CARDIFF
CAERDYDD

THE OFFICIAL ICAEW DIRECTORY OF FIRMS 2009

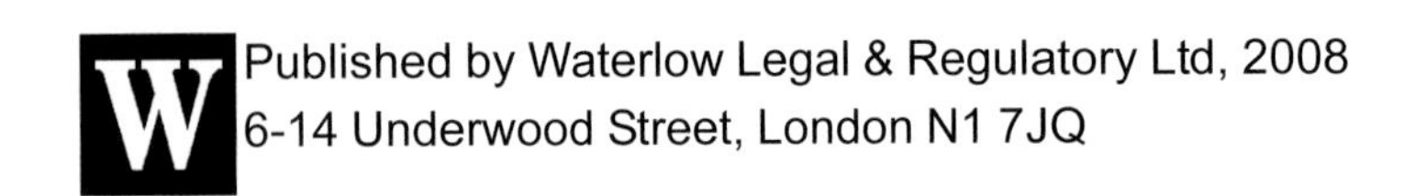
Published by Waterlow Legal & Regulatory Ltd, 2008
6-14 Underwood Street, London N1 7JQ

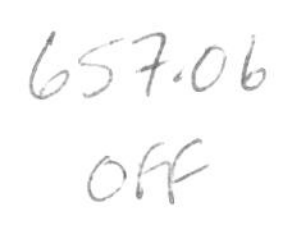

Editorial enquiries
T +44 (0)20 7549 8633
F +44 (0)20 7324 2366
Contact: Anjana Solanki
E asolanki@waterlow.com

Sales enquiries
T +44 (0)20 7566 8227
F +44 (0)20 7324 2341
Contact: Kate Parkinson
E kparkinson@waterlow.com

A catalogue entry for this book is available from the British Library.

ISBN 978-1-85783-100-9

Typesetting by Data Standards, Frome, Somerset
Printed in Great Britain by Polestar Wheatons, Exeter.

Details notified after 1 September 2008 may not be included.

ICAEW
Chartered Accountants' Hall
PO Box 433
Moorgate Place
London EC2P 2BJ
UK
T +44 (0)20 7920 8100
F +44 (0)20 7920 0547

Wolters Kluwer (UK) Limited
145 London Road
Kingston upon Thames
Surrey KT2 6SR
UK
T +44 (0)844 561 8166
F +44 (0)20 8247 1184

The Official ICAEW Directory of Firms **is also available in regional formats and online at www.icaewfirms.co.uk**

CONTENTS

David Furst FCA
President

The role of chartered accountants in the world's economies has never been more important. People making financial decisions need knowledge and guidance based on the highest technical and ethical standards.

Our members provide this better than anyone. They are trained to challenge people and organisations to think and act differently, to provide clarity and rigour, and so help create and sustain prosperity.

The Institute provides leadership and practical support to over 130,000 members in more than 160 countries. We create the environment in which their skills are constantly developed, recognised and valued. We shape opinion, understanding and delivery, to ensure the highest standards in business and in the public interest.

The Institute is a founding member of the Global Accounting Alliance which represents over 700,000 members worldwide.

Because of us, people can do business with confidence.

ANALYSIS OF MEMBERS

The three charts below provide a snapshot of ICAEW membership as at 1 July 2008. Members have been profiled by their sector of work, age and gender. Firm size has been profiled by number of partners.

MEMBERS BY WORK SECTOR

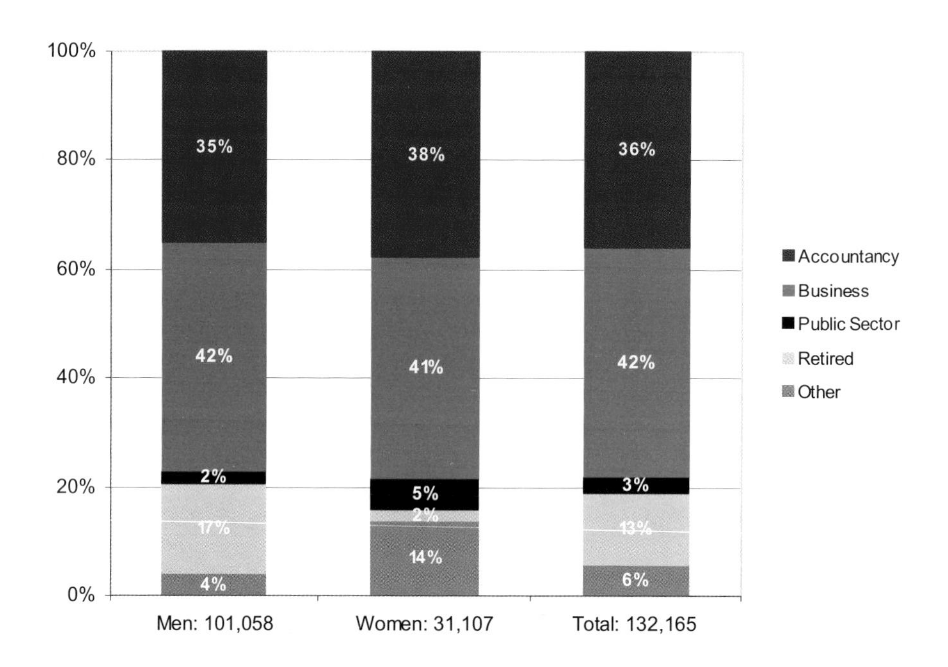

MEMBERS BY AGE AND GENDER

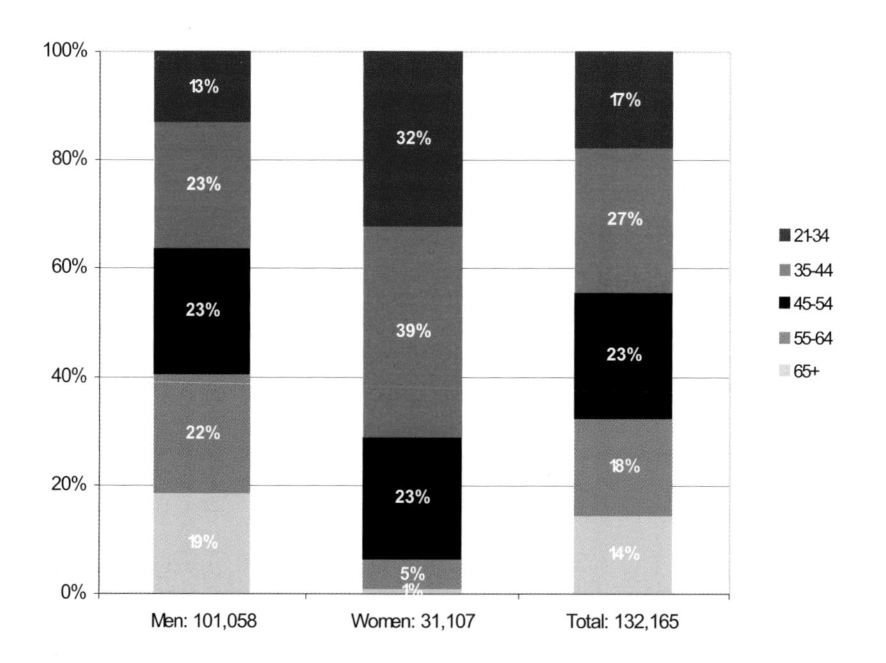

FIRM SIZE BY PARTNERS

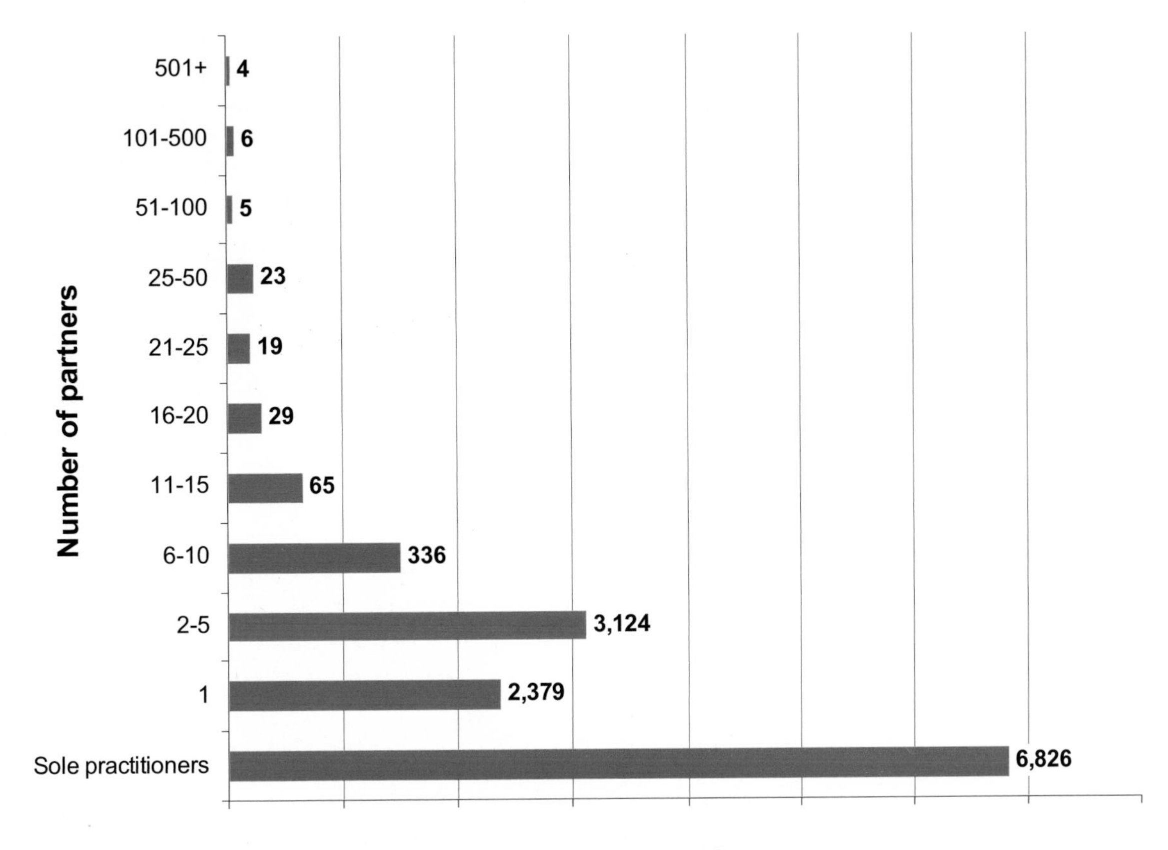

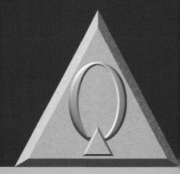

CHOOSING YOUR CHARTERED ACCOUNTANT

WHAT TO LOOK FOR

- A chartered accountant will have the letters ACA or FCA after his or her name.
- Find a chartered accountant before you start your business.
- Look for a firm which is similar in size to yours; they will be more understanding of the issues and problems you will face.
- Do they have experience of your sector and type of business?
- What is their reputation? Will they be acceptable to third parties, eg, finance providers, shareholders?
- For audit, investment business or insolvency work, make sure the chartered accountant is authorised to undertake the work.
- A practising ICAEW member firm is entitled to use the ICAEW member firm logo, as shown below, to promote itself as a member of the Institute.

MAKING CONTACT

- Invest time in finding the right accountant. It's a long-term relationship.
- Telephone between three and six firms and arrange to meet with at least three of them.
- Check in advance whether the first meeting to discuss their appointment is free of charge; specific advice may be charged for.
- Tell them what you are planning to do and check whether they offer the services you will need to build your business.
- Tell them the accounting records you keep. Can they suggest improvements?
- Ask for their comments on your business plan. If you need finance, you may need a plan. How much would they charge to do one with you?
- If you also want personal financial advice, check whether they can provide this.
- Establish what the fees will be and when they are payable.
- Establish who at the firm will be dealing with your work – it may not only be the person you are meeting with.
- Do you get on with this person? Is this someone you can work with? Do you feel happy that he or she will be able to help you develop your business?
- Ask to speak to existing clients – references are always important.
- After appointing your chartered accountant, you should receive a letter setting out their terms and conditions.
- Advice on specific investments needs FSA authorisation (some chartered accountants are authorised to do this). Otherwise chartered accountants can give generic advice which may prove a useful basis for subsequent discussions with an FSA-authorised investment business adviser.

AFTER THE APPOINTMENT

- Your chartered accountant should always keep in touch, not just at the year-end.
- You must tell your chartered accountant as soon as possible of changes in your business, problems, circumstances, etc.
- After your accounts have been prepared, you should receive a letter setting out future tax liabilities.
- Don't be afraid to tap into your chartered accountant's knowledge for help with running your business or financial affairs.
- Review your chartered accountant's charges every three to five years.
- From time to time, assess whether your accountant's services still match your business needs.
- If you decide to sell your business, tell your chartered accountant – he or she could plan to minimise tax liabilities and even help with the sale.
- Chartered accountants can answer most questions you may have about business or financial matters – or they know someone who can.

THOUGHT LEADERSHIP FROM THE ICAEW

The ICAEW has a range of thought leadership programmes looking at public policy issues and questions of long-term interest to the profession.

***FinanceDirection* – the thought leadership programme of the Finance and Management Faculty**

Boards of businesses around the world play a vital role in wealth creation and economic development. To deliver its strategy, the leadership of any organisation establishes internal structures and allocates staff to best suit the needs of the organisation. Of course, the needs of an organisation will change over time and as the board and senior management try to find more efficient and effective ways of managing the business.

Change impacts a finance function as much as other parts of the organisation. The role of a finance function and its leadership, the finance director, or CFO, should not be taken for granted.

The responsibilities of, and the resources allocated to, a finance function vary between organisations. The scope of activities, including the associated business systems that a finance function is responsible for and the other areas with which it is directly or indirectly involved, may vary substantially from organisation to organisation and across cultures. There is no 'right' model and no one country has necessarily achieved an optimum solution. Finance functions continue to evolve.

One aspect of the evolution of a finance function is the board's expectations of the finance director. As the business and regulatory environment gets ever more complex, boards' responsibilities will increase and their role will become ever more challenging. To rise to these challenges, boards need support.

Market Foundations

Market activity is the means by which society benefits from the comparative advantages held by the individuals within it. Society benefits when markets are efficient and when they deliver desired public policy outcomes.

Such markets will have as their foundations: participants (whether as principals, agents or advisers) who can trust and be trusted; accepted, predictable and transparent standards of behaviour; and effective and efficient mechanisms to intervene in the markets when necessary to correct the behaviour.

Those foundations have often built up in markets in an ad hoc fashion: can they be improved to further enhance market effectiveness and efficiency?

Areas of examination will include:

- what the public interest is;
- the role of professionalism in society; and
- whether the rights and obligations of some types of legal entity are more effective than others.

We will also be taking forward existing work on:

- ethical behaviour
- regulation
- economic crime.

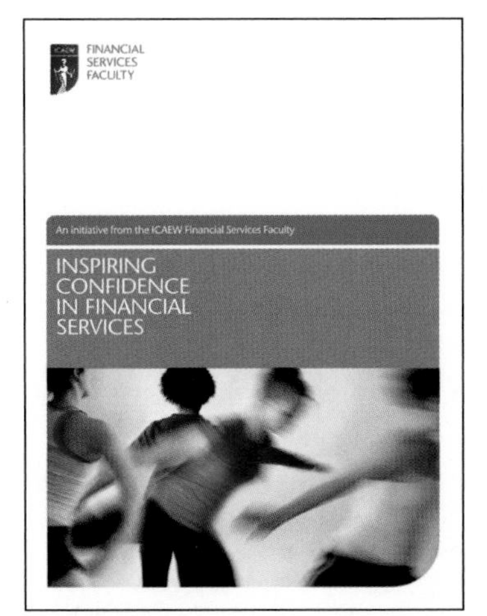

***Inspiring Confidence in Financial Services* – the thought leadership programme of the Financial Services Faculty**

Confidence is vital to financial services. The *Inspiring Confidence in Financial Services* campaign will take a leading role in debating issues affecting confidence in the financial services sector. It will develop new insights and ideas by asking questions about financial services providers, consumers and regulators, how they interact with each other and the information flows between them.

In order to have stable, efficient markets that support consumer interests and sustain wider economic development, it is necessary to draw together these elements. We will explore aspects of this through our four themes of:

- responsible providers
- responsible consumers
- better regulation
- better information.

Making Information Systems Work – the thought leadership programme of the Information Technology Faculty

Information technology is central to the operation of all organisations today, and consumes increasingly significant levels of corporate resources. This presents many opportunities to drive or support business growth. However, as systems cross new organisational boundaries and become ever-more complex, the challenges of effective implementation are greater than ever. These are challenges to the business, not just IT, and require engagement from all across the organisation in the effective management and use of technology.

The IT Faculty's *Making Information Systems Work* initiative aims to engage a wide audience in debating and addressing some of these challenges.

This initiative will provide a truly independent and objective viewpoint in the debate. Taking stock of the wide range of existing literature in the area, we will explore key underlying questions in managing IT today, challenge common assumptions and clarify the areas of real contention. By doing this, we can move the debate forward and focus attention on issues which require further research and discussion.

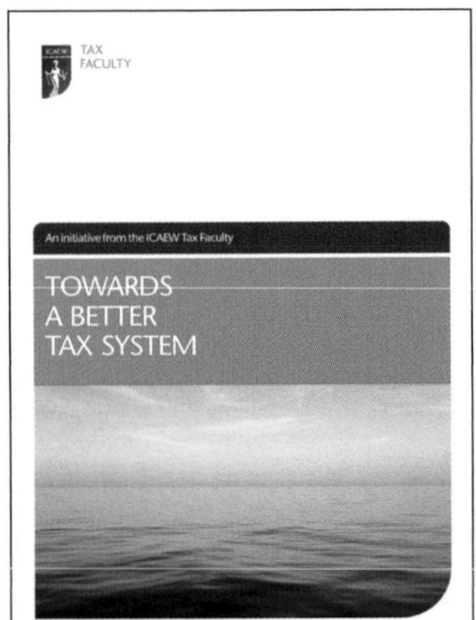

Towards a Better Tax System – the thought leadership programme of the Tax Faculty

The need to improve tax systems is as great as ever, and there is growing international debate about what works best for taxpayers as a whole. The *Towards a Better Tax System* programme addresses the practical challenges faced when designing and implementing changes to tax systems.

The ICAEW Tax Faculty will pursue its work under three main heads: business, people and delivery. The aim of this programme is to consider the challenges faced by tax systems and help shape solutions suitable for the 21st century. We intend to involve stakeholders including taxpayers and intermediaries, policy makers, tax administrations and academics.

Chartered accountants have a unique perspective on tax. They work both in, and with, business and are able to offer practical and informed views based on daily experience.

Since its formation in 1991, the ICAEW Tax Faculty has been engaged in thought leadership work. It hosts the annual Hardman Lecture in which a leading figure from the tax world, or from government, addresses a critical tax policy issue. This is the most prestigious event in the UK tax calendar.

re: Assurance

Businesses rely on sources of information to make economic decisions. Confidence diminishes when there are uncertainties around the integrity and credibility of information or its fitness for purpose. Where businesses or stakeholders identify a particular need to build confidence in information and reinforce relationships of trust, external assurance can play a valuable role. An independent expert expressing assurance on information provides a strong signal that reports are trustworthy.

Through the *re: Assurance* initiative, the ICAEW is promoting dialogue about assurance services: finding out where new services could help strengthening markets and support economic confidence and answering demands for practical guidance to meet emerging market needs.

Based on the framework issued by the international standard setter, the Audit and Assurance Faculty has published a range of practical guidance for businesses and practitioners who support them.

- On audit-exempt companies – useful materials explaining chartered accountant services for audit-exempt companies.
- On business relationships – a series of best practice guidance on assurance services on business relationships, typically on internal controls.
- On non-financial information – examining the types of non-financial information on which external assurance reports are currently provided and practical challenges in this developing area.

For more information on all the ICAEW's thought leadership programmes, visit **www.icaew.com/thoughtleadership**

ICAEW ENTERPRISE SURVEY REPORT 2008 KEY FINDINGS

The ICAEW *Annual Enterprise Survey*, now in its twelfth year, draws upon the expertise of our members working at the heart of business. In doing so, it provides a unique annual picture of the opportunities and challenges facing businesses around the world.

In addition to the *UK Enterprise Survey Report 2008*, this year, for the first time the survey included responses from chartered accountants in three key global regions. These included, the remainder of the EU, the Far East (Hong Kong, Singapore and Malaysia) and the US.

Each year, The ICAEW does more than just report on the aspirations and concerns of enterprise in its annual *Enterprise Survey*. We use the results of the survey to help inform and influence governments, to better encourage entrepreneurship and so better contribute to economic growth.

By sharing the *Enterprise Survey* results and related policy positions with ministers internationally, parliamentarians, officials and a range of stakeholders nationally and regionally, we raise the profile of chartered accountants with key decision makers . The survey itself amply demonstrates the knowledge, experience and judgement of chartered accountants holding key positions in all sizes of business across all sections of the economy. Our contribution to the public debate on enterprise also helps to demonstrate the role of practitioners as facilitators of enterprise - key business and finance advisers to entrepreneurs.

For a copy of the full report, please email enterprise@icaew.com, or for more information on enterprise and what the ICAEW does to support it, go to **www.icaew.com/enterprise**

UK KEY FINDINGS AT A GLANCE

ECONOMIC ISSUES

- Nearly two-thirds of UK businesses say that the credit crunch has had a negative effect on their organisation – one in five 'very negative'.
- Those in Construction & Housing, Real Estate & Property Services and Banking, Financial Services & Insurance have been the most strongly affected.
- Most of those affected say that the credit crunch has increased borrowing costs, reduced revenue growth and made forward planning more difficult.
- Most businesses affected believe that the credit crunch will last until at least the latter part of 2009 or 2010.
- Most UK businesses expect the turbulence in financial markets, changes in global commodity prices and changes in consumer demand to impact negatively on their business this year, with medium-sized businesses particularly pessimistic about their effect.

GROWTH

- In spite of the credit crunch, more than 8 in 10 UK businesses are still planning turnover growth over the next two years, although growth targets are a little lower than in 2007.
- One in three respondents are looking for annual growth rates in excess of 10%, with 11% targeting over 30% p.a.
- Micro businesses have more ambitious growth targets than in 2007, but others, particularly small and medium businesses, have reduced turnover growth plans.
- Increasing profitability remains the key financial objective, but more are looking to increase cash balances and pay down debt.
- Competition is by far the strongest barrier to growth (59% critical/strong), but many feel they are held back by regulation (38%), lack of leadership (33%) and technical skills (38%) and the cost of labour (34%).

GLOBALISATION

- Nearly two-thirds of respondent companies have at least one of the three attributes of globalised engagement – customers, operations or outsourcing outside the UK – a small increase since 2007.
- Respondents remain positive about the impact of continuing globalisation on their business: 42% view it positively (down marginally from 44% in 2007).
- Banking, Financial Services & Insurance and IT & Communications are the most positive sectors on globalisation, Manufacturing & Engineering remains the sector most conscious of the risks.
- In an increasingly global marketplace, many UK businesses are looking to develop and enhance their product offering and extend their global trading footprint.
- Administrative, regulatory and legal considerations are considered the main barriers to international expansion by UK businesses.
- Many UK businesses say that their global engagement has been affected by exchange rate movements and changes in raw material costs.
- Just over half (51%) of UK businesses have plans to enter new markets or expand market share outside the UK, although the focus tends to be nearer home this year, in the EU and Middle East.

REGULATION

- 53% of UK businesses say that the regulatory and taxation environment in the UK is not business-friendly.
- The total cost to UK businesses of implementing new legislation is estimated at up to £11.3bn.
- The cost to micro and small businesses has increased significantly since the 2007 survey and they carry an increasingly heavy share of the burden.
- Employment legislation, employment tax and business tax changes are seen as the main hindrances to the operation and development of UK businesses, with employment tax most often singled out as the greatest cost.
- Disciplinary, dismissal and grievance procedures are considered the most burdensome aspect of employment legislation.

KEY FINDINGS OF OTHER REGIONS AT A GLANCE

OTHER EU BUSINESSES

- Generally feel a little less impacted by the credit crunch than those in other regions and are less likely to report many of the negative effects on their organisation.
- Show the highest level of global engagement (94%), and in particular are most likely to have customers outside their own country (93%), reflecting the comparative ease of trading across borders.
- Are more likely than those in other regions to look to increase both trading and outsourcing in other countries over the next five years.
- Share with the UK a perception that their domestic regulatory and taxation environment is not business-friendly, feeling particularly burdened by employment tax and legislation.

FAR EAST BUSINESSES

- Are as likely as those in other regions to report the negative impact of the credit crunch on their business. However, they also perceive some benefit to have come from it. More than in any other region, they see increased opportunities for acquisitions and sales and anticipate a less negative impact this year from changes in consumer demand.
- Predict an earlier end to the impact of the credit crunch, with as many as 40% not expecting it to affect their organisation for more than a year.
- See more serious barriers to their growth, however more of them are aiming for turnover growth than in any other region. Apart from increasing profitability, increasing shareholder rewards is a key driver.
- Are more likely than others to say that their business has been affected by recent exchange rate movements and changes in raw material costs, and see more serious barriers to their international expansion. Nevertheless, they are far more likely than those in other regions to regard continued globalisation of markets as having a positive impact on their business (81%).
- Describe their domestic regulatory and taxation environment as business-friendly (87%).
- Are more likely than those in other regions to regard many aspects of regulation and taxation as a help rather than a hindrance to their operation and development.

US BUSINESSES

- Are similar to the UK in reporting the negative impact of the credit crunch on their organisation and are more likely than those in other regions to say that it has reduced their ability to finance acquisitions and reduced their planned staffing levels.
- Generally are less likely than others to expect negative effects this year from changes in global commodity prices or exchange rates.
- Are a little more likely than others to see increasing profitability as their key business objective over the next two years.
- Have slightly lower levels of global engagement than those in the EU or Far East, but they are the most likely to outsource outside their own country in an administrative or commercial capacity (50%), especially to India (35%).
- Feel their domestic regulatory and taxation environment to be more business-friendly than those in Europe, however they are the most likely to consider financial reporting and corporate governance requirements to be a hindrance to their operation and development.

SME FUNDING ADVISER SCHEME

Most small businesses wanting finance for their business turn to their bank. They are often surprised when the bank asks why they want the money, what will they use the money for, how much do they want, do they have any security and when do they plan to repay it? But there is one question which often puzzles them most - have they considered other options?

Small and medium sized business owners generally do not have the time (or possibly the motivation) to study the alternative sources and types of finance available to their business, let alone recite the advantages and disadvantages of each. But help is at hand. Many chartered accountants have this knowledge and have helped many businesses to raise finance, on occasions helping the same client more than once. However many business people think of chartered accountants only in terms of advice on tax, preparing accounts and auditing financial statements.

For this reason we started a new scheme in 2007– the SME (for Small and Medium Enterprise) Funding Adviser scheme. Under this scheme practising (providing services to the public) members can choose to highlight their firms' ability to help businesses to raise finance.

We have grouped the different types of business finance into 10 different 'specialisms' (see below). In our new database each firm lists the business finance specialism(s) it offers, so if you already know which form of finance you need, you can search for the advisers meeting this need within your area. However, many SMEs don't know which form of finance they require or would prefer to talk to an adviser who has a wider range of knowledge and experience of many forms of business finance. In the ICAEW scheme these firms with wider experience are described as 'SME Funding Advisers'. Practices with these wider skills can be separately searched on our online database. SME Funding Advisers will have experience of helping businesses raise equity finance, which is particularly important for high growth businesses lacking security or a track record which probably rules out funding their needs totally through bank finance – loans and overdrafts.

Whether it is a particular form of finance you want or if you would like advice on the full range of financing options The ICAEW SME Funding Adviser scheme can provide a firm to help. For full details on the types of finance, their advantages and disadvantages and any further considerations please refer to the Institute website at **www.icaew.com/enterprise**

The 10 specialisms in this scheme are:

- Bank loans and overdrafts including Small Firms Loan Guarantee
- Business plans for bank and equity finance
- Business start-up (eg, own funds, friends and family finance)
- Small scale equity finance (eg, Business Angels)
- Asset finance
- Corporate finance (including acquisitions and mergers, equity issues, management buyouts and raising or restructuring debt)
- Grants
- Invoice discounting and factoring
- Leasing and hire purchase
- Share valuations

CHARTERED ACCOUNTANT SERVICES FOR AUDIT-EXEMPT COMPANIES

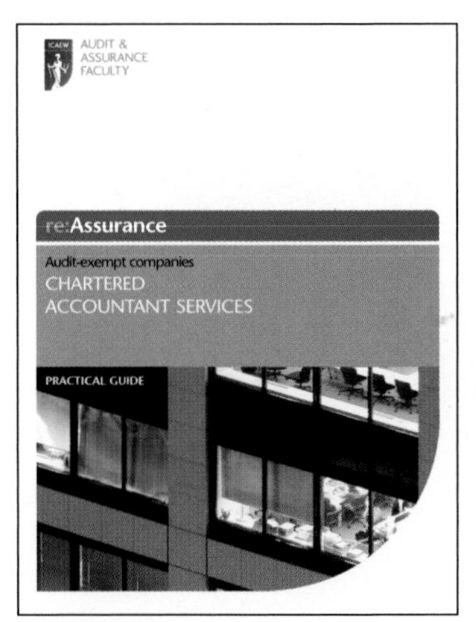

Many companies with a turnover of less than £6.5m (applicable for periods on or after 6 April 2008) can take advantage of provisions in the Companies Act, which allow them to be exempted from having an audit. This means that there are options to choose from the services chartered accountants provide. You may wish to have a voluntary statutory audit, but if you decide to take advantage of audit exemption, a company can have, for example, the ICAEW Assurance Service or accounts compilation service.

The ICAEW Assurance Service may be suitable for companies that want an independent assurance report on their unaudited annual accounts to obtain a degree of comfort. Alternatively, chartered accountants can help compile accounts.

To assist the process of choosing the right service, the Institute has also developed a practical guide for audit-exempt companies, which explains three main services that chartered accountants provide on the accounts – voluntary statutory audit, the ICAEW Assurance Service and accounts compilation.

For full details, visit **www.icaew.com/assuranceservice**

UK DISTRICT SOCIETIES AND REGIONS

Regions		District Societies	Number of Members
1	East England	Beds, Bucks & Herts; East Anglian; South Essex	13,219
2	East Midlands	Leicestershire & Northamptonshire; Nottingham, Derby & Lincoln	5,537
3	London	London; Croydon & District	32,930
4	North West	Isle of Man; Liverpool; Manchester; North West	10,590
5	Northern	Northern	2,927
6	South East	South Eastern; Southern; Thames Valley	19,588
7	South West	South Western; West of England	7,379
8	Wales	South Wales	2,238
9	West Midlands	Birmingham & West Midlands; Staffs, Salop & Wolverhampton	7,862
10	Yorkshire and Humber	Humberside & District Sheffield & District; West Yorkshire	7,886
11	Institute Members in Scotland		1,367

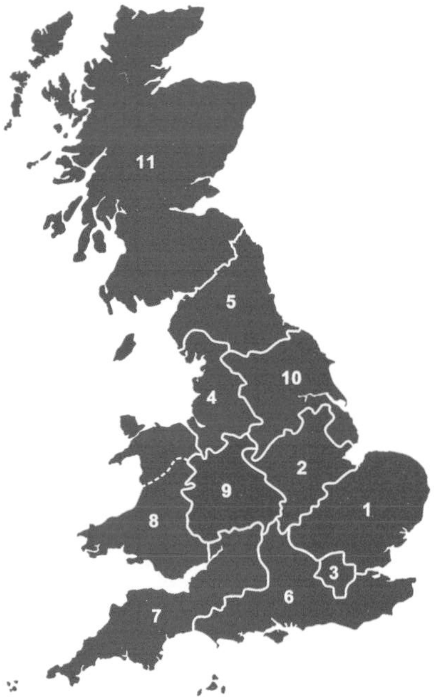

REGIONS WORLDWIDE

Regions		Number of Members
1	Americas	4,599
2	Africa	1,248
3	Europe	116,749
4	Asia	6,361
5	Australasia	3,208

REGIONAL AND DISTRICT SOCIETY CONTACTS

The network of 10 regional offices in England and Wales plays a key role in raising the profile of the Institute around the country, through building relationships with key stakeholders and by ensuring that members' views are promoted effectively on business issues.

The 22 district societies plus the Institute Members in Scotland serve local needs and interests, and supplement locally many of the services which the Institute provides nationally. They also act as a channel for members of the public wanting the services of a chartered accountant. If you are unable to contact the relevant region or district society, you can telephone the regional services department at the Institute in London, on +44 (0)20 7920 8412.

REGIONAL OFFICES

EAST ENGLAND REGION

REGIONAL OFFICE
Compass House, Vision Park, Chivers Way
Histon, Cambridge CB4 9AD
T +44 (0)1223 257 873 F +44 (0)1223 257 810
E eastengland@icaew.com

REGIONAL DIRECTOR
Phillippa Bourne
T +44 (0)1223 257 874 F +44 (0)1223 257 810
M +44 (0)7876 035 926 E phillippa.bourne@icaew.com

REGIONAL COORDINATOR
Debbie Kimpton
T +44 (0)1223 257 873 F +44 (0)1223 257 810
E debbie.kimpton@icaew.com

DISTRICT SOCIETIES IN THIS REGION
Beds, Bucks & Herts Society of Chartered Accountants
East Anglian Society of Chartered Accountants
South Essex Society of Chartered Accountants

EAST MIDLANDS REGION

REGIONAL OFFICE
Cumberland House, 35 Park Row, Nottingham NG1 6EE
T +44 (0)115 988 6062 F +44 (0)115 988 6226
E eastmidlands@icaew.com

REGIONAL DIRECTOR
Gill Sykes
T +44 (0)115 988 6063 F +44 (0)115 988 6226
M +44 (0)7876 035 952 E gill.sykes@icaew.com

REGIONAL COORDINATOR
Stephen Chapman
T +44 (0)115 988 6062 F +44 (0)115 988 6226
E stephen.chapman@icaew.com

DISTRICT SOCIETIES IN THIS REGION
Leicestershire & Northamptonshire Society of Chartered Accountants
Nottingham, Derby & Lincoln Society of Chartered Accountants

LONDON REGION

REGIONAL OFFICE
Chartered Accountants' Hall, PO Box 433, Moorgate Place
London EC2P 2BJ
T +44 (0)20 7920 8682 F +44 (0)20 7920 8648
E london@icaew.com

REGIONAL DIRECTOR
Ian Strange
T +44 (0)20 7920 8788
M +44 (0)7876 035 933 E ian.strange@icaew.com

REGIONAL EXECUTIVE
Elizabeth Russell
T +44 (0)20 7920 8562
E elizabeth.russell@icaew.com

DISTRICT SOCIETIES IN THIS REGION
London Society of Chartered Accountants
Croydon & District Society of Chartered Accountants

NORTH WEST REGION

REGIONAL OFFICE
Cinnamon House, Cinnamon Brow
Fearnhead, Warrington WA2 0XP
T +44 (0)1925 661 858 F +44 (0)1925 661 828
E northwest@icaew.com

REGIONAL DIRECTOR
Mark Hale
T +44 (0)1925 661 859 F +44 (0)1925 661 828
M +44 (0)7921 698 056 E mark.hale@icaew.com

REGIONAL COORDINATOR
Helen Payen
T +44 (0)1925 661 858 F +44 (0)1925 661 828
E helen.payen@icaew.com

DISTRICT SOCIETIES IN THIS REGION
Isle of Man Society of Chartered Accountants
Liverpool Society of Chartered Accountants
Manchester Chartered Accountants
North West Society of Chartered Accountants

NORTHERN REGION

REGIONAL OFFICE
Rotterdam House, 116 Quayside
Newcastle upon Tyne NE1 3DY
T +44 (0)191 206 4548 F +44 (0)191 206 4239
E northern@icaew.com

REGIONAL DIRECTOR
Keith Proudfoot
T +44 (0)191 206 4550 F +44 (0)191 206 4239
M +44 (0)7876 035 942 E keith.proudfoot@icaew.com

REGIONAL COORDINATOR
Marie Rice
T +44 (0)191 206 4548 F +44 (0)191 206 4239
M +44 (0)7876 035 951 E marie.rice@icaew.com

DISTRICT SOCIETY IN THIS REGION
Northern Society of Chartered Accountants

SOUTH EAST REGION

REGIONAL OFFICE
3000 Cathedral Hill, Guildford, Surrey GU2 7YB
T +44 (0)1483 246 561 F +44 (0)1483 245 117
E southeast@icaew.com

REGIONAL DIRECTOR

Fay Webster
T +44 (0)1483 246 562 F +44 (0)1483 245 117
M +44 (0)7918 196 050 E fay.webster@icaew.com

REGIONAL COORDINATOR

Michelle Higgins
T +44 (0)1483 246 561 F +44 (0)1483 245 117
E michelle.higgins@icaew.com

DISTRICT SOCIETIES IN THIS REGION

South Eastern Society of Chartered Accountants
Southern Society of Chartered Accountants
Thames Valley Society of Chartered Accountants

SOUTH WEST REGION

REGIONAL OFFICE

1 Friary, Temple Quay, Bristol BS1 6EA
T +44 (0)117 344 5045 F +44 (0)117 344 5046
E southwest@icaew.com

REGIONAL DIRECTOR

John Blake
T +44 (0)117 344 5603 F +44 (0)117 344 5046
M +44 (0)7793 834 326 E john.blake@icaew.com

REGIONAL COORDINATOR

Debra Morris
T +44 (0)117 344 5045 F +44 (0)117 344 5046
E debra.morris@icaew.com

DISTRICT SOCIETIES IN THIS REGION

South Western Society of Chartered Accountants
West of England Society of Chartered Accountants

WALES BUSINESS CENTRE

REGIONAL OFFICE

Regus House, Falcon Drive, Cardiff Bay, Cardiff CF10 4RU
T +44 (0)29 2050 4595 F +44 (0)29 2050 4199
E wales@icaew.com; cymru@icaew.com

REGIONAL DIRECTOR

David Lermon
T +44 (0)29 2050 4596 F +44 (0)29 2050 4199
M +44 (0)7876 035 935 E david.lermon@icaew.com

REGIONAL COORDINATORS

Emma Friedl / Fiona Washbrook
T +44 (0)29 2050 4595 F +44 (0)29 2050 4199
E wales@icaew.com; cymru@icaew.com

DISTRICT SOCIETY IN THIS REGION

South Wales Society of Chartered Accountants

WEST MIDLANDS REGION

REGIONAL OFFICE

2nd Floor, 3 Brindleyplace, Birmingham B1 2JB
T +44 (0)121 697 7002 F +44 (0)121 698 8618
E westmidlands@icaew.com

REGIONAL DIRECTOR

Nigel Hastilow
T +44 (0)121 697 7015 F +44 (0)121 698 8618
M +44 (0)7876 035 940 E nigel.hastilow@icaew.com

REGIONAL COORDINATOR

Linda Conway
T +44 (0)121 697 7002 F +44 (0)121 698 8618
E linda.conway@icaew.com

EVENTS MANAGER

Sebastian Hargreaves
T +44 (0)121 697 7003 F +44 (0)121 698 8618
E sebastian.hargreaves@icaew.com

DISTRICT SOCIETIES IN THIS REGION

Birmingham and West Midlands Society of Chartered Accountants
Staffs, Salop and Wolverhampton Society of Chartered Accountants

YORKSHIRE & HUMBER REGION

REGIONAL OFFICE

Suite G39, 1200 Century Way, Thorpe Park Business Park
Colton, Leeds LS15 8ZA
T +44 (0)113 251 5669 F +44 (0)113 251 5399
E yorks-humberside@icaew.com

REGIONAL DIRECTOR

Chris Manners
T +44 (0)113 251 5666 F +44 (0)113 251 5399
M +44 (0)7753 715 812 E chris.manners@icaew.com

REGIONAL COORDINATOR

Gillian North
T +44 (0)113 251 5669 F +44 (0)113 251 5399
E gillian.north@icaew.com

DISTRICT SOCIETIES IN THIS REGION

Humberside and District Society of Chartered Accountants
Sheffield & District Society of Chartered Accountants
West Yorkshire Society of Chartered Accountants

DISTRICT SOCIETY CONTACTS

1. BEDS, BUCKS & HERTS SOCIETY OF CHARTERED ACCOUNTANTS

President: Peter Tucker FCA
Dickinsons, Enterprise House, Beesons Yard, Bury Lane, Rickmansworth WD3 1DS
T +44 (0)1923 776 818
E pdt@dickinsons.co.uk
Regional Executive: Katherine Bowyer
PO Box 721, Horseheath, Cambridge CB1 6WZ
T +44 (0)1799 584 456 F +44 (0)1799 584 910
E katherine.bowyer@icaew.com; bbhsca@icaew.com
Branches: no recognised branches

2. BIRMINGHAM AND WEST MIDLANDS SOCIETY OF CHARTERED ACCOUNTANTS

President: Andeep Mangal ACA
Thaper & Co, Harpal House, 14 Holyhead Road, Birmingham B21 0LT
T +44 (0)121 554 7266
E andeep@thaper.co.uk
Regional Executive: Terry Smythe
PO Box 110, Wellington TF1 6QX
T +44 (0)1952 251 932 F +44 (0)1952 240 114
E terry.smythe@icaew.com; bwmsca@icaew.com
Branches: Warwickshire Society, Worcestershire Society (contact district society)

3. CROYDON & DISTRICT SOCIETY OF CHARTERED ACCOUNTANTS

President: Nick Lawson
155 Cherry Orchard Road, Croydon CR0 6BF
T +44 (0)20 8681 2664
E nicklawson@gmail.com
Regional Executive: Jacquie Fairclough
PO Box 2436, Purley CR8 2NX
T +44 (0)20 8763 6261 F +44 (0)20 8660 1754
E jacquie.fairclough@icaew.com; croydonsca@icaew.com
Branches: no recognised branches

4. EAST ANGLIAN SOCIETY OF CHARTERED ACCOUNTANTS

President: Paul Leech FCA
Deloitte & Touche, Stonecutter Court, 1 Stonecutter Street, London EC4V 4TR
T +44 (0)20 7303 5398
E pleech@deloitte.co.uk
Regional Executives: Margaret Jackson and Michelle May-Jones
St Andrews Castle, 33 St Andrews Street South, Bury St Edmunds IP33 3PH
T +44 (0)1284 774 730 F +44 (0)1284 774 732
E margaret.jackson@icaew.com; michelle.may-jones@icaew.com; eastangliansca@icaew.com
Branches: Cambridge Society; Ipswich & Colchester Society; Norfolk & Norwich Society (contact district society)

5. HUMBERSIDE AND DISTRICT SOCIETY OF CHARTERED ACCOUNTANTS

President: Owen Finn FCA
48 Spindlewood, Elloughton, Brough, East Yorkshire HU15 1LL
T +44 (0)1482 370 085
E owen@premier-eng.co.uk
Regional Executive: Alexia Bahadur
PO Box 101, Willerby, Hull HU10 6XX
T +44 (0)1430 434 762 F +44 (0)1132 515 399
E alexia.bahadur@icaew.com; humbersidesca@icaew.com
Branches: Grimsby & North Lincolnshire Society (contact district society)

6. LEICESTERSHIRE AND NORTHAMPTONSHIRE SOCIETY OF CHARTERED ACCOUNTANTS

President: Kaaeed Mamujee BSc ACA
M-Cubed, 9 Stoughton Close, Oadby, Leicester LE2 4DT
T +44 (0)7725 562 020
E kmamujee@m-cubed.org
Regional Executive: Vicky Nicholas
PO Box 717, Spratton, Northampton NN6 8WP
T +44 (0)1604 821 558 F +44 (0)1604 821 570
E vicky.nicholas@icaew.com; lansca@icaew.com
Branches: no recognised branches

7. LIVERPOOL SOCIETY OF CHARTERED ACCOUNTANTS

President: Michael Cox FCA
Grant Thornton UK LLP, 1st Floor, Royal Liver Buildings, Pier Head, Liverpool L3 1PS
T +44 (0)151 224 7200
E michael.cox@gtuk.com
Regional Executive: Alex Pilkington
PO Box 471, Wigan WN2 1WY
T +44 (0)1942 497 015 F +44 (0)1942 497 014
E alex.pilkington@icaew.com; liverpoolsca@icaew.com
Branches: Chester & North Wales Society, Southport Society (contact district society), Isle of Man Society (independent society)
T +44 (0)1624 662 788

8. LONDON SOCIETY OF CHARTERED ACCOUNTANTS

President: Derek Felstead FCA
Flat 24, Tignel Court, Boddington Gardens, London W3 9AR
T +44 (0)20 8992 2465
E dmfelstead@aol.com
For general enquiries, please contact:
Regional Executive: Elizabeth Russell
Chartered Accountants' Hall, PO Box 43, Moorgate Place, London EC2P 2BJ
T +44 (0)20 7920 8682 F +44 (0)20 7920 8648
E lsca@icaew.com
For information regarding the LSCA annual dinner/city lunch, please contact:
Regional Executive: Karen Franklin
PO Box 19496, Chingford E4 6WX
T +44 (0)20 8524 6257 F +44 (0)20 8524 8112
E karen.franklin@icaew.com
Branches: North London Society (contact district society)

9. MANCHESTER CHARTERED ACCOUNTANTS

President: Rodger Owen FCA
5 Midge Hall Drive, Bamford, Rochdale OL11 4AX
T +44 (0)161 834 2700
E r.owen@manchestercentral.co.uk
Regional Executive: Astrid Leather
PO Box 480, Northwich, Cheshire CW9 9AG
T +44 (0)1606 892 594 F +44 (0)1606 892 943
E astrid.leather@icaew.com; manchestersca@icaew.com
Branches: Bolton Society (contact district society)

10. NORTH WEST SOCIETY OF CHARTERED ACCOUNTANTS

President: Martin Shaw BEng ACA
Fletchers Farm, Water Street, Brindle, Chorley PR6 8NH
T +44 (0)1925 832 794
E martin.w.shaw@bnfl.com
Regional Executive: Melanie Christie
PO Box 273, Leyland PR26 7WS
T +44 (0)1772 641 163 F +44 (0)1772 433 235
E melanie.christie@icaew.com; northwestsca@icaew.com
Branches: no recognised branches

11. NORTHERN SOCIETY OF CHARTERED ACCOUNTANTS

President: Jim Summers BA FCA
Suite 15, Grainger Suite, Dobson House, Regent Centre, Newcastle upon Tyne NE3 3PF
T +44 (0)191 233 6328
E jg_summers@yahoo.co.uk
Regional Executive: Marie Rice
Rotterdam House, 116 Quayside, Newcastle upon Tyne NE1 3DY
T +44 (0)191 206 4548 F +44 (0)191 206 4239
E marie.rice@icaew.com; northernsca@icaew.com
Branches: Cumberland Society, Teesside Society, Tyne & Wear Society (contact district society)

12. NOTTINGHAM, DERBY AND LINCOLN SOCIETY OF CHARTERED ACCOUNTANTS

President: Kevin Slack FCA
Mabe Allen, 50 Osmaston Road, Derby DE1 2HU
T +44 (0)1332 345 265
E kevinslack@mabeallen.co.uk
Regional Executive: Elaine Franklin
PO Box 8543, Nottingham NG16 9AE
T +44 (0)1773 811 010 F +44 (0)1773 863 441
E elaine.franklin@icaew.com; nottinghamsca@icaew.com
Branches: Derby Society, Lincoln & South Lincolnshire Society, Nottingham Society (contact district society)

13. SHEFFIELD & DISTRICT SOCIETY OF CHARTERED ACCOUNTANTS

President: Chris Heaton ACA
CHCT, 6 Home Farm, Wortley, Sheffield S35 7DT
T +44 (0)114 283 1385
E chris@chct.co.uk
Regional Executives: Carmel Smithson, Kirsten Glasby-Hemmings
The Blades Enterprise Centre, Greystones Suite, Sheffield United Football Club, John Street, Sheffield S2 4SU
T +44 (0)114 292 2415 F +44 (0)114 292 2417
E carmel.smithson@icaew.com; kirsten.glasby-hemmings@icaew.com; sheffieldsca@icaew.com
Branches: no recognised branches

14. SOUTH EASTERN SOCIETY OF CHARTERED ACCOUNTANTS

President: Mike Arnold FCA
25 Sergison Road, Haywards Heath, RH16 1HX
T +44 (0)1444 457 465
E michaeljarnold@btinternet.com
Regional Executive: Emma Ware
PO Box 300, Ashford TW15 1WJ
T +44 (0)1932 788 772 F +44 (0)1932 781 987
E emma.ware@icaew.com; southeasternsca@icaew.com
Branches: no recognised branches

15. SOUTH ESSEX SOCIETY OF CHARTERED ACCOUNTANTS

President: Richard Lock FCA
256 Old Church Road, Chingford, London E4 8BT
T +44 (0)20 8523 7549
E locktax@tiscali.co.uk
Regional Executive: Linda Howard
2nd Floor, Parker House, 104A Hutton Road, Shenfield, Essex CM15 8NE
T/F +44 (0)1277 204 130
E linda.howard@icaew.com; southessexsca@icaew.com
Branches: no recognised branches

16. SOUTH WALES SOCIETY OF CHARTERED ACCOUNTANTS

President: Gary Partridge ACA
PricewaterhouseCoopers, One Kingsway, Cardiff CF10 3PW
T +44 (0)29 2023 7000
E gary.partridge@uk.pwc.com
Regional Executives: Emma Friedl / Fiona Washbrook
Wales Business Centre, Regus House, Falcon Drive, Cardiff Bay, Cardiff CF10 4RU
T +44 (0)29 2050 4595 F +44 (0)29 2050 4199
E wales@icaew.com; cymru@icaew.com
Branches: Cardiff & District Society, Gwent & Powys Society, Swansea & West Wales Society (contact district society)

17. SOUTH WESTERN SOCIETY OF CHARTERED ACCOUNTANTS

President: Clive Brown BA FCA
Sound Accounts, 26 Ladymeade, Ilminster, Somerset TA19 0EA
T +44 (0)1460 54705
E cbrown@soundaccountsltd.co.uk
Regional Executive: Trudi Coles
PO Box 80, Launceston PL15 7BB
T/F +44 (0)1566 86090
E trudi.coles@icaew.com; southwesternsca@icaew.com
Branches: Cornwall and Plymouth Society, Exeter and District Society and Somerset Society (contact district society)

18. SOUTHERN SOCIETY OF CHARTERED ACCOUNTANTS

President: Norman Armstrong BSc ACA
Grant Thornton UK LLP, Manor Court, Barnes Wallis Road, Segensworth, Fareham PO15 5GT
T +44 (0)1489 864 276
E norman.armstrong@gtuk.com
Regional Executive: Marietta Maidman
PO Box 423, Southampton S031 0AB
T +44 (0)1489 582 838 F +44 (0)1489 565 726
E marietta.maidman@icaew.com; southernsca@icaew.com
Branches: no recognised branches

19. STAFFS, SALOP & WOLVERHAMPTON SOCIETY OF CHARTERED ACCOUNTANTS

President: Valerie Wood ACA
77 Constance Avenue, Trentham, Stoke on Trent ST4 8TE
T +44 (0)1782 744 144
E valerie205@btinternet.com
Regional Executive: Terry Smythe
PO Box 110, Wellington TF1 6QX
T +44 (0)1952 251 932 F +44 (0)1952 240 114
E terry.smythe@icaew.com; bwmsca@icaew.com
Branches: Warwickshire Society, Worcestershire Society (contact district society)

20. THAMES VALLEY SOCIETY OF CHARTERED ACCOUNTANTS

President: David Duvall MA FCA
39 Hudson Road, Woodley, Reading RG5 4EN
T +44 (0)778 965 4969
E dduvall@cvdfk.com
Regional Executive: Sue Pye
PO Box 425, Redhill RH1 2GX
T +44 (0)1737 773 863 F +44 (0)1737 770 393
E sue.pye@icaew.com; thamesvalleysca@icaew.com
Branches: no recognised branches

21. WEST OF ENGLAND SOCIETY OF CHARTERED ACCOUNTANTS

President: Lee Aston ACA
KPMG, 100 Temple Street, Bristol BS1 6AG
T +44 (0)117 905 6000
E lee.aston@kpmg.co.uk
Regional Executive: Karen Evans
PO Box 51, Bristol BS16 1FH
T/F +44 (0)117 910 4965
M +44 (0)7876 035 944 E karen.evans@icaew.com

22. WEST YORKSHIRE SOCIETY OF CHARTERED ACCOUNTANTS

President: Merryck Lowe ACA
Alvarez & Marsal Europe Limited, 1 Canada Square (10th Floor), Canary Wharf, London E14 5AA
T +44 (0)20 7715 5220
E mlowe@alvarezandmarsal.com
Regional Executive: Esta Andrews
PO Box 1508, Huddersfield HD1 9HB
T +44 (0)1484 428 022 F +44 (0)1484 428 524
E esta.andrews@icaew.com; westyorkshiresca@icaew.com
Branches: Bradford Society, Huddersfield Society, York Society (contact district society)

23. INSTITUTE MEMBERS IN SCOTLAND

President: Melanie Wilson ACA CTA MAAT
Systematic Tax & Accounting, 39/3 Pilrigh Heights, Edinburgh EH6 5FD
T +44 (0)8453 880 265
E melaniejwilson@gmail.com
Regional Executive: Fiona Ormiston
PO Box 26198, Dunfermline KY12 8ZD
T +44 (0)1383 885 645
E fiona.ormiston@icaew.com

INSTITUTE INFORMATION

ADDRESSES

The Institute of Chartered Accountants in England and Wales
PO Box 433
Chartered Accountants' Hall
Moorgate Place
London EC2P 2BJ
UK
T +44 (0)20 7920 8100 F +44 (0)20 7920 0547
www.icaew.com

Metropolitan House
321 Avebury Boulevard
Milton Keynes MK9 2FZ
UK
T +44 (0)1908 248 100 F +44 (0)1908 691 165
www.icaew.com

European Office
221 Rue de la Loi
B-1040 Brussels
Belgium
T +32 (0)2 230 3272 F +32 (0)2 230 2851
www.icaew.com/europe

China Office
Room 706A Tower E1 Oriental Plaza
No.1 East Chang An Avenue Dong Cheng District
Beijing
100738 China
T +86 10 8518 8622 F +86 10 8518 7980
www.icaew.com/china

Hong Kong Office
27th Floor
Wu Chung House
213 Queen's Road East
Wanchai, Hong Kong
T +852 2287 7277 F +852 2575 8925
www.icaew.com/hongkong

Malaysia Office
Level 2 Chulan Tower
3 Jalan Conlay
50450 Kuala Lumpur, Malaysia
T +6 (03)2171 6022 F +6 (03)2171 6025
www.icaew.com/malaysia

OFFICE HOLDERS

President - David Furst FCA
Deputy-President - Martin Hagen FCA
Vice-President - Gerald Russell FCA
Chief Executive - Michael Izza FCA

USEFUL TELEPHONE NUMBERS

The Institute provides members with a wide range of services to help them keep up to date professionally. Direct line numbers for some of the most frequently used services are listed below:

ACA training .... +44 (0)1908 248 040
Audit and Assurance Faculty .... +44 (0)20 7920 8493
Communications .... +44 (0)20 7920 8633
Continuing Professional Development .... +44 (0)1908 248 293
Corporate Finance Faculty .... +44 (0)20 7920 8685
Esca restaurant .... +44 (0)20 7920 8626
Ethics helpline service .... +44 (0)1908 248 258
Finance and Management Faculty .... +44 (0)20 7920 8508
Financial Reporting Faculty .... +44 (0)20 7920 3511
Financial Services Faculty .... +44 (0)20 7920 8417
Information Centre .... +44 (0)1908 248 186
Insolvency licensing .... +44 (0)1908 546 262
IT Faculty .... +44 (0)20 7920 8481
Library and Information Service .... +44 (0)20 7920 8620
Media relations .... +44 (0)20 7920 8630
Membership enquiries and subscriptions .... +44 (0)1908 248 250
Money Laundering helpline .... +44 (0)1908 248 320
Practice Assurance helpline .... +44 (0)1908 546 388
Practice Advisory Services .... +44 (0)1908 248 032
President's Appointments Scheme .... +44 (0)1908 248 037
Regulatory support .... +44 (0)1908 546 302
Special Interest Groups .... +44 (0)1908 248 186
Support members .... +44 (0)800 917 3526
Tax Faculty .... +44 (0)20 7920 8646
Technical enquiries service .... +44 (0)1908 248 025

ENQUIRIES

Enquiries from the general public and from members relating to the services provided by the Institute, or other general matters should be directed to the Institute, switchboard T +44 (0)20 7920 8100.

SENIOR MANAGEMENT TEAM

Chief Executive
Michael Izza, FCA T +44 (0)20 7920 8419
Executive Director, Finance and Operations
Robin Fieth, FCA T +44 (0)20 7920 8464
Executive Director, Learning & Professional Development
Dr Raymond Madden, FRSA T +44 (0)20 7920 8563
Executive Director, Professional Standards
Vernon Soare, CPFA T +44 (0)20 7920 8787
Executive Director, Technical
Robert Hodgkinson, FCA T +44 (0)20 7920 8492

CCH

CCH, a division of Wolters Kluwer (UK) Limited is a unique organisation that delivers integrated, seamless solutions to help take accountancy and finance professionals to new levels of excellence and efficiency. The **CCH** name is one of the longest-established and most trusted in this market – both in the UK and globally – making it the supplier of choice to the accountancy market.
CEO Wolters Kluwer (UK) Limited: Catherine Wolfe

ACCOUNTANCY MAGAZINE

Accountancy is the Institute of Chartered Accountants in England and Wales' monthly magazine, providing accountancy professionals with:

- relevant and topical news accountants must know
- authoritative analysis of current events
- exclusive surveys and insights into the latest business and accountancy trends
- in-depth technical analysis
- the latest accounting standards, and
- sections dedicated to practice, financial reporting, tax, business finance, technology and law.

Total net circulation for the period end June 2008 is 150,456.

For subscription information please contact the subscriptions department on T +44 (0)844 561 8162.

Accountancy Online is an internet news service providing free daily updates on professional and business news, regular surveys, useful links and subscription-based access to *Accountancy* magazine in electronic format. Visit *Accountancy Online* at **www.accountancymagazine.com**
Editorial Director: Douglas Broom
Editor: Sally Percy

CCH FEE PROTECTION AND CONSULTANCY

CCH Fee Protection and Consultancy supply guaranteed advice, practical assistance and training not only on matters relating to taxation issues, but also to employment, workplace safety and environmental issues.

CCH Fee Protection and Consultancy offer insurance policies that protect accountants' fees should their clients be investigated by HM Revenue and Customs. These policies are underwritten by DAS Legal Expenses Insurance Company Limited, the UK's largest legal expenses insurer.

The policy can cover up to £50,000 per claim for representation costs to deal with:

- self assessment full and aspect enquiries and in depth accounts investigations
- employer compliance disputes (PAYE, P11D, NIC), and
- VAT disputes.

CCH Fee Protection and Consultancy also have a number of advice lines that are not only for queries relating to taxation, eg clients in accountancy practices also have access to the **Business Support Helpline**, as do those of their clients who take up fee protection insurance.

The **Business Support Helpline** is a specialist service that provides immediate telephone advice and guidance across a whole range of business issues.

Its multi-disciplined team of consultants provides reliable, practical solutions, based on a wide knowledge and experience of matters relating to: payroll employment and personnel, health and safety, company and contract law, landlord and tenant, consumer sales law, company secretarial, copyright and patents and debt collection.

For more information about **CCH Fee Protection and Consultancy** and any of its products please call T +44 (0)800 542 6648 E tax@cch.co.uk or visit our website at **www.cch.co.uk**

CCH INFORMATION

CCH Information packages offer solutions to information needs in a variety of formats and media:

- looseleaf reference works ensuring comprehensive, accurate and up-to-date information
- electronic reference services – available online (see **www.cchinformation.com** below) and in CD-ROM format
- newsletters – available in both print and online
- books, special reports and bulletins, and
- telephone advice helplines staffed by experts in their field – providing unlimited, friendly, authoritative advice.

All new product development is carefully researched before publication ensuring that the final content produced is what is needed and is in the most appropriate format for the customer. All our content is produced by experts and is independently reviewed to ensure that it is reliable and up to date.

For the latest catalogue please call customer services on T +44 (0)844 561 8166 E customerservices@cch.co.uk or visit our website at **www.cch.co.uk**

Accounting & Business Research is a quarterly research journal. It contains articles by leading academics on business and accounting topics. For subscription information please contact the subscriptions department on T +44 (0)20 8247 1637.
Director: Robert McKay

WWW.CCHINFORMATION.COM

www.cchinformation.com is a unique online information resource for accountants and tax advisers in practice and business. It provides a complete, bespoke information solution which will satisfy all the needs of the different parts of business, including direct and indirect taxation; tax investigations; accountancy, auditing and assurance; corporate governance; risk management; financial management and business advice.

It is a unique site because no other UK site can equal the breadth and depth of tax, accountancy, audit and business content available at www.cchinformation.com. You subscribe to just the content your business needs and you control access so that the right information reaches the right people at the right time.

For more information or to register for a free 14-day trial please call T +44 (0)870 777 2906 E cchcustomerservices@cch.co.uk or visit our website at **www.cchinformation.com**

CCH PROFESSIONAL DEVELOPMENT

Through **CCH Professional Development** we offer a comprehensive choice of seminars and courses to accountants, tax and finance professionals ranging from introductory through to those designed to meet the needs of the most experienced practitioner. As **CCH Seminars Online**, we have developed an online CPD service, accessed from the desktop, for accountants in practice and others who wish to keep abreast of the latest developments in tax, audit and accounting, particularly accountants in commerce and industry and financial advisers.

For further information on **CCH Professional Development** please call T +44 (0)20 7824 8257 or E info@cchseminars.co.uk.

CCH SOFTWARE

CCH Software provides a series of solutions designed to help manage routine processes and key tasks, helping to ensure legal compliance and increasing the effectiveness of businesses by saving them time and money. The portfolio of applications range from management software, risk assessment, tax, audit and reporting tools, through to computer-based and online training packages.

For further information on **CCH Software** please call Customer Services on T +44 (0)1483 775 070 E info@cchgroup.co.uk or visit our website at **www.cch.co.uk**
Director: Simon Crompton

SERVICES FOR ICAEW MEMBERS

VALUE FROM INSTITUTE MEMBERSHIP

The ICAEW gives members the tools and assistance necessary to thrive in their chosen field, by promoting trust in our brand, and by building on our collective reputation at home and abroad as the leading UK body of finance professionals offering world-class qualifications, thought leadership and clear insight into professional and technical issues.

The Institute is continually developing its portfolio of products and services to ensure members have access to the most useful and relevant support available. Here is an overview of what the Institute offers its members, full details of which can be found at **www.icaew.com/members**

ICAEW WEBSITE

The Institute's website **(www.icaew.com)** provides a wealth of news and information for anyone with an interest in accountancy. The site includes details on how to become a chartered accountant, the services chartered accountants offer and the online edition of the *Directory of Firms*.

Members can log into their own dedicated area of the site **(www.icaew.com/members)** using their membership number and password where they will find details of member services, technical helplines, events and personalised information from faculties and regions.

INFORMATION AND ADVICE

The Library Enquiry Service provides members with information on a range of topics from dividends to tax and company information. Most enquiries are answered straight away and are always responded to within 24 hours. Members can also borrow books, which are posted out free of charge.

The library website offers free online resources, including articles from major business and trade journals, UK and international market research reports, country information, European tax rates and 200 eBooks. Visit **www.icaew.com/library**

We keep members up-to-date via a variety of media including our electronic newsletters – *Business Alert*, *Practice Society Alert*, *Young Professionals Alert* or *International Alert* – for which members can register online.

The experienced and knowledgeable Ethics and Technical Advisory teams offer friendly, free and expert advice, in strict confidence, to all members, students and affiliates of the Institute.

ETHICS

Ethics Advisory Services advises on ethical dilemmas in both business and practice sectors, including providing guidance on interpretation and compliance with the *Members' Handbook*.
T +44 (0)1908 248 258 E ethics@icaew.com
www.icaew.com/ethicsadvice

TECHNICAL ENQUIRIES SERVICE

The Technical Enquiries Service provides technical advice on a wide range of subjects including accounting, company law, charities and auditing, but not taxation, T +44 (0)1908 248 025
www.icaew.com/technicalenquiries

TECHNICAL STRATEGY DEPARTMENT

The Technical Strategy Department maintains and enhances the Institute's global reputation for thought leadership and technical excellence, and develops and promotes technical policy in order to influence the regulatory and professional environment affecting members. The Department also supports the ICAEW's engagement with European and global bodies and provides guidance to members on a wide variety of issues affecting the profession. Please see **www.icaew.com/technical** for further information.

CONFIDENTIALITY

Enquirers' details are treated in strict confidence and not divulged to third parties, including other departments of the Institute, unless an enquirer asks for this to be done or consents to it. Membership details are requested and brief details of enquiries are kept in order to provide a record in case the member needs to rely on it at a later date.

MONEY LAUNDERING HELPLINE

This is a helpline service to offer advice on all aspects of compliance with the money laundering legislation. The service is provided by the Institute's Advisory Services Team. T +44 (0)1908 248 320
www.icaew.com/moneylaundering

SUPPORT MEMBERS

Support members provide immediate, totally confidential and non-judgemental support to all members of the Institute whenever they are in difficulty. They are all volunteers who give some of their time to help other members. There are support members in each of the regions and district society areas and they come from a variety of business, practice and other backgrounds.

Experience has shown that in nearly all cases members can benefit from contacting a support member. Often simply discussing a problem with a support member can help to identify a way forward. So that you can feel completely at ease in contacting a support member in what might be a difficult or sensitive situation, all of the volunteers are exempt from the duty to report misconduct in their support role. Whatever your circumstances, support members are there to help.
T Freephone +44 (0)800 917 3526 (normal call charges apply if you are calling from outside the UK).
www.icaew.com/supportmembers

FACULTIES AND SPECIAL INTEREST GROUPS

For a small subscription fee, members can further develop their professional knowledge by joining one of the Institute's seven faculties and eleven special interest groups.

With over 35,000 members, the faculties provide an essential source of technical expertise to help maintain professional excellence, the latest knowledge of good practice, thought leadership and invaluable networking opportunities. The faculties include audit and assurance, corporate finance, finance and management, financial reporting, financial services, information technology; and tax. For more information, please visit **www.icaew.com/faculties**

The special interest groups provide our members with practical support, information and the chance to network with their peers when working in, or for, a particular sector. The groups are: charity and voluntary sector; entertainment and media; farming and rural business; forensic; healthcare; interim management; non-executive directors; public sector; solicitors; tourism and hospitality and valuation. For more information, please visit **www.icaew.com/sigs**

MEMBERSHIP PRODUCTS AND SERVICES

The Institute chooses partners who are able to provide our members with a range of products to assist them in their lifestyles and professional lives. From finance and insurance products to car rental and directory advertising, the Institute has selected products to suit everyone. Visit **www.icaew.com/memberoffers** for full details.

PRESIDENT'S APPOINTMENTS SCHEME

The Institute maintains a database of members and others who are specialists in arbitration, mediation and expert determination. If you are seeking an independent valuation of shares in a company, have a partnership dispute or need the services of a forensic accountant as an expert witness, this scheme can help.

For more information or a copy of the scheme guidelines,
T +44 (0)1908 248 037 or visit **www.icaew.com/presappts**

ACA

The ACA is the premier finance-based qualification for business leaders. It is internationally acknowledged as the 'gold-standard' accountancy qualification and inspires business confidence.

Training for the ACA takes between three and five years with exams, on-the-job experience and structured study. Successful students are awarded the designatory letters ACA which enables them to practice as a chartered accountant. Today, ACAs work in over 160 countries around the world.

The ACA represents achievement across a breadth of financial and business skills that other qualifications can only aspire to. The professional recognition and reputation of qualified ACAs speaks for itself: 67%* of FTSE 100 qualified accountants acting as finance director or CEO have an ACA. That's more than four times the number holding any other single qualification.

To register to train ACA students, please visit **www.icaew.com/employers** or T +44 (0)1908 248 038.

To study for the ACA qualification across the world, learn more about the qualification and search for available training vacancies visit **www.icaew.com/careers** or T +44 (0)1908 248 040.

CORPORATE FINANCE QUALIFICATION

The Corporate Finance (CF) qualification is designed exclusively for corporate finance practitioners and was developed by the ICAEW, in partnership with the Canadian Institute of Chartered Accountants.

This international qualification combines comprehensive technical knowledge and skills with practical application, high level strategy and comprises two stages.

- Diploma level delivers the technical skills, knowledge and best practice technique, required for today's high performing corporate financiers.
- Advanced Diploma focuses on real-life corporate finance experience and deal management. It takes the development of the technical knowledge to the highest level of practical application.

Dependent on your location, there will be an entry requirement relating to the local legal and regulatory aspects of your jurisdiction. In the UK, the Certificate in Corporate Finance, delivered by the Securities & Investment Institute (SII) is required before starting the Diploma level (exemptions are available).

Successful candidates who have completed the required stages and acquired the requisite work experience will be awarded the CF designation. This denotes success, status and commitment to professional excellence.

For more information, visit **www.cfqualification.com**
E cfqualification@icaew.com or T +44 (0)1908 248 293.

INTERNATIONAL FINANCIAL REPORTING STANDARDS (IFRS)

The IFRS learning and assessment programme has been developed by IFRS specialists and is relevant to both accountants and non-accountants who are required to implement, use or are affected by IFRS.

Available at Certificate level, this self taught programme is completely flexible allowing individuals to learn anywhere and at any time. Supported by learning materials consisting of a learning manual, interactive online learning environment and an online certificated assessment. The assessment will demonstrate and verify the individual's knowledge and understanding to help meet IFRS requirements with confidence.

For more information, visit **www.icaew.com/ifrs**
E ifrs@icaew.com or T +44 (0)1908 248 293.

**Accountancy*, October/November 2006

MBA ESSENTIALS

MBA Essentials is designed to inspire, motivate and develop managers in just five days. This tailored programme considers management strategy; its implementation and how best to measure it; marketing; results-driven leadership and concludes with practical application.

The programme underlines the principles, tools and applications used for strategy, enabling participants to challenge and improve processes and appreciate the different styles of leadership.

Experienced practitioners and academic experts deliver the programme in small study groups, which aids the learning process and provides the opportunity for one-on-one sessions with peers and tutors.

This programme is ideal for managers operating at all levels who require a refresher course, together with those wishing to improve management performance and strategic outlook; and is the perfect taster opportunity for someone considering a full MBA.

For more information, visit **www.icaew.com/mbaessentials**
E mbaessentials@icaew.com or T +44 (0)1908 248 293.

DIPLOMA IN CHARITY ACCOUNTING

Through this specialist postgraduate diploma individuals are given a comprehensive insight into the different aspects of the voluntary sector, alongside in-depth training in charity finance and accounting.

The diploma is a classroom-based course provided by Cass Business School, London, which is open to graduates and individuals who are looking to develop their career and extend their professional skills in charity finance and accounting.

On successful completion, individuals are awarded a postgraduate diploma and credits to help achieve an MSc. Individuals will also acquire the designatory letters, DChA, which acknowledges expertise in charity accounting at the highest level and up to 12 months free membership to the Charity and Voluntary Sector Special Interest Group, if not already a member.

For more information, visit **www.icaew.com/charityaccounting**
E charityaccounting@icaew.com or T +44 (0)1908 248 293.

CERTIFICATE IN FINANCE, ACCOUNTING AND BUSINESS

The Certificate in Finance, Accounting and Business (CFAB) qualification aims to give individuals the opportunity to develop essential knowledge for today's business environment. Consisting of the professional stage of the ACA, the modules include: Business and Finance, Management Information, Accounting (mandatory), Law, Assurance and Principles of Taxation, which provide individuals with a wealth of business, finance and accounting fundamentals.

CFAB can be gained within one year and consists of a flexible learning and assessment structure, which enables individuals to learn at their own pace.

The qualification is ideal for those who are interested in a career in finance, business and accounting or for those who work within these sectors.

For more information, visit **www.icaew.com/cfab**
E cfab@icaew.com or T +44 (0)1908 248 293.

BUSINESS SUSTAINABILITY PROGRAMME

The Business Sustainability Programme aims to help raise the awareness of the business case for corporate responsibility and the issues which face companies now and in the future.

Consisting of five modules, the programme is an easily accessible e-learning programme which takes the user on a journey from potentially a basic level of knowledge through to confidence in understanding how an organisation can benefit from doing business differently. The programme is abundant with flexibility; the content can be tailored to the organisation, it is not time sensitive and the modules can be taken in stages.

The programme will address the financial perspective of corporate responsibility and will be of interest, not only to those who work in an accounting and finance environment, but also to all business professionals. Equally it can be used as part of an induction or training programme for individuals who operate at all levels within business, practice and the public sector.

For more information,visit **www.icaew.com/bsp**
E bsp@icaew.com or T +44 (0)1908 248 293.

PATHWAYS TO MEMBERSHIP

The Pathways to Membership programme has been established to enable members of ACCA, CIPFA and CIMA to gain membership to the ICAEW by passing an Examination of Experience. To be eligible applicants must have at least five years' relevant work experience and two sponsors who are already ICAEW members.

The benefits of ICAEW membership for the individual include the opportunity to expand and refresh their knowledge base, networking opportunities, technical representation, advice and support throughout their career. For firms it also supports succession planning by increasing the pool of potential partners.

For further information, visit **www.icaew.com/pathways** or
T +44 (0)1908 248 040.

CONTINUING PROFESSIONAL DEVELOPMENT (CPD)

To maintain 'professionalism by association' for ICAEW members and to protect the exceptional reputation of the Institute in its own right, it is imperative that all members comply with their CPD obligations. To meet the requirements members must:

- reflect on their responsibilities, undertake appropriate development activities and consider the impact of those development activities, on an ongoing basis
- provide a signed declaration on an annual basis
- if asked to do so, submit evidence to back their declaration.

For further information, visit **www.icaew.com/cpd** or
T +44 (0)1908 248 293.

RECORDS TEAM

Members' Registrar: Daniel Quint

The Members Records Team maintains the details of the Institute's members and member firms. The department also deals with:

- enquiries about entries in the *List of Members* and *Directory of Firms*
- applications for reciprocal membership
- applications for re-admission
- resignations.

The department can be contacted by T +44 (0)1908 248 054 or T +44 (0)1908 248 248, F +44 (0)1908 248 064, or
E members.records@icaew.com, readmissions@icaew.com, resignations@icaew.com

MEMBERS INFORMATION

Enquiries about the current status of a member or member firm should be made by T +44 (0)9066 140 906. Calls cost 60p per minute. Enquiries made from outside the UK should
E members.registration@icaew.com. The department also:

- provides membership and registration
- provides letters of confirmation of membership, including Notarising and seeking Apostiles from the Foreign & Commonwealth Office and foreign embassies
- issues of associate, fellow and practising certificates.

The department can be contacted by T +44 (0)1908 248 250, by F +44 (0)1908 248 069, or E members.registration@icaew.com

CHARTERED ACCOUNTANTS' HALL

All the function rooms at Chartered Accountants' Hall are available for hire, from the smallest meeting room for eight, to the spacious Great Hall which seats over 300. Member firms benefit from a 10% discount on all bookings throughout the year.

Open Monday to Friday, 12:00 – 14:00, the Esca restaurant offers high quality food every day, while the wine bar has a lighter menu for those with less time. The restaurant can also be hired for private dinners and receptions.

For full details on room hire and the restaurant,
T +44 (0)20 7920 8613, E cahall@icaew.com, or visit
www.cahall.co.uk

MEMBER FIRM BRAND MARK

Raising the profile of chartered accountants and the professional reputation of our members has never been more important. To support this, the ICAEW launched a new corporate identity in January 2007. Our new brand mark is instantly recognisable, with a simple accessible design that will have significant impact wherever it is used.

Taking the main elements of the Institute brand mark, we have designed a specific member firm brand mark as shown below. As a member firm, using the brand mark will endorse your commitment to quality and integrity of the accountancy profession. It will also enable you to align your firm with any Institute promotional activity and help to strengthen the main ICAEW brand.

Only practising member firms can use the member firm brand mark. If you need to check your entitlement to use the mark, please contact the ICAEW information centre on:

T +44 (0)1908 248 186
F +44 (0)1908 248 069
E information.centre@icaew.com

The member firm brand mark and guidelines are available for download from **www.icaew.com**

HOW TO USE THE DIRECTORY

The Official ICAEW Directory of Firms is published in two formats. The main directory is a hardback national version, which lists details of firms throughout the UK and worldwide. This directory is available from Waterlow Legal & Regulatory Ltd priced £107 or £99 (for Institute members). The directory also appears in 10 regional versions, each of which list firms in that region. The breakdown of these regions is as follows:
East England, East Midlands, London, North West, Northern, South East, South West, Wales, West Midlands and Yorkshire and Humber.

To order a copy of your regional directory, please contact Matthew Holley on T +44 (0)20 566 8280 or E mholley@waterlow.com.

If you are looking for a chartered accountant in your area, please contact your nearest district society using the list on page 25 of the directory.

Entries in this directory are organised alphabetically by town. Entries within each town are also alphabetical. To find the names of firms in a given town, turn to the relevant town name.

Use the specialisations index to identify firms according to specific service requirements.

If you know the name of the firm you are looking for, you can use the index at the back of the directory.

All firms eligible for entry in the directory were contacted during its compilation. Where no response was received, only minimum details appear.

Three areas of accountancy work are regulated by statute: investment business, audit and insolvency. Details on each of these areas are given below.

INVESTMENT BUSINESS AUTHORISATION

Under the Financial Services and Markets Act 2000, firms that wish to recommend specific investment business products have to be authorised to do so by the Financial Services Authority (FSA).
The Institute can license firms to provide a wide range of investment advice, including advice on private company shares and selling investments, and advice on general insurances and mortgages, that arises out of or is complementary to another service. The directory indicates which form of authorisation a firm has.

AUDIT REGULATION

Under Part II of the Companies Act 2006, firms which wish to undertake company audit work must be registered with either the Institute or another recognised supervisory body (RSB). If firms wish to promote company audit services they may choose to publicise the fact that they are registered auditors. There is no obligation to do so. This directory indicates whether a firm which has chosen to promote its company audit services is registered with the Institute or with another RSB.

INSOLVENCY LICENCE

If an office promotes insolvency work, at least one individual at that office must be a licensed insolvency practitioner. Licensed insolvency practitioners will hold an insolvency licence, issued either by this Institute or by another recognised professional body (RPB).

Entries for firms eligible to undertake work in these areas may include one or more of the legends below:

◎ registered by The Institute of Chartered Accountants in England and Wales to carry out company audit work

◎ registered by another RSB to carry out company audit work

◎ regulated by The Institute of Chartered Accountants in England and Wales for a range of investment business activities

◎ authorised and regulated by the Financial Services Authority for investment business

◎ licensed by another DPB to carry on investment business

◎ individual(s) licensed for insolvency work by the Institute of Chartered Accountants in England and Wales

◎ individual(s) licensed for insolvency work by another RPB

PRACTICE ASSURANCE

Practice Assurance (a compulsory scheme of practice review) applies to all members who hold a practising certificate and who offer accountancy services to the public. These members are required to comply with four published, principles-based standards. In most cases, practising certificate holders will be monitored through an annual return and a visit to 'member firms', whether or not they use the description chartered accountant.

Where a practising certificate holder works within a 'mixed' firm, the firm's parent body will undertake the monitoring, under reciprocal arrangements. If there is no parent body, the Institute will monitor the individual.

Member firms that are subject to Practice Assurance monitoring and that comply with the principles-based standards are entitled to use the Institute's logo and Practice Assurance legend.

EXPLANATION OF TERMS AND SYMBOLS

Accountancy firms not marked ▽, ★ or ▼ are composed wholly of chartered accountant members of this Institute.

▽ against the name of a firm indicates that the firm is composed wholly of accountants who are members of one or another of the three Institutes of Chartered Accountants in Great Britain and Ireland (namely: this Institute, The Institute of Chartered Accountants of Scotland and The Institute of Chartered Accountants in Ireland).

★ against the name of a firm indicates that the firm is not composed wholly of members of one or another of the three Institutes of Chartered Accountants in Great Britain and Ireland.

▼ against the name of an organisation indicates an overseas organisation which, although associated with a member firm, does not include a member of the Institute as either a partner or director.

Ⓜ against the name of a firm indicates that the firm operates as management consultants.

◈ listed in the SME Funding Adviser Scheme (see p.23)

Example

GREAVES & CO
White Lodge, 33 Woodside Road,
Woodford Green IG8 0TW
Tel: 020 8506 1002
Principal: ICAEW Member
C.M.Greaves

HASLERS
Johnston House, 8 Johnston Road,
Woodford Green IG8 0XA
Tel: 020 8504 3344
Fax: 020 8506 5100
E-Mail: advice@haslers.com
Web: http://www.haslers.com
Training Contracts Available.
Resident Partners/Directors:
ICAEW Members

M.J.Anderson, S.Baskin, S.J.Blake, M.P. Gould, R.A.J.Hooper, L.A.Jacobs, P.D. Kurup, G.C.Reed, S.M.Simmons
Non ICAEW Members
J O'Shea
Other Offices:
Lion House, 72 Chapel Street, Netherton, Dudley, West Midlands DY2 9PF
(Tel: 01384 238141)

Registered by the ICAEW to carry out company audit work

Regulated by the ICAEW for a range of investment business activities

Individual(s) licensed for insolvency work by the ICAEW

SPECIALISATIONS - SERVICES

Bankruptcies, Corporate Finance, Corporate Recovery, Disposal of Businesses, Divorce/ Matrimonial, Expert Witnesses in Litigation, Forensic Accounting, Investigations, Liquidations, Reorganisations and Company Reconstructions

SPECIALISATIONS - TAXATION

Back Duty, Planning

General Description: With some 80 staff and 10 partners we are one of the largest independent firms in the London/Essex border area. We aim to provide a high quality service with a personal touch. In addition to tax and corporate compliance work, we are particularly known for our expertise in tax planning, insolvency, corporate finance, financial services and computer consultancy.

DEFINITIONS OF SERVICES AND SPECIALISATIONS

Entries in this directory list various services and specialisations offered by firms of chartered accountants. These have been split into the following categories:

- financial reporting
- audit and assurance
- taxation
- business recovery – insolvency
- investment business
- business – general advice
- forensic accounting
- IT
- sector specialisations

Below you will find definitions of items within these categories, apart from the final one which is self-explanatory.

FINANCIAL REPORTING

ACCOUNTS PREPARATION
The preparation of finalised accounts of businesses, companies or other organisations from the basic accounting records. This includes limited companies and partnership/sole trader accounts.

AUDIT EXEMPTION REPORT
The accounts of limited liability companies where the company is small enough not to require an audit.

FINANCIAL REPORTING
The preparation of accounts to comply with the statutory requirements and applicable accounting standards.

FOREIGN SUBSIDIARY COMPANIES IN THE UK
The preparation of the accounts of foreign companies trading in the UK.

INTERNATIONAL FINANCIAL REPORTING STANDARDS (IFRS)
The preparation of limited liability accounts to international accounting standards.

LIMITED COMPANIES
Advice on all aspects of financial reporting and taxation that affect limited companies and limited liability partnerships.

LIMITED COMPANY ACCOUNTS
The preparation of accounts of limited companies.

LIMITED LIABILITY PARTNERSHIP
The preparation of accounts of partnerships where one or more partners has limited liability.

PARTNERSHIP/SOLE TRADER ACCOUNTS
The preparation of accounts of unincorporated entities.

AUDIT AND ASSURANCE

ASSURANCE SERVICES
The evaluation by a professional accountant of subject matter that is the responsibility of another party using identified suitable criteria, expressing a conclusion that provides the intended user with a level of assurance about that subject matter.

AUDIT
The provision of audit services by an independent auditor.

AUDIT - PRIVATE COMPANY
For companies above a certain turnover level and some other organisations, there is a legal requirement for a report on the accounts by an independent auditor, registered with the Institute of Chartered Accountants in England and Wales or another recognised supervisory body.

AUDIT - PUBLIC COMPANY
As well as undertaking the audit, advice can be given on Stock Exchange reporting requirements and compliance with accounting standards.

INTERNAL AUDIT
The function, carried out within an organisation, of examining, evaluating and reporting on accounting and other controls on the operations of the organisation.

TAXATION

BACK DUTY
See 'Investigations and enquiries'.

CAPITAL GAINS TAX - LIMITED COMPANIES
Advice on taxation of gains or losses arising from the disposal of business assets.

CAPITAL GAINS - PERSONAL
Advice on taxation of gains or losses arising from the disposal of personal assets.

CORPORATE
Advice on the rules that apply in respect of corporate transactions and in particular the tax implications of corporate groups.

CUSTOMS DUTY
Tax paid on goods exported or imported and advice on the reliefs available.

EMPLOYEE TAXATION
Advice to employees on the tax on income earned from their employment and advice to employers.

ESTATE AND INHERITANCE
Inheritance tax planning.

ESTATE PLANNING
Advice on planning the most effective way of passing on your wealth to future generations.

EXECUTORSHIP
Either acting as the named executor in a will or advising executors on the steps to be taken.

FOREIGN NATIONALS IN THE UK
Advice on the effect of UK taxation on foreign individuals and advice for their employers.

INVESTIGATIONS AND ENQUIRIES
Assessing and negotiating with HMRC, for example on tax underpaid in previous years as a result of failing to provide adequate information about income to the tax authorities.

NATIONAL INSURANCE ADVICE
Advice both to employers and employees on the effect of National Insurance contributions on salary and benefits.

OFFSHORE COMPANIES
Advice on the taxation of companies domiciled offshore.

PARTNERSHIPS AND SOLE TRADERS
Calculation and agreement of the tax liability of partnerships and sole traders arising from their business activities.

PAYE ADVICE
Assistance with the Pay As You Earn (PAYE) system of tax collection.

PAYROLL SERVICE AND ADVICE
The provision of a payroll service and advice on payroll matters.

PERSONAL
Advice on all aspects of tax as it affects the individual, including self assessment.

SELF ASSESSMENT ADVICE
Among many other aspects, this includes advice about record-keeping, tax returns and the systems for the payment of tax.

SMALL TRADERS
Advice on all aspects of taxation of small businesses, such as retailers.

TAXATION
All aspects of tax work for companies, businesses and individuals, including preparing computations, dealing with HMRC and advising on taxation.

TRUSTEESHIP
Advice on the use of trusts and also acting as a trustee.

TRUSTS
How trusts are taxed and their use in tax planning.

UK COMPANIES OVERSEAS
The tax implications of UK companies trading overseas.

UK NATIONALS OVERSEAS
Advice on the effect of UK and overseas taxation on UK nationals working overseas.

UK SUBSIDIARIES OF OVERSEAS MULTINATIONALS
Advice for UK subsidiaries of overseas multinationals to ensure compliance with UK tax laws.

VALUE ADDED TAX
Advice on complying with, and the incidence of, VAT on business transactions.

BUSINESS RECOVERY - INSOLVENCY

ADMINISTRATION
A rescue procedure under which a licensed insolvency practitioner is appointed to a company, which either is, or seems likely to become, unable to pay its debts. (See also 'Corporate recovery'.)

BANKRUPTCIES
Dealing with personal insolvency.

CORPORATE RECOVERY
The provision of advice and assistance to companies facing financial difficulties.

LIQUIDATIONS
Dealing with insolvencies of businesses by which a company ceases and has its assets collected and liabilities satisfied for as the assets will allow.

REORGANISATIONS AND COMPANY RECONSTRUCTIONS
Advice on schemes of rearrangement to assist companies over financial difficulties including administration.

INVESTMENT BUSINESS

FINANCIAL PLANNING AND ADVICE
Advice can be given on aspects of financial planning, both for individuals and for businesses.

PENSIONS ADVICE
Advice on the most suitable pension or insurance arrangements, either for an individual or for a company wishing to establish a pension scheme.

PLANNING
Advice on how to arrange transactions in the most tax-beneficial manner.

BUSINESS - GENERAL ADVICE

ACQUISITIONS AND MERGERS
Advice on all aspects of taking over or merging with another enterprise, including identification of other suitable businesses and negotiating agreements.

BOOK-KEEPING
The provision of a book-keeping service for clients running their own business.

BOOK-KEEPING SYSTEMS
Advice on manual and computerised methods of recording your accounting transactions.

COMPANY FORMATION
Formation of a limited liability company including documentation, name availability and provision of the Memorandum and Articles and statutory registers.

COMPANY SECRETARIAL SERVICE
Advice on and assistance with keeping statutory records of shareholders, directors and other company information.

DATA PROCESSING SERVICES
The provision of computerised reports, usually of an accounting nature, from basic information supplied by you.

DEBT COUNSELLING
On a personal level, how to control your spending and deal with the repayment of a mortgage and other arrears.

DISPOSAL OF BUSINESSES
Assistance with all aspects of disposing of your business, including finding potential buyers, negotiating and taxation advice.

DIVORCE/MATRIMONIAL
Advice on taxation and other aspects of divorce and marriage.

EUROPE
Advice on trading with or setting up businesses within the EU.

FRANCHISING
Advice on all aspects of franchising from both the franchisor and franchisee perspective.

INVESTMENT APPRAISAL
An examination of the merits of different forms of investment, whether to retain an investment and, if FSA authorised, whether to make certain investments.

MANAGEMENT ACCOUNTING CONSULTANCY
Advice on establishing an efficient system of management reporting and interpretation of the information recorded.

MANAGEMENT ADVICE TO BUSINESS
Advice on financial and other management aspects of controlling your business.

MANAGEMENT CONSULTANCY
Investigation and advice on specific managerial, financial and operational aspects of your business.

OUTSOURCING - FINANCIAL SERVICES
Undertaking the processing of transactions on behalf of others eg, insurance, banking, investment and other financial services.

OVERSEAS COUNTRIES
The accountancy and management issues of investing and trading overseas.

PENSION SCHEME ACCOUNTING
Administration of a business pension scheme which might include a membership database, record of contributions, running bank accounts, paying benefits and preparation of scheme accounts.

RISK MANAGEMENT
Profiling the risks faced by a business (such as business interruption and fraud) and developing a strategy for dealing with them.

TAKEOVERS
Advice and assistance throughout the whole process of taking over another organisation.

FOREIGN CURRENCIES ADVICE
Advice on trading in the euro and other currency.

FORENSIC ACCOUNTING

EXPERT WITNESS IN LITIGATION
To act as an independent expert in legal and arbitration cases where specialist financial comment is required.

FORENSIC ACCOUNTING
Using accounting, auditing and investigative skills to assist enquiries which are likely to result in a case in a court of law, hence requires knowledge of rules of evidence.

IT

COMPUTER CONSULTANTS
Advice on the selection of computer hardware.

COMPUTER SYSTEMS AND CONSULTANCY
Advice on how your business can benefit from the use of Information and Communications Technology (ICT) including use of accounting software.

COMPUTERISED ACCOUNTING SYSTEMS
The provision of advice and assistance with the implementation of computerised accounting systems.

E-COMMERCE
Advice on doing business on the internet.

INFORMATION TECHNOLOGY
Using other communications tools for business applications.

THE OFFICIAL ICAEW DIRECTORY OF FIRMS 2009

SPECIALISATION INDEX

FINANCIAL REPORTING

ACCOUNTS PREPARATION

United Kingdom

ABERGAVENNY .... Dorrell Oliver Ltd
ABINGDON .... Mark Wells Consulting Ltd
ALTRINCHAM ... Stephen Hobson BA FCA
BECKENHAM .... Hammonds
BIRMINGHAM .... A.K. Patel & Co
James, Stanley & Co
Mason Law LLP
Syedain & Co
BLYTH .... G D Hakin & Co
BOLTON .... Bentleys
BRADFORD .... Andrew S. Parker
David Allen Associates
BRAINTREE .... Lambert Chapman LLP
BRIGHTON ..... Lucraft, Hodgson & Dawes
Wilson Sandford (Brighton) Ltd
BRISTOL .... Evans & Partners
Evans & Partners
Mensis Ltd
BUCKHURST HILL .... Dutchmans
BURNLEY .... K M Business Solutions Ltd
BUXTON .... ABC Accountants
CAMBERLEY .... RSH Accounting
CANNOCK Shelvoke, Pickering, Janney & Co
CARDIFF .... Groves Davey Ltd
CHELMSFORD .... Bird Luckin Ltd
Lambert Chapman LLP
CHELTENHAM .... William Hinton Ltd
COLCHESTER .... Elizabeth Burden
J.Kirkwood & Co
COVENTRY .... Sheth & Co
CROYDON .... D.S. & Co
Hamilton-Eddy & Co
The McCay Partnership
Saleemi Associates
DERBY .... R.V. Hoad & Co
DOUGLAS ..... Baker Tilly Isle of Man LLC
Charles Fargher
Crowe Morgan
Matthew Edwards & Co
PKF (Isle of Man) LLC
DUNMOW .... Bird Luckin Ltd
EASTBOURNE ...... Kenneth M. Bradshaw
EASTLEIGH .... Walji & Co Private Clients Ltd
EDGWARE .... Harris Kafton
Seafields
ELY .... Youngman & Co
ENFIELD .... B. Wright & Co
EXMOUTH .... John Wheeler
FARNHAM .... Milne Eldridge & Co
Taylor Cocks
Wise & Co
GERRARDS CROSS Godfrey Anderson & Co
GRANTHAM .... Callow & Holmes
HARLOW .... Giess Wallis Crisp
HARROW .... AZR Ltd
Hill Wooldridge & Co
HARTLEPOOL .... Wm Fortune & Son
HASTINGS .... Deeks Evans
HIGH WYCOMBE .... Seymour Taylor
HOVE .... Wilson Sandford Ltd
HYDE .... Graham H. Wood & Co
ILFORD .... Fredericks Ltd
INGATESTONE .... Taylor, Viney & Marlow
IPSWICH .... Ensors
JERSEY .... Alex Picot
Le Sueur, Ireson & Co
Mazars Channel Islands Ltd
Rosscot Ltd
KETTERING .... Meadows
KING'S LYNN .... Stephenson Smart
KINGSTON UPON THAMES . David Howard Garners Ltd
LEEDS .... Whitesides
LEIGHTON BUZZARD ..... Ian N. Edwards
LINCOLN .... Nicholsons
LONDON E16 .... Eafton & Co
LONDON EC1 .... FW Stephens
Morwood-Leyland & Co
LONDON EC2 .... Everett & Son
LONDON N13 ...... John Crook & Partners
LONDON N14 .... Bond Partners LLP
LONDON N20 .... Gerald Edelman
Harris Lipman LLP
Kallis & Partners
LONDON N22 .... C.Babs-Jonah & Co
LONDON N3 .... Alexander-Passe & Co
FMCB
Paul Perlin & Co
SPW Poppleton & Appleby
SPW (UK) LLP
LONDON N8 .... A.K. Suleman
LONDON NW1 .... Creasey Alexander & Co
H.W. Fisher & Co
Winston Gross & Co
LONDON NW11 .... H & H Associates
LONDON NW3 .... Nyman Libson Paul
LONDON NW4 .... Dodd Harris
LONDON NW9 .... De Susman & Co
LONDON SE19 .... API Partnership Ltd
LONDON SE3 .... Susan Stelfox
LONDON SW1 .... Helmores
Matthew Edwards & Co
Smith & Hutchinson
LONDON SW12 .... The Decimal Place
LONDON SW19 .... Coulthards
Howell Wade
LONDON W1 .... Arthur G Mead
Citroen Wells
Civvals
David Smith & Co
Gerald Edelman
Sayers Butterworth LLP
LONDON W11 .... Katz & Co
LONDON W13 .... Merchant & Co
LONDON W4 .... Flinthams
LONDON W5 .... Levy & Partners
Levy + Partners Ltd
LONDON WC1 .... Rayner Essex LLP
LONDON WC2 .... Arnold Hill & Co
Bourner Bullock
LUTON .... Miller & Co
MAIDENHEAD .... Hale & Co
Higgins Day
MALDON .... Lambert Chapman LLP
MANCHESTER .... Beever and Struthers
Haffner, Hoff & Co
Horwath Clark Whitehill LLP
UHY Hacker Young Manchester LLP
MILTON KEYNES .... Bourner Bullock
Chancery (UK) LLP
Jaquest & Co
Keens Shay Keens Milton Keynes
MacIntyre Hudson LLP
R.J. Cladd
MORECAMBE .... Coates & Co
MORETON-IN-MARSH .... Tayabali-Tomlin Ltd
NESTON .... Driffield & Co
NEW MALDEN .... Nasir Mahmud
NEWBURY .... Maughans Ltd
NEWCASTLE UPON TYNE ...... Business Consultancy Services
Tait Walker
NEWHAVEN .... Intelligent Blue Ltd
NORTHAMPTON .... J.R. Watson & Co
NORTHWICH .... Howard Worth
NOTTINGHAM .... Higson & Co
Keith Willis Associates Ltd
OXFORD .... Taylor Cocks
PETERSFIELD .... Barter Durgan & Muir Ltd
PORTSMOUTH .... The Taylor Cocks Partnership Ltd
PRESTON .... TLL Accountants Ltd
Turpin Lucas Lees
Whitehead & Aldrich
PURLEY .... Rebello & Co
READING .... Avalon Accounting
Holland MacLennan & Co
Taylor Cocks
Vale & West
REIGATE .... EC Accountancy
RICHMOND ...... The Hughes Consultancy
PK Partners LLP
RUGBY .... C H Ivens & Co
RUISLIP .... Grant Harrod
Warneford Gibbs
SALE .... Armitt & Co
SALFORD .... P. David Levinson
SEVENOAKS .... Brebners
SHEFFIELD .... Barber Harrison & Platt
SOUTH CROYDON .... Sargent & Co
SOUTHAMPTON .... Roches
Rule Datlen Mann
ST ALBANS .... Jane M. Andrews
Rayner Essex LLP
STALYBRIDGE .... Roberts Toner LLP
STRATFORD-UPON-AVON .. Grenfell James
SUTTON COLDFIELD .... Bissell & Brown Ltd
SWANSEA .... Bevan & Buckland
Gerald Thomas & Co
UXBRIDGE .... Pinkney Keith Gibbs
WAKEFIELD .... Dix Vogan Ltd
WARRINGTON .... Voisey & Co
WATFORD ...... JSA Business Services LLP
JSA Services Ltd
Turnbull Associates
WELLS .... Rendell & Co
WELWYN .... R.S. Partnership
WEST BYFLEET ...... Gibson Hewitt & Co
WESTCLIFF-ON-SEA .... Brannans
WEYBRIDGE .... Southworth & Co
TWP
WICKFORD .... Hamilton Brading
WILMSLOW .... Jane Foy & Co
Sandison Easson & Co
WIMBORNE .... The Taylor Cocks Partnership Ltd
WOKING .... C.E. Petty & Co
WORTHING .... Carpenter Box LLP
WREXHAM .... Guy Walmsley & Co
YORK .... Wild & Co

Overseas

BERMUDA, Hamilton .... Mazars
CYPRUS, Nicosia .... Abacus Ltd
CYPRUS, Lefkosa, Mersin 10 .. D.K. Deniz & Co
CYPRUS, Nicosia .... Ernst & Young
GREECE, Athens .. KPMG Certified Auditors AE
IRAN, Tehran .... A.M. Mahallati & Co
NIGERIA, Lagos .... Horwath Dafinone
POLAND, Warsaw Baker Tilly Smoczynski & Partners Sp. z o.o.
SPAIN, Madrid .... Eurocontrol Asesores Contables

AUDIT EXEMPTION REPORT

United Kingdom

BEACONSFIELD ..... HLB Vantis Audit plc
BIRMINGHAM .... A.K. Patel & Co
DOUGLAS .... PKF (Isle of Man) LLC
EPSOM .... HLB Vantis Audit plc
HARROW .... AZR Ltd
HIGH WYCOMBE .... Seymour Taylor
ILFORD .... Fredericks Ltd
INGATESTONE .... Taylor, Viney & Marlow
LEICESTER .... HLB Vantis Audit plc
LONDON E17 .... Michael Barrs and Co
LONDON EC1 .... HLB Vantis Audit plc
LONDON EC2 .... Everett & Son
LONDON N22 .... C.Babs-Jonah & Co
LONDON N3 .... FMCB
Paul Perlin & Co
LONDON NW1 .... H.W. Fisher & Co
LONDON SE19 .... API Partnership Ltd
LONDON W1 .... Arthur G Mead
HLB Vantis Audit plc
LONDON W13 .... Merchant & Co
LONDON W5 .... Levy & Partners
Levy + Partners Ltd
LOUGHTON .... HLB Vantis Audit plc
MANCHESTER .... Beever and Struthers
MIDDLESBROUGH ... HLB Vantis Audit plc
NORTHAMPTON .... J.R. Watson & Co
SIDCUP .... HLB Vantis Audit plc
ST ALBANS .... HLB Vantis Audit plc
WATFORD .... Turnbull Associates
WESTCLIFF-ON-SEA .... Brannans

FINANCIAL REPORTING

United Kingdom

DOUGLAS .... PKF (Isle of Man) LLC
EDINBURGH .... IFRS 2009 Ltd
INGATESTONE .... Taylor, Viney & Marlow
LEWES .... Knill James
LONDON SE19 .... API Partnership Ltd
LONDON SW12 .... The Decimal Place
LONDON W4 .... Flinthams
MANCHESTER .... Beever and Struthers
MILTON KEYNES .... Bourner Bullock
Chancery (UK) LLP
Keens Shay Keens Milton Keynes
RICHMOND .... Feltonpumphrey
PK Partners LLP
WESTCLIFF-ON-SEA .... Brannans

Overseas

IRAN, Tehran .... A.M. Mahallati & Co
NIGERIA, Lagos .... Horwath Dafinone
POLAND, Warsaw Baker Tilly Smoczynski & Partners Sp. z o.o.

FOREIGN SUBSIDIARY COMPANIES

United Kingdom

BEDFORD .... Keens Shay Keens Ltd
BRACKNELL .... Invest in UK Ltd
HALESOWEN .... Nicklin LLP
HIGH WYCOMBE .... Seymour Taylor
LONDON EC1 .... FW Stephens
LONDON NW1 .... H.W. Fisher & Co
LONDON NW3 .... Nyman Libson Paul
LONDON SE19 .... API Partnership Ltd
LONDON W1 .... Citroen Wells
Sayers Butterworth LLP
MILTON KEYNES .... Bourner Bullock
Keens Shay Keens Milton Keynes
RICKMANSWORTH .... Dickinsons
STANMORE .... Lawrence Grant
WEYBRIDGE .... MGI Midgley Snelling

Overseas

POLAND, Warsaw Baker Tilly Smoczynski & Partners Sp. z o.o.
SPAIN, Madrid .... Eurocontrol Asesores Contables

INTERNATIONAL REPORTING STANDARDS (IFRS)

United Kingdom

DOUGLAS .... PKF (Isle of Man) LLC
EDINBURGH .... IFRS 2009 Ltd
GLOUCESTER .... Hazlewoods LLP
HIGH WYCOMBE .... Seymour Taylor
LIVERPOOL .... Chadwick LLP
LONDON EC1 .... Lubbock Fine
LONDON EC2 .... Everett & Son
LONDON N14 .... Bond Partners LLP
LONDON NW1 .... H.W. Fisher & Co
LONDON W1 .... Jenson Solutions Ltd
MANCHESTER .... Chadwick LLP
MILTON KEYNES ..... Chancery (UK) LLP

Overseas

CYPRUS, Nicosia .... HLB Afxentiou Ltd
IRAN, Tehran .... A.M. Mahallati & Co
NIGERIA, Lagos .... Horwath Dafinone
POLAND, Warsaw Baker Tilly Smoczynski & Partners Sp. z o.o.

LIMITED COMPANIES

United Kingdom

BERKHAMSTED .... Harts
BIRMINGHAM .... A.K. Patel & Co
BRAINTREE .... Jaynes & Co
BRISTOL .... Mensis Ltd
CHELTENHAM .... William Hinton Ltd
DOUGLAS .... PKF (Isle of Man) LLC
ESHER .... Holmes & Co
GRANTHAM .... Callow & Holmes
GUILDFORD .... Randall Greene
HARROW .... Alliotts
ILFORD .... Fredericks Ltd
INGATESTONE .... Taylor, Viney & Marlow
KIDDERMINSTER ...... G.H.Herbert & Co
KINGSTON UPON THAMES . David Howard
LEEDS .... Whitesides
LONDON EC2 .... Everett & Son
LONDON N3 .... FMCB
Paul Perlin & Co
LONDON NW1 .... H.W. Fisher & Co
LONDON NW4 .... Dodd Harris
LONDON SE19 .... API Partnership Ltd
LONDON SW18 .... Chicksand Gordon Avis Ltd
LONDON W1 .... Arthur G Mead
MILTON KEYNES ..... Chancery (UK) LLP
Jaquest & Co
MORETON-IN-MARSH .... Tayabali-Tomlin Ltd
NEWCASTLE UPON TYNE ...... Business Consultancy Services
NEWHAVEN .... Intelligent Blue Ltd
NORTHAMPTON .... J.R. Watson & Co
READING .... Avalon Accounting
Vale & West
SALFORD .... P. David Levinson
SOUTHAMPTON .... Roches
SWANSEA .... Bevan & Buckland
Gerald Thomas & Co
UXBRIDGE .... Pinkney Keith Gibbs
WESTCLIFF-ON-SEA .... Brannans

Overseas

IRAN, Tehran .... A.M. Mahallati & Co

LIMITED COMPANY ACCOUNTS

United Kingdom

ABINGDON .... Mark Wells Consulting Ltd
ALTRINCHAM ... Stephen Hobson BA FCA
AMERSHAM .... Cansdales
BARNET .... Debson & Co
BATH .... Berkeley Bate
BECKENHAM .... Hammonds
BEDFORD .... Gregory Wildman
BIRMINGHAM .... A.K. Patel & Co
J W Scrivens & Co Ltd
BISHOP'S STORTFORD ...... Walton & Co
BRADFORD .... Andrew S. Parker
BRAINTREE .... Jaynes & Co
BRIGHTON .... Antrams
Lucraft, Hodgson & Dawes
BRISTOL .... Mensis Ltd
CARDIFF .... Groves Davey Ltd
CHALFONT ST. GILES ...... Lawson & Co
CHELTENHAM .... William Hinton Ltd
COVENTRY .... Sheth & Co
CROYDON .... D.S. & Co
The McCay Partnership
DERBY .... R.V. Hoad & Co
DOUGLAS .... Charles Fargher
Matthew Edwards & Co
PKF (Isle of Man) LLC
EDGWARE .... Seafields
FARNHAM .... Milne Eldridge & Co
Taylor Cocks
HARLOW .... Parry & Co
HARROW .... AZR Ltd
HERTFORD .... Gary J. Cansick & Co
Philip T. Chave & Co
HIGH WYCOMBE .... Seymour Taylor
HYDE .... Graham H. Wood & Co
ILFORD .... Fredericks Ltd
INGATESTONE .... Taylor, Viney & Marlow
JERSEY .... Le Sueur, Ireson & Co
KING'S LYNN .... Stephenson Smart
LONDON E16 .... Eafton & Co
LONDON E17 .... Michael Barrs and Co
LONDON N13 ...... John Crook & Partners
LONDON N20 .... Gerald Edelman
Harris Lipman LLP
LONDON N22 .... C.Babs-Jonah & Co
LONDON N3 .... FMCB
Paul Perlin & Co
SPW Poppleton & Appleby
SPW (UK) LLP
LONDON NW1 .... Creasey Alexander & Co
H.W. Fisher & Co
Winston Gross & Co
LONDON NW11 .... Tuchbands
LONDON SE19 .... API Partnership Ltd
LONDON SE25 .... Soteriou Christou Ltd
LONDON SW1 .... Helmores
Matthew Edwards & Co
Smith & Hutchinson
LONDON SW17 ...... Wadud Patwari & Co
LONDON SW18 .... LBCo Ltd

LONDON SW19 .... Howell Wade
LONDON SW3 .... Dennis R. Waters
LONDON SW4 .... Willis Burnell Ltd
LONDON W1 .... Civvals
Gerald Edelman
Sayers Butterworth LLP
LONDON W13 .... Merchant & Co
LONDON W5 .... Levy & Partners
Levy + Partners Ltd
MAIDENHEAD .... Higgins Day
MAIDSTONE .... Michael D. Nichols
MANCHESTER .... Beever and Struthers
Haffner, Hoff & Co
UHY Hacker Young Manchester LLP
MORECAMBE .... Coates & Co
MORETON-IN-MARSH .... Tayabali-Tomlin Ltd
NESTON .... Driffield & Co
NEWBURY .... Maughans Ltd
NEWCASTLE UPON TYNE .... Tait Walker
NEWHAVEN .... Intelligent Blue Ltd
NORTHAMPTON .... J.R. Watson & Co
Paul Slater & Co
NOTTINGHAM .... Huw Williams Ltd
Keith Willis Associates Ltd
OXFORD .... Taylor Cocks
PETERSFIELD .... Barter Durgan & Muir Ltd
PORTSMOUTH .... The Taylor Cocks Partnership Ltd
PRESTON .... TLL Accountants Ltd
Turpin Lucas Lees
Whitehead & Aldrich
READING .... Avalon Accounting
Taylor Cocks
RICHMOND .... PK Partners LLP
SALFORD .... P. David Levinson
SEVENOAKS .... Brebners
SOUTH CROYDON .... Sargent & Co
STRATFORD-UPON-AVON .. Grenfell James
SURBITON .... Stevensons
SUTTON COLDFIELD .... Bissell & Brown Ltd
TUNBRIDGE WELLS .... Auker Hutton
UXBRIDGE .... Pinkney Keith Gibbs
WATFORD .... JSA Services Ltd
Turnbull Associates
WEST WICKHAM .... Daniels & Co
WESTCLIFF-ON-SEA .... Brannans
WICKFORD .... Hamilton Brading
WILMSLOW .... Jane Foy & Co
WIMBORNE .... The Taylor Cocks Partnership Ltd
WOKING .... C.E. Petty & Co
WREXHAM .... Guy Walmsley & Co
YORK .... Wild & Co

Overseas

IRAN, Tehran .... A.M. Mahallati & Co

LIMITED LIABILITY PARTNERSHIP

United Kingdom

AMERSHAM .... Cansdales
HARROW .... AZR Ltd
INGATESTONE .... Taylor, Viney & Marlow
LONDON EC1 .... Lubbock Fine
LONDON EC2 .... Everett & Son
LONDON N22 .... C.Babs-Jonah & Co
LONDON N3 .... Paul Perlin & Co
LONDON NW1 .... H.W. Fisher & Co
LONDON NW3 .... Nyman Libson Paul
LONDON SE19 .... API Partnership Ltd
LONDON W5 .... Levy & Partners
Levy + Partners Ltd
MANCHESTER .... Beever and Struthers
MILTON KEYNES ..... Chancery (UK) LLP
Keens Shay Keens Milton Keynes
NEWHAVEN .... Intelligent Blue Ltd
NORTHAMPTON .... J.R. Watson & Co
RICHMOND .... PK Partners LLP
RUISLIP .... Grant Harrod
SEVENOAKS .... Brebners
WESTCLIFF-ON-SEA .... Brannans

PARTNERSHIP/SOLE TRADER ACCOUNTS

United Kingdom

ABINGDON .... Mark Wells Consulting Ltd
ALTRINCHAM ... Stephen Hobson BA FCA
AMERSHAM .... Cansdales
BARNET .... Debson & Co
BATH .... Berkeley Bate
BECKENHAM .... Hammonds
BEDFORD .... Gregory Wildman
BIRMINGHAM .... A.K. Patel & Co
J W Scrivens & Co Ltd
BISHOP'S STORTFORD ...... Walton & Co
BRADFORD .... Andrew S. Parker
BRAINTREE .... Jaynes & Co
BRIGHTON .... Antrams
Lucraft, Hodgson & Dawes
BRISTOL .... Mensis Ltd
CANNOCK Shelvoke, Pickering, Janney & Co
CHALFONT ST. GILES ...... Lawson & Co
CHELTENHAM .... William Hinton Ltd
CROYDON .... D.S. & Co
Hamilton-Eddy & Co
The McCay Partnership
DAVENTRY .... Stephen Franklin FCA CTA
DERBY .... R.V. Hoad & Co
DOUGLAS .... Charles Fargher
Matthew Edwards & Co
PKF (Isle of Man) LLC
EDGWARE .... Seafields
FARNHAM .... Milne Eldridge & Co
HARLOW .... Giess Wallis Crisp
Parry & Co
HARROW .... Alliotts
AZR Ltd
HERTFORD .... Gary J. Cansick & Co
Philip T. Chave & Co
HIGH WYCOMBE .... Seymour Taylor
HYDE .... Graham H. Wood & Co
ILFORD .... Fredericks Ltd
INGATESTONE .... Taylor, Viney & Marlow
KING'S LYNN .... Stephenson Smart
LEEDS .... Whitesides
LEIGHTON BUZZARD ..... Ian N. Edwards
LONDON E16 .... Eafton & Co
LONDON E17 .... Michael Barrs and Co
LONDON EC2 .... Everett & Son
LONDON N13 ...... John Crook & Partners
LONDON N22 .... C.Babs-Jonah & Co
LONDON N3 .... Alexander-Passe & Co
FMCB
Paul Perlin & Co
SPW Poppleton & Appleby
LONDON NW1 .... H.W. Fisher & Co
Winston Gross & Co
LONDON NW11 .... Tuchbands
LONDON SE10 .... Med Act
LONDON SE19 .... API Partnership Ltd
LONDON SW1 .... Helmores
LONDON SW17 ...... Wadud Patwari & Co
LONDON SW18 .... Chicksand Gordon Avis Ltd
LBCo Ltd
LONDON SW4 .... Willis Burnell Ltd
LONDON W1 .... David Smith & Co
Sayers Butterworth LLP
LONDON W13 .... Merchant & Co
LONDON W5 .... Levy & Partners
Levy + Partners Ltd
LONDON WC2 .... Bourner Bullock
MAIDENHEAD .... Higgins Day
MAIDSTONE .... Michael D. Nichols
MANCHESTER .... Beever and Struthers
MILTON KEYNES .... Bourner Bullock
Chancery (UK) LLP
MORECAMBE .... Coates & Co
MORETON-IN-MARSH .... Tayabali-Tomlin Ltd
NESTON .... Driffield & Co
NEWBURY .... Maughans Ltd
NEWCASTLE UPON TYNE ...... Business Consultancy Services
NEWHAVEN .... Intelligent Blue Ltd
NORTHAMPTON .... J.R. Watson & Co
Paul Slater & Co
NOTTINGHAM .... Huw Williams Ltd
Keith Willis Associates Ltd
PETERSFIELD .... Barter Durgan & Muir Ltd
PRESTON .... Whitehead & Aldrich
READING .... Avalon Accounting
Vale & West
RICHMOND .... PK Partners LLP
RUISLIP .... Grant Harrod
SALFORD .... P. David Levinson
SEVENOAKS .... Brebners
STRATFORD-UPON-AVON .. Grenfell James
TUNBRIDGE WELLS .... Auker Hutton
UXBRIDGE .... Pinkney Keith Gibbs
WATFORD .... Turnbull Associates
WEMBLEY .... S. Syedain & Co
WESTCLIFF-ON-SEA .... Brannans
WICKFORD .... Hamilton Brading
WILMSLOW .... Jane Foy & Co
Sandison Easson & Co
WREXHAM .... Guy Walmsley & Co

AUDIT & ASSURANCE

ASSURANCE SERVICES

United Kingdom

CHELMSFORD .... Bird Luckin Ltd
DOUGLAS .... PKF (Isle of Man) LLC
DUNMOW .... Bird Luckin Ltd
EDINBURGH .... IFRS 2009 Ltd
HALESOWEN .... Nicklin LLP
JERSEY .... Mazars Channel Islands Ltd
Rosscot Ltd
LONDON EC1 .... FW Stephens
LONDON N14 .... Bond Partners LLP
LONDON W4 .... Flinthams
LONDON WC2 .... Bourner Bullock
MAIDENHEAD .... Hale & Co
MANCHESTER .... Alexander & Co
Beever and Struthers
MILTON KEYNES .... Bourner Bullock
NORTHAMPTON .... J.R. Watson & Co
READING .... Vale & West
STOKE-ON-TRENT .... Moore Stephens
WESTCLIFF-ON-SEA .... Brannans

Overseas

CYPRUS, Lefkosa, Mersin 10 .. D.K. Deniz & Co
CYPRUS, Nicosia .... Ernst & Young

GREECE, Athens .. KPMG Certified Auditors AE
IRAN, Tehran .... A.M. Mahallati & Co
SPAIN, Madrid .... Eurocontrol Auditores SL

AUDIT

United Kingdom

ABERGAVENNY .... Dorrell Oliver Ltd
ALTRINCHAM ... Stephen Hobson BA FCA
BEACONSFIELD ..... HLB Vantis Audit plc
BECKENHAM .... Hammonds
BEDFORD .... Gregory Wildman
BISHOP'S STORTFORD ...... Walton & Co
BLYTH .... G D Hakin & Co
BOLTON .... Bentleys
BRADFORD .... Andrew S. Parker
BRIGHTON .... Antrams
BRISTOL .... Evans & Partners
Evans & Partners
BUCKHURST HILL .... Dutchmans
BURNLEY .... K M Business Solutions Ltd
CANNOCK Shelvoke, Pickering, Janney & Co
CHALFONT ST. GILES ...... Lawson & Co
CHELMSFORD .... Bird Luckin Ltd
CHELTENHAM .... William Hinton Ltd
COLCHESTER .... Butt Cozens
Elizabeth Burden
Whittle & Co
COVENTRY .... Sheth & Co
CROYDON .... D.S. & Co
Hamilton-Eddy & Co
The McCay Partnership
Saleemi Associates
DERBY .... Johnson Tidsall
R.V. Hoad & Co
DOUGLAS ..... Baker Tilly Isle of Man LLC
Crowe Morgan
Matthew Edwards & Co
PKF (Isle of Man) LLC
DUNMOW .... Bird Luckin Ltd
EASTLEIGH .... Walji & Co Private Clients Ltd
EDGWARE .... Harris Kafton
ELY .... Youngman & Co
EPSOM .... HLB Vantis Audit plc
FARNHAM .... Milne Eldridge & Co
Taylor Cocks
Wise & Co
GRANTHAM .... Callow & Holmes
GUERNSEY .... Saffery Champness
Saffery Champness
HARLOW .... Giess Wallis Crisp
HARROW .... AZR Ltd
Hill Wooldridge & Co
HARTLEPOOL .... Wm Fortune & Son
HASTINGS .... Deeks Evans
HERTFORD .... Gary J. Cansick & Co
HIGH WYCOMBE .... Seymour Taylor
HOVE .... Wilson Sandford Ltd
HYDE .... Graham H. Wood & Co
ILFORD .... Fredericks Ltd
INGATESTONE .... Taylor, Viney & Marlow
IPSWICH .... Ensors
JERSEY .... Alex Picot
Le Rossignol, Scott Warren and Partners
Le Sueur, Ireson & Co
Mazars Channel Islands Ltd
Rosscot Ltd
KINGSTON UPON THAMES .... Garners Ltd
LEEDS .... Whitesides
LEICESTER .... HLB Vantis Audit plc
LEWES .... Knill James
LINCOLN .... Nicholsons
LIVERPOOL .... Chadwick LLP
LONDON E14 .... Littlejohn
LONDON E16 .... Eafton & Co
LONDON E17 .... Michael Barrs and Co
LONDON EC1 .... FW Stephens
Higgisons
HLB Vantis Audit plc
LONDON EC2 .... Everett & Son
LONDON EC4 .... Knox Cropper
LONDON N12 .... Anthony Tiscoe & Co
LONDON N13 ...... John Crook & Partners
LONDON N14 .... Bond Partners LLP
LONDON N20 .... Gerald Edelman
Harris Lipman LLP
Kallis & Partners
LONDON N3 .... FMCB
Paul Perlin & Co
SPW Poppleton & Appleby
SPW (UK) LLP
LONDON NW1 .... H.W. Fisher & Co
LONDON NW3 .... Nyman Libson Paul
LONDON NW9 .... De Susman & Co
LONDON SE19 .... API Partnership Ltd
LONDON SW1 .... Helmores
Matthew Edwards & Co
LONDON SW17 ...... Wadud Patwari & Co
LONDON SW18 .... LBCo Ltd
LONDON SW19 .... Coulthards
Howell Wade
LONDON W1 .... Arthur G Mead
Citroen Wells
Elman Wall Ltd
F. Winter & Co LLP
Gerald Edelman
HLB Vantis Audit plc
Sayers Butterworth LLP
LONDON W11 .... Katz & Co
LONDON W4 .... Flinthams
LONDON W5 .... Levy & Partners
Levy + Partners Ltd
LONDON WC1 .... Rayner Essex LLP
LONDON WC2 .... Arnold Hill & Co
Bourner Bullock
LOUGHTON .... Haslers
HLB Vantis Audit plc
LUTON .... Miller & Co
MAIDENHEAD .... Hale & Co
Higgins Day
MANCHESTER .... Beever and Struthers
Chadwick LLP
Horwath Clark Whitehill LLP
UHY Hacker Young Manchester LLP
MIDDLESBROUGH ... HLB Vantis Audit plc
MILTON KEYNES .... Bourner Bullock
Chancery (UK) LLP
Jaquest & Co
Keens Shay Keens Milton Keynes
MacIntyre Hudson LLP
NEW MALDEN .... Nasir Mahmud
NEWCASTLE UPON TYNE .... Tait Walker
NORTHAMPTON .... J.R. Watson & Co
Paul Slater & Co
NORTHWICH .... Howard Worth
NOTTINGHAM .... Higson & Co
Keith Willis Associates Ltd
OXFORD .... Taylor Cocks
PORTSMOUTH .... The Taylor Cocks Partnership Ltd
PRESTON .... TLL Accountants Ltd
Turpin Lucas Lees
Whitehead & Aldrich
PURLEY .... Rebello & Co
READING .... Avalon Accounting
Taylor Cocks
Vale & West
RICHMOND .... Feltonpumphrey
PK Partners LLP
ROYSTON .... WKH
RUGBY .... C H Ivens & Co
SALFORD .... P. David Levinson
SALISBURY ..... Nexia Smith & Williamson Audit Ltd
SEVENOAKS .... Brebners
SHEFFIELD .... Barber Harrison & Platt
SIDCUP .... HLB Vantis Audit plc
SOUTHAMPTON .... Roches
Rule Datlen Mann
ST ALBANS .... HLB Vantis Audit plc
Rayner Essex LLP
STRATFORD-UPON-AVON .. Grenfell James
SUTTON COLDFIELD .... Bissell & Brown Ltd
SWANSEA .... Bevan & Buckland
Gerald Thomas & Co
UXBRIDGE .... Pinkney Keith Gibbs
WAKEFIELD .... Dix Vogan Ltd
WALTON-ON-THAMES Byrne, Palmer & Co
WELWYN .... R.S. Partnership
WESTCLIFF-ON-SEA .... Brannans
WEYBRIDGE .... MGI Midgley Snelling
Southworth & Co
TWP
WICKFORD .... Hamilton Brading
WIMBORNE .... The Taylor Cocks Partnership Ltd
WORTHING .... Carpenter Box LLP
WREXHAM .... Guy Walmsley & Co

Overseas

CYPRUS, Lefkosa, Mersin 10 .. D.K. Deniz & Co
CYPRUS, Nicosia .... Ernst & Young
HLB Afxentiou Ltd
CYPRUS, Limassol .... N Constantinou & Co Audit Ltd
HONG KONG, Wan Chai .. C.C. Kwong & Co
IRAN, Tehran .... A.M. Mahallati & Co
LUXEMBOURG, Luxembourg HT Group S.A.
NIGERIA, Lagos .... Horwath Dafinone
POLAND, Warsaw Baker Tilly Smoczynski & Partners Sp. z o.o.
SWITZERLAND, Zollikon Graham Associates AG

AUDIT — PRIVATE COMPANY

United Kingdom

AMERSHAM .... Cansdales
BEACONSFIELD ..... HLB Vantis Audit plc
BERKHAMSTED .... Harts
BIRMINGHAM .... A.K. Patel & Co
James, Stanley & Co
BOLTON .... Barlow Andrews

BRAINTREE ... Jaynes & Co
Lambert Chapman LLP
BRIGHTON ... Lucraft, Hodgson & Dawes
CARDIFF ... Groves Davey Ltd
CHELMSFORD ... Lambert Chapman LLP
DOUGLAS ... Matthew Edwards & Co
PKF (Isle of Man) LLC
DUDLEY ... Price Pearson
EPSOM ... HLB Vantis Audit plc
FARNBOROUGH Howard Lee, Fellows & Co
FARNHAM ... Taylor Cocks
GAINSBOROUGH ... Wright Vigar Ltd
HARROGATE ... Holeys
HARROW ... AZR Ltd
Leftley Rowe & Co
HAYWARDS HEATH ... PRB Martin Pollins LLP
HOVE ... Atkinsons
ILFORD ... Fredericks Ltd
INGATESTONE ... Taylor, Viney & Marlow
KIDDERMINSTER ... Price Pearson Ltd
KING'S LYNN ... Stephenson Smart
LEICESTER ... HLB Vantis Audit plc
LINCOLN ... Wright Vigar Ltd
LONDON E16 ... Eafton & Co
LONDON EC1 ... FW Stephens
HLB Vantis Audit plc
LONDON N3 ... FMCB
Paul Perlin & Co
LONDON NW11 ... Tuchbands
LONDON NW3 ... Nyman Libson Paul
LONDON NW9 ... De Susman & Co
LONDON SE25 ... Soteriou Christou Ltd
LONDON SE3 ... Susan Stelfox
LONDON SW1 ... Matthew Edwards & Co
Smith & Hutchinson
LONDON SW14 . White Hart Associates LLP
LONDON W1 ... Citroen Wells
Civvals
David Smith & Co
Fisher, Sassoon & Marks
HLB Vantis Audit plc
LONDON W11 ... Wright Vigar Ltd
LONDON W13 ... Merchant & Co
LONDON W5 ... Levy & Partners
Levy + Partners Ltd
LONDON WC2 ... Bourner Bullock
LOUGHTON ... HLB Vantis Audit plc
MANCHESTER ... Beever and Struthers
MIDDLESBROUGH ... HLB Vantis Audit plc
MILTON KEYNES ... Bourner Bullock
NEW MALDEN ... Atkinsons
NEWBURY ... Maughans Ltd
OXFORD ... Taylor Cocks
PETERSFIELD ... Barter Durgan & Muir Ltd
PORTSMOUTH ... Rothman Pantall & Co
The Taylor Cocks Partnership Ltd
READING ... Taylor Cocks
RETFORD ... Wright Vigar Ltd
SIDCUP ... HLB Vantis Audit plc
SLEAFORD ... Wright Vigar Ltd
SLOUGH ... Charles Stuart LLP
SOUTH CROYDON ... Sargent & Co
ST ALBANS ... HLB Vantis Audit plc
STALYBRIDGE ... Roberts Toner LLP
STOCKTON-ON-TEES ... Lyons & Co
TUNBRIDGE WELLS ... Creaseys
Foot Davson
WATFORD ... JSA Business Services LLP
WESTCLIFF-ON-SEA ... Brannans
WIMBORNE ... The Taylor Cocks Partnership Ltd

Overseas

CYPRUS, Nicosia ... Ernst & Young
IRAN, Tehran ... A.M. Mahallati & Co
NIGERIA, Lagos ... Horwath Dafinone
POLAND, Warsaw Baker Tilly Smoczynski & Partners Sp. z o.o.

AUDIT — PUBLIC COMPANY

United Kingdom

BEACONSFIELD ... HLB Vantis Audit plc
DOUGLAS ... PKF (Isle of Man) LLC
EPSOM ... HLB Vantis Audit plc
LEICESTER ... HLB Vantis Audit plc
LONDON EC1 ... FW Stephens
HLB Vantis Audit plc
LONDON W1 ... HLB Vantis Audit plc
LOUGHTON ... HLB Vantis Audit plc
MANCHESTER ... Beever and Struthers
MIDDLESBROUGH ... HLB Vantis Audit plc
SIDCUP ... HLB Vantis Audit plc
ST ALBANS ... HLB Vantis Audit plc

Overseas

CYPRUS, Nicosia ... Ernst & Young
IRAN, Tehran ... A.M. Mahallati & Co
NIGERIA, Lagos ... Horwath Dafinone
POLAND, Warsaw Baker Tilly Smoczynski & Partners Sp. z o.o.

INTERNAL AUDIT

United Kingdom

AMERSHAM ... Cansdales
DOUGLAS ... PKF (Isle of Man) LLC
GRAVESEND ... Internal Audit Services Ltd
MANCHESTER ... Beever and Struthers
ST ALBANS ... M.R. Aldridge

Overseas

CYPRUS, Nicosia ... Ernst & Young
NIGERIA, Lagos ... Horwath Dafinone
POLAND, Warsaw Baker Tilly Smoczynski & Partners Sp. z o.o.

PENSION SCHEME AUDITORS

United Kingdom

BIRMINGHAM ... Mason Law LLP
BISHOP'S STORTFORD ... Walton & Co
BRIGHTON ... Lucraft, Hodgson & Dawes
DOUGLAS ... PKF (Isle of Man) LLC
FARNBOROUGH Howard Lee, Fellows & Co
HIGH WYCOMBE ... Seymour Taylor
INGATESTONE ... Taylor, Viney & Marlow
LIVERPOOL ... Hurst (Liverpool) LLP
LONDON EC2 ... Everett & Son
LONDON EC4 ... Target Winters
LONDON N3 ... Paul Perlin & Co
LONDON W1 ... Ash Shaw LLP
MANCHESTER ... Beever and Struthers
NORTHAMPTON ... J.R. Watson & Co
SHEFFIELD ... Barber Harrison & Platt
WESTCLIFF-ON-SEA ... Brannans

Overseas

CYPRUS, Nicosia ... Ernst & Young

TAXATION

BACK DUTY

United Kingdom

AMERSHAM ... Cansdales
BRISTOL ... Evans & Partners
BURNLEY ... Ashworth Moulds
CANNOCK Shelvoke, Pickering, Janney & Co
CARDIFF ... Chris Madge & Co
CLEVEDON ... Chris Madge & Co
CROYDON ... D.S. & Co
DERBY ... Tax Investigation Services
DUDLEY ... Price Pearson
HOVE ... Atkinsons
KIDDERMINSTER ... Price Pearson Ltd
LONDON EC1 ... FW Stephens
Higgisons
LONDON N14 ... Bond Partners LLP
LONDON N3 ... Paul Perlin & Co
LONDON NW1 ... Creasey Alexander & Co
LONDON NW3 ... Nyman Libson Paul
LONDON NW9 ... De Susman & Co
LONDON W1 ... Chris Madge & Co
LONDON W13 ... Merchant & Co
LONDON W5 ... Levy & Partners
Levy + Partners Ltd
NEW MALDEN ... Atkinsons
TORPOINT ... C.E. Taylor
WESTCLIFF-ON-SEA ... Brannans

Overseas

NIGERIA, Lagos ... Horwath Dafinone

CAPITAL GAINS — LIMITED COMPANIES

United Kingdom

BIRMINGHAM ... A.K. Patel & Co
BOLTON ... Barlow Andrews
BRISTOL ... Mensis Ltd
Phillip Corbin
CROYDON ... D.S. & Co
GODALMING ... Delia Orme
ILFORD ... Fredericks Ltd
INGATESTONE ... Taylor, Viney & Marlow
LEEDS ... Whitesides
LEICESTER ... Powrie Appleby LLP
LONDON E14 ... Littlejohn
LONDON N3 ... Paul Perlin & Co
LONDON SW13 ... C.J. Cook & Co
LONDON W5 ... Levy & Partners
Levy + Partners Ltd
MANCHESTER ... Beever and Struthers

MILTON KEYNES ..... Chancery (UK) LLP
NORTHAMPTON .... J.R. Watson & Co
READING .... Avalon Accounting
STOCKPORT .... The TACS Partnership
WESTCLIFF-ON-SEA .... Brannans

Overseas

NIGERIA, Lagos .... Horwath Dafinone
POLAND, Warsaw Baker Tilly Smoczynski & Partners Sp. z o.o.

CAPITAL GAINS — PERSONAL

United Kingdom

BIRMINGHAM .... A.K. Patel & Co
BRISTOL .... Mensis Ltd
Phillip Corbin
BROMLEY .... Pauline Lonsdale
BURTON-ON-TRENT .... Nicholson Blythe Ltd
CHALFONT ST. GILES ...... Lawson & Co
CROYDON .... D.S. & Co
DAVENTRY .... Stephen Franklin FCA CTA
EASTLEIGH .... Romeril Martin
GODALMING .... Delia Orme
ILFORD .... Fredericks Ltd
INGATESTONE .... Taylor, Viney & Marlow
LEEDS .... Whitesides
LEICESTER .... Powrie Appleby LLP
LONDON E14 .... Littlejohn
LONDON EC1 .... FW Stephens
LONDON N22 .... C.Babs-Jonah & Co
LONDON N3 .... Paul Perlin & Co
LONDON NW1 .... Winston Gross & Co
LONDON SE19 .... API Partnership Ltd
LONDON SW13 .... C.J. Cook & Co
LONDON SW19 .... Miss E A Parks
LONDON W1 .... Civvals
Sayers Butterworth LLP
LONDON W13 .... Merchant & Co
LONDON W5 .... Levy & Partners
Levy + Partners Ltd
MANCHESTER .... Beever and Struthers
MATLOCK .... Anne Griffiths
MILTON KEYNES ..... Chancery (UK) LLP
NEWBURY .... Paul M Bowers
NORTHAMPTON .... J.R. Watson & Co
READING .... Avalon Accounting
RICHMOND .... PK Partners LLP
RUISLIP .... Grant Harrod
Warneford Gibbs
SOUTHAMPTON .... Roches
STOCKPORT .... The TACS Partnership
WATFORD .... Turnbull Associates
WESTCLIFF-ON-SEA .... Brannans

CUSTOMS DUTY

United Kingdom

BRISTOL .... Mensis Ltd
CARDIFF .... Chris Madge & Co
CLEVEDON .... Chris Madge & Co
LONDON E14 .... Littlejohn
LONDON W1 .... Chris Madge & Co
NEWCASTLE-UNDER-LYME.............
Barringtons Ltd
READING .... Vale & West

Overseas

POLAND, Warsaw Baker Tilly Smoczynski & Partners Sp. z o.o.

EMPLOYEE

United Kingdom

BROMLEY .... Pauline Lonsdale
GODALMING .... Delia Orme
HARROW .... Alliotts
LEICESTER .... Powrie Appleby LLP
LEIGHTON BUZZARD ..... Ian N. Edwards
LONDON EC1 .... FW Stephens
LONDON N3 .... Paul Perlin & Co
LONDON SE19 .... API Partnership Ltd
LONDON SW19 .... Miss E A Parks
MANCHESTER .... Beever and Struthers
READING .... Avalon Accounting
STOCKPORT .... The TACS Partnership
WESTCLIFF-ON-SEA .... Brannans
WILMSLOW .... Sandison Easson & Co

Overseas

IRAN, Tehran .... A.M. Mahallati & Co

ESTATE AND INHERITANCE

United Kingdom

AMERSHAM .... Cansdales Ltd
BIRMINGHAM .... Clement Keys
Mason Law LLP
BOLTON .... Barlow Andrews
BRAINTREE .... Lambert Chapman LLP
BROMLEY .... Pauline Lonsdale
COLCHESTER .... Whittle & Co
DAVENTRY .... Stephen Franklin FCA CTA
DOUGLAS .... PKF (Isle of Man) LLC
EASTLEIGH .... Romeril Martin
Rothman Pantall & Co
FARNHAM .... Taylor Cocks
GODALMING .... Delia Orme
GUILDFORD .... Randall Greene
HASLEMERE .... Knox Cropper
LEICESTER .... Powrie Appleby LLP
LEIGH-ON-SEA .... Walsh & Co
LONDON E14 .... Littlejohn
LONDON EC1 .... FW Stephens
LONDON SE19 .... API Partnership Ltd
LONDON SW14 .... Andrew B Tappin
LONDON W1 ...... Sayers Butterworth LLP
LONDON W13 .... Merchant & Co
LONDON W5 .... Levy & Partners
Levy + Partners Ltd
LOUGHTON .... Haslers
MANCHESTER .... Beever and Struthers
MILTON KEYNES ..... Chancery (UK) LLP
Keens Shay Keens Milton Keynes
NEWBURY .... Paul M Bowers
NORTHAMPTON .... J.R. Watson & Co
NOTTINGHAM .... Huw Williams Ltd
NUNEATON .... Nicola Fisher Financial Planning Ltd
OXFORD .... Taylor Cocks
PLYMOUTH .... Parkhurst Hill
PORTSMOUTH .... The Taylor Cocks Partnership Ltd
READING .... Taylor Cocks
SWANSEA .... Bevan & Buckland
Gerald Thomas & Co
WATFORD .... Myers Clark
Turnbull Associates
WESTCLIFF-ON-SEA .... Brannans
WEYBRIDGE .... TWP
WILMSLOW .... Sandison Easson & Co
WIMBORNE .... The Taylor Cocks Partnership Ltd
Ward Goodman Ltd

ESTATE PLANNING

United Kingdom

AMERSHAM .... Cansdales
Cansdales Ltd
BRISTOL .... Geoff Gollop & Co Ltd
BUCKHURST HILL .... Dutchmans
BURNLEY .... Ashworth Moulds
CARDIFF .... Groves Davey Ltd
DOUGLAS .... PKF (Isle of Man) LLC
GODALMING .... Delia Orme
GUILDFORD .... Randall Greene
HARLOW .... Giess Wallis Crisp
HOVE .... Atkinsons
ILKESTON .... Gorings
IPSWICH .... Ensors
JERSEY .... Alex Picot
Rosscot Ltd
LEICESTER .... Powrie Appleby LLP
LEIGH-ON-SEA .... Walsh & Co
LONDON EC1 .... FW Stephens
Lubbock Fine
LONDON N14 .... Bond Partners LLP
LONDON SE19 .... API Partnership Ltd
LONDON W1 .... Citroen Wells
Sayers Butterworth LLP
LONDON WC1 .... haysmacintyre
LONDON WC2 .... Bourner Bullock
MAIDENHEAD .... Hale & Co
MANCHESTER .... Beever and Struthers
Cassons
MILTON KEYNES ..... Keens Shay Keens Milton Keynes
NEW MALDEN .... Atkinsons
PLYMOUTH .... Parkhurst Hill
PRESTON .... Titus Thorp & Ainsworth
ROSSENDALE .... Cassons
STOCKTON-ON-TEES .... Benson Wood Ltd
WAKEFIELD .... Dix Vogan Ltd
WESTCLIFF-ON-SEA .... Brannans
WEYBRIDGE .... TWP

EXECUTORSHIP

United Kingdom

BRAINTREE .... Jaynes & Co
BROMLEY .... Pauline Lonsdale
BUCKHURST HILL .... Dutchmans
BURNLEY .... Ashworth Moulds
DOUGLAS .... PKF (Isle of Man) LLC
EASTLEIGH .... Rothman Pantall & Co
GODALMING .... Delia Orme
GUILDFORD .... Randall Greene
HARROW .... Alliotts
LONDON EC1 .... FW Stephens
LONDON SE19 .... API Partnership Ltd
LONDON SW14 .... Andrew B Tappin
LONDON W1 .... Citroen Wells
Sayers Butterworth LLP
MANCHESTER .... Beever and Struthers
PRESTON .... Titus Thorp & Ainsworth
READING .... Vale & West
WATFORD .... Myers Clark
WESTCLIFF-ON-SEA .... Brannans

FOREIGN NATIONALS IN THE UK

United Kingdom

BARNET .... Debson & Co
BROMLEY .... Pauline Lonsdale
COBHAM .... Wellden Turnbull LLP
DOUGLAS .... PKF (Isle of Man) LLC

GODALMING . . . . Delia Orme
HIGH WYCOMBE . . . . Seymour Taylor
JERSEY . . . . Caversham
LEICESTER . . . . Powrie Appleby LLP
LONDON E14 . . . . Littlejohn
LONDON EC1 . . . . FW Stephens
Lubbock Fine
LONDON EC4 . . . . Target Winters
LONDON N12 . . . . Anthony Tiscoe & Co
LONDON N14 . . . . Bond Partners LLP
LONDON N3 . . . . Paul Perlin & Co
LONDON NW3 . . . . Nyman Libson Paul
LONDON SE19 . . . . API Partnership Ltd
LONDON SW1 . . . . Helmores
LONDON SW19 . . . . Miss E A Parks
LONDON W1 . . . . Citroen Wells
Sayers Butterworth LLP
LONDON W5 . . . . Johnsons Financial Management Ltd
LONDON WC2 . . . . Bourner Bullock
MANCHESTER . . . . Beever and Struthers
MILTON KEYNES . . . . Jaquest & Co
RICHMOND . . . . PK Partners LLP
STANMORE . . . . Lawrence Grant
TUNBRIDGE WELLS . . . . Creaseys
WATFORD . . . . Turnbull Associates
WESTCLIFF-ON-SEA . . . . Brannans
WEYBRIDGE . . . . MGI Midgley Snelling

INVESTIGATIONS

United Kingdom

BIRMINGHAM . . . . Clement Keys
BRISTOL . . . . Evans & Partners
CARDIFF . . . . Chris Madge & Co
Harris Lipman LLP
CHALFONT ST. GILES . . . . . . Lawson & Co
CHESTER LE STREET. . . . . . . Straughans Ltd
CLEVEDON . . . . Chris Madge & Co
COLCHESTER . . . . Butt Cozens
CROYDON . . . . D.S. & Co
DERBY . . . . Tax Investigation Services
DOUGLAS . . . . . Baker Tilly Isle of Man LLC
PKF (Isle of Man) LLC
FARNHAM . . . . Taylor Cocks
HALIFAX . . . . Riley & Co
HARROW . . . . LINK
HOUNSLOW . . . . Charles Stuart LLP
KING'S LYNN . . . . Stephenson Smart
LEEDS . . . . Bartfields Business Services LLP
Bartfields (UK) Ltd
LONDON EC1 . . . . Lubbock Fine
LONDON N14 . . . . Bond Partners LLP
LONDON N20 . . . . Harris Lipman LLP
LONDON N22 . . . . C.Babs-Jonah & Co
LONDON N3 . . . . SPW (UK) LLP
LONDON SW1 . . . . Sterling Hay
LONDON W1 . . . . Chris Madge & Co
Citroen Wells
Elman Wall Ltd
LONDON WC1 . . . . FTI Forensic Accounting Ltd
Griffins
Rayner Essex LLP
LOUGHTON . . . . Haslers
MANCHESTER . . . . Alexander & Co
Beever and Struthers
CLB Coopers
OXFORD . . . . Taylor Cocks
PORTSMOUTH . . . . The Taylor Cocks Partnership Ltd
READING . . . . Taylor Cocks
SEVENOAKS . . . . Samuels
SHEFFIELD . . . . The P&A Partnership
SLOUGH . . . . Charles Stuart LLP
ST ALBANS . . . . Harris Lipman LLP
Rayner Essex LLP
STOCKPORT . . . . The TACS Partnership
WATFORD . . . . Turnbull Associates
WESTCLIFF-ON-SEA . . . . Brannans
WIMBORNE . . . . The Taylor Cocks Partnership Ltd
WOKING . . . . Barnbrook Sinclair Ltd

Overseas

IRAN, Tehran . . . . A.M. Mahallati & Co
POLAND, Warsaw Baker Tilly Smoczynski & Partners Sp. z o.o.

NATIONAL INSURANCE ADVICE

United Kingdom

BRISTOL . . . . Mensis Ltd
CROYDON . . . . D.S. & Co
HARROW . . . . Alliotts
LONDON N3 . . . . Paul Perlin & Co
LONDON SE19 . . . . API Partnership Ltd
MANCHESTER . . . . Beever and Struthers
RUSHDEN . . . . Peter Arrowsmith FCA
WESTCLIFF-ON-SEA . . . . Brannans

Overseas

IRAN, Tehran . . . . A.M. Mahallati & Co

OFFSHORE COMPANIES

United Kingdom

BARNET . . . . Debson & Co
DOUGLAS . . . . . Baker Tilly Isle of Man LLC
PKF (Isle of Man) LLC
GUERNSEY . . . . Sphere Management Ltd
HOVE . . . . Atkinsons
JERSEY . . . . Caversham
HLB Jackson Fox
Le Sueur, Ireson & Co
Rosscot Ltd
LEICESTER . . . . Powrie Appleby LLP
LONDON N14 . . . . Bond Partners LLP
LONDON SE19 . . . . API Partnership Ltd
LONDON W1 . . . . Citroen Wells
LONDON W5 . . . . Johnsons Financial Management Ltd
NEW MALDEN . . . . Atkinsons
PORT ST. MARY . . . . Young and Associates Ltd
STANMORE . . . . Lawrence Grant
TUNBRIDGE WELLS . . . . Creaseys
WESTCLIFF-ON-SEA . . . . Brannans

Overseas

CYPRUS, Nicosia . . Athinodorou & Zevedeou Ltd
CYPRUS, Lefkosa, Mersin 10 . . D.K. Deniz & Co
CYPRUS, Limassol . . . . N Constantinou & Co Audit Ltd
FRANCE, Paris . . . . Dixon Wilson
LUXEMBOURG, Luxembourg HT Group S.A.
SPAIN, Marbella . . . . Spence Clarke & Co

PARTNERSHIPS AND SOLE TRADERS

United Kingdom

BATH . . . . Berkeley Bate
BERKHAMSTED . . . . Harts
BIRMINGHAM . . . . A.K. Patel & Co
BRISTOL . . . . Mensis Ltd
CANNOCK Shelvoke, Pickering, Janney & Co
CHALFONT ST. GILES . . . . . . Lawson & Co
CHELTENHAM . . . . William Hinton Ltd
CROYDON . . . . D.S. & Co
DAVENTRY . . . . Stephen Franklin FCA CTA
ESHER . . . . Holmes & Co
GODALMING . . . . Delia Orme
GRANTHAM . . . . Callow & Holmes
HASLEMERE . . . . Knox Cropper
HERTFORD . . . . Gary J. Cansick & Co
ILFORD . . . . Fredericks Ltd
INGATESTONE . . . . Taylor, Viney & Marlow
LEEDS . . . . Whitesides
LEICESTER . . . . Powrie Appleby LLP
LEIGHTON BUZZARD . . . . . Ian N. Edwards
LONDON EC1 . . . . FW Stephens
Lubbock Fine
LONDON N22 . . . . C.Babs-Jonah & Co
LONDON N3 . . . . FMCB
Paul Perlin & Co
SPW Poppleton & Appleby
SPW (UK) LLP
LONDON NW1 . . . . Creasey Alexander & Co
LONDON NW4 . . . . Dodd Harris
LONDON NW6 . . . . Tony Stitt
LONDON SE10 . . . . Med Act
LONDON SE19 . . . . API Partnership Ltd
LONDON SW1 . . . . Sterling Hay
LONDON SW12 . . . . The Decimal Place
LONDON SW17 . . . . . . Wadud Patwari & Co
LONDON SW19 . . . . Miss E A Parks
LONDON SW3 . . . . Dennis R. Waters
LONDON W1 . . . . Arthur G Mead
F. Winter & Co LLP
Sayers Butterworth LLP
LONDON W13 . . . . Merchant & Co
LONDON W5 . . . . Levy & Partners
Levy + Partners Ltd
MAIDSTONE . . . . Michael D. Nichols
MANCHESTER . . . . Beever and Struthers
MATLOCK . . . . Anne Griffiths
MILTON KEYNES . . . . . Chancery (UK) LLP
Jaquest & Co
Keens Shay Keens Milton Keynes
R.J. Cladd
MORETON-IN-MARSH . . . . Tayabali-Tomlin Ltd
NEWBURY . . . . Paul M Bowers
NEWCASTLE UPON TYNE . . . . . . Business Consultancy Services
READING . . . . Avalon Accounting
Vale & West
RICHMOND . . . . PK Partners LLP
RUISLIP . . . . Grant Harrod
SOUTHAMPTON . . . . Roches
UXBRIDGE . . . . Pinkney Keith Gibbs
WATFORD . . . . Turnbull Associates
WEST BYFLEET . . . . Gibson Hewitt Outsourcing Ltd
WEST WICKHAM . . . . Daniels & Co
WESTCLIFF-ON-SEA . . . . Brannans
WILMSLOW . . . . Sandison Easson & Co
YORK . . . . Wild & Co

PAYE ADVICE

United Kingdom

BRISTOL . . . . Mensis Ltd
CARDIFF . . . . Chris Madge & Co
CLEVEDON . . . . Chris Madge & Co
CROYDON . . . . D.S. & Co
HIGH WYCOMBE . . . . Seymour Taylor
ILFORD . . . . Fredericks Ltd
INGATESTONE . . . . Taylor, Viney & Marlow
LONDON N3 . . . . FMCB

Paul Perlin & Co
LONDON NW1 .... Winston Gross & Co
LONDON SE19 .... API Partnership Ltd
LONDON SW1 .... Sterling Hay
LONDON W1 .... Chris Madge & Co
LONDON W13 .... Merchant & Co
LONDON W5 .... Levy & Partners
Levy + Partners Ltd
MANCHESTER .... Beever and Struthers
MILTON KEYNES ..... Chancery (UK) LLP
MORECAMBE .... Coates & Co
WATFORD .... Turnbull Associates
WESTCLIFF-ON-SEA .... Brannans
WILMSLOW .... Sandison Easson & Co

Overseas

NIGERIA, Lagos .... Horwath Dafinone

PAYROLL SERVICE AND ADVICE

United Kingdom

ALTRINCHAM ... Stephen Hobson BA FCA
BECKENHAM .... Hammonds
BEDFORD .... Gregory Wildman
BERKHAMSTED .... Harts
BIRMINGHAM .... A.K. Patel & Co
Clement Keys
J W Scrivens & Co Ltd
BRACKNELL .... Invest in UK Ltd
BRAINTREE .... Lambert Chapman LLP
BRIGHTON .... Antrams
Lucraft, Hodgson & Dawes
Wilson Sandford (Brighton) Ltd
BRISTOL .... Evans & Partners
Evans & Partners
Mensis Ltd
BUCKHURST HILL .... Dutchmans
BURNLEY .... K M Business Solutions Ltd
BUXTON .... ABC Accountants
CANNOCK Shelvoke, Pickering, Janney & Co
CARDIFF .... Groves Davey Ltd
CHELMSFORD .... Bird Luckin Ltd
CHELTENHAM .... William Hinton Ltd
COLCHESTER .... Elizabeth Burden
CROYDON .... D.S. & Co
The McCay Partnership
Saleemi Associates
DUNMOW .... Bird Luckin Ltd
EAST MOLESEY .... Christie Buchanan
EDGWARE .... Seafields
FARNHAM .... Milne Eldridge & Co
Wise & Co
GERRARDS CROSS Godfrey Anderson & Co
GREENFORD .... RehncyShaheen
HARLOW .... Giess Wallis Crisp
HARROW .... AZR Ltd
Leftley Rowe & Co
HERTFORD .... Philip T. Chave & Co
HIGH WYCOMBE .... Seymour Taylor
HOVE .... Wilson Sandford Ltd
HYDE .... Graham H. Wood & Co
ILFORD .... Fredericks Ltd
INGATESTONE .... Taylor, Viney & Marlow
IPSWICH .... Ensors
KIDDERMINSTER ...... G.H.Herbert & Co
KING'S LYNN .... Stephenson Smart
KINGSTON UPON THAMES . David Howard
Garners Ltd
LANCASTER .... Langdale
LEEDS .... Whitesides
LIVERPOOL .... Chadwick LLP
LONDON E17 .... Michael Barrs and Co
LONDON EC1 .... FW Stephens
Kingswood
LONDON N20 .... Gerald Edelman
LONDON N3 .... FMCB
Paul Perlin & Co
SPW (UK) LLP
LONDON NW11 ..... Edmund Wright & Co
LONDON SE19 .... API Partnership Ltd
LONDON SE25 .... Soteriou Christou Ltd
LONDON SE3 .... Susan Stelfox
LONDON SW1 .... Smith & Hutchinson
LONDON SW12 .... The Decimal Place
LONDON SW18 .... Chicksand Gordon Avis Ltd
LONDON SW3 .... Dennis R. Waters
LONDON SW4 .... Willis Burnell Ltd
LONDON W1 .... Citroen Wells
Gerald Edelman
Sayers Butterworth LLP
LONDON W11 .... Katz & Co
LONDON W13 .... Merchant & Co
LONDON W5 .... Levy & Partners
Levy + Partners Ltd
LONDON WC2 .... Bourner Bullock
LUTON .... Miller & Co
MAIDENHEAD .... Hale & Co
Higgins Day
MAIDSTONE .... Michael D. Nichols
MANCHESTER .... Beever and Struthers
Chadwick LLP
MILTON KEYNES Keens Shay Keens Milton Keynes
MORECAMBE .... Coates & Co
MORETON-IN-MARSH .... Tayabali-Tomlin Ltd
NEWCASTLE UPON TYNE .... Tait Walker
NEWHAVEN .... Intelligent Blue Ltd
NORTHAMPTON .... J.R. Watson & Co
Paul Slater & Co
NOTTINGHAM .... Huw Williams Ltd
PETERSFIELD .... Barter Durgan & Muir Ltd
PORTSMOUTH .... David Bailey
PRESTON .... Whitehead & Aldrich
PURLEY .... Rebello & Co
READING .... Avalon Accounting
Holland MacLennan & Co
Vale & West
REIGATE .... EC Accountancy
RICHMOND .... Feltonpumphrey
The Hughes Consultancy
PK Partners LLP
ROYSTON .... WKH
RUISLIP .... Warneford Gibbs
SALE .... Armitt & Co
SHEFFIELD .... Barber Harrison & Platt
SLOUGH .... Charles Stuart LLP
ST ALBANS .... Jane M. Andrews
UXBRIDGE .... Pinkney Keith Gibbs
WAKEFIELD .... Dix Vogan Ltd
WALTON-ON-THAMES Byrne, Palmer & Co
WARRINGTON .... Voisey & Co
WATFORD .... JSA Services Ltd
Turnbull Associates
WELWYN .... R.S. Partnership
WEMBLEY .... S. Syedain & Co
WEST BYFLEET .... Gibson Hewitt Outsourcing Ltd
WESTCLIFF-ON-SEA .... Brannans
WEYBRIDGE .... GCA
TWP
WICKFORD .... Hamilton Brading
WIRRAL .... Morris & Co
WREXHAM .... Guy Walmsley & Co

Overseas

LUXEMBOURG, Luxembourg HT Group S.A.
NIGERIA, Lagos .... Horwath Dafinone
POLAND, Warsaw Baker Tilly Smoczynski & Partners Sp. z o.o.

PERSONAL

United Kingdom

ASHTEAD .... David Beckman & Co Ltd
AYLESBURY .... P.G.Jeffery
BATH .... Berkeley Bate
Roland J. Adamson
BERKHAMSTED .... Harts
BIRMINGHAM .... A.K. Patel & Co
BRADFORD .... Andrew S. Parker
David Allen Associates
BRISTOL .... Mensis Ltd
BROMLEY .... Pauline Lonsdale
BUCKHURST HILL .... Dutchmans
BURTON-ON-TRENT .... Nicholson Blythe Ltd
CANNOCK Shelvoke, Pickering, Janney & Co
CHELTENHAM .... William Hinton Ltd
CROYDON .... D.S. & Co
DAVENTRY .... Stephen Franklin FCA CTA
EASTLEIGH .... Romeril Martin
FARNHAM .... Wise & Co
GODALMING .... Delia Orme
GUILDFORD .... Morley Tippett
Randall Greene
HERTFORD .... Gary J. Cansick & Co
ILFORD .... Fredericks Ltd
INGATESTONE .... Taylor, Viney & Marlow
LEICESTER .... Powrie Appleby LLP
LEIGHTON BUZZARD ..... Ian N. Edwards
LONDON E14 .... Littlejohn
LONDON EC1 .... FW Stephens
LONDON N3 .... FMCB
Paul Perlin & Co
LONDON NW1 .... Creasey Alexander & Co
H.W. Fisher & Co
LONDON NW6 .... Tony Stitt
LONDON SW1 .... Smith & Hutchinson
Sterling Hay
LONDON SW12 .... The Decimal Place
LONDON SW13 .... C.J. Cook & Co
LONDON SW19 .... Miss E A Parks
LONDON W1 .... Arthur G Mead
Citroen Wells
Sayers Butterworth LLP
LONDON W13 .... Merchant & Co
LONDON W5 .... Levy & Partners
Levy + Partners Ltd
MANCHESTER .... Beever and Struthers
UHY Hacker Young Manchester LLP
MILTON KEYNES Keens Shay Keens Milton Keynes
MORETON-IN-MARSH .... Tayabali-Tomlin Ltd
NEWBURY .... Paul M Bowers
NEWCASTLE UPON TYNE ...... Business Consultancy Services
READING .... Avalon Accounting
RICHMOND .... Feltonpumphrey
PK Partners LLP
RUISLIP .... Grant Harrod
SALFORD .... P. David Levinson
SOUTH CROYDON .... Sargent & Co
UXBRIDGE .... Pinkney Keith Gibbs
WATFORD .... Turnbull Associates
WESTCLIFF-ON-SEA .... Brannans
WILMSLOW .... Sandison Easson & Co
WOKING .... C.E. Petty & Co

YORK .... Mary Matthews

Overseas

FRANCE, Paris .... Dixon Wilson
GREECE, Athens .. KPMG Certified Auditors AE
IRAN, Tehran .... A.M. Mahallati & Co

SELF ASSESSMENT ADVICE

United Kingdom

ANDOVER .... Brady Scrace Ltd
AYLESBURY .... P.G.Jeffery
BERKHAMSTED .... Harts
BIRMINGHAM .... A.K. Patel & Co
BRAINTREE .... Jaynes & Co
BRISTOL .... Mensis Ltd
Phillip Corbin
CANNOCK Shelvoke, Pickering, Janney & Co
CHALFONT ST. GILES ...... Lawson & Co
COLCHESTER .... J.Kirkwood & Co
DAVENTRY .... Stephen Franklin FCA CTA
DOUGLAS .... PKF (Isle of Man) LLC
EDGWARE .... Harris Kafton
ESHER .... Holmes & Co
HARLOW .... Parry & Co
HARROW .... LINK
HORSHAM .... David Langley
HOVE .... Atkinsons
ILFORD .... Fredericks Ltd
INGATESTONE .... Taylor, Viney & Marlow
KIDDERMINSTER ...... G.H.Herbert & Co
KINGSTON UPON THAMES . David Howard
LEEDS .... Whitesides
LONDON E16 .... Eafton & Co
LONDON E17 .... Michael Barrs and Co
LONDON EC1 .... FW Stephens
Kingswood
LONDON N3 .... FMCB
Paul Perlin & Co
SPW (UK) LLP
LONDON NW1 .... Winston Gross & Co
LONDON NW4 .... Dodd Harris
LONDON NW6 .... Tony Stitt
LONDON SE10 .... Med Act
LONDON SE19 .... API Partnership Ltd
LONDON SE25 .... Soteriou
Christou Ltd
LONDON SW1 .... Sterling Hay
LONDON SW13 .... C.J. Cook & Co
LONDON SW17 ...... Wadud Patwari & Co
LONDON SW18 .... Chicksand Gordon
Avis Ltd
LONDON SW19 .... Miss E A Parks
LONDON W1 .... Arthur G Mead
Civvals
LONDON W13 .... Merchant & Co
LONDON W5 .... Levy & Partners
Levy + Partners Ltd
MAIDSTONE .... Michael D. Nichols
MANCHESTER .... Beever and Struthers
MATLOCK .... Anne Griffiths
MILTON KEYNES .... R.J. Cladd
MORECAMBE .... Coates & Co
NEW MALDEN .... Atkinsons
NEWBURY .... Paul M Bowers
NEWCASTLE UPON TYNE ...... Business
Consultancy Services
NEWHAVEN .... Intelligent Blue Ltd
NORTHAMPTON .... J.R. Watson & Co
Paul Slater & Co
NOTTINGHAM .... Huw Williams Ltd
PINNER .... Douglas Collier Ltd
READING .... Avalon Accounting
Vale & West
REIGATE .... EC Accountancy
RUISLIP .... Grant Harrod
Warneford Gibbs
SALE .... Armitt & Co
SOUTH CROYDON .... Sargent & Co
SURBITON .... Stevensons
TUNBRIDGE WELLS .... Auker Hutton
WATFORD .... Turnbull Associates
WESTCLIFF-ON-SEA .... Brannans

Overseas

NIGERIA, Lagos .... Horwath Dafinone

SMALL TRADERS

United Kingdom

AYLESBURY .... P.G.Jeffery
BERKHAMSTED .... Harts
BIRMINGHAM .... A.K. Patel & Co
BRISTOL .... Mensis Ltd
BURTON-ON-TRENT .... Nicholson
Blythe Ltd
DAVENTRY .... Stephen Franklin FCA CTA
DERBY .... R.V. Hoad & Co
ESHER .... Holmes & Co
ILFORD .... Fredericks Ltd
INGATESTONE .... Taylor, Viney & Marlow
KINGSTON UPON THAMES . David Howard
LEIGHTON BUZZARD ..... Ian N. Edwards
LONDON N22 .... C.Babs-Jonah & Co
LONDON N3 .... FMCB
Paul Perlin & Co
LONDON NW3 .... Fisher Phillips
LONDON SE19 .... API Partnership Ltd
LONDON SE25 .... Soteriou
Christou Ltd
LONDON SW1 .... Smith & Hutchinson
LONDON SW13 .... C.J. Cook & Co
LONDON SW3 .... Dennis R. Waters
LONDON W1 .... Arthur G Mead
Lewis Golden & Co
LONDON W13 .... Merchant & Co
LONDON W5 .... Levy & Partners
Levy + Partners Ltd
MANCHESTER .... Beever and Struthers
MILTON KEYNES .... R.J. Cladd
NEWCASTLE UPON TYNE ...... Business
Consultancy Services
NEWHAVEN .... Intelligent Blue Ltd
PORTSMOUTH .... David Bailey
PRESTON .... TLL Accountants Ltd
Turpin Lucas Lees
READING .... Avalon Accounting
RUISLIP .... Grant Harrod
WATFORD .... Turnbull Associates
WESTCLIFF-ON-SEA .... Brannans

TAXATION

United Kingdom

ALTRINCHAM ... Stephen Hobson BA FCA
AMERSHAM .... Cansdales
BARNET .... Debson & Co
BECKENHAM .... Hammonds
BEDFORD .... Gregory Wildman
BIRMINGHAM .... A.K. Patel & Co
Clement Keys
J W Scrivens & Co Ltd
James, Stanley & Co
BISHOP'S STORTFORD ...... David J. Trill
BLYTH .... G D Hakin & Co
BOLTON .... Bentleys
BRADFORD .... Andrew S. Parker
BRAINTREE .... Lambert Chapman LLP
BRIGHTON .... Antrams
Lucraft, Hodgson & Dawes
Wilson Sandford
(Brighton) Ltd
BRISTOL .... Evans & Partners
Evans & Partners
Phillip Corbin
BUCKHURST HILL .... Dutchmans
BURNLEY .... Ashworth Moulds
K M Business Solutions Ltd
BUXTON .... ABC Accountants
CANNOCK Shelvoke, Pickering, Janney & Co
CARDIFF .... Groves Davey Ltd
CHELMSFORD .... Bird Luckin Ltd
Lambert Chapman LLP
CHELTENHAM .... William Hinton Ltd
CHESTER .... Sullivan & Co
COLCHESTER .... Elizabeth Burden
J.Kirkwood & Co
COVENTRY .... Sheth & Co
CROYDON .... D.S. & Co
Hamilton-Eddy & Co
The McCay Partnership
Saleemi Associates
DERBY .... John V. Woodward
Johnson Tidsall
R.V. Hoad & Co
DOUGLAS ..... Baker Tilly Isle of Man LLC
Charles Fargher
PKF (Isle of Man) LLC
DUNMOW .... Bird Luckin Ltd
EASTBOURNE ...... Kenneth M. Bradshaw
EASTLEIGH .... Walji & Co Private
Clients Ltd
EDGWARE .... Harris Kafton
Seafields
EDINBURGH ...... Andrew PD Cramb BSc
ENFIELD .... B. Wright & Co
EXMOUTH .... John Wheeler
FARNHAM .... Milne Eldridge & Co

Taylor Cocks
Wise & Co
GERRARDS CROSS Godfrey Anderson & Co
GODALMING .... Delia Orme
GUERNSEY .... Saffery Champness
Saffery Champness
GUILDFORD .... Randall Greene
HALESOWEN .... Nicklin LLP
HARLOW .... Giess Wallis Crisp
Parry & Co
HARROW .... AZR Ltd
Hill Wooldridge & Co
HASTINGS .... Deeks Evans
HERTFORD .... Philip T. Chave & Co
HIGH WYCOMBE .... Seymour Taylor
HORSHAM .... David Langley
HOVE .... Wilson Sandford Ltd
HYDE .... Graham H. Wood & Co
ILFORD .... Fredericks Ltd
INGATESTONE .... Taylor, Viney & Marlow
JERSEY .... Mazars Channel Islands Ltd
Rosscot Ltd
KINGSTON UPON THAMES . David Howard
Garners Ltd
LANCASTER .... Langdale
LEEDS .... Bartfields Business Services LLP
Bartfields (UK) Ltd
Whitesides
LEICESTER .... Powrie Appleby LLP
LEIGH-ON-SEA .... Walsh & Co
LEIGHTON BUZZARD ..... Ian N. Edwards
LEWES .... Knill James
LIVERPOOL .... Chadwick LLP
LLANDUDNO .... Gareth Hughes &
Company Ltd
LONDON E16 .... Eafton & Co
LONDON E17 .... Michael Barrs and Co
LONDON EC1 .... Lubbock Fine
LONDON EC2 .... Everett & Son
LONDON N13 ...... John Crook & Partners
LONDON N20 .... Gerald Edelman
Harris Lipman LLP
Kallis & Partners
LONDON N3 .... Alexander-Passe & Co
FMCB
Paul Perlin & Co
SPW Poppleton & Appleby
SPW (UK) LLP
LONDON N8 .... A.K. Suleman
LONDON NW1 .... H.W. Fisher & Co
Winston Gross & Co
LONDON NW11 ..... Edmund Wright & Co
LONDON NW6 .... Tony Stitt
LONDON SE19 .... API Partnership Ltd
LONDON SW1 .... Helmores
LONDON SW12 .... Child & Child
Accountants Ltd
LONDON SW14 .... Andrew B Tappin
White Hart Associates LLP
LONDON SW17 ...... Wadud Patwari & Co
LONDON SW18 .... Chicksand Gordon
Avis Ltd
LBCo Ltd
LONDON SW19 .... Coulthards
Med Act
LONDON SW4 .... Willis Burnell Ltd
LONDON W1 .... Citroen Wells
David Smith & Co
Elman Wall Ltd
F. Winter & Co LLP
Gerald Edelman
Rosenthal & Co
LONDON W4 .... Flinthams
LONDON W5 .... Levy & Partners
Levy + Partners Ltd
LONDON WC1 .... Rayner Essex LLP
LONDON WC2 .... Arnold Hill & Co

Bourner Bullock
LOUGHTON .... Haslers
LUTON .... Miller & Co
MAIDENHEAD .... Hale & Co
Higgins Day
MAIDSTONE .... Michael D. Nichols
MALDON .... Lambert Chapman LLP
MANCHESTER .... Beever and Struthers
Chadwick LLP
Horwath Clark Whitehill LLP
UHY Hacker Young Manchester LLP
MILTON KEYNES .... Bourner Bullock
Keens Shay Keens Milton Keynes
MacIntyre Hudson LLP
MORECAMBE .... Coates & Co
MORETON-IN-MARSH .... Tayabali-
Tomlin Ltd
NESTON .... Driffield & Co
NEW MALDEN .... Nasir Mahmud
NEWBURY .... Maughans Ltd
NEWCASTLE UPON TYNE ...... Business
Consultancy Services
Tait Walker
NEWHAVEN .... Intelligent Blue Ltd
NORTHAMPTON .... J.R. Watson & Co
NORTHWICH .... Howard Worth
NORTHWOOD .... Rosenthal & Co
NOTTINGHAM .... Higson & Co
OXFORD .... Taylor Cocks
PETERSFIELD .... Barter Durgan &
Muir Ltd
PORTSMOUTH ...... Rothman Pantall & Co
The Taylor Cocks
Partnership Ltd
PRESTON .... James Todd & Co
Whitehead & Aldrich
PURLEY .... Rebello & Co
READING .... Holland MacLennan & Co
Taylor Cocks
Vale & West
REIGATE .... EC Accountancy
P.J. Lindsay
RICHMOND .... Feltonpumphrey
The Hughes Consultancy
RUGBY .... C H Ivens & Co
SALE .... Armitt & Co
SALFORD .... P. David Levinson
SEVENOAKS .... Brebners
SHEFFIELD .... Barber Harrison & Platt
SOUTHAMPTON .... Hopper Williams &
Bell Ltd
Roches
Rule Datlen Mann
SOUTHPORT .... Eaves and Co
ST ALBANS .... Rayner Essex LLP
STALYBRIDGE .... Roberts Toner LLP
STOCKPORT .... The TACS Partnership
STOKE-ON-TRENT .... Moore Stephens
STRATFORD-UPON-AVON .. Grenfell James
SURBITON .... Stevensons
SUTTON COLDFIELD .... Bissell &
Brown Ltd
SWANSEA .... Bevan & Buckland
Gerald Thomas & Co
UXBRIDGE .... Pinkney Keith Gibbs
WALTON-ON-THAMES Byrne, Palmer & Co
WATFORD ...... JSA Business Services LLP
WELWYN .... R.S. Partnership
WEYBRIDGE .... MGI Midgley Snelling
WICKFORD .... Hamilton Brading
WILMSLOW .... Jane Foy & Co
Sandison Easson & Co
WIMBORNE .... The Taylor Cocks
Partnership Ltd
WORTHING .... Carpenter Box LLP
WREXHAM .... Guy Walmsley & Co

Overseas

CYPRUS, Lefkosa, Mersin 10 .. D.K. Deniz & Co
CYPRUS, Nicosia .... Ernst & Young
HLB Afxentiou Ltd
Savvas E Savvides Ltd
LUXEMBOURG, Luxembourg HT Group S.A.
NIGERIA, Lagos .... Horwath Dafinone
POLAND, Warsaw Baker Tilly Smoczynski & Partners Sp. z o.o.
SPAIN, Madrid .... Eurocontrol Asesores Contables
SPAIN, Marbella .... Spence Clarke & Co

TRUSTEESHIP

United Kingdom

CROYDON .... Hamilton-Eddy & Co
DOUGLAS .... Crowe Morgan
PKF (Isle of Man) LLC
EASTLEIGH .... Rothman Pantall & Co
GODALMING .... Delia Orme
GUILDFORD .... Randall Greene
JERSEY .... Alex Picot
Caversham
LONDON EC1 .... FW Stephens
LONDON SW1 .... Helmores
LONDON SW14 .... Andrew B Tappin
LONDON W1 .... David Smith & Co
LONDON WC2 .... Arnold Hill & Co
MANCHESTER .... Beever and Struthers
PETERSFIELD .... Barter Durgan &
Muir Ltd
WESTCLIFF-ON-SEA .... Brannans

Overseas

CYPRUS, Nicosia .... Abacus Ltd
Ernst & Young
FRANCE, Paris .... Dixon Wilson

TRUSTS

United Kingdom

BIRMINGHAM .... Clement Keys
BRADFORD .... David Allen Associates
BRAINTREE .... Lambert Chapman LLP
BROMLEY .... Pauline Lonsdale
CHELMSFORD .... Bird Luckin Ltd
CHESTER LE STREET
.... Straughans Ltd
DAVENTRY .... Stephen Franklin FCA CTA
DOUGLAS .... PKF (Isle of Man) LLC
EASTLEIGH .... Romeril Martin
Rothman Pantall & Co
GODALMING .... Delia Orme
GUILDFORD .... Morley Tippett
Randall Greene
HASLEMERE .... Knox Cropper
HOVE .... Atkinsons
JERSEY .... Caversham
HLB Jackson Fox
Rosscot Ltd
LEICESTER .... Powrie Appleby LLP
LONDON E14 .... Littlejohn
LONDON EC1 .... FW Stephens
Higgisons
Lubbock Fine
LONDON N14 .... Bond Partners LLP
LONDON N3 .... Paul Perlin & Co
LONDON NW1 .... H.W. Fisher & Co
LONDON W1 .... Citroen Wells
Sayers Butterworth LLP
MANCHESTER .... Beever and Struthers
MILTON KEYNES ..... Chancery (UK) LLP

NEW MALDEN .... Atkinsons
NEWBURY .... Paul M Bowers
NORTHAMPTON .... J.R. Watson & Co
NOTTINGHAM .... Huw Williams Ltd
NUNEATON .... Nicola Fisher Financial Planning Ltd
PRESTON .... Titus Thorp & Ainsworth
READING .... Vale & West
RICHMOND .... PK Partners LLP
SHEFFIELD .... Barber Harrison & Platt
STANMORE .... Lawrence Grant
SWANSEA .... Bevan & Buckland
WATFORD .... Myers Clark
WESTCLIFF-ON-SEA .... Brannans
WEYBRIDGE .... TWP

Overseas

FRANCE, Paris .... Dixon Wilson

UK COMPANIES OVERSEAS

United Kingdom

DOUGLAS .... PKF (Isle of Man) LLC
LEICESTER .... Powrie Appleby LLP
LIVERPOOL .... Hurst (Liverpool) LLP
LONDON NW11 .... Tuchbands
LONDON W1 .... Citroen Wells
OXFORD .... The MGroup Partnership
STANMORE .... Lawrence Grant
TUNBRIDGE WELLS .... Creaseys
WESTCLIFF-ON-SEA .... Brannans

Overseas

POLAND, Warsaw Baker Tilly Smoczynski & Partners Sp. z o.o.
SPAIN, Marbella .... Spence Clarke & Co

UK NATIONALS OVERSEAS

United Kingdom

BRISTOL .... Mensis Ltd
BROMLEY .... Pauline Lonsdale
DOUGLAS .... PKF (Isle of Man) LLC
EPSOM .... Hakim Fry
GODALMING .... Delia Orme
LEICESTER .... Powrie Appleby LLP
LEIGH-ON-SEA .... Walsh & Co
LONDON EC1 .... FW Stephens
Lubbock Fine
LONDON EC4 .... Target Winters
LONDON W1 .... Citroen Wells
STANMORE .... Lawrence Grant
TUNBRIDGE WELLS .... Creaseys
WESTCLIFF-ON-SEA .... Brannans

Overseas

FRANCE, Paris .... Dixon Wilson
POLAND, Warsaw Baker Tilly Smoczynski & Partners Sp. z o.o.
SPAIN, Marbella .... Spence Clarke & Co

UK SUBSIDIARIES OF OVERSEAS MULTINATIONALS

United Kingdom

AMERSHAM .... Cansdales
BEDFORD .... Gregory Wildman
BERKHAMSTED .... Harts
COBHAM .... Wellden Turnbull LLP
DOUGLAS .... PKF (Isle of Man) LLC
FARNBOROUGH Howard Lee, Fellows & Co
HARROW .... Leftley Rowe & Co
HIGH WYCOMBE .... Seymour Taylor
HOUNSLOW .... Charles Stuart LLP
HOVE .... Parkers Business Services Ltd
LIVERPOOL .... Hurst (Liverpool) LLP
LONDON E14 .... Littlejohn
LONDON EC1 .... FW Stephens
Lubbock Fine
LONDON EC2 .... Everett & Son
LONDON EC4 .... Target Winters
LONDON N12 .... Anthony Tiscoe & Co
LONDON N14 .... Bond Partners LLP
LONDON NW1 .... BRAL Ltd
LONDON SE19 .... API Partnership Ltd
LONDON SW13 .... C.J. Cook & Co
LONDON W1 .... Bowker Orford
Citroen Wells
Elman Wall Ltd
LONDON W5 .... Johnsons Financial Management Ltd
LONDON WC2 .... Bourner Bullock
MILTON KEYNES Keens Shay Keens Milton Keynes
NORTHAMPTON .... Hawsons
RICKMANSWORTH .... Dickinsons
SLOUGH .... Charles Stuart LLP
STANMORE .... Lawrence Grant
SURBITON .... Richard Morgan and Co
TUNBRIDGE WELLS .... Creaseys
WEYBRIDGE .... MGI Midgley Snelling
Ward Williams Ltd

VALUE ADDED TAX

United Kingdom

AMERSHAM .... Cansdales
BIRMINGHAM .... A.K. Patel & Co
Clement Keys
BOLTON .... Bentleys
BRISTOL .... Mensis Ltd
CANNOCK Shelvoke, Pickering, Janney & Co
CARDIFF .... Chris Madge & Co
CHELMSFORD .... Bird Luckin Ltd
CLEVEDON .... Chris Madge & Co
DOUGLAS ..... Baker Tilly Isle of Man LLC
PKF (Isle of Man) LLC
EASTLEIGH .... Rothman Pantall & Co
GERRARDS CROSS Godfrey Anderson & Co
HARROW .... AZR Ltd
HOVE .... Atkinsons
ILFORD .... Fredericks Ltd
INGATESTONE .... Taylor, Viney & Marlow
LONDON E14 .... Littlejohn
LONDON E17 .... Michael Barrs and Co
LONDON EC1 .... FW Stephens
Morwood-Leyland & Co
LONDON EC4 .... Knox Cropper
LONDON N3 .... FMCB
Paul Perlin & Co
LONDON NW1 .... H.W. Fisher & Co
LONDON SE19 .... API Partnership Ltd
LONDON SE25 .... Soteriou
Christou Ltd
LONDON SW19 .... Mark Buffery
LONDON W1 .... Chris Madge & Co
Sayers Butterworth LLP
LONDON W5 .... Levy & Partners
Levy + Partners Ltd
LOUGHTON .... Haslers
MAIDSTONE .... Michael D. Nichols
MANCHESTER .... Beever and Struthers
UHY Hacker Young Manchester LLP
MILTON KEYNES .... Bourner Bullock
Chancery (UK) LLP
MacIntyre Hudson LLP
NEW MALDEN .... Atkinsons
NEWCASTLE-UNDER-LYME.............
Barringtons Ltd
NORTHAMPTON .... J.R. Watson & Co
READING .... Avalon Accounting
SALE .... Armitt & Co
SHEFFIELD .... Barber Harrison & Platt
WESTCLIFF-ON-SEA .... Brannans

Overseas

IRAN, Tehran .... A.M. Mahallati & Co
NIGERIA, Lagos .... Horwath Dafinone
POLAND, Warsaw Baker Tilly Smoczynski & Partners Sp. z o.o.

BUSINESS RECOVERY & INSOLVENCY

BANKRUPTCIES

United Kingdom

AMERSHAM .... Wilkins Kennedy
BIRMINGHAM .... Begbies Traynor Ltd
Vantis Business Recovery Services
BRIGHTON .... Begbies Traynor Ltd
Jeremy Knight & Co
BRISTOL .... Begbies Traynor
CARDIFF .... Begbies Traynor Ltd
Harris Lipman LLP
CHICHESTER .... Stonham.Co
EDINBURGH .... Begbies Traynor Ltd
EGHAM .... Wilkins Kennedy
EXETER .... Begbies Traynor Ltd
GLASGOW .... Begbies Traynor Ltd
GUILDFORD .... Wilkins Kennedy
HALIFAX .... Begbies Traynor Ltd
HELSTON .... Purnells
HORNCHURCH ... Vantis Business Recovery Services
HUDDERSFIELD .... Wilkinson & Co
IVYBRIDGE .... Richard J. Smith & Co
LEEDS .... Begbies Traynor

Begbies Traynor
Geoffrey Martin & Co
LEICESTER ...... Vantis Business Recovery Services
LIVERPOOL .... Begbies Traynor Ltd
Parkin S. Booth & Co
LONDON EC1 .... Kingston Smith & Partners LLP
Lubbock Fine
LONDON EC2 .... Harris Lipman LLP
LONDON EC3 .... Begbies Traynor Ltd
LONDON N12 ..... David Rubin & Partners
LONDON N14 .... Bond Partners LLP
LONDON N20 .... Harris Lipman LLP
LONDON N3 .... SPW Poppleton & Appleby
SPW (UK) LLP
LONDON SE1 .... Wilkins Kennedy
LONDON W1 .... Citroen Wells
Geoffrey Martin & Co
Vantis Business Recovery Services
LONDON W2 ...... Gregory Michaels & Co
LONDON WC1 .... Griffins
LOUGHTON .... Haslers
ThorntonRones Ltd
MANCHESTER .... Begbies Traynor Ltd
MARKET DRAYTON .... Barringtons Ltd
MARLOW Vantis Business Recovery Services
MILTON KEYNES .... Begbies Traynor
NEWCASTLE UPON TYNE .... Tait Walker
NEWCASTLE-UNDER-LYME............. Barringtons Ltd
NEWPORT .... Barringtons Ltd
NOTTINGHAM .... Begbies Traynor Ltd
ORPINGTON .... Wilkins Kennedy
PRESTON .... Begbies Traynor Ltd
RICHMOND .... Pococks
SALISBURY .... Begbies Traynor
SHEFFIELD .... The P&A Partnership
SOUTHEND-ON-SEA .... Begbies Traynor Ltd
Wilkins Kennedy
ST ALBANS .... Harris Lipman LLP
Kingston Smith & Partners LLP
Vantis Business Recovery Services
STEVENAGE .... Wilder Coe
STOKE-ON-TRENT .... Begbies Traynor Ltd
Moore Stephens
TONBRIDGE ..... Vantis Business Recovery Services
TRURO .... Richard J. Smith & Co
UXBRIDGE ... L + A Business Recovery LLP
WATFORD .... Myers Clark
WEST BYFLEET ...... Gibson Hewitt & Co
WORTHING .... Vantis Business Recovery Services

Overseas

POLAND, Warsaw Baker Tilly Smoczynski & Partners Sp. z o.o.

CORPORATE RECOVERY

United Kingdom

AMERSHAM .... Wilkins Kennedy
BIRMINGHAM .... Begbies Traynor Ltd
Vantis Business Recovery Services
BRIGHTON .... Begbies Traynor Ltd
Jeremy Knight & Co
BRISTOL .... Begbies Traynor
CARDIFF .... Begbies Traynor Ltd
Harris Lipman LLP
CHICHESTER .... Stonham.Co
DOUGLAS .... PKF (Isle of Man) LLC
EDINBURGH .... Begbies Traynor Ltd
EGHAM .... Wilkins Kennedy
EXETER .... Begbies Traynor Ltd
GLASGOW .... Begbies Traynor Ltd
GUILDFORD .... Wilkins Kennedy
HALIFAX .... Begbies Traynor Ltd
HELSTON .... Purnells
HORNCHURCH ... Vantis Business Recovery Services
IPSWICH .... Ensors
IVYBRIDGE .... Richard J. Smith & Co
LEEDS .... Begbies Traynor
Begbies Traynor
Geoffrey Martin & Co
LEICESTER ...... Vantis Business Recovery Services
LIVERPOOL .... Begbies Traynor Ltd
Parkin S. Booth & Co
LONDON EC1 ... Kingston Smith & Partners LLP
Lubbock Fine
LONDON EC2 .... Harris Lipman LLP
LONDON EC3 .... Begbies Traynor Ltd
LONDON N12 ..... David Rubin & Partners
LONDON N14 .... Bond Partners LLP
LONDON N20 .... Gerald Edelman
Harris Lipman LLP
LONDON N3 .... SPW Poppleton & Appleby
SPW (UK) LLP
LONDON NW1 .... H.W. Fisher & Co
LONDON SE1 .... Wilkins Kennedy
LONDON W1 .... Citroen Wells
Geoffrey Martin & Co
Gerald Edelman
Vantis Business Recovery Services
LONDON WC1 .... Griffins
LOUGHTON .... Haslers
ThorntonRones Ltd
MANCHESTER .... Begbies Traynor Ltd
CLB Coopers
MARKET DRAYTON .... Barringtons Ltd
MARLOW Vantis Business Recovery Services
MILTON KEYNES .... Begbies Traynor
NEWCASTLE UPON TYNE .... Tait Walker
NEWCASTLE-UNDER-LYME............. Barringtons Ltd
NEWPORT .... Barringtons Ltd
NOTTINGHAM .... Begbies Traynor Ltd
ORPINGTON .... Wilkins Kennedy
PRESTON .... Begbies Traynor Ltd
RICHMOND .... Pococks
SALISBURY .... Begbies Traynor
SHEFFIELD .... Barber Harrison & Platt
The P&A Partnership
SOUTHEND-ON-SEA .... Begbies Traynor Ltd
Wilkins Kennedy
ST ALBANS .... Harris Lipman LLP
Kingston Smith & Partners LLP
Vantis Business Recovery Services
STEVENAGE .... Wilder Coe
STOKE-ON-TRENT .... Begbies Traynor Ltd
Moore Stephens
TONBRIDGE ..... Vantis Business Recovery Services
TRURO .... Richard J. Smith & Co
UXBRIDGE ... L + A Business Recovery LLP
WELLS .... Rendell & Co
WEST BYFLEET ...... Gibson Hewitt & Co
WORTHING ...... Vantis Business Recovery Services

Overseas

CYPRUS, Nicosia .... Ernst & Young
IRAN, Tehran .... A.M. Mahallati & Co
POLAND, Warsaw Baker Tilly Smoczynski & Partners Sp. z o.o.

LIQUIDATIONS

United Kingdom

AMERSHAM .... Wilkins Kennedy
BIRMINGHAM .... Begbies Traynor Ltd
Vantis Business Recovery Services
BRIGHTON .... Begbies Traynor Ltd
Jeremy Knight & Co
BRISTOL .... Begbies Traynor
CARDIFF .... Begbies Traynor Ltd
Harris Lipman LLP
CHICHESTER .... Stonham.Co
DERBY .... Johnson Tidsall
DOUGLAS ..... Baker Tilly Isle of Man LLC
PKF (Isle of Man) LLC
EDINBURGH .... Begbies Traynor Ltd
EGHAM .... Wilkins Kennedy
EXETER .... Begbies Traynor Ltd
GLASGOW .... Begbies Traynor Ltd
GUILDFORD .... Wilkins Kennedy
HALIFAX .... Begbies Traynor Ltd
HELSTON .... Purnells
HORNCHURCH ... Vantis Business Recovery Services
HUDDERSFIELD .... Wilkinson & Co
IVYBRIDGE .... Richard J. Smith & Co
LEEDS .... Begbies Traynor
Begbies Traynor
Geoffrey Martin & Co
LEICESTER ...... Vantis Business Recovery Services
LIVERPOOL .... Begbies Traynor Ltd
Parkin S. Booth & Co
LONDON EC1 ... Kingston Smith & Partners LLP
Lubbock Fine
LONDON EC2 .... Harris Lipman LLP
LONDON EC3 .... Begbies Traynor Ltd
LONDON N12 ..... David Rubin & Partners
LONDON N14 .... Bond Partners LLP
LONDON N20 .... Gerald Edelman
Harris Lipman LLP
LONDON N3 .... SPW Poppleton & Appleby
SPW (UK) LLP
LONDON SE1 .... Wilkins Kennedy
LONDON W1 .... Citroen Wells
Geoffrey Martin & Co
Gerald Edelman
Vantis Business Recovery Services
LONDON W2 ...... Gregory Michaels & Co
LONDON WC1 .... Griffins
LOUGHTON .... Haslers
ThorntonRones Ltd
MALDON .... Barrie Harding & Co
MANCHESTER .... Begbies Traynor Ltd
CLB Coopers
MARKET DRAYTON .... Barringtons Ltd
MARLOW Vantis Business Recovery Services
MILTON KEYNES .... Begbies Traynor
NEWCASTLE UPON TYNE .... Tait Walker
NEWCASTLE-UNDER-LYME............. Barringtons Ltd
NEWPORT .... Barringtons Ltd
NOTTINGHAM .... Begbies Traynor Ltd
ORPINGTON .... Wilkins Kennedy
PLYMOUTH .... Tony Jopson & Co Ltd

PRESTON .... Begbies Traynor Ltd
RICHMOND .... Pococks
SALISBURY .... Begbies Traynor
SEVENOAKS .... Brebners
SHEFFIELD .... The P&A Partnership
SOUTHEND-ON-SEA .... Begbies Traynor Ltd
Wilkins Kennedy
ST ALBANS .... Harris Lipman LLP
Kingston Smith & Partners LLP
Vantis Business Recovery Services
STEVENAGE .... Wilder Coe
STOKE-ON-TRENT .... Begbies Traynor Ltd
Moore Stephens
TONBRIDGE ..... Vantis Business Recovery Services
TRURO .... Richard J. Smith & Co
UXBRIDGE ... L + A Business Recovery LLP
WATFORD .... Myers Clark
WELLS .... Rendell & Co
WEST BYFLEET ...... Gibson Hewitt & Co
WORTHING ...... Vantis Business Recovery Services

Overseas

CYPRUS, Nicosia .... Ernst & Young
POLAND, Warsaw Baker Tilly Smoczynski & Partners Sp. z o.o.
SPAIN, Marbella .... Spence Clarke & Co

REORGANISATIONS AND COMPANY RECONSTRUCTIONS

United Kingdom

AMERSHAM .... Cansdales
Wilkins Kennedy
BRIGHTON .... Begbies Traynor Ltd
Jeremy Knight & Co
COLCHESTER .... Butt Cozens
EGHAM .... Wilkins Kennedy
GRAVESEND .... Internal Audit Services Ltd
GUILDFORD .... Wilkins Kennedy
HELSTON .... Purnells
LEEDS .... Begbies Traynor
Begbies Traynor
Geoffrey Martin & Co
LONDON E1 .... UHY Corporate Finance Ltd
LONDON EC1 ... Kingston Smith & Partners LLP
Lubbock Fine
LONDON EC2 .... Harris Lipman LLP
LONDON EC3 .... Begbies Traynor Ltd
LONDON N14 .... Bond Partners LLP
LONDON SE1 .... Wilkins Kennedy
LONDON W1 .... Geoffrey Martin & Co
LOUGHTON .... Haslers
MANCHESTER .... Begbies Traynor Ltd
ORPINGTON .... Wilkins Kennedy
SOUTHEND-ON-SEA ..... Wilkins Kennedy
ST ALBANS . Kingston Smith & Partners LLP
STEVENAGE .... Wilder Coe
STOKE-ON-TRENT .... Moore Stephens
UXBRIDGE ... L + A Business Recovery LLP
WEST BYFLEET ...... Gibson Hewitt & Co

Overseas

CYPRUS, Nicosia .... Ernst & Young
IRAN, Tehran .... A.M. Mahallati & Co
POLAND, Warsaw Baker Tilly Smoczynski & Partners Sp. z o.o.

INVESTMENT BUSINESS

FINANCIAL PLANNING AND ADVICE

United Kingdom

ABERGAVENNY .... Dorrell Oliver Ltd
ACCRINGTON .... Haworths Ltd
AMERSHAM .... Cansdales
Cansdales Ltd
BIRMINGHAM .... Mason Law LLP
BUCKHURST HILL .... Dutchmans
CANNOCK Shelvoke, Pickering, Janney & Co
CROYDON .... Hamilton-Eddy & Co
EASTLEIGH .... Rothman Pantall & Co
Walji & Co Private Clients Ltd
EPSOM .... Vantis Financial Management Ltd
FARNHAM .... Milne Eldridge & Co
GUERNSEY .... Saffery Champness
HALESOWEN .... Nicklin LLP
HIGH WYCOMBE .... Seymour Taylor
IPSWICH .... Ensors
LEICESTER .... Vantis Financial Management Ltd
LEIGH-ON-SEA .... Walsh & Co
LINCOLN .... Nicholsons
LONDON EC1 .... FW Stephens
Higgisons
LONDON N14 .... Bond Partners LLP
LONDON N3 .... FMCB
Paul Perlin & Co
LONDON NW11 ..... Edmund Wright & Co
LONDON SE19 .... API Partnership Ltd
LONDON SW1 .... Helmores
LONDON W1 .... Citroen Wells
Vantis Financial Management Ltd
LONDON WC1 .... haysmacintyre
MAIDENHEAD .... Hale & Co
MANCHESTER Horwath Clark Whitehill LLP
MILTON KEYNES ..... Chancery (UK) LLP
Keens Shay Keens Milton Keynes
NEWCASTLE UPON TYNE .... Tait Walker
NORTHAMPTON .... J.R. Watson & Co
NORTHWICH .... Howard Worth
PETERSFIELD .... Barter Durgan & Muir Ltd
RUGBY .... C H Ivens & Co
WEYBRIDGE .... TWP
WILMSLOW .... Sandison Easson & Co

Overseas

CYPRUS, Nicosia .... Ernst & Young
IRAN, Tehran .... A.M. Mahallati & Co

PENSIONS ADVICE

United Kingdom

ACCRINGTON .... Haworths Ltd
AMERSHAM .... Cansdales Ltd
CANNOCK Shelvoke, Pickering, Janney & Co
EASTLEIGH .... Rothman Pantall & Co
EPSOM .... Vantis Financial Management Ltd
LEICESTER .... Vantis Financial Management Ltd
LONDON EC1 .... FW Stephens
LONDON W1 .... Citroen Wells
Vantis Financial Management Ltd
MANCHESTER .... Beever and Struthers
Cassons
NEWCASTLE UPON TYNE .... Tait Walker
ROSSENDALE .... Cassons
SWANSEA .... Bevan & Buckland
Gerald Thomas & Co
WILMSLOW .... Sandison Easson & Co

PLANNING

United Kingdom

AMERSHAM .... Cansdales
Cansdales Ltd
BOLTON .... Bentleys
COLCHESTER .... Butt Cozens
CROYDON .... D.S. & Co
EPSOM .... Vantis Financial Management Ltd
GUILDFORD .... Randall Greene
LEICESTER .... Vantis Financial Management Ltd
LEIGH-ON-SEA .... Walsh & Co
LONDON EC1 .... FW Stephens
Kingswood
LONDON N3 .... Paul Perlin & Co
LONDON SW13 .... C.J. Cook & Co
LONDON W1 .... Citroen Wells
Vantis Financial Management Ltd
MANCHESTER .... Beever and Struthers
UHY Hacker Young Manchester LLP
READING .... Avalon Accounting
SOUTHAMPTON .... Rule Datlen Mann
WILMSLOW .... Sandison Easson & Co

Overseas

IRAN, Tehran .... A.M. Mahallati & Co

BUSINESS & GENERAL ADVICE

ACQUISITIONS AND MERGERS

United Kingdom

AMERSHAM .... Wilkins Kennedy
BEDFORD .... Gregory Wildman
BIRMINGHAM .... Begbies Traynor Ltd
Clement Keys
BRAINTREE .... Lambert Chapman LLP
BURNLEY .... Ashworth Moulds
CHELMSFORD .... Bird Luckin Ltd
DOUGLAS .... PKF (Isle of Man) LLC
DUDLEY .... Price Pearson
EGHAM .... Wilkins Kennedy
GUILDFORD .... Wilkins Kennedy
HARLOW .... Giess Wallis Crisp
HARROW .... Alliotts
HERTFORD .... Wilkins Kennedy
HIGH WYCOMBE .... Seymour Taylor
HOVE .... Wilson Sandford Ltd
KIDDERMINSTER .... Price Pearson Ltd
LEICESTER .... Kemp Taylor LLP
LIVERPOOL .... Chadwick LLP
LONDON E1 .... UHY Corporate Finance Ltd
LONDON E14 .... Littlejohn
LONDON EC1 .... Kingswood
LONDON EC4 .... Castle Corporate Finance Ltd
LONDON N14 .... Bond Partners LLP
LONDON NW1 .... Fisher Corporate plc

Jade Securities Ltd
LONDON NW11 . . . . H & H Associates
LONDON SE1 . . . . Wilkins Kennedy
LONDON W1 . . . . Jenson Solutions Ltd
Vantis Corporate Finance Ltd
LONDON WC1 . . . . Rayner Essex LLP
LOUGHTON . . . . Haslers
MANCHESTER . . . . A2E Venture Catalyst Ltd
Alexander & Co
Beever and Struthers
Chadwick LLP
UHY Hacker Young Manchester LLP
MATLOCK . . . . Libcus Ltd
MILTON KEYNES . . . . . Chancery (UK) LLP
NEWCASTLE UPON TYNE . . . . Tait Walker
ORPINGTON . . . . Wilkins Kennedy
READING . . . . Turner Barratt Corporate Finance Ltd
REIGATE . . . . Samuels Corporate Ltd
RICHMOND . . . . PK Partners LLP
Pococks
ROMFORD . . . . Chegwidden & Co
ROMSEY . . . . Wilkins Kennedy
ROYSTON . . . . WKH
SALISBURY . . . . Mynott's
SOUTHEND-ON-SEA . . . . . Wilkins Kennedy
ST ALBANS . . . . Rayner Essex LLP
STOURBRIDGE . . . . Nick Pritchard
WATFORD . . . . Myers Clark
WEYBRIDGE . . . . Ward Williams Ltd
WIMBORNE . . . . Ward Goodman Ltd
WINCHESTER . . . . Wilkins Kennedy

Overseas

CYPRUS, Nicosia . . . . Ernst & Young
FALKLAND ISLANDS, Stanley . . . . . Wilkins Kennedy
GREECE, Athens . . KPMG Certified Auditors AE
IRAN, Tehran . . . . A.M. Mahallati & Co
NIGERIA, Lagos . . . . Horwath Dafinone
POLAND, Warsaw Baker Tilly Smoczynski & Partners Sp. z o.o.

ADMINISTRATION

United Kingdom

DOUGLAS . . . . Crowe Morgan
JERSEY . . . . Alex Picot
LONDON N12 . . . . . David Rubin & Partners
LONDON NW1 . . . . BRAL Ltd
LONDON W1 . . . . Geoffrey Martin & Co
Jenson Solutions Ltd
LONDON WC1 . . . . Griffins
MAIDSTONE . . . . Michael D. Nichols
NEWHAVEN . . . . Intelligent Blue Ltd
SHEFFIELD . . . . The P&A Partnership
WESTCLIFF-ON-SEA . . . . Brannans

Overseas

CYPRUS, Nicosia . . . . Abacus Ltd
IRAN, Tehran . . . . A.M. Mahallati & Co

BOOK-KEEPING

United Kingdom

ALTRINCHAM . . . Stephen Hobson BA FCA
BECKENHAM . . . . Hammonds
BEDFORD . . . . Gregory Wildman
BIRMINGHAM . . . . A.K. Patel & Co
BRADFORD . . . . David Allen Associates
BRIGHTON . . . . . Lucraft, Hodgson & Dawes
BRISTOL . . . . Mensis Ltd
BUXTON . . . . ABC Accountants
CAMBERLEY . . . . RSH Accounting
CANNOCK Shelvoke, Pickering, Janney & Co
CHELMSFORD . . . . Bird Luckin Ltd
CROYDON . . . . D.S. & Co
The McCay Partnership
Saleemi Associates
DERBY . . . . R.V. Hoad & Co
DOUGLAS . . . . Charles Fargher
PKF (Isle of Man) LLC
EDGWARE . . . . Seafields
FARNHAM . . . . Milne Eldridge & Co
Taylor Cocks
Wise & Co
GREENFORD . . . . RehncyShaheen
HALIFAX . . . . Riley & Co
HARLOW . . . . Giess Wallis Crisp
HARROW . . . . AZR Ltd
Hill Wooldridge & Co
Leftley Rowe & Co
HOVE . . . . Atkinsons
ILFORD . . . . Fredericks Ltd
INGATESTONE . . . . Taylor, Viney & Marlow
IPSWICH . . . . Ensors
JERSEY . . . . Mazars Channel Islands Ltd
KING'S LYNN . . . . Stephenson Smart
KINGSTON UPON THAMES . David Howard
LEEDS . . . . Whitesides
LONDON E17 . . . . Michael Barrs and Co
LONDON EC1 . . . . FW Stephens
Higgisons
LONDON N3 . . . . Paul Perlin & Co
SPW Poppleton & Appleby
SPW (UK) LLP
LONDON NW1 . . . . BRAL Ltd
H.W. Fisher & Co
LONDON SE19 . . . . API Partnership Ltd
LONDON SE3 . . . . Susan Stelfox
LONDON SW1 . . . . Helmores
Smith & Hutchinson
LONDON SW12 . . . . The Decimal Place
LONDON W1 . . . . Citroen Wells
Civvals
Sayers Butterworth LLP
LONDON W5 . . . . Levy & Partners
Levy + Partners Ltd
LONDON WC1 . . . . Rayner Essex LLP
LONDON WC2 . . . . Arnold Hill & Co
MAIDENHEAD . . . . Hale & Co
Higgins Day
MAIDSTONE . . . . Michael D. Nichols
MANCHESTER . . . . UHY Hacker Young Manchester LLP
MATLOCK . . . . Libcus Ltd
MILTON KEYNES . . . . . Chancery (UK) LLP
Keens Shay Keens Milton Keynes
MacIntyre Hudson LLP
MORECAMBE . . . . Coates & Co
MORETON-IN-MARSH . . . . Tayabali-Tomlin Ltd
NEW MALDEN . . . . Atkinsons
NEWHAVEN . . . . Intelligent Blue Ltd
OXFORD . . . . Taylor Cocks
PETERSFIELD . . . . Barter Durgan & Muir Ltd
PORTSMOUTH . . . . The Taylor Cocks Partnership Ltd
PURLEY . . . . Rebello & Co
READING . . . . Avalon Accounting
Taylor Cocks
REIGATE . . . . EC Accountancy
RICHMOND . . . . Feltonpumphrey
PK Partners LLP
SALE . . . . Armitt & Co
SEVENOAKS . . . . Brebners
ST ALBANS . . . . Rayner Essex LLP
UXBRIDGE . . . . Pinkney Keith Gibbs
WATFORD . . . . . . JSA Business Services LLP
Turnbull Associates
WESTCLIFF-ON-SEA . . . . Brannans
WEYBRIDGE . . . . TWP
WILMSLOW . . . . Jane Foy & Co
WIMBORNE . . . . The Taylor Cocks Partnership Ltd
WOKING . . . . C.E. Petty & Co

Overseas

CYPRUS, Nicosia . . . . Abacus Ltd
CYPRUS, Lefkosa, Mersin 10 . . D.K. Deniz & Co
CYPRUS, Nicosia . . . . Ernst & Young
GREECE, Athens . . KPMG Certified Auditors AE
IRAN, Tehran . . . . A.M. Mahallati & Co
LUXEMBOURG, Luxembourg HT Group S.A.
NIGERIA, Lagos . . . . Horwath Dafinone
POLAND, Warsaw Baker Tilly Smoczynski & Partners Sp. z o.o.
SWITZERLAND, Zollikon Graham Associates AG

BOOK-KEEPING SYSTEMS

United Kingdom

BURNLEY . . . . K M Business Solutions Ltd
DOUGLAS . . . . PKF (Isle of Man) LLC
KINGSTON UPON THAMES . David Howard
LEEDS . . . . Whitesides
LONDON N3 . . . . Paul Perlin & Co
LONDON SE19 . . . . API Partnership Ltd
LONDON W1 . . . . Arthur G Mead
LONDON W5 . . . . Levy & Partners
Levy + Partners Ltd
LONDON WC2 . . . . Bourner Bullock
MILTON KEYNES . . . . Bourner Bullock
NEWHAVEN . . . . Intelligent Blue Ltd
WEST BYFLEET . . . . Gibson Hewitt Outsourcing Ltd
WESTCLIFF-ON-SEA . . . . Brannans

Overseas

IRAN, Tehran . . . . A.M. Mahallati & Co
NIGERIA, Lagos . . . . Horwath Dafinone
SPAIN, Madrid . . . . Eurocontrol Asesores Contables

COMPANY FORMATION

United Kingdom

AMERSHAM . . . . Cansdales
BEDFORD . . . . Gregory Wildman
BISHOP'S STORTFORD . . . . . . Walton & Co
BRIGHTON . . . . . Lucraft, Hodgson & Dawes
Wilson Sandford (Brighton) Ltd
BRISTOL . . . . Mensis Ltd
BURNLEY . . . . K M Business Solutions Ltd
CANNOCK Shelvoke, Pickering, Janney & Co
CARDIFF . . . . Groves Davey Ltd
CROYDON . . . . The McCay Partnership
DERBY . . . . R.V. Hoad & Co
DOUGLAS . . . . Crowe Morgan
PKF (Isle of Man) LLC
EDGWARE . . . . Seafields
EDINBURGH . . . . IFRS 2009 Ltd
FARNHAM . . . . Milne Eldridge & Co
HARLOW . . . . Giess Wallis Crisp
HARROW . . . . AZR Ltd
Leftley Rowe & Co
HASLEMERE . . . . Knox Cropper
HERTFORD . . . . Gary J. Cansick & Co

HIGH WYCOMBE .... Seymour Taylor
HOVE .... Wilson Sandford Ltd
HYDE .... Graham H. Wood & Co
ILFORD .... Fredericks Ltd
INGATESTONE .... Taylor, Viney & Marlow
JERSEY .... Alex Picot
Rosscot Ltd
LEEDS .... Whitesides
LONDON E16 .... Eafton & Co
LONDON E17 .... Michael Barrs and Co
LONDON EC1 .... FW Stephens
Higgisons
Morwood-Leyland & Co
LONDON N22 .... C.Babs-Jonah & Co
LONDON N3 .... Alexander-Passe & Co
FMCB
Paul Perlin & Co
SPW Poppleton & Appleby
SPW (UK) LLP
LONDON SE19 .... API Partnership Ltd
LONDON SW1 .... Helmores
LONDON SW12 .... The Decimal Place
LONDON W1 .... Citroen Wells
Sayers Butterworth LLP
LONDON W5 .... Levy & Partners
Levy + Partners Ltd
LONDON WC1 .... Rayner Essex LLP
LOUGHTON .... Haslers
LUTON .... Miller & Co
MAIDENHEAD .... Hale & Co
MAIDSTONE .... Michael D. Nichols
MATLOCK .... Libcus Ltd
MILTON KEYNES ..... Chancery (UK) LLP
Keens Shay Keens Milton Keynes
MORETON-IN-MARSH .... Tayabali-Tomlin Ltd
PETERSFIELD .... Barter Durgan & Muir Ltd
PRESTON .... TLL Accountants Ltd
Turpin Lucas Lees
Whitehead & Aldrich
PURLEY .... Rebello & Co
READING .... Holland MacLennan & Co
RICHMOND .... PK Partners LLP
Pococks
ST ALBANS .... Rayner Essex LLP
STANMORE .... Lawrence Grant
SURBITON .... Stevensons
TUNBRIDGE WELLS .... Auker Hutton
WESTCLIFF-ON-SEA .... Brannans
WICKFORD .... Hamilton Brading
WOKING .... Barnbrook Sinclair Ltd
WORTHING .... Carpenter Box LLP

Overseas

CYPRUS, Nicosia .... Abacus Ltd
CYPRUS, Lefkosa, Mersin 10 .. D.K. Deniz & Co
CYPRUS, Nicosia .... Ernst & Young
CYPRUS, Limassol .... N Constantinou & Co Audit Ltd
HONG KONG, Wan Chai .. C.C. Kwong & Co
IRAN, Tehran .... A.M. Mahallati & Co
LUXEMBOURG, Luxembourg HT Group S.A.
NIGERIA, Lagos .... Horwath Dafinone
POLAND, Warsaw Baker Tilly Smoczynski & Partners Sp. z o.o.
SPAIN, Marbella .... Spence Clarke & Co
SWITZERLAND, Zollikon Graham Associates AG

COMPANY SECRETARIAL SERVICE

United Kingdom

BECKENHAM .... Hammonds
BRIGHTON ..... Lucraft, Hodgson & Dawes
BRISTOL .... Mensis Ltd
CARDIFF .... Groves Davey Ltd
CHELMSFORD .... Bird Luckin Ltd
CROYDON .... Hamilton-Eddy & Co
The McCay Partnership
DOUGLAS .... Crowe Morgan
PKF (Isle of Man) LLC
DUNMOW .... Bird Luckin Ltd
EDINBURGH .... IFRS 2009 Ltd
FARNHAM .... Milne Eldridge & Co
Wise & Co
HARROW .... AZR Ltd
Hill Wooldridge & Co
HIGH WYCOMBE .... Seymour Taylor
ILFORD .... Fredericks Ltd
INGATESTONE .... Taylor, Viney & Marlow
JERSEY .... Alex Picot
Rosscot Ltd
KINGSTON UPON THAMES . David Howard
Garners Ltd
LONDON E16 .... Eafton & Co
LONDON E17 .... Michael Barrs and Co
LONDON EC1 .... FW Stephens
Kingswood
Morwood-Leyland & Co
LONDON EC4 .... Target Winters
LONDON N20 .... Gerald Edelman
Harris Lipman LLP
LONDON N3 .... FMCB
Paul Perlin & Co
LONDON NW1 .... Creasey Alexander & Co
H.W. Fisher & Co
LONDON SE19 .... API Partnership Ltd
LONDON SW1 .... Helmores
Smith & Hutchinson
LONDON SW18 .... LBCo Ltd
LONDON W1 .... Citroen Wells
Gerald Edelman
Sayers Butterworth LLP
LONDON W5 .... Levy & Partners
Levy + Partners Ltd
LONDON WC2 .... Bourner Bullock
LOUGHTON .... Haslers
LUTON .... Miller & Co
MAIDENHEAD .... Hale & Co
MANCHESTER .... Beever and Struthers
UHY Hacker Young Manchester LLP
MILTON KEYNES .... Bourner Bullock
Keens Shay Keens Milton Keynes
MORETON-IN-MARSH .... Tayabali-Tomlin Ltd
NORTHAMPTON .... J.R. Watson & Co
PETERSFIELD .... Barter Durgan & Muir Ltd
READING .... Avalon Accounting
Vale & West
RICHMOND .... PK Partners LLP
STRATFORD-UPON-AVON .. Grenfell James
UXBRIDGE .... Pinkney Keith Gibbs
WESTCLIFF-ON-SEA .... Brannans
WILMSLOW .... Jane Foy & Co
WREXHAM .... Guy Walmsley & Co

Overseas

CYPRUS, Nicosia .... Abacus Ltd
Ernst & Young
IRAN, Tehran .... A.M. Mahallati & Co
LUXEMBOURG, Luxembourg HT Group S.A.
NIGERIA, Lagos .... Horwath Dafinone

DATA PROCESSING SERVICES

United Kingdom

BEDFORD .... Gregory Wildman
BRISTOL .... Mensis Ltd
EXMOUTH .... John Wheeler
FARNHAM .... Milne Eldridge & Co
LONDON EC1 .... FW Stephens
PETERSFIELD .... Barter Durgan & Muir Ltd
RICHMOND .... PK Partners LLP
WATFORD ...... JSA Business Services LLP
WESTCLIFF-ON-SEA .... Brannans

Overseas

IRAN, Tehran .... A.M. Mahallati & Co
NIGERIA, Lagos .... Horwath Dafinone

DEBT COUNSELLING

United Kingdom

CHICHESTER .... Stonham.Co
LONDON N3 .... SPW (UK) LLP
MALDON .... Barrie Harding & Co
RICHMOND .... Pococks
WESTCLIFF-ON-SEA .... Brannans

DISPOSAL OF BUSINESSES

United Kingdom

AMERSHAM .... Wilkins Kennedy
BIRMINGHAM .... Begbies
Traynor Ltd
BURNLEY .... Ashworth Moulds
CHELMSFORD ..... Lambert Chapman LLP
DUDLEY .... Price Pearson
EGHAM .... Wilkins Kennedy
GUILDFORD .... Wilkins Kennedy
HERTFORD .... Wilkins Kennedy
HIGH WYCOMBE .... Seymour Taylor
KIDDERMINSTER .... Price Pearson Ltd
LONDON E1 .... UHY Corporate Finance Ltd
LONDON E14 .... Littlejohn
LONDON NW1 .... Fisher Corporate plc
H.W. Fisher & Co
Jade Securities Ltd
LONDON SE1 .... Wilkins Kennedy
LONDON W1 .... Citroen Wells
Vantis Corporate Finance Ltd
LONDON W5 .... Levy & Partners
Levy + Partners Ltd
LOUGHTON .... Haslers
MANCHESTER .... Beever and Struthers
NEWCASTLE UPON TYNE .... Tait Walker
NEWHAVEN .... Intelligent Blue Ltd
ORPINGTON .... Wilkins Kennedy
READING .... Turner Barratt Corporate Finance Ltd
RICHMOND .... Pococks
ROMFORD .... Chegwidden & Co
ROMSEY .... Wilkins Kennedy
SALISBURY .... Mynott's
SOUTHEND-ON-SEA ..... Wilkins Kennedy
STEVENAGE .... Wilder Coe
STOCKTON-ON-TEES .... Lyons & Co
STOURBRIDGE .... Nick Pritchard
WATFORD .... Myers Clark
WESTCLIFF-ON-SEA .... Brannans
WINCHESTER .... Wilkins Kennedy

Overseas

FALKLAND ISLANDS, Stanley ..... Wilkins Kennedy

DIVORCE/MATRIMONIAL

United Kingdom

BIRMINGHAM .... Clement Keys
COBHAM .... Wellden Turnbull LLP
LONDON EC1 .... FW Stephens
LONDON EC2 .... CRA International (UK) Ltd
RGL LLP
LONDON WC1 .... FTI Forensic Accounting Ltd
LOUGHTON .... Haslers
MANCHESTER .... Beever and Struthers
MATLOCK .... Libcus Ltd
NORWICH .... Walton Dodge Forensic
OXFORD .... The MGroup Partnership
WESTCLIFF-ON-SEA .... Brannans
WIMBORNE .... Ward Goodman Ltd

EUROPE

United Kingdom

LONDON EC1 .... FW Stephens
LONDON NW1 .... BRAL Ltd
LONDON WC2 .... Bourner Bullock
MILTON KEYNES .... Bourner Bullock
PLYMOUTH .... Parkhurst Hill
STANMORE .... Lawrence Grant
TUNBRIDGE WELLS .... Creaseys

Overseas

POLAND, Warsaw Baker Tilly Smoczynski & Partners Sp. z o.o.

FEASIBILITY STUDIES

United Kingdom

COLCHESTER .... Butt Cozens
LONDON EC2 .... RGL LLP
LONDON N22 .... C.Babs-Jonah & Co
MATLOCK .... Libcus Ltd
RICHMOND .... Pococks
WELLS .... Mark Shelton
WESTCLIFF-ON-SEA .... Brannans

Overseas

IRAN, Tehran .... A.M. Mahallati & Co
NIGERIA, Lagos .... Horwath Dafinone

FRANCHISING

United Kingdom

CHESTER .... Morris & Co
FOLKESTONE .... Beresfords
WESTCLIFF-ON-SEA .... Brannans
WIRRAL .... Morris & Co

Overseas

POLAND, Warsaw Baker Tilly Smoczynski & Partners Sp. z o.o.

INVESTMENT APPRAISAL

United Kingdom

AMERSHAM .... Cansdales Ltd
DOUGLAS .... PKF (Isle of Man) LLC
LONDON E1 .... UHY Corporate Finance Ltd
LONDON EC2 .... RGL LLP
LONDON W1 .... Jenson Solutions Ltd
MANCHESTER .... Cassons
MILTON KEYNES ..... Chancery (UK) LLP
ROSSENDALE .... Cassons
WESTCLIFF-ON-SEA .... Brannans

Overseas

IRAN, Tehran .... A.M. Mahallati & Co

MANAGEMENT ACCOUNTING CONSULTANCY

United Kingdom

AMERSHAM .... Cansdales
BIRMINGHAM .... James, Stanley & Co
BRIDGEND .... Medrus UK Ltd
BRISTOL .... Mensis Ltd
CAMBERLEY .... RSH Accounting
CHELMSFORD .... Bird Luckin Ltd
COLCHESTER .... Butt Cozens
DOUGLAS .... PKF (Isle of Man) LLC
DUNMOW .... Bird Luckin Ltd
FARNBOROUGH Howard Lee, Fellows & Co
GRAVESEND .... Alpha Advice
HARROW .... AZR Ltd
Leftley Rowe & Co
HERTFORD .... Gary J. Cansick & Co
LANCASTER .... Langdale
LEEDS .... Whitesides
LIVERPOOL .... Chadwick LLP
LONDON N22 .... C.Babs-Jonah & Co
LONDON N3 .... Paul Perlin & Co
LONDON SW4 .... Willis Burnell Ltd
LONDON W1 .... Civvals
LONDON W5 .... Levy & Partners
Levy + Partners Ltd
MAIDENHEAD .... Hale & Co
MANCHESTER .... Beever and Struthers
Chadwick LLP
UHY Hacker Young Manchester LLP
MILTON KEYNES ..... Chancery (UK) LLP
RICHMOND .... PK Partners LLP
SALE .... Armitt & Co
SEVENOAKS .... Brebners
WARRINGTON .... Voisey & Co
WESTCLIFF-ON-SEA .... Brannans

Overseas

IRAN, Tehran .... A.M. Mahallati & Co
POLAND, Warsaw Baker Tilly Smoczynski & Partners Sp. z o.o.
SWITZERLAND, Zollikon Graham Associates AG

MANAGEMENT ADVICE TO BUSINESS

United Kingdom

AMERSHAM .... Cansdales
Cansdales Ltd
BECKENHAM .... Hammonds
BEDFORD .... Gregory Wildman
BRAINTREE .... Jaynes & Co
Lambert Chapman LLP
BRIDGEND .... Medrus UK Ltd
BRIGHTON ..... Lucraft, Hodgson & Dawes
BRISTOL .... Mensis Ltd
BURNLEY .... Ashworth Moulds
K M Business Solutions Ltd
BUXTON .... ABC Accountants
CAMBERLEY .... John J May
CARDIFF .... Groves Davey Ltd
CHELMSFORD ..... Lambert Chapman LLP
COLCHESTER .... Butt Cozens
Wood & Disney Ltd
CROYDON .... D.S. & Co
DERBY .... Johnson Tidsall
DOUGLAS .... Charles Fargher
EXMOUTH .... John Wheeler
FARNHAM .... Milne Eldridge & Co
Taylor Cocks
GRAVESEND .... Alpha Advice
HAMPTON .... AKCA Consulting Ltd
HARROW .... Alliotts
HIGH WYCOMBE .... Seymour Taylor
INGATESTONE .... Taylor, Viney & Marlow
IPSWICH .... Ensors
JERSEY .... Rosscot Ltd
KINGSTON UPON THAMES . David Howard
LANCASTER .... Langdale
LEWES .... Knill James
LINCOLN .... Nicholsons
LONDON EC1 .... FW Stephens
Kingswood
Lubbock Fine
LONDON EC2 .... Everett & Son
LONDON EC4 .... 2020 CA Ltd
LONDON N1 .... CPP
LONDON N14 .... Bond Partners LLP
LONDON N3 .... Paul Perlin & Co
LONDON NW11 ..... Edmund Wright & Co
LONDON SW1 .... Helmores
LONDON W1 .... Jenson Solutions Ltd
LONDON W5 .... Levy & Partners
Levy + Partners Ltd
LONDON WC2 .... Arnold Hill & Co
Bourner Bullock
LOUGHTON .... Haslers
MALDON .... Lambert Chapman LLP
MATLOCK .... Libcus Ltd
MILTON KEYNES .... Bourner Bullock
Keens Shay Keens Milton Keynes
MacIntyre Hudson LLP
NORTHAMPTON .... J.R. Watson & Co
NOTTINGHAM .... Keith Willis Associates Ltd
OXFORD .... Taylor Cocks
PETERSFIELD .... Barter Durgan & Muir Ltd
PORTSMOUTH .... The Taylor Cocks Partnership Ltd
PRESTON .... James Todd & Co
READING .... Taylor Cocks
RICHMOND ...... The Hughes Consultancy
PK Partners LLP
Pococks
SOUTHAMPTON .... Hopper Williams & Bell Ltd
STOKE-ON-TRENT .... Moore Stephens
STRATFORD-UPON-AVON .. Grenfell James
SURBITON .... Richard Morgan and Co
SUTTON COLDFIELD .... Bissell & Brown Ltd
TUNBRIDGE WELLS .... Creaseys
WATFORD ...... JSA Business Services LLP
WEYBRIDGE .... MGI Midgley Snelling TWP
WIMBORNE .... The Taylor Cocks Partnership Ltd
YORK .... Wild & Co

Overseas

NIGERIA, Lagos .... Horwath Dafinone
POLAND, Warsaw Baker Tilly Smoczynski & Partners Sp. z o.o.

MANAGEMENT CONSULTANCY

United Kingdom

ABINGDON .... Mark Wells Consulting Ltd
BECKENHAM .... Hammonds
CARMARTHEN .... Clay Shaw Butler Ltd
CHELMSFORD .... Bird Luckin Ltd
CHESTER .... Sullivan & Co
CROYDON .... D.S. & Co
DOUGLAS .... Charles Fargher
PKF (Isle of Man) LLC
EDINBURGH .... IFRS 2009 Ltd
FARNHAM .... Taylor Cocks
HAMPTON .... AKCA Consulting Ltd
HARLOW .... Giess Wallis Crisp
LEEDS .... Whitesides
LONDON EC4 .... 2020 CA Ltd
LONDON W1 .... Citroen Wells
LONDON WC2 .... Bourner Bullock
MANCHESTER .... A2E Venture Catalyst Ltd
Beever and Struthers
MATLOCK .... Libcus Ltd
MILTON KEYNES .... Bourner Bullock
OXFORD .... Taylor Cocks
PORTSMOUTH .... The Taylor Cocks Partnership Ltd
READING .... Taylor Cocks
Vale & West
RICHMOND .... Pococks
WELWYN .... R.S. Partnership
WESTCLIFF-ON-SEA .... Brannans
WIMBORNE .... The Taylor Cocks Partnership Ltd

Overseas

IRAN, Tehran .... A.M. Mahallati & Co
NIGERIA, Lagos .... Horwath Dafinone

OUTSOURCING - FINANCIAL SERVICES

United Kingdom

AMERSHAM .... Wilkins Kennedy
BOLTON .... Barlow Andrews
BRIDGEND .... Medrus UK Ltd
EAST MOLESEY .... Christie Buchanan
EGHAM .... Wilkins Kennedy
GUILDFORD .... Wilkins Kennedy
HERTFORD .... Wilkins Kennedy
HIGH WYCOMBE .... Seymour Taylor
LONDON NW1 .... BRAL Ltd
LONDON SE1 .... Wilkins Kennedy
MANCHESTER .... Beever and Struthers
NEWCASTLE UPON TYNE .... Tait Walker
ORPINGTON .... Wilkins Kennedy
RICHMOND .... Feltonpumphrey
The Hughes Consultancy
PK Partners LLP
ROMSEY .... Wilkins Kennedy
WATFORD .... JSA Services Ltd
Myers Clark
WEST BYFLEET .... Gibson Hewitt Outsourcing Ltd
WESTCLIFF-ON-SEA .... Brannans
WINCHESTER .... Wilkins Kennedy

Overseas

FALKLAND ISLANDS, Stanley .... Wilkins Kennedy

OVERSEAS COUNTRIES

United Kingdom

GRAVESEND .... Alpha Advice
JERSEY .... Alex Picot
STANMORE .... Lawrence Grant
TUNBRIDGE WELLS .... Creaseys
WESTCLIFF-ON-SEA .... Brannans
WEYBRIDGE .... MGI Midgley Snelling

Overseas

IRAN, Tehran .... A.M. Mahallati & Co

RISK MANAGEMENT

United Kingdom

GRAVESEND .... Internal Audit Services Ltd
JERSEY .... Mazars Channel Islands Ltd
MANCHESTER .... Beever and Struthers
ST ALBANS .... M.R. Aldridge
STEVENAGE .... Wilder Coe
WESTCLIFF-ON-SEA .... Brannans

Overseas

CYPRUS, Nicosia .... Ernst & Young

TAKEOVERS

United Kingdom

DOUGLAS .... PKF (Isle of Man) LLC
HARROW .... Alliotts
LOUGHTON .... Haslers
NEWCASTLE UPON TYNE .... Tait Walker
ROMFORD .... Chegwidden & Co
WESTCLIFF-ON-SEA .... Brannans

Overseas

IRAN, Tehran .... A.M. Mahallati & Co

SECTOR SPECIALISATIONS

ADVERTISING/DESIGN AGENCIES

United Kingdom

BLACKBURN .... PM & M Corporate Finance Ltd
LONDON EC1 .... Higgisons
LONDON N1 .... CPP
LONDON N3 .... Paul Perlin & Co
LONDON SE19 .... API Partnership Ltd
LONDON SW18 .... LBCo Ltd
LONDON W1 .... Kingston Smith LLP
LONDON WC1 .... Lee Associates Audit Ltd
LONDON WC2 .... Bourner Bullock
RICHMOND .... The Hughes Consultancy
WESTCLIFF-ON-SEA .... Brannans

AGRICULTURE

United Kingdom

ACCRINGTON .... Haworths Ltd
ALTON .... Sheen Stickland LLP
AMERSHAM .... Cansdales
ASHFORD .... Chavereys
BLACKBURN .... PM & M Corporate Finance Ltd
BRAINTREE .... Lambert Chapman LLP
CHELMSFORD .... Lambert Chapman LLP
CHELTENHAM .... Hazlewoods LLP
CHICHESTER .... Stonham.Co
DORCHESTER .... Edwards & Keeping
GUILDFORD .... Morley Tippett
HERTFORD .... Wilkins Kennedy
LOUGHBOROUGH .... Turner & Smith
MALDON .... Lambert Chapman LLP
MARKET DRAYTON .... Barringtons Ltd
Stubbs Parkin & South
NEWPORT .... Barringtons Ltd
NORTHAMPTON .... J.R. Watson & Co
Mark L. Aldridge & Co
NORTHWICH .... Murray Smith
RINGWOOD .... Graham Latham Ltd
ROYSTON .... WKH
STAFFORD .... Dean Statham
SWANSEA .... John F Harvey
TAUNTON .... Mitchells
WADEBRIDGE .... R.L. Statton
WELLS .... Mark Shelton
WINCHESTER .... Martin and Co

Overseas

POLAND, Warsaw ... Baker Tilly Smoczynski & Partners Sp. z o.o.

ARCHITECTS/SURVEYORS

United Kingdom

BLACKBURN ... PM & M Corporate Finance Ltd
CHICHESTER ... Stonham.Co
LEEDS ... Whitesides
LEICESTER ... Kemp Taylor LLP
LONDON E2 ... Leonard Jones & Co
LONDON EC1 ... FW Stephens
LONDON N1 ... CPP
LONDON N3 ... Paul Perlin & Co
LONDON SE19 ... API Partnership Ltd
LONDON SW18 ... LBCo Ltd
LONDON W13 ... Merchant & Co
LONDON W4 ... Flinthams
LONDON WC1 ... haysmacintyre
Lee Associates Audit Ltd
RICHMOND ... The Hughes Consultancy
ROMFORD ... Chegwidden & Co
WATFORD ... Myers Clark
WESTCLIFF-ON-SEA ... Brannans

ARTISTS/GRAPHIC DESIGNERS

United Kingdom

AMERSHAM ... Cansdales
BRIGHTON ... Feist Hedgethorne Ltd
LEATHERHEAD ... Rochman Goodmans
LEICESTER ... Kemp Taylor LLP
LONDON N3 ... Mac Kotecha & Co
Paul Perlin & Co
LONDON SE19 ... API Partnership Ltd
LONDON W1 ... Bowker Orford
Citroen Wells
Kingston Smith LLP
LONDON W12 ... Godfrey Accounting
LONDON WC1 ... Lee Associates Audit Ltd
WATFORD ... Turnbull Associates
WESTCLIFF-ON-SEA ... Brannans

BANKS/FINANCIAL INSTITUTIONS

United Kingdom

EDINBURGH ... IFRS 2009 Ltd
GRAVESEND ... Alpha Advice
LONDON EC2 ... RGL LLP
LONDON W1 ... Fisher, Sassoon & Marks

Overseas

CYPRUS, Nicosia ... Ernst & Young
IRAN, Tehran ... A.M. Mahallati & Co
NIGERIA, Lagos ... Horwath Dafinone

BARRISTERS

United Kingdom

BEDFORD ... Keens Shay Keens Ltd
BIRMINGHAM ... J W Scrivens & Co Ltd
CHICHESTER ... Stonham.Co
EAST GRINSTEAD ... Place Campbell
LEEDS ... Whitesides
LONDON EC4 ... Target Winters
LONDON N3 ... FMCB
SPW (UK) LLP
LONDON SW1 ... Sterling Hay
LONDON W1 ... Arthur G Mead
Citroen Wells
MANCHESTER ... Beever and Struthers
Cassons
Haffner, Hoff & Co
RINGWOOD ... Vincent Clemas
ROSSENDALE ... Cassons
STANMORE ... Lawrence Grant

CATERING/RESTAURANTS

United Kingdom

BLACKBURN ... PM & M Corporate Finance Ltd
LONDON EC1 ... Westbury
LONDON N1 ... CPP
LONDON N3 ... Paul Perlin & Co
LONDON NW1 ... H.W. Fisher & Co
LONDON NW3 ... Fisher Phillips
LONDON SE19 ... API Partnership Ltd
LONDON SW14 ... White Hart Associates LLP
LONDON W1 ... Civvals
Lewis Golden & Co
LONDON W13 ... Merchant & Co
LONDON WC1 ... haysmacintyre
WESTCLIFF-ON-SEA ... Brannans

CHARITIES

United Kingdom

ALTON ... Sheen Stickland LLP
AMERSHAM ... C D Nash Ltd
Cansdales
Wilkins Kennedy
BARNET ... Debson & Co
BARROW-IN-FURNESS ... Melville & Co
BIRMINGHAM ... Clement Keys
BISHOP'S STORTFORD ... Walton & Co
BLACKBURN ... PM & M Corporate Finance Ltd
BOLTON ... Bentleys
BUCKHURST HILL ... Dutchmans
BURNLEY ... Ashworth Moulds
K M Business Solutions Ltd
CARMARTHEN ... Clay Shaw Butler Ltd
CHELMSFORD ... Lambert Chapman LLP
CHESTER ... Morris & Co
CHICHESTER ... Stonham.Co
COLCHESTER ... Whittle & Co
CROYDON ... Britt & Keehan
DOUGLAS ... PKF (Isle of Man) LLC
DUDLEY ... G.P. Brookes
DURHAM ... Jane Ascroft Accountancy Ltd
EASTLEIGH ... Rothman Pantall & Co
EGHAM ... Wilkins Kennedy
ESHER ... Holmes & Co
FARNBOROUGH ... Howard Lee, Fellows & Co
GAINSBOROUGH ... Wright Vigar Ltd
GUILDFORD ... Wilkins Kennedy
HALIFAX ... Riley & Co
HARROW ... Leftley Rowe & Co
HERTFORD ... Wilkins Kennedy
HIGH WYCOMBE ... Seymour Taylor
KINGSTON UPON THAMES ... David Howard
LEEDS ... Ian Pickup & Co
LEICESTER ... Kemp Taylor LLP
LINCOLN ... Wright Vigar Ltd
LONDON E14 ... Littlejohn
LONDON E16 ... Eafton & Co
LONDON E17 ... Kim D Hooper
LONDON E2 ... Leonard Jones & Co
LONDON EC1 ... FW Stephens
Lubbock Fine
Westbury
LONDON EC2 ... Everett & Son
Gotham Erskine
LONDON EC4 ... Knox Cropper
Target Winters
LONDON N12 ... Anthony Tiscoe & Co
LONDON N14 ... Bond Partners LLP
LONDON N3 ... FMCB
Paul Perlin & Co
LONDON N4 ... Harry Nicolaou & Co Ltd
LONDON NW1 ... H.W. Fisher & Co
LONDON NW3 ... Maurice Apple
Nyman Libson Paul
LONDON SE1 ... Wilkins Kennedy
LONDON SE19 ... API Partnership Ltd
LONDON SW1 ... Helmores
LONDON SW19 ... Coulthards
LONDON W1 ... Citroen Wells
David Smith & Co
Lewis Golden & Co
LONDON W11 ... GMAK
Wright Vigar Ltd
LONDON W4 ... Flinthams
LONDON W5 ... Levy & Partners
Levy + Partners Ltd
LONDON W8 ... Keith, Vaudrey & Co
LONDON WC1 ... haysmacintyre
LONDON WC2 ... Bourner Bullock
LOUGHTON ... Haslers
MANCHESTER ... Beever and Struthers
Haffner, Hoff & Co
Slade & Cooper
Slade & Cooper Ltd
MILTON KEYNES ... Bourner Bullock
Keens Shay Keens Milton Keynes
NORTHAMPTON ... J.R. Watson & Co
ORPINGTON ... Wilkins Kennedy
OXFORD ... Peter J Stevenson
PLYMOUTH ... Parkhurst Hill
PRESTON ... TLL Accountants Ltd
Turpin Lucas Lees
RETFORD ... Wright Vigar Ltd
RICKMANSWORTH ... Nicola Anderson FCA FCIE
RINGWOOD ... Vincent Clemas
ROMSEY ... Wilkins Kennedy
RUISLIP ... Grant Harrod
SALISBURY ... Mark Merrill
SANDHURST ... Symons
SHEFFIELD ... Barber Harrison & Platt
SLEAFORD ... Wright Vigar Ltd
SOUTH CROYDON ... Sargent & Co
SOUTHEND-ON-SEA ... Wilkins Kennedy

STEVENAGE .... Clarity
STOCKTON-ON-TEES .... Lyons & Co
TUNBRIDGE WELLS .... Creaseys
Foot Davson
WATFORD .... Myers Clark
WEST WICKHAM .... Daniels & Co
WESTCLIFF-ON-SEA .... Brannans
WEYBRIDGE .... Ward Williams Ltd
WINCHESTER .... Wilkins Kennedy
WIRRAL .... Morris & Co

Overseas

FALKLAND ISLANDS, Stanley ..... Wilkins Kennedy
POLAND, Warsaw Baker Tilly Smoczynski & Partners Sp. z o.o.

CHURCH

United Kingdom

ALTON .... Sheen Stickland LLP
AMERSHAM .... C D Nash Ltd
Cansdales
CHICHESTER .... Stonham.Co
DUDLEY .... G.P. Brookes
LONDON E16 .... Eafton & Co
LONDON W13 .... Merchant & Co
LONDON W8 .... Keith, Vaudrey & Co
LOUGHTON .... Haslers
ORPINGTON .... Hewsons
OXFORD .... Peter J Stevenson
SANDHURST .... Symons

CLOTHING/TEXTILES

United Kingdom

BLACKBURN .... PM & M Corporate Finance Ltd
LONDON N3 .... FMCB
SPW (UK) LLP
LONDON SE19 .... API Partnership Ltd
LONDON W1 .... Citroen Wells
Civvals
LOUGHTON .... Haslers
WESTCLIFF-ON-SEA .... Brannans

Overseas

NIGERIA, Lagos .... Horwath Dafinone

CLUBS/ASSOCIATIONS

United Kingdom

BIRMINGHAM .... Cairns Bailey & Co
BRAINTREE .... Jaynes & Co
EASTLEIGH .... Rothman Pantall & Co
FARNBOROUGH Howard Lee, Fellows & Co
LONDON EC1 .... FW Stephens
LONDON SE19 .... API Partnership Ltd
LONDON W13 .... Merchant & Co
LONDON W8 .... Keith, Vaudrey & Co
LOUGHTON .... Haslers
NORTHAMPTON .... J.R. Watson & Co
PONTEFRACT .... HBH
Holmes Beaumont & Holroyd
READING .... Vale & West
RUISLIP .... Warneford Gibbs
WALTON-ON-THAMES Byrne, Palmer & Co
WATFORD .... Myers Clark
WESTCLIFF-ON-SEA .... Brannans

CONSTRUCTION

United Kingdom

AMERSHAM .... Wilkins Kennedy
BRAINTREE .... Lambert Chapman LLP
BRIDGEND .... Medrus UK Ltd
BRISTOL .... Andrew Waters & Associates Ltd
CARMARTHEN .... Clay Shaw Butler Ltd
CHELMSFORD ..... Lambert Chapman LLP
CHICHESTER .... Stonham.Co
DONCASTER .... Royston Parkin
EGHAM .... Wilkins Kennedy
FARNBOROUGH Howard Lee, Fellows & Co
GUILDFORD .... Wilkins Kennedy
HERTFORD .... Wilkins Kennedy
HIGH WYCOMBE .... Seymour Taylor
KINGSTON UPON THAMES . David Howard
LEEDS .... Whitesides
LEICESTER .... Kemp Taylor LLP
LONDON EC1 .... FW Stephens
Higgisons
LONDON SE1 .... Wilkins Kennedy
LONDON SE19 .... API Partnership Ltd
LONDON SW1 .... Helmores
LONDON SW19 .... Med Act
MANCHESTER .... UHY Hacker Young Manchester LLP
NEWHAVEN .... Intelligent Blue Ltd
NORTHAMPTON .... J.R. Watson & Co
ORPINGTON .... Wilkins Kennedy
RICHMOND ...... The Hughes Consultancy
ROMSEY .... Wilkins Kennedy
SOUTHAMPTON .... Hopper Williams & Bell Ltd
SOUTHEND-ON-SEA ..... Wilkins Kennedy
WESTCLIFF-ON-SEA .... Brannans
WINCHESTER .... Wilkins Kennedy

Overseas

IRAN, Tehran .... A.M. Mahallati & Co
NIGERIA, Lagos .... Horwath Dafinone

CORPORATE

United Kingdom

ALTON .... Sheen Stickland LLP
BIRMINGHAM .... Taxcare Ltd
BLACKBURN .... PM & M Corporate Finance Ltd
BRADFORD .... Andrew S. Parker
CANNOCK Shelvoke, Pickering, Janney & Co
CHELMSFORD .... Bird Luckin Ltd
COLCHESTER .... Butt Cozens
COVENTRY .... Sheth & Co
CROYDON .... D.S. & Co
DOUGLAS .... PKF (Isle of Man) LLC
DUNMOW .... Bird Luckin Ltd
EDINBURGH .... IFRS 2009 Ltd
LEEDS .... Whitesides
LONDON E14 .... Littlejohn
LONDON EC1 .... FW Stephens
LONDON EC2 .... Everett & Son
LONDON N3 .... FMCB
Paul Perlin & Co
SPW Poppleton & Appleby
LONDON NW3 .... Nyman Libson Paul
LONDON SE19 .... API Partnership Ltd
LONDON SW13 .... C.J. Cook & Co
LONDON W1 .... Citroen Wells
LOUGHTON .... Haslers
MANCHESTER .... Beever and Struthers
UHY Hacker Young Manchester LLP
MILTON KEYNES Keens Shay Keens Milton Keynes
READING .... Avalon Accounting
Vale & West
REIGATE .... EC Accountancy
STOCKPORT .... The TACS Partnership
WESTCLIFF-ON-SEA .... Brannans

Overseas

GREECE, Athens .. KPMG Certified Auditors AE
IRAN, Tehran .... A.M. Mahallati & Co
POLAND, Warsaw Baker Tilly Smoczynski & Partners Sp. z o.o.

DENTISTS/OPTICIANS

United Kingdom

ALTON .... Sheen Stickland LLP
BIRMINGHAM .... A.K. Patel & Co
J W Scrivens & Co Ltd
BLACKBURN .... PM & M Corporate Finance Ltd
BRISTOL .... Evans & Partners
BURNLEY .... Ashworth Moulds
BUXTON .... ABC Accountants
CHELTENHAM .... Hazlewoods LLP
CHESTER .... Morris & Co
CORSHAM .... Clear Vision Accountancy Ltd
CROYDON .... Saleemi Associates
DONCASTER .... Royston Parkin
EGHAM .... Wilkins Kennedy
HARROW .... Leftley Rowe & Co
LEEDS .... Whitesides
LONDON EC1 .... Higgisons
LONDON N3 .... Mac Kotecha & Co
Paul Perlin & Co
LONDON SE19 .... API Partnership Ltd
LONDON SW18 .... Chicksand Gordon Avis Ltd
LONDON W1 .... Arthur G Mead
Citroen Wells
Civvals
F. Winter & Co LLP
LONDON W13 .... Merchant & Co
LONDON W4 .... Flinthams
LOUGHTON .... Haslers
MANCHESTER .... Beever and Struthers
Cassons
MILTON KEYNES Keens Shay Keens Milton Keynes
NORTHAMPTON .... J.R. Watson & Co
PLYMOUTH .... Parkhurst Hill
ROSSENDALE .... Cassons
RUISLIP .... Grant Harrod
SHEFFIELD .... Barber Harrison & Platt
Gordon & Hood
SOUTHEND-ON-SEA ..... Wilkins Kennedy
STANMORE .... Lawrence Grant
STOCKPORT .... Tatton & Fletcher
WESTCLIFF-ON-SEA .... Brannans
WIRRAL .... Morris & Co

DOCTORS

Sandison Easson & Co
www.sandisoneasson.co.uk
Rex Buildings, Alderley Road, Wimslow, Cheshire
SK9 1HY
Tel: 01625 527 351

United Kingdom

- ACCRINGTON ... Haworths Ltd
- ALTON ... Sheen Stickland LLP
- AMERSHAM ... C D Nash Ltd
- Cansdales
- BEXHILL-ON-SEA ... Honey Barrett Ltd
- BIRMINGHAM ... A.K. Patel & Co
- Clement Keys
- J W Scrivens & Co Ltd
- BLACKBURN ... PM & M Corporate Finance Ltd
- BRIGHTON ... Feist Hedgethorne Ltd
- BUCKHURST HILL ... Dutchmans
- BURNLEY ... Ashworth Moulds
- K M Business Solutions Ltd
- CHESTER ... Morris & Co
- COLBY ... David J. Hill & Co
- CROYDON ... Saleemi Associates
- FARNBOROUGH Howard Lee, Fellows & Co
- FARNHAM ... Taylor Cocks
- GLOUCESTER ... Little & Co
- HALESOWEN ... HSP Nicklin
- HARROW ... Charles Rippin & Turner
- HATFIELD ... Keelings Ltd
- HUDDERSFIELD ... Wheawill & Sudworth
- KIDDERMINSTER ... Lambert & Co
- LEEDS ... Whitesides
- LONDON SE10 ... Med Act
- LONDON SE19 ... API Partnership Ltd
- LONDON SW18 ... Chicksand Gordon Avis Ltd
- LONDON SW19 ... Med Act
- LONDON SW3 ... Dennis R. Waters
- LONDON W1 ... Arthur G Mead
- Bowker Orford
- Citroen Wells
- Civvals
- David Smith & Co
- Rosenthal & Co
- LONDON W13 ... Merchant & Co
- LONDON W4 ... Flinthams
- LOUGHTON ... Haslers
- MACCLESFIELD ... Josolyne & Co
- MANCHESTER ... Beever and Struthers
- Cassons
- Hall Liddy
- MILTON KEYNES Keens Shay Keens Milton Keynes
- NORTHWOOD ... Rosenthal & Co
- OXFORD ... Taylor Cocks
- PLYMOUTH ... Parkhurst Hill
- PORTSMOUTH ... The Taylor Cocks Partnership Ltd
- READING ... Taylor Cocks
- ROMFORD ... Chegwidden & Co
- ROSSENDALE ... Cassons
- RUISLIP ... Grant Harrod
- SHEFFIELD ... Barber Harrison & Platt
- Gordon & Hood
- SLOUGH ... Charles Stuart LLP
- SOUTHEND-ON-SEA ... Wilkins Kennedy
- STAFFORD ... Dean Statham
- STANMORE ... Lawrence Grant
- STOCKTON-ON-TEES ... Benson Wood Ltd
- WATFORD ... Myers Clark
- Turnbull Associates
- WESTCLIFF-ON-SEA ... Brannans
- WILMSLOW ... Sandison Easson & Co
- WIMBORNE ... The Taylor Cocks Partnership Ltd
- WIRRAL ... Morris & Co
- WITNEY ... Williamson West

ELECTRONICS

United Kingdom

- CHICHESTER ... Stonham.Co
- LONDON EC2 ... RGL LLP
- LONDON SE19 ... API Partnership Ltd
- LONDON SW18 ... Chicksand Gordon Avis Ltd
- PLYMOUTH ... Parkhurst Hill

Overseas

- IRAN, Tehran ... A.M. Mahallati & Co

ENGINEERS

United Kingdom

- BLACKBURN ... PM & M Corporate Finance Ltd
- CHICHESTER ... Stonham.Co
- GRAVESEND ... Alpha Advice
- LEEDS ... Whitesides
- LONDON W4 ... Flinthams
- LONDON WC1 ... Lee Associates Audit Ltd
- WATFORD ... JSA Services Ltd
- Turnbull Associates
- WESTCLIFF-ON-SEA ... Brannans

ENTERTAINERS

United Kingdom

- BIRMINGHAM ... Clement Keys
- BRIGHTON ... Feist Hedgethorne Ltd
- BURNLEY ... Ashworth Moulds
- EPSOM ... Bevis & Co
- HERTFORD ... Wilkins Kennedy
- LONDON EC1 ... Higgisons Lubbock Fine
- LONDON N12 ... Eric R. Jenkins
- LONDON N3 ... FMCB
- Paul Perlin & Co
- LONDON NW1 ... Creasey Alexander & Co
- H.W. Fisher & Co
- LONDON NW3 ... Nyman Libson Paul
- LONDON SW1 ... Ross Bennet-Smith
- LONDON SW14 ... Farrow Accounting & Tax Ltd
- LONDON SW18 ... Chicksand Gordon Avis Ltd
- LONDON W1 ... Blinkhorns
- Bowker Orford
- Citroen Wells
- David Smith & Co
- F. Winter & Co LLP
- Harris & Trotter LLP
- Lewis Golden & Co
- LONDON W9 ... Ryan & Co
- LONDON WC1 ... Lee Associates Audit Ltd
- LONDON WC2 ... Coppards
- MANCHESTER ... Cassons
- RICHMOND ... The Hughes Consultancy
- ROSSENDALE ... Cassons
- WESTCLIFF-ON-SEA ... Brannans

Overseas

- SPAIN, Marbella ... Spence Clarke & Co

ENTERTAINMENT CENTRES

United Kingdom

- WESTCLIFF-ON-SEA ... Brannans

ESTATE AGENTS

United Kingdom

- CHICHESTER ... Stonham.Co
- FARNBOROUGH Howard Lee, Fellows & Co
- GLOUCESTER ... Hazlewoods LLP
- LEEDS ... Whitesides
- LONDON EC1 ... FW Stephens
- LONDON NW1 ... Creasey Alexander & Co
- LONDON SE19 ... API Partnership Ltd
- LONDON SW1 ... Helmores
- LONDON SW18 ... Chicksand Gordon Avis Ltd
- LONDON W1 ... Bowker Orford
- Civvals
- LONDON W13 ... Merchant & Co
- MILTON KEYNES Keens Shay Keens Milton Keynes
- NORTHAMPTON ... J.R. Watson & Co
- PLYMOUTH ... Parkhurst Hill
- SOUTHEND-ON-SEA ... Wilkins Kennedy
- WATFORD ... Myers Clark
- WESTCLIFF-ON-SEA ... Brannans

FOOD INDUSTRY

United Kingdom

- BLACKBURN ... PM & M Corporate Finance Ltd
- LONDON SE19 ... API Partnership Ltd
- PRESCOT ... Sergents
- WELLS ... Mark Shelton
- WESTCLIFF-ON-SEA ... Brannans

Overseas

- IRAN, Tehran ... A.M. Mahallati & Co

NIGERIA, Lagos	Horwath Dafinone

FSA MEMBERS

United Kingdom

AMERSHAM	Cansdales Ltd
BRISTOL	Geoff Gollop & Co Ltd
CHICHESTER	Stonham.Co
EGHAM	Wilkins Kennedy
HIGH WYCOMBE	Seymour Taylor
LONDON E14	Littlejohn
LONDON EC1	FW Stephens
	Higgisons
	Lubbock Fine
LONDON N14	Bond Partners LLP
LONDON SE1	Wilkins Kennedy
LONDON SE19	API Partnership Ltd
LONDON SW1	Helmores
	Sterling Hay
LONDON SW18	LBCo Ltd
LONDON W1	Citroen Wells
	Edward Ratnam FCA
	Fisher, Sassoon & Marks
LONDON W4	Flinthams
LONDON WC1	haysmacintyre
LOUGHTON	Haslers
MANCHESTER	Beever and Struthers
	UHY Hacker Young Manchester LLP
NORTHAMPTON	J.R. Watson & Co
ORPINGTON	Wilkins Kennedy
SOUTHEND-ON-SEA	Wilkins Kennedy

HIGHER EDUCATION/RESEARCH ESTABLISHMENTS

United Kingdom

LIVERPOOL	Chadwick LLP
LONDON EC2	Everett & Son
LONDON EC4	Knox Cropper
MANCHESTER	Chadwick LLP
WESTCLIFF-ON-SEA	Brannans

HORTICULTURE

United Kingdom

ALTON	Sheen Stickland LLP
ASHFORD	Chavereys
CHICHESTER	Stonham.Co
PRESTON	TLL Accountants Ltd
	Turpin Lucas Lees

HOTELS/PUBLIC HOUSES

United Kingdom

BEAMINSTER	Sarum Management Services Ltd
BLACKBURN	PM & M Corporate Finance Ltd
CARLISLE	Saint & Co
CHICHESTER	Stonham.Co
DOUGLAS	PKF (Isle of Man) LLC
EASTLEIGH	Rothman Pantall & Co
HARROW	LINK
LONDON N3	SPW (UK) LLP
LONDON SW1	Helmores
LONDON SW3	Dennis R. Waters
LONDON W1	Arthur G Mead
	Civvals
LONDON WC1	haysmacintyre
LOUGHTON	Haslers
NEWHAVEN	Intelligent Blue Ltd
NOTTINGHAM	Dawes & Sutton
PRESCOT	Sergents
SOUTHAMPTON	Hopper Williams & Bell Ltd
SOUTHEND-ON-SEA	Wilkins Kennedy
WESTCLIFF-ON-SEA	Brannans
WEYBRIDGE	GCA

HOUSING CO-OPERATIVES

United Kingdom

AMERSHAM	Cansdales
LONDON EC2	Gotham Erskine
LONDON EC4	Knox Cropper

HUMAN RESOURCES

United Kingdom

CHELMSFORD	Lambert Chapman LLP
WESTCLIFF-ON-SEA	Brannans

Overseas

NIGERIA, Lagos	Horwath Dafinone

INSURANCE ADVICE

United Kingdom

PENRITH	O'Reilly

INSURANCE BROKERS

United Kingdom

AMERSHAM	Wilkins Kennedy
BURNLEY	Ashworth Moulds
CHICHESTER	Stonham.Co
EASTLEIGH	Rothman Pantall & Co
EGHAM	Wilkins Kennedy
HERTFORD	Wilkins Kennedy
LONDON E14	Littlejohn
LONDON EC1	Higgisons
LONDON SE1	Wilkins Kennedy
LONDON SE19	API Partnership Ltd
LONDON W1	Lewis Golden & Co
LONDON W4	Flinthams
LOUGHTON	Haslers
MARKET DRAYTON	Stubbs Parkin & South
ORPINGTON	Wilkins Kennedy
RICHMOND	The Hughes Consultancy
SOUTHEND-ON-SEA	Wilkins Kennedy
WATFORD	Myers Clark
WESTCLIFF-ON-SEA	Brannans

Overseas

FALKLAND ISLANDS, Stanley	Wilkins Kennedy

JOURNALISTS/WRITERS/COPYWRITERS

United Kingdom

LEATHERHEAD	Rochman Goodmans
LONDON N1	CPP
LONDON N3	Paul Perlin & Co
LONDON NW1	H.W. Fisher & Co
LONDON NW3	Fisher Phillips
LONDON SE19	API Partnership Ltd
LONDON W1	Citroen Wells
LONDON WC1	Lee Associates Audit Ltd
WESTCLIFF-ON-SEA	Brannans

LEISURE INDUSTRY

United Kingdom

AMERSHAM	Cansdales
BLACKBURN	PM & M Corporate Finance Ltd
DOUGLAS	PKF (Isle of Man) LLC
LONDON SE19	API Partnership Ltd
LONDON W1	Elman Wall Ltd
NEWHAVEN	Intelligent Blue Ltd
NOTTINGHAM	Dawes & Sutton
PRESCOT	Sergents
WESTCLIFF-ON-SEA	Brannans

LLOYDS UNDERWRITERS

United Kingdom

CHICHESTER	Stonham.Co
LONDON E14	Littlejohn
WATFORD	Myers Clark

MANUFACTURING

United Kingdom

AMERSHAM	Cansdales
BLACKBURN	PM & M Corporate Finance Ltd
BURNLEY	Ashworth Moulds
	K M Business Solutions Ltd
CHICHESTER	Stonham.Co
DOUGLAS	PKF (Isle of Man) LLC
LEEDS	Whitesides
LONDON EC2	Everett & Son
	RGL LLP
LONDON N14	Bond Partners LLP
MANCHESTER	Beever and Struthers
MILTON KEYNES	Keens Shay Keens Milton Keynes
SOUTHEND-ON-SEA	Wilkins Kennedy
WESTCLIFF-ON-SEA	Brannans

Overseas

NIGERIA, Lagos	Horwath Dafinone

MEDIA

United Kingdom

BIRMINGHAM .... Clement Keys
BRIDGEND .... Medrus UK Ltd
EPSOM .... Bevis & Co
LEATHERHEAD ...... Rochman Goodmans
LONDON E2 .... Leonard Jones & Co
LONDON EC1 .... Lubbock Fine
LONDON EC2 .... RGL LLP
LONDON N12 .... Anthony Tiscoe & Co
LONDON N14 .... Bond Partners LLP
LONDON N3 .... Paul Perlin & Co
LONDON NW1 .... Creasey Alexander & Co
H.W. Fisher & Co
LONDON NW3 .... Nyman Libson Paul
LONDON SE19 .... API Partnership Ltd
LONDON SW1 .... Ross Bennet-Smith
LONDON SW14 ...... Farrow Accounting & Tax Ltd
LONDON W1 .... Blinkhorns
Bowker Orford
Harris & Trotter LLP
Kingston Smith LLP
LONDON W6 .... Media Finance
LONDON WC1 .... haysmacintyre
Lee Associates Audit Ltd
LONDON WC2 .... Bourner Bullock
MILTON KEYNES .... Bourner Bullock
SEVENOAKS .... Brebners
SURBITON .... Richard Morgan and Co
WESTCLIFF-ON-SEA .... Brannans

NEW MEDIA

United Kingdom

LONDON EC1 .... FW Stephens
Lubbock Fine
LONDON EC4 .... 2020 CA Ltd
LONDON N14 .... Bond Partners LLP
LONDON W1 .... Bowker Orford
LONDON WC1 .... Lee Associates Audit Ltd
LONDON WC2 .... Bourner Bullock
MILTON KEYNES .... Bourner Bullock
WATFORD .... Turnbull Associates
WESTCLIFF-ON-SEA .... Brannans

Overseas

LUXEMBOURG, Luxembourg HT Group S.A.

NURSING HOMES/CLINICS

United Kingdom

BLACKBURN .... PM & M Corporate Finance Ltd
CHELTENHAM .... Hazlewoods LLP
CHICHESTER .... Stonham.Co
LONDON E14 .... Littlejohn
LONDON EC4 .... Target Winters
LONDON SE19 .... API Partnership Ltd
LONDON SW18 .... Chicksand Gordon Avis Ltd
LOUGHTON .... Haslers
MANCHESTER .... Beever and Struthers
SOUTHAMPTON .... Hopper Williams & Bell Ltd
STANMORE .... Lawrence Grant
WATFORD .... Myers Clark
WESTCLIFF-ON-SEA .... Brannans
WEYBRIDGE .... TWP

OIL/PETROLEUM INDUSTRIES

United Kingdom

EDINBURGH .... IFRS 2009 Ltd
LONDON EC1 .... Lubbock Fine
LONDON EC2 .... RGL LLP
LONDON N12 .... Anthony Tiscoe & Co

Overseas

IRAN, Tehran .... A.M. Mahallati & Co

PAPER/PRINTING/ PUBLISHING

United Kingdom

CHICHESTER .... Stonham.Co
LONDON E14 .... Littlejohn
LONDON N1 .... CPP
LONDON NW3 .... Fisher Phillips
LONDON SE19 .... API Partnership Ltd
LONDON W1 .... Bowker Orford
NORTHAMPTON .... J.R. Watson & Co

Overseas

NIGERIA, Lagos .... Horwath Dafinone

PROPERTY

United Kingdom

ALTON .... Sheen Stickland LLP
AMERSHAM .... Wilkins Kennedy
BLACKBURN .... PM & M Corporate Finance Ltd
BRIGHTON .... Feist Hedgethorne Ltd
CROYDON .... Saleemi Associates
EGHAM .... Wilkins Kennedy
GUILDFORD .... Wilkins Kennedy
HERTFORD .... Wilkins Kennedy
HOUNSLOW .... Charles Stuart LLP
KINGSTON UPON THAMES . David Howard
LEEDS .... Whitesides
LONDON EC1 .... FW Stephens
LONDON N14 .... Bond Partners LLP
LONDON N3 .... FMCB
Mac Kotecha & Co
Paul Perlin & Co
LONDON NW1 .... H.W. Fisher & Co
LONDON SE1 .... Wilkins Kennedy
LONDON SE19 .... API Partnership Ltd
LONDON SW19 .... WSM Partners LLP
LONDON W1 .... Citroen Wells
Civvals
Lewis Golden & Co
LONDON WC1 .... haysmacintyre
LOUGHTON .... Haslers
MAIDENHEAD .... Hale & Co
MANCHESTER .... Beever and Struthers
Haffner, Hoff & Co
MILTON KEYNES Keens Shay Keens Milton Keynes
NEWHAVEN .... Intelligent Blue Ltd
NORTHAMPTON .... J.R. Watson & Co
ORPINGTON .... Wilkins Kennedy
READING .... Vale & West
ROMSEY .... Wilkins Kennedy
SOUTHAMPTON .... Hopper Williams & Bell Ltd
SOUTHEND-ON-SEA ..... Wilkins Kennedy
WATFORD .... Turnbull Associates
WESTCLIFF-ON-SEA .... Brannans
WINCHESTER .... Wilkins Kennedy

Overseas

FALKLAND ISLANDS, Stanley ..... Wilkins Kennedy
IRAN, Tehran .... A.M. Mahallati & Co
POLAND, Warsaw Baker Tilly Smoczynski & Partners Sp. z o.o.

PROPERTY DEVELOPMENT

United Kingdom

AMERSHAM .... Cansdales
BLACKBURN .... PM & M Corporate Finance Ltd
BRISTOL .... Andrew Waters & Associates Ltd
CHELMSFORD ..... Lambert Chapman LLP
CHICHESTER .... Stonham.Co
CROYDON .... D.S. & Co
DOUGLAS .... PKF (Isle of Man) LLC
EASTLEIGH .... Rothman Pantall & Co
FARNBOROUGH Howard Lee, Fellows & Co
KINGSTON UPON THAMES . David Howard
LEICESTER .... Kemp Taylor LLP
LONDON EC1 .... FW Stephens
Higgisons
Lubbock Fine
LONDON N20 .... Gerald Edelman
LONDON NW1 .... H.W. Fisher & Co
LONDON NW3 .... Fisher Phillips
LONDON SE19 .... API Partnership Ltd
LONDON SW1 .... Helmores
LONDON SW18 .... LBCo Ltd
LONDON W1 .... Citroen Wells
Civvals
Gerald Edelman
Harris & Trotter LLP
Lewis Golden & Co
LONDON WC1 .... Lee Associates Audit Ltd
LONDON WC2 .... Bourner Bullock
LOUGHBOROUGH .... Turner & Smith
MANCHESTER .... UHY Hacker Young Manchester LLP
MILTON KEYNES .... Bourner Bullock
NEWHAVEN .... Intelligent Blue Ltd
SLOUGH .... Charles Stuart LLP
STANMORE .... Parker Cavendish
WESTCLIFF-ON-SEA .... Brannans
WEYBRIDGE .... TWP

Overseas

IRAN, Tehran .... A.M. Mahallati & Co
NIGERIA, Lagos .... Horwath Dafinone

SPAIN, Marbella .... Spence Clarke & Co

PROPERTY INVESTMENT

United Kingdom

AMERSHAM .... Cansdales
BLACKBURN .... PM & M Corporate Finance Ltd
BOLTON .... Barlow Andrews
CAMBERLEY .... RSH Accounting
CROYDON .... D.S. & Co
DOUGLAS .... PKF (Isle of Man) LLC
EASTLEIGH .... Rothman Pantall & Co
LONDON EC1 .... FW Stephens
Lubbock Fine
Westbury
LONDON N20 .... Gerald Edelman
LONDON N22 .... C.Babs-Jonah & Co
LONDON NW3 .... Nyman Libson Paul
LONDON SE19 .... API Partnership Ltd
LONDON SW1 .... Helmores
LONDON SW19 .... Howell Wade
WSM Partners LLP
LONDON W1 .... Blinkhorns
Citroen Wells
Civvals
Gerald Edelman
Harris & Trotter LLP
Lewis Golden & Co
LONDON W13 .... Merchant & Co
LONDON W4 .... Flinthams
LONDON WC2 .... Bourner Bullock
LOUGHBOROUGH .... Turner & Smith
MANCHESTER .... Haffner, Hoff & Co
UHY Hacker Young Manchester LLP
MILTON KEYNES .... Bourner Bullock
NORTHAMPTON .... J.R. Watson & Co
SLOUGH .... Charles Stuart LLP
STANMORE .... Parker Cavendish
TUNBRIDGE WELLS .... Creaseys
WESTCLIFF-ON-SEA .... Brannans
WEYBRIDGE .... TWP

Overseas

IRAN, Tehran .... A.M. Mahallati & Co
NIGERIA, Lagos .... Horwath Dafinone
POLAND, Warsaw Baker Tilly Smoczynski & Partners Sp. z o.o.
SPAIN, Marbella .... Spence Clarke & Co

REGISTERED SOCIAL LANDLORDS

United Kingdom

AMERSHAM .... Cansdales
HATFIELD .... Keelings Ltd
LONDON SE19 .... API Partnership Ltd
LONDON SW17 ...... Wadud Patwari & Co
MANCHESTER .... Beever and Struthers

RETAILERS

United Kingdom

AMERSHAM .... Cansdales
BURNLEY .... K M Business Solutions Ltd
CROYDON .... Saleemi Associates
DONCASTER .... Royston Parkin
HIGH WYCOMBE .... Seymour Taylor
LONDON N3 .... FMCB
Paul Perlin & Co
LONDON NW3 .... Fisher Phillips
LONDON SE19 .... API Partnership Ltd
LONDON W1 .... Citroen Wells
Civvals
LONDON W5 .... Levy & Partners
Levy + Partners Ltd
WATFORD .... Turnbull Associates
WESTCLIFF-ON-SEA .... Brannans

Overseas

POLAND, Warsaw Baker Tilly Smoczynski & Partners Sp. z o.o.

ROAD HAULAGE AND DISTRIBUTION

United Kingdom

BLACKBURN .... PM & M Corporate Finance Ltd
CHICHESTER .... Stonham.Co
LONDON E14 .... Littlejohn
WESTCLIFF-ON-SEA .... Brannans

RUBBER AND PLASTICS INDUSTRY

United Kingdom

MILTON KEYNES Keens Shay Keens Milton Keynes

SCHOOLS

United Kingdom

AMERSHAM .... Cansdales
CHELMSFORD ..... Lambert Chapman LLP
EAST MOLESEY .... Christie Buchanan
LONDON E14 .... Littlejohn
LONDON SW1 .... Helmores
LONDON W13 .... Merchant & Co
LONDON W4 .... Flinthams
LONDON W8 .... Keith, Vaudrey & Co
LONDON WC1 .... haysmacintyre
LOUGHTON .... Haslers
MANCHESTER .... Beever and Struthers
MILTON KEYNES Keens Shay Keens Milton Keynes
PRESCOT .... Sergents
WATFORD .... Myers Clark
WESTCLIFF-ON-SEA .... Brannans

SOLICITORS

United Kingdom

ALTON .... Sheen Stickland LLP
AMERSHAM .... Cansdales
Wilkins Kennedy
BARNET .... Debson & Co
BIRMINGHAM .... Clement Keys
J W Scrivens & Co Ltd
BLACKBURN .... PM & M Corporate Finance Ltd
BUCKHURST HILL .... Dutchmans
BURNLEY .... Ashworth Moulds
K M Business Solutions Ltd
CARMARTHEN .... Clay Shaw Butler Ltd
CHELTENHAM .... Hazlewoods LLP
CHICHESTER .... Stonham.Co
COBHAM .... Wellden Turnbull LLP
DOUGLAS .... PKF (Isle of Man) LLC
EGHAM .... Wilkins Kennedy
FARNHAM .... Taylor Cocks
GLOUCESTER .... Little & Co
GUILDFORD .... Wilkins Kennedy
HALIFAX .... Riley & Co
HARROW .... LINK
HASLEMERE .... Knox Cropper
HERTFORD .... Wilkins Kennedy
HIGH WYCOMBE .... Seymour Taylor
HUDDERSFIELD .... Wheawill & Sudworth
LEEDS .... Whitesides
LONDON E14 .... Littlejohn
LONDON E2 .... Leonard Jones & Co
LONDON EC1 .... FW Stephens
Higgisons
Lubbock Fine
LONDON EC2 .... Everett & Son
LONDON EC4 .... Target Winters
Tarrant Green & Co
LONDON N12 .... Anthony Tiscoe & Co
LONDON N14 .... Bond Partners LLP
LONDON N3 .... FMCB
LONDON NW1 .... Creasey Alexander & Co
H.W. Fisher & Co
LONDON SE1 .... Wilkins Kennedy
LONDON SE19 .... API Partnership Ltd
LONDON SW1 .... Helmores
LONDON SW17 ...... Wadud Patwari & Co
LONDON SW18 .... Chicksand Gordon
Avis Ltd
LBCo Ltd
LONDON W1 .... Bowker Orford
Citroen Wells
Civvals
Elman Wall Ltd
Lewis Golden & Co
LONDON W13 .... Merchant & Co
LONDON W4 .... Flinthams
LONDON W5 .... Johnsons Financial Management Ltd
Levy & Partners
Levy + Partners Ltd
LONDON WC1 .... haysmacintyre
LONDON WC2 .... Bourner Bullock
LOUGHBOROUGH .... Turner & Smith
LOUGHTON .... Haslers
MAIDENHEAD .... Hale & Co
MANCHESTER .... Beever and Struthers
Cassons
UHY Hacker Young Manchester LLP
MARKET DRAYTON Stubbs Parkin & South
MILTON KEYNES .... Bourner Bullock
Keens Shay Keens Milton Keynes
NEWCASTLE UPON TYNE .... Stephenson Coates
NORTHAMPTON .... J.R. Watson & Co
NORTHWICH .... Bennett Brooks & Co Ltd.
ORPINGTON .... Wilkins Kennedy
OXFORD .... Taylor Cocks
PLYMOUTH .... Parkhurst Hill
PORTSMOUTH .... The Taylor Cocks Partnership Ltd
READING .... Taylor Cocks
Vale & West
RINGWOOD .... Vincent Clemas
ROSSENDALE .... Cassons
RUISLIP .... Warneford Gibbs
SEVENOAKS .... Samuels
SHEFFIELD .... Barber Harrison & Platt
SLOUGH .... Charles Stuart LLP
SOUTHAMPTON .... Roches
SOUTHEND-ON-SEA ..... Wilkins Kennedy
STAFFORD .... Dean Statham
STANMORE .... Lawrence Grant
STOCKTON-ON-TEES .... Benson Wood Ltd
Lyons & Co
TUNBRIDGE WELLS .... Creaseys
WATFORD .... Myers Clark
WESTCLIFF-ON-SEA .... Brannans

WIMBORNE .... The Taylor Cocks Partnership Ltd

TRADE ASSOC/UNIONS/FRIENDLY SOCIETIES

United Kingdom

LONDON NW1 .... H.W. Fisher & Co
LONDON W8 .... Keith, Vaudrey & Co
MANCHESTER .... Beever and Struthers
WESTCLIFF-ON-SEA .... Brannans

Overseas

NIGERIA, Lagos .... Horwath Dafinone

TRADERS — GENERAL

United Kingdom

AMERSHAM .... Cansdales
CHICHESTER .... Stonham.Co
LEIGHTON BUZZARD ..... Ian N. Edwards
LONDON N3 .... Paul Perlin & Co
SPW (UK) LLP
LONDON SE19 .... API Partnership Ltd
LONDON SW17 ...... Wadud Patwari & Co
LONDON SW18 .... LBCo Ltd
LONDON W1 .... Citroen Wells
LONDON W13 .... Merchant & Co
LONDON W5 .... Levy & Partners
Levy + Partners Ltd
NEWHAVEN .... Intelligent Blue Ltd
SEVENOAKS .... Brebners
WESTCLIFF-ON-SEA .... Brannans

TRADERS — LUXURY ITEMS

United Kingdom

LONDON SE19 .... API Partnership Ltd
WESTCLIFF-ON-SEA .... Brannans

TRANSPORT

United Kingdom

DOUGLAS .... PKF (Isle of Man) LLC
GRAVESEND .... Alpha Advice
LONDON EC1 .... Higgisons
LONDON SE19 .... API Partnership Ltd

Overseas

IRAN, Tehran .... A.M. Mahallati & Co

TRAVEL INDUSTRY

United Kingdom

BLACKBURN .... PM & M Corporate Finance Ltd
BURNLEY .... Ashworth Moulds
LONDON EC1 .... Higgisons
LONDON SE19 .... API Partnership Ltd
LONDON SW14 . White Hart Associates LLP
LONDON W1 .... Civvals
Elman Wall Ltd
Elman Wall
LONDON W4 .... Flinthams
LOUGHBOROUGH .... Turner & Smith
MANCHESTER .... UHY Hacker Young Manchester LLP
RICHMOND ...... The Hughes Consultancy
WESTCLIFF-ON-SEA .... Brannans

FORENSIC ACCOUNTING

EXPERT WITNESSES IN LITIGATION

United Kingdom

AMERSHAM .... Wilkins Kennedy
BEDFORD .... Derek A Parry
BIRMINGHAM .... Clement Keys
BRAINTREE .... Lambert Chapman LLP
BRIGHTON .... Hartley Fowler LLP
BROUGHTON-IN-FURNESS ... Accounting Evidence Ltd
CARDIFF .... Chris Madge & Co
Harris Lipman LLP
CHESTER .... Morris & Co
CLEVEDON .... Chris Madge & Co
DOUGLAS .... PKF (Isle of Man) LLC
DROITWICH .... Ormerod Rutter Ltd
EASTLEIGH .... Rothman Pantall & Co
EGHAM .... Wilkins Kennedy
GLOUCESTER .... Hazlewoods LLP
Little & Co
GUILDFORD .... Wilkins Kennedy
HARLOW .... Giess Wallis Crisp
HERTFORD .... Wilkins Kennedy
HIGH WYCOMBE .... Seymour Taylor
IVYBRIDGE .... Richard J. Smith & Co
LEEDS .... Begbies Traynor
Mall & Co
LONDON E14 .... Littlejohn
LONDON EC1 .... Kingswood
Morwood-Leyland & Co
LONDON EC2 .... CRA International (UK) Ltd
Everett & Son
RGL LLP
LONDON EC3 .... Begbies Traynor Ltd
LONDON N12 ..... David Rubin & Partners
LONDON N14 .... Bond Partners LLP
LONDON N20 .... Harris Lipman LLP
LONDON NW1 .... Fisher Forensic
H.W. Fisher & Co
LONDON NW4 .... Frenkels Ltd
LONDON SE1 .... Wilkins Kennedy
LONDON W1 .... Chris Madge & Co
Citroen Wells
Sim Kapila
Vantis Forensic Accounting & Dispute Resolution
LONDON WC1 .... FTI Forensic Accounting Ltd
LONDON WC2 .... Bourner Bullock
LOUGHTON .... Haslers
MANCHESTER .... Beever and Struthers
Begbies Traynor Ltd
Cassons
MILTON KEYNES .... Bourner Bullock
MIRFIELD .... Chris Makin Mediator
NEWCASTLE-UNDER-LYME............. Barringtons Ltd
NORTHWICH .... Bennett Brooks & Co Ltd.
NORWICH .... Walton Dodge Forensic
ORPINGTON .... Wilkins Kennedy
PETERBOROUGH .... Rawlinsons
RINGWOOD .... Vincent Clemas
ROSSENDALE .... Cassons
SEVENOAKS .... Samuels
SOUTHEND-ON-SEA ..... Wilkins Kennedy
ST ALBANS .... Harris Lipman LLP
STEVENAGE .... Wilder Coe
TAUNTON .... Mitchells
TRURO .... Richard J. Smith & Co
WELLS .... Mark Shelton
WEST BYFLEET ...... Gibson Hewitt & Co
Gibson Hewitt Outsourcing Ltd
WEYBRIDGE .... Ward Williams Ltd
WILMSLOW .... Fenczuk & Co

Overseas

IRAN, Tehran .... A.M. Mahallati & Co
POLAND, Warsaw Baker Tilly Smoczynski & Partners Sp. z o.o.

FORENSIC ACCOUNTING

United Kingdom

AMERSHAM .... Wilkins Kennedy
BEDFORD .... Derek A Parry
BIRMINGHAM .... Clement Keys
BOLTON .... Bentleys

BRIGHTON .... Financial Forensics LLP
Hartley Fowler LLP
BROUGHTON-IN-FURNESS ... Accounting Evidence Ltd
CARDIFF .... Chris Madge & Co
Harris Lipman LLP
CHESTER .... Sullivan & Co
CHICHESTER .... Stonham.Co
CLEVEDON .... Chris Madge & Co
COVENTRY .... Prime Accountants Group Ltd
DOUGLAS ..... Baker Tilly Isle of Man LLC
PKF (Isle of Man) LLC
DROITWICH .... Ormerod Rutter Ltd
EXMOUTH .... Tandy & Co
GLOUCESTER .... Little & Co
GRANTHAM .... Callow & Holmes
HATFIELD .... Hassell Forensic Accounting Ltd
HERTFORD .... Wilkins Kennedy
HORNCHURCH .... Robertson Milroy Ltd
HOVE .... Atkinsons
HUDDERSFIELD .... Wheawill & Sudworth
IVYBRIDGE .... Richard J. Smith & Co
JERSEY .... Mazars Channel Islands Ltd
Rosscot Ltd
LEEDS .... Bartfields Business Services LLP
Bartfields (UK) Ltd
Begbies Traynor
Mall & Co
LEICESTER .... WM Proserv
LIVERPOOL .... Hurst (Liverpool) LLP
LONDON E14 .... Littlejohn
LONDON EC2 .... CRA International (UK) Ltd
RGL LLP
LONDON EC3 .... Begbies Traynor Ltd
LONDON EC4 .... Tarrant Green & Co
LONDON N12 ..... David Rubin & Partners
LONDON N14 .... Bond Partners LLP
LONDON N20 .... Harris Lipman LLP
LONDON NW1 .... Fisher Forensic
H.W. Fisher & Co
LONDON NW4 .... Frenkels Ltd
LONDON SW3 .... Dennis R. Waters
LONDON W1 .... Chris Madge & Co
Citroen Wells
Sim Kapila
Vantis Forensic Accounting & Dispute Resolution
LONDON WC1 .... FTI Forensic Accounting Ltd
LOUGHTON .... Haslers
MANCHESTER .... Alexander & Co
Beever and Struthers
Begbies Traynor Ltd
Cassons
MILTON KEYNES ..... Chancery (UK) LLP
Keens Shay Keens Milton Keynes
NEW MALDEN .... Atkinsons
NEWCASTLE UPON TYNE .... Stephenson Coates
Tait Walker
NORTHWICH .... Bennett Brooks & Co Ltd.
NORWICH .... Walton Dodge Forensic
ORPINGTON .... Wilkins Kennedy
RICHMOND .... PK Partners LLP
ROSSENDALE .... Cassons
SEVENOAKS .... Samuels
SHEFFIELD .... Barber Harrison & Platt
ST ALBANS .... Harris Lipman LLP
STEVENAGE .... Wilder Coe
TORPOINT .... C.E. Taylor
TRURO .... Richard J. Smith & Co
WELLS .... Mark Shelton
WILMSLOW .... Fenczuk & Co

Overseas

NIGERIA, Lagos .... Horwath Dafinone
POLAND, Warsaw Baker Tilly Smoczynski & Partners Sp. z o.o.

IT

COMPUTER CONSULTANTS

United Kingdom

BRIGHTON .... Feist Hedgethorne Ltd
CROYDON .... D.S. & Co
FLEET .... JCS Associates
HARROW .... LINK
LONDON EC2 .... CRA International (UK) Ltd
RGL LLP
LONDON EC4 .... 2020 CA Ltd
LONDON N3 .... FMCB
Paul Perlin & Co
LONDON SW18 .... Chicksand Gordon Avis Ltd
LBCo Ltd
LONDON W1 .... Bowker Orford
LONDON W13 .... Merchant & Co
LONDON W5 .... Levy & Partners
Levy + Partners Ltd
LONDON WC2 .... Bourner Bullock
STANMORE .... Lawrence Grant
UCKFIELD .... Maitland Ltd
WATFORD .... JSA Services Ltd

Overseas

LUXEMBOURG, Luxembourg HT Group S.A.

COMPUTER SYSTEMS AND CONSULTANCY

United Kingdom

CARDIFF .... Groves Davey Ltd
CHELMSFORD .... Bird Luckin Ltd
CROYDON .... D.S. & Co
DUNMOW .... Bird Luckin Ltd
HASTINGS .... Deeks Evans
HERTFORD .... Philip T. Chave & Co
LONDON E14 .... Littlejohn
LONDON N14 .... Bond Partners LLP
LONDON N20 .... Harris Lipman LLP
LONDON N3 .... Paul Perlin & Co
LONDON NW11 .... H & H Associates
LONDON W5 .... Levy & Partners
Levy + Partners Ltd
LONDON WC2 .... Bourner Bullock
MAIDENHEAD .... Hale & Co
NORTHAMPTON .... J.R. Watson & Co
PETERSFIELD .... Barter Durgan & Muir Ltd
PRESTON .... Whitehead & Aldrich
READING .... Vale & West
STRATFORD-UPON-AVON .. Grenfell James
WESTCLIFF-ON-SEA .... Brannans

Overseas

NIGERIA, Lagos .... Horwath Dafinone

COMPUTERISED ACCOUNTING SYSTEMS

United Kingdom

BEDFORD .... Gregory Wildman
BURNLEY .... K M Business Solutions Ltd
CARDIFF .... Groves Davey Ltd
DOUGLAS .... PKF (Isle of Man) LLC
EAST GRINSTEAD .... Brooks & Co
HARLOW .... Giess Wallis Crisp
JERSEY .... Rosscot Ltd
KINGSTON UPON THAMES . David Howard
LANCASTER .... Langdale
LEEDS .... Bartfields Business Services LLP
Bartfields (UK) Ltd
Whitesides
LLANDUDNO .... Gareth Hughes & Company Ltd
LONDON N3 .... Paul Perlin & Co
LONDON NW11 .... H & H Associates
LONDON SW4 .... Willis Burnell Ltd
LONDON W5 .... Levy & Partners
Levy + Partners Ltd
MILTON KEYNES Keens Shay Keens Milton Keynes
NEW MALDEN .... Atkinsons
NOTTINGHAM .... Keith Willis Associates Ltd
PORTSMOUTH .... David Bailey
WATFORD .... Myers Clark
WESTCLIFF-ON-SEA .... Brannans

Overseas

IRAN, Tehran .... A.M. Mahallati & Co
NIGERIA, Lagos .... Horwath Dafinone

E-COMMERCE

United Kingdom

HARROGATE .... Holeys
LONDON EC1 .... FW Stephens Westbury
LONDON EC4 .... 2020 CA Ltd
LONDON N14 .... Bond Partners LLP
LONDON NW11 .... H & H Associates
LONDON NW3 .... Nyman Libson Paul
LONDON W1 .... Bowker Orford

INFORMATION TECHNOLOGY

United Kingdom

HOVE .... Atkinsons
LONDON EC1 .... FW Stephens Higgisons
LONDON EC2 .... RGL LLP
LONDON EC4 .... 2020 CA Ltd
LONDON N3 .... Paul Perlin & Co
LONDON WC2 .... Bourner Bullock
NEW MALDEN .... Atkinsons
WESTCLIFF-ON-SEA .... Brannans

THE OFFICIAL ICAEW DIRECTORY OF FIRMS 2009

LONDON

LONDON E1

A.D.HARVERD
c/o Carter Backer Winter, Enterprise House, 21 Buckle Street, London E1 8EH

ACCTECH CONSULTING
51 Fashion Street, London, E1 6PX

AHMAD & CO
41A Brick Lane, London, E1 6PU

CARTER BACKER WINTER ◈
Enterprise House, 21 Buckle Street, London, E1 8NN
Tel: 020 7309 3800
Website: http://www.cbw.co.uk
Resident Partners/Directors: ICAEW Members
J A G Alexander, M J Carter, R H Davis, D P Kramer, P Luscombe, P D Smethurst, P Winter
Resident Partners (Non-ICAEW Members):
H A Lipman, V Shah, P R Woosey
Registered by the ICAEW to carry out company audit work
Regulated by the ICAEW for a range of investment business activities
Individual(s) licensed for insolvency work by the ICAEW
Individual(s) licensed for insolvency work by another RPB

CHARIOT HOUSE LTD
42 Alie Street, London, E1 8DA

EAFTON & CO
3rd Floor, 101 Commercial Road, London, E1 1RD

HABIB RAHMAN & CO ◈
233 Whitechapel Road, London, E1 1DB

HASLOCKS LTD
46-48 East Smithfield, London, E1W 1AW
Tel: 020 7265 0606
Resident Partners/Directors: ICAEW Members
C G Haslock

KSA
228 Shoreditch High Street, London, E1 6PJ

LEMON & CO
221 Shoreditch High Street, London, E1 6PP
Tel: 020 7247 1922
Fax: 020 7247 1478
Email: accountant@lemonco.co.uk
Website: http://www.lemonco.co.uk
Date Established: 1888
Resident Partners/Directors: ICAEW Members
I B Boustead
Resident Partners (Non-ICAEW Members):
M Thompson
Registered by the ICAEW to carry out company audit work
Regulated by the ICAEW for a range of investment business activities

MAZARS CORPORATE FINANCE LTD ◈
Tower Bridge House, St Katharines Way, London, E1W 1AA

MAZARS LLP ◈
Tower Bridge House, St Katharines Way, London, E1W 1DD
Tel: 020 7063 4000
Resident Partners/Directors: ICAEW Members
S A Brice, S M Bullock, A Carey, H C Clarke, L J R Decaen, S A Eden, D J Evans, A J Fraser, A J Goldsworthy, M J Grice, N C Grummitt, A Heffron, D R P Herbinet, F C Hotston Moore, A J Hubbard, K B Hurst, M Y Jooma, R A Karmel, R W Metcalfe, A N Mole, G C Morley, R H Neate, S M G Russell, R Stevens, R C Tidbury, R J Weston, G M Williams
Resident Partners (Non-ICAEW Members):
C J Blundell, J P Bradley, J L Brice, P D Forrest, R J Green, R H Jones, S M Joseph, R Lang, I J Pickford, N L E Rilbollet, M E Rodriguez-Piza, S N Skeels, P G Willians, A M Whitfield
Registered by the ICAEW to carry out company audit work
Authorised and regulated by the Financial Services Authority for investment business
Individual(s) licensed for insolvency work by the ICAEW

MOHAMMAD SHAH & CO
100 Mile End Road, London, E1 4UN

OCTOKHAN
2nd Floor, 94a Whitechapel, High Street, London E1 7RA

P & CO
No. 13, 2 Artichoke Hill, London, E1W 2DE

P AND CO
Unit 13, 2 Artichoke Hill, London, E1W 2DE

P AND CO LLP
Unit 13, 2 Artichoke Hill, London, E1W 2DE
Tel: 020 7264 0390
Website: http://www.p-co.co.uk
Training Contracts Available.
Resident Partners/Directors: ICAEW Members
S Pitayanukul
Registered by the ICAEW to carry out company audit work
Languages Spoken:
Japanese, Thai, Chinese

PITAYANUKUL & CO LTD
No. 13, 3rd Floor, 2 Artichoke Hill, London, E1W 2DE

R AHMED & CO
37 New Road, London, E1 1HE
Tel: 020 7375 3075
Principal: ICAEW Member
A Ahmed

RASHED SHAHEEDEE & CO
Chytel House, 160-164 Mile End Road, London, E1 4LJ

S.ASGHAR & CO
93-95 Commercial Road, 2nd Floor, London, E1 1RD

SABERA & CO
126 Middlesex Street, London, E1 7HY

TBW
42 Alie Street, London, E1 8DA

UHY CORPORATE FINANCE LTD ◈
Quadrant House, 17 Thomas More Street, Thomas More Square, London E1W 1YW
Tel: 020 7216 4600
Email: l.sacker@uhy-uk.com
Website: http://www.uhy-uk.com/corpfinance
Resident Partners/Directors: ICAEW Members
M P W Egan, L Sacker, H P Spencer
Authorised and regulated by the Financial Services Authority for investment business

SPECIALISATIONS – BUSINESS & GENERAL ADVICE

Acquisitions and Mergers
Disposal of Businesses
Investment Appraisal

SPECIALISATIONS – BUSINESS RECOVERY & INSOLVENCY

Reorganisations and Company Reconstructions

General Description: Services include AIM and PLUS admissions, pre-IPO, equity, venture capital, company sale and purchase, investigations and due diligence. Authorised to approve financial promotions.

UHY HACKER YOUNG LLP
Quadrant House, 17 Thomas More Street, Thomas More Square, London E1W 1YW
Tel: 020 7216 4600
Email: london@uhy-uk.com
Website: http://www.uhy-uk.com
Resident Partners/Directors: ICAEW Members
A Andronikou, B B Bhattacharyya, G C K Chong, I R Cohen, J E Easton, M P W Egan, M Giddens, P M Hollins, C N Jones, A M Kaye, D S Levy, C J Lowry, C R Maugham, L Sacker, H P Spencer, M Waterman
Non-resident Partners (ICAEW Members):
J P Warsop
Resident Partners (Non-ICAEW Members):
L Hornan, D E Murphy, J E C Lim, V J Vadgama, P A Kubik, S Newark, M Kiely, C Wright
Registered by the ICAEW to carry out company audit work
Regulated by the ICAEW for a range of investment business activities
General Description: A top 20 firm providing professional accounting and tax services to a broad spectrum of clients. See our website for details.

UHY JACKSON BLY
Quadrant House, 17 Thomas More Street, Thomas More Square, London E1W 1YW

WATLINGTON SECURITIES LTD
36 Elder Street, London, E1 6BT
Tel: 020 7456 9600
Fax: 020 7377 2946
Resident Partners/Directors: ICAEW Members
A G Ebel, B J Hallett, A P Stirling
Regulated by the ICAEW for a range of investment business activities

LONDON E2

ARMSTRONG & CO
Unit 4A, Printing House Yard, Hackney Road, London E2 7PR
Tel: 020 7613 2586
Email: hq@armco.co.uk
Principal: ICAEW Member
A D Armstrong
Registered by the ICAEW to carry out company audit work

LEONARD JONES & CO
1 Printing House Yard, London, E2 7PR
Tel: 020 7739 8790
Email: enquiries@leonardjones.co.uk
Resident Partners/Directors: ICAEW Members
A L Carter, D A Lyons
Registered by the ICAEW to carry out company audit work
Regulated by the ICAEW for a range of investment business activities

continued

LEONARD JONES & CO *cont*

SPECIALISATIONS – SECTOR

Architects/Surveyors
Charities
Media
Solicitors

General Description: We provide a full range of business support, accounting and tax services.

M.K. CHOWDHURY & CO
250 Bethnal Green Road, London, E2 0AA
Tel: 020 7729 9394
Principal: ICAEW Member
M K H Chowdhury

LONDON E4

B & M ACCOUNTANCY LTD
52 Dale View Avenue, Chingford, London, E4 6PL

BARROW & CO ★ ◈
Jackson House, Station Road, Chingford, London E4 7BU
Tel: 020 8524 8134
Resident Partners/Directors: ICAEW Members
R M Barrow

CARTER CLARK ★
Meridian House, 62 Station Road, North Chingford, London E4 7BA
Tel: 020 8524 1447
Resident Partners/Directors: ICAEW Members
A J Clark

CLAY RATNAGE DAFFIN & CO LTD
Doric House, 132 Station Road, Chingford, London E4 6AB

DAVID J. WENHAM & CO
7 Victoria Road, London, E4 6BY

DUDHIA LEWIN MYERS ASSOCIATES LTD
98 Chingford Mount Road, South Chingford, London, E4 9AA
Tel: 020 8503 2211
Resident Partners/Directors: ICAEW Members
Z Dudhia

EAST LONDON ACCOUNTANCY SERVICES ★
7 Norbury Road, London, E4 8JX

FINDLAY, WETHERFIELD, SCOTT & CO
135/137 Station Road, Chingford, London, E4 6AG

GARDEZI JAY & CO
Hamilton House, 4a The Avenue, London, E4 9LD

GARDEZI JAY & CO
Security House, 485 Hale End Road, London, E4 9PT

J E BUTLER & CO
222 The Avenue, Highams Park, London, E4 9SE
Tel: 020 8531 9128
Principal: ICAEW Member
J E Butler

JACKSON & JACKSON ◈
33 Chingford Mount Road, London, E4 8LU
Tel: 020 8527 6912

JACKSON & JACKSON ACCOUNTANTS LTD ◈
33 Chingford Mount Road, London, E4 8LU
Tel: 020 8527 6912
Resident Partners/Directors: ICAEW Members
H R Jackson

LESSER & CO ◈
147 Station Road, North Chingford, London, E4 6AG
Tel: 020 8524 2556
Fax: 020 8529 9097
Email: enquiries@lesserandco.com
Website: http://www.lesserandco.com
Principal: ICAEW Member
S M Lesser

Registered by the ICAEW to carry out company audit work

Authorised and regulated by the Financial Services Authority for investment business

Languages Spoken:
Italian

See display advertisement near this entry.

PRICE BAILEY LLP ◈
500 Larkshall Road, Highams Park, London, E4 9HH
Tel: 020 8531 0505
Website: http://www.pricebailey.co.uk
Resident Partners/Directors: ICAEW Members
A J Sanderson
Resident Partners (Non-ICAEW Members):
H W Sears

Registered by the ICAEW to carry out company audit work

Authorised and regulated by the Financial Services Authority for investment business

PRICE BAILEY PRIVATE CLIENT LLP
500 Larkshall Road, Highams Park, London, E4 9HH

REYNOLDS & CO
Meridian House, 7 The Avenue, Highams Park, London E4 9LB

STEPHEN MALME
51 Mornington Road, North Chingford, London, E4 7DT

LONDON E5

FRANCIS & CO
100 Clarence Road, London, E5 8HB

LONDON E6

CHEEMA GOFFE & CO ◈
26 Plashet Grove, East Ham, London, E6 1AE
Tel: 020 8552 6786
Principal: ICAEW Member
D S Cheema

LYNCH & CO
194 Lonsdale Avenue, Newham, London, E6 3PP

LONDON E8

EAST LONDON ACCOUNTANCY SERVICES
62 Beechwood Road, London, E8 3DY

EMMANUEL STEPHENS & CO
62 Beechwood Road, London, E8 3DY

LESKIN GALLER
338 Kingsland Road, London, E8 4DA

LONDON E11

A A JAMAL TAX CONSULTANTS LTD
28 Fairlop Road, London, E11 1BN

A. MANNAN & CO
14 Norman Road, Leytonstone, London, E11 4PX

BARNES ROFFE LLP
Leytonstone House, Leytonstone, London, E11 1HR
Tel: 020 8988 6100
Resident Partners/Directors: ICAEW Members
P Bonnell, A Cheason, P W Hughes, M B Smith, G M Wallace

FRIEDMANS
Summit House, 13 High Street, Wanstead, London E11 2AA

JEFFERY EDELMAN & CO
22 Draycot Road, London, E11 2NX
Tel: 020 8530 7241
Principal: ICAEW Member
J Edelman

MYERS HOGG & CO
3 Lemna Road, Leytenstone, London, E11 1JL
Tel: 020 988 8070
Principal: ICAEW Member
G M Hogg

THP LTD
34-40 High Street, Wanstead, London, E11 2RJ
Tel: 020 8989 5147
Website: http://www.thp.co.uk
Training Contracts Available.
Resident Partners/Directors: ICAEW Members
J P Christie, H E Godwin, A C Hart, J B Hearne, C D Johnson, K A Mallett, G H Nottage

WARREN D MISKIN
2 Forest Close, Snaresbrook, London, E11 1PY

LONDON E14

ABELL MORLISS
167 Cannon Workshops, Cannon Drive, London, E14 4AS

ABELL MORLISS LTD
167 Cannon Workshops, Cannon Drive, London, E14 4AS

EDWARDS H.G.
34 Capstan Square, London, E14 3EU

F D SOLUTIONS ★
8 Pepper Street, Glengall Bridge, London, E14 9RP
Tel: 020 7512 1110
Resident Partners/Directors: ICAEW Members
M G Durham, S H Walters

HADLEYS & CO ◈
5 Malvern House, 199 Marsh Wall, Meridan Gate, London E14 9YT
Tel: 020 7001 7770
Principal: ICAEW Member
K Mehmood

I C HOBBS
1 Park Place, Canary Wharf, London, E14 4HJ

J.J. KEEFE
77 The Wheel House, Burrells Wharf, Westferry Road, London E14 3TB

LITTLEJOHN

LITTLEJOHN ★ ◈
1 Westferry Circus, Canary Wharf, London, E14 4HD
Tel: 020 7516 2200
Fax: 020 7987 9707
Email: info@clblf.com
Website: http://www.clblf.com
Date Established: 1875
Training Contracts Available.
Resident Partners/Directors: ICAEW Members
J E Brew, A H F Campbell, N A Coulson, I M Cowan, D R M Frame, E H Hindson, P W Hopper, A J Knapp, N M C Light, M R Ling, S A Morrison, J C Needham, C A Palmer, C Papa, J A Perry, A M Rana, M P Reddihough, A D Roberts, D W Roberts, J P Rummins, A J Sheridan, M T Stenson, D A Thompson, D H Tout
Resident Partners (Non-ICAEW Members):
I H Singer, R W Jones, T K Moore, C R Mead

Registered by the ICAEW to carry out company audit work

Authorised and regulated by the Financial Services Authority for investment business

SPECIALISATIONS – AUDIT & ASSURANCE
Audit

SPECIALISATIONS – BUSINESS & GENERAL ADVICE
Acquisitions and Mergers
Disposal of Businesses

SPECIALISATIONS – FORENSIC ACCOUNTING
Expert Witnesses in Litigation
Forensic Accounting

SPECIALISATIONS – IT
Computer Systems and Consultancy

SPECIALISATIONS – SECTOR
Charities
Corporate
FSA Members
Insurance Brokers
Lloyds Underwriters
Nursing Homes/Clinics
Paper/Printing/Publishing
Road Haulage and Distribution
Schools
Solicitors

SPECIALISATIONS – TAXATION
Capital Gains — Limited Companies
Capital Gains — Personal
Customs Duty
Estate and Inheritance
Foreign Nationals in the UK
Personal
Trusts
UK Subsidiaries of Overseas Multinationals
Value Added Tax

General Description: Strong relationships, substantial partner involvement, honest answers and intelligent solutions from an independent, top 30 firm of accountants and advisers. From our base in London's Canary Wharf, we serve a wide range of business and private clients and through our independent membership of Polaris International, we are represented by an association that encompasses 170 firms operating in 90 countries.

LITTLEJOHN CORPORATE SERVICES LTD ★
1 Westferry Circus, London, E14 4HD

LITTLEJOHN PAYROLL SERVICES LTD ★
1 Westferry Circus, Canary Wharf, London, E14 4HD

LITTLEJOHN WEALTH MANAGEMENT LTD ★
1 Westferry Circus, Canary Wharf, London, E14 4HD

MEER & CO
1 Cochrane House, Admirals Way, Canary Wharf, London E14 9UD

RBS ACCOUNTANTS LTD
Suite 16, Beaufort Court, Admirals Way, Sth Quay, London E14 9XL
Tel: 020 7537 9043
Website: http://www.rbsca.com
Resident Partners/Directors: ICAEW Members
K K J Shah
See display advertisement near this entry.

SANSONS ◈
35 Beaufort Court, Admirals Way, South Quay Waterside, London E14 9XL
Tel: 020 7537 1600
Principal: ICAEW Member
S Sood

TOM MADGE
18 Chilcot Close, London, E14 6AN

LONDON E15

APPLEBY & WOOD ★ ◈
40 The Lock Building, 72 High Street, London, E15 2QB
Tel: 020 8534 0383
Resident Partners/Directors: ICAEW Members
R R Oswald

LB GROUP LTD
1 Vicarage Lane, Stratford, London, E15 4HF

LONDON E16

EAFTON & CO
143 Varley Road, London, E16 3NR
Tel: 0870 242 4364
Fax: 0870 242 4368
Email: efatona@hotmail.com
Principal: ICAEW Member
E A Fatona

continued

EAFTON & CO *cont*
Other Offices:3rd Floor, 101 Commercial Road, London E1 1RD
Registered by the ICAEW to carry out company audit work
SPECIALISATIONS – AUDIT & ASSURANCE
Audit
Audit — Private Company
SPECIALISATIONS – BUSINESS & GENERAL ADVICE
Company Formation
Company Secretarial Service
SPECIALISATIONS – FINANCIAL REPORTING
Accounts Preparation
Limited Company Accounts
Partnership/Sole Trader Accounts
SPECIALISATIONS – SECTOR
Charities
Church
SPECIALISATIONS – TAXATION
Self Assessment Advice
Taxation

LONDON E17

ANDERSON ROSS
Waltham Forest Business Centre, 5 Blackhorse Lane, London, E17 6DS
Tel: 020 8523 2228
Resident Partners/Directors: ICAEW Members
N Savomy, H J Wooller

GILLIAN MCKAY ACCOUNTANCY SERVICES
13 Pasquier Road, Walthamstow, London, E17 6HB

GOLDIN & CO ◈
105 Hoe Street, Walthamstow, London, E17 4SA
Tel: 020 8520 8659
Principal: ICAEW Member
I A Goldin

I.A. KAY & CO
306 Hoe Street, Walthamstow, London, E17 9PX

JEEWA & CO
91 Cairo Road, Walthamstow, London, E17 3BB

KIM D HOOPER
58 Knebworth Avenue, London, E17 5AJ
Tel: 020 8527 7648
Principal: ICAEW Member
K D Hooper
SPECIALISATIONS – SECTOR
Charities

KLEIN EVANGELOU ★
368 Forest Road, London, E17 5JF

KOUNNIS AND PARTNERS PLC ★
Sterling House, Fulbourne Road, Walthamstow, London E17 4EE

M AKRAM & CO
109 Farmilo Road, Walthamstow, London, E17 8JN

MICHAEL BARRS AND CO
395 Hoe Street, Walthamstow, London, E17 9AP
Tel: 020 8520 6844
Fax: 020 8521 0874
Email: info@mbarrs.co.uk
Principal: ICAEW Member
M Barrs
Registered by the ICAEW to carry out company audit work
Regulated by the ICAEW for a range of investment business activities
SPECIALISATIONS – AUDIT & ASSURANCE
Audit
SPECIALISATIONS – BUSINESS & GENERAL ADVICE
Book-keeping
Company Formation
Company Secretarial Service
SPECIALISATIONS – FINANCIAL REPORTING
Audit Exemption Report
Limited Company Accounts
Partnership/Sole Trader Accounts
SPECIALISATIONS – TAXATION
Payroll Service and Advice
Self Assessment Advice
Taxation
Value Added Tax
See display advertisement near this entry.

TEMPLETONS (UK) LTD
309 Hoe Street, London, E17 9BG

LONDON E18

ALAN PATIENT & CO
1 The Shrubberies, George Lane, South Woodford, London E18 1BD
Tel: 020 8532 9843
Principal: ICAEW Member
A S Patient

BEAVERS ◈
3 The Shrubberies, George Lane, London, E18 1BD

BJ SEXTON & CO
2 The Shrubberies, George Lane, South Woodford, London E18 1BE

CATON FRY & CO LTD
Essex House, 7-8 The Shrubberies, George Lane, London E18 1BD
Tel: 020 8530 1900
Email: info@catonfry.com
Resident Partners/Directors: ICAEW Members
C A Caton, E O Caton, J E Caton
Registered by the ICAEW to carry out company audit work

COMPANY CONTRACTS AND SERVICES LTD
11 The Shrubberies, George Lane, London, E18 1BD

CROFTS & CO
7 Orestes Court, 39 Woodford Road, South Woodford, London E18 2EF

GEOFFREY LITTLE & CO
22 Orford Road, London, E18 1PY

IAN J. SHANKS FCA
25 Lancaster Avenue, South Woodford, London, E18 1QF
Tel: 020 8989 3729
Principal: ICAEW Member
I J Shanks

MARK NORDEN & CO LTD ◈
158 Hermon Hill, South Woodford, London, E18 1QH
Tel: 020 8530 0720
Resident Partners/Directors: ICAEW Members
M Norden

MARK SMITH & CO
Rear of, 8 The Shubberies, George Lane, South Woodford, London E18 1BD

REIN & CO
Elliot House, 109 George Lane, South Woodford, London E18 1AN

ROBERT OLLMAN & CO
11 The Shrubberies, George Lane, London, E18 1BD

S.J. HERTZBERG & CO
18 Glebelands Avenue, South Woodford, London, E18 2AB

STANLEY KENNER & CO LTD
3 Walbrook, Woodford Road, South Woodford, London E18 2EG

STEPHEN MILLER
37 High View Road, South Woodford, London, E18 2HL
Tel: 020 8989 4187
Principal: ICAEW Member
S D Miller

STEPHEN R. BELL
30 Avon Way, South Woodford, London, E18 2AR
Tel: 020 8530 5291
Principal: ICAEW Member
S R Bell

WOLF TAYLOR ◈
107 George Lane, London, E18 1AN
Tel: 020 8530 4162
Fax: 020 8530 1205
Email: geoff@wolftaylor.com
Website: http://www.wolftaylor.com
Date Established: 1980
Resident Partners/Directors: ICAEW Members
A Taylor, G M Wolf
Registered by the ICAEW to carry out company audit work

LONDON EC1

ACCOUNTING POLICY ADVISORY LTD
47 Dickinson Court, 15 Brewhouse Yard, London, EC1V 4JX

ADBELL INTERNATIONAL LTD
Finsgate, 5-7 Cranwood Street, London, EC1V 9EE

AIMS - KEVIN LLEWELYN-EVANS
21 Northampton Square, London, EC1V 0AJ

ALFRED HENRY CORPORATE FINANCE LTD
1st Floor Finsgate, 5/7 Cranwood Street, London, EC1V 9EE

AMIN PATEL & SHAH ★
1st Floor, 334-336 Goswell Road, London, EC1V 7RP

ARRAM BERLYN GARDNER
30 City Road, London, EC1Y 2AB
Tel: 020 7330 0000
Fax: 020 7330 0001
Email: abg@abggroup.co.uk
Website: http://www.abggroup.co.uk
Date Established: 1966
Resident Partners/Directors: ICAEW Members
P Berlyn, G Jackson, P G S Morris, J A Piper
Non-resident Partners (ICAEW Members):
L S Lazarus, G Berlyn, H J Rose, M Segal
Resident Partners (Non-ICAEW Members):
M Rubinson, F Zekia
Registered by the ICAEW to carry out company audit work
Regulated by the ICAEW for a range of investment business activities
General Description: Arram Berlyn Gardner was established in 1966 and has developed a strong client base throughout the country, in particular, London and the South East. We have a reputation for a personal and responsive partner-led service to our clients, which include sole traders, partnerships and private companies and their directors. The purpose of this firm is to provide imaginative and quality solutions to our clients' tax, financial and business problems in ways that enhance their prosperity and to exceed clients' expectations in terms of quality, service and value.

ASH PULLAN
Epworth House, 25 City Road, London, EC1Y 1AR

ASHINGS ◈
Barbican House, 26-34 Old Street, London, EC1V 9QQ

BEGBIES CHETTLE AGAR ◈
Epworth House, 25 City Road, London, EC1Y 1AR
Tel: 020 7628 5801
Website: http://www.begbieschettleagar.co.uk
Resident Partners/Directors: ICAEW Members
R G Maples, J Payne, D M Valentine, C P Wain
Resident Partners (Non-ICAEW Members):
J N Staines

BEGBIES CHETTLE AGAR LTD ◈
Epworth House, 25 City Road, London, EC1Y 1AR

BLACKSTONE FRANKS CORPORATE FINANCE
Barbican House, 26-34 Old Street, London, EC1V 9QR
Tel: 020 7250 3300
Website: http://www.blackstonefranks.com

BLACKSTONE FRANKS LLP ◈
Barbican House, 26-34 Old Street, London, EC1V 9QR
Tel: 020 7250 3300
Email: lblackstone@blackstones.co.uk
Website: http://www.blackstonefranks.com
Resident Partners/Directors: ICAEW Members
L R Blackstone, R W Maas, S V Thakrar
Resident Partners (Non-ICAEW Members):
S Ahmed
General Description: International and UK tax planning. Mergers and acquisitions. Corporate finance. General business, Audit and accountancy services.

BLEVINS FRANKS LTD
Barbican House, 26-34 Old Street, London, EC1V 9QQ
Tel: 020 7336 1000
Email: ali.alidina@blevinsfranks.com
Website: http://www.blevinfranks.com
Resident Partners/Directors: ICAEW Members
B H R Alidina

BOND PARTNERS LLP
111 Charterhouse Street, London, EC1M 6AW

CRITCHLEYS
10 Charterhouse Square, London, EC1 N6LQ

DAVISON & SHINGLETON ◈
Boundary House, 91-93 Charterhouse Street, London, EC1M 6HR
Tel: 020 7490 4221
Training Contracts Available.
Resident Partners/Directors: ICAEW Members
R Davison, C L Hollinghurst, A K Shingleton
Registered by the ICAEW to carry out company audit work
Regulated by the ICAEW for a range of investment business activities

DOUGLAS WADKIN
Douglas Wadkin, 11 Amwell Street, London, EC1R 1UL
Tel: 020 7713 8306
Fax: 020 7713 8315
Email: doug@dougwadkin.com
Principal: ICAEW Member
D J Wadkin

EDEN CONSULTANTS LTD
24 Cloth Fair, London, EC1A 7JQ

F W STEPHENS TAXATION LTD
Third Floor, 24 Chiswell Street, London, EC1Y 4XY
Tel: 020 7382 1820
Fax: 020 7382 1821
Email: info@fwstephens.co.uk
Resident Partners/Directors: ICAEW Members
E Clapton, S T Linley, O S Skinner, R A Stevens

FINANCE ASSOCIATES LTD
Boundary House, 91-93 Charterhouse Street, London, EC1M 6HR

FORD, BULL, WATKINS
Clerks Well House, 20 Britton Street, London, EC1M 5TU

FORDHAMS & CO ★ ◈
Second Floor, 61 Old Street, London, EC1V 9HX
Tel: 020 7253 6363
Resident Partners/Directors: ICAEW Members
M Akhtaruzzaman, I F Nurbhai

FRASER SAMUELSON
2nd Floor, 145-157 St John Street, London, EC1V 4PY

FRASER SAMUELSON LTD
2nd Floor, 145-157 St John Street, London, EC1V 4PY

FW STEPHENS ◈
Third Floor, 24 Chiswell Street, London, EC1Y 4YX
Tel: 020 7382 1820
Email: info@fwstephens.co.uk
Website: http://www.fwstephens.co.uk
Date Established: 1908
Training Contracts Available.
Resident Partners/Directors: ICAEW Members
E Clapton, M J Cook, S T Linley, A H Miller, J C O'Brien, M O'Brien, M S T Procter, C S Reeve-Tucker, O S Skinner, R A Stevens, S P Tanner
Resident Partners (Non-ICAEW Members):
J P Crowder

Registered by the ICAEW to carry out company audit work

Regulated by the ICAEW for a range of investment business activities

SPECIALISATIONS – AUDIT & ASSURANCE
Assurance Services
Audit
Audit — Private Company
Audit — Public Company

SPECIALISATIONS – BUSINESS & GENERAL ADVICE
Book-keeping
Company Formation
Company Secretarial Service
Data Processing Services
Divorce/Matrimonial
Europe
Management Advice to Business

SPECIALISATIONS – FINANCIAL REPORTING
Accounts Preparation
Foreign Subsidiary Companies

SPECIALISATIONS – INVESTMENT BUSINESS
Financial Planning and Advice
Pensions Advice
Planning

SPECIALISATIONS – IT
E-commerce
Information Technology

SPECIALISATIONS – SECTOR
Architects/Surveyors
Charities
Clubs/Associations
Construction
Corporate
Estate Agents
FSA Members
New Media
Property
Property Development
Property Investment
Solicitors

SPECIALISATIONS – TAXATION
Back Duty
Capital Gains — Personal
Employee
Estate and Inheritance
Estate Planning
Executorship
Foreign Nationals in the UK
Partnerships and Sole Traders
Payroll Service and Advice
Personal
Self Assessment Advice
Trusteeship
Trusts
UK Nationals Overseas
UK Subsidiaries of Overseas Multinationals
Value Added Tax

General Description: FW Stephens are a leading group of chartered accountants, business advisers and taxation consultants and independent financial advisers, with strong international connections. Founded on traditional values our name is synonymous with experience, expertise, imagination and most of all vision. For further information please refer to our website or contact Richard Stevens or Simon Linley.
See display advertisement near this entry.

GORDON LEIGHTON ▽
3rd Floor, 20-23 Greville Street, London, EC1N 8SS

GORDON LEIGHTON LTD
20-23 Greville Street, London, EC1N 8SS

HAMMOND KNIGHT
2nd Floor, 145-157 St John Street, London, EC1V 4PY

HAT GROUP OF ACCOUNTANTS
12 Cock Lane, London, EC1A 9BU

HIGGISONS
Higgison House, 381/383 City Road, London, EC1V 1NW
Tel: 020 7 837 4433
Fax: 020 7833 1701
Email: admin@higgisons.com
DX: 400206 FINSBURY 2
Website: http://www.higgisons.com
Resident Partners/Directors: ICAEW Members
D J Frampton, J J McHale, I Shillinglaw

Registered by the ICAEW to carry out company audit work

Regulated by the ICAEW for a range of investment business activities

SPECIALISATIONS – AUDIT & ASSURANCE
Audit

SPECIALISATIONS – BUSINESS & GENERAL ADVICE
Book-keeping
Company Formation

SPECIALISATIONS – INVESTMENT BUSINESS
Financial Planning and Advice

SPECIALISATIONS – IT
Information Technology

SPECIALISATIONS – SECTOR
Advertising/Design Agencies
Construction
Dentists/Opticians
Entertainers
FSA Members
Insurance Brokers
Property Development
Solicitors
Transport
Travel Industry

SPECIALISATIONS – TAXATION
Back Duty
Trusts

General Description: The firm has been established for 40 years and specialises in assisting privately owned business in all financial matters including start ups, banking and finance arrangements and back duty investigations.

HLB VANTIS AUDIT PLC
82 St John Street, London, EC1M 4JN
Tel: 020 7417 0417
Website: http://www.hlbvantisaudit.com
Training Contracts Available.

Registered by the ICAEW to carry out company audit work

Regulated by the ICAEW for a range of investment business activities

SPECIALISATIONS – AUDIT & ASSURANCE
Audit
Audit — Private Company
Audit — Public Company

SPECIALISATIONS – FINANCIAL REPORTING
Audit Exemption Report

HOLBORN ACCOUNTANCY TUITION LTD
12 Cock Lane, London, EC1A 9BU

IFRS CONSULTING.COM
47 Dickinson Court, 15 Brewhouse Yard, London, EC1V 4JX

JEFFREYS HENRY & CO
Finsgate, 5-7 Cranwood Street, London, EC1V 9EE

JEFFREYS HENRY LLP
Finsgate, 5-7 Cranwood Street, London, EC1V 9EE

KINGSTON SMITH & PARTNERS LLP
Devonshire House, 60 Goswell Road, London, EC1M 7AD
Tel: 020 7566 4020
Resident Partners/Directors: ICAEW Members
D A Benton, M Bridge, S L Bright, N S J Brooks, M A Burchmore, E M Carder, P Chadda, A P Craddock, S J De Lord, D Djanogly, M D Fecher, N M Finlayson, R M Garrick, K E Halstead, M K Hindson, P R Holgate, A J Houstoun, G W Howells, C C Hughes, C W Ireton, C J Lane, M J Meadows, A Merron, D J Montgomery, G A Morgan, M A Muirhead, S Neal, M B Penfold, H M Powell, J R Riches, I Robert, P E M Samrah, J P Seymour, A N Shaw, M N Sinclair, M J Snyder, J Staniforth, T F J Stovold, R N Surman, J Sutcliffe, P J Timms, M Twum-Ampofo, G A Tyler, J I Walsh
Individual(s) licensed for insolvency work by the ICAEW

SPECIALISATIONS – BUSINESS RECOVERY & INSOLVENCY
Bankruptcies
Corporate Recovery
Liquidations
Reorganisations and Company Reconstructions

KINGSTON SMITH LLP
Devonshire House, 60 Goswell Road, London, EC1M 7AD
Tel: 020 7566 4000
Fax: 020 7566 4010
Email: ks@kingstonsmith.co.uk
Website: http://www.kingstonsmith.co.uk
Resident Partners/Directors: ICAEW Members
N S J Brooks, M A Burchmore, A P Craddock, S J De Lord, D

Djanogly, M D Fecher, N M Finlayson, R M Garrick, M K Hindson, P R Holgate, A J Houstoun, C C Hughes, C J Lane, M J Meadows, G A Morgan, M A Muirhead, S Neal, H M Powell, J R Riches, A N Shaw, M J Snyder, J Staniforth, T F J Stovold, J Sutcliffe, P J Timms, M Twum-Ampofo, J I Walsh

Registered by the ICAEW to carry out company audit work

Regulated by the ICAEW for a range of investment business activities

KINGSWOOD ◈

3 Coldbath Square, London, EC1R 5HL
Tel: 020 7841 0000
Fax: 020 7841 0009
Email: kingswood@kingswood.org.uk
Website: http://www.kingswood.org.uk
Resident Partners/Directors: ICAEW Members
J F Massing, H S Moss

Registered by the ICAEW to carry out company audit work

Authorised and regulated by the Financial Services Authority for investment business

SPECIALISATIONS – BUSINESS & GENERAL ADVICE

Acquisitions and Mergers
Company Secretarial Service
Management Advice to Business

SPECIALISATIONS – FORENSIC ACCOUNTING

Expert Witnesses in Litigation

SPECIALISATIONS – INVESTMENT BUSINESS

Planning

SPECIALISATIONS – TAXATION

Payroll Service and Advice
Self Assessment Advice

General Description: Commercial firm providing corporate finance and accounting services to the SME business sector including private companies and family businesses.

KINGSWOOD CORPORATE FINANCE LTD ◈

3 Coldbath Square, London, EC1R 5HL
Tel: 020 7841 0000
Resident Partners/Directors: ICAEW Members
J F Massing, H S Moss

KLSA

Klaco House, 28-30 St John's Square, London, EC1M 4DN
Tel: 020 7490 5525
Fax: 020 7490 4876
Email: enquiries@klsa.net
Website: http://www.klsa.net
Resident Partners/Directors: ICAEW Members
A M K Shah, K D Shah
Non-resident Partners (ICAEW Members):
H R Shah
Resident Partners (Non-ICAEW Members):
M Abdulla, S Chheda, V Doshi

Registered by the ICAEW to carry out company audit work

Regulated by the ICAEW for a range of investment business activities
Individual(s) licensed for insolvency work by the ICAEW

LITHGOW, NELSON & CO

Premier House, 12-13 Hatton Garden, London, EC1N 8AN
Tel: 020 7269 9510
Resident Partners/Directors: ICAEW Members
R Barr, P J Gee

Registered by the ICAEW to carry out company audit work

Regulated by the ICAEW for a range of investment business activities

LUBBOCK FINE ◈

Russell Bedford House, City Forum, 250 City Road, London EC1V 2QQ
Tel: 020 7490 7766
Fax: 020 7490 5102
Email: enquiries@lubbockfine.co.uk
Website: http://www.lubbockfine.co.uk
Resident Partners/Directors: ICAEW Members
S C Banks, L C Facey, J Gitter, G G Goodyear, R Majithia, L D Newman, R M Rich, N D P Shah, P N Shah, M Turner
Resident Partners (Non-ICAEW Members):
M Sans, P Blackburn
Registered by the ICAEW to carry out company audit work

SPECIALISATIONS – BUSINESS & GENERAL ADVICE

Management Advice to Business

SPECIALISATIONS – BUSINESS RECOVERY & INSOLVENCY

Bankruptcies
Corporate Recovery
Liquidations
Reorganisations and Company Reconstructions

SPECIALISATIONS – FINANCIAL REPORTING

International Reporting Standards (IFRS)
Limited Liability Partnership

SPECIALISATIONS – SECTOR

Charities
Entertainers
FSA Members
Media
New Media
Oil/Petroleum Industries
Property Development
Property Investment
Solicitors

SPECIALISATIONS – TAXATION

Estate Planning
Foreign Nationals in the UK
Investigations
Partnerships and Sole Traders
Taxation
Trusts
UK Nationals Overseas
UK Subsidiaries of Overseas Multinationals

General Description: Lubbock Fine is a significant independent firm of chartered accountants, committed to providing our clients with a world class service. For full details please see our website.

M.S. PAUL

Buchanan House, 24-30 Holborn, London, EC1N 2HS

THE MARTLET PARTNERSHIP LLP

43 Charterhouse Square, London, EC1M 6EW

MOORE STEPHENS LLP

1-3 Snow Hill, London, EC1A 2DH
Tel: 020 7334 9191
Resident Partners/Directors: ICAEW Members
D Gregory

MORGAN CORPORATE FINANCE LTD

82 St Johns Street, London, EC1M 4JN

MORWOOD-LEYLAND & CO ◈

Suite 48, 88-90 Hatton Garden, London, EC1N 8PN
Tel: 07000 265395
Principal: ICAEW Member
A M Morwood-Leyland

SPECIALISATIONS – BUSINESS & GENERAL ADVICE

Company Formation
Company Secretarial Service

SPECIALISATIONS – FINANCIAL REPORTING

Accounts Preparation

SPECIALISATIONS – FORENSIC ACCOUNTING

Expert Witnesses in Litigation

SPECIALISATIONS – TAXATION

Value Added Tax

N.S. AMIN & CO

334-336 Goswell Rd, London, EC1V 7RP

NIGEL WILSON & CO ★

Third Floor, 111 Charterhouse Street, London, EC1M 6AW

PANNELL KERR FORSTER ▼

Farringdon Place, 20 Farringdon Road, London, EC1M 3AP

PKF (UK) LLP

Farringdon Place, 20 Farringdon Road, London, EC1M 3AP
Tel: 020 7065 0000
Email: info.london@uk.pkf.com
Website: http://www.pkf.co.uk
Resident Partners/Directors: ICAEW Members
P L Armstrong, S J Barnsdall, R S Bint, J B Cassidy, C Cox, K G Crofton Martin, D M Dearman, T A Drew, M R Goodchild, B J Hamblin, J A Harris, S P Harrison, S P Holgate, J R Homewood, A J Huddleston, N Y Kissun, P J Long, H R Mathew-Jones, I F Mathieson, K R Mistry, P R Pallett, D J Pomfret, G M Singleton, C W Stewart, B D Tash, J D Welch, N M Whitaker
Resident Partners (Non-ICAEW Members):
R Barnard, S P Bayfield, R J Clarke, A D Foreman, J Gilligan, C L Hardaker, L E Lloyd-Thomas, P McAllister, M Moine, G Myton, T Roberts, M Ross, R Weighell, P Fisher, R Grant

Registered by the ICAEW to carry out company audit work

Authorised and regulated by the Financial Services Authority for investment business
Individual(s) licensed for insolvency work by the ICAEW

PLANIT SERVICES LTD

Lansdowne House, City Forum, 250 City Road, London EC1V 2PU
Tel: 020 7251 8690
Resident Partners/Directors: ICAEW Members
A D Learer

RAMON LEE & PARTNERS

Kemp House, 152-160 City Road, London, EC1V 2DW

S.L. SMITH & CO

Barbican House, 26-34 Old Street, London, EC1V 9QR
Tel: 020 7608 2288
Principal: ICAEW Member
S L Smith

SAYER VINCENT

8 Angel Gate, City Road, London, EC1V 2SJ
Tel: 020 7841 6360
Resident Partners/Directors: ICAEW Members
P M Craig, H C E Elliott, J A Miller, C L Sayer

SHARON RAMDENEE
93 Vesage Court, 8a Leather Lane, London, EC1N 7RF

SILVER ALTMAN LTD ◈
8 Baltic Street East, London, EC1Y 0UP

SMITHFIELD ACCOUNTANTS LLP ◈
117 Charterhouse Street, London, EC1M 6AA
Tel: 020 7253 3757
Resident Partners/Directors: ICAEW Members
R A Harvey, E Poli

SOUTHWELL, TYRRELL & CO
9 Newbury Street, London, EC1A 7HU

STEELE ROBERTSON GODDARD ◈
28 Ely Place, London, EC1N 6AA
Tel: 020 7269 9700
Fax: 020 7269 9701
Email: email@srgcas.com
Website: http://www.srgcas.com
Date Established: 2004
Resident Partners/Directors: ICAEW Members
A N Bloom, T A Lording, T R S J Meadows, D J Skeet, H C Wood
Non-resident Partners (Non-ICAEW Members):
J R Park
Other Offices: Glasgow (Tel: 0141 221 9922)
Registered by the ICAEW to carry out company audit work
Licensed by another DPB to carry on investment business
General Description: General practice with a range of specific areas of expertise.

VALENTINE ELLIS & CO ★
Preacher's Court, The Charterhouse, Charterhouse Square, London EC1M 6AS
Tel: 020 7253 6302
Resident Partners/Directors: ICAEW Members
R E Coward

VANTAGE
Lower Ground Floor, 20-24 Kirby Street, London, EC1N 8TS

VANTIS GROUP LTD
82 St John Street, London, EC1M 4JN
Tel: 020 7417 0417
Website: http://www.vantisplc.com/london
Resident Partners/Directors: ICAEW Members
J E Allen, T Applin, P K Ashton, P F Jackson, R W Thornton
General Description: ICAEW Registered.

WEST & CO
325 City Road, London, EC1V 1LJ

WEST, WAKE, PRICE & CO
4 Chiswell Street, London, EC1Y 4UP

WESTBURY ◈
145/157 St John Street, London, EC1V 4PY
Tel: 020 7253 7272
Fax: 020 7253 0814
Email: info@westbury.co.uk
Resident Partners/Directors: ICAEW Members
J R Dabek, A J Gittins, H Graham, K Graham, P D Klinger, N Padden, N C Pearson, N S Springer
Resident Partners (Non-ICAEW Members):
R Lele
Registered by the ICAEW to carry out company audit work
Regulated by the ICAEW for a range of investment business activities

SPECIALISATIONS – IT

E-commerce

SPECIALISATIONS – SECTOR

Catering/Restaurants
Charities
Property Investment

General Description: Full range of audit, accounting, taxation and business services, with strong international connections.
Languages Spoken:
Italian, French, Hebrew

WESTBURY COMPUTER SERVICES
145/157 St John Street, London, EC1V 4PY

WESTBURY PAYROLL SERVICES
145/157 St John Street, London, EC1V 4PY

WESTBURY SECRETARIAL SERVICES
145/157 St John Street, London, EC1V 4PY

WILSON STEVENS ACCOUNTANCY LTD
Third Floor, 111 Charterhouse Street, London, EC1M 6AW

WORMALD ACCOUNTANTS LTD
7th Floor, 63-66 Hatton Garden, London, EC1N 8RS

LONDON EC2

ASH & ASSOCIATES ◈
2 London Wall Buildings, London Wall, London, EC2M 5PP
Tel: 020 7256 9911
Principal: ICAEW Member
A K Aggarwal

AVAR & COMPANY LTD ◈
Interactive House, 46 Great Eastern Street, London, EC2A 3EP

BENEDICT MACKENZIE LLP
62 Wilson Street, London, EC2A 2BU
Tel: 020 7247 1174
Website: http://www.benemack.com
Resident Partners/Directors: ICAEW Members
A P M Benedict, L Pagden, I D Williams
Individual(s) licensed for insolvency work by another RPB

BENEDICT MCQUEEN
62 Wilson Street, London, EC2A 2BU
Tel: 020 7247 1174

CLOKE & CO
Warnford Court, Throgmorton Street, London, EC2N 2AT

CRA INTERNATIONAL (UK) LTD
99 Bishopsgate, London, EC2M 3XD
Tel: 020 7664 3700
Fax: 020 7664 3998
Email: info@lee-and-allen.com
Website: http://www.lee-and-allen.com
Resident Partners/Directors: ICAEW Members
T J Allen, D J Lee, L Steadman
Other Offices: North America, Europe, SE Asia, Australasia and Middle East

SPECIALISATIONS – BUSINESS & GENERAL ADVICE

Divorce/Matrimonial

SPECIALISATIONS – FORENSIC ACCOUNTING

Expert Witnesses in Litigation
Forensic Accounting

SPECIALISATIONS – IT

Computer Consultants

General Description: CRA International incorporates Lee & Allen Consulting Ltd. Lee & Allen is the established boutique forensic accounting and forensic computing firm.

CROUCH CHAPMAN ◈
62 Wilson Street, London, EC2A 2BU
Tel: 020 7782 0007
Email: info@crouchchapman.co.uk
Website: http://www.crouchchapman.co.uk
Resident Partners/Directors: ICAEW Members
K J Chapman, K L Foster, N M Heath, R P Howard
Registered by the ICAEW to carry out company audit work
Regulated by the ICAEW for a range of investment business activities
Individual(s) licensed for insolvency work by another RPB

DAVID HUNT
25 Moorgate, London, EC2R 6AY

DENNY SULLIVAN & ASSOCIATES LLP ◈
Blackwell House, Guildhall Yard, London, EC2V 5AE
Tel: 020 7713 1600
Resident Partners/Directors: ICAEW Members
A W Denny

EVERETT & SON ◈
35 Paul Street, London, EC2A 4UQ
Tel: 020 7628 0857
Fax: 020 7628 7253
Email: advice@everettgroup.co.uk
Website: http://www.everettgroup.co.uk
Date Established: 1900
Training Contracts Available.
Resident Partners/Directors: ICAEW Members
J N Cross, J Griffin
Other Offices:3 Park Place, St James, London SW1A 1LP (Tel: 020 7629 0166)
Overseas Offices: Lugano, Switzerland (Affiliated Office)
Registered by the ICAEW to carry out company audit work
Regulated by the ICAEW for a range of investment business activities

SPECIALISATIONS – AUDIT & ASSURANCE

Audit
Pension Scheme Auditors

SPECIALISATIONS – BUSINESS & GENERAL ADVICE

Management Advice to Business

SPECIALISATIONS – FINANCIAL REPORTING

Accounts Preparation
Audit Exemption Report
International Reporting Standards (IFRS)
Limited Companies
Limited Liability Partnership
Partnership/Sole Trader Accounts

SPECIALISATIONS – FORENSIC ACCOUNTING

Expert Witnesses in Litigation

SPECIALISATIONS – SECTOR

Charities
Corporate
Higher Education/Research Establishments
Manufacturing
Solicitors

SPECIALISATIONS – TAXATION

Taxation
UK Subsidiaries of Overseas Multinationals

Languages Spoken:
French, German

EVERETT HORDER LTD
35 Paul Street, London, EC2A 4UQ

EVERGREEN ◈
2 London Wall Buildings, London Wall, London, EC2M 5UU
Tel: 020 7448 5150
Principal: ICAEW Member
J S Bal

THE GALLAGHER PARTNERSHIP LLP ◈
PO Box 698, 2nd Floor, Titchfield House, 69/85 Tabernacle Street, London EC2A 4RR
Tel: 020 7490 7774
Resident Partners/Directors: ICAEW Members
I A Arian, S D Clarke, D A Kozuba-Kozubska, M J Palmer, R S Palmer

GALLAGHERS ◈
PO Box 698, 2nd Floor, Titchfield House, 69/85 Tabernacle Street, London EC2A 4RR
Tel: 020 7490 7774

GEO LITTLE SEBIRE & CO
Victoria House, 64 Paul Street, London, EC2A 4TT

GOTHAM ERSKINE
52-58 Tabernacle Street, London, EC2A 4NJ
Tel: 020 7490 1880
Email: mail@gothamerskine.co.uk
Website: http://www.gothamerskine.co.uk
Registered by the ICAEW to carry out company audit work
Individual(s) licensed for insolvency work by another RPB

SPECIALISATIONS – SECTOR

Charities
Housing Co-operatives

GOTHAM ERSKINE LLP
52-58 Tabernacle Street, London, EC2A 4NJ

GRANT THORNTON UK LLP
30 Finsbury Square, London, EC2P 2YU
Tel: 020 7184 4300
Resident Partners/Directors: ICAEW Members
S J Akers, J A Bartlett, A D Conquest, P A Cooper, S J Cornmell, S K Croston, P M Dawson, J Earp, M G Ellis, P Flatley, M A Goddard, I D Gorham, H Hamedani, M J Hore, I Jacob, S J Keen, R C Kemsley, P R Keown, A Lees, S J Longfield, S J Lowe, D M Mason, R J Matyszczyk, D A S Maxwell, D A Medland, R H Pick, S J Quest, P J Secrett, A L Stopford, P D Storey, M J Swales, D S Taylor, M J Thornton, G D Williams
Resident Partners (Non-ICAEW Members):
P D Allen, G D Beaney, P Cook, J Corbould, H Dickson, C Foster, S Greenhalgh, K Hellard, A L Hosking, M McGrath, T P Newbery, N Ruddock, F Owen, A Ward, N S Wood

HARRIS LIPMAN LLP ◈
New Broad Street House, 35 New Broad Street, London, EC2M 1NH
Tel: 0845 338 5292
Fax: 0845 338 5293
Email: mail@harris-lipman.co.uk
Website: http://www.harris-lipman.co.uk
Resident Partners/Directors: ICAEW Members
F Khalastchi
Non-resident Partners (ICAEW Members):
M J Atkins, B D Lewis
Non-resident Partners (Non-ICAEW Members):
J D Cullen, M Hall
Other Offices: London N20, Reading, St Albans, Cardiff
Individual(s) licensed for insolvency work by the ICAEW

SPECIALISATIONS – BUSINESS RECOVERY & INSOLVENCY

Bankruptcies
Corporate Recovery
Liquidations
Reorganisations and Company Reconstructions

General Description:
Specialists in corporate recovery, bankruptcies, expert witness in litigation, forensic accounting, liquidations, investigations.

HOWARTH ARMSBY
New Broad Street House, 35 New Broad Street, London, EC2M 1NH

J.S. PHILLIPS
62 Cromwell Tower, Barbican, London, EC2Y 8DD

KINETIC PARTNERS
1 London Wall, Level 10, London, EC2Y 5HB

KINETIC PARTNERS
One London Wall, Level 10, London, EC2Y 5HB

KINETIC PARTNERS AUDIT LLP
One London Wall, Level 10, London, EC2Y5HB

KINETIC PARTNERS IRELAND
One London Wall, Level 10, London, EC2Y 5HB

KROGH & PARTNERS LTD
823 Salisbury House, 29 Finsbury Circus, London, EC2M 5QQ

LAIPETERS & CO
New Broad Street House, 35 New Broad Street, London, EC2M 1NH

LINN MAGGS GOLDWIN
2-4 Great Eastern Street, London, EC2A 3NT

LITCHFIELDS ◈
5 Luke Street, London, EC2A 4PX
Tel: 020 7729 7290
Resident Partners/Directors: ICAEW Members
R H Shah

LOGICUM LTD
13 Austin Friars, London, EC2N 2JX

THE MACDONALD PARTNERSHIP
Level 25, Tower 42, 25 Old Broad Street, London EC2N 1HQ

THE MACDONALD PARTNERSHIP PLC
Level 25, Tower 42, 25 Old Broad Street, London EC2N 1HQ

MAURICE J. BUSHELL & CO ◈
Curzon House, 64 Clifton Street, London, EC2A 4HB

NEXIA SMITH & WILLIAMSON AUDIT LTD
25 Moorgate, London, EC2R 6AY

NUMERION ASSOCIATES LLP
2 London Wall Buildings, London Wall, London, EC2M 5UU
Tel: 020 7448 5234
Website: http://www.numerion.co.uk
Resident Partners/Directors: ICAEW Members
I I Aziz, S Aziz

OPPENHEIM AND COMPANY LTD
52 Great Eastern Street, London, EC2A 3EP
Tel: 020 7613 3525
Resident Partners/Directors: ICAEW Members
B H Oppenheim

OPPENHEIM SCROXTON
52 Great Eastern Street, London, EC2A 3EP
Tel: 020 7613 4045
Principal: ICAEW Member
J M Scroxton
Registered by the ICAEW to carry out company audit work
Regulated by the ICAEW for a range of investment business activities

PERRYS
34 Threadneedle Street, London, EC2R 8AY

PERSONAL DEBT SOLUTIONS (PDS)
Level 25, Tower 42, 25 Old Broad Street, London EC2N 1HQ

PETER J YARDLEY & CO
Unit 36, 50 Willow Street, London, EC2A 4BH

PRICE BAILEY LLP
2nd Floor, New Liverpool House, 15 Eldon Street, London EC2M 7LD
Tel: 020 7065 2660
Website: http://www.pricebailey.co.uk
Resident Partners/Directors: ICAEW Members
I D Coombes, P F Gillman, R L Vass
Resident Partners (Non-ICAEW Members):
H W Sears
Registered by the ICAEW to carry out company audit work
Authorised and regulated by the Financial Services Authority for investment business
Individual(s) licensed for insolvency work by the ICAEW

PRICE BAILEY PRIVATE CLIENT LLP
2nd Floor, New Liverpool House, 15 Eldon Street, London EC2M 7LD

RGL LLP

Devonshire Buildings, 16-17 Devonshire Square, London, EC2M 4SQ
Tel: 020 7247 4804
Fax: 020 7247 4970
Email: expert@uk.rgl.com
Website: http://www.rgl.com

Training Contracts Available.

Resident Partners/ Directors: ICAEW Members
K J Harding, A S Levitt, C M Rawlin, J H F Stanbury

Resident Partners (Non-ICAEW Members):
K Tuffin

Overseas Offices: Atlanta, Charlotte, Chicago, Dallas, Denver, Indianapolis, Los Angeles, New York, Orange County, Perth, Portland, Sacramento, San Diego, San Francisco, Seattle, Singapore, St Louis, Sydney, Tokyo

INVESTOR IN PEOPLE

SPECIALISATIONS – BUSINESS & GENERAL ADVICE
Divorce/Matrimonial
Feasibility Studies
Investment Appraisal

SPECIALISATIONS – FORENSIC ACCOUNTING
Expert Witnesses in Litigation
Forensic Accounting

SPECIALISATIONS – IT
Computer Consultants
Information Technology

SPECIALISATIONS – SECTOR
Banks/Financial Institutions
Electronics
Manufacturing
Media
Oil/Petroleum Industries

General Description: RGL is a worldwide firm of forensic accountants and consultants. We quantify claims in insurance and litigation, determine value and advise on related issues. We also specialise in Forensic Technology and Regulatory and Competition Finance.

Languages Spoken:
Afrikaans, Dutch, Finnish, French, German, Greek, Italian, Japanese, Russian, Spanish, Swedish, Ukrainian

RSM BENTLEY JENNISON ◈

2nd Floor, 45 Moorfields, London, EC2Y 9AE
Tel: 020 7920 3200
Fax: 020 7920 3201
Resident Partners/Directors: ICAEW Members
P D Coleman, D G Talbot
Registered by the ICAEW to carry out company audit work
Authorised and regulated by the Financial Services Authority for investment business

RSM BENTLEY JENNISON ◈

30-34 Moorgate, London, EC2R 6DN
Tel: 020 7433 2980
Fax: 020 7433 2999
Email: richard.plumb@rsmbentleyjennison.com
Website: http://www.rsmbentleyjennison.com
Registered by the ICAEW to carry out company audit work
Authorised and regulated by the Financial Services Authority for investment business

SIDDIQI & CO

3rd Floor, 39 Tabernacle Street, London, EC2A 4AA

SMITH & WILLIAMSON LTD

25 Moorgate, London, EC2R 6AY
Tel: 020 7131 4000
Fax: 020 7631 0741
Email: firstname.lastname@smith.williamson.co.uk
Website: http://www.smith.williamson.co.uk
Resident Partners/Directors: ICAEW Members
J T Boadle, N J Cartwright, P F Garwood, B K Livingston, J D E Money, A Murphy, G D Pearce, N J Reeve, A C Spicer, K P Stopps
Non-resident Partners (ICAEW Members):
S R L Cork, M P Fosberry, I J A Anderson, H Dobson, I G R Grant, J W Hender, A J Penman, R Pugh, M T Sharratt, C P Shepard, C M Stannard, J H Voyez, N P A Wallis
General Description: Smith & Williamson is an independent professional and financial services group employing over 1400 people. We are leading providers of investment management, financial advisory and accountancy services to private clients, professional practices and mid-sized companies. Nexia Smith & Williamson Audit (Bristol) LLP provides audit services to complement the specialist financial advisory services provided by Smith & Williamson.

SMITH & WILLIAMSON LLP

25 Moorgate, London, EC2R 6AY
Tel: 020 7131 4000

TENON LTD

Salisbury House, 31 Finsbury Circus, London, EC2M 5SQ
Tel: 020 7628 2040

TMP

Level 25, Tower 42, 25 Old Broad Street, London EC2N 1HQ

WARR & CO

Suite 39, 2 London Wall Buildings, London Wall, London EC2M 5UU

WHALE ROCK LTD

2nd Floor, 53 Gresham Street, London, EC2V 7AY

WHALE ROCK PROFESSIONAL SERVICES GROUP

2nd Floor, 50 Gresham Street, London, EC2V 7AY
Tel: 0844 893 0811

LONDON EC3

BEGBIES TRAYNOR LTD

32 Cornhill, London, EC3V 3BT
Tel: 020 7398 3800
Website: http://www.begbies-traynor.com
Resident Partners/Directors: ICAEW Members
N G Atkinson, P M Davis, N R Hood, D M Lawler, N J Mather, C Morris

SPECIALISATIONS – BUSINESS RECOVERY & INSOLVENCY

Bankruptcies
Corporate Recovery
Liquidations
Reorganisations and Company Reconstructions

SPECIALISATIONS – FORENSIC ACCOUNTING

Expert Witnesses in Litigation
Forensic Accounting

BLEVINS FRANKS LTD

3rd Floor, 29-30 Cornhill, London, EC3V 3ND

BTG MCINNES CORPORATE FINANCE

32 Cornhill, London, EC3V 3BT

DIXON WILSON

4 Royal Mint Court, London, EC3N 4HJ
Tel: 020 7680 8100
Email: dw@dixonwilson.co.uk
Website: http://www.dixonwilson.com
Training Contracts Available.
Resident Partners/Directors: ICAEW Members
G L Chambers, H Clark, J K Kidgell, R J Leonard, D C Mellor, D H Nelson, S R Oldfield, P J Pickles, S F Rees, S M Rose, G Spinks, J L Sutton, S J Wakefield, M V Waterman
Non-resident Partners (ICAEW Members):
P J Howes, J R Benford
Non-resident Partners (Non-ICAEW Members):
S Lemaître
Overseas Offices: 19 Avenue de l'opéra 75001 Paris

Regulated by the ICAEW for a range of investment business activities

Languages Spoken:
French
See display advertisement near this entry.

HAMPDEN TAX CONSULTANTS LTD

85 Gracechurch Street, London, EC3V 0AA

P.E. SHIRLEY LLP

24 Lime Street, London, EC3M 7HS

PEARLMAN ROSE ★

48A/49A Aldgate High Street, London, EC3N 1AL

SIGMA 2002 LLP

45-47 Cornhill, London, EC3V 3PF

SIGMA PARTNERSHIP

45-47 Cornhill, London, EC3V 3PF
Resident Partners/Directors: ICAEW Members
J L P Seet

STONHAM.CO

9 St Clare Street, London, EC3N 1LQ

STREETS LLP ◈

Lloyds Building, 12 Leadenhall Street, London, EC3V 1LP
Tel: 020 7816 5827
Email: info@streetsweb.co.uk
Website: http://www.streetsweb.co.uk
Non-resident Partners (ICAEW Members):
P Tutin

LONDON EC4

chartered accountants

2020 CA LTD ◈

1 St Andrew's Hill, London, EC4V 5BY
Tel: 020 7246 3030
Email: info@2020.co.uk
Website: http://www.2020.co.uk
Resident Partners/Directors: ICAEW Members
S Hay, S J Kelly

SPECIALISATIONS – BUSINESS & GENERAL ADVICE

Management Advice to Business
Management Consultancy

SPECIALISATIONS – IT

Computer Consultants
E-commerce
Information Technology

SPECIALISATIONS – SECTOR

New Media

BAKER TILLY

5 Old Bailey, London, EC4M 7AF
Tel: 020 7002 8600
Resident Partners/Directors: ICAEW Members
A Aneizi, R H Donaldson, P T Elliot, A S R Hynd
Resident Partners (Non-ICAEW Members):
E Grant, K E Sandwell

BAKER TILLY

5 Old Bailey, London, EC4M 7AF

BAKER TILLY RESTRUCTURING AND RECOVERY LLP

5 Old Bailey, London, EC4M 7AF
Tel: 020 7002 8600
Resident Partners/Directors: ICAEW Members
S P Bower, P G Cooper, A Lovett, M B Taub
Resident Partners (Non-ICAEW Members):
L M Brittain, G L Carton-Kelly, B A Mackay, M Rollings, T E Callaghan

BAKER TILLY TAX AND ADVISORY SERVICES LLP

5 Old Bailey, London, EC4M 7AF
Tel: 020 7002 8600
Resident Partners/Directors: ICAEW Members
A Aneizi, S P Bower, P G Cooper, R H Donaldson, P T Elliot, A S R Hynd, A Lovett, M B Taub
Resident Partners (Non-ICAEW Members):
L M Brittain, B A Mackay, G L Carton-Kelly, T E Callaghan, E G Grant, M Rollings, K E Sandwell

BALLAMY WOODHOUSE

Albert Buildings, 49 Queen Victoria Street, London, EC4N 4SA

BEECHAMS LLP

3rd Floor, 167 Fleet Street, London, EC4A 2EA
Tel: 020 7427 5700
Resident Partners/Directors: ICAEW Members
P A Bloom, D A Maxwell, R B Parmar, S M Ufland

BOROUGHS ★

6 New Street Square, London, EC4A 3AQ

BURFORD AND PARTNERS LLP

Bridge House, 181 Queen Victoria Street, London, EC4V 4DZ

BUZZACOTT

12 New Fetter Lane, London, EC4A 1AG

BUZZACOTT LLP

12 New Fetter Lane, London, EC4A 1AG
Tel: 020 7556 1200
Fax: 020 7556 1212
Email: enquiries@buzzacott.co.uk
Website: http://www.buzzacott.co.uk
Resident Partners/Directors: ICAEW Members
J P Ager, C R Cooper, A.De Lacey, M P Farmar, E A Finch, A S Francis, D N Jarman, A McQuater, K Patel, A K Savjani, G F M Wheatley, M C Worsey
Resident Partners (Non-ICAEW Members):
D T Matheson, A B Hopson, T Egan, R Cobbold, D L Aldrich, J M Dillingham, S W Mackenzie, N M O Pursey, A O Coker

Registered by the ICAEW to carry out company audit work

Authorised and regulated by the Financial Services Authority for investment business

CALDWELL & BRAHAM ▽

1st Floor, 5 Breams Buildings, London, EC4A 1DY
Tel: 020 7404 0600
Fax: 020 7404 0900
Email: info@caldwellandbraham.co.uk
Website: http://www.caldwellandbraham.co.uk
Date Established: 1940
Resident Partners/Directors: ICAEW Members
P Vannozzi
Non-resident Partners (ICAEW Members):
A J Bailey
Resident Partners (Non-ICAEW Members):
N A H Brecker
Other Offices: Dartford

Registered by the ICAEW to carry out company audit work

Regulated by the ICAEW for a range of investment business activities

CASTLE CORPORATE FINANCE LTD ◈

8-10 New Fetter Lane, London, EC4A 1RS
Tel: 01732 400123
Website: http://www.castlecf.com
Resident Partners/Directors: ICAEW Members
M A Norrie

Regulated by the ICAEW for a range of investment business activities

SPECIALISATIONS – BUSINESS & GENERAL ADVICE

Acquisitions and Mergers

CORNELIUS, BARTON & CO

Mitre House, 44-46 Fleet Street, London, EC4Y 1BN
Tel: 020 7583 5577
Principal: ICAEW Member
H P Sethi

CW ENERGY TAX CONSULTANTS LTD

Fleet House, 8-12 New Bridge Street, London, EC4V 6AL

DAVID GREY & CO LTD

175/177 Temple Chambers, Temple Avenue, London, EC4Y 0DB

DELOITTE & TOUCHE LLP ◈
Athene Place, 66 Shoe Lane, London, EC4A 3BQ
Tel: 020 7936 3000
Website: http://www.deloitte.co.uk
Resident Partners/Directors: ICAEW Members
A H Abhyankar, M J D Adams, M K Adams, P J Avis, T M Awan, A K Balcombe, D C Beanland, J Belsey, A Birkett, R A Bradbury, N S Bramwell, C D Cahill, D Caukill, S P Charge, R K Chopra, I E Clark, M J Clatworthy, J F Cox, S C Creedy Smith, J A Curwen, N J Dargan, W J I Dodwell, G P Dootson, N G Edwards, D J Evans, K Folwell-Davies, K J Garrison, D E Graham, P W R Gratton, B M Griffin, G J Griffiths, A J Grimstone, J R Hammond, A S Harris, J W Hinton, O P Holder, M J Howell, C J Hyams, D R James, N J Jeal, D Johnston, N B Kahn, N J Kerr, S R Knight, J I Leake, R A Lloyd-Owen, G C Loftus, T J Macdonald, C D Mackinnon, I A Macmillan, T M Mahapatra, L A Manning, J F Maxey, K I McFarlane, P D Mills, A J Newsome, H M H Nicholson, A G Paisley, C Pearson, D Quantrill, J D Richards, J S Sahota, M F K Saunders, D D Scott, A Shah, M R Shah, F K A Silcock, I R Sparshott, A V Walton, C Ward, C N Warren, D B Watkinson, J A P Williams, R M Williams, L H Young, P E Zimmerman

DELOITTE & TOUCHE LLP
3 New Street Square, London, EC4A 3BT
Tel: 020 7936 3000
Website: http://www.deloitte.co.uk
Resident Partners/Directors: ICAEW Members
N D Carrington, S E Gutteridge, H D F Hatton, F L Ilett, W R H Inglis, A C Kaye, P M Lobb, P F Maher, P J Maher, A J Pollock, N J Prior, A J Scrimgeour, M D Sullivan, I D Williams

DELOITTE & TOUCHE LLP
2 New Street Square, London, EC4A 3BZ
Tel: 020 7936 3000
Website: http://www.deloitte.co.uk
Resident Partners/Directors: ICAEW Members
J A Adam, S Almond, I Amiri, T W Archer, M R Barber, J C Bentley, D S Bettesworth, J W Bird, C W Brough, I Brown, R A Buck, A R Butterworth, R B Cattell, M S Chahal, A Chapman, D F Cobb, N O Coles, J M Conneely, J P Connolly, D S Cook, S R Counsell, E J Cox, D J O Cruickshank, J P Cullinane, A G Daley, M E Donaldson, M J A Eadon, M Ewing, J R Ferguson, P Franek, A G Gwyther, K A Hackshall, G J Hamilton-Deeley, E J Hanson, I M Hook, K J Houldsworth, R I Howard, C G Hudson, N A Hudson, C D Hughes, D J Hume, M E Jones, P K Kakoullis, A J Kelly, B A Kenny, S H Kerton-Johnson, D J King, Y Konii, I S Krieger, M R Lee-Amies, J A Leigh, S D Letts, S G Ley, M Y Manuel, J D Marsh, C Maton, R A Matthews, N J Mercer, N M Mitchell, J D Moore, A D Morris, A J Morris, J G Murphy, R R J Muschamp, K L Newman, P J Newman, J V Niblett, D A Noon, R M Norton, P S J O'Donoghue, A Ogram, P F Parsons, Z Patel, D J Paterson, J W Phipps, V Poole, T M Powell, C J F Reay, M M Reilly, G O Richardson, M A Saluveer, P J A Saunders, H J Shekle, S L Shillingford, A K J Simmonds, J P Small, A J Spooner, D Sproul, R W Syratt, J S Thomas, W G Touche, I P Waller, R W Warburton, S A Ward, R H Webber, B Whitehead, A J Whitton, K Wild, J N Wright, B Yeomans, J C S Young, M S Zelkha

DELOITTE & TOUCHE LLP ◈
Stonecutter Court, 1 Stonecutter Street, London, EC4A 4TR
Tel: 020 7936 3000
Website: http://www.deloitte.co.uk
Resident Partners/Directors: ICAEW Members
M J Boyle, H J Davies, A P Goulden, P K Moller, N R Owen, R K Punt, N J Sandall, N Slater, H Vega-Lozano, N G Warner, R L Widdas, M H Wilkinson

DELOITTE & TOUCHE LLP ◈
Hill House, 1 Little New Street, London, EC4A 3TR
Tel: 020 7936 3000
Website: http://www.deloitte.co.uk
Resident Partners/Directors: ICAEW Members
D S Anthony, A J Arterton, C A Atha, D J Barnes, S W Barnett, M N Batham, S Z H Bokhari, A L Bond, C Bouch, C J Bradbrook, C L Britton, G J Bullock, G Bunting, J Casson, A Chaudhuri, A P Clark, R P Collins, T W Davy, A J Downes, E J Dungworth, C Faulkner, M Goodey, O W Grundy, K A Hale, S C Hardy, D Haria, D K Keeble, J A Kilby, A Kyriakidis, J Le Blan, T O Lewthwaite, M J Lloyd, N Lovejoy, C M Lynch, N R McCrea, K McNicholls, C V Mellor, R M Miles, P R Muir, P G Nicklin, K M Potts, W A Ramsay, M Rana, C C Rawlings, M G Rhys, G A Robb, A P Rothery, D J Rush, M P Rust, T D Steel, P R Stephenson, C M Thomson, A G Todd, V Vedi, W G Weaver, S G Weston, J G Whitehead, M W Williams, N T Wood, J D Wyer

GROSS KLEIN ◈
6 Breams Buildings, London, EC4A 1QL
Tel: 020 7242 2212
Resident Partners/Directors: ICAEW Members
H A Gross, A P Klein, M J Wood

GROSS, KLEIN & PARTNERS ★
6 Breams Buildings, London, EC4A 1QL
Tel: 020 7242 2212
Resident Partners/Directors: ICAEW Members
H A Gross, A P Klein

GROSVENOR PARTNERS LLP
6-7 Ludgate Square, London, EC4M 7AS
Tel: 020 7213 0470
Email: info@grosvenor-partners.co.uk
Website: http://www.grosvenor-partners.co.uk
Resident Partners/Directors: ICAEW Members
M P Bassford, C A Bugden, K Petrou

General Description: View our website for a comprehensive list of our services.

HORWATH CLARK WHITEHILL LLP
St Bride's House, 10 Salisbury Square, London, EC4Y 8EH
Tel: 020 7842 7100
Resident Partners/Directors: ICAEW Members
T J Baines, R J M L Baker, N D Bostock, D W K Chitty, L M Cooper, G R Cranston, H R Creed, D J Devon, P Fay, P R Framjee, D A Furst, S J Gale, S A Harvie, N Hashemi, J A Hetherington, M E Hicks, M A B Israel, S J Kirby, C L Malcolm, D C Mellor, A Penketh, A J Pianca, E Sloper, P Varley, T J Williams

HORWATH SMALL BUSINESS CENTRE
St Brides House, 10 Salisbury Square, London, EC4Y 8EH

KENNARD COUSINS & ASSOCIATES LTD
8 Little Trinity Lane, London, EC4V 2AN

KNOX CROPPER
8-9 Well Court, London, EC4M 9DN
Tel: 020 7332 6400
Fax: 020 7248 9225
Email: kc@knoxcropper.co.uk
Website: http://www.knoxcropper.co.uk
Training Contracts Available.
Resident Partners/Directors: ICAEW Members
J D Jones, K P Lally, G N C D Stevenson

Registered by the ICAEW to carry out company audit work

Regulated by the ICAEW for a range of investment business activities

SPECIALISATIONS – AUDIT & ASSURANCE
Audit

SPECIALISATIONS – SECTOR
Charities
Higher Education/Research Establishments
Housing Co-operatives

SPECIALISATIONS – TAXATION
Value Added Tax

KPMG LLP
8 Salisbury Square, London, EC4Y 8BB
Tel: 020 7311 1000
Website: http://www.kpmg.co.uk
Resident Partners/Directors: ICAEW Members
A J Aldridge, N Amin, M R Anderson, R E Anderson, N D Andrews, G P Armitage, R Aronson, M St J Ashley, T Aston, R N Austin, T Aw, E S Awty, J Awty, M A Bacon, N Bacon, M R Baillache, R A Bainbridge, I R Bannatyne, K I R Bannister, M F Barradell, E A Bassett, A D Bates, R I Bawden, C V Ben-Nathan, R Bennison, P Bishop, M D Blake, S G Bligh, I K Bone, S P Bonney, A J Brennan, R J Brent, P F Brice, K S Briggs, R D Broadbelt, P D A Brook, T J Brown, A A Buckle, D J Burlison, J D Cain, R M Campbell, B K Carter, F J P Carter, A G Cates, D S Cazeaux, A R Cecil, N Chandler, A P Cheadle, N J Chism, R J Clarke, E A Claydon, S A Cole, S A Collins, S J Collins, J W Conway, C I S Cook, S J Cooper, S R Cormack, M T Coughtrey, A F Cox, I A Cummings, J Daboo, G S Dalal, P M Davidson, A M Davies, N G S Davies, D M Defroand, I A Dewar, R C J Di Vito, H L Dickinson, W G H Dickinson, B J Dilley, E F C Donaldson, J M Downer, J D Driver, S T Dumasia, K J Durward, D G R Eastwood, N J Edmonds, J O Edwards, L S Edwards, D Elliott, J M H

Ellison, D J Elms, M T Farlow, S R F Figgis, D I Fletcher, T K Franks, E K Fraser, F C Fry, P E Furneaux, M D Gabriel, I P Gomes, R J A Gorsuch, H G D Green, J G Griffith-Jones, J A H Groom, J J Guppy, J J Guy, M A Halley, A M Halsey, T Harding, N E Harman, M J Harper, R G Hathaway, R Heis, H R Hepburn, L G Hickey, D N Hicks, S E Hill, J L Hills, W E J Holland, H R Horgan, J E Hughes, P R Hughes, J Hughff, A P Hulse, A J Hunter, M E J Hutchinson, B D Jackson, C J Jenkins, P R Johnson, A D K Johnston, J H Kelly, R S Kharegat, P A Kirkbright, P A Korolkiewicz, R M Krajewski, I G Latter, J S Leach, M J Lewis, R P Lewis, D J Littleford, A Lobo, P Long, J L Lowes, J K Luke, J Machin, L J Main, M V Maloney, A G Marshall, C S Martin, P D L B Marwood, S C A Masters, D V Matthews, S J M McCallion, R G McCarthy, M J McDonagh, M J McGowan, M.V. McLoughlin, S K G McNaught, W R C Meredith, M J Metcalf, B Michael, M Michael, S P Miller, J M Mills, A C Milner, J D T Milsom, K P Moore, J M J Morgan, J A Morris, A J Morrison, M M L Morrissey, C J G Moulder, H M Munro, S J N Murphy, F V H Neate, A F J Neden, B R Nelson, R J Newby, S R Nicholls, A M Nicholson, K Nicholson, D A Nickson, C M North, C M O'Brien, N T O'Brien, D J O'Keeffe, R I Ohrenstein, J N Oldcorn, J B Osborne, S P Osmer, J J Outen, C J Oxborough, S R Oxley, S R Palmer, I M Parker, S Parker, D A Parkes, H N Patel, R O Paterson, J A Pearce, B L Pearcy, A J Pearson, M A Peck, G M Penfold, M S Penney, J P Pickering, R Pinckard, A Plavsic, I D Pontefract, N W J Pratt, R S Price, N B Priestley, A J Pyle, M A Quest, P G Read, R H Reid, P A J Richards, C L Richmond, M S Robinson, A M Rocker, M J Roden, C J Rodgers, D W Rogers, S D Ryder, P A G Sanderson, P K Sawdon, D A Sayer, A J Sayers, R M Seale, S J Secker, M J D Sephton, D J Shah, S Shah, N K Sharma, W Shaul, S P Sherman, F F M Short, P Smart, S G Smith, W E Southwood, C J Spall, R W Spedding, S G Spellman, J S Spratt, B J Stapleton, M H Stevenson, A C Stirling, J F Storey, A Suchak, M Summerfield, T D N Surridge, A J Sykes, P Terry, S Thakkar, J H E Thompson, M H Thompson, A J Tickel, D A T Todd, P J Tombleson, J R Tucker, A Vials, J E Vines, H R Von Bergen, H L Walker, M P Wareing, G R Warrington, J R M White, R G Whittington, K M Wightman, A J Wilcox, J C Wilkinson, C J Williams, N G D Williams, J P L Woolf, R M Yasue, J A Zatouroff

Resident Partners (Non-ICAEW Members):
J P Abbott, J D B Anderson, C A Austin, S Balmer, S M Barrett, R Bayly, C E Beer, B A Brookes, B J Brown, J W A Burns, M A Byrne, M A Carter, R Carter, R M Cartwright, A C Christian, B Clark, T Clifford, A F C Collins, S Crisp, M P H Davison, N C Dexter, D Djurasevich, A G Downey, M A Elysee, D Fairs, A D Fellowes, P Fenton, C Fitzpatrick, J Flood, G J Fox, C S Fyles, J J Gallagher, S Gallagher, A Gavan, S J C Gilbert, D J Green, N B Griffin, A Harkin, G Harley, J M Harlow, J K Harris, M J Harris, P J Harrison, A T Hartley, A J Hickman, R Hill, S W Hindle, E Hodgart, I Hopkinson, E Howard, C A Hunt, J P Hunt, R Iferenta, L Jagger, J Jenkins, T R Jones, A Kennedy, D W Kilshaw, P Kirby, O Kirby-Johnson, S Lane, C Laverty, M Lindsay, S J Machin, D Madoc-Jones, M N Marshall, Q C Maxwell-Jackson, R J McCombe, E J McCormick, D A McCorquodale, P McCoy, F McDermott, T C McGinness, S P McGrady, P McIntyre, D McPhee, R Metelerkamp, R G Michie, A Monro, C J Morgan, J B Moriarty, S Munce, J S Neighbour, M Newton, C A Nicholson, T F O'Connell, S Rae, S Ranger, D C Reynolds, M Richards, T R Roff, G C Ross, R S Ross, P Rowe, G S Russell, F B Sangster, J Santoro, C J Scott, M Scott, T Scott, R Scully, R Shalom, B Sharma, R Sharman, N P Sherlock, D R Simpson, D Skinner, M Smedley, G Smith, M Spears, J Stankler, A C Steel, M J Stephens, T J Stone, O R Tant, D S Thomas, J Thomas, M Q Thomas, N Thomas, P Tippin, R W Turnbull, W Upton, N P Urry, T G Urwin, M Vaessen, J Vaughan, M Walker, J M Wardrop, N Warwick, L P L West, R W White, M Williamson

LADIMEJI & CO
Five Kings House, 1 Queen Street Place, London, EC4R 1QS

MACINTYRE HUDSON CORPORATE FINANCE LTD ◈
New Bridge Street House, 30-34 New Bridge Street, London, EC4V 6BJ
Tel: 020 7429 4100
Website: http://www.macintyrehudson.co.uk
Resident Partners/Directors: ICAEW Members
M J Kay
Authorised and regulated by the Financial Services Authority for investment business

MACINTYRE HUDSON LLP ◈
New Bridge Street House, 30-34 New Bridge Street, London, EC4V 6BJ
Tel: 020 7429 4100
Website: http://www.macintyrehudson.co.uk
Resident Partners/Directors: ICAEW Members
S J Barber, A E Burnham, J C Burwood, J Coverdale, V A F Dauppe, M J Kay, H K Lewis, R J Midgley, I R Mowbray, M D Payne, R Shaunak, C N Sutton, G L Young
Regulated by the ICAEW for a range of investment business activities

MARSH HAMMOND LTD
26 Farringdon Street, London, EC4A 4AB

MARSH HAMMOND & PARTNERS LLP
26 Farringdon Street, London, EC4A 4AB

MERCER & HOLE ◈
76 Shoe Lane, London, EC4A 3JB
Tel: 020 7353 1597
Website: http://www.mercerhole.co.uk
Resident Partners/Directors: ICAEW Members
H Cain, A J Crook, R I Jamieson, C Laughton

MERCER & HOLE TRUSTEES LTD
76 Shoe Lane, London, EC4A 3JB
Tel: 020 7353 1597
Resident Partners/Directors: ICAEW Members
A V B Broke

MIDICORP
Fleet House, 8-12 New Bridge Street, London, EC4V 6AL

MIDICORP CORPORATE FINANCE LTD
Fleet House, 8-12 New Bridge Street, London, EC4V 6AL

MOORE STEPHENS & CO ★
St Pauls House, 8-12 Warwick Lane, London, EC4M 7BP

MOORE STEPHENS LLP ◈
St Pauls House, 8-12 Warwick Lane, London, EC4M 7BP

MOORE STEPHENS LLP
Hillgate House, 26 Old Bailey, London, EC4M 7HW
Tel: 020 7334 9191

NICHOLSON & CO
Suite 21, 3 Ludgate Square, London, EC4M 7AS

P & C
6th Floor, 32 Ludgate Hill, London, EC4M 7DR

P & C
32 Ludgate Hill, London, EC4M 7DR

PB RECOVERY
26 Farringdon Street, London, EC4A 4AB

PORTMAN & CO
6th Floor, 32 Ludgate Hill, London, EC4M 7DR

PORTMAN & CO LLP
6th Floor, 32 Ludgate Hill, London, EC4M 7DR

PRENTIS & CO
Vintners Place, 68 Upper Thames Street, London, EC4V 3BJ

PRICEWATERHOUSE-COOPERS
Plumtree Court, London, EC4A 4HT

PRICEWATERHOUSE-COOPERS LLP
Plumtree Court, London, EC4A 4HT
Tel: 020 7583 5000
Resident Partners/Directors: ICAEW Members
M C Batten, S Bellars, R W Birchall, R C Boys-Stones, P B Buckle, A P Clark, G M Davies, S M Drury, K J D Ellis, J J N W Fisher, M D Gercke, R N A Gordon, L Frazer, B J Hornsby, M A F Hunter, M J A Jervis, W Kenyon, G J Lagerberg, C J Lemar, B G Lochead, A V Lomas, M J Magee, S G E O'Hare, A R Palmer, J G Parr, S A Pearson, A A W Pepper, J G A Phillips, S J Phizackerley, Z P Randeria, S J Russell, I Schneider, D Y Schwarzmann, R V Y Setchim, P N Spratt, H Swanston, C J Temple, J P Terry, G R Yeandle

PRICEWATERHOUSE-COOPERS LLP
St Andrews House, 18-20 St Andrew Street, London, EC4A 3AY

RAWLINSON & HUNTER★ ◈
Eighth Floor, 6 New Street Square, New Fetter Lane, London EC4A 3AQ
Tel: 020 7842 2000
Fax: 020 7842 2080
Email: firstname.lastname@rawlinson-hunter.com
Website: http://www.rawlinson-hunter.com
Resident Partners/Directors: ICAEW Members
P A Baker, C J A Bliss, R Drennan, S P Jennings, J C

continued

RAWLINSON & HUNTER *cont*
Kelly, R B Melling, D C Rawlings, A Shilling
Non-resident Partners (ICAEW Members):
P M Prettejohn, K S Nagra, M Harris, F J Stephens
Resident Partners (Non-ICAEW Members):
S Ousley, D G Barker
Overseas Offices: Australia, Bermuda, British Virgin Islands, Cayman Islands, Guernsey, Jersey, Monaco, London, New Zealand, Switzerland

Registered by the ICAEW to carry out company audit work

Regulated by the ICAEW for a range of investment business activities

General Description:
Rawlinson & Hunter is an independent international practice of chartered accountants which was established in 1933. To meet the extensive international requirements of our clients, we employ over 430 people and operate ten offices worldwide. We provide a wide spectrum of professional services to the private and corporate clients. The partners are dedicated to understanding the clients' needs and are fully supported by highly qualified staff and sophisticated technology. Our experience in areas of UK and international taxation and trust law have given the firm an established reputation as one of the leaders in this field. The firm's philosophy is to provide long-term support to clients, often stretching over generations. To ensure this continuity the firm is committed to remaining independent in the future and thus maintaining our fundamental commitment to personal service to all our clients, from the small family trust to the multi-national corporation.
Languages Spoken:
French, German, Spanish

REES POLLOCK
35 New Bridge Street, London, EC4V 6BW

TARGET WINTERS
29 Ludgate Hill, London, EC4M 7JE
Tel: 020 7919 9100
Fax: 020 7919 9019
Website: http://www.targetwinters.co.uk

Registered by the ICAEW to carry out company audit work

Regulated by the ICAEW for a range of investment business activities

SPECIALISATIONS – AUDIT & ASSURANCE
Pension Scheme Auditors

SPECIALISATIONS – BUSINESS & GENERAL ADVICE
Company Secretarial Service

SPECIALISATIONS – SECTOR
Barristers
Charities
Nursing Homes/Clinics
Solicitors

SPECIALISATIONS – TAXATION
Foreign Nationals in the UK
UK Nationals Overseas
UK Subsidiaries of Overseas Multinationals

General Description: A leading business and accounting firm with offices in London, Bath, Reading and Rugby. Authorised provision of financial services.

TARRANT GREEN & CO
2 Priory Court, Pilgrim Street, London, EC4V 6DE
Tel: 01438 869644
Email: tarrantgreen@btconnect.com
Principal: ICAEW Member
R T B Green

SPECIALISATIONS – FORENSIC ACCOUNTING
Forensic Accounting

SPECIALISATIONS – SECTOR
Solicitors

THORNHILL SCOTT LTD
Albert Buildings, 49 Queen Victoria Street, London, EC4N 4SA

VALERIE HOYLE
7 Gough House, 6 Bolt Court, London, EC4A 3DQ

LONDON N1

CHEESMANS ◈
4 Aztec Row, Berners Road, London, N1 0PW
Tel: 020 7354 3914
Principal: ICAEW Member
C A Cheesman

CPP ◈
81 Essex Road, Islington, London, N1 2SF
Tel: 020 7880 7272
Email: enquiries@cppca.co.uk
Website: http://www.cpp-accountants.com
Principal: ICAEW Member
P V Ciccone

Registered by the ICAEW to carry out company audit work

SPECIALISATIONS – BUSINESS & GENERAL ADVICE
Management Advice to Business

SPECIALISATIONS – SECTOR
Advertising/Design Agencies
Architects/Surveyors
Catering/Restaurants
Journalists/Writers/Copywriters
Paper/Printing/Publishing

General Description: CPP is dedicated to assisting the growth of SMEs by the design, implementation and maintenance of management information systems augmented by the provision of management advice.

DEREK ROTHERA & CO ◈
Units 15 & 16, 7 Wenlock Road, London, N1 7SL
Tel: 020 7226 1199
Fax: 020 7226 9446
Email: derek@rothera.com
Principal: ICAEW Member
D J Rothera

Registered by the ICAEW to carry out company audit work

Authorised and regulated by the Financial Services Authority for investment business

EPPY LTD
101 White Lion Street, London, N1 9PF
Tel: 020 7837 5604
Resident Partners/Directors: ICAEW Members
A I Rogove, I J Rogove

FINANCIAL FORENSICS LLP
52 Mildmay Road, London, N1 4NG

H. RAINSBURY & CO ◈
15 Duncan Terrace, London, N1 8BZ
Tel: 020 7837 4870
Fax: 020 7833 1975
Resident Partners/Directors: ICAEW Members
A N Bolsom, R L Hodge

Registered by the ICAEW to carry out company audit work

Regulated by the ICAEW for a range of investment business activities

PATSONS
Suraj Chambers, 53 Islington Park Street, London, N1 1QB

PJMA
PO Box 58218, London, N1 4XN

ROGOVE & CO
101 White Lion Street, London, N1 9PF

UPPER STREET ACCOUNTS LTD
3 Tolpuddle Street, Islington, London, N1 0XT

LONDON N2

ABELESSKOLNICK
Langley House, Park Road, London, N2 8EX

AMK RUSSELL MARKS
21 Aylmer Parade, Aylmer Road, London, N2 0AT

ANTHONY, WELLS & CO
19 Norrice Lea, London, N2 0RD
Tel: 020 8455 7733
Principal: ICAEW Member
A A Wells

CHAKRABORTY & CO
19 Elmfield Road, East Finchley, London, N2 8EB

DON FISHER & CO
101 High Road, East Finchley, London, N2 8AG

FENTON & CO
7 Bancroft Avenue, London, N2 0AR
Tel: 020 8341 3577
Principal: ICAEW Member
A Feigenbaum

GROSS KLEIN ◈
PO Box 27004, London, N2 0WS
Tel: 020 7242 2212

HAROLD D. NASS
20 Heath View, London, N2 0QA

IAN SKOLNICK & CO
Langley House, Park Road, London, N2 8EX

IVAN LAYMAN
10 Ferrour Court, 17 King Street, London, N2 8PB

J.R. LEVY
57 Brim Hill, London, N2 0HA

JON CATTY & CO
12 Durham Road, London, N2 9DN
Tel: 020 8444 1228
Principal: ICAEW Member
J Catty

KENNETH CORDIERO
26 Baronsmere Road, London, N2 9QE

LANGLEY GROUP LLP
Langley House, Park Road, East Finchley, London N2 8EX

MORRIS SULTMAN & CO
15b Southern Road, East Finchley, London, N2 9LH

P.R.HARTLEY
PO Box 27075, London, N2 0FZ
Tel: 020 8731 9745
Principal: ICAEW Member
P R Hartley

ROSS FRANKLIN LTD
18 Park Hall Road, East Finchley, London, N2 9PU

RUSSELL MARKS LTD
21 Aylmer Parade, Aylmer Road, London, N2 0AT

S.B.SHAH & CO
97 Brim Hill, London, N2 0EZ
Tel: 020 8444 9962
Principal: ICAEW Member
S B Shah

STEWART LAITNER & CO
17 Bancroft Avenue, East Finchley, London, N2 0AR

VSP
23a Lyttelton Road, Hampstead Garden Suburb, London, N2 0DN

VSP LTD
23a Lyttleton Road, Hampstead Garden Suburb, London, N2 0DN

WINNINGTONS
1 Winnington Road, London, N2 0TP
Tel: 020 8209 1092
Resident Partners/Directors: ICAEW Members
J B Grant, L J Grant

LONDON N3

A & CO ACCOUNTANTS LTD
35 Ballards Lane, London, N3 1XW

ADLER SHINE LLP
Aston House, Cornwall Avenue, London, N3 1LF
Tel: 020 8371 3000
Resident Partners/Directors: ICAEW Members
A S Banday, P A Gale, D A Garcia, P O'Rourke, J L Shine, L K Taub, C Taylor, K H Woolf

ALEXANDER-PASSE & CO
44 North Crescent, Finchley, London, N3 3LL
Tel: 020 8371 1500
Fax: 020 8371 1501
Email: gaptax@aol.com
Website: http://www.alexanderpasse.co.uk
SPECIALISATIONS – BUSINESS & GENERAL ADVICE
Company Formation
SPECIALISATIONS – FINANCIAL REPORTING
Accounts Preparation
Partnership/Sole Trader Accounts
SPECIALISATIONS – TAXATION
Taxation

ALEXANDER-PASSE & CO
10 North Crescent, London, N3 3LL

BERG KAPROW LEWIS LLP
35 Ballards Lane, London, N3 1XW

BLAKE WELTMAN & CO
25 Dollis Park, Finchley, London, N3 1HJ

BLAKE WELTMAN & CO
Sovereign House, 1 Albert Square, London, N3 1QB

BOSECO ◈
309 Regents Park Road, London, N3 1DP

BRIAN BEN CAMISSAR & CO
38 Hendon Lane, London, N3 1TT
Tel: 020 8346 3795
Principal: ICAEW Member
B B Camissar

BRIAN BERG LTD
35 Ballards Lane, London, N3 1XW

BRIAN J WOLKIND LTD
35 Ballards Lane, London, N3 1XW

BROOKS GREEN
Abbey House, 342 Regents Park Rd, London, N3 2LJ

FAROUK IBRAHIM
12 North Crescent, Finchley, London, N3 3LL
Tel: 020 8349 0901
Principal: ICAEW Member
F Ibrahim

FMCB
Hathaway House, Popes Drive, Finchley, London N3 1QF
Tel: 020 8346 6446
Fax: 020 8349 3990
Email: fmcb@fmcb.co.uk
Website: http://www.fmcb.co.uk
Training Contracts Available.
Resident Partners/Directors: ICAEW Members
N Anayiotos, S N Freeda, G W Zeiderman, J D Zinkin
Registered by the ICAEW to carry out company audit work
Regulated by the ICAEW for a range of investment business activities
SPECIALISATIONS – AUDIT & ASSURANCE
Audit
Audit — Private Company
SPECIALISATIONS – BUSINESS & GENERAL ADVICE
Company Formation
Company Secretarial Service
SPECIALISATIONS – FINANCIAL REPORTING
Accounts Preparation
Audit Exemption Report
Limited Companies
Limited Company Accounts
Partnership/Sole Trader Accounts
SPECIALISATIONS – INVESTMENT BUSINESS
Financial Planning and Advice
SPECIALISATIONS – IT
Computer Consultants
SPECIALISATIONS – SECTOR
Barristers
Charities
Clothing/Textiles
Corporate
Entertainers
Property
Retailers
Solicitors
SPECIALISATIONS – TAXATION
Partnerships and Sole Traders
PAYE Advice
Payroll Service and Advice
Personal
Self Assessment Advice
Small Traders
Taxation
Value Added Tax
General Description: We are a general accountancy practice committed to providing a comprehensive, professional and timely service, incorporating the latest information technology, yet retaining the personal approach.
Languages Spoken: Greek

GOODBRIDGE LTD
Abbey House, 342 Regents Park Road, London, N3 2LJ

IRVING SILVERMAN
52 Mayflower Lodge, Regents Park Road, London, N3 3HX

J GOODMAN ACCOUNTING SERVICES LTD
24 Lyndhurst Gardens, London, N3 1TB
Tel: 020 8343 1258
Resident Partners/Directors: ICAEW Members
J H M Goodman FCA

JACKSON FELDMAN & CO ★
Alexander House, 3 Shakespeare Road, Finchley, London N3 1XE
Tel: 020 8346 7272
Fax: 020 8346 2631
Email: m.feldman@jfaccount.com
Resident Partners/Directors: ICAEW Members
J P Nettleton, A Parker
Resident Partners (Non-ICAEW Members):
M S Feldman, D K Vora
Registered by another RSB to carry out company audit work

JAMES ECKHARDT
2 Queensborough Court, North Circular Road, London, N3 3JP

JEFF HARTSTONE LTD
35 Ballards Lane, London, N3 1XW

MAC KOTECHA & CO ★
Lichfield House, 2 Lichfield Grove, London, N3 2JP
Tel: 020 8346 0391
Website: http://www.mackotecha.co.uk
Resident Partners/Directors: ICAEW Members
M K Kotecha
SPECIALISATIONS – SECTOR
Artists/Graphic Designers
Dentists/Opticians
Property

MOSS GOODMAN
24 Lyndhurst Gardens, Finchley, London, N3 1TB
Tel: 020 8343 1258
Email: jg@mossgoodman.com
Principal: ICAEW Member
J H M Goodman FCA

NEIL GRAHAM LTD
35 Ballards Lane, London, N3 1XW

NR BETTS & CO
44 Squires Lane, Finchley, London, N3 2AT

PAUL PERLIN & CO ◈
Trojan House, 34 Arcadia Avenue, London, N3 2JU
Tel: 020 8371 5111
Fax: 020 8371 5112
Email: admin@perlin.co.uk
Website: http://www.perlin.co.uk
Date Established: 1979

continued

PAUL PERLIN & CO

cont

Resident Partners/ Directors: ICAEW Members
F Franco, P L Perlin

Registered by the ICAEW to carry out company audit work

Regulated by the ICAEW for a range of investment business activities

SPECIALISATIONS – AUDIT & ASSURANCE
Audit
Audit — Private Company
Pension Scheme Auditors

SPECIALISATIONS – BUSINESS & GENERAL ADVICE
Book-keeping
Book-keeping Systems
Company Formation
Company Secretarial Service
Management Accounting Consultancy
Management Advice to Business

SPECIALISATIONS – FINANCIAL REPORTING
Accounts Preparation
Audit Exemption Report
Limited Companies
Limited Company Accounts
Limited Liability Partnership
Partnership/Sole Trader Accounts

SPECIALISATIONS – INVESTMENT BUSINESS
Financial Planning and Advice
Planning

SPECIALISATIONS – IT
Computer Consultants
Computer Systems and Consultancy
Computerised Accounting Systems
Information Technology

SPECIALISATIONS – SECTOR
Advertising/Design Agencies
Architects/Surveyors
Artists/Graphic Designers
Catering/Restaurants
Charities
Corporate
Dentists/Opticians
Entertainers
Journalists/Writers/ Copywriters
Media
Property
Retailers
Traders — General

SPECIALISATIONS – TAXATION
Back Duty
Capital Gains — Limited Companies
Capital Gains — Personal
Employee
Foreign Nationals in the UK
National Insurance Advice
Partnerships and Sole Traders
PAYE Advice
Payroll Service and Advice
Personal
Self Assessment Advice
Small Traders
Taxation
Trusts
Value Added Tax

RICHARD ANTHONY & CO

13 Station Road, Finchley, London, N3 2SB
Tel: 020 8349 0353
Resident Partners/Directors: ICAEW Members
M Barnett, A M Hassan, P Horesh, A Levy, A V Simons, R I Simons, B Singh, P A Taylor

RICHARD NORTON & CO

342 Regents Park Road, London, N3 2LJ
Tel: 020 8346 8890
Principal: ICAEW Member
R J Norton

ROGGER & CO

5 Grass Park, Finchley, London, N3 1UB
Tel: 020 8346 7530
Principal: ICAEW Member
J R Rogger

RUTH NAFTALIN

14 Park Crescent, London, N3 2NJ
Tel: 020 8346 2915
Principal: ICAEW Member
R M Naftalin

SANDES

45 Arden Road, London, N3 3AD

SIDNEY BERMAN FCA

24 Riverside Gardens, Finchley, London, N3 3GR
Tel: 020 8343 4481
Principal: ICAEW Member
S Berman

SPENCER HYDE LTD ◈

272 Regents Park Road, London, N3 3HN
Tel: 020 8343 0583
Fax: 020 8343 0587
Resident Partners/Directors: ICAEW Members
S J McGuinness

Resident Partners (Non-ICAEW Members):
A B Jomehri, A Gurnah, S Dooreemeeah

Registered by the ICAEW to carry out company audit work

Regulated by the ICAEW for a range of investment business activities

SPW POPPLETON & APPLEBY ★ ◈

Gable House, 239 Regents Park Road, London, N3 3LF
Tel: 020 8371 5000
Fax: 020 8346 8588
Email: enquiries@spwca.com
Resident Partners/Directors: ICAEW Members
D L Platt, S A Shah, H J Sorsky, P J Winter
Resident Partners (Non-ICAEW Members):
C Shah, M S Solomons
Individual(s) licensed for insolvency work by another RPB

SPECIALISATIONS – AUDIT & ASSURANCE
Audit

SPECIALISATIONS – BUSINESS & GENERAL ADVICE
Book-keeping
Company Formation

SPECIALISATIONS – BUSINESS RECOVERY & INSOLVENCY
Bankruptcies
Corporate Recovery
Liquidations

SPECIALISATIONS – FINANCIAL REPORTING
Accounts Preparation
Limited Company Accounts
Partnership/Sole Trader Accounts

SPECIALISATIONS – SECTOR
Corporate

SPECIALISATIONS – TAXATION
Partnerships and Sole Traders
Taxation

General Description: A multi-discipline practice offering personal partner attention to each client.

SPW (UK) LLP

Gable House, 239 Regents Park Road, London, N3 3LF
Tel: 020 8371 5000
Fax: 020 8346 8588
Email: enquiries@spwca.com
Website: http://www.spwca.com
Resident Partners/Directors: ICAEW Members
D L Platt, S A Shah, H J Sorsky, P J Winter
Resident Partners (Non-ICAEW Members):
C R Shah, M S E Solomons
Registered by the ICAEW to carry out company audit work

SPECIALISATIONS – AUDIT & ASSURANCE
Audit

SPECIALISATIONS – BUSINESS & GENERAL ADVICE
Book-keeping
Company Formation
Debt Counselling

SPECIALISATIONS – BUSINESS RECOVERY & INSOLVENCY
Bankruptcies
Corporate Recovery
Liquidations

SPECIALISATIONS – FINANCIAL REPORTING
Accounts Preparation
Limited Company Accounts

SPECIALISATIONS – SECTOR
Barristers
Clothing/Textiles
Hotels/Public Houses
Traders — General

SPECIALISATIONS – TAXATION
Investigations
Partnerships and Sole Traders
Payroll Service and Advice
Self Assessment Advice
Taxation

Languages Spoken:
Gujarati, Arabic

STERLINGS LTD ◈

Lawford House, Albert Place, London, N3 1QA

STEVEN HOCKING-ROBINSON LTD

35 Ballards Lane, London, N3 1XW

STEWART BENNETT LTD

35 Ballards Lane, London, N3 1XW

VASWANI & CO

29a Hendon Avenue, Finchley Central, London, N3 1UJ

WOLFSON ASSOCIATES LTD

1st Floor, 314 Regents Park Road, Finchley, London N3 2LT
Tel: 020 8349 4911
Fax: 020 8343 1045
Email: admin@wolfsonassociates.co.uk
Resident Partners/Directors: ICAEW Members
I Wolfson, K Wolfson

Registered by the ICAEW to carry out company audit work

Authorised and regulated by the Financial Services Authority for investment business

LONDON N4

A. E. IOANNOU & CO

407 Green Lanes, London, N4 1EY

BARCANT BEARDON LLP
8 Blackstock Mews, Islington, London, N4 2BT
Tel: 020 7704 9368
Website: http://www.barcantbeardon.co.uk
Resident Partners/Directors: ICAEW Members
D Beardon, M V Khatri
Resident Partners (Non-ICAEW Members):
R Barcant

HARRY NICOLAOU & CO
38b Stroud Green Road, London, N4 3ES
Tel: 020 7281 1188
Principal: ICAEW Member
H Nicolaou

HARRY NICOLAOU & CO LTD
38b Stroud Green Road, London, N4 3ES
Tel: 020 7281 1188
Resident Partners/Directors: ICAEW Members
H Nicolaou
SPECIALISATIONS – SECTOR
Charities

IOANNOU & CO
407B Green Lanes, London, N4 1EY

ODOOM & CO
59 Upper Tollington Park, London, N4 4DD

TASOS PAPALOIZOU
167 Stroud Green Road, Finsbury Park, London, N4 3PZ

LONDON N5

HIGGINSON
53 Battledean Road, Highbury, London, N5 1UX

HOWARD HARRISON
9 Ardilaun Road, London, N5 2QR
Tel: 020 7354 1233
Principal: ICAEW Member
H R Harrison

LONDON N6

A.M. ACCOUNTANTS LTD ◈
63 Highgate High Street, London, N6 5JX
Tel: 020 8348 3378
Resident Partners/Directors: ICAEW Members
M A Markham

ANTHONY MARKHAM & CO ◈
63 Highgate High Street, London, N6 5JX
Tel: 020 8348 3378
Resident Partners/Directors: ICAEW Members
M A Markham

ANTHONY MARKHAM & CO
63 Highgate High Street, Highgate, London, N6 5JX
Tel: 020 8348 3378
Resident Partners/Directors: ICAEW Members
M A Markham

B H WHITE & CO
51 Fordington Road, Highgate, London, N6 4TH

G.B.C HUGHES
15 Holly Lodge Gardens, London, N6 6AA

KHOKHAR & CO
85 Shepherds Hill, Highgate, London, N6 5RG

MARKS CAMERON DAVIES & CO ◈
3 Hampstead Lane, London, N6 4RS
Tel: 020 8340 1984
Principal: ICAEW Member
A Marks

MICHAEL ANTHONY MARKHAM ◈
63 Highgate High Street, Highgate, London, N6 5JX

LONDON N7

AKDAG & CO
1st Floor South, 332-336 Holloway Road, London, N7 6NJ

C A PITTS & CO
Omnibus Business Centre, 39-41 North Road, London, N7 9DP

CHRISTOPHER & CO
51A Anson Road, London, N7 0AR

D'AURIA, QUICK & TANNA ★
Antonia House, 262 Holloway Road, London, N7 6NG

FREEMAN LAWRENCE & PARTNERS ◈
Spectrum Studios, 2 Manor Gardens, London, N7 6ER
Tel: 020 7272 7025

FREEMAN LAWRENCE & PARTNERS LTD ◈
Spectrum Studios, 2 Manor Gardens, London, N7 6ER
Tel: 020 7272 7025
Resident Partners/Directors: ICAEW Members
S A Freeman

THURSTON WATTS & CO
39-41 North Road, London, N7 9DP
Tel: 020 7607 0977
Principal: ICAEW Member
S N Samji

LONDON N8

A.K. SULEMAN ◈
11 Clovelly Road, Hornsey, London, N8 7RL
Tel: 020 8340 4380
Email: aksuleman@ukgateway.net
Principal: ICAEW Member
A K Suleman
SPECIALISATIONS – FINANCIAL REPORTING
Accounts Preparation
SPECIALISATIONS – TAXATION
Taxation

GCP ACCOUNTANCY SERVICES LTD
54 Nelson Road, Crouch End, London, N8 9RT

JULIA PODMORE
54 Nelson Road, Crouch End, London, N8 9RT

PORTMAN & CO
5 High Street, Hornsey, London, N8 7PS

LONDON N10

CLARKE & CO
59 Curzon Road, Muswell Hill, London, N10 2RB
Tel: 020 8444 7979
Principal: ICAEW Member
J L Clarke

COLLINGS & CO
49 Wilton Road, Muswell Hill, London, N10 1LX
Tel: 020 8883 9185
Principal: ICAEW Member
S D Collings

CORNEL PARTNERS LTD
117 Alexandra Park Road, Muswell Hill, London, N10 2DP

JANET R. BANNING
11 Teresa Walk, Muswell Hill, London, N10 3LL

JONATHAN KENDAL & CO
4 Holt Close, London, N10 3HW

MICHAEL POLLARD
12 Creighton Avenue, London, N10 1NU

P.LAVERY & COMPANY LTD
64 Grosvenor Road, Muswell Hill, London, N10 2DS

Q M HUSAIN & CO LTD
37 Grove Avenue, Muswell Hill, London, N10 2AS

QAZI M HUSAIN
37 Grove Avenue, Muswell Hill, London, N10 2AS

LONDON N11

DODHIA & CO
3 Tewkesbury Terrace, London, N11 2LT
Principal: ICAEW Member
J V Dodhia

I ALAM
7 Tash Place, New Southgate, London, N11 1PA

J.B. COUTINHO & CO
46 Eleanor Road, London, N11 2QS

JOHN R HETHERINGTON
7 Seafield Road, London, N11 1AR
Tel: 020 8368 7220
Principal: ICAEW Member
J R Hetherington

LAMBOUS & CO
327 Bowes Road, London, N11 1BA

LAURENCE LINCHIS
32 Greenway Close, Colney Hatch Lane, London, N11 3NS

LONDON N12

A.K. LTD
8 Percy Road, North Finchley, London, N12 8BU

ANTHONY TISCOE & CO
Brentmead House, Britannia Road, London, N12 9RU
Tel: 020 8343 8749
Email: tony@tiscoe.fsnet.co.uk
Principal: ICAEW Member
A M Tiscoe
Registered by the ICAEW to carry out company audit work
SPECIALISATIONS – AUDIT & ASSURANCE
Audit
SPECIALISATIONS – SECTOR
Charities
Media
Oil/Petroleum Industries
Solicitors
SPECIALISATIONS – TAXATION
Foreign Nationals in the UK
UK Subsidiaries of Overseas Multinationals

ASH COMPANY AUDIT LTD
19 Greenbank, London, N12 8AS

BAGINSKY COHEN
930 High Road, London, N12 9RT

BALLARDS NEWMAN (FINCHLEY) LTD
Apex House, Grand Arcade, London, N12 0EH
Tel: 020 8446 3114
Resident Partners/Directors: ICAEW Members
D L Cohen, R Muller, L M Perkin

BRAMIL ASSOCIATES ★
Rex House, 354 Ballards Lane, North Finchley, London N12 0DD

CARSON & CO
Finchley House, 707 High Road, Finchley, London N12 0BT

CHATRATH & CO
8 Cissbury Ring North, London, N12 7AN
Tel: 020 8445 3021
Principal: ICAEW Member
S S Chatrath
Other Offices:3rd Floor, 12/13 Little Newport Street, London WC2H 7JY
(Tel: 020 7434 1463)
(Fax: 020 7437 4388)

COOPERS
Apex House, Grand Arcade, Tally Ho Corner, London N12 0EH

D.J. COLOM & CO
1st Floor, Hillside House, 2-6 Friern Park, North Finchley, London N12 9BT
Tel: 020 8446 1404
Email: info@djcolom.co.uk
Principal: ICAEW Member
D J Colom

DAVID PELHAM & CO
39 Christchurch Avenue, London, N12 0DG

DAVID RUBIN & PARTNERS
Pearl Assurance House, 319 Ballards Lane, North Finchley, London N12 8LY
Tel: 020 8343 5900
Fax: 020 8446 2994
Email: [addressee]@drpartners.com
Website: http://www.drpartners.com
Resident Partners/Directors: ICAEW Members
H K Lan, A D Miller, D A Rubin
Non-resident Partners (ICAEW Members):
P R Appleton
Non-resident Partners (Non-ICAEW Members):
R Reeken
Other Offices:26-28 Bedford Row, London WC1R 4HE (Tel: 020 7400 7900), JSA House, 110 The Parade, Watford WD1 2GB
(Tel: 01923 251811)
Individual(s) licensed for insolvency work by the ICAEW

SPECIALISATIONS – BUSINESS & GENERAL ADVICE
Administration

SPECIALISATIONS – BUSINESS RECOVERY & INSOLVENCY
Bankruptcies
Corporate Recovery
Liquidations

SPECIALISATIONS – FORENSIC ACCOUNTING
Expert Witnesses in Litigation
Forensic Accounting

DEFRIES WEISS LLP
311 Ballards Lane, London, N12 8LY

EA ASSOCIATES ◈
869 High Road, North Finchley, London, N12 8QA
Tel: 020 8445 5500
Website: http://www.eaassocates.co.uk
Resident Partners/Directors: ICAEW Members
E Evagora, T Vassiliades
Resident Partners (Non-ICAEW Members):
A Christoforou, J Frangoudis
Registered by the ICAEW to carry out company audit work
Regulated by the ICAEW for a range of investment business activities
General Description: Energetic firm specialising in accounting and management advice to small and medium enterprises.

ERIC R. JENKINS
104 Southover, London, N12 7HD
Tel: 020 8446 2673
Principal: ICAEW Member
E R Jenkins

SPECIALISATIONS – SECTOR
Entertainers

ERRINGTON LANGER PINNER
Pyramid House, 956 High Road, Finchley, London N12 9RX
Tel: 020 8446 6911
Resident Partners/Directors: ICAEW Members
R N Errington, M S Pinner

F A KERIN
92 Woodgrange Avenue, North Finchley, London, N12 0PS
Tel: 020 8445 2302
Principal: ICAEW Member
F A Kerin

IAN COBDEN & CO
Rowlandson House, 289-293 Ballards Lane, London, N12 8NP

J.B. COOKE & CO
2nd Floor, Hillside House, 2-6 Friern Park, North Finchley, London N12 N12 9BT
Tel: 020 8446 7744
Email: jon@joncooke1@demon.co.uk
Principal: ICAEW Member
J B Cooke

ROBERT JACKSON MANAGEMENT LTD
41 Avondale Avenue, Woodside Pk, Finchley, London N12 8ER

JOSEPH KOKKINOS & CO
335a Ballards Lane, London, N12 8LT

K.J. PITTALIS & CO ★
Global House, 303 Ballards Lane, London, N12 8NP

LEAPMAN WEISS
Hillside House, 2-6 Friern Park, North Finchley, London N12 9BT

LEIGH & CO
2nd Floor, Brentmead House, Britannia Road, London N12 9RU

LEIGH ADAMS LLP
Brentmead House, Britannia House, London, N12 9RU

LEONARD FINN & CO
Brentmead House, Britannia Road, London, N12 9RU
Tel: 020 8446 6767
Resident Partners/Directors: ICAEW Members
D M Finn, L I Finn

LEONARD FINN & CO SERVICES LTD
Brentmead House, Britannia Road, London, N12 9RU
Tel: 020 8446 6767
Resident Partners/Directors: ICAEW Members
L I Finn

LEWIS NESTEL & CO
17 Woodside Avenue, London, N12 8AN

LYONS LEONIDOU
Galla House, 695 High Rd, North Finchley, London N12 0BT
Tel: 020 8445 0112
Email: leo@lyonsleonidou.com
Website: http://www.lyonsleonidou.com
Principal: ICAEW Member
L A Leonidou
Registered by the ICAEW to carry out company audit work

M.H. LINTON & CO
Brentmead House, Britannia Road, London, N12 9RU

M J LEAF & CO
Melville House, 8-12 Woodhouse Road, Finchley, London N12 0RG
Tel: 020 8445 0184
Principal: ICAEW Member
M J Leaf

M.S. IACOVOU & CO
6 Thyra Grove, North Finchley, London, N12 8HB

NEILS LTD
Finchley House, 707 High Road, Finchley, London N12 0BT

NEWTON & GARNER ◈
Apex House, Grand Arcade, North Finchley, London N12 0EJ

NYC & CO ★
36 Birkbeck Road, London, N12 8DZ

P&A ASSOCIATES ★
30 Offham Slope, Woodside Park, London, N12 7BZ

PAMELA MORROW
88 Linkside, Finchley, London, N12 7LG

POSNER LYONS
38a Northiam, Woodside Park, London, N12 7HA
Tel: 020 8492 0666
Principal: ICAEW Member
J L Posner

RHCO
727-729 High Road, Finchley, London, N12 0BJ

ROSSTAX LTD
Britannia House, 958 High Road, Finchley, London N12 9RY

AT & RT CONSULTANTS LTD
7 Michleham Down, London, N12 7JJ

S HARRISON
6 Albany, 38-40 Alexandra Grove, North Finchley, London N12 8NN
Tel: 020 8446 8062
Principal: ICAEW Member
S C Harrison

S. JIWA & CO
41 The Woodlands, London, N12 0DU

S. POOLE & CO
4 Norbury Court, 897 High Road, Finchley, London N12 8QZ
Tel: 020 8445 9220
Principal: ICAEW Member
S A Poole

SHELLEY & PARTNERS ◈
Brentmead House, Britannia Road, London, N12 9RU
Tel: 020 8446 6767
Training Contracts Available.
Resident Partners/Directors: ICAEW Members
K D Buddhdev, L I Finn

SMS ABACUS & CO LTD
Rowlandson House, 289-293 Ballards Lane, London, N12 8NP
Tel: 020 8343 7171
Resident Partners/Directors: ICAEW Members
J C Mehta, K Shahabuddin, K F Shahabuddin

SPIRO NEIL
Finchley House, 707 High Road, Finchley, London N12 0BT

TORRINGTONS
Hillside House, 2-6 Friern Park, London, N12 9FB

TORRINGTONS LTD
Hillside House, 2-6 Friern Park, North Finchley, London N12 9FB

LONDON N13

BHASKAR BHAVSAR LTD
36 Tottenhall Road, London, N13 6HX

CHRIS SKARPARIS & CO LTD
10(b) Aldermans Hill, Palmers Green, London, N13 4PJ
Tel: 020 8882 3225
Email: enquiries@cskarparis.co.uk
Website: http://www.cskarparis.co.uk
Resident Partners/Directors: ICAEW Members
C Skarparis
Registered by the ICAEW to carry out company audit work

CHRYSOSTOMOU & CO LTD
407 Green Lanes, Palmers Green, London, N13 4JD

CPS & CO
10a Aldermans Hill, Palmers Green, London, N13 4PJ

GEORGIADES CHARALAMBOU & CO ★
283 Green Lanes, London, N13 4XS

HENDERSON & CO
87 Devonshire Road, Palmers Green, London, N13 4QU

HETHERINGTON & CO, ★
Second Floor, 289 Green Lanes, Palmers Green, London N13 4XS

HURKAN SAYMAN & CO ★
291-293 Green Lanes, Palmers Green, London, N13 4XS
Tel: 020 8886 9222
Resident Partners/Directors: ICAEW Members
E Hurer, F H Khundkar, P D Patel

HURKANS
291-293 Green Lanes, Palmers Green, London, N13 4XS

JOHN CROOK & PARTNERS ◈
255 Green Lanes, Palmers Green, London, N13 4XE
Tel: 020 8886 0187
Email: mail@johncrookandpartners.co.uk
Website: http://www.johncrookandpartners.co.uk
Resident Partners/Directors: ICAEW Members
P Bridges, J A Crook, B D Hunt, I A Hunt, G G Prosser, M Woodgate
Registered by the ICAEW to carry out company audit work
Regulated by the ICAEW for a range of investment business activities

SPECIALISATIONS – AUDIT & ASSURANCE

Audit

SPECIALISATIONS – FINANCIAL REPORTING

Accounts Preparation
Limited Company Accounts
Partnership/Sole Trader Accounts

SPECIALISATIONS – TAXATION

Taxation

MAURICE GOLEND & CO
271 Green Lanes, London, N13 4XP
Tel: 020 8882 8000
Principal: ICAEW Member
L M Golend

RONNIE DAVIDSON ACCOUNTANCY & TAXATION SERVICES
Flat D, 4 Cranley Gardens, London, N13 4LS

T.M. WATTS & CO
42 Wentworth Gardens, Palmers Green, London, N13 5SN
Tel: 020 8350 1901
Principal: ICAEW Member
T M Watts

THOMAS ALEXANDER & CO
590 Green Lanes, Palmers Green, London, N13 5RY

W.H. GEAR
119 Bourne Hill, London, N13 4BE
Tel: 020 8886 2737
Principal: ICAEW Member
W H Gear

LONDON N14

BELL & CO
37 The Vale, Southgate, London, N14 6HR

BOND PARTNERS LLP ◈
The Grange, 100 High Street, London, N14 6TB
Tel: 0870 850 6007
Fax: 0870 850 6008
Email: info@bondpartners.co.uk
DX: 34310 SOUTHGATE
Website: http://www.bondpartners.co.uk
Date Established: 2004
Resident Partners/Directors: ICAEW Members
M D Marcus, C Morfakis, T Papanicola
Non-resident Partners (ICAEW Members):
C Brewster
Resident Partners (Non-ICAEW Members):
M P Michaelides, G Ioannides, S Hadjiyiangou, V Constantinou, J Daglish, T Alexander, S Sapkota
Non-resident Partners (Non-ICAEW Members):
A Johnson, S Christofi, D Betts, J Munnery, T Hudson, M Whitemead, B Cue, M King, D Griffiths, W Sharpe
Other Offices: Alcester, Bath, Boston, Harwich, Hessle, Newcastle, Norwich, Preston, Thorne, London (City), Brighton, Buntingford, Liverpool, Stoke-on-Trent
Overseas Offices: Cyprus, Germany, Malta, Spain, Portugal, South Africa, Gibraltar, Switzerland, Russia, China, Australia
Registered by another RSB to carry out company audit work
Licensed by another DPB to carry on investment business
Individual(s) licensed for insolvency work by another RPB

SPECIALISATIONS – AUDIT & ASSURANCE

Assurance Services
Audit

SPECIALISATIONS – BUSINESS & GENERAL ADVICE

Acquisitions and Mergers
Management Advice to Business

SPECIALISATIONS – BUSINESS RECOVERY & INSOLVENCY

Bankruptcies
Corporate Recovery
Liquidations
Reorganisations and Company Reconstructions

SPECIALISATIONS – FINANCIAL REPORTING

Accounts Preparation
International Reporting Standards (IFRS)

SPECIALISATIONS – FORENSIC ACCOUNTING

Expert Witnesses in Litigation
Forensic Accounting

SPECIALISATIONS – INVESTMENT BUSINESS

Financial Planning and Advice

SPECIALISATIONS – IT

Computer Systems and Consultancy
E-commerce

SPECIALISATIONS – SECTOR

Charities
FSA Members
Manufacturing
Media
New Media
Property
Solicitors

SPECIALISATIONS – TAXATION

Back Duty
Estate Planning
Foreign Nationals in the UK
Investigations
Offshore Companies
Trusts
UK Subsidiaries of Overseas Multinationals

General Description: We are an enterprising independent firm offering the full range of specialist audit, tax planning and corporate recovery services.

Languages Spoken:
Nepalese, Polish, Ukranian, Russian, Greek, French, Mandarin, Hindi, Gujarati

CHARLES ELLINAS & CO ◈
15 York Gate, Southgate, London, N14 6HS
Tel: 020 8886 7161
Principal: ICAEW Member
C G Ellinas

CK PARTNERSHIP LTD
1 Old Court Mews, 311a Chase Road, London, N14 6JS
Tel: 020 8886 1800
Resident Partners/Directors: ICAEW Members
G Christou, R Koppa

DAVID WEST
24 The Woodlands, London, N14 5RN

EASEBAY LTD ◈
Frovi House, 284B Chase Road, Southgate, London N14 6HF
Tel: 020 8882 4111
Resident Partners/Directors: ICAEW Members
E Costas

EVERETT WONG & CO
51 The Mall, Southgate, London, N14 6LR
Tel: 020 8886 5882
Principal: ICAEW Member
C H Everett

FREEMANS
Solar House, 282 Chase Road, London, N14 6NZ

FREEMANS PARTNERSHIP LLP
Solar House, 282 Chase Road, London, N14 6NZ

HEPPLEWHITE & CO
20 Selborne Road, Southgate, London, N14 7DH

IRVING D. SCHRYBER ◈
90 Friars Walk, London, N14 5LN
Tel: 020 8368 1741
Principal: ICAEW Member
I D Schryber

J.NEVILLE BECKMAN & CO
7 Osidge Lane, London, N14 5JD
Tel: 020 8361 8959
Principal: ICAEW Member
J N Beckman

MICHAEL COLE & CO ◈
10 Cecil Road, London, N14 5RJ
Tel: 020 8368 2446
Principal: ICAEW Member
M M Cole

MONTE ARORA & CO
43 Burleigh Gardens, Southgate, London, N14 5AJ

MORPHAKIS STELIOS & CO
22 Parkway, Southgate, London, N14 6QU

NOTT & CO
24 Chase Road, Southgate, London, N14 4EU
Tel: 020 8882 8389
Principal: ICAEW Member
P C Nott

PEACE OF MIND (ACCOUNTANCY & TAX) LTD
21 Orchard Avenue, Southgate, London, N14 4NB

PHILLIPS SPYROU LLP
2 Old Court Mews, 311a Chase Road, London, N14 6JS

R.K. RAJA & CO
21 Whitehouse Way, London, N14 7LX
Tel: 020 8361 6200
Principal: ICAEW Member
R K Raja
Registered by the ICAEW to carry out company audit work

ROBERT WONG & CO
51 The Mall, Southgate, London, N14 6LR

ROY ASSOCIATES LTD
77 Burleigh Gardens, Southgate, London, N14 5AJ

S P SPYROU & CO
Unit 2, Old Court Mews, 311a Chase Road, Southgate, London N14 N14 6JS

SARA GRAFF & CO
28 Minchenden Crescent, Southgate, London, N14 7EL
Tel: 020 8882 6847
Principal: ICAEW Member
S J Graff

SOUTHGATE ACCOUNTING
81 Ulleswater Road, Southgate, London, N14 7BN
Tel: 020 8882 9856
Principal: ICAEW Member
W B Flynn

TKG PARTNERSHIP LTD
Frovi House, 284b Chase Road, London, N14 6HF

V.S. SHAH & CO
3 Lakenheath, Oakwood, London, N14 4RJ

WINSTON FOX NUR & CO
Crown House, 2a Ashfield Parade, Southgate, London N14 5EJ

WR BOSTOCK
6 Lakenheath, Oakwood, London, N14 4RN

LONDON N15

HAGER STENHOUSE & CO ★
206 High Road, London, N15 4NP
Tel: 020 8801 6038
Resident Partners/Directors: ICAEW Members
S Y Steinhaus

SIMON WINEGARTEN AND CO
13 Hurstdene Gardens, London, N15 6NA
Tel: 020 8800 1717
Principal: ICAEW Member
S Winegarten

VENITT AND GREAVES
115 Craven Park Road, London, N15 6BL
Tel: 020 8802 4782
Principal: ICAEW Member
M A Venitt

LONDON N16

B. EHREICH & CO
113 Manor Road, London, N16 5PB

JT ANALYTICS
4 Leadale Road, London, N16 6DA

REIFER & CO
23 Craven Walk, London, N16 6BS

ROY HISCOCK
9OC Lordship Park, London, N16 5UA

SIMON TESLER AND ASSOCIATES
149 Albion Road, London, N16 9JU

SUGARWHITE ASSOCIATES
5 Windus Road, London, N16 6UT

LONDON N17

NIELSENS ◈
The Gatehouse, 784-788 High Road, Tottenham, London N17 0DA
Tel: 020 8801 6262
Resident Partners/Directors: ICAEW Members
S P Dubb, M R Mandalia, D U Shah

VALLANCE LODGE & CO ◈
Units 082 - 086, 555 White Hart Lane, London, N17 7RN
Tel: 020 8888 3800
Principal: ICAEW Member
M Y Manjra

LONDON N19

CARLINGTONS
17 Poynings Road, London, N19 5LH

SIMPLY CHURCHES LTD
17 Heathville Road, London, N19 3AL
Tel: 07963 003199
Resident Partners/Directors: ICAEW Members
J M M Helm

LONDON N20

ALG ★
Brook Point, 1412-1420 High Road, London, N20 9BH

ANNE CONNEELY & CO
199 Friern Barnet Lane, Whetstone, London, N20 0NN

D. FREEMAN & CO
Gateways Lodge, 76a Oakleigh Park North, London, N20 9AS
Tel: 020 8445 0499
Principal: ICAEW Member
D D Freeman

DAVID ISAACS & CO
2nd Floor, Walsingham House, 1331-1337 High Road, Whetstone, London N20 N20 9HR

DJM ACCOUNTANTS LLP
Fourth Floor, Brook Point, 1412 High Road, London N20 9BH
Tel: 020 8343 6170
Resident Partners/Directors: ICAEW Members
D Jacobs, J H Mendlesohn

FREEDMANS
Northway House, 5th Floor, Suite 504-505, 1379 High Road, Whetstone London N20 9LP

G.T. ASSOCIATES
The Limes, 1339 High Road, Whetstone, London N20 9HR

G. TAN & CO
88 Ventnor Drive, London, N20 8BS
Tel: 020 8445 5783
Principal: ICAEW Member
G H Tan

GERALD EDELMAN ◈
Edelman House, 1238 High Road, Whetstone, London N20 0LH
Tel: 020 8492 5600
Fax: 020 8492 5601
Email: gemail@geraldedelman.com
Website: http://www.geraldedelman.com
Resident Partners/Directors: ICAEW Members
D B Atkinson, D A Convisser, S H Rosenberg, N Summer, H J Wallis
Non-resident Partners (ICAEW Members):
C R Burns, M Harris, R H Kleiner, S P Coleman
Resident Partners (Non-ICAEW Members):
B Hoffman, A C Shah, D S Patel, G W Thomas
Other Offices: London W1
Registered by the ICAEW to carry out company audit work
Regulated by the ICAEW for a range of investment business activities
Individual(s) licensed for insolvency work by another RPB

SPECIALISATIONS – AUDIT & ASSURANCE
Audit

SPECIALISATIONS – BUSINESS & GENERAL ADVICE
Company Secretarial Service

SPECIALISATIONS – BUSINESS RECOVERY & INSOLVENCY
Corporate Recovery
Liquidations

SPECIALISATIONS – FINANCIAL REPORTING
Accounts Preparation
Limited Company Accounts

SPECIALISATIONS – SECTOR
Property Development
Property Investment

SPECIALISATIONS – TAXATION
Payroll Service and Advice
Taxation

Languages Spoken:
French, German

GREEN & PETER
The Limes, 1339 High Road, Whetstone, London N20 9HR

HARRIS LIPMAN LLP◈
2 Mountview Court, 310 Friern Barnet Lane, London, N20 0YZ
Tel: 020 8446 9000
Fax: 020 8446 9537
Email: mail@harris-lipman.co.uk
DX: 132890 WHETSTONE 2
Website: http://www.harris-lipman.co.uk
Resident Partners/ Directors:
ICAEW Members
M J Atkins, M D T Bernstein, N D Chajet, B D Lewis
Non-resident Partners (ICAEW Members):
F Khalastchi
Resident Partners (Non-ICAEW Members):
A Shah, M Hall
Non-resident Partners (Non-ICAEW Members):
J D Cullen
Other Offices: Corporate recovery offices in EC1M, Reading, Cardiff and St Albans
Registered by the ICAEW to carry out company audit work
Regulated by the ICAEW for a range of investment business activities
Individual(s) licensed for insolvency work by the ICAEW
SPECIALISATIONS – AUDIT & ASSURANCE
Audit
SPECIALISATIONS – BUSINESS & GENERAL ADVICE
Company Secretarial Service
SPECIALISATIONS – BUSINESS RECOVERY & INSOLVENCY
Bankruptcies
Corporate Recovery
Liquidations
SPECIALISATIONS – FINANCIAL REPORTING
Accounts Preparation
Limited Company Accounts
SPECIALISATIONS – FORENSIC ACCOUNTING
Expert Witnesses in Litigation
Forensic Accounting
SPECIALISATIONS – IT
Computer Systems and Consultancy
SPECIALISATIONS – TAXATION
Investigations
Taxation
General Description:
Specialists in corporate recovery, bankruptcies, expert witness in litigation, forensic accounting, liquidations, investigations.

HOWARD FRANK LTD
Turnberry House, 1404-1410 High Road, Whetstone, London N20 9BH

JEFFREY GOLD & CO
Turnberry House, 1404-1410 High Road, Whetstone, London N20 9BH

JOSEPH PAUL & CO
21 Oakleigh Road North, London, N20 9HE

JOSEPH PAUL & CO LTD
21 Oakleigh Road North, London, N20 9HE

JPL ★
110 Chandos Avenue, London, N20 9DZ

JPL
110 Chandos Avenue, London, N20 9DZ

JPL ACCOUNTANCY SERVICES LTD
110 Chandos Avenue, London, N20 9DZ

KALLIS & PARTNERS ★
Mountview Court, 1148 High Road, Whetstone, London N20 0RA
Tel: 020 8446 6699
Fax: 020 8492 6099
Email: chris@kallisandpartners.co.uk
Resident Partners/Directors:
ICAEW Members
C Pieri
Resident Partners (Non-ICAEW Members):
J Pieri
Registered by another RSB to carry out company audit work
SPECIALISATIONS – AUDIT & ASSURANCE
Audit
SPECIALISATIONS – FINANCIAL REPORTING
Accounts Preparation
SPECIALISATIONS – TAXATION
Taxation

KEITH J. SHULMAN
11 Harley Court, High Road, Whetstone, London, N20 0QD

KEITH JONES
3 Tudor Grove, Church Crescent, London, N20 0JW
Tel: 020 8361 4884
Principal: ICAEW Member
K J Jones

KLEINMAN GRAHAM
Turnberry House, 1404 -1410 High Road, Whetstone, London N20 9BH
Tel: 020 8446 4325
Resident Partners/Directors:
ICAEW Members
J S Bennett, P R Kleinman
See display advertisement near this entry.

L.JUNE HUGHES
34 Weirdale Av, Whetstone, London, N20 0AG

LACOME & CO
116 Totteridge Lane, London, N20 8JH

LACOME & CO
116 Totteridge Lane, Totteridge, London, N20 8JH

LACOME & CO LTD
116 Totteridge Lane, London, N20 8JH

M.ARIS & CO
Northway House, 1379 High Road, Whetstone, London N20 9LP
Tel: 020 8492 1770
Resident Partners/Directors:
ICAEW Members
M A Aris, N Aris

M.P. SAUNDERS & CO
2nd Floor, Walsingham House, 1331-1337 High Road, Whetstone, London N20 N20 9HR

MCCORMACK & ASSOCIATES ★
Euro House, 1394-1400 High Road, London, N20 9BH
Tel: 020 8445 5566
Resident Partners/Directors:
ICAEW Members
N M Patani, H H Shah, R Shah

MACINTYRE HUDSON LLP ◈
Euro House, 1394 High Road, Whetstone, London N20 9YZ
Tel: 020 8446 0922
Website: http://www.macintyrehudson.co.uk
Resident Partners/Directors: ICAEW Members
H S Gill, G C Gleghorn, S J Hinds, C K Jackson, B M Sharkey, C F Stratton
Resident Partners (Non-ICAEW Members):
N C May
Regulated by the ICAEW for a range of investment business activities

MH & CO
Euro House, 1394 High Road, Whetstone, London N20 9YZ

MICHAEL REEVES & CO
12 Harmsworth Way, Totteridge, London, N20 8JU

MUNRO'S
1341 High Road, Whetstone, London, N20 9HR

NEXIA SMITH & WILLIAMSON AUDIT LTD
Prospect House, 2 Athenaeum Road, Whetstone, London N20 9YU

NIREN BLAKE ★
Brook Point, 1412-1420 High Road, London, N20 9BH

PASCALL & CO
47 Park Way, Whetstone, London, N20 0XN

PETER LAWRENCE
The Lindens, 8 Oaklands Road, Totteridge, London N20 8BA

PHILIPS
1160 High Rd, London, N20 0RA
Tel: 020 8445 0004
Principal: ICAEW Member
P K Soteri

R. MARCHANT & CO ◈
42 Oakleigh Park South, London, N20 9JN
Tel: 020 8445 4724
Principal: ICAEW Member
R Marchant

RAYMOND HARRIS
3 Golfside Close, London, N20 0RD

SMITH & WILLIAMSON LTD
Prospect House, 2 Athenaeum Road, Whetstone, London N20 9YU
Tel: 020 8492 8600
Resident Partners/Directors: ICAEW Members
D J Hall, V T Winspeare
Resident Partners (Non-ICAEW Members):
N Antoniou, S R L Cork, G O Everett
General Description: Smith & Williamson is an independent professional and financial services group employing over 1400 people. We are leading providers of investment management, financial advisory and accountancy services to private clients, professional practices and mid-sized companies. Nexia Smith & Williamson Audit (Bristol) LLP provides audit services to complement the specialist financial advisory services provided by Smith & Williamson.

TUNG SING & CO
26 Oakleigh Park South, London, N20 9JU
Tel: 020 8445 7312
Principal: ICAEW Member
C M Y Tung Sing

LONDON N21

ADAM ARMSBY
1st Floor, 725 Green Lanes, Winchmore Hill, London N21 3RX

ALEXANDER LAWSON JACOBS
1 Kings Avenue, London, N21 3NA

ALEXANDER LAWSON JACOBS LTD
1 Kings Avenue, London, N21 3NA
Tel: 020 8370 7250
Resident Partners/Directors: ICAEW Members
N I Koumettou

ANDREA TERRONI
28 Beechdale, Winchmore Hill, London, N21 3QG

C.L. BATSFORD
69 Grange Park Avenue, Winchmore Hill, London, N21 2LN

COLIN S. JOHNSON
95 Old Park Ridings, Grange Park, London, N21 2EJ

COLIN S. JOHNSON FCA
95 Old Park Ridings, Grange Park, London, N21 2EJ
Tel: 020 8360 9131

CORPORATE MANAGEMENT SERVICES LTD ◈
16 Park View, Winchmore Hill, London, N21 1QX
Tel: 020 8882 9332
Resident Partners/Directors: ICAEW Members
Peter J Delf

D.A. METSON
12 Orchardmede, Winchmore Hill, London, N21 2DL

D.W.DAWES & CO
4 Cranwich Avenue, Winchmore Hill, London, N21 2BB

FSP (UK) LTD
87 Firs Park Avenue, Winchmore Hill, London, N21 2PU

G.A. PEARLMAN
159 Wynchgate, London, N21 1QT

G FELDMAN & CO LTD
5 Stone Hall Road, London, N21 1LR
Tel: 020 8364 0219
Resident Partners/Directors: ICAEW Members
G I Feldman

GM ASSOCIATES
7 Viga Road, Grange Park, London, N21 1HH
Tel: 020 8364 2420
Principal: ICAEW Member
G I Moscrop

GPMA
Devon House, Church Hill, London, N21 1LE

GRAEME BRUCE & PARTNERS
911 Green Lanes, London, N21 2QP

J.W. ARNOLD & CO
59A Station Road, Winchmore Hill, London, N21 3NB
Tel: 020 8360 4009
Principal: ICAEW Member
J Arnold

K. RUSSELL & CO
9 The Orchard, Winchmore Hill, London, N21 2DN

M TUMBRIDGE & CO
20 Anderson Close, London, N21 1TH

NEXIA POYIADJIS ★
21 Kent Road, Winchmore Hill, London, N21 2JH

R.A. BRAND
20 Houndsden Road, Winchmore Hill, London, N21 1LT

R.J.C. DAVEY
124 Old Park Ridings, Grange Park, London, N21 2EP

RAMSAY BROWN AND PARTNERS
Ramsay House, 18 Vera Avenue, Grange Park, London N21 1RA
Tel: 020 8370 7700
Resident Partners/Directors: ICAEW Members
K L Perry, S Singer, L M Slavin, J A Stone

ROBERT L. WILES
33 Bush Hill, Winchmore Hill, London, N21 2BT
Tel: 020 8360 1315
Principal: ICAEW Member
R L Wiles

TAT ACCOUNTING LTD
26 Hillfield Park, London, N21 3QH

VITTIS & CO
21 Hillfield Park, Winchmore Hill, London, N21 3QJ
Tel: 020 8882 7154
Principal: ICAEW Member
M Christou

LONDON N22

BACHA AND BACHA ◈
Stirling House, 107 Stirling Road, London, N22 5BN
Tel: 020 8881 8686
Resident Partners/Directors: ICAEW Members
Y Bacha

BUSINESS EXPERTS
37 Palace Gates Road, London, N22 7BW

C.BABS-JONAH & CO ◈
Guardian House, 655 Lordship Lane, Wood Green, London N22 5LA
Tel: 020 8881 6671
Fax: 020 8888 4256
Email: ck_babsjonah@yahoo.co.uk
Mobile: 07833 321211
Date Established: 1972
Principal: ICAEW Member
C B Jonah
Overseas Offices:62 Akanro Str, Ilasamaja Apapa-Oshodi Expressway, PO Box 3772, Apapa, Lagos (Tel: 00 234 4524594)

SPECIALISATIONS – BUSINESS & GENERAL ADVICE

Company Formation
Feasibility Studies
Management Accounting Consultancy

SPECIALISATIONS – FINANCIAL REPORTING

Accounts Preparation
Audit Exemption Report
Limited Company Accounts
Limited Liability Partnership
Partnership/Sole Trader Accounts

SPECIALISATIONS – SECTOR

Property Investment

SPECIALISATIONS – TAXATION

Capital Gains — Personal
Investigations
Partnerships and Sole Traders
Small Traders

General Description: Business Plan & Business Start-Ups; Cost Projection & Feasibility Study; Annual Accounts & Payroll Services; Property & Mortgage Accounts; Self Assessment & VAT Returns; Specialist in Resolving Tax Investigations; Computer Consultancy Services.

DATTA & CO
58 Whittington Road, London, N22 8YF
Tel: 020 8889 6376
Principal: ICAEW Member
G S Datta

DAVID GEDGE & CO
38 Sirdar Road, London, N22 6RG
Tel: 020 8889 6967
Principal: ICAEW Member
D R Gedge

JOSEPH ANDERSON BEADLE & CO
196 High Road, London, N22 8HH

N. ZAMAN & CO
35a Westbury Avenue, London, N22 6BS

XHI CONSULTING LTD
144 Victoria Road, London, N22 7XQ

LONDON NW1

ADDISON, BEYER, GREEN & CO
233-237 Old Marylebone Road, London, NW1 5QT
Tel: 020 7724 6060
Resident Partners/Directors: ICAEW Members
R M Coe, M S Kraitt, S S Landy

AIMS ACCOUNTANTS FOR BUSINESS
3 Park Road, London, NW1 6AS
Tel: 020 7616 6629
Website: http://www.aims.co.uk

ANDREW MILLER & CO
110 Gloucester Avenue, Primrose Hill, London, NW1 8HX
Tel: 020 7722 1820
Email: info@milleraccountants.co.uk
Website: http://www.milleraccountants.co.uk

ANTHONISZ NEVILLE LLP
1st Floor, 105-111 Euston Street, London, NW1 2EW

BATER PAUL
11 Chalfont Court, 236 Baker Street, London, NW1 5RS

BLICK ROTHENBERG ◈
12 York Gate, Regent's Park, London, NW1 4QS
Tel: 020 7486 0111
Website: http://www.blickrothenberg.com
Resident Partners/Directors: ICAEW Members
J A Brown, S M Bruck, J R Ellis, R M Fabian, M E Hart, D G Jordan, M G Korn, C I Lehmann, J A Newman, M Pandya, R M Rothenberg, W D Rothenberg, A J Sanford, M G D Scoltock, N Shah, T M Shaw, C J Shepherd, S Wagman
Resident Partners (Non-ICAEW Members):
R A Pearce, A Beech, T Ryland
Registered by the ICAEW to carry out company audit work
Authorised and regulated by the Financial Services Authority for investment business

BR VAT RECLAIM
12 York Gate, Regents Park, London, NW1 4QS

BRAL
12 York Gate, Regents Park, London, NW1 4QS

BRAL LTD
12 York Gate, Regents Park, London, NW1 4QS
Tel: 020 7487 3886
Website: http://www.bral.com
Resident Partners/Directors: ICAEW Members
A L Boronte, J A Brown, R M Rothenberg
Resident Partners (Non-ICAEW Members):
P Deters

SPECIALISATIONS – BUSINESS & GENERAL ADVICE
Administration
Book-keeping
Europe
Outsourcing - Financial Services

SPECIALISATIONS – TAXATION
UK Subsidiaries of Overseas Multinationals

General Description: BRAL is a multi-lingual provider of outsourced accounting services to UK businesses and overseas companies setting up in the UK and Europe. Services range from entity establishment and UK tax advice to online accounting, book-keeping and payroll.

BRIAN COHEN
88 Camden Road, London, NW1 9EA

BUTTERS GATES & CO
107 Bell Street, London, NW1 6TL

CAPE AND DALGLEISH ◈
22 Melton Street, Euston Square, London, NW1 2BT

CAVERNHAM LLP ◈
85-87 Bayham Street, London, NW1 0AG
Tel: 020 7788 4300
Resident Partners/Directors: ICAEW Members
P I Macorison, A R O Williams

CDS,CHARTERED ACCOUNTANTS
88-90 Camden Road, London, NW1 9EA

CHAMBERLAINS
First Floor, 22 Stephenson Way, London, NW1 2LE

CHAMBERLAINS UK LLP
First Floor, 22 Stephenson Way, London, NW1 2LE

CHANDLERS
85-87 Bayham Street, London, NW1 0AG

CHARLES WILLIAM LTD
115 Hampstead Road, London, NW1 3EE

CREASEY ALEXANDER & CO
Parkgate House, 33A Pratt St, London, NW1 0BG
Tel: 020 7267 0167
Email: mail@creaseyalexander.co.uk
Principal: ICAEW Member
A P Creasey
Registered by the ICAEW to carry out company audit work
Regulated by the ICAEW for a range of investment business activities

SPECIALISATIONS – BUSINESS & GENERAL ADVICE
Company Secretarial Service

SPECIALISATIONS – FINANCIAL REPORTING
Accounts Preparation
Limited Company Accounts

SPECIALISATIONS – SECTOR
Entertainers
Estate Agents
Media
Solicitors

SPECIALISATIONS – TAXATION
Back Duty
Partnerships and Sole Traders
Personal

DANGOOR & CO
36 Chester Close North, Regents Park, London, NW1 4JE
Tel: 020 8961 2770
Principal: ICAEW Member
R P Dangoor

DRENNAN & CO
1 Chamberlain Street, London, NW1 8XB
Tel: 020 7483 1575
Principal: ICAEW Member
R G Drennan

FISHER CORPORATE PLC ◈
Acre House, 11/15 William Road, London, NW1 3ER
Tel: 020 7388 7000
Resident Partners/Directors: ICAEW Members
P A C Beber, P A Beer, C J Hazard, G A Miller
Other Offices: Acre House, 3-5 Hyde Road, Watford, Hertfordshire WD17 4WP (Tel: 01923 698340) (Fax: 01923 698341)
Authorised and regulated by the Financial Services Authority for investment business

SPECIALISATIONS – BUSINESS & GENERAL ADVICE
Acquisitions and Mergers
Disposal of Businesses

FISHER FORENSIC ◈
Acre House, 11/15 William Road, London, NW1 3ER
Tel: 020 7388 7000
Other Offices: Acre House, 3-5 Hyde Road, Watford, Hertfordshire WD17 4WP (Tel: 01923 698340) (Fax: 01923 698341)
Regulated by the ICAEW for a range of investment business activities

SPECIALISATIONS – FORENSIC ACCOUNTING
Expert Witnesses in Litigation
Forensic Accounting

FORENSIC ACCOUNTING SOLUTIONS
85-87 Bayham Street, Camden Town, London, NW1 0AG

GARO & CO
27 Daventry Street, London, NW1 6TD

GRANT THORNTON UK LLP
Grant Thornton House, 22 Melton Street, Euston Square, London NW1 2EP
Tel: 020 7383 5100
Resident Partners/Directors: ICAEW Members
R Aitken, S C Almond, D P Ascott, T A J Back, S Barnes, J A Bartlett, E J Best, G T Beveridge, M S Bhagrath, M Bowler, D N Brooks, M R Byers, M J Cardiff, A J Chande, M J Cleary, C E Corner, T G De, D J Dunckley, S Edmonds, I M Evans, L A Field, D H Fisher, P Flatley, P J Gamson, M N Gardner, J M Grant, P F Green, H Hamedani, J P Hargaden, C S Hartnell, K V Hiddleston, M J Hore, O C Hutton-Potts, P M Jackson, P A Jones, R C Kemsley, F C Lagerberg, A Lees, I D Luder, S Maslin, R J Matyszczyk, D A S Maxwell, D C McDonnell, D A Medland, M A M Merali, J D Mew, D F Miller, S C Morris, L Naylor, N S Page, A N Richards, S V Romanovitch, P M Rowley, C A Rudge, H Self, B R Shearer, M B Shierson, I V Smart, C Smith, D R W Smith, A F E Stewart, A L Stopford, R J Tremeer, M R Ward, P R Westerman, D M Whitehead, H C Wilson, R D Withecombe
Resident Partners (Non-ICAEW Members):
R S Burrows, P V Cutler, M Henshaw, S Sangar, G C Stone, L P Kehoe, K Thorne, K J Eddy, D Beeton, C J Fathers, E Briou, D Neumann, P V Roberts, D

continued

GRANT THORNTON UK LLP *cont*
Willams, S M Shepley, A Bristow, S Kumar, P Dossett, L Parkin

H W FISHER & COMPANY LTD ◈
Acre House, 11/15 William Road, London, NW1 3ER
Tel: 020 7388 7000
Resident Partners/Directors: ICAEW Members
P A C Beber, P A Beer, A J Bernstein, D L Birne, D W Breger, S Burns, J S Challis, M B Davis, C J Hazard, S M Katz, A K Lester, B Lindsey, S P Mehta, E Meyer, G A Miller, R Nathan, A R W Parfitt, A G Rich, N S Samani, R A Saville, D S Selwyn, N N Siganporia, A Subramaniam, M A Taylor, N J Thaker, J S Trent
Resident Partners (Non-ICAEW Members):
A Thompson, B Johnson
Other Offices: Acre House, 3-5 Hyde Road, Watford, Hertfordshire WD17 4WP (Tel: 01923 698340) (Fax: 01923 698341)

Registered by the ICAEW to carry out company audit work

Regulated by the ICAEW for a range of investment business activities

H.W. FISHER & CO ◈
Acre House, 11-15 William Road, London, NW1 3ER
Tel: 020 738 8700
Website: http://www.hwfisher.co.uk
Training Contracts Available.
Resident Partners/Directors: ICAEW Members
P A C Beber, P A Beer, A J Bernstein, D L Birne, D W Breger, S Burns, J S Challis, C J Hazard, S M Katz, A K Lester, B Lindsey, S P Mehta, E Meyer, G A Miller, R Nathan, A G Rich, N S Samani, R A Saville, D S Selwyn, N N Siganporia, A Subramaniam, M A Taylor, N J Thaker, J S Trent
Resident Partners (Non-ICAEW Members):
A Thompson, B Johnson
Other Offices: Acre House, 3-5 Hyde Road, Watford, Hertfordshire WD17 4WP (Tel: 01923 698340) (Fax: 01923 698341)

Registered by the ICAEW to carry out company audit work

Regulated by the ICAEW for a range of investment business activities

Individual(s) licensed for insolvency work by the ICAEW

SPECIALISATIONS – AUDIT & ASSURANCE
Audit

SPECIALISATIONS – BUSINESS & GENERAL ADVICE
Book-keeping
Company Secretarial Service
Disposal of Businesses

SPECIALISATIONS – BUSINESS RECOVERY & INSOLVENCY
Corporate Recovery

SPECIALISATIONS – FINANCIAL REPORTING
Accounts Preparation
Audit Exemption Report
Foreign Subsidiary Companies
International Reporting Standards (IFRS)
Limited Companies
Limited Company Accounts
Limited Liability Partnership
Partnership/Sole Trader Accounts

SPECIALISATIONS – FORENSIC ACCOUNTING
Expert Witnesses in Litigation
Forensic Accounting

SPECIALISATIONS – SECTOR
Catering/Restaurants
Charities
Entertainers
Journalists/Writers/Copywriters
Media
Property
Property Development
Solicitors
Trade Assoc/Unions/Friendly Societies

SPECIALISATIONS – TAXATION
Personal
Taxation
Trusts
Value Added Tax

JADE SECURITIES LTD ◈
Acre House, 11/15 William Road, London, NW1 3ER
Tel: 020 7388 2636
Fax: 020 7380 4900
Email: jade@hwfisher.co.uk
Website: http://www.jade-securities.co.uk
Resident Partners/Directors: ICAEW Members
P A C Beber, M A Shulman

Regulated by the ICAEW for a range of investment business activities

SPECIALISATIONS – BUSINESS & GENERAL ADVICE
Acquisitions and Mergers
Disposal of Businesses

LISA SCOTT
22 St Augustines Road, London, NW1 9RN

MAK ASSOCIATES
Regent House, 72-76 Eversholt Street, Euston, London NW1 1BY

MANSFIELD & CO
55 Kentish Town Road, Camden Town, London, NW1 8NX
Tel: 020 7482 2022
Principal: ICAEW Member
D F L Mansfield

MORLEY & CO
83 Marathon House, 200 Marylebone Road, London, NW1 5PL

MORRISON FORENSIC
97 Camden Road, London, NW1 9HA
Tel: 07740 475400
Principal: ICAEW Member
D N Morrison

NAREN PATEL & CO
126 Royal College Street, London, NW1 0TA

NAZMAN ◈
55 Rossmore Court, Park Road, London, NW1 6XY

NEWMAN & CO
Regent House, 1 Pratt Mews, London, NW1 0AD
Tel: 020 7554 4840
Fax: 020 7388 8324
Email: partners@newmanandco.com
Resident Partners/Directors: ICAEW Members
F T Chin, C Newman

NORRIS GILBERT
143 Ivor Court, 209 Gloucester Place, London, NW1 6BT
Tel: 020 7262 0805
Fax: 020 7724 5357
Email: norris.gilbert@btconnect.com
Principal: ICAEW Member
N Gilbert

PETER BENNETTS LTD
51 Albert Street, London, NW1 7LX
Resident Partners/Directors: ICAEW Members
P L Bennetts

PORTMAN PARTNERSHIP LTD
36 Gloucester Avenue, Primrose Hill, London, NW1 7BB

R G CONSULTANCY
12 York Gate, Regent's Park, London, NW1 4QS

RICHARD L. OWEN
6 Chester Gate, Regents Park, London, NW1 4JH

SHAH DODHIA & CO ◈
First Floor, 22 Stephenson Way, Euston, London NW1 2LE
Tel: 020 7380 0222
Resident Partners/Directors: ICAEW Members
C Shah, S B Shah

SHULMAN & CO ★
35a Huntsworth Mews, Gloucester Place, London, NW1 6DB

WILDER COE ◈
233-237 Old Marylebone Road, London, NW1 5QT
Tel: 020 7724 6060
Fax: 020 7724 6070
Email: advice@wildercoe.co.uk
Website: http://www.wildercoe.co.uk
Resident Partners/Directors: ICAEW Members
M Bordoley, B L Chew, R M Coe, S S Landy, J Pattani, M R Saunders
Non-resident Partners (ICAEW Members):
N Cowan
Resident Partners (Non-ICAEW Members):
T Cook

Registered by the ICAEW to carry out company audit work

Regulated by the ICAEW for a range of investment business activities

WINSTON FOX & CO
34 Arlington Road, London, NW1 7HU
Tel: 020 7388 4143
Email: awinston@winstonfox.co.uk
Principal: ICAEW Member
A J Winston

WINSTON GROSS & CO ◈
34 Arlington Road, London, NW1 7HU
Tel: 020 7388 4048
Email: bgross@winstongross.co.uk
Website: http://www.winstongross.co.uk
Date Established: 1990
Resident Partners/Directors: ICAEW Members
B Gross, A J Winston

Registered by the ICAEW to carry out company audit work

Regulated by the ICAEW for a range of investment business activities

SPECIALISATIONS – FINANCIAL REPORTING
Accounts Preparation
Limited Company Accounts
Partnership/Sole Trader Accounts

SPECIALISATIONS – TAXATION
Capital Gains — Personal
PAYE Advice
Self Assessment Advice
Taxation

LONDON NW2

ALAN MILLER & CO
102A The Broadway, Cricklewood, London, NW2 3EJ

ARGENT & CO ◈
20 Burgess Hill, London, NW2 2DA

COMPLETE TAX SOLUTIONS
Second Floor, Cardiff House, Tilling Road, London NW2 1LJ

D. DAVE & CO
60 Kenwyn Drive, London, NW2 7NT

DAVID EXELL ASSOCIATES
10 Pattison Road, Childs Hill, London, NW2 2HH

DAVID JOSEPH & CO LTD
Suite 109, Atlas Business Centre, Oxgate Lane, London NW2 7HJ

JACOBS & CO
152-154 Coles Green Road, London, NW2 7HD

JEFFREY GOLD & CO
AJP Business Centre, 152-154 Coles Green Road, London, NW2 7HD

JOSEPH MORRIS & CO
Suite 109, Atlas Business Centre, Oxgate Lane, London NW2 7HJ

P.T. BHIMJIYANI & CO
124 Chatsworth Road, London, NW2 5QU

SHENKER & CO LTD
Hanover House, 385 Edgware Road, London, NW2 6BA

SHENKERS
Hanover House, 385 Edgware Road, London, NW2 6BA

SILVERMANS AP LTD
Hanover House, 385 Edgware Road, London, NW2 6LD

ZAMAN & CO
27 Dollis Hill Lane, London, NW2 6JH

LONDON NW3

AEL PARTNERS LLP
2nd Floor, 201 Haverstock Hill, London, NW3 4QG

AIMS - BRYAN CRYSTOL
13 Walham Court, 111 Haverstock Hill, London, NW3 4SD

B.A. ABRAHAM
40A Primrose Gardens, London, NW3 4TP

BRACKMAN CHOPRA LLP
8 Fairfax Mansions, Finchley Road, Swiss Cottage, London, NW3 6JY

BRENNER & CO
7 Pavilion Court, Mount Vernon, Frognal Rise, London NW3 6PZ

CLAYTON, STARK & CO
5th Floor, Charles House, 108-110 Finchley Road, London, NW3 5JJ
Tel: 020 7431 4200
Fax: 020 7431 6112
Email: csco@claytonstark.co.uk
Date Established: 1954
Resident Partners/Directors: ICAEW Members
J L Budhdeo, N J Kariya, A Mitchell
Registered by the ICAEW to carry out company audit work
Regulated by the ICAEW for a range of investment business activities

DAVID GRANT ◈
Suite 48, 571 Finchley Road, Hampstead, London NW3 7BN
Tel: 0845 108 2450
Website: http://www.addup.info
Resident Partners/Directors: ICAEW Members
D N Grant

DAVID LEWIS & CO
Flat 1, 16 Lindfield Gardens, Hampstead, London NW3 6PU

FERNANDEZ
35 Tudor Close, London, NW3 4AG

FISHER PHILLIPS ◈
Summit House, 170 Finchley Road, London, NW3 6BP
Tel: 020 7483 6100
Fax: 020 7435 0152
Email: info@fisherphillips.co.uk
Date Established: 1945
Resident Partners/Directors: ICAEW Members
G R Ornstein, P P Sykes, R Ward, A K Woricker
Registered by the ICAEW to carry out company audit work
Regulated by the ICAEW for a range of investment business activities
SPECIALISATIONS – SECTOR
Catering/Restaurants
Journalists/Writers/Copywriters
Paper/Printing/Publishing
Property Development
Retailers
SPECIALISATIONS – TAXATION
Small Traders

HOPKINS CONSULTING
5 Heath Hurst Road, Hampstead, London, NW3 2RU

HOWARD S. MARKHAM & CO ◈
10 Perrin's Lane, Hampstead, London, NW3 1QY
Tel: 020 7794 0171
Principal: ICAEW Member
H S Markham

J DENZA
85 Redington Road, London, NW3 7RR

JANE WAKSMAN ACA
4 Byron Mews, London, NW3 2NQ

JAYSON BUSINESS CONSULTANTS LTD
Hillsdown House, PO Box No 47362, 32 Hampstead High Street, London NW3 1WJ

JAYSON CONSULTING
Hillsdown House, PO Box No 47362, 32 Hampstead High Street, London NW3 1WJ

JEFFREY JAMES
First Floor, 421A Finchley Road, Hampstead, London NW3 6HJ

K. NARAIN & CO
6A Belsize Square, London, NW3 4HT

K.S. TAN & CO
1st Floor, 10/12 New College Parade, Finchley Road, London NW3 5EP
Tel: 020 7586 1280
Fax: 020 7586 5921
Email: mail@kstan.co.uk
Website: http://www.kstan.co.uk
Principal: ICAEW Member
K S Tan
Registered by the ICAEW to carry out company audit work
Individual(s) licensed for insolvency work by the ICAEW

THE KBSP PARTNERSHIP ◈
Harben House, Harben Parade, Finchley Road, London NW3 6LH
Tel: 020 7586 3841
Website: http://www.kbsp.co.uk
Resident Partners/Directors: ICAEW Members
T F Berkley, T Curzon, J Landau, M L Marks, A Y Melinek, J H Simmons
Resident Partners (Non-ICAEW Members):
D H Stockman

LAURENCE BARD
33 Platts Lane, Hampstead, London, NW3 7NN

LAURENCE BARD LTD
33 Platts Lane, Hampstead, London, NW3 7NN

M.I. BUNDHUN
Apartment 3, 15 Wedderburn Road, London, NW3 5QS

MAURICE APPLE ◈
3rd Floor, Marlborough House, 179-189 Finchley Road, London NW3 6LB
Tel: 020 7642 4556
Email: apm@maurice-apple.co.uk
Website: http://www.maurice-apple.co.uk
Resident Partners/Directors: ICAEW Members
A P M Myers, M A Silver
Registered by the ICAEW to carry out company audit work
Regulated by the ICAEW for a range of investment business activities
SPECIALISATIONS – SECTOR
Charities

MICHAEL I. KAYSER
12A Belsize Park Gardens, London, NW3 4LD

MICHELLE EVERITT
25D Fitzjohn's Avenue, London, NW3 5JY

HARROD NEILSON & CO
8 Fairfax Mansions, Finchley Road, London, NW3 6JY
Tel: 020 7372 1144
Principal: ICAEW Member
D Harrod

Nyman
LIBSON
PauL

NYMAN LIBSON PAUL
Regina House, 124 Finchley Road, London, NW3 5JS
Tel: 020 7433 2400
Fax: 020 7433 2401
Email: mail@nlpca.co.uk
DX: 38864 SWISS COTTAGE
Website: http://www.nlpca.co.uk
Date Established: 1933
Training Contracts Available.
Resident Partners/Directors: ICAEW Members
P J Decker, K P Dias, A S Katten, R Lloyd, J Newman, R J Paul, R S Paul, A D Pins, L E Pittal, J M Pope, P G Taiano
Resident Partners (Non-ICAEW Members):
A Clark, A Saleh
Other Offices: Room 107, Pinewood Studios, Pinewood Road, Iver Heath, Bucks SL0 0NH
Registered by the ICAEW to carry out company audit work

continued

NYMAN LIBSON PAUL *cont*
Regulated by the ICAEW for a range of investment business activities
SPECIALISATIONS – AUDIT & ASSURANCE
Audit
Audit — Private Company
SPECIALISATIONS – FINANCIAL REPORTING
Accounts Preparation
Foreign Subsidiary Companies
Limited Liability Partnership
SPECIALISATIONS – IT
E-commerce
SPECIALISATIONS – SECTOR
Charities
Corporate
Entertainers
Media
Property Investment
SPECIALISATIONS – TAXATION
Back Duty
Foreign Nationals in the UK
General Description: A full range of tax and accounting services. Specialist knowledge of film, TV, video, the theatre and all aspects of the entertainment industry, E-Commerce, charities and property companies.

P.C MARKS & CO
10 Carlton Close, West Heath Road, London, NW3 7UA

RICHARD H. HARTLEY
College House, 4a New College Parade, Finchley Road, London NW3 5EP

RICHARD YONG & CO
293 Finchley Road, London, NW3 3PX

SAHNI & CO LTD
55 Maresfield Gardens, London, NW3 5TE

SHULMAN & CO ★
52 Redington Road, Hampstead, London, NW3 7RS

LONDON NW4

AARON ZIMBLER ASSOCIATES
49 Watford Way, Hendon, London, NW4 3JH

ACCOUNTANCY EXPERTS LTD.
6 Shirehall Park, Hendon, London, NW4 2QL

AIMS - STUART A WILLIAMSON FCA
8 Sydney Grove, London, NW4 2EH

ANWAR ISLAM & CO
12 Cheyne Walk, London, NW4 3QJ
Tel: 020 8202 1655
Principal: ICAEW Member
A L M A Islam

CHRIS LO
23 Rowsley Avenue, London, NW4 1AP
Tel: 020 8203 2298
Email: ktlo88@hotmail.com
Principal: ICAEW Member
L K T Lo Neng Fong

DAVID FISHEL ACCOUNTANCY SERVICES LTD
59a Brent Street, London, NW4 2EA
Tel: 020 8203 2021
Resident Partners/Directors: ICAEW Members
D H Fishel

DODD HARRIS
35/37 Brent Street, London, NW4 2EF
Tel: 020 8203 9155
Email: info@doddharris.com
Resident Partners/Directors: ICAEW Members
J D Epstein, D A Jaye
SPECIALISATIONS – FINANCIAL REPORTING
Accounts Preparation
Limited Companies
SPECIALISATIONS – TAXATION
Partnerships and Sole Traders
Self Assessment Advice

ELIJAH & CO
Churchill House, 137 Brent Street, Hendon, London NW4 4DJ

FRENKELS LTD
Churchill House, 137 Brent Street, London, NW4 4DJ
Tel: 020 8457 2929
Resident Partners/Directors: ICAEW Members
J R Frenkel
SPECIALISATIONS – FORENSIC ACCOUNTING
Expert Witnesses in Litigation
Forensic Accounting

GROSS KLEIN
Penny Farthing, 32 Manor Hall Avenue, Hendon, London NW4 1NX

H. MORRIS & CO
6 Shirehall Park, Hendon, London, NW4 2QL

J.W. WOODROW & CO
141 Station Road, Hendon, London, NW4 4NJ

JACOB CHARLES & CO
Sentinel House, Sentinel Square, Brent Street, London NW4 2EP

JACQUELINE DAVIDSON
17 Wykeham Road, London, NW4 2TB

JEFFREY H. KAHAN
5 Aprey Gardens, London, NW4 2RH

K.S. SOLOMONS & CO
6 Raleigh Close, Hendon, London, NW4 2TA
Tel: 020 8202 8915
Principal: ICAEW Member
K S Solomons
Licensed by another DPB to carry on investment business

LANDAU BAKER LTD ◈
Mountcliff House, 154 Brent Street, London, NW4 2DP

LAURENCE S.ROSS
12 Kings Close, London, NW4 2JT
Tel: 020 8203 2370
Fax: 020 8922 3321
Email: laurence.ross@lineone.net
Mobile: 07941 195743
Principal: ICAEW Member
L S Ross

MARTIN J. REICH & CO
41 Boyne Ave, London, NW4 2JL
Tel: 020 8203 8091
Principal: ICAEW Member
M J Reich

MARTIN MAY
399 Hendon Way, London, NW4 3LH

MMAS LTD
399 Hendon Way, London, NW4 3LH

N.SAHA & CO
21 Parade Mansions, Hendon Central, London, NW4 3JR

PETER HOCKLEY & CO
Buckingham Chambers, 45 Vivian Avenue, London, NW4 3XA
Tel: 020 8202 2266
Principal: ICAEW Member
P M Hockley

PYLIOTIS ASSOCIATES
157 Great North Way, London, NW4 1PP
Tel: 020 8203 0647
Principal: ICAEW Member
R S Pyliotis

RASHMI SHAH & CO
62 Bertram Road, Hendon, London, NW4 3PP

RIPE ◈
Suite 9 Stirling House, Breasy Place, 9 Burroughs Gardens, London NW4 4AU
Tel: 020 8359 1205
Website: http://www.ripefinancial.com
Resident Partners (Non-ICAEW Members):
P Glazer

RIPE LLP
Suite 9 Stirling House, Breasy Place, 9 Burroughs Gardens, London NW4 4AU
Tel: 020 8359 1205
Resident Partners/Directors: ICAEW Members
R D Glazer

RONALD FUSS & CO
18 Tenterden Gardens, London, NW4 1TE

ROSENFELD & CO
6 Vivian Avenue, London, NW4 3YA

S SHAIKH
19 Faber Gardens, Hendon, London, NW4 4NP
Tel: 020 8202 8803
Principal: ICAEW Member
S Shaikh

SASSOON SALEH
13 Woodward Avenue, London, NW4 4NU

SHERMAN BASS TRENT & CO
8 Tenterden Drive, London, NW4 1ED

SHINE GARFEN & CO
210 Hendon Way, London, NW4 3NE

SINCLAIR HARRIS
46 Vivian Avenue, Hendon Central, London, NW4 3XP

STEPHEN C STONE & CO
32 Green Lane, London, NW4 2NG

WALLACE SIMSON
Buckingham Chambers, 45 Vivian Avenue, Hendon, London NW4 3XA
Tel: 020 8202 2266
Principal: ICAEW Member
W Simson

WARWICK DURHAM & CO
Senator House, 2 Graham Road, Hendon Central, London NW4 3HJ

LONDON NW5

DUB & CO ★
7 Torriano Mews, Torriano Avenue, London, NW5 2RZ

FREDERICKS
Highgate Business Centre, 33 Greenwood Place, London, NW5 1LB
Tel: 020 7482 1144

FREDERICKS 2001 LTD
Highgate Business Centre, 33 Greenwood Place, London, NW5 1LB
Tel: 020 7482 1144
Resident Partners/Directors: ICAEW Members
J E Chrastek, J F Grassan

KEN FRYER
56 Athlone Street, London, NW5 4LL
Tel: 07041 492171

PRINCE & CO
23 Willes Road, London, NW5 3DT

RICHARD DAVISON ASSOCIATES
Studio 32, Highgate Studios, 53-79 Highgate Road, London NW5 1TL

RICHARD DAVISON ASSOCIATES
Studio 320, Highgate Studios, 53-79 Highgate Road, London NW5 1TL

LONDON NW6

AIMS - CHRISTOPHER HALDER
23 Ingham Road, London, NW6 1DG

ALAN HEYWOOD & CO
78 Mill Lane, West Hampstead, London, NW6 1JZ
Tel: 020 7435 0101
Resident Partners/Directors: ICAEW Members
A Heywood, S G Parekh

ANDY BLACKSTONE
50 Maygrove Road, London, NW6 2EB

AYNESLEY WALTERS COHEN LTD
Suite A, 4-6 Canfield Place, London, NW6 3BT

BARRY PAYDON & CO
Dunluce House, 4/8a Canfield Gardens, London, NW6 3BS

DAVID STONE
16 Goldhurst Terrace, London, NW6 3HU
Tel: 020 7328 4578
Principal: ICAEW Member
D Stone

DAVID SUMMERS & CO
Argo House, Kilburn Park Road, London, NW6 5LF

DAVID SUMMERS & CO LTD
Argo House, Kilburn Park Road, London, NW6 5LF
Tel: 020 7644 0478
Resident Partners/Directors: ICAEW Members
C Haria, D Summers

F.T. GIEBEL & CO
68a Hillfield Road, West Hampstead, London, NW6 1QA

FINANCIAL ANGELS LTD ◈
7 Plaza Parade, Maida Vale, London, NW6 5RP

GOLDWINS
75 Maygrove Road, West Hampstead, London, NW6 2EG

GOLDWINS LTD
75 Maygrove Road, West Hampstead, London, NW6 2EG

HAFEEZ & CO ◈
41 Willesden Lane, London, NW6 7RF
Tel: 020 7328 6769
Principal: ICAEW Member
S M H Qureshi

HARRIS & CO ◈
4-6 Canfield Place, London, NW6 3BT
Tel: 020 7372 2300
Principal: ICAEW Member
N B Harris

KHATIBI & ASSOCIATES ◈
Office 29, Merlin House, 122-126 Kilburn High Road, London NW6 4HY
Tel: 020 7604 4378
Principal: ICAEW Member
I Khatibi

LEVY COHEN & CO ★
37 Broadhurst Gardens, London, NW6 3QT
Tel: 020 7624 2251
Resident Partners/Directors: ICAEW Members
R C Shahmoon

LEWIS-SIMLER
4-5 Coleridge Gardens, Swiss Cottage, London, NW6 3QH

PAUL LYNTON ACA
36 Mutrix Road, London, NW6 4QG

PAYNE & CO
16 Ingham Road, West Hampstead, London, NW6 1DE

PURCELLS
4 Quex Road, London, NW6 4PJ

RAHMAN & CO
3 Narcissus Road, London, NW6 1TJ

THE INCOME TAX RETURN SERVICE
75 Maygrove Road, West Hampstead, London, NW6 2EG

TONY STITT
257 Goldhurst Terrace, London, NW6 3EP
Tel: 020 7624 9388
Mobile: 07831 770636
Principal: ICAEW Member
A V P Stitt
Regulated by the ICAEW for a range of investment business activities
SPECIALISATIONS – TAXATION
Partnerships and Sole Traders
Personal
Self Assessment Advice
Taxation

LONDON NW7

B.S. GREENBERG & CO
2 The Reddings, Mill Hill, London, NW7 4JR
Tel: 020 8906 9846
Principal: ICAEW Member
B S Greenberg

BOOKEY & CO
319 Trafalgar House, Grenville Place, London, NW7 3SA

IAN SKOLNICK & CO
Trafalgar House, Grenville Place, London, NW7 3SA

JAFFERY'S
113 Devonshire Road, Mill Hill, London, NW7 1EA
Tel: 020 8346 1728
Principal: ICAEW Member
M M K Jaffer

JJ ACCOUNTANCY LTD
33-35 Daws Lane, London, NW7 4SD

LAURENCE SCODIE
PO Box 11194, 35B Flower Lane, London, NW7 2JG

LIU WARD & ASSOCIATES
Trafalgar House, 1 Grenville Place, Mill Hill, London NW7 3SA

LWA
Trafalgar House, 1 Grenville Place, Mill Hill, London NW7 3SA

MICHAEL SINCLAIR
Trafalgar House, Grenville Place, Mill Hill, London NW7 3SA
Tel: 020 8905 4478
Principal: ICAEW Member
M Schachter

MICHAEL WONG & CO
23 Hillside Grove, London, NW7 2LS
Tel: 020 8906 3578
Principal: ICAEW Member
M S H Wong

MLA ASSOCIATES LTD
Unit 7, Granard Business Centre, Bunns Lane, Mill Hill, London NW7 2DQ

N.R. SHARLAND & CO
Concorde House, Grenville Place, Mill Hill, London NW7 3SA

NAIR & CO
6 Thornfield Avenue, London, NW7 1LS

NG & CO ◈
Flat 12, Holland Court, Page Street, Mill Hill, London NW7 2DJ
Tel: 020 8201 1888
Principal: ICAEW Member
K Ng

NORMAN WARNER & CO
8 Maxwelton Close, Mill Hill, London, NW7 3NA

PRAVIN VYAS
31 Sylvan Avenue, London, NW7 2JH
Tel: 020 8959 7644
Principal: ICAEW Member
P D Vyas

RICHARD COWEN
Trafalgar House, Grenville Place, London, NW7 3SA

RICHARD YONG & CO
100 Hale Lane, London, NW7 3SE

ROBINSON STEWART & CO
7 Granard Business Centre, Bunns Lane, Mill Hill, London NW7 2DQ
Tel: 020 8906 2232
Principal: ICAEW Member
J S Robinson

SACKMAN & CO LTD
Laynes House, 526-528 Watford Way, London, NW7 4RS

SCOTT & CO
8 Sunbury Gardens, Mill Hill, London, NW7 3SG
Tel: 020 8906 2345
Principal: ICAEW Member
A L Scott

STEINBERG PLATT
643 Watford Way, Apex Corner, Mill Hill, London, NW7 3JR
Tel: 020 8959 0440
Fax: 020 8959 0288
Email: info@steinbergplatt.com
Resident Partners/Directors: ICAEW Members
A M Platt, S M Steinberg
Registered by the ICAEW to carry out company audit work
Regulated by the ICAEW for a range of investment business activities

STEVE REYNOLDS
Suite 125, 6 The Broadway, Mill Hill, London NW7 3LL
Tel: 05602 546209
Email: sreynoldsaccounts@btinternet.com
Website: http://www.sreynoldsaccounts.com
Mobile: 07946 591477
Principal: ICAEW Member
S M Reynolds

LONDON NW8

CH & CO LTD
8 Belgrave Gardens, London, NW8 0RB

GROMAN & CO ◈
5 Violet Hill, St Johns Wood, London, NW8 9EB
Tel: 020 7624 0101
Principal: ICAEW Member
A I Groman

J. AFZAL & CO ◈
23 Grove Hall Court, Hall Road, London, NW8 9NR
Tel: 020 7289 2166
Principal: ICAEW Member
J Afzal

JOHN LEWIS
42-48 Charlbert Street, St Johns Wood, London, NW8 7BU

MARTIN GREENE RAVDEN
55 Loudoun Road, St John's Wood, London, NW8 0DL

MARTIN GREENE RAVDEN LLP
55 Loudoun Road, St John's Wood, London, NW8 0DL

MGR AUDIT LTD
55 Loudoun Road, St Johns Wood, London, NW8 0DL

MILTON AVIS ★
Wellington Building, 28-32 Wellington Road, St John's Wood, London NW8 9SP
Tel: 020 7483 9215
Resident Partners/Directors: ICAEW Members
S C Goh, S J Young

ROBERT EVANS
23 Clifton Hill, St Johns Wood, London, NW8 0QE

SCODIE DEYONG LLP ◈
85 Frampton Street, London, NW8 8NQ
Tel: 020 7535 2700
Resident Partners/Directors: ICAEW Members
L S Deyong, M G Jacobs, L C Kuyper, M Scodie, S J Sefton
Resident Partners (Non-ICAEW Members):
M E James, D Arad

STEPHEN SCHICK
31 Abbey Gardens, London, NW8 9AS
Tel: 020 7328 9723
Email: stephen.schick@btopenworld.com
Principal: ICAEW Member
S E Schick

LONDON NW9

A.M. GARFIELD
120 Salmon Street, Kingsbury, London, NW9 8NL

CHRISTOU & CO
132 Salmon Street, London, NW9 8NT
Tel: 020 8200 8617
Principal: ICAEW Member
A Christou

DE SUSMAN & CO
9th Floor, Hyde House, Edgware Road, Hendon, London NW9 6LH
Tel: 020 8200 8383
Fax: 020 8200 8384
Email: desusmanco@binternet.com
Principal: ICAEW Member
D De
Registered by the ICAEW to carry out company audit work
Regulated by the ICAEW for a range of investment business activities
SPECIALISATIONS – AUDIT & ASSURANCE
Audit
Audit — Private Company
SPECIALISATIONS – FINANCIAL REPORTING
Accounts Preparation
SPECIALISATIONS – TAXATION
Back Duty

DHARUN & CO ACCOUNTANTS & AUDITORS LTD
19 Tintern Avenue, London, NW9 0RH

THE FRASER CONSULTANCY LTD
Alpha House, 646c Kingsbury Road, London, NW9 9HN

FRASERS YOUNG LTD
Alpha House, 646c Kingsbury Road, Kingsbury, London NW9 9HN

GATES FREEDMAN & CO
9th Floor, Hyde House, The Hyde, London NW9 6LQ
Tel: 020 8975 1030
Fax: 020 8975 1031
Email: david@gatesfreedman.co.uk
Principal: ICAEW Member
D C N Freedman
Registered by the ICAEW to carry out company audit work

J.W. PERRY & CO
4th Floor, Hyde House, The Hyde, Edgware Road, London NW9 6LH

KAJAINE LTD
First Floor, Alpine House, Unit 2, Honeypot Lane, London NW9 9RX

KESHANI & CO
506 Kingsbury Road, London, NW9 9HE
Tel: 020 8206 2919
Fax: 020 8206 2082
Email: mebs@keshani.com
Website: http://www.keshani.com
Date Established: 1982
Resident Partners/Directors: ICAEW Members
M Keshani
Regulated by the ICAEW for a range of investment business activities

MACKENZIE FIELD
4th Floor Hyde House, The Hyde, Edgware Road, London NW9 6LA

NAIM AHMED & CO
Knightsbridge House, Kingsbury Road, London, NW9 8XG
Tel: 020 8201 3431
Fax: 020 8201 3438
Email: nahmedco@aol.com
Principal: ICAEW Member
N Ahmed
Registered by the ICAEW to carry out company audit work

PETER E. BYRNE
68 Lavender Avenue, Kingsbury, London, NW9 8HE
Tel: 020 8205 3561
Principal: ICAEW Member
P E Byrne

S DUTT & CO
42 Dunster Drive, London, NW9 8EJ

SJS TAX LTD
Symal House, 423 Edgware Road, London, NW9 0HU

SOARES & CO
1A Colin Parade, Edgware Road, Colindale, London, NW9 6SG

STEPHEN SAMUEL & CO
269 Edgware Road, London, NW9 6NB

TANNA & CO
13 Sheaveshill Parade, Sheaveshill Avenue, London, NW9 6RS

UDAI PARMAR & CO LTD ◈
29 New Way Road, London, NW9 6PL
Tel: 020 8931 0504
Email: udai@udaiparmar.co.uk
Website: http://www.udaiparmar.co.uk
Resident Partners/Directors: ICAEW Members
U S Parmar

WULAR KAUL & CO
61 Colin Crescent, London, NW9 6EU

WULAR KAUL DHOUL & CO
61 Colin Crescent, London, NW9 6EU

YG EATON & CO LTD
Alpine House, Unit 2, 1st Floor, Honeypot Lane, London NW9 9RX
Tel: 020 8206 0077
Resident Partners/Directors: ICAEW Members
R Barve, Y K Gupta

LONDON NW10

A. JACKSON-JAKUBOWSKI
32C Craven Park Road, Harlesden, London, NW10 4AB

ACCOUNTANCY SERVICES LONDON LTD
Suite 401/402, Cumberland House, 80 Scrubs Lane, London NW10 6RF

AMIN & CO
98 Fleetwood Road, Dollis Hill, London, NW10 1NN

C.R.V. GUDKA & CO
306 Neasden Lane, London, NW10 0AD
Tel: 020 8208 1414
Principal: ICAEW Member
C R V Gudka

CHAPMANS ASSOCIATES LTD
3 Coombe Road, London, NW10 0EB

D.WALD & CO
18 Sapcote Trading Centre, Dudden Hill Lane, London, NW10 2DH
Tel: 020 8451 3939
Principal: ICAEW Member
D I L Wald

GARETH MOORS & CO
31 Holland Road, London, NW10 5AH

K K ASSOCIATES
517 Crown House, North Circular Road, Park Royal, London NW10 7PN

MATRIX ◈
112/113 Cumberland House, 80 Scrubs Lane, London, NW10 6RF
Tel: 020 8968 8000
Resident Partners/Directors: ICAEW Members
N Raizada, F Yussouf

PETER WILLIAMS & CO
68 Herbert Gardens, London, NW10 3BU
Tel: 020 89601388
Principal: ICAEW Member
P J Williams

WILLIAMS
Jade House, 67 Park Royal Road, London, NW10 7JJ

YUSSOUF & CO
Suite 401/402, Cumberland House, 80 Scrubs Lane, London NW10 6RF

LONDON NW11

A.J. BRACEINER & CO
Park House, Russell Gardens, Golders Green, London NW11 9NJ
Tel: 020 8905 5432
Principal: ICAEW Member
A J Braceiner

ABIGAIL SAYAGH
12 Beverley Gardens, London, NW11 9DG

ALAN LINDSEY & CO
23 Gresham Gardens, London, NW11 8NX
Tel: 020 8455 2882
Fax: 020 8455 1214
Email: acclindsey@aol.com
Website: http://www.accountantslondon.uk.com
Principal: ICAEW Member
A M Lindsey
Registered by the ICAEW to carry out company audit work
Authorised and regulated by the Financial Services Authority for investment business
General Description: The firm specialises in national and international tax and financial advice. The principal was a member of the ICAEW Council from 1988 to 2007.

ALBERT HECKSCHER & CO
13 Alba Court, Alba Gardens, London, NW11 9NP

ALEXANDER & CO
220 The Vale, London, NW11 8SR

BEN ADLER ASSOCIATES ◈
3rd Floor, Roman House, 296 Golders Green Road, London NW11 9PY

COHEN ARNOLD ◈
New Burlington House, 1075 Finchley Road, Temple Fortune, London NW11 0PU
Tel: 020 8731 0777
Fax: 020 8731 0778
Email: davidgoldberg@cohenarnold.com
Website: http://www.cohenarnold.com
Date Established: 1938
Resident Partners/Directors: ICAEW Members
D M Birns, A J Cohen, D Goldberg, B Leigh, D B Myers, J A Neumann, J Schonberg, J N Schwarz
Resident Partners (Non-ICAEW Members):
D S Davis, D Yu
Registered by the ICAEW to carry out company audit work
Regulated by the ICAEW for a range of investment business activities

DAVID HERSKINE & CO
45 Hurstwood Road, Temple Fortune, London, NW11 0AX

DTE BUSINESS ADVISORY SERVICES LTD
Park House, 26 North End Road, London, NW11 7PT

E F COHEN & CO
21A Russell Gardens, London, NW11 9NJ

EBERT & CO
9 Windsor Court, Golders Green Road, London, NW11 9PP

EDMUND WRIGHT & CO
90 The Ridgeway, London, NW11 9RU
Tel: 020 8201 8600
Email: edmundwright@beancounter.biz
Principal: ICAEW Member
R E Wright
Registered by the ICAEW to carry out company audit work
Regulated by the ICAEW for a range of investment business activities
SPECIALISATIONS – BUSINESS & GENERAL ADVICE
Management Advice to Business
SPECIALISATIONS – INVESTMENT BUSINESS
Financial Planning and Advice
SPECIALISATIONS – TAXATION
Payroll Service and Advice
Taxation

FADAVI & CO LTD
8b Accommodation Road, London, NW11 8ED

FAIZ & CO
8b Accommodation Road, Golders Green, London, NW11 8ED
Tel: 020 8819 6931

FAIZ & CO LTD
8b Accommodation Road, Golders Green, London, NW11 8ED
Tel: 020 8819 6931
Resident Partners/Directors: ICAEW Members
B Faiz-Mahdavi

FOX ASSOCIATE LLP
Britanic House, 17 Highfield Road, London, NW11 9LS

FOX SHARER LLP
Britannic House, 17 Highfield Road, London, NW11 9LS

GERALD KREDITOR & CO ◈
Hallswelle House, 1 Hallswelle Road, London, NW11 0DH
Tel: 020 8209 1535
Fax: 020 8209 1923
Email: admin@geraldkreditor.co.uk
Resident Partners/Directors: ICAEW Members
M Rosen, I S Sivlal, J Smulovitch, P P Smulovitch
Resident Partners (Non-ICAEW Members):
I S Sivlal
Registered by the ICAEW to carry out company audit work
Regulated by the ICAEW for a range of investment business activities

GILBERT, ALLAN & CO
8 Rodborough Road, London, NW11 8RY

GLAZERS ◈
843 Finchley Road, London, NW11 8NA

GOODMAN & CO
14 Basing Hill, Golders Green, London, NW11 8TH

GRUNBERG & CO ◈
10-14 Accommodation Road, Golders Green, London, NW11 8ED

H & H ASSOCIATES ◈
18 Connaught Drive, Finchley, London, NW11 6BJ
Tel: 020 8209 0835
Website: http://www.hhassociates.co.uk
Resident Partners/Directors: ICAEW Members
H Hardoon
SPECIALISATIONS – BUSINESS & GENERAL ADVICE
Acquisitions and Mergers
SPECIALISATIONS – FINANCIAL REPORTING
Accounts Preparation
SPECIALISATIONS – IT
Computer Systems and Consultancy
Computerised Accounting Systems
E-commerce

HAMILTON, GOODMAN & CO
22 Hill Rise, London, NW11 6NA

HAMMER & CO
Flat 13, Alba Court, Alba Gardens, London NW11 9NP
Tel: 020 8455 9123

HAMMER & CO ACCOUNTANTS LTD
13 Alba Court, Alba Gardens, London, NW11 9NP
Tel: 020 8455 9123
Resident Partners/Directors: ICAEW Members
A Hammer

JOHN GALPERT
6 Montpelier Rise, London, NW11 9SS

JOSEPH KAHAN ASSOCIATES
923 Finchley Road, London, NW11 7PE

JOSEPH KAHAN ASSOCIATES LLP
923 Finchley Road, London, NW11 7PE

M. WECHSLER
48 Brookside Road, London, NW11 9NE
Tel: 020 8458 8856
Principal: ICAEW Member
M Wechsler

MARTIN + HELLER
5 North End Road, London, NW11 7RJ

MARTIN SKLAN & CO
133 Golders Green Road, London, NW11 8HJ
Tel: 020 8458 4433
Principal: ICAEW Member
A Martin-Sklan

MAWSON BRESKAL & CO ★
Bishops House, Monkville Avenue, London, NW11 0AH
Tel: 020 8458 8636
Resident Partners/Directors: ICAEW Members
G Breskal

MICHAEL, PASHA & CO
220 The Vale, London, NW11 8SR

MINAYAN & CO LTD
8b Accomodation Road, London, NW11 8ED
Tel: 020 8209 1646
Resident Partners/Directors: ICAEW Members
F Minaeian

MOUNT KATTEN & CO
35 Temple Gardens, London, NW11 0LP
Tel: 020 8458 5329
Principal: ICAEW Member
I Katzenberg

N L TUCHBAND
925 Finchley Road, London, NW11 7PE

R FULENA AND CO
41 Britten Close, Wellgarth Road, London, NW11 7HQ

R J TAYLOR
26 Midholm, Hampstead Garden Suburb, London, NW11 6LN

RAYMOND BIRNS
20 Woodstock Avenue, London, NW11 9SL
Tel: 020 8458 3159
Principal: ICAEW Member
R Birns

S L GALPERT & CO
6 Montpelier Rise, London, NW11 9SS

S.L. GALPERT & CO LTD
6 Montpelier Rise, London, NW11 9SS

SEYMOUR KING
2nd Floor, Hillview House, 1 Hallswelle Parade, London NW11 0DL

SINCLAIR ASSOCIATES ◈
Roman House, 296 Golders Green Road, London, NW11 9PT
Tel: 020 8455 0011

SINCLAIR UK ASSOCIATES LTD ◈
Roman House, 296 Golders Green Road, London, NW11 9PT
Tel: 020 8455 0011
Resident Partners/Directors: ICAEW Members
D G Sinclair

STANTON & CO
6 Princes Park Avenue, London, NW11 0JP

STERN ASSOCIATES
2 Helenslea Avenue, London, NW11 8ND

TUCHBANDS ★
925 Finchley Road, London, NW11 7PE
Tel: 020 8458 8727
Fax: 020 8209 1557
Email: info@tuchbands.com
Website: http://www.tuchbands.com
Resident Partners/Directors: ICAEW Members
P A Woolfson
Resident Partners (Non-ICAEW Members):
N Poli

Registered by the ICAEW to carry out company audit work

Regulated by the ICAEW for a range of investment business activities

SPECIALISATIONS – AUDIT & ASSURANCE
Audit — Private Company

SPECIALISATIONS – FINANCIAL REPORTING
Limited Company Accounts
Partnership/Sole Trader Accounts

SPECIALISATIONS – TAXATION
UK Companies Overseas

VARBECK LTD
56 Highfield Avenue, London, NW11 9UD

THE ZANE PARTNERSHIP
925 Finchley Road, London, NW11 7PE

LONDON SE1

1ST OPTION CONSULTING
Lyon House, 160-166 Borough High Street, London, SE1 1JR

1ST OPTION CONSULTING SERVICES LTD
Lyon House, 160-166 Borough High Street, London Bridge, London SE1 1JR

AKE SERVICES LTD
20 Anchor Terrace, 3-13 Southwark Bridge Road, London, SE1 9HQ

ANDREW RATCLIFFE
1 Hays Lane, London, SE1 2RD

CHANDA ASSOCIATES
23 King Edward Walk, London, SE1 7PR
Tel: 020 7928 3786
Principal: ICAEW Member
R Chanda

CHAPMAN DAVIS LLP
2 Chapel Court, London, SE1 1HH
Tel: 020 7357 6008
Resident Partners/Directors: ICAEW Members
J C Davis, R J Palmer

CONDUIT BUSINESS INFORMATION
9 Maltings Place, Tower Bridge Road, London, SE1 3JB

COULTHARDS MACKENZIE
International House, 39-45 Bermondsey Street, London, SE1 3XF

DAVERT BANKS & CO
11 St Saviours Wharf, Mill Street, London, SE1 2BE

DAVID ANTHONY & CO
5 The Gateway, Rathmore Road, London, SE7 7QW

E.C. BROWN & BATTS ◈
Delta House, 175-177 Borough High Street, London, SE1 1HR

ERNST & YOUNG LTD
1 More London Place, London, SE1 2AF

ERNST & YOUNG EUROPE LLP
Becket House, 1 Lambeth Palace Road, London, SE1 7EU

ERNST & YOUNG LLP
1 More London Place, London, SE1 2AF
Tel: 020 7951 2000
Fax: 020 7951 1345
Resident Partners/Directors: ICAEW Members
S J Abbott, L J Sass, C P Alexander, J E L Anderson, A Anthony, D P J Arnold, G P Atkins, J M Babiak, I J J Baggs, A C Baker, V Balakrishnan, K L Barrow, A J Barton, J A Bates, A A Beecher, S D Bell, A J Belton, M Bevington, A R Bloom, J Bourne, C S Bowles, M N M Boyd, R S Brown, M P Burke, W N Bussey, M J Buxton, S L Callaghan, D G Canning-Jones, E H Carruthers, C G Cartmell, B A Castell, J R Charlton, H L Cleaton-Roberts, A R E Clifford, S E Clifford, J D E Close, J G Cole, J L Constantine, N C Corp, M J D Corson, R Cubbage, T J A Curry, P H Curtis, S M Date, T N Davison, J W Dean, G J Deuchar, A Duncan, L J Ed, R J Engineer, M Evans, D A Eyre, D G Fairhurst, K S Farr, R N Findlater, M Fishman, J C Flaherty, I R Francis, E W Gardner, D A Gaunt, G M George, H T Gill, K D Gill, D J Gittleson, A J Glover, A Godfrey, N K Gomer, T R Gordon, A H F Grant, N J Gray, P J Green, S R Gregory, C Grounds, P Haberman, N L Halkes, R A Hall, J H Harley, R A Harper, J A Headley, R D J Heath, K M Honey, C G Honnywill, C Hooper, T V Howard, C W O Hughes, G H Hughes, R K Indge, R C Ireland, S G Ivermee, S M Jennings, A D Jones, N G O Jones, R D Jowitt, N Kaul, D W Lambert, S C Lang, D J Larnder, T A F Leary, T J Leggett, J A Lenton, J R Lester, J R Liver, S E Long, A J Love, R J Lowe, M D Lynch-Bell, K P Macauley, P G Maddox, H D Martin, P H Martin, A M Mawji, C E McAree, T B McCartney, M D A McCormick, R R McCracken, A H McCrae, J F McCready, K McGregor, J M McIlroy, A J McIntyre, J E Meader, M C Mealey, T M Medak, S P Michaelson, A J Millar, A S Millings, M E Mills, J E W Morris, T J Morris, R J Murray, E Mustafa, S A Nash, A C Nicholls, A C P Noble, G K Norman, D Oldknow, R Overend, S J Parkinson, N Pasricha, I M Paterson, K Paterson, S M Pearson, R K Perkin, S T Perry, R A J Phillip, N J Philpott, N H Pickersgill, S J Porter, G Prothero, W Rainey, L S Rattigan, D L Read, R Rees-Pulley, L K Roberts, J A Robertson-Kellie, J L Robson, R A C Roman, T J Rooke, S M Routledge, D L Royce, G W Russell, I F Sadler, D A Sage, R C Sandwell, C Sanger, P E R Sater, I A Scott, M A Semple, K W Senior, R A Shah, F F Sheffield, F D Small, R A Smee, R G Solomon, P H Spence, E Stanton, J A Stanton, T J Steel, P T Stevens, M A Stilwell, A Swarbrick, M H Taylor, S C Taylor, A D Tivey, R E Upton, D L Vaughan, A J Vickery, P I Wallace, A Walton, R J Ward, G S J Watkins, L W Watson, A Whitaker, D J Whitecross, I J P Whitlock, G Wild, I R Wilkie, D L Wilkinson, S J Williams, K A Williamson, K G Williamson, N J Willis, S P Wills, R W Wilson, R F Winchester, A D Woosey, J A Worth, J A Young, P J Young

EYOP LLP
1 More London Place, London, SE1 2AF

GREENBACK ALAN LLP ◈
11 Raven Wharf, Lafone Street, London, SE1 2LR
Tel: 020 7403 5959
Fax: 020 7403 3111
Email: gba@greenback-alan.co.uk
Website: http://www.greenback-alan.co.uk
Resident Partners/Directors: ICAEW Members
M K Christy, S A Dabby, A S Green
Resident Partners (Non-ICAEW Members):
N Nicolaou, T Sian

INTANGIBLE BUSINESS
9 Maltings Place, 169 Tower Bridge Road, London, SE1 3JB
Tel: 020 7089 9236

INTANGIBLE BUSINESS LTD
9 Maltings Place, 169 Tower Bridge Road, London, SE1 3JB

JB WILKINS KENNEDY
Bridge House, London Bridge, London, SE1 9QR

K.J. DESAI & CO
51 Lafone Street, London, SE1 2LX

KEITH REYNOLDS ASSOCIATES
Ground Floor, 135 Bermondsey Street, London, SE1 3UW
Tel: 020 7403 0366
Principal: ICAEW Member
J K Reynolds

MARTYN CHILVERS & CO
Long Lane Studios, 142-152 Long Lane, London, SE1 4BS
Tel: 020 7407 1676
Principal: ICAEW Member
M L Chilvers

O'FARRELL
1 Chaucer Drive, London, SE1 5TA
Tel: 020 7252 2583
Principal: ICAEW Member
W O'Farrell

PARKER RANDALL
9 Bickels Yard, 151-153 Bermondsey Street, London, SE1 3HA

PARKER RANDALL LLP
9 Bickels Yard, 151-153 Bermondsey Street, London Bridge, London SE1 3HA

PATEL DODHIA & CO
4 Trinity Street, London, SE1 1DB

PK PARTNERS LLP
Suite 7, The Hop Exchange, 24 Southwark Street, London SE1 1TY

PRICE FIRMAN
Prince Consort House, Albert Embankment, London, SE1 7TJ

PRICEWATERHOUSE-COOPERS
6 Hay's Lane, London, SE1 2HB

PRICEWATERHOUSE-COOPERS
Hay's Galleria, 1 Hays Lane, London, SE1 2RD

PRICEWATERHOUSE-COOPERS
10-18 Union Street, London, SE1 1SZ

PRICEWATERHOUSE-COOPERS LLP
10-18 Union Street, London, SE1 1SZ
Tel: 020 7583 5000
Resident Partners/Directors: ICAEW Members
D W Adair, R M Bailey, P Boorman, A M Debell, J B Grosvenor, J L Scott, P Wallace

PRICEWATERHOUSE-COOPERS LLP
Hays Galleria, 1 Hays Lane, London, SE1 2RD
Tel: 020 7583 5000
Resident Partners/Directors: ICAEW Members
M Amin, G I A Armfield, M Barling, S Barnes, P V Barrow, M E Batten, S Berryman, J W E Bichard, M N Bolton, J R Bromfield, P J L Calnan, J R Calvert-Davies, R J Clark, P E C Clarke, R S Collier, K A Corcoran, A D Crawford-Ingle, H J Daubeney, I F Davis, A E Devoy, I E Dilks, N M S Drewett, P A Evans, M G Falconer, J D Forbes, J M R Foster, B J Furness, R G Gardiner, D W Grace, C F Graham, A J Gray, I J L Griffiths, A M Hamilton, M N Higgin, S Higgins, A G Hill, M N Hine, J J Holloway, J P Howe, H R A Hudson, S D Hunt, C F Ilako, K Ingram, G R Ireland, P C Jeffrey, H D Jenkins, J R Jensen, D M J Jessup, C P Jones, A Kail, R J Keers, D G Ketteringham, S B Kundu, K S Laing-Williams, P C Maybrey, M.E.McLaren, D J McNab, D L Meek, A C M Morris, P H Nash, P J Newberry, M P Newman, D M Newton, R Oldfield, R G Palmer, D A Pedropillai, G M Phillips, G P N Phillips, J M Picton, R J Pollard, C W Potter, G J Powell, J D Preston, R M L Pugh, P S Purewal, A N Ratcliffe, P G Rivett, R Rowe, C C Rowland, P S Samaratunga, T M Stephen, G E Stylianides, J H Tattersall, D J Taylor, N J D Terry, P G Tew, C E Thompson, N J Vooght, P Wilkin, J J T Woodhouse, C J Woolcott, S J Wooldridge

PRICEWATERHOUSE-COOPERS LLP
6 Hay's Lane, London, SE1 2HB
Tel: 020 7583 5000

REEVES+NEYLAN LLP
Colechurch House, 1 London Bridge Walk, London, SE1 2SX
Tel: 020 7407 7604
Resident Partners/Directors: ICAEW Members
P D Hudson
Registered by the ICAEW to carry out company audit work
Regulated by the ICAEW for a range of investment business activities

RICKARDS(1993)LTD
Unit 2, Market Yard Mews, 194 Bermondsey Street, London SE1 3TJ

ROLAND KLEPZIG LTD
42 Copperfield Street, London, SE1 0DY
Tel: 020 7620 3005
Resident Partners/Directors: ICAEW Members
R P Klepzig

S.N. BARTARYA
75 Weston Street, London, SE1 3RS

STEWARD & CO
151 Borough High Street, London, SE1 1HR

T.R. SHAW
7 Gladstone Street, London, SE1 6EY

TAYLOR MEDCRAFT AND CO
The Garden Flat, County Hall, London, SE1 7GN
Tel: 020 7021 0340
Principal: ICAEW Member
A G Taylor

WALTERS ASSOCIATES
Unit B, 15 Bell Yard Mews, Bermondsey Street, London SE1 3TY
Tel: 020 7403 8558

WILKINS KENNEDY ◈
Bridge House, London Bridge, London, SE1 9QR
Tel: 020 7403 1877
Website: http://www.wilkinskennedy.com
Resident Partners/Directors: ICAEW Members
C B Baynes, S R Golder, P A Goodman, D R Graves, R T Haslam, J Howard, P R Manning, W J B Payne, R D Reynolds, R C P Smith, C G Wiseman
Resident Partners (Non-ICAEW Members):
A M Cork, J C Selby
Other Offices: Amersham, Ashford, Egham, Guildford,
continued

WILKINS KENNEDY *cont*
Hertford, Orpington, Reading, Romsey, Southend, Winchester
Overseas Offices: Stanley, Falkland Islands
Registered by the ICAEW to carry out company audit work
Regulated by the ICAEW for a range of investment business activities
Individual(s) licensed for insolvency work by another RPB

SPECIALISATIONS – BUSINESS & GENERAL ADVICE
Acquisitions and Mergers
Disposal of Businesses
Outsourcing - Financial Services

SPECIALISATIONS – BUSINESS RECOVERY & INSOLVENCY
Bankruptcies
Corporate Recovery
Liquidations
Reorganisations and Company Reconstructions

SPECIALISATIONS – FORENSIC ACCOUNTING
Expert Witnesses in Litigation

SPECIALISATIONS – SECTOR
Charities
Construction
FSA Members
Insurance Brokers
Property
Solicitors
Languages Spoken:
French, German

LONDON SE2

SAIFUDDIN & CO
253 Wickham Lane, Abbey Wood, London, SE2 0NX

LONDON SE3

AIMS-MARTIN FOLEY ◈
4 Grotes Place, London, SE3 0QH
Tel: 020 8297 5022

B.A. KIRK & CO ◈
21A Ulundi Road, Blackheath, London, SE3 7UQ
Tel: 020 8858 3051
Principal: ICAEW Member
B A Kirk

LANDERGAN & CO
42 Whetstone Road, London, SE3 8PX

LEVETT CHARLES & CO (BLACKHEATH)
237 Westcombe Hill, Blackheath, London, SE3 7DW
Tel: 020 8858 4303
Principal: ICAEW Member
S A Saward

THE LIFE OF RILEY LTD
20 Humber Road, Blackheath, London, SE3 7LT

RICHARD HEWSON & CO
21 Corner Green, London, SE3 9JJ

SMITH & EADES
113 Humber Road, Blackheath, London, SE3 7LW

SUSAN STELFOX ◈
46 The Keep, Blackheath, London, SE3 0AF
Tel: 020 8318 4848
Fax: 020 8297 8041
Email: susan.stelfox@susanstelfox.co.uk
Principal: ICAEW Member
S Stelfox
Registered by the ICAEW to carry out company audit work
Regulated by the ICAEW for a range of investment business activities

SPECIALISATIONS – AUDIT & ASSURANCE
Audit — Private Company

SPECIALISATIONS – BUSINESS & GENERAL ADVICE
Book-keeping

SPECIALISATIONS – FINANCIAL REPORTING
Accounts Preparation

SPECIALISATIONS – TAXATION
Payroll Service and Advice

ZANDAN LTD ◈
4 Grotes Place, Blackheath, London, SE3 0QH
Tel: 020 8297 5022
Principal: ICAEW Member
M J Foley

LONDON SE4

COMPLETION ACCOUNTS LTD
19 St Margarets Road, London, SE4 1YL

SHABBIR & CO
248 Brockley Road, London, SE4 2SF
Tel: 020 8691 2942
Resident Partners/Directors: ICAEW Members
M A Saleemi, G Shabbir
See display advertisement near this entry.

LONDON SE5

ATHENA & CO ◈
189 John Ruskin Street, London, SE5 0PT
Tel: 05601 392135
Principal: ICAEW Member
A C K Wan

CHELEPIS WATSON
Chelco House, 39 Camberwell Church Street, London, SE5 8TR
Tel: 020 7703 6602
Fax: 020 7701 4635
Email: office@chelepiswatson.co.uk
Resident Partners/Directors: ICAEW Members
P S Dunn, G Georgiou, N F Springer, M G Tsielepis, P L Wallyn
Resident Partners (Non-ICAEW Members):
M C Voniatis
Registered by the ICAEW to carry out company audit work

CHELEPIS WATSON
39 Camberwell Church Street, London, SE5 8TR

CHELEPIS WATSON LTD
Chelco House, 39 Camberwell Church Street, London, SE5 8TR

RICHARD SAMSON
21 Coldharbour Lane, London, SE5 9NR

T.R. SOUTH & CO
214 Ruskin Park House, Champion Hill, London, SE5 8TN

LONDON SE6

AIMS ACCOUNTANTS
84 Crantock Road, London, SE6 2QP
Tel: 020 8695 8618
Principal: ICAEW Member
R L Murphy

PATRICK HERELLE
88 Daneby Road, Catford, London, SE6 2QG
Tel: 020 8697 6732
Principal: ICAEW Member
P Herelle

PETER LOUTH AND CO
18 Westdown Road, Catford, London, SE6 4RL
Tel: 020 8690 8231
Principal: ICAEW Member
P Louth

T. BURTON & CO
178 Brownhill Rd, Catford, London, SE6 2DJ

LONDON SE9

DENNY SULLIVAN & ASSOCIATES LLP ◈
155 Greenvale Road, Eltham, London, SE9 1PG
Tel: 020 7713 1600

EUAN WILLIAMS
55 Glenesk Road, Eltham, London, SE9 1AH

J.C BEAMES & CO
4 The Crossway, Mottingham, London, SE9 4JJ

M.P. GRIMES & CO
154a Eltham High Street, Eltham, London, SE9 1BJ
Tel: 020 8850 8280
Principal: ICAEW Member
M P Grimes

NICHOLS & CO (ACCOUNTANCY) LTD
Unit 7, Mulberry Place, Pinnell Road, London SE9 6AR

STANLEY HELM LTD
17 Court Yard, London, SE9 5PR

LONDON SE10

IAN MURRAY & CO
40 Stockwell Street, London, SE10 8EY

MED ACT ◈
107 Old Woolwich Road, Greenwich, London, SE10 9PP
Tel: 020 8544 0300
Email: medact@medact.eu
Principal: ICAEW Member
R H Russell
Other Offices:107 Old Woolwich Road, Greenwich, London, SE10 9PP

SPECIALISATIONS – FINANCIAL REPORTING
Partnership/Sole Trader Accounts

SPECIALISATIONS – SECTOR
Doctors

SPECIALISATIONS – TAXATION
Partnerships and Sole Traders
Self Assessment Advice

SUSAN FIELD
Neptune House, 70 Royal Hill, London, SE10 8RF

SUSAN FIELD LTD
Neptune House, 70 Royal Hill, London, SE10 8RF

LONDON SE11

BEAR SPACE LTD
9 Denny Crescent, London, SE11 4UY

BEAR SPACE FINANCE AND MANAGEMENT LLP
9 Denny Crescent, London, SE11 4UY

LONDON SE12

GURAM & CO
130 Marvels Lane, Grove Park, London, SE12 9PG

R.E.JONES & CO ◈
132 Burnt Ash Road, Lee, London, SE12 8PU
Tel: 020 8318 1417
Resident Partners/Directors: ICAEW Members
L J Cox

S. BERI & CO
74 Burnt Ash Road, Lee, London, SE12 8PY

S. BERI & CO LTD
74 Burnt Ash Road, Lee, London, SE12 8PY

LONDON SE13

ANDREW CROSS & CO ★
The Plaza Building, Lee High Road, Lewisham, London SE13 5PT

CHASE REEVES & CO LTD
Chase House, 90 Springbank Road, London, SE13 6SX

CONRADI MORRISON
207 Lewisham High Street, London, SE13 6LY
Tel: 020 8318 1336
Fax: 020 8463 0331
Email: admin@conradimorrison.co.uk
Website: http://www.conradimorrison.co.uk
Non-resident Partners (ICAEW Members):
P L Wallyn, P G Runacres
Resident Partners (Non-ICAEW Members):
K D Hardie
Non-resident Partners (Non-ICAEW Members):
S B Ison
Registered by the ICAEW to carry out company audit work

CONRADI MORRISON (SOUTH EAST) LLP
207 Lewisham High Street, London, SE13 6LY
Tel: 020 8318 1336
Email: admin@conradimorrison.co.uk
Resident Partners/Directors: ICAEW Members
P L Wallyn
Resident Partners (Non-ICAEW Members):
K D Hardie
Non-resident Partners (Non-ICAEW Members):
P L Wallyn, S B Ison, P S Dunn
Registered by the ICAEW to carry out company audit work
Regulated by the ICAEW for a range of investment business activities

NEWNHAM & CO
65 Morden Hill, London, SE13 7NP

S.G. RIPLEY & CO
157 Lewisham Road, London, SE13 7PZ
Tel: 020 8852 6926
Resident Partners/Directors: ICAEW Members
M J Hodgson-Barker, S G Ripley

S.G. RIPLEY & CO LTD Ⓜ
157 Lewisham Road, London, SE13 7PZ
Tel: 020 8852 6629
Resident Partners/Directors: ICAEW Members
M J Hodgson-Barker, S G Ripley

SYLVA & CO
105 Loampit Vale, Lewisham, London, SE13 7TG
Tel: 020 8694 8669
Principal: ICAEW Member
S I C Okoye

WAGSTAFF, ROWLAND & HUNTLEY ★
27 Lewisham High St, London, SE13 5AF

LONDON SE14

BACCMA CONSULTING (MG BACCHUS)
92 Jerningham Road, Telegraph Hill, London, SE14 5NW

LONDON SE16

AMATI UK LTD
39 Plover Way, London, SE16 7TS
Tel: 020 7870 9890
Resident Partners/Directors: ICAEW Members
J L Macarthur

COCKE, VELLACOTT & HILL
Unit 3, Dock Offices, Surrey Quays Road, Surrey Quays, London Se16 SE16 2XU
Tel: 020 7394 1717
Fax: 020 7740 1673
Email: cvandh@c-v-h.co.uk
Resident Partners/Directors: ICAEW Members
C W Brailey, J A Russell
Registered by the ICAEW to carry out company audit work

DAS UK LTD
1st Floor, Windsor House, 1270 London Road, London SW16 4DH

JPCA LTD
17 City Business Centre, Lower Road, London, SE16 2XB

MARTYN POOLE & CO
35 St Olav's Court, Lower Road, Rotherhithe, London, SE16 2XB

POOLE MORDANT LLP
35 City Business Centre, St Olav's Court, Rotherhithe, London SE16 2XB
Tel: 020 7232 0707
Resident Partners/Directors: ICAEW Members
M R Poole

LONDON SE18

BAJARIA, GIBBS & CO ◈
72 Plumstead High Street, London, SE18 1SL
Tel: 020 8854 5591
Principal: ICAEW Member
C S Lau

MARK R WILLIAMS LLP
362 Shooters Hill Road, London, SE18 4LS

MAURICE G. WOOD PARTNERSHIP
69 Plumstead Common Road, Plumstead, London, SE18 3AX

THE ROY SOKHAL GROUP ◈
Suite 235, 2nd Floor, Island Business Centre, 18-36 Wellington Street, Woolwich, London Se18 SE18 6PF
Tel: 020 8316 1300
Principal: ICAEW Member
J P R Sokhal

SIMPSON, WREFORD & CO
Wellesley House, Duke of Wellington Avenue, Royal Arsenal, London SE18 6SS

LONDON SE19

AIMS - ROBERT BULL
4 Park Lodge, 80 Auckland Road, London, SE19 2DF

API PARTNERSHIP LTD
75 Westow Hill, London, SE19 1TX
Tel: 020 8761 2213
Resident Partners/Directors: ICAEW Members
C T Jobanputra, P Karageorghis, A Sotiriou

SPECIALISATIONS – AUDIT & ASSURANCE
Audit

SPECIALISATIONS – BUSINESS & GENERAL ADVICE
Book-keeping
Book-keeping Systems
Company Formation
Company Secretarial Service

SPECIALISATIONS – FINANCIAL REPORTING
Accounts Preparation
Audit Exemption Report
Financial Reporting
Foreign Subsidiary Companies
Limited Companies
Limited Company Accounts
Limited Liability Partnership
Partnership/Sole Trader Accounts

SPECIALISATIONS – INVESTMENT BUSINESS
Financial Planning and Advice

SPECIALISATIONS – SECTOR
Advertising/Design Agencies
Architects/Surveyors
Artists/Graphic Designers
Catering/Restaurants
Charities
Clothing/Textiles
Clubs/Associations
Construction
Corporate
Dentists/Opticians
Doctors
Electronics
Estate Agent

continued

API PARTNERSHIP LTD *cont*
Food Industry
FSA Members
Insurance Brokers
Journalists/Writers/Copywriters
Leisure Industry
Media
Nursing Homes/Clinics
Paper/Printing/Publishing
Property
Property Development
Property Investment
Registered Social Landlords
Retailers
Solicitors
Traders — General
Traders — Luxury Items
Transport
Travel Industry

SPECIALISATIONS – TAXATION

Capital Gains — Personal
Employee
Estate and Inheritance
Estate Planning
Executorship
Foreign Nationals in the UK
National Insurance Advice
Offshore Companies
Partnerships and Sole Traders
PAYE Advice
Payroll Service and Advice
Self Assessment Advice
Small Traders
Taxation
UK Subsidiaries of Overseas Multinationals
Value Added Tax
See display advertisement near this entry.

BROOKFIELD & CO
52 Church Road, Crystal Palace, London, SE19 2EZ

CHELEPIS WATSON LTD
67 Westow Street, London, SE19 3RW

GIBSONS ◈
Foresters Hall, 25-27 Westow Street, London, SE19 3RY
Tel: 020 8916 1212
Fax: 020 8916 1211
Email: gibsons@gibsonsllp.com
Date Established: 1986
Resident Partners/Directors: ICAEW Members
G C Gibbs, S.C. O'Neill, C O Ogunsola
Resident Partners (Non-ICAEW Members):
S Brennan, P Buck
Registered by another RSB to carry out company audit work

J DIGBY-ROGERS
13 Gipsy Hill, London, SE19 1QG

PATEL KHANDERIA & CO
9 Hitherwood Drive, London, SE19 1XA

PEGG ROBERTSON LTD
67 Westow Street, London, SE19 3RW
Tel: 020 8768 6266
Email: admin@peggrobertson.co.uk
Website: http://www.peggrobertson.co.uk
Resident Partners/Directors: ICAEW Members
P S Dunn, P L Wallyn
Registered by the ICAEW to carry out company audit work
Regulated by the ICAEW for a range of investment business activities

R. BULL
4 Park Lodge, 80 Auckland Road, London, SE19 2DF

ROBERT TYDEMAN & CO
58 Gipsy Hill, Upper Norwood, London, SE19 1PD
Tel: 020 8265 6894
Principal: ICAEW Member
R K Tydeman

THORNTON SPRINGER INTERNATIONAL LTD
67 Westow Street, Upper Norwood, London, SE19 3RW

THORNTON SPRINGER LLP
67 Westow Street, Upper Norwood, London, SE19 3RW
Tel: 020 8771 8661
Email: ts@thorntonspringer.co.uk
Resident Partners/Directors: ICAEW Members
P S Dunn, N F Springer, P L Wallyn
Resident Partners (Non-ICAEW Members):
S B Ison, S A Kaye, D J Ankrah
Registered by the ICAEW to carry out company audit work
Regulated by the ICAEW for a range of investment business activities

LONDON SE20

THAUOOS & CO
201 High Street, Penge, London, SE20 7PF

THOMPSON & HUNTER
10 Genoa Road, London, SE20 8ES

LONDON SE21

BHATIA, SONNADARA & CO ★
74 Alleyn Park, West Dulwich, London, SE21 8SF

J.TAYLOR SERVICES LTD
172 Burbage Road, London, SE21 7AG

RODERICK C HOLE
28 Rouse Gardens, Alleyn Park, London, SE21 8AF

LONDON SE22

BENNETT & CO ★
16 Upland Road, Dulwich, London, SE22 9GG

FELLS ACCOUNTING SERVICES
130 Friern Road, East Dulwich, London, SE22 0AY

K.A.JEFFRIES & CO
18 Melbourne Grove, London, SE22 8RA

NICHOLAS NG AND CO
201 Lordship Lane, Dulwich, London, SE22 8HA

NICHOLAS NG AND COMPANY LTD
201 Lordship Lane, Dulwich, London, SE22 8HA

LONDON SE23

SHEA & CO LTD
105 Stansted Road, London, SE23 1HH

TAYLOR ASSOCIATES
23 St Germans Road, Forest Hill, London, SE23 1RH

LONDON SE24

A.S. ZANETTOS & CO
4 Croxted Mews, 286A/288 Croxted Road, Nr. Dulwich Village, London SE24 9DA

AIMS - ANDREW GARRAN
61 Beckwith Road, London, SE24 9LQ

LONDON SE25

ACCOUNTANCY GROUP
SVS House, Oliver Grove, London, SE25 6EJ

SOTERIOU CHRISTOU
6A Dickenson's Place, London, SE25 5HL

SOTERIOU CHRISTOU LTD
6a Dickenson's Place, London, SE25 5HL
Tel: 020 8655 2252
Website: http://www.soteriouchristou.co.uk
Resident Partners/Directors: ICAEW Members
P Soteriou
Registered by the ICAEW to carry out company audit work

SPECIALISATIONS – AUDIT & ASSURANCE

Audit — Private Company

SPECIALISATIONS – FINANCIAL REPORTING

Limited Company Accounts

SPECIALISATIONS – TAXATION

Payroll Service and Advice
Self Assessment Advice

Small Traders
Value Added Tax

WRIGHT & CO
57 High Street, South Norwood, London, SE25 6EF

LONDON SE26

BAMBURY & CO
Flat 4, Goodwood House, Park Court, Lawrie Park Road, London Se26 SE26 6EQ

K.S. POTTER
16 Peckarmans Wood, London, SE26 6RY

K. S. POTTER, FCA
16 Peckarmans Wood, London, SE26 6RY

MICHAEL WHEELER
8 Hall Drive, Sydenham, London, SE26 6XB
Tel: 020 8778 2687
Principal: ICAEW Member
M J Wheeler

MILLER DAVIES ◈
Unit A3, Broomsleigh Business Park, Worsley Bridge Road, London SE26 5BN
Tel: 020 8695 8210
Fax: 020 8695 8211
Email: info@millerdavies.co.uk
Resident Partners/Directors: ICAEW Members
R J Bedford, M R Davies
Registered by the ICAEW to carry out company audit work
Regulated by the ICAEW for a range of investment business activities

MORRISON & CO
4 Crescent Wood Road, Sydenham Hill, London, SE26 6RU

LONDON SE27

GIWA-OSAGIE DFK & CO ★
116 Glennie Road, London, SE27 0LU

LONDON SW1

A J MEASURES
157-197 Buckingham Palace Road, London, SW1W 9SP

A.M. WAJIH FCA
44 Clabon Mews, London, SW1X 0EH
Tel: 020 7225 0020
Principal: ICAEW Member
A M Wajih

THE ACCOUNTS BUREAU LTD
1 Warwick Row, London, SW1E 5ER
Tel: 020 7808 7177
Resident Partners/Directors: ICAEW Members
M M Weston
See display advertisement near this entry.

AEGIS ACCOUNTING SERVICES
New Zealand House, 9th Floor, 80 Haymarket, London SW1Y 4TQ

ALLAN AS LTD ◈
14 Vincent Square Mansions, Walcott Street, London, SW1P 2NT
Tel: 0845 838 7445

BEECHCROFT ASSOCIATES LTD ◈
Greencoat House, Francis Street, London, SW1P 1DH
Tel: 020 7233 6111
Resident Partners/Directors: ICAEW Members
T J Gerhard, F A Lilley, S Mollett, J R Terry

CITADEL BLACKSTAR TAX CONSULTANTS LLP
11 St James's Place, London, SW1A 1NP

BRIAN HARRIS & CO
1st Floor, Trafalgar House, 11 Waterloo Place, London SW1Y 4AU

BUCKINGHAM CORPORATE FINANCE LTD
57A Catherine Place, London, SW1E 6DY

BUSINESS TAX SERVICES LTD
26th Floor, Portland House, Bressenden Place, London SW1E 5BG

C. HYDE-COOPER
74 Claverton Street, London, SW1V 3AX

CALDER & CO
1 Regent Street, London, SW1Y 4NW
Tel: 020 7839 6655
Email: info@calders.net
Date Established: 1883
Resident Partners/Directors: ICAEW Members
T Badiani, P K S Ewen, D J Gallagher, D J Lyon, I M Rosmarin
Registered by the ICAEW to carry out company audit work
Regulated by the ICAEW for a range of investment business activities
General Description: A broad range of services provided.

CARLESS STEBBINGS & CO
31 Westminster Palace Gardens, Artillery Row, London, SW1P 1RR
Tel: 020 7222 7272
Principal: ICAEW Member
P J Stevens

CASTLE JOHNS
1 Warwick Row, London, SW1E 5ER
Tel: 020 7808 7482
Fax: 01233 625111
Email: info@castlejohns.co.uk
Website: http://www.castlejohns.co.uk
Principal: ICAEW Member
P J Castle

CATALYST CORPORATE FINANCE LLP
5th Floor, 12-18 Grosvenor Gardens, London, SW1W 0DH
Tel: 020 7881 2960
Resident Partners/Directors: ICAEW Members
R A J Bailey, S P Currie, B Evans, T W Evans, R A D Holden, M S Humphries

CHARLES WAKELING & CO
72-73 Wilton Road, Victoria, London, SW1V 1DE
Tel: 020 7931 8877
Resident Partners/Directors: ICAEW Members
H R Johnson

COOPER HATHAWAY LTD
The Ground Floor, Suite G1, Buckingham Court, 78 Buckingham Gate, London SW1E 6PE

EVERETT & SON
3 Park Place, St James's, London, SW1 1LP

F.W. SMITH, RICHES & CO
18-19 Pall Mall, London, SW1Y 5LU

FREEMAN & PARTNERS
30 St James Street, London, SW1A 1HB
Tel: 020 7925 0770
Resident Partners/Directors: ICAEW Members
F A Dada, R Wattrus

GEORGE HAY & CO
83 Cambridge Street, Pimlico, London, SW1V 4PS
Tel: 020 7630 0582
Fax: 020 7630 1502
Email: info@georgehay.com
Website: http://www.georgehay.com
Date Established: 1939
Training Contracts Available.
Resident Partners/Directors: ICAEW Members
N D Christy, J P P Craik, P A Ventham

continued

GEORGE HAY & CO *cont*
Resident Partners (Non-ICAEW Members):
M Davis
Registered by the ICAEW to carry out company audit work
Regulated by the ICAEW for a range of investment business activities
General Description: The firm was founded in 1939 and moved to Pimlico, London, in 1983. It is well established, medium sized, giving a personal service to clients. Its clients range from the small trader to medium-sized limited company and it has a large tax department specialising in personal and corporate tax.
See display advertisement near this entry.

HELMORES
Grosvenor Gardens House, 35-37 Grosvenor Gdns, London, SW1W 0BY
Tel: 020 7828 3156
Email: nch@helmores.co.uk
Website: http://www.helmores.co.uk
Resident Partners/Directors: ICAEW Members
M J V Guillem, N C Hough, D P Howorth, J B McGinley
Resident Partners (Non-ICAEW Members):
H S Virdee
Registered by the ICAEW to carry out company audit work
Authorised and regulated by the Financial Services Authority for investment business
SPECIALISATIONS – AUDIT & ASSURANCE
Audit
SPECIALISATIONS – BUSINESS & GENERAL ADVICE
Book-keeping
Company Formation
Company Secretarial Service
Management Advice to Business
SPECIALISATIONS – FINANCIAL REPORTING
Accounts Preparation
Limited Company Accounts
Partnership/Sole Trader Accounts
SPECIALISATIONS – INVESTMENT BUSINESS
Financial Planning and Advice
SPECIALISATIONS – SECTOR
Charities
Construction
Estate Agents
FSA Members
Hotels/Public Houses
Property Development
Property Investment
Schools
Solicitors
SPECIALISATIONS – TAXATION
Foreign Nationals in the UK
Taxation
Trusteeship
General Description: The firm has been established for over 80 years. Located next to Victoria Station, we offer a full range of accountancy, taxation and financial services to a broad range of clients from small private businesses to the UK subsidiaries of major European companies. We place great emphasis on providing a personal service tailored to individual client needs.

IRIDIS LTD
5th Floor, 24 Buckingham Gate, London, SW1E 6LB

JOHN K HICKS & CO
36a Sloane Gardens, London, SW1W 8DJ
Tel: 020 7730 2773
Principal: ICAEW Member
J K Hicks

KENT & CO
Grosvenor Gardens House, 35/37 Grosvenor Gardens, London, SW1W 0BS
Tel: 020 7828 5456
Principal: ICAEW Member
N S Kent

L.A. GURRIE
203 Collingwood House, Dolphin Square, London, SW1V 3ND

MAGUS
100 Rochester Row, London, SW1P 1JP

MATTHEW EDWARDS & CO
86 Jermyn Street, St James, London, SW1Y 6AW
Tel: 020 7930 7111
Fax: 020 7930 7444
Non-resident Partners (ICAEW Members):
M Wickers, N Morris
Other Offices: Clinch's House, Lord Street, Douglas, Isle of Man IM99 1RZ
(Tel: 01624 663166)
(Fax: 01624 677108)
Overseas Offices: First Floor, Riverview House, 21-23 City Quay, Dublin 2
(Tel: 00 353 1 675 3140)
(Fax: 00 353 1 675 3150)
Registered by the ICAEW to carry out company audit work
Regulated by the ICAEW for a range of investment business activities
SPECIALISATIONS – AUDIT & ASSURANCE
Audit
Audit — Private Company
SPECIALISATIONS – FINANCIAL REPORTING
Accounts Preparation
Limited Company Accounts

THE MONEY FARM COMPANY SERVICES LTD
1st Floor, 1 Warwick Row, London, SW1E 5ER

MS&CO
Suite 16, Grosvenor Gardens House, 35-37 Grosvenor Gardens, London SW1W 0BS

N DUNHILL & CO
23A Moreton Terrace, Pimlico, London, SW1V 2NS
Tel: 020 7821 0500
Principal: ICAEW Member
N V A Dunhill

NICHOLAS ANDREW & CO LTD
39-40 St James's Place, London, SW1A 1NS

NORMAN ALEXANDER & CO
Suite 191, 5th Floor, Grosvenor Gardens House, 35-37 Grosvenor Gardens, London Sw1w SW1W 0BS
Tel: 020 7976 5505
Fax: 020 7976 5424
Email: office@normanalexander.co.uk
Resident Partners/Directors: ICAEW Members
W H Hertzberg, R J Kite
Registered by the ICAEW to carry out company audit work

RAWI & CO
128 Ebury Street, London, SW1W 9QQ

ROBERT TAYLOR ASSOCIATES LTD ◈
100 Pall Mall, St James's, London, SW1Y 5HP

ROBSON LEE
1st Floor, 1 Warwick Row, London, SW1E 5ER

ROSS BENNET-SMITH
Charles House, 5-11 Regent Street, St James, London SW1Y 4LR
Tel: 020 7930 6000
Fax: 020 7930 7070
Website: http://www.rossbennetsmith.com
Resident Partners/Directors: ICAEW Members
A Bennet-Smith, S L Ross
Resident Partners (Non-ICAEW Members):
D Ross
Registered by the ICAEW to carry out company audit work
Regulated by the ICAEW for a range of investment business activities
SPECIALISATIONS – SECTOR
Entertainers
Media
General Description: One of the leading firms in the world specialising in entertainment, media, sport and high net worth individuals.

SAUNDERS, WOOD & CO ◈
The White House, 140A Tachbrook Street, London, SW1V 2NE
Tel: 020 7821 0455
Email: admin@saunders-wood.co.uk
Website: http://www.saunders-wood.co.uk
Date Established: 1959
Resident Partners/Directors: ICAEW Members
J Robson, J A Wood, N J Wood
Resident Partners (Non-ICAEW Members):
P R Wood
Registered by the ICAEW to carry out company audit work
Regulated by the ICAEW for a range of investment business activities

SMITH & HUTCHINSON ◈
New Zealand House, 9th Floor, 80 Haymarket, London SW1Y 4TQ
Tel: 020 7968 2780
Fax: 020 7930 0258
Resident Partners/Directors: ICAEW Members
A P C Fox, R M Smith
Registered by the ICAEW to carry out company audit work
Regulated by the ICAEW for a range of investment business activities
SPECIALISATIONS – AUDIT & ASSURANCE
Audit — Private Company
SPECIALISATIONS – BUSINESS & GENERAL ADVICE
Book-keeping
Company Secretarial Service
SPECIALISATIONS – FINANCIAL REPORTING
Accounts Preparation
Limited Company Accounts
SPECIALISATIONS – TAXATION
Payroll Service and Advice
Personal
Small Traders
General Description: General practice but with strong European links, Zurich associated office.

STERLING HAY ◈
100 Pall Mall, London,
SW1Y 5HP
Tel: 020 7664 8888
Fax: 020 7664 8686
Email: mail@sterlinghay.com
Website: http://
www.sterlinghay.com
Other Offices: Kingfisher
House, 21-23 Elmfield Road,
Bromley, BR1 1LT

SPECIALISATIONS – SECTOR

Barristers
FSA Members

SPECIALISATIONS – TAXATION

Investigations
Partnerships and Sole Traders
PAYE Advice
Personal
Self Assessment Advice

THINKFINE LTD
1 Ebury Mews, London,
SW1W 9NX

THROGMORTON UK LTD
33 St James's Square, London,
SW1Y 4JS

VIRTUAL FINANCE LTD
Suite 19, 34 Buckingham Palace
Road, London, SW1W 0RH
Tel: 020 7754 5983
Resident Partners/Directors:
ICAEW Members
D B Maniar

WELLERS ★
Stuart House, 55 Catherine
Place, London, SW1E 6DY

LONDON SW2

HARDY & CO
166 Streatham Hill, London,
SW2 4RU

HARDY & COMPANY LTD
166 Streatham Hill, London,
SW2 4RU

MARK A. GUTHRIE & CO
43-45 Acre Lane, London,
SW2 5TN

W S MANTZ & CO
90 Brixton Hill, London,
SW2 1QN

LONDON SW3

DENNIS R. WATERS ◈
6 Arundel Court, Jubilee Place,
London, SW3 3TJ
Tel: 020 7351 2842
Website: http://
www.dennisrwaters.com
Principal: ICAEW Member
D R Waters

Registered by the ICAEW to carry out company audit work

Regulated by the ICAEW for a range of investment business activities

SPECIALISATIONS – FINANCIAL REPORTING

Limited Company Accounts

SPECIALISATIONS – FORENSIC ACCOUNTING

Forensic Accounting

SPECIALISATIONS – SECTOR

Doctors
Hotels/Public Houses

SPECIALISATIONS – TAXATION

Partnerships and Sole Traders
Payroll Service and Advice
Small Traders

KIT & CO
63 Egerton Gardens, London,
SW3 2DA

L.H. NEWMAN & CO ◈
148 Walton Street, London,
SW3 2JJ
Tel: 020 7589 6855
Fax: 020 7584 3585
Website: http://
www.lhnewman.co.uk
Principal: ICAEW Member
L H Newman

Registered by the ICAEW to carry out company audit work

Regulated by the ICAEW for a range of investment business activities

PETER MARSHALL
38 Oakley Street, London,
SW3 5HA

LONDON SW4

ANNA LONG
58 Crescent Lane, London,
SW4 9PU

ATKIN & CO
75 The Chase, Clapham,
London, SW4 0NR

IAN RECORDON
25A Bromfelde Road, London,
SW4 6PP

KENNEDY & CO
5 Gauden Road, London,
SW4 6LR

N. HARRIS & CO
Jaybee House, 155-157a
Clapham High Street, London,
SW4 7SY
Tel: 020 7622 0181
Principal: ICAEW Member
N Harris

WILLIS BURNELL LTD
Spectrum House, 9 Bromells
Road, London, SW4 0BN
Tel: 0870 777 6138
Email: willisburnell@aol.com
Resident Partners/Directors:
ICAEW Members
S W Burnell

SPECIALISATIONS – BUSINESS & GENERAL ADVICE

Management Accounting
Consultancy

SPECIALISATIONS – FINANCIAL REPORTING

Limited Company Accounts
Partnership/Sole Trader
Accounts

SPECIALISATIONS – IT

Computerised Accounting
Systems

SPECIALISATIONS – TAXATION

Payroll Service and Advice
Taxation

LONDON SW5

ROGER PURCELL LLP
202 Old Brompton Road,
London, SW5 0BU
Tel: 020 7370 3028
Resident Partners/Directors:
ICAEW Members
R B A Purcell

LONDON SW6

ASTON & CO
132 Walham Green Court,
Moore Park Road, Fulham,
London SW6 2PX

AUSTIN MICHAELIDES LTD
Riverbank House, 1 Putney
Bridge Approach, London,
SW6 3JD

B.S. WOUDSTRA
69 Chesilton Road, London,
SW6 5AA

BARTON LITTLE & CO
1 Fernhurst Road, London,
SW6 7JN

BLUE DOT CONSULTING LTD ◈
Riverbank House, Business
Centre, 1 Putney Bridge
Approach, London SW6 3JD
Tel: 020 7384 6800
Website: http://
www.bluedotconsulting.co.uk
Resident Partners/Directors:
ICAEW Members
M J C Austin

CHANTER, BROWNE & CURRY
1 Plato Place, 72-74 St Dionis
Road, London, SW6 4TU
Tel: 020 7384 2647
Website: http://
www.chanterbrowne.co.uk
Principal: ICAEW Member
P G Browne

CW NOEL & CO
97 Harbord Street, London,
SW6 6PN

DAVIS & CO ★
331 Lillie Road, London,
SW6 7NR

DJS ACCOUNTING SERVICES
3a Crabtree Lane, Fulham,
London, SW6 6LP

GRAHAM CRUICKSHANK BA FCA
35 Whittingstall Road, London,
SW6 4EA
Tel: 020 7731 2827
Principal: ICAEW Member
G D Cruickshank

HAGGARDS CROWTHER
Matrix Studios, 91 Peterborough
Road, London, SW6 3BU
Tel: 020 7384 6550
Email: tim@haggards.co.uk
Resident Partners/Directors:
ICAEW Members
A D D Haggard, T M D Haggard
Resident Partners (Non-ICAEW Members):
P N Crowther

HEXTALL MEAKIN
Argon House, Argon Mews,
London, SW6 1BJ

HEXTALL MEAKIN LTD ◈
Argon House, Argon Mews,
London, SW6 1BJ
Tel: 020 7381 2022
Fax: 020 7385 1087
Email: admin@
hextallmeakin.co.uk
Website: http://
www.hextallmeakin.co.uk
Date Established: 1986
Resident Partners/Directors:
ICAEW Members
T Hextall, G R Meakin
Non-resident Partners (ICAEW Members):
A Morley
Other Offices: Beckett House, 4
Bridge St, Salisbury, Wilts SP1
2LX
(Tel: 01722 414445)
(Fax: 01722 414196)

Registered by the ICAEW to carry out company audit work

Regulated by the ICAEW for a range of investment business activities

General Description: We are a twelve strong team. In addition to running a general practice, we concentrate on working with small and medium sized businesses. Our aim is to help owners develop businesses which work so that their owners can choose not to.

Languages Spoken:
French

HOLDEN & CO
P.O. Box 229, London,
SW6 4UX

JOHN PURVIS & CO
Riverbank House, 1 Putney
Bridge Approach, Fulham,
London SW6 3JD

MCKELVIE & CO
82 Wandsworth Bridge Road,
Fulham, London, SW6 2TF

MANCHANDA AND CO
22 Doneraile Street, Fulham, London, SW6 6EN

MRS P.V.R. RICHARDS
34 Queensmill Road, London, SW6 6JS
Tel: 020 7381 9543
Principal: ICAEW Member
P V R Richards

OLIVER PLUMMER & CO ◈
1-5 Lillie Road, London, SW6 1TX
Tel: 020 7381 0100
Principal: ICAEW Member
O J Plummer

PETER HUNT & CO
Argon House, Argon Mews, Fulham Broadway, London SW6 1BJ

ROBERT V. ASHDOWN
75 Brookville Road, London, SW6 7BH

WARRENER STEWART ◈
Harwood House, 43 Harwood Road, London, SW6 4QP
Tel: 020 7731 6163
Website: http://www.warrenerstewart.com
Resident Partners/Directors: ICAEW Members
J A P Broers, G J Chapman, C P Edney, N D Morgan, D M Talbot
Registered by the ICAEW to carry out company audit work
Regulated by the ICAEW for a range of investment business activities

WYATTS ◈
York House, 1 Seagrave Road, London, SW6 1RP

LONDON SW7

DAVID MOK ◈
10 Queensberry Mews West, South Kensington, London, SW7 2DU
Tel: 020 7581 3362
Principal: ICAEW Member
D H H Mok

GRIFFITHS LTD
Suite 108, 56 Gloucester Road, London, SW7 4UB
Tel: 020 7376 2122
Resident Partners/Directors: ICAEW Members
D M A Griffiths
See display advertisement near this entry.

NEUHOFF & CO
Flat 1, 33 Rutland Gate, London, SW7 1PA

LONDON SW8

DUNBAR & CO (CORPORATE SERVICES) LTD
70 South Lambeth Road, London, SW8 1RL

SBM & CO
117 Fentiman Road, London, SW8 1JZ
Tel: 020 7582 9473
Fax: 020 7587 1966
Email: info@sbmandco.com
Website: http://www.sbmandco.com
Resident Partners/Directors: ICAEW Members
P McAlpine, S B McAlpine
Registered by the ICAEW to carry out company audit work

LONDON SW9

ELLEN HOLYHEAD
36 Hargwyne Street, Stockwell, London, SW9 9RG

LONDON SW10

CHARLES D.B. PUGH
2 Priory Walk, London, SW10 9SP

COLIN GLOVER & CO
23 Carlyle Court, Chelsea Harbour, London, SW10 0UQ

J LOCKS LTD
Flat 18, 5 Elm Park Gardens, London, SW10 9QQ
Tel: 020 7351 1733

PATRICK JENKINS & CO
214 Harbour Yard, Chelsea Harbour, London, SW10 0XD

LONDON SW11

AHMEDANI & CO
46 Wycliffe Road, London, SW11 5QR

BLUNT MCLAREN & CO LTD
3 Old Garden House, The Lanterns, Bridge Lane, London SW11 3AD

C BELL LTD
22 Garfield Road, London, SW11 5PN

HODGSON HICKIE
4 Dovedale Studios, 465 Battersea Park Road, London, SW11 4LR
Tel: 020 7652 2222
Resident Partners/Directors: ICAEW Members
R A Hickie, E Hodgson

JOSEPH KHEDOORY
3 Calico House, Plantation Wharf, London, SW11 3TN

JOSEPH TSEYOUNGSUN ◈
Tempo House, 15 Falcon Road, London, SW11 2PH

N J HADFIELD
47 Brynmaer Road, London, SW11 4EN

NICOL AND CO
28 Whistlers Avenue, London, SW11 3TS

PETER F SELLEY & CO
84 Belleville Road, London, SW11 6PP

REZA SAMII
5 Calico Row, Plantation Wharf, Battersea, London SW11 3YH

SAMPSON WEST & CHRISTO
4 The Old Garden House, The Lanterns, Bridge Lane, London SW11 3AD

V.L. RAINSFORD
31b Thirsk Road, Battersea, London, SW11 5SU

WADLAN LEY
119 Battersea Business Centre, Lavender Hill, London, SW11 5QL
Tel: 020 7228 6531
Principal: ICAEW Member
J Ley

WALTON & CO ★
Unit 4, Dovedale Studios, 465 Battersea Park Road, London SW11 4LR

LONDON SW12

A C DINARDO
2A Cornford Grove, Balham, London, SW12 9JF

CHILD & CHILD ACCOUNTANTS LTD
49 Cavendish Road, Clapham, London, SW12 0BL
Tel: 020 8675 8006
Website: http://www.childandchild.biz
Resident Partners/Directors: ICAEW Members
J Child, R J Child

SPECIALISATIONS – TAXATION
Taxation

THE DECIMAL PLACE
8 Blandfield Road, London, SW12 8BG
Tel: 020 8675 3355
Fax: 020 8675 1716
Email: richard@thedecimalplace.co.uk
Website: http://www.thedecimalplace.co.uk

SPECIALISATIONS – BUSINESS & GENERAL ADVICE

Book-keeping
Company Formation

SPECIALISATIONS – FINANCIAL REPORTING

Accounts Preparation
Financial Reporting

SPECIALISATIONS – TAXATION

Partnerships and Sole Traders
Payroll Service and Advice
Personal

General Description: Small accountancy firm offering a genuinely personal service.
Languages Spoken:
Mandarin, Cantonese, Gujarati

HARRIS COOMBS & CO ★
5 Jaggard Way, London, SW12 8SG
Tel: 020 8675 6880
Email: mailbox@harriscoombs.co.uk
Resident Partners/Directors: ICAEW Members
R C P Coombs
Registered by the ICAEW to carry out company audit work
Licensed by another DPB to carry on investment business

PEARSON ◈
12 Old Park Avenue, London, SW12 8RH

RAZZLE LTD
8 Blandfield Road, London, SW12 8BG

SHARDLOW & CO
61a Gosberton Road, London, SW12 8LG

V K MEHTA & CO
25 Balham High Road, London, SW12 9AL

VKM ACCOUNTANTS LTD
25 Balham High Road, London, SW12 9AL

LONDON SW13

AIMS - ALASTAIR CAMERON
48 Lowther Road, Barnes, London, SW13 9NU

AIMS - RONALD POLLOCK
7 Ellison Road, Barnes, London, SW13 0AD

C.J. COOK & CO
24A Suffolk Road, Barnes, London, SW13 9NB
Tel: 020 8748 6933
Fax: 020 8748 6933
Email: cjcbarnessw13@hotmail.com
Principal: ICAEW Member
C J Cook
Regulated by the ICAEW for a range of investment business activities

SPECIALISATIONS – INVESTMENT BUSINESS

Planning

SPECIALISATIONS – SECTOR

Corporate

SPECIALISATIONS – TAXATION

Capital Gains — Limited Companies
Capital Gains — Personal
Personal
Self Assessment Advice
Small Traders
UK Subsidiaries of Overseas Multinationals

DAVID WADSWORTH & CO
47 Merthyr Terrace, Barnes, London, SW13 8DL

GLENN W START & CO
24 Wyatt Drive, Barnes, London, SW13 8AA

J.G.K. BELL
1 Westwood Gardens, Barnes, London, SW13 0LB
Tel: 020 8878 1865
Principal: ICAEW Member
J G K Bell

PETER SABINE & CO ◈
17 Keble Place, London, SW13 8HJ

LONDON SW14

ANDREW B TAPPIN
18 East Sheen Avenue, London, SW14 8AS
Tel: 020 8287 8825
Fax: 020 8711 2579
Email: andrew.tappin@blueyonder.co.uk
Principal: ICAEW Member
A B Tappin

SPECIALISATIONS – TAXATION

Estate and Inheritance
Executorship
Taxation
Trusteeship

BLYTHE & CO
206 Upper Richmond Road West, East Sheen, London, SW14 8AH

BLYTHE FINANCIAL LTD
206 Upper Richmond Road West, East Sheen, London, SW14 8AH

CHARLES VASEY & CO
75 Richmond Park Road, East Sheen, London, SW14 8JY

CRIPPS DRANSFIELD
206 Upper Richmond Road West, London, SW14 8AH

DAVID WELLS FCA
14 Dukes Court, 77 Mortlake High Street, London, SW14 8HS
Tel: 020 8876 6790
Principal: ICAEW Member
D J R Wells

DELLAL & CO
5 Park Drive, London, SW14 8RB
Tel: 020 8876 3074
Principal: ICAEW Member
D Dellal

FARROW ACCOUNTING
Worple Court, 94-95 South Worple Way, London, SW14 8ND

FARROW ACCOUNTING & TAX LTD
Worple Court, 94-95 South Worple Way, London, SW14 8ND
Tel: 020 8876 8020
Email: info@farrowaccounting.com
Resident Partners/Directors: ICAEW Members
N C Farrow

SPECIALISATIONS – SECTOR

Entertainers
Media

GILLIAN EDWARDES-KER
29 Shalstone Road, Mortlake, London, SW14 7HP
Tel: 020 8876 2657
Principal: ICAEW Member
G C Edwardes-Ker

GORDON DEWAR
19 Gilpin Avenue, East Sheen, London, SW14 8QX

H.A. BURTON
17 Hertford Avenue, East Sheen, London, SW14 8EF

SHAN KENNEDY LTD
71 Palewell Park, London, SW14 8JJ

SHERYL CAIN LTD
237 Sheen Lane, London, SW14 8LE
Tel: 020 8878 4318
Resident Partners/Directors: ICAEW Members
S M Cain

V KAPADIA & CO ◈
53 Sheen Lane, London, SW14 8AB
Tel: 020 8392 1099
Principal: ICAEW Member
V V Kapadia

V KAPADIA & CO ◈
53 Sheen Lane, London, SW14 8AB
Tel: 020 8392 1099

V KAPADIA & CO LTD ◈
53 Sheen Lane, London, SW14 8AB
Tel: 020 8392 1099
Resident Partners/Directors: ICAEW Members
V V Kapadia

WHITE HART ASSOCIATES LLP ★
East House, 109 South Worple Way, London, SW14 8TN
Tel: 020 8878 8383
Fax: 020 8392 2451
Email: wha.acp@btinternet.com
Website: http://www.whitehartassociates.com
Mobile: 07867 793071
Resident Partners/Directors: ICAEW Members
M J Siddiqui
Resident Partners (Non-ICAEW Members):
M S Siddiqui, C Photi, N A Spoor, M Caldicott
Registered by the ICAEW to carry out company audit work

SPECIALISATIONS – AUDIT & ASSURANCE

Audit — Private Company

SPECIALISATIONS – SECTOR

Catering/Restaurants
Travel Industry

SPECIALISATIONS – TAXATION

Taxation

General Description: Travel industry specialists - ATOL, ABTA and IATA. Complete licensing and bonding expertise.
Languages Spoken:
Greek, Urdu, Punjabi

LONDON SW15

ANDERSON NEAL
No 1 The Mews, 6 Putney Common, London, SW15 1HL
Tel: 020 8789 4460
Email: mcorbitt@andersonneal.co.uk

ANDERSON NEAL LTD
1 The Mews, 6 Putney Common, London, SW15 1HL

ATC
5 Castle Court, 1 Brewhouse Lane, London, SW15 2JJ

CFO CONSULTING LTD ◈
Flat 2, 27 Disraeli Road, Putney, London SW15 2DR
Tel: 020 8788 7640
Resident Partners/Directors: ICAEW Members
P H Rossiter

ELIZABETH PADUA & CO
21 Bangalore Street, Putney, London, SW15 1QD

G. F. TRAYLEN
15 Holmbush Road, Putney, London, SW15 3LE

GAIRDNERS
17 Larpent Avenue, Putney, London, SW15 6UP

HORDER ADEY ◈
13 Princeton Court, 53-55 Felsham Road, Putney, London SW15 1AZ
Tel: 020 8789 8588
Email: email@haca.co.uk
Website: http://www.haca.co.uk
Resident Partners/Directors: ICAEW Members
L B Adey, N I Horder
Registered by the ICAEW to carry out company audit work
Regulated by the ICAEW for a range of investment business activities

JACKSON TAYLOR
162/164 Upper Richmond Road, Putney, London, SW15 2SL

JOHN WHITE
1 Egliston Road, London, SW15 1AL

KNAPTON & CO
5 Highdown Road, Putney, London, SW15 5BU

LILES MORRIS ★
Park House, 233 Roehampton Lane, London, SW15 4LB
Tel: 020 8785 4690
Resident Partners/Directors: ICAEW Members
T R T Morris
Resident Partners (Non-ICAEW Members):
F P Helsby
Registered by the ICAEW to carry out company audit work

LINK KAPLAN LTD
166 Upper Richmond Road, London, SW15 2SH

M.R. HENDERSON
32 Granard Avenue, London, SW15 6HJ

MACCALLUM SLATOR ◈
70 Upper Richmond Road, London, SW15 2RP
Tel: 020 8874 5585

NABARRO
151 Putney High Street, London, SW15 1TA

NIGEL WRIGHT CORPORATE FINANCE
11 Danemere Street, Putney, London, SW15 1LT

REZA SAMII
Flat 19, Cornerways, 1 Daylesford Avenue, London SW15 5QP

STUART MOFFATT
53 Crestway, London, SW15 5DB

SUSANNA RUSSELL-SMITH FCA
249 Upper Richmond Road, Putney, London, SW15 6SW
Tel: 020 8788 1447
Principal: ICAEW Member
Susanna Russell-Smith

WHITEMOOR
17 Mexfield Road, London, SW15 2RG

LONDON SW16

ABBOTT GREELEY
1433b London Road, Norbury, London, SW16 4AW

ANGELA JOSEPH & CO
35 Northside, Streatham Common North, London, SW16 3HR

APRP LTD ◈
91 Sunnyhill Road, Stratham, London, SW16 2UG
Tel: 020 8769 6375
Resident Partners/Directors: ICAEW Members
P B Patel

ARIF MALIDA ◈
66 Moyser Road, London, SW16 6SQ
Tel: 020 8769 5705
Principal: ICAEW Member
A Malida

DOSHI & CO
1st Floor, Windsor House, 1270 London Road, London SW16 4DH

M.U. AHMED & CO
28 Christian Fields, Norbury, London, SW16 3JZ
Tel: 020 8764 1056
Principal: ICAEW Member
M U Ahmed

P.V.SCLAVERANO
29 Gibson's Hill, Norbury, London, SW16 3JR

PAULA THOMAS
25 Westcote Road, Streatham, London, SW16 6BN
Tel: 020 8677 4721
Principal: ICAEW Member
P Thomas

RAMESH A. PATEL & CO
28 Pollards Hill North, Norbury, London, SW16 4NL

ROBERT WONG & CO
68 Pendennis Road, Streatham, London, SW16 2SP

S.U. TAMURI
1 Forrest Gardens, London, SW16 4LP
Tel: 020 8764 7390
Principal: ICAEW Member
S U Tamuri

SIVA NAMASIVAYAM
7 Beckway Road, Norbury, London, SW16 4HB

TRAIN CONSULTING LTD
42 Ryecroft Road, London, SW16 3EQ

LONDON SW17

ELLEN ENGLISH
99 St James's Drive, London, SW17 7RP

ERNEST CLARK & CO
26 St Catherines Close, London, SW17 7UA

JAMES FRANCIS & CO ◈
32 Wontner Road, Upper Tooting, London, SW17 7QT

PAUL HIGGINS
2C Church Lane, Tooting, London, SW17 9PP

RCI (LONDON) LTD
782 Garratt Lane, London, SW17 0LZ

WADUD PATWARI & CO
10 Tooting Bec Road, London, SW17 8BD
Tel: 020 8672 3634
Fax: 020 8672 3600
Email: mawpatwari@aol.com
Principal: ICAEW Member
M A W Patwari
Registered by the ICAEW to carry out company audit work
Regulated by the ICAEW for a range of investment business activities

SPECIALISATIONS – AUDIT & ASSURANCE
Audit

SPECIALISATIONS – FINANCIAL REPORTING
Limited Company Accounts
Partnership/Sole Trader Accounts

SPECIALISATIONS – SECTOR
Registered Social Landlords
Solicitors
Traders — General

SPECIALISATIONS – TAXATION
Partnerships and Sole Traders
Self Assessment Advice
Taxation

ZAIDI & CO
Amen Corner, 241 Mitcham Road, London, SW17 9JQ

LONDON SW18

CHICKSAND GORDON AVIS
12 Northfields Prospect, Putney Bridge Road, London, SW18 1PE
Tel: 020 8874 6131

CHICKSAND GORDON AVIS LTD
12 Northfields Prospect, Putney Bridge Road, London, SW18 1PE
Tel: 020 8874 6131
Fax: 020 8874 6101
Email: stan@stanchicksand.co.uk
Website: http://www.stanchicksand.co.uk
Mobile: 07979 758953
Resident Partners/Directors: ICAEW Members
S B Chicksand, A J Taylor

Registered by the ICAEW to carry out company audit work

SPECIALISATIONS – FINANCIAL REPORTING
Limited Companies
Partnership/Sole Trader Accounts

SPECIALISATIONS – IT
Computer Consultants

SPECIALISATIONS – SECTOR
Dentists/Opticians
Doctors
Electronics
Entertainers
Estate Agents
Nursing Homes/Clinics
Solicitors

SPECIALISATIONS – TAXATION
Payroll Service and Advice
Self Assessment Advice
Taxation

See display advertisement near this entry.

EKAS
24 Parkside, Knightsbridge, London, SW18 7JW

F&R RUSSELL
33 Frewin Road, London, SW18 3LR

FITZGERALDS ◈
40 Ringford Road, London, SW18 1RR
Tel: 020 8870 0954
Principal: ICAEW Member
T J Fitzgerald

FRANKLIN
320 Garratt Lane, Earlsfield, London, SW18 4EJ
Tel: 020 8871 3047
Resident Partners/Directors: ICAEW Members
A J Franklin, S R Franklin

HUSAIN BULMAN & CO
258 Merton Road, London, SW18 5JL

LBCO LTD
16 Northfields Prospect Business Centre, Northfields, London, SW18 1PE
Tel: 020 88711440
Fax: 020 8871 1396
Email: enquiry@leesbuckley.co.uk
Website: http://www.leesbuckley.co.uk
Resident Partners/Directors: ICAEW Members
L G Lees-Buckley
Registered by the ICAEW to carry out company audit work
Licensed by another DPB to carry on investment business

SPECIALISATIONS – AUDIT & ASSURANCE
Audit

SPECIALISATIONS – BUSINESS & GENERAL ADVICE
Company Secretarial Service

SPECIALISATIONS – FINANCIAL REPORTING
Limited Company Accounts
Partnership/Sole Trader Accounts

SPECIALISATIONS – IT
Computer Consultants

SPECIALISATIONS – SECTOR
Advertising/Design Agencies
Architects/Surveyors
FSA Members
Property Development
Solicitors
Traders — General

SPECIALISATIONS – TAXATION
Taxation

General Description: A highly computerised practice providing a full range of services with an emphasis on quality and the accessibility of principal and staff.
Languages Spoken:
French

MCDERMOTT & CO
1 Centre Square, Hardwicks Way, London, SW18 4AW
Tel: 020 7198 8411
Principal: ICAEW Member
B P McDermott

SAMERA LTD
5 Morie Studios, Morie Street, London, SW18 1SL

SARAH HENRY
24 Frewin Road, London, SW18 3LP

STEPHEN JAY ◈
17 Geraldine Road, Wandsworth, London, SW18 2NR
Tel: 020 8874 2592
Fax: 020 8355 4134
Email: stephen.jay@ntlworld.com
Date Established: 1992
Principal: ICAEW Member
S J Jay

WILKINSON LATHAM
5 College Mews, Saint Ann's Hill, London, SW18 2SJ

LONDON SW19

A MAQBOOL & CO LTD
192 Haydons Road, Wimbledon, London, SW19 8TR

ABDUL MUHITH
209 Merton Road, London, SW19 1EE

ACCOUNTING & FINANCIAL SOLUTIONS (LONDON) LTD ◈
66 Norman Road, Wimbledon, London, SW19 1BN
Tel: 020 8540 0303
Resident Partners/Directors: ICAEW Members
M T Brown

B DAVIS COULTHARDS
162-164 Arthur Road, London, SW19 8AQ

BERKOVI & CO ◈
Cygnet House, 98 Graham Road, London, SW19 3SS
Tel: 020 8543 0705
Principal: ICAEW Member
A J Berkovi

BUSINESS TAX SERVICES LTD
58 Vineyard Hill Road, Wimbledon, London, SW19 7JH

CATHARINE MADGIN
33 Murray Road, Wimbledon, London, SW19 4PD
Tel: 020 8946 4718
Principal: ICAEW Member
C J Madgin

COULTHARDS
162-164 Arthur Road, Wimbledon, London, SW19 8AQ
Tel: 020 8944 1180
Fax: 020 8944 0863
Email: info@bdc-ca.co.uk

SPECIALISATIONS – AUDIT & ASSURANCE
Audit

SPECIALISATIONS – FINANCIAL REPORTING
Accounts Preparation

SPECIALISATIONS – SECTOR
Charities

SPECIALISATIONS – TAXATION
Taxation

COULTHARDS LTD
162-164 Arthur Road, London, SW19 8AQ

COWLEY & CO
73 Arthur Road, London, SW19 7DP
Tel: 020 8879 0596
Principal: ICAEW Member
A M Cowley

CROSSMOUNT
Highlands House, 165 The Broadway, Wimbledon, London SW19 1NE

EKAS
Masons Yard, 34 High Street, Wimbledon Village, London SW19 5BY

FINANCIAL PROFESSIONAL SUPPORT SERVICES
Olympic House, 196 The Broadway, London, SW19 1RY

FINANCIAL PROFESSIONAL SUPPORT SERVICES LLP
Olympic House, 196 The Broadway, London, SW19 1RY

G A HELLINGS LTD
53 Queens Road, Wimbleon, London, SW19 8NP

GORDONS KNIGHT & CO LTD
Pendragon House, 170 Merton High Street, London, SW19 1AY

HARTLEY FOWLER LLP ◈
4th Floor, Tuition House, 27-37 St Georges Road, Wimbledon, London SW19 4EU
Tel: 020 8946 1212
Fax: 020 8947 0998
Email: info.ldn@hartleyfowler.com
Website: http://www.hartleyfowler.com
Training Contracts Available.
Resident Partners/Directors: ICAEW Members
R M Morris, J K Upson
Registered by the ICAEW to carry out company audit work
Regulated by the ICAEW for a range of investment business activities

HEENA PATEL BA ACA
25 Burghley House, Somerset Road, London, SW19 5JB

HOWELL WADE ◈
55 Church Road, Wimbledon Village, London, SW19 5DQ
Tel: 020 8947 6912
Email: mail@howellwade.com
Principal: ICAEW Member
A B Warren
Registered by the ICAEW to carry out company audit work
Regulated by the ICAEW for a range of investment business activities

continued

HOWELL WADE *cont*

SPECIALISATIONS – AUDIT & ASSURANCE

Audit

SPECIALISATIONS – FINANCIAL REPORTING

Accounts Preparation
Limited Company Accounts

SPECIALISATIONS – SECTOR

Property Investment

General Description: Full range of services. Independent members of UK200 Group. Special offers at www.howellwade.com.

KHAN WAHAB SHAFIQUE RAHMAN & CO
136 Merton High Street, London, SW19 1BA

KWSR & CO
136 Merton High Street, London, SW19 1BA

MARK BUFFERY ◈
123 Dora Road, London, SW19 7JT
Tel: 020 8288 9975
Email: mark@suas.co.uk
Principal: ICAEW Member
M C Buffery

SPECIALISATIONS – TAXATION

Value Added Tax

MARK JONES & CO
9a Southside Common, London, SW19 4TL
Tel: 020 8739 0181
Principal: ICAEW Member
M P Jones

MARK W WATSON ◈
Flat 4, Gresham Way, Wimbledon Park, London SW19 8ED
Tel: 020 8944 0572
Principal: ICAEW Member
M W Watson

MED ACT
36 Lancaster Road, Wimbledon, London, SW19 5DD
Tel: 020 8544 0300

SPECIALISATIONS – SECTOR

Construction
Doctors

SPECIALISATIONS – TAXATION

Taxation

MERCHANTS ◈
3 Gordondale Road, Wimbledon Park, London, SW19 8EN
Tel: 020 8946 5990
Principal: ICAEW Member
J Merchant

MISS E A PARKS
68 Murray Road, Wimbledon, London, SW19 4PE
Tel: 020 8944 9423
Website: http://www.misseaparks.co.uk
Principal: ICAEW Member
E A Parks

SPECIALISATIONS – TAXATION

Capital Gains — Personal
Employee
Foreign Nationals in the UK
Partnerships and Sole Traders
Personal
Self Assessment Advice

MITCHELL RODRIGUES & CO LTD
Suite 14 Zeal House, 8 Deer Park Road, London, SW19 3GY
Tel: 020 8542 8839
Resident Partners/Directors: ICAEW Members
C T Simmons

MITROD
Suite 14, Zeal House, 8 Deer Park Road, London SW19 3GY

MOHAMMAD SHAH & CO
209 Merton Road, South Wimbledon, London, SW19 1EE

MRS C.M. EDGE BSC FCA
2 Kingswood Road, London, SW19 3NE

MUSTAFA A. DATOO
144 Dorset Road, Merton Park, London, SW19 3EF
Tel: 020 8540 7006
Principal: ICAEW Member
M A L Datoo

NEWPORT & CO
198 Kingston Road, London, SW19 3NU

PAUL FURRER & CO ◈
2nd Floor Tuition House, 27-37 St Georges Road, Wimbledon, London SW19 4EU
Tel: 020 8947 2445
Email: paul@paulfurrer.co.uk
Principal: ICAEW Member
P S Furrer
General Description: Comprehensive range of accountancy & business advisory services.
Languages Spoken: French, Spanish

REAY & KING
87 High Street, Wimbledon, London, SW19 5EG
Tel: 020 8947 9919
Principal: ICAEW Member
R J Evans

RICHARD FLOYD & CO
170 Dorset Road, London, SW19 3EF
Tel: 020 8547 1888

ROBERT LYONS & CO
Flat 1, 42 Marryat Road, Wimbledon, London SW19 5BD

SIMON COWLEY
73 Arthur Road, London, SW19 7DP
Tel: 020 8879 0596
Principal: ICAEW Member
S C Cowley

STROVER, LEADER & CO ◈
Barry House, 20/22 Worple Road, Wimbledon, London SW19 4DH
Tel: 020 8947 2345
Fax: 020 8947 2233
Email: gen@stroverleader.co.uk
Website: http://www.stroverleader.co.uk
Date Established: 1973
Resident Partners/Directors: ICAEW Members
J A R Ironmonger, D L Roberts, J Y R Strover
Registered by the ICAEW to carry out company audit work
Authorised and regulated by the Financial Services Authority for investment business

THOMAS HARRIS LTD
The 1929 Building, Merton Abbey Mills, 18 Watermill Way, London SW19 2RD

WSM
Pinnacle House, 17/25 Hartfield Road, Wimbledon, London SW19 3SE

WSM PARTNERS LLP
Pinnacle House, 17/25 Hartfield Road, Wimbledon, London SW19 3SE
Tel: 020 8543 3991
Fax: 020 8543 5547
Email: wsm@wsm.co.uk
Website: http://www.wsmproperty.com
Training Contracts Available.
Resident Partners/Directors: ICAEW Members
S C C Marsh, G F M Stebbing, P J Windsor

Resident Partners (Non-ICAEW Members):
W Patterson

Registered by the ICAEW to carry out company audit work

Regulated by the ICAEW for a range of investment business activities

INVESTOR IN PEOPLE

SPECIALISATIONS – SECTOR

Property
Property Investment

WSM PROPERTY
Pinnacle House, 17/25 Hartfield Road, Wimbledon, London SW19 3SE

LONDON SW20

A. CALDARA
10 Crossway, West Wimbledon, London, SW20 9JA

ARGENTA ASSOCIATES
15 Ernle Road, Wimbledon Common, London, SW20 0HH

DEIRDRE A THOMAS
45a Cottenham Park Road, London, SW20 0SB
Tel: 020 8947 7191
Fax: 020 8947 7774
Email: deirdre.thomas@btinternet.com
Principal: ICAEW Member
D A Thomas

Registered by the ICAEW to carry out company audit work

Regulated by the ICAEW for a range of investment business activities

GEORGE F Y LEW & CO
78 Westway, Raynes Park, London, SW20 9LS

N D MYATT & CO
194 Coombe Lane, London, SW20 0QT

PAUL MARKS & CO ◈
3 Lansdowne Road, London, SW20 8AP
Tel: 020 8947 9567
Principal: ICAEW Member
P M Stankiewicz

ROBIN DARBYSHIRE FCA
43 Ethelbert Road, Wimbledon, London, SW20 8QE

ROGER MATHEWS
10 Durrington Park Road, Wimbledon, London, SW20 8NX
Tel: 020 8971 2116
Principal: ICAEW Member
R G Mathews

TRIGG & CO
1 Merton Mansions, Bushey Road, London, SW20 8DQ

LONDON W1

3SIXTY HOLDINGS LTD
295 Regent Street, London, W1B 2HL

A.R. MUNSON ◈
8 Devonshire Mews West, London, W1G 6QE
Tel: 020 7486 7023
Principal: ICAEW Member
A R Munson

ACCOUNTRUST LTD
Royalty House, 32 Sackville Street, Mayfair, London W1S 3EA

ADAMS MITCHELL ★ ◈
109 Gloucester Place, London, W1U 6JW
Tel: 020 7486 2234
Resident Partners/Directors: ICAEW Members
A R Mitchell

ADLER SHINE LLP
15 Hanover Square, London, W1S 1HS

AGUTTER-KHANDERIA
First Floor, 85a Great Portland Street, London, W1W 7LT

ALBERDALE PARTNERS LTD
12 Curzon Street, London, W1J 5HL

ARTHUR G MEAD ★
Adam House, 1 Fitzroy Square, London, W1T 5HE
Tel: 020 7387 6046
Fax: 020 7383 0435
Email: gerry@agmead.co.uk

Date Established: 1929

Resident Partners/ Directors: ICAEW Members
G F J McKey

Resident Partners (Non-ICAEW Members):
V G McKey

Registered by the ICAEW to carry out company audit work

SPECIALISATIONS – AUDIT & ASSURANCE

Audit

SPECIALISATIONS – BUSINESS & GENERAL ADVICE

Book-keeping Systems

SPECIALISATIONS – FINANCIAL REPORTING

Accounts Preparation
Audit Exemption Report
Limited Companies

SPECIALISATIONS – SECTOR

Barristers
Dentists/Opticians
Doctors
Hotels/Public Houses

SPECIALISATIONS – TAXATION

Partnerships and Sole Traders
Personal
Self Assessment Advice
Small Traders

See display advertisement near this entry.

ASA & CO ◈
Regent House Business Centre, 24/25 Nutford Place, Marble Arch, London W1H 5YN

ASH SHAW LLP
211 Piccadilly, London, W1J 9HF
Tel: 020 7917 2987
Fax: 020 7917 2988
Resident Partners/Directors: ICAEW Members
G J Burton, T Jarvis

Registered by the ICAEW to carry out company audit work

SPECIALISATIONS – AUDIT & ASSURANCE

Pension Scheme Auditors

AUDITEX
2 Sheraton Street, London, W1F 8BH

AUERBACH HOPE ★
58/60 Berners Street, London, W1T 3JS
Tel: 020 7637 4121
Fax: 020 7636 5330
Email: info@auerbachhope.co.uk
Website: http://www.auerbachhope.co.uk
Date Established: 1945
Resident Partners/Directors: ICAEW Members
I Fishman, J S Marco, I A Randolph, H R Reuben, J Shah
Resident Partners (Non-ICAEW Members):
J Coker, W Ahmad

Registered by the ICAEW to carry out company audit work

Authorised and regulated by the Financial Services Authority for investment business

B.N. REDPATH & CO
42 Berkeley Square, London, W1J 5AW

BARNES ROFFE LLP
13 Albemarle Street, London, W1S 4HJ
Tel: 020 7529 7660
Resident Partners/Directors: ICAEW Members
S A Corner

BARTRUM LERNER ★
39A Welbeck Street, London, W1G 8DH

BDO STOY HAYWARD LLP
55 Baker Street, London, W1U 7EU
Tel: 020 7486 5888
Fax: 020 7487 3686
Resident Partners/Directors: ICAEW Members
M N K Aldridge, P Alexander, D M Anderson, R S Aziz, S G Bartlett, S B Benaim, P C Bennett, S B Bevan, M Bomer, S C Bourne, J H M Breach, K J Britten, D I Campbell, D K Campbell, N H Carter-Pegg, P C J Chidgey, R J Citron, C D Clark, G C Clayworth, G J Clipsham, M J Cobb, M Cohen, I P Cooper, K D Crossthwaite, P F Daniel, I A Daniels, J M Dennison, D I Dover, P M Eagland, N A Eastaway, R J Eastell, F E Fernie, A L Foyle, A R Frais, J C H Frost, N A R Fung-On, S Gerber, D H Gilbert, M H Goldstein, C J Grove, S Gupta, A W Harris, P J Hemington, I A R Henderson, S J Herring, L S Jefferson, G H Jones, M W Kaye, S W Knight, L Lackey, P R Lavercombe, J Le Poidevin, A M Levene, R J Levy, D I C Lowson, G Macgregor, D C A Mathias, S R G McNaughton, R J Merson, D J Miles, J L Nedas, J S Newman, A D Nygate, M A O'Leary, A J Perkins, I R Plunkett, D A Porter, M J Prangley, P N A M Prince, G D Quigley, P C Rayney, A L Sayers, C J Searle, H L Sharma, M J Shaw, M A Sherfield, P Spencer, S M J Surrey, A C D Tapp, D M Taylor, N A Udal, A S Viner, A J A Ware, A C White, M R White, B R Wilkinson, C I Williams, D S Williams, J M Willmott
Resident Partners (Non-ICAEW Members):
J J Bannon, A W Butterworth, A Caldwell, S E Dayman, D H Ellis, E A E Howard, E P Magrin, S J Michaels, J J R Pinder, R J Tierney, M Ware, W M Walton, T J Moore, R N Miller, P L Ayres, B J Barnes, A J Buchanan, B J Goldman, J P Hickman, A J Hume, C R Ives, R Spilg, A J Spillett, K A Stubbs, A Bailey, A R Evans, A Flint, D N G Hughes, H J Jones, D L Kasmir, C E Le Jeune, D A J Mitchell, T M Payne, M S R Welby

BENJAMIN, TAYLOR & CO ◈
5 Wigmore Street, London, W1U 1HY
Tel: 020 7636 7176

continued

BENJAMIN, TAYLOR & CO
cont
Resident Partners/Directors: ICAEW Members
S Cowan, J Diner, P Goldstein

BERLEY ◈
76 New Cavendish Street, London, W1G 9TB

BJCA LTD
211-212 Piccadilly, Piccadilly, London, W1V 9LD

BLINKHORNS ★
27 Mortimer Street, London, W1T 3BL
Tel: 020 7636 3702
Fax: 020 7636 0335
Email: info@blinkhorns.co.uk
Website: http://www.blinkhorns.co.uk
Resident Partners/Directors: ICAEW Members
D M Cramer, M A L Datoo, G S Stern, S J Wharton
Resident Partners (Non-ICAEW Members):
R P Kent, G P Martin, G A Thomas, J R Trott
Registered by the ICAEW to carry out company audit work
Regulated by the ICAEW for a range of investment business activities
SPECIALISATIONS – SECTOR

Entertainers
Media
Property Investment

Languages Spoken:
French, Swahili, German, Afrikaans, Gujarati

BOOTHBY BAKER & CO
9 Wimpole Street, London, W1G 9SG
Tel: 020 7079 0330
Principal: ICAEW Member
G G Boothby

BOROUMAND & ASSOCIATES ★
6th Floor, 94-96 Wigmore Street, London, W1U 3RF
Tel: 020 7486 0488
Resident Partners/Directors: ICAEW Members
H Noorizadeh

BOWKER ORFORD
15/19 Cavendish Place, London, W1G 0DD
Tel: 020 7636 6391
Fax: 020 7580 3909
Email: mail@bowkerorford.com
Website: http://www.bowkerorford.com
Resident Partners/Directors: ICAEW Members
R S Parmar
Resident Partners (Non-ICAEW Members):
J S Goh, P M Davis
Registered by the ICAEW to carry out company audit work
Regulated by the ICAEW for a range of investment business activities
SPECIALISATIONS – IT
Computer Consultants
E-commerce
SPECIALISATIONS – SECTOR

Artists/Graphic Designers
Doctors
Entertainers
Estate Agents
Media
New Media
Paper/Printing/Publishing
Solicitors

SPECIALISATIONS – TAXATION
UK Subsidiaries of Overseas Multinationals

Languages Spoken:
Spanish

BRADLEY-HOARE & CO
31 Harley Street, London, W1G 9QS

BREBNERS ◈
The Quadrangle, 180 Wardour Street, London, W1F 8LB
Tel: 020 7734 2244
Email: partners@brebners.com
Website: http://www.brebners.com
Training Contracts Available.
Resident Partners/Directors: ICAEW Members
M R J Burton, J B Chamberlain, J Craig, S J Cryer, R S Gregory, M J Harris, P J Heath, T E J Smith, M N Widdowson
Resident Partners (Non-ICAEW Members):
D R Taylor, M Taylor, R S Ward, A Sonah
Registered by the ICAEW to carry out company audit work
Authorised and regulated by the Financial Services Authority for investment business
Individual(s) licensed for insolvency work by the ICAEW

BRETT ADAMS
25 Manchester Square, London, W1U 3PY
Tel: 020 7486 8985
Resident Partners/Directors: ICAEW Members
J B Cohen, S Davidson

BRIDGE BUSINESS RECOVERY LLP
3rd Floor, 39-45 Shaftesbury Avenue, London, W1D 6LA
Tel: 020 7025 6130
Resident Partners/Directors: ICAEW Members
S T Bennett, M J C Oldham

BROWN MCLEOD LTD
10 Three Kings Yard, Mayfair, London, W1K 4JR
Tel: 020 7495 7429

BUTLER & CO ◈
Walmar House, 288-292 Regent Street, London, W1B 3AL
Tel: 020 7436 3343
Fax: 020 7436 5302
Email: k_shah@butler-co.com
Website: http://www.butler-co.com
Resident Partners/Directors: ICAEW Members
M S Desai, S Y Phadke, K N Shah
Registered by the ICAEW to carry out company audit work
Authorised and regulated by the Financial Services Authority for investment business
General Description: We offer a full range of accountancy, taxation and financial services. Our specialisations include UK taxation, offshore services, IT solutions, financial planning and investigations.

C C YOUNG & CO LTD
1st Floor, 48 Poland Street, London, W1F 7ND

CAMERON BAUM
88 Crawford Street, London, W1H 2EJ

CAMERON BAUM LTD
88 Crawford Street, London, W1H 2EJ

CARNELIAN
7a Wyndham Place, London, W1H 1PN
Tel: 020 7723 9040

CARNELIAN BUSINESS SERVICES LTD ◈
7a Wyndham Place, London, W1H 1PN
Tel: 020 7723 9040
Resident Partners/Directors: ICAEW Members
S Aggarwal

CHARLES MARCUS
42 Brook Street, London, W1K 5DB

CHILTERN TAX SUPPORT FOR PROFESSIONALS LTD
55 Baker Street, London, W1U 7EU

CHOWDHURY AHAMMAD & CO
4th Floor, 36 East Castle Street, London, W1W 8DP
Tel: 020 7580 8070
Principal: ICAEW Member
U C Ahammad

CHRIS MADGE & CO
212 Piccadilly, London, W1J 9HG
Tel: 020 7917 9452
Website: http://www.chris-madge.co.uk

SPECIALISATIONS – FORENSIC ACCOUNTING
Expert Witnesses in Litigation
Forensic Accounting

SPECIALISATIONS – TAXATION
Back Duty
Customs Duty
Investigations
PAYE Advice
Value Added Tax

CITROEN WELLS ◈
Devonshire House, 1 Devonshire Street, London, W1W 5DR
Tel: 020 7304 2000
Fax: 020 7304 2020
Email: jonathan.prevezer@citroenwells.co.uk
Website: http://www.citroenwells.co.uk
Date Established: 1952
Training Contracts Available.
Resident Partners/Directors: ICAEW Members
M S Bailey, N J Brennan, H M Charles, P M Friede, M Higgins, D J B Kidd, D Marks, J W Prevezer, D H Rodney, S Simou
Resident Partners (Non-ICAEW Members):
E A Lanham, M K Mehta, W Lian, A Thurlow, K Richardson
Registered by the ICAEW to carry out company audit work
Regulated by the ICAEW for a range of investment business activities
Individual(s) licensed for insolvency work by another RPB
SPECIALISATIONS – AUDIT & ASSURANCE
Audit
Audit — Private Company

SPECIALISATIONS – BUSINESS & GENERAL ADVICE

Book-keeping
Company Formation
Company Secretarial Service
Disposal of Businesses
Management Consultancy

SPECIALISATIONS – BUSINESS RECOVERY & INSOLVENCY

Bankruptcies
Corporate Recovery
Liquidations

SPECIALISATIONS – FINANCIAL REPORTING

Accounts Preparation
Foreign Subsidiary Companies

SPECIALISATIONS – FORENSIC ACCOUNTING

Expert Witnesses in Litigation
Forensic Accounting

SPECIALISATIONS – INVESTMENT BUSINESS

Financial Planning and Advice
Pensions Advice
Planning

SPECIALISATIONS – SECTOR

Artists/Graphic Designers
Barristers
Charities
Clothing/Textiles
Corporate
Dentists/Opticians
Doctors
Entertainers
FSA Members
Journalists/Writers/ Copywriters
Property
Property Development
Property Investment
Retailers
Solicitors
Traders — General

SPECIALISATIONS – TAXATION

Estate Planning
Executorship
Foreign Nationals in the UK
Investigations
Offshore Companies
Payroll Service and Advice
Personal
Taxation
Trusts
UK Companies Overseas
UK Nationals Overseas
UK Subsidiaries of Overseas Multinationals

Languages Spoken:
French, German, Hebrew

CITYCAS LTD ◈
Room 540 Fifth Floor, Linen Hall, 162-168 Regents Street, London W1B 5TF
Tel: 0845 606 6567
Resident Partners/Directors: ICAEW Members
P M Cullen, S Pahwa

CIVVALS ◈
Marble Arch House, 66-68 Seymour Street, London, W1H 5AF
Tel: 020 7258 3461
Email: aamir@civvals.co.uk
Website: http://www.civvals.co.uk
Resident Partners/Directors: ICAEW Members
L N Fagan, M A Kazi, S Pollack, A N Siganporia

Registered by the ICAEW to carry out company audit work

Regulated by the ICAEW for a range of investment business activities

SPECIALISATIONS – AUDIT & ASSURANCE

Audit — Private Company

SPECIALISATIONS – BUSINESS & GENERAL ADVICE

Book-keeping
Management Accounting Consultancy

SPECIALISATIONS – FINANCIAL REPORTING

Accounts Preparation
Limited Company Accounts

SPECIALISATIONS – SECTOR

Catering/Restaurants
Clothing/Textiles
Dentists/Opticians
Doctors
Estate Agents
Hotels/Public Houses
Property
Property Development
Property Investment
Retailers
Solicitors
Travel Industry

SPECIALISATIONS – TAXATION

Capital Gains — Personal
Self Assessment Advice

CIVVALS ELLAM LTD
Marble Arch House, 66-68 Seymour Street, London, W1H 5AF

CLARKSON HYDE LLP
70 Conduit Street, London, W1S 2GF
Tel: 020 7022 0050
Email: enquiries@clarksonhyde.com
Website: http://www.clarksonhyde.com
Resident Partners/Directors: ICAEW Members
M E Coomber, R F John
Other Offices:137-143 High Street, Sutton, Surrey SM1 1JH

CLAYMAN & CO
189 Bickenhall Mansions, Bickenhall Street,Baker Street, London, W1U 6BX

CLEARWATER CORPORATE FINANCE LLP
1st Floor, 71 Broadwick Street, London, W1F 9QY

CLIVE PARRITT ◈
One Heddon Street, London, W1B 4BD
Tel: 020 7470 7233
Principal: ICAEW Member
C A Parritt

COMPANY AUDITS LTD
12 Upper Berkeley Street, London, W1H 7QD

CONVEX CAPITAL LTD ◈
1 Berkeley Street, Mayfair, London, W1J 8DJ

COOPER MURRAY
Fifth Floor, Tennyson House, 159-165 Great Portland Street, London W1W 5PA

COUSINS BRETT
20 Bulstrode Street, London, W1U 2JW

CROWLEY YOUNG ASSOCIATES LTD
10 Berkeley Street, London, W1J 8DP

CW & G PARTNERSHIP LLP ◈
68 Great Portland Street, London, W1W 7NG
Tel: 020 7637 3717
Resident Partners/Directors: ICAEW Members
A T Coomber, A L Weiner

Registered by the ICAEW to carry out company audit work

Regulated by the ICAEW for a range of investment business activities

DALES EVANS & CO LTD
88/90 Baker Street, London, W1U 6TQ

DALY, HOGGETT & CO
5-11 Mortimer Street, London, W1T 3HS
Tel: 020 7637 7906
Email: info@dalyhoggett.co.uk
Website: http://www.dalyhoggett.co.uk
Resident Partners/Directors: ICAEW Members
D J Bartlett, R V F Brianti
Resident Partners (Non-ICAEW Members):
O J Gould
Other Offices: Rickmansworth

Registered by the ICAEW to carry out company audit work

Authorised and regulated by the Financial Services Authority for investment business

DANIEL AUERBACH & COMPANY LLP ★
9 Mansfield Street, London, W1G 9NY

DANIEL WHITEFIELD LTD
26-28 Hallam Street, London, W1W 6NS

DARBY TWYMAN JONES
427 Linen Hall, 162-168 Regent Street, London, W1B 5TD

DAVE & CO
54/62 Regent Street, London, W1B 5RE

DAVID BACON FCA
Suite 2, First Floor, 1 Duchess Street, London W1W 6AN

DAVID SMITH & CO
41 Welbeck Street, London, W1G 8HH
Tel: 020 7224 1004
Fax: 020 7486 8705
Email: dcsmithco@aol.com
Principal: ICAEW Member
D C Smith

Registered by the ICAEW to carry out company audit work

Regulated by the ICAEW for a range of investment business activities

SPECIALISATIONS – AUDIT & ASSURANCE

Audit — Private Company

SPECIALISATIONS – FINANCIAL REPORTING

Accounts Preparation
Partnership/Sole Trader Accounts

SPECIALISATIONS – SECTOR

Charities
Doctors
Entertainers

SPECIALISATIONS – TAXATION

Taxation
Trusteeship

DB ASSOCIATES LTD
82Z Portland Place, London, W1B 1NS

DE WARRENNE WALLER AND CO LTD
211 Piccadilly, London, W1J 9HF
Tel: 020 7958 1710

DEREK R. GRAY
82z Portland Place, London, W1B 1NS

DOVER CHILDS TYLER ★
7-9 Swallow Street, London, W1R 8DT

DTE CORPORATE RECOVERY AND INSOLVENCY SERVICES LTD
1 Great Cumberland Place, London, W1H 7LW

EDWARD RATNAM FCA
Suite 419, 40 Warren Street, London, W1T 6AF
Tel: 0845 458 9462
Email: edratnam@clara.co.uk
Date Established: 2001
Principal: ICAEW Member
E I Ratnam

SPECIALISATIONS – SECTOR

FSA Members

General Description: Bespoke accountancy services for FSA members in small firms.

ELMAN WALL
5-7 John Princes Street, London, W1G 0JN

SPECIALISATIONS – SECTOR

Travel Industry

ELMAN WALL LTD ◈
5-7 John Princes Street, London, W1G 0JN
Tel: 020 7493 9595
Email: jonw@elmanwall.co.uk
Website: http://www.elmanwall.co.uk
Resident Partners/Directors: ICAEW Members
R D Eisen, I R Palmer, J Wall

Registered by the ICAEW to carry out company audit work

Regulated by the ICAEW for a range of investment business activities

SPECIALISATIONS – AUDIT & ASSURANCE

Audit

SPECIALISATIONS – SECTOR

Leisure Industry
Solicitors
Travel Industry

SPECIALISATIONS – TAXATION

Investigations
Taxation
UK Subsidiaries of Overseas Multinationals

General Description: We are a full service firm that provides expert, professional advice with dedication and friendliness. We also are leading specialists to the travel industry.

ELMAN WALL TRAVEL ACCOUNTANTS
5-7 John Princes Street, London, W1G 0JN

ELWELL WATCHORN & SAXTON LLP
41 Welbeck Street, London, W1G 8EA

F. WINTER & CO LLP
Ramillies House, 2 Ramillies Street, London, W1F 7LN
Tel: 020 7437 1137
Fax: 020 7494 1038
Email: admin@fwinter.co.uk
Resident Partners/Directors: ICAEW Members
H Khakhria, P S Sharma

Registered by the ICAEW to carry out company audit work

Regulated by the ICAEW for a range of investment business activities

SPECIALISATIONS – AUDIT & ASSURANCE

Audit

SPECIALISATIONS – SECTOR

Dentists/Opticians
Entertainers

SPECIALISATIONS – TAXATION

Partnerships and Sole Traders
Taxation

FISHER, SASSOON & MARKS
43-45 Dorset Street, London, W1U 7NA
Tel: 020 7935 8111
Fax: 020 7487 3893
Email: arose@fsm.org.uk
Website: http://www.fsm.org.uk
Resident Partners/Directors: ICAEW Members
J Marks, A Rose

SPECIALISATIONS – AUDIT & ASSURANCE

Audit — Private Company

SPECIALISATIONS – SECTOR

Banks/Financial Institutions
FSA Members

FRIEND LLP
43-45 Portman Square, London, W1H 6HN

GARSIDE & CO LLP ◈
6 Vigo Street, London, W1S 3HF
Tel: 020 7439 1050
Fax: 020 7439 1060
Email: stephen@garside.co.uk
Website: http://www.garside.co.uk
Resident Partners/Directors: ICAEW Members
S B Garside, D Russell

Registered by the ICAEW to carry out company audit work

Authorised and regulated by the Financial Services Authority for investment business

GEOFFREY MARTIN & CO ★
7-8 Conduit Street, London, W1S 2XF
Tel: 020 7495 1100

SPECIALISATIONS – BUSINESS & GENERAL ADVICE

Administration

SPECIALISATIONS – BUSINESS RECOVERY & INSOLVENCY

Bankruptcies
Corporate Recovery
Liquidations
Reorganisations and Company Reconstructions

GERALD EDELMAN ◈
25 Harley Street, London, W1G 9BR
Tel: 020 7299 1400
Fax: 020 7299 1401
Email: gemail@geraldedelman.co.uk
Website: http://www.geraldedelman.com
Resident Partners/Directors: ICAEW Members
C R Burns, S P Coleman, M Harris, R H Kleiner
Non-resident Partners (ICAEW Members):
D B Atkinson, D A Convisser, S H Rosenberg, N Summer, H J Wallis
Non-resident Partners (Non-ICAEW Members):
B Hoffman, A C Shah, D S Patel, G W Thomas
Other Offices: Whetstone, London N20

Registered by the ICAEW to carry out company audit work

Regulated by the ICAEW for a range of investment business activities
Individual(s) licensed for insolvency work by another RPB

SPECIALISATIONS – AUDIT & ASSURANCE

Audit

SPECIALISATIONS – BUSINESS & GENERAL ADVICE

Company Secretarial Service

SPECIALISATIONS – BUSINESS RECOVERY & INSOLVENCY

Corporate Recovery
Liquidations

SPECIALISATIONS – FINANCIAL REPORTING

Accounts Preparation
Limited Company Accounts

SPECIALISATIONS – SECTOR

Property Development
Property Investment

SPECIALISATIONS – TAXATION

Payroll Service and Advice
Taxation

GMG ROBERTS
47 Queen Anne Street, London, W1G 9JG
Tel: 020 7486 8686
Resident Partners/Directors: ICAEW Members
J E Granat, R Granat, H A Mehdyoun

GODSON & CO
6/7 Pollen Street, London, W1S 1NJ
Tel: 020 7495 5916
Fax: 020 7495 5918
Email: rgodson@godsons.co.uk
Principal: ICAEW Member
R G Godson

GOLDSMITH & CO
67 Upper Berkeley Street, London, W1H 7QX

GOLDWYNS
13 David Mews, Porter Street, London, W1U 6EQ

GOLDWYNS
13 David Mews, Porter Street, London, W1U 6EQ
Tel: 020 7935 1762
Resident Partners/Directors: ICAEW Members
T M Motyer, M A Myers

GOLDWYNS (LONDON) LTD
13 David Mews, Porter Street, London, W1U 6EQ
Tel: 020 7935 1762
Resident Partners/Directors: ICAEW Members
T M Motyer, M A Myers

GOODMAN JONES LLP ◈
29-30 Fitzroy Square, London, W1T 6LQ
Tel: 020 7388 2444
Email: info@goodmanjones.com
Website: http://www.goodmanjones.com
Training Contracts Available.
Resident Partners/Directors: ICAEW Members
M P G Austin, J C Bates, G P Bursack, J M Finesilver, J R Flitter, M D Goldstein, W E Grossman, R C Morris, L M Phillips, P J Rogol, A Sharma, S I Wildman, P H Woodgate
Resident Partners (Non-ICAEW Members):
C Suleyman

Registered by the ICAEW to carry out company audit work

GOODMAN JONES PARTNERSHIP
29-30 Fitzroy Square, London, W1T 6LQ
Tel: 020 7388 2444
Resident Partners/Directors: ICAEW Members
M P G Austin, J C Bates, G P Bursack, J M Finesilver, J R

Flitter, M D Goldstein, W E Grossman, R C Morris, L M Phillips, P J Rogol, A Sharma, S I Wildman, P H Woodgate
Resident Partners (Non-ICAEW Members):
C Suleyman

GORRIE WHITSON
18 Hand Court, London, WC1V 6JF

GRIFFIN STONE, MOSCROP & CO
41 Welbeck Street, London, W1G 8EA

HADLEY & CO
1-7 Harley Street, London, W1G 9QD

HAINES WATTS CORPORATE FINANCE ★
211 Regent Street, London, W1B 4NF
Resident Partners/Directors:
ICAEW Members
G M Laughton

HALPERN AND CO ◈
20 Berkeley Street, London, W1J 8EE
Tel: 020 7491 7410
Fax: 020 7491 7411
Email: david@halpernandco.com
Resident Partners/Directors:
ICAEW Members
D Halpern

HARDWICK & MORRIS
41 Great Portland Street, London, W1W 7LA

HAROLD EVERETT WREFORD
32 Wigmore Street, London, W1U 2RP
Tel: 020 7535 5900
Resident Partners/Directors:
ICAEW Members
M Bayer, S Cymerman, G P Golbey, M D Isaacs, D J Scott, J Sloneem

HARRIS & TROTTER LLP
65 New Cavendish Street, London, W1G 7LS
Tel: 020 7467 6300
Fax: 020 7467 6363
Email: mail@harrisandtrotter.co.uk
Website: http://www.harrisandtrotter.co.uk
Resident Partners/Directors:
ICAEW Members
J M Boas, S M Garbutta, S E Haffner, C E Harris, R M Harris, H M Lask, N J Newman, R M Selwyn, D R Walters, M Webber

SPECIALISATIONS – SECTOR

Entertainers
Media
Property Development
Property Investment

HAZLEMS FENTON ◈
Palladium House, 1-4 Argyll Street, London, W1F 7LD
Tel: 020 7437 7666
Email: info@hazlemsfenton.com
DX: 9081 WEST END
Website: http://www.hazlemsfenton.com
Resident Partners/Directors:
ICAEW Members
L Angel, P Aswani, J M Barron, S R N Fenton, S H Jaffe, M M Krieger, M J Levitt, R P Tenzer
Registered by the ICAEW to carry out company audit work
Regulated by the ICAEW for a range of investment business activities

SPECIALISATIONS – AUDIT & ASSURANCE

Audit
Audit — Private Company
Audit — Public Company

SPECIALISATIONS – FINANCIAL REPORTING

Audit Exemption Report

HAZLEMS FINANCIAL LTD
Palladium House, 1-4 Argyll Street, London, W1F 7LD

HERBERT REIMERS
Office 404, 4th Floor, Albany House, 324-326 Regent Street, London W1B 3HH

HEYWARDS
6th Floor, Remo House, 310-312 Regent Street, London W1B 3BS
Tel: 020 7299 8150
Website: http://www.heywards.co.uk
Resident Partners/Directors:
ICAEW Members
S Patel, P N Samuels, H B Strudwick

HIGGINS FAIRBAIRN & CO ◈
71 Duke Street, London, W1K 5NY
Tel: 020 7355 4629
Resident Partners/Directors:
ICAEW Members
F W Higgins, B C Patel
Registered by the ICAEW to carry out company audit work
Authorised and regulated by the Financial Services Authority for investment business
Languages Spoken:
Chinese, French

HLB VANTIS AUDIT PLC
66 Wigmore Street, London, W1U 2SB
Tel: 020 7467 4000
Website: http://www.hlbvantisaudit.com
Training Contracts Available.
Resident Partners/Directors:
ICAEW Members
I Hughes
Registered by the ICAEW to carry out company audit work
Regulated by the ICAEW for a range of investment business activities

HOLBECK HARTMAN & DEEN
12 Upper Berkeley Street, London, W1H 7QD

HOWARD BLOOM
8 Hinde Street, London, W1U 3BE

HOWARD BLOOM LTD
8 Hinde Street, London, W1U 3BE

HW CORPORATE FINANCE LLP
7-10 Chandos Street, London, W1G 1LG
Tel: 02380 111310

HWCA LTD ◈
7-10 Chandos Street, Cavendish Square, London, W1G 9DQ
Tel: 020 7323 2131
Resident Partners/Directors:
ICAEW Members
G C Fairclough, A S Minifie, Y A Patel

HWSEG LTD
7-10 Chandos Street, Cavendish Square, London, W1G 9DQ

HYMAN ASSOCIATES
1 Cato Street, London, W1H 5HG

HYMAN CAPITAL SERVICES LTD
25 Duke Street, London, W1U 1LD

ICON CORPORATE FINANCE ◈
53 Davies Street, London, W1K 5JH
Tel: 020 7152 6375
Principal: ICAEW Member
A C Bristow

IVAN SOPHER & CO
15 Hanover Square, London, W1S 1HS

J B KLEIN & PARTNERS ★
10 Argyll Street, London, W1F 7TQ
Tel: 020 7440 3810
Resident Partners/Directors:
ICAEW Members
J B Klein

J.B. MARKS & CO
88 Crawford Street, London, W1H 2EJ

J.M. SHAH & CO
24 Old Bond Street, London, W1S 4AP
Tel: 020 7499 4431
Email: info@jmshah.co.uk
Website: http://www.jmshah.co.uk
Date Established: 1979
Principal: ICAEW Member
J M Shah
Registered by the ICAEW to carry out company audit work

JACOB, TING & CO
40 Homer Street, London, W1H 4NL

JAMIESON STONE ◈
26 Eastcastle Street, London, W1W 8DQ
Tel: 020 7580 1810
Principal: ICAEW Member
M R Stone

JASSENS
34 Seymour Street, London, W1H 7JE

JENSON SOLUTIONS LTD ◈
Communications House, 26 York Street, London, W1V 6PZ
Tel: 020 7788 7539
Resident Partners/Directors:
ICAEW Members
P N Jenkinson

SPECIALISATIONS – BUSINESS & GENERAL ADVICE

Acquisitions and Mergers
Administration
Investment Appraisal
Management Advice to Business

SPECIALISATIONS – FINANCIAL REPORTING

International Reporting Standards (IFRS)

THE JMO PRACTICE ◈
7 Harley Street, London, W1G 9QD

JONES & PARTNERS
Fifth Floor, 26-28 Great Portland Street, London, W1W 8AS

KC PARTNERS
1st Floor, 76 New Bond Street, London, W1S 1RX

KERBURN ROSE CAPITAL LTD
83 Baker Street, London, W1U 6AG

KHMM
Lisbon House, 173 Wardour Street, London, W1F 8WT

KING & KING
Roxburghe House, 273-287 Regent Street, London, W1B 2HA

KINGSTON SMITH LLP
141 Wardour Street, London, W1F 0UT
Tel: 0207 304 4646
Fax: 020 7304 4647
Email: ks@kingstonsmith.co.uk
Website: http://www.kingstonsmith.co.uk
Resident Partners/Directors: ICAEW Members
E M Carder, G W Howells, C W Ireton, A Merron, G A Tyler

SPECIALISATIONS – SECTOR

Advertising/Design Agencies
Artists/Graphic Designers
Media

LAWRENCE B LADENHEIM
Suite 725, 19-21 Crawford Street, London, W1H 1PJ

THE LAWRENCE WOOLFSON PARTNERSHIP
1 Bentinck Street, London, W1U 2ED

THE LEAMAN PARTNERSHIP LLP
51 Queen Anne Street, London, W1G 9HS

LEIGH CARR ◈
72 New Cavendish Street, London, W1G 8AU
Tel: 020 7580 7788
Fax: 020 7580 8877
Email: leighcarr@btinternet.com
Resident Partners/Directors: ICAEW Members
R A De Souza, P Herelle, J S Natt, R.J. O'Gorman, I P Sugarman
Resident Partners (Non-ICAEW Members):
N A Jin, R T Whitcomb
Registered by the ICAEW to carry out company audit work
Regulated by the ICAEW for a range of investment business activities
General Description: Founded over 70 years ago, the modern Leigh Carr offer a wide variety of services including audit and accountancy work, management buy-outs, tax planning and compliance, mergers & acquisitions, forensic accountancy.

LEIGH PHILIP & PARTNERS
1/6 Clay Street, London, W1U 6DA
Tel: 020 7486 4889
Fax: 020 7486 4885
Email: mail@lpplondon.co.uk
Training Contracts Available.
Resident Partners/Directors: ICAEW Members
L A Genis, I D Sassoon, A M Shaw
Registered by the ICAEW to carry out company audit work
Regulated by the ICAEW for a range of investment business activities

LEIGH SAXTON GREEN ★
Clearwater House, 4-7 Manchester Street, London, W1U 3AE

LEWIS & CO
19 Goodge Street, London, W1T 2PH
Tel: 020 7580 9049
Email: admin@lewis-and-co.com
Principal: ICAEW Member
R W Lewis

LEWIS GOLDEN & CO ◈
40 Queen Anne Street, London, W1G 9EL
Tel: 020 7580 7313
Fax: 020 7580 2179
Email: fca@lewis-golden.co.uk
Website: http://www.lewis-golden.co.uk
Date Established: 1950
Training Contracts Available.
Resident Partners/Directors: ICAEW Members
N W Benson, D C Edwards, A G Moss, A R Parker, S J Webber
Resident Partners (Non-ICAEW Members):
G G Kinch, K Mitchell
Registered by the ICAEW to carry out company audit work
Regulated by the ICAEW for a range of investment business activities

SPECIALISATIONS – SECTOR

Catering/Restaurants
Charities
Entertainers
Insurance Brokers
Property
Property Development
Property Investment
Solicitors

SPECIALISATIONS – TAXATION

Small Traders

LINDFORD & CO
One Duchess Street, London, W1W 6AN
Tel: 020 7637 2244
Website: http://www.lindford.com
Principal: ICAEW Member
T J Lindford

LITTLESTONE MARTIN GLENTON
73 Wimpole Street, London, W1G 8AZ
Tel: 020 7535 1650
Resident Partners/Directors: ICAEW Members
V R Drexler, D G Humphrey, R H Weston, M J Wright

LYNDOE REEVE
34/36 Maddox Street, London, W1S 1PD
Tel: 020 7629 9679
Fax: 020 7499 0387
Email: peter@lyndoe-reeve.demon.co.uk
Principal: ICAEW Member
P M Reeve

M.C. LANDAU
88-90 Crawford Street, London, W1H 2EJ

MCBRIDES
31 Harley Street, London, W1G 9QS
Tel: 020 7467 1700
Principal: ICAEW Member
P McBride

MACCORKINDALE INTERNATIONAL PARTNERS ★
13 Harley Street, London, W1G 9QG
Tel: 020 7636 1888
Resident Partners/Directors: ICAEW Members
P D Maccorkindale

MACKENZIE FIELD
28 Savile Row, London, W1S 2EU

MCR ★
43-45 Portman Square, London, W1H 6LY

MAGUS PARTNERS LLP
65 Duke Street, London, W1K 5AJ

MARRIOTS LLP
Allan House, 10 John Princes Street, London, W1G 0AH

MATHIE, NEAL, DANCER & CO
93-95 Gloucester Place, London, W1U 6JG

MG AUDIT (LONDON) LTD
93-95 Gloucester Place, London, W1U 6JG

MG CONTRACTOR SERVICES
93-95 Gloucester Place, London, W1U 6JG

MG CONTRACTOR SERVICES LTD
93-95 Gloucester Place, London, W1U 6JG

MICHAEL GOLDSTEIN & CO
1 Harley Street, London, W1G 9QD
Tel: 020 7291 4548
Principal: ICAEW Member
M Goldstein

MICHAEL KENTAS & CO
72 Wimpole Street, London, W1G 9RP

MICHAEL KENTAS & CO LTD
72 Wimpole Street, London, W1G 9RP
Tel: 020 7935 7741
Resident Partners/Directors: ICAEW Members
M Kentas

MIDDLETON PARTNERS ★
38 Langham Street, London, W1W 7AR

MND (LONDON) LTD
93-95 Gloucester Place, London, W1U 6JG

MODIPLUS ★
37 Warren Street, London, W1T 6AD

MODIPLUS LTD
37 Warren Street, London, W1T 6AD

N.D. PILBROW
5th Floor, 35 Davies Street, London, W1K 4LS
Tel: 020 3195 6473

NABARRO
3/4 Great Marlborough Street, London, W1F 7HH

NATHAN MAKNIGHT
1 Berkeley Street, London, W1J 8DJ

NEWBERY CHAPMAN LLP
Adam House, 14 New Burlington Street, London, W1S 3BQ

NEWMAN PETERS PANAYI LLP ◈
19 Fitzroy Square, London, W1T 6EQ
Tel: 020 7388 1208
Resident Partners/Directors: ICAEW Members
Y M A Bulmer, R H Newman, R J Peters

NICHOLAS PETERS & CO
18-22 Wigmore Street, London, W1U 2RG
Tel: 020 7462 6900
Resident Partners/Directors: ICAEW Members
P Petrou

NORTON LEWIS & CO
246/248 Great Portland St, London, W1W 5JL
Tel: 020 7387 5351
Principal: ICAEW Member
G N Norton

NUMERICA CAPITAL MARKETS LTD ◈
66 Wigmore Street, London, W1U 2SB

NYMAN LINDEN
105 Baker Street, London, W1U 6NY

OLIVINE CAPITAL PARTNERS LTD ◈
26 Devonshire Place, London, W1G 6JE

P C MAVRON & CO LTD
38 South Molton Street, Mayfair, London, W1K 5RL
Tel: 0870 870 4141
Resident Partners/Directors:
ICAEW Members
P C Mavron

PANACO INTERNATIONAL LTD
First Floor, 27 Gloucester Place, London, W1U 8HU

PAWLEY & MALYON
52 Queen Anne Street, London, W1G 9LA

PERRYS ◈
12 Old Bond Street, London, W1S 4PW
Tel: 020 7408 4442

PK PARTNERS LLP
38a Homer Street, London, W1H 4NH

PKB UNDERWOOD LAMB ◈
77 Brook Street, London, W1K 4HY

PKB UNDERWOOD LAMB LLP
77 Brook Street, London, W1K 4HY

REDFORD & CO
1st Floor, 64 Baker Street, London, W1U 7GB

REDFORD & CO LTD
1st Floor, 64 Baker Street, London, W1U 7GB
Tel: 020 7224 2444
Resident Partners/Directors:
ICAEW Members
M J Redford, P N Redford

REVILL PEARCE
58 Queen Anne Street, London, W1G 8HW

RICHES & CO ★
1 Duchess Street, London, W1W 6AN

ROBERTS & PARTNERS
47 Queen Anne Street, London, W1G 9JG

ROBINSON RUSHEN
47 Queen Anne Street, London, W1G 9JG

ROCHMAN GOODMANS
Accurist House, 44 Baker Street, London, W1U 7AL

ROSENTHAL & CO ◈
20-21 Cato Street, London, W1H 5JQ
Tel: 020 7258 0800
Email: robert@rcrosenthal.co.uk

SPECIALISATIONS – SECTOR

Doctors

SPECIALISATIONS – TAXATION

Taxation

ROSENTHAL, HASS & CO
Pitt House, 120 Baker Street, London, W1U 6TU
Tel: 020 7299 9840
Email: mail@rosenthalhass.com
Website: http://www.rosenthalhass.com
Resident Partners/Directors:
ICAEW Members
R E Isaacson, C C Rosenthal, S J Truman
Resident Partners (Non-ICAEW Members):
M M Jaffer

Registered by the ICAEW to carry out company audit work

Regulated by the ICAEW for a range of investment business activities

S H LANDES LLP ◈
5th Floor, Walmar House, 288 Regent Street, London W1B 3AL
Tel: 020 7637 5666
Resident Partners/Directors:
ICAEW Members
S H Landes

Registered by the ICAEW to carry out company audit work

Regulated by the ICAEW for a range of investment business activities

SAM ROGOFF & CO
2nd Floor, 167-169 Great Portland Street, London, W1W 5PF

SANDERS ◈
1 Bickenhall Mansions, Bickenhall Street, London, W1U 6BP
Tel: 020 7317 0040
Principal: ICAEW Member
S B Sanders

SANDISON EASSON & GORDON
7-10 Chandos Street, Cavendish Square, London, W1G 9DQ

SANDISON LANG & CO
12 Harley Street, London, W1N 1AA

SAUNDERS & CO
29 Harcourt Street, London, W1H 4HS

SAYERS BUTTERWORTH LLP ◈
18 Bentinck Street, London, W1U 2AR
Tel: 020 7935 8504
Email: enquiries@sayersb.co.uk
Website: http://www.sayersb.co.uk
Date Established: 1900
Resident Partners/Directors:
ICAEW Members
D M Burke, M C Dunne, P E Ffitch, A G Mahoney, M W Wright

SPECIALISATIONS – AUDIT & ASSURANCE

Audit

SPECIALISATIONS – BUSINESS & GENERAL ADVICE

Book-keeping
Company Formation
Company Secretarial Service

SPECIALISATIONS – FINANCIAL REPORTING

Accounts Preparation
Foreign Subsidiary Companies
Limited Company Accounts
Partnership/Sole Trader Accounts

SPECIALISATIONS – TAXATION

Capital Gains — Personal
Estate and Inheritance
Estate Planning
Executorship
Foreign Nationals in the UK
Partnerships and Sole Traders
Payroll Service and Advice
Personal
Trusts
Value Added Tax

General Description: Founded in 1900, the firm is a general practice with a strong tax and commercial bias. It has a reputation built on a high quality personal service to clients. Please visit www.sayersb.co.uk.

SCANNELL & ASSOCIATES ★
212 Piccadilly, London, W1J 9HG

SEDLEY RICHARD LAURENCE VOULTERS
1 Conduit Street, London, W1S 2XA
Tel: 020 7287 9595
Website: http://www.srlv.co.uk
Training Contracts Available.
Resident Partners/Directors:
ICAEW Members
L W Finger, S P Jeffery, P M Maranzana, S Marks, M H L Ossman, R B Rosenberg, A Verma, M Voulters

SG ASSOCIATES LTD
82z Portland Place, London, W1B 1NS

SHAH DHANANI & CO ★
23 Harcourt Street, London, W1H 4HJ

SHARPE FAIRBROTHER
67-69 George Street, London, W1U 8LT

SHEARS & DUBE'
52-53 Margaret Street, London, W1W 8SQ

SHELLEY STOCK HUTTER
7-10 Chandos Street, London, W1G 9DQ

SHELLEY STOCK HUTTER LLP
7-10 Chandos Street, London, W1G 9DQ

SILVER LEVENE ★
Silvene House, 37 Warren Street, London, W1T 6AD
Tel: 020 7383 3200
Resident Partners/Directors:
ICAEW Members
M I Franks, S L George, P R A Grossmark, H E Mehta, U J Modi, R B Perez

SIM KAPILA ◈
St Georges House, 14-17 Wells Street, London, W1T 3PD
Tel: 020 7636 7699
Email: rkapila@simkapila.co.uk
Resident Partners/Directors:
ICAEW Members
R Kapila, G E Sim
Registered by the ICAEW to carry out company audit work

SPECIALISATIONS – FORENSIC ACCOUNTING

Expert Witnesses in Litigation
Forensic Accounting

General Description: Sim Kapila is a "niche" practice specialising in forensic and investigative accountancy.

SIMMONDS & CO
Suite 3, 7 Paddington Street, London, W1U 5QQ

SIMMONS GAINSFORD LLP
5th Floor, 7-10 Chandos Street, London, W1G 9DQ
Tel: 020 7447 9000
Fax: 020 7447 9001
Email: excellence@simmonsgainsford.co.uk
Website: http://www.simmonsgainsford.co.uk

Date Established: 1976

Resident Partners/Directors:
ICAEW Members
P Austin, O A H W Dodd, J Goldman, S M Jennings, J Lewis, R V Patel, Abdultaiyab Pisavadi, M S Pizer, D J Pumfrey, W W P Sing, S M Strauss, H Sze, R C Thakerar, R D Ward

Non-resident Partners (ICAEW Members):
C Stebbing

Resident Partners (Non-ICAEW Members):
D L Hersey, N Wight

Other Offices:52 New Town, Uckfield, East Sussex TN22 5DE

continued

SIMMONS GAINSFORD LLP *cont*
Registered by the ICAEW to carry out company audit work
Regulated by the ICAEW for a range of investment business activities

INVESTOR IN PEOPLE

SIMON SILVER-MYER
8 Durweston Street, London, W1H 1EW

SINCLAIRS ★
32 Queen Anne Street, London, W1G 8HD

SMALLFIELD, CODY & CO
5 Harley Place, Harley Street, London, W1G 8QD

SOCHALLS ◈
9 Wimpole Street, London, W1G 9SR
Tel: 020 7291 1000
Resident Partners/Directors: ICAEW Members
B D Sochall

STEPHEN H ROSS & CO
Elliott House, 28A Devonshire Street, London, W1G 6PS

STEVEN FRIEND & CO LTD
12 Newburgh Street, Soho, London, W1F 7RP

SUMMERS & CO
6 Jacobs Well Mews, London, W1U 3DY
Tel: 020 7935 0123
Email: info@sumco.co.uk
Resident Partners/Directors: ICAEW Members
A G Summers, R Summers

TAX SAVERS U.K. LTD
Elliott House, 28A Devonshire Street, London, W1G 6PS

TAXATION SERVICES (LONDON) LTD
93-95 Gloucester Place, London, W1U 6JG

TAXATION SERVICES MG GROUP
93-95 Gloucester Place, London, W1U 6JG

TENON LTD
66 Chiltern Street, London, W1V 4JT

TENON LTD
66 Chiltern St, London, W1U 4JT
Tel: 020 7535 1400

TENON LTD
Sherlock House, 73 Baker Street, London, W1U 6RD
Tel: 020 7935 5566

TENON LTD
3rd Floor Egmont House, 25-31 Tavistock Place, London, WC1H 9SF
Tel: 020 7554 4660

TENON AUDIT LTD
66 Chiltern Street, London, W1U 4JT
Tel: 020 7535 1400

THOMPSON TARAZ
3 New Burlington Mews, London, W1B 4QB

THOMPSON TARAZ LLP
3 New Burlington Mews, London, W1B 4QB

VANTIS BUSINESS RECOVERY SERVICES
66 Wigmore Street, London, W1U 2SB
Tel: 0207 467 4000
Website: http://www.vantisplc.com/businessrecovery
Individual(s) licensed for insolvency work by another RPB

SPECIALISATIONS – BUSINESS RECOVERY & INSOLVENCY
Bankruptcies
Corporate Recovery
Liquidations

VANTIS CORPORATE FINANCE LTD ◈
66 Wigmore Street, London, W1U 2SB
Tel: 020 7467 4000
Website: http://www.vantisplc.com/corporatefinance
Resident Partners/Directors: ICAEW Members
J Ward
Resident Partners (Non-ICAEW Members):
P Marsden
Authorised and regulated by the Financial Services Authority for investment business

SPECIALISATIONS – BUSINESS & GENERAL ADVICE
Acquisitions and Mergers
Disposal of Businesses

VANTIS FINANCIAL MANAGEMENT LTD
66 Wigmore Street, London, W1U 2SB
Tel: 020 7467 4000
Website: http://www.vantisplc.com/financialmanagement
Authorised and regulated by the Financial Services Authority for investment business

SPECIALISATIONS – INVESTMENT BUSINESS
Financial Planning and Advice
Pensions Advice
Planning

VANTIS FORENSIC ACCOUNTING & DISPUTE RESOLUTION
66 Wigmore Street, London, W1U 2SB
Tel: 020 7467 4000
Website: http://www.vantisplc.com/forensic
Resident Partners/Directors: ICAEW Members
D A Stern

SPECIALISATIONS – FORENSIC ACCOUNTING
Expert Witnesses in Litigation
Forensic Accounting

General Description: CEDR accredited.

VANTIS GROUP LTD
66 Wigmore Street, London, W1U 2SB
Tel: 020 7467 4000
Website: http://www.vantisplc.com/london
Resident Partners/Directors: ICAEW Members
C Crown, P A Musgrave
General Description: ICAEW Registered.

VIRTUALBPO
Medius House, 2 Sheraton Street, London, W1F 8BH

VIRTUALBPO LTD
Medius House, 2 Sheraton Street, London, W1F 8BH

WARD DIVECHA LTD
29 Welbeck Street, London, W1G 8DA
Tel: 020 7486 9893
Fax: 020 7487 5557
Email: info@warddivecha.co.uk
Website: http://www.warddivecha.co.uk
Resident Partners/Directors: ICAEW Members
A R Divecha
Registered by the ICAEW to carry out company audit work
Regulated by the ICAEW for a range of investment business activities

WEBSTERS
Baker Street Chambers, 136 Baker Street, London, W1U 6UD

WELBECK ASSOCIATES
31 Harley Street, London, W1G 9QS

WELBECK ASSOCIATES LTD
31 Harley Street, London, W1G 9QS

WESTON KAY ◈
73/75 Mortimer Street, London, W1W 7SQ

WIGGIN'S
3 Wigmore Place, London, W1U 2LN

WILLIAM EVANS & PARTNERS
20 Harcourt Street, London, W1H 4HG

WINGRAVE YEATS LTD
65 Duke Street, London, W1K 5AJ
Tel: 020 7495 2244
Resident Partners/Directors: ICAEW Members
G L Bates, C C Jenkins, T I Roberts, K Moran, M Jones

WINGRAVE YEATS PARTNERSHIP LLP ◈
65 Duke Street, London, W1K 5AJ
Tel: 020 7495 2244
Fax: 020 7499 9442
Email: info@wingrave.co.uk
Website: http://www.wingrave.co.uk
Date Established: 1983
Resident Partners/Directors: ICAEW Members
G L Bates, C C Jenkins, M L Jones, Miss K L Moran, T I Roberts
Resident Partners (Non-ICAEW Members):
P K Hedges
Registered by the ICAEW to carry out company audit work
Regulated by the ICAEW for a range of investment business activities
General Description: See website for further details.

WM PROSERV LLP
Devlin House, 36 St George Street, Mayfair, London W1S 2FJ

WONG & CO
2nd Floor, Astoria House, 62 Shaftesbury Avenue, London, W1D 6LT

WPA AUDIT LTD
26 Grosvenor Street, Mayfair, London, W1K 4QW

WSS FORENSIC ACCOUNTING ◈
25 Manchester Square, London, W1U 3PY
Tel: 020 7224 6700
Principal: ICAEW Member
W S Starr

LONDON W2

ASTON DRAYCOTT
Caprini House, 163/173 Praed Street, London, W2 1RH
Tel: 020 7402 2223
Fax: 020 7724 2105
Email: info@astondraycott.com
Website: http://www.astondraycott.com
Principal: ICAEW Member
C Atalianis

BAHRAM ALIMORADIAN & CO
76 Braithwaite Tower, Hall Place, London, W2 1LR

BRIGHT GRAHAME MURRAY
131 Edgware Road, London, W2 2AP
Tel: 020 7402 7444
Fax: 020 7402 8444
Email: post@bgm.co.uk
Website: http://www.bgm.co.uk
Date Established: 1934
Training Contracts Available.
Resident Partners/Directors: ICAEW Members
M Colclough, M C N Cole, L A Delamere, R L Feld, K L Levine, A Miraj, R K Moore, P A Rodney, A P Rotman, J D C Wakefield
Registered by the ICAEW to carry out company audit work
Regulated by the ICAEW for a range of investment business activities

BSS ASSOCIATES LTD ◈
Gresham House, 116 Sussex Gardens, London, W2 1UA

CHONG & CO
Flat 4, 55 Lancaster Gate, London, W2 3NA

ELLIOTTS SHAH ◈
2nd Floor, 5 - 11 Westbourne Grove, London, W2 4UA
Tel: 020 7221 3601
Fax: 020 7221 2036
Email: info@elliottsshah.co.uk
Resident Partners/Directors: ICAEW Members
S D Ballantine, M Haria, A R Shah, N Shah, P R Shah, N Yip
Resident Partners (Non-ICAEW Members):
W Wan
Registered by the ICAEW to carry out company audit work

GREGORY MICHAELS & CO
6 Southwick Mews, Paddington, London, W2 1JG
Tel: 020 7723 1816
Fax: 020 7706 2090
Email: gregory.michaels@hotmail.co.uk
Website: http://www.insolvency.co.uk/ip/gregory.htm
Principal: ICAEW Member
M C Ioannou
Registered by the ICAEW to carry out company audit work
Regulated by the ICAEW for a range of investment business activities
Individual(s) licensed for insolvency work by the ICAEW
SPECIALISATIONS – BUSINESS RECOVERY & INSOLVENCY
Bankruptcies
Liquidations

H.W.M. CARTWRIGHT LTD
22 Shrewsbury Mews, Chepstow Road, London, W2 5PN

IAN FRANSES ASSOCIATES ★
24 Conduit Place, London, W2 1EP
Tel: 020 7262 1199
Resident Partners/Directors: ICAEW Members
I S R Franses

J.M. ASSOCIATES
21A Craven Terrace, London, W2 3QH

JOHN WARWICK & CO
Flat 308 Peninsula Apartments, 4 Praed Street, Paddington, London W2 1JE
Tel: 020 7723 3467
Principal: ICAEW Member
J A Warwick

KINETIC PARTNERS AUDIT LLP
3 Sheldon Square, London, W2 6PS

M.A. SHIATIS YOUNG & CO ▽
23 Craven Terrace, Lancaster Gate, London, W2 3QH

M. PARMAR & CO
1st Floor, 244 Edgware Road, London, W2 1DS
Tel: 020 7724 8272
Principal: ICAEW Member
M A Parmar

MAWS & ASSOCIATES ◈
132a Westbourne Terrace, London, W2 6QJ

STEIN RICHARDS ◈
10 London Mews, London, W2 1HY
Tel: 020 7402 7070

STEIN RICHARDS LTD ◈
10 London Mews, London, W2 1HY
Tel: 020 7402 7070
Resident Partners/Directors: ICAEW Members
R G Hyams, R I Nissen

LONDON W3

ANNABEL YOUNG
26 Spencer Road, London, W3 6DW

BEEVERS & CO
44 Chatsworth Gardens, Acton, London, W3 9LW
Tel: 020 8896 2011
Principal: ICAEW Member
T Beevers

CLARKE & CO
Acorn House, 33 Churchfield Road, Acton, London W3 6AY
Tel: 020 8993 5931
Training Contracts Available.
Resident Partners/Directors: ICAEW Members
P A Cambray, N Law Pak Chong, K K Pandya, M T Stower
Registered by the ICAEW to carry out company audit work
Authorised and regulated by the Financial Services Authority for investment business

CSJ FINANCIAL SOLUTIONS LTD
122 High Street, Acton, London, W3 6QX

KOTHARI & CO ★
Unit 1, Acton Hill Mews Business Centre, 310/328 Uxbridge Road, London W3 9QU

KUMAR STRATEGIC CONSULTANTS LTD ◈
255-261 Horn Lane, Acton, London, W3 9EH

MICHAEL STERN & CO
61 Shalimar Gardens, Acton, London, W3 9JG

REDDY SIDDIQUI ★ ◈
Park View, 183-189 The Vale, London, W3 7RW

RICHARD IAN & CO
Unit 3, Portal West Business Centre, 6 Portal Way, Acton, London W3 W3 6RU

S.C. DEVANI & CO ◈
37 High Street, Acton, London, W3 6ND
Tel: 020 8992 3506
Fax: 020 8992 9549
Email: scdevani@aol.com
Principal: ICAEW Member
S C Devani
Registered by the ICAEW to carry out company audit work
Regulated by the ICAEW for a range of investment business activities

SAGOO & CO
122 High Street, London, W3 6QX

VINCENT BIFULCO & CO LTD
47 Cumberland Park, London, W3 6SX
Tel: 020 8992 7348
Resident Partners/Directors: ICAEW Members
V Bifulco

WEM & CO ◈
Savoy House, Savoy Circus, London, W3 7DA

LONDON W4

AKHTAR & CO
454-458 Chiswick High Road, London, W4 5TT
Tel: 020 8742 3563
Email: info@akhtarandco.com
Principal: ICAEW Member
N Akhtar

ANGLOPOL LTD
12 Florence Road, Chiswick, London, W4 5DP

ASHON
Sental House, 66 Waldeck Road, Strand on the Green, London W4 3NU

ASHON LTD
Sental House, 66 Waldeck Road, Strand on the Green, London W4 3NU

BLYTH & CO
Sental House, 66 Waldeck Road, Strand-on-the-Green, London W4 3NU

BOYDELL & CO
89 Chiswick High Road, London, W4 2EF
Tel: 020 8995 6281
Principal: ICAEW Member
M B Boydell

BRYAN AND RIDGE ★ ◈
The Gatehouse, 2 Devonhurst Place, Heathfield Terrace, London W4 4JD
Tel: 020 8994 9627
Website: http://www.ouradviceaddsup.com
Resident Partners/Directors: ICAEW Members
E M Ridge, N B Ridge

CHARLES CARNE
49 Windmill Road, London, W4 1RN

FLINTHAMS
277-279 Chiswick High Road, London, W4 4PU
Tel: 020 8742 1015
Email: amc@flinthams.co.uk
Training Contracts Available.
Principal: ICAEW Member
A L McCartney
Registered by the ICAEW to carry out company audit work
Regulated by the ICAEW for a range of investment business activities
SPECIALISATIONS – AUDIT & ASSURANCE
Assurance Services
Audit
SPECIALISATIONS – FINANCIAL REPORTING
Accounts Preparation
Financial Reporting
SPECIALISATIONS – SECTOR
Architects/Surveyors
Charities
Dentists/Opticians
Doctors
Engineers
FSA Members
Insurance Brokers
Property Investment
Schools
Solicitors
Travel Industry

continued

FLINTHAMS *cont*
SPECIALISATIONS – TAXATION
Taxation

FRENCH ASSOCIATES
The Swan Centre, Fishers Lane, Chiswick, London W4 1RX

GRASHOFF & CO
35 Whellock Road, London, W4 1DY
Tel: 020 8995 4748
Website: http://www.taxandmoney.co.uk

GRASHOFF & CO LTD
35 Whellock Road, London, W4 1DY
Tel: 020 8995 4748
Resident Partners/Directors: ICAEW Members
T Grashoff

JONES FISHER DOWNES ★
Corner House, 21 Coombe Road, Chiswick, London W4 2HR

M.C. BOGARD
22 Dukes Avenue, London, W4 2AE

MANDY SANDERS
6 Waldeck Road, Chiswick, London, W4 3NP
Tel: 07973 600909
Principal: ICAEW Member
M Sanders

MAURICE GLOVER
31 Burnaby Gardens, London, W4 3DR

MY BEAN COUNTER
1 Rusthall Avenue, London, W4 1BW

PHILIP HUDSON & CO
454-458 Chiswick High Road, London, W4 5TT

QUANTUM
Oxford House, 24 Oxford Road North, London, W4 4DH

ROBERT KO & CO ◈
33 Crofton Avenue, London, W4 3EW
Tel: 07714 768816
Principal: ICAEW Member
R S W Ko

SPIERS & CO
72 Fielding Road, Chiswick, London, W4 1DB
Tel: 020 8742 2811
Resident Partners/Directors: ICAEW Members
P T Falvey, H P Singh

LONDON W5

ABEL ATASHROO & CO
3 Elm Grove Road, Ealing, London, W5 3JH

ASHFORTH LLP
93 Bramley Road, Ealing, London, W5 4ST

CHEUNG & CO
342 Windmill Road, London, W5 4UR

CPL AUDIT LTD ◈
44 Mountfield Road, Ealing, London, W5 2NQ

D.M. MORJARIA
69 Lynwood Road, Ealing, London, W5 1JG

DAUMAN & CO LTD
9 Station Parade, Uxbridge Road, Ealing Common, London, W5 3LD

DAVID MOED
8 Hart Grove, London, W5 3NB

G H WALA & CO
7 Kingfield Road, London, W5 1LD

GKP PARTNERSHIP
44 Mountfield Road, Ealing, London, W5 2NQ

HARRY ALVAREZ FCA
51 Ranelagh Road, Ealing, London, W5 5RP
Tel: 020 8579 4926
Principal: ICAEW Member
H L Alvarez

JAY PATEL & CO
278 Northfield Avenue, Ealing, London, W5 4UB
Tel: 020 8579 5153
Principal: ICAEW Member
J G Patel

JOHNSONS
2nd Floor, 109 Uxbridge Road, London, W5 5TL

JOHNSONS FINANCIAL MANAGEMENT LTD ◈
2nd Floor, 109 Uxbridge Road, London, W5 5TL
Tel: 020 8567 3451
Email: mail@johnsonsca.com
Website: http://www.johnsonsca.com
Resident Partners/Directors: ICAEW Members
S E Murad, D M Turner

Registered by the ICAEW to carry out company audit work

Regulated by the ICAEW for a range of investment business activities

SPECIALISATIONS – SECTOR
Solicitors

SPECIALISATIONS – TAXATION
Foreign Nationals in the UK
Offshore Companies
UK Subsidiaries of Overseas Multinationals

Languages Spoken:
Spanish

LEVY & PARTNERS
86-88 South Ealing Road, London, W5 4QB

LEVY + PARTNERS LTD
86-88 South Ealing Road, London, W5 4QB
Tel: 020 8932 1932
Fax: 020 8932 0122
Email: arvind@levyandpartners.com
Website: http://www.levyandpartners.com
Date Established: 1964
Resident Partners/Directors: ICAEW Members
R N Bhargava, A L Joshi

Registered by the ICAEW to carry out company audit work

Regulated by the ICAEW for a range of investment business activities

SPECIALISATIONS – AUDIT & ASSURANCE
Audit
Audit — Private Company

SPECIALISATIONS – BUSINESS & GENERAL ADVICE
Book-keeping
Book-keeping Systems
Company Formation
Company Secretarial Service
Disposal of Businesses
Management Accounting Consultancy
Management Advice to Business

SPECIALISATIONS – FINANCIAL REPORTING
Accounts Preparation
Audit Exemption Report
Limited Company Accounts
Limited Liability Partnership
Partnership/Sole Trader Accounts

SPECIALISATIONS – IT
Computer Consultants
Computer Systems and Consultancy
Computerised Accounting Systems

SPECIALISATIONS – SECTOR
Charities
Retailers
Solicitors
Traders — General

SPECIALISATIONS – TAXATION
Back Duty
Capital Gains — Limited Companies
Capital Gains — Personal
Estate and Inheritance
Partnerships and Sole Traders
PAYE Advice
Payroll Service and Advice
Personal
Self Assessment Advice
Small Traders

Taxation
Value Added Tax
General Description: Established since 1964. Has a wide compass of experience and specialisation. Partner is a member of the Chartered Institute of Taxation.
See display advertisement near this entry.

M FLETCHER & CO
2 Ealing Park Gardens, London, W5 4EU

MAINARD LTD
7 Kingfield Road, London, W5 1LD

NEILL & CO
26 New Broadway, Ealing, London, W5 2XA
Tel: 020 8567 7711
Principal: ICAEW Member
J A Kiernander

STERN & COMPANY LTD
12-15 Hanger Green, Ealing, London, W5 3AY

LONDON W6

DALY MANDEL ◈
186 Hammersmith Road, London, W6 7DJ
Tel: 020 8748 3290

DONALD M. SMITH
Hadleigh House, 5 Rivercourt Road, London, W6 9LD

JOHN HAYWARD ASSOCIATES
4 Marco Road, Hammersmith, London, W6 0PN
Tel: 020 8748 9276
Principal: ICAEW Member
J A I Hayward

KANCELARIA UK LTD ◈
214 King Street, Hammersmith, London, W6 0RA
Tel: 020 8741 2345
Resident Partners/Directors: ICAEW Members
J Szczepanski

LAKESEL LTD
PO Box 47168, London, W6 6AY

LESLIE MICHAEL LIPOWICZ & CO ◈
Accounts House, 16 Dalling Road, Hammersmith, London W6 0JB

MARY-LOUISE WEDDERBURN
57 Beryl Road, London, W6 8JS
Tel: 020 8748 8630
Principal: ICAEW Member
M Wedderburn

MEDIA FINANCE ◈
Riverside Studios, Crisp Road, London, W6 9RL
Tel: 020 8237 1074
Website: http://www.mediafinance.co.uk

SPECIALISATIONS – SECTOR

Media
General Description: Specialising in Financial and business advice, including part-time Finance Director services, for the media and creative sector.

MEDIA FINANCE LTD
Riverside Studios, Crisp Road, London, W6 9RL

MICHAEL LEONG AND CO
43 Overstone Road, London, W6 0AD
Tel: 020 8741 2181

MICHAEL LEONG AND COMPANY LTD
43 Overstone Road, London, W6 0AD
Tel: 020 8741 2181
Resident Partners/Directors: ICAEW Members
M C L Leong

PARVEZ & CO
20 Greyhound Road, London, W6 8NX

PETER BROOK
15 Luxemburg Gardens, Brook Green, London, W6 7EA

S.J.M. DENT
22a Bradmore Park Road, London, W6 0DT
Tel: 020 8741 1144
Principal: ICAEW Member
S J M Dent

THOMAS COOKE ◈
1 Kilmarsh Road, London, W6 0PL
Tel: 020 8748 8080
Website: http://www.thomascooke.co.uk
Principal: ICAEW Member
T J M Cooke

WELLINGTON MEDIA LTD
49 Rannoch Road, London, W6 9SS

LONDON W7

GROVER & CO
Anmol House, 173 Uxbridge Road, Hanwell, London W7 3TH

KAPASI & CO
20 Highland Avenue, London, W7 3RF

LOVELLS
44 Elthorne Park Road, Hanwell, London, W7 2JA

LONDON W8

ABASY YATES & CO
27 Lexham Gardens, London, W8 5JJ

C.R.S. LINK
4 Brunswick Gardens, London, W8 4AJ
Tel: 020 7229 0430
Principal: ICAEW Member
C R S Link

CHANCELLERS ★
67 Earls Court Road, Kensington, London, W8 6EF
Tel: 020 7937 3309
Fax: 020 7376 1592
Email: kensington@chancellers.co.uk
Registered by the ICAEW to carry out company audit work

CLENTON LTD ◈
11 Old Court House, Old Court Place, London, W8 4PD
Tel: 02031 552020
Resident Partners/Directors: ICAEW Members
D P Patel

HORSLEY & CO
4 Palmerston House, 60 Kensington Place, London, W8 7PU

KEITH, VAUDREY & CO
First Floor, 15 Young Street, London, W8 5EH
Tel: 020 7795 6535
Fax: 020 7937 6433
Email: keithvaud@aol.com
Date Established: 1987
Resident Partners/Directors: ICAEW Members
J I E Borucki, T H Vaudrey
Registered by the ICAEW to carry out company audit work
SPECIALISATIONS – SECTOR

Charities
Church
Clubs/Associations
Schools
Trade Assoc/Unions/Friendly Societies
Languages Spoken:
Polish

M. EMANUEL ◈
5 Lexham Gardens Mews, Kensington, London, W8 5JQ
Tel: 020 7370 7986
Principal: ICAEW Member
M S Emanuel

MILNCRAIG LTD
12 Vicarage Gardens, London, W8 4AH

NEIL SIMPSON & CO
St James House, 13 Kensington Square, London, W8 5HD
Tel: 01992 505788

ROBERT MCDONALD
15 Vicarage Gate, London, W8 4AA
Tel: 020 7937 4774
Principal: ICAEW Member
R McDonald

ROBERTS & CO
136 Kensington Church Street, London, W8 4BH

RODNEY S. W. RICHARDS
3 Shaftesbury Villas, Allen Street, London, W8 6UZ

WARD & CO
First Floor, 15 Young Street, London, W8 5EH

Z DUDHIA & COMPANY LTD ◈
4 Hornton Place, London, W8 4LZ
Tel: 020 7938 3742
Resident Partners/Directors: ICAEW Members
Z Dudhia

LONDON W9

C A RYAN & CO LTD
4F Shirland Mews, London, W9 3DY

COLE & CO
400 Harrow Rd, London, W9 2HU

GALE GARDNER & CO LTD
4F Shirland Mews, London, W9 3DY

HAVILAND & CO
11 Biddulph Road, London, W9 1JA

MELANIE HAYWOOD
5 Essendine Road, London, W9 2LS

MONIQUE LAW
129 Randolph Avenue, London, W9 1DN

PAREKHS
16 Sevington Street, Maida Hill, London, W9 2QN
Tel: 020 7289 2870
Principal: ICAEW Member
R R D Parekh

RYAN & CO
4F Shirland Mews, London, W9 3DY
Tel: 020 8960 0961
Email: ryan@ryanandco.com
SPECIALISATIONS – SECTOR

Entertainers
General Description: Music industry specialists.

LONDON W10

A F KABINI & CO
14 Conlan Street, London, W10 5AR

HILTON CONSULTING
117 Buspace Studios, Conlan Street, London, W10 5AP

HILTON CONSULTING LTD
119 The Hub, 300 Kensal Road, London, W10 5BE
Tel: 020 8969 6956
Resident Partners/Directors: ICAEW Members
B J Warren

MILNE & CO
1 Highlever Road, London, W10 6PP

LONDON W11

GMAK
5/7 Vernon Yard, Portobello Road, London, W11 2DX
Tel: 020 7229 3591
Email: angela@gmak.co.uk
Website: http://www.gmak.co.uk
Resident Partners/Directors: ICAEW Members
Guy Mayers
Resident Partners (Non-ICAEW Members):
A Ktistakis
SPECIALISATIONS – SECTOR
Charities

GMAK SERVICES LTD ◈
5-7 Vernon Yard, Portobello Road, London, W11 2DX

KATZ & CO ◈
135 Notting Hill Gate, London, W11 3LB
Tel: 020 7727 6692
Fax: 020 7792 2481
Email: sk@katzandco.co.uk
Website: http://www.katzandco.co.uk
Mobile: 07803 583323
Date Established: 1980
Principal: ICAEW Member
S A Katz
Registered by another RSB to carry out company audit work
SPECIALISATIONS – AUDIT & ASSURANCE
Audit
SPECIALISATIONS – FINANCIAL REPORTING
Accounts Preparation
SPECIALISATIONS – TAXATION
Payroll Service and Advice
General Description: Established in 1983 in general practice, now also specialising in financial and management control consultancy, and computerisation.
See display advertisement near this entry.

N.D. PILBROW
Flat 5, 139 Holland Park Avenue, London, W11 4UT

O J KILKENNY & CO LTD
6 Lansdowne Mews, London, W11 3BH

S J HOOK
38A Ledbury Road, London, W11 2AB

WRIGHT VIGAR LTD ◈
1st Floor, 13 Needham Road, London, W11 2RP
Tel: 020 7229 4362
Website: http://www.wrightvigar.co.uk
Resident Partners/Directors: ICAEW Members
J E O'Hern
Other Offices: Lincoln, Gainsborough, Retford, Sleaford
SPECIALISATIONS – AUDIT & ASSURANCE
Audit — Private Company
SPECIALISATIONS – SECTOR
Charities

LONDON W12

ANTHONY, WELLS & CO
Room 3607, BBC White City, London, W12 7TS
Tel: 020 8752 6871

BRANNANS ★
63 Stowe Road, London, W12 8BE

FRIXOU & CO
71 Goldhawk Road, Shepherds Bush, London, W12 8EG

GODFREY ACCOUNTING
33 Vespan Road, Shepherds Bush, London, W12 9QG
Tel: 020 8749 4354
Principal: ICAEW Member
H J Godfrey
SPECIALISATIONS – SECTOR
Artists/Graphic Designers

J.A.GORDON STEWART & CO ◈
29 Greenside Road, London, W12 9JQ
Tel: 020 8743 0974
Principal: ICAEW Member
J A Gordon Stewart

MICHAEL D.H. ILLINGWORTH
36 Ormiston Grove, London, W12 0JT

LONDON W13

ALISON GURKIN CONSULTANTS
41 Culmington Road, Ealing, London, W13 9NJ

BHANOT & CO
First Floor, 126-128 Uxbridge Road, Ealing, London W13 8QS

EUREKA BUSINESS CONSULTANTS LTD ◈
223 Cavendish Avenue, London, W13 0JZ

GOODALL & CO
Abacus House, Manor Road, London, W13 0AS

HARVEY & CO
76a Uxbridge Road, Ealing, London, W13 8RA
Tel: 020 8567 4607
Principal: ICAEW Member
H S Dhaliwal

HUGH CLARK
84 Cleveland Road, Ealing, London, W13 8AH

J HAGG & CO
75 Camborne Avenue, London, W13 9QZ

J.N. LYONS
13 Woodbury Park Road, Ealing, London, W13 8DD

JAY & CO
15 Alexandria Road, Ealing, London, W13 0NP

JAY & CO LONDON LTD ◈
15 Alexandria Road, Ealing, London, W13 0NP
Tel: 020 8840 6620
Website: http://www.jay-co.co.uk
Mobile: 07947 245503
Resident Partners/Directors: ICAEW Members
J M Chitroda
Registered by another RSB to carry out company audit work
General Description: Audits, Accountancy, Tax Advice.

LAMBROU & CO ◈
223 Cavendish Avenue, Ealing, London, W13 0JZ

MANAKTALA & CO
17 Leeland Mansions, Leeland Road, West Ealing, London, W13 9HE

MARRIOTTS
32 Westfield Road, Ealing, London, W13 9JL

MAURICE & CO ◈
71 Coldershaw Road, Ealing, London, W13 9DU
Tel: 020 8840 7756
Principal: ICAEW Member
P C Q C Chow Yick Cheung

MERCHANT & CO
84 Uxbridge Road, West Ealing, London, W13 8RA
Tel: 020 8579 7933
Fax: 020 8579 7935
Email: info@merchantco.co.uk

Resident Partners/Directors: ICAEW Members
L C Clements, D W Ford, G H Freemantle

Registered by the ICAEW to carry out company audit work

Regulated by the ICAEW for a range of investment business activities

SPECIALISATIONS – AUDIT & ASSURANCE

Audit — Private Company

SPECIALISATIONS – FINANCIAL REPORTING

Accounts Preparation
Audit Exemption Report
Limited Company Accounts
Partnership/Sole Trader Accounts

SPECIALISATIONS – IT

Computer Consultants

SPECIALISATIONS – SECTOR

Architects/Surveyors
Catering/Restaurants
Church
Clubs/Associations
Dentists/Opticians
Doctors
Estate Agents
Property Investment
Schools
Solicitors
Traders — General

SPECIALISATIONS – TAXATION

Back Duty
Capital Gains — Personal
Estate and Inheritance
Partnerships and Sole Traders
PAYE Advice
Payroll Service and Advice
Personal
Self Assessment Advice
Small Traders

General Description: We are a well established (circa 1920) three partner firm in general practice servicing the needs of both individuals and organisations. We employ highly trained staff, all of whom are qualified, including a tax manager. The firm is fully computerised. We specialise in assisting all types of Schools by way of financial consultancy, bursarial services, audit accountancy and Independent Examination work, as well as providing tax and accountancy services to members of the medical profession. We would welcome the opportunity to help you grow your business soundly, in a friendly and efficient manner, at a fair and reasonable cost.

Languages Spoken:
German

See display advertisement near this entry.

RON MACHELL
204 Northfield Avenue, London, W13 9SJ
Tel: 020 8567 2928
Principal: ICAEW Member
R Machell

SEFTON SOLOMON
Peterden House, 1a Leighton Road, West Ealing, London W13 9EL

LONDON W14

CR WALLIS
5a Warwick Gardens, London, W14 8PH

FOWLER & HARE
Third Floor, Crown House, 72 Hammersmith Road, London W14 8TH

HAMSUN & HOGATE ◈
Unit 2, Bramber Court, Bramber Road, London W14 9PW
Tel: 020 7381 6622
Principal: ICAEW Member
A M S Lakha

JAFFER & CO ★
7 Hazlitt Mews, Hazlitt Road, London, W14 0JZ

MAJAINAH SADRA LTD ◈
2 Martin House, 179-181 North End Road, London, W14 9NL
Tel: 020 7385 6276
Resident Partners/Directors: ICAEW Members
N Majainah, K S Sadra

MJ LERMIT
9 Tennyson Mansions, Queen's Club Gardens, London, W14 9TJ

PHILIP DE NAHLIK
89 Barons Keep, Gliddon Road, London, W14 9AX

R.N. VIRK & CO
25 Anley Road, West Kensington, London, W14 0BZ
Tel: 020 7602 7279
Principal: ICAEW Member
R N Virk

RAKMANS
85 Oakwood Court, Abbotsbury Road, Holland Park, London W14 8JZ

REES & CO
10 Dryden Mansions, Queens Club Gardens, London, W14 9RG

LONDON WC1

1ST CONTACT ACCOUNTANTS LTD
Castlewood House, 77-91 New Oxford Street, London, WC1A 1DG

1ST CONTACT ACCOUNTING
Castlewood House, 77-91 New Oxford Street, London, WC1A 1DG
Tel: 020 7759 5326
Resident Partners/Directors: ICAEW Members
A M Deakin

THE ACCOUNTS DEPT. LTD
3 Cromer Street, London, WC1H 8LS

THE ACCOUNTS DEPT. LTD
253 Gray's Inn Road, London, WC1X 8QT

ANDREW MURRAY & CO ★ ◈
144-146 Kings Cross Road, London, WC1X 9DU

ANTONY BATTY & COMPANY LLP
3 Field Court, Gray's Inn, London, WC1R 5EF
Tel: 020 7831 1234
Resident Partners/Directors: ICAEW Members
W A Batty

ARDNERS
18 Hand Court, London, WC1V 6JF

B N JACKSON NORTON ★
1 Gray's Inn Square, Gray's Inn, London, WC1R 5AA

BAKER TILLY
2 Bloomsbury Street, London, WC1B 3ST

BAKER TILLY & CO LTD
2 Bloomsbury Street, London, WC1B 3ST
Tel: 020 7413 5100
Resident Partners/Directors: ICAEW Members
J E Bugden, J C Chapman, D J Punt, J D Warner

BAKER TILLY CORPORATE FINANCE LLP
2 Bloomsbury Street, London, WC1B 3ST
Tel: 020 7413 5100
Resident Partners/Directors: ICAEW Members
K Denham, S J Mason, A D Pierre, C R V Taylor, N J Tristem, P R Watts, R White
Resident Partners (Non-ICAEW Members):
J A Randall, D Gwilliam

BAKER TILLY TAX AND ADVISORY SERVICES LLP
2 Bloomsbury Street, London, WC1B 3ST

continued

BAKER TILLY TAX AND ADVISORY SERVICES LLP
cont
Tel: 020 7413 5100
Resident Partners/Directors: ICAEW Members
E C Banks, S H Berger, D S Clark, R J Coates, G M Craig Waller, K Denham, D J Fenton, H Freedman, T G Fussell, P R Ginman, S J Govey, M E Harwood, W P Hogan, L P Longe, S J Mason, P S Newman, K J Phillips, A D Pierre, R H Spooner, M F Stean, C R V Taylor, N J Tristem, N D Ware, P R Watts, R White, V P Wood
Resident Partners (Non-ICAEW Members):
M S Benson, R D Jones, A M McLaren, J A Randall, D Gwilliam

BAKER TILLY UK AUDIT LLP
2 Bloomsbury Street, London, WC1B 3ST
Tel: 020 7413 5100
Resident Partners/Directors: ICAEW Members
E C Banks, D S Clark, R J Coates, G M Craig Waller, D J Fenton, H Freedman, M E Harwood, J M W Hudson, P S Newman, A D Pierre, D C Taylor, N J Tristem, N D Ware, P R Watts, R White
Resident Partners (Non-ICAEW Members):
D Blacher

BIPIN KOTECHA
123 Queen Alexandra Mansions, Tonbridge Street, London, WC1H 9DW
Tel: 020 7833 0471
Principal: ICAEW Member
B Kotecha

BORN ASSOCIATES LTD
24 Bedford Square, London, WC1B 3HN

BSG VALENTINE
2nd Floor, Lynton House, 7/12 Tavistock Square, London, WC1H 9BQ
Tel: 020 7393 1111
Fax: 020 7393 1122
Email: info@bsgvalentine.com
Website: http://www.bsgvalentine.com
Resident Partners/Directors: ICAEW Members
A M Athanasiou, M Benson, D S Burke, N R Colaco, M Gandz, R Gulrajani, D L Lee, B M Mackenzie, M Nicolaou, N Patel, S C Poluck, N Strong
Resident Partners (Non-ICAEW Members):
M G Mapara
Registered by the ICAEW to carry out company audit work
Authorised and regulated by the Financial Services Authority for investment business

CHANTREY VELLACOTT DFK LLP
Russell Square House, 10-12 Russell Square, London, WC1B 5LF
Tel: 020 7509 9000
Fax: 020 7436 8884
Email: info@cvdfk.com
Website: http://www.cvdfk.com
Resident Partners/Directors: ICAEW Members
M E Adams, I C Blackman, S J Bonner, M J Cannon, N R N Gooch, H Hampartsoumian, C A Heath, M R Hewitt-Boorman, C D James, G M Jones, J A Keating, S A Kilbane, M E Lamb, C N Malacrida, K A McCaffrey, J H Metcalf, P J Moss, K A Murphy, R P R O'Beirne, J H Owen, J Sanghrajka, I B Staunton, A P R Steinthal, R H Toone, M J Tovey
Resident Partners (Non-ICAEW Members):
A Hyde, J C Heath, C M Jones, L J Steppings, D Clarke, M D Kinsella, T J Waters
Other Offices: Brighton & Hove, Colchester, Croydon, Leicester, Northampton, Stevenage, Reading, Watford
Registered by the ICAEW to carry out company audit work
Regulated by the ICAEW for a range of investment business activities
Individual(s) licensed for insolvency work by the ICAEW

INVESTOR IN PEOPLE

CINDERHALL LTD
37a Great Percy Street, London, WC1X 9RD

COUCH, BRIGHT, KING & CO ◈
91 Gower Street, London, WC1E 6AB
Tel: 020 7387 4264
Fax: 020 7388 9966
Email: accountants@cbk.co.uk
Resident Partners/Directors: ICAEW Members
D R Cates, A C Oakes, A P Shepherd
Resident Partners (Non-ICAEW Members):
B J Leach
Registered by the ICAEW to carry out company audit work
Regulated by the ICAEW for a range of investment business activities

CV CAPITAL LLP ◈
10-12 Russell Square, London, WC1B 5LF

DAVID RUBIN & PARTNERS
First Floor, 26-28 Bedford Row, London, WC1R 4HE

DOUGLAS SHANKS LLP
1 Procter Street, London, WC1V 6PG

EDMUNDS RICHMOND LTD ◈
32 Bloomsbury Street, London, WC1B 3QJ

FMCB CORPORATE FINANCE LLP
22a Theobalds Road, London, WC1X 8PF

FSPG
21 Bedford Square, London, WC1B 3HH

FTI FORENSIC ACCOUNTING LTD
Midtown, 322 High Holborn, London, WC1V 7PB
Tel: 020 7427 0011
Fax: 020 7979 7501
Email: info@forensicaccounting.co.uk
Website: http://www.forensicaccounting.co.uk
Training Contracts Available.
Resident Partners/Directors: ICAEW Members
R Bairoliya, J M Glass, J H Hudson, S D Lewin, A A J Mainz, I F S Trumper, D J Y Wreford
Resident Partners (Non-ICAEW Members):
J D Walker, B B Johnson

SPECIALISATIONS – BUSINESS & GENERAL ADVICE
Divorce/Matrimonial

SPECIALISATIONS – FORENSIC ACCOUNTING
Expert Witnesses in Litigation
Forensic Accounting

SPECIALISATIONS – TAXATION
Investigations

GOLDBLATTS
24 Gray's Inn Road, London, WC1X 8HP

GOLDBLATTS LTD
24 Gray's Inn Road, London, WC1X 8HP

GRIFFINS ★
Tavistock House South, Tavistock Square, London, WC1H 9LG
Tel: 020 7554 9600
Fax: 020 7554 9666
Email: insol@griffins.net
DX: 122017 TAVISTOCK SQUARE 2
Website: http://www.griffins.net
Resident Partners/Directors: ICAEW Members
K A Goldfarb
Resident Partners (Non-ICAEW Members):
S J Hunt
Other Offices: St Albans
Individual(s) licensed for insolvency work by the ICAEW

SPECIALISATIONS – BUSINESS & GENERAL ADVICE
Administration

SPECIALISATIONS – BUSINESS RECOVERY & INSOLVENCY
Bankruptcies
Corporate Recovery
Liquidations

SPECIALISATIONS – TAXATION
Investigations

HAINES WATTS
Egmont House, 25-31 Tavistock Place, London, WC1H 9SF
Tel: 020 7833 4155
Resident Partners/Directors: ICAEW Members
M L Cass, G M Laughton, J R P Moughton, M Perry, C G Segal, P Simmons, R A Welland, D H Yudt

HARD DOWDY
23-28 Great Russell Street, London, WC1B 3NG
Tel: 020 7436 2171
Resident Partners (Non-ICAEW Members):
T J Waters

haysmacintyre

HAYSMACINTYRE ◈
Fairfax House, 15 Fulwood Place, London, WC1V 6AY
Tel: 020 7969 5500
Fax: 020 7969 5600
Email: marketing@haysmacintyre.com
Website: http://www.haysmacintyre.com
Training Contracts Available.
Resident Partners/Directors: ICAEW Members
A Ball, J R Beard, A M Broome, I J R Cliffe, D Cox, G A Crowther, N M Gillam, A M Gregory-Jones, A M Halsey, N M Hanlon, R M Jackson, M F Jessa, B A E Pritchard, D R Riley, D J E Sewell, R N Simpson, B A Watson, R J Weaver, S C Wilks, T L Young
Resident Partners (Non-ICAEW Members):
G Elliott, N Landsman
Registered by the ICAEW to carry out company audit work
Regulated by the ICAEW for a range of investment business activities

SPECIALISATIONS – INVESTMENT BUSINESS
Financial Planning and Advice

SPECIALISATIONS – SECTOR

Architects/Surveyors
Catering/Restaurants
Charities
FSA Members
Hotels/Public Houses
Media
Property
Schools
Solicitors

SPECIALISATIONS – TAXATION

Estate Planning

General Description: haysmacintyre, Chartered Accountants and tax advisers, works in a variety of sectors (e.g. real estate, charities, professional practices, media, sports and private clients) providing high quality auditing and assurance, business and personal taxation, corporate finance, financial services and other business support services to SMEs. haysmacintyre is a member of MSI, an international alliance of independent accounting and legal firms with over 250 member firms in 100 countries.

HOPKINS CONSULTING
1 Procter Street, London, WC1V 6PG

HURKAN SAYMAN & CO ★
5-15 Cromer Street, London, WC1H 8LS

J B STEPHENSON
Third Floor, 3 Field Court, Grays Inn, London WC1R 5EF

JACOBS SASSOON
3 Stedham Place, New Oxford Street, London, WC1A 1HU

JACOBS SASSOON LTD
3 Stedham Place, New Oxford Street, London, WC1A 1HU

JEREMY SCHOLL & CO
20-21 Jockey's Fields, London, WC1R 4BW

JS2 LTD
17 Doughty Street, London, WC1N 2PL

KEITH RAFFAN & CO LTD
2nd Floor, 36 Great Russell Street, London, WC1B 3QB

LEE ASSOCIATES AUDIT LTD
5 Southampton Place, London, WC1A 2DA
Tel: 020 7025 4600
Fax: 020 7025 4666
Email: mail@leeassociates.co.uk
Website: http://www.leeassociates.co.uk
Resident Partners/Directors: ICAEW Members
R B Davis, S Rawal, O G Sargent
Registered by the ICAEW to carry out company audit work

SPECIALISATIONS – SECTOR

Advertising/Design Agencies
Architects/Surveyors
Artists/Graphic Designers
Engineers
Entertainers
Journalists/Writers/Copywriters
Media
New Media
Property Development

LEE ASSOCIATES LLP
5 Southampton Place, London, WC1A 2DA

LEON CHARLES LTD
247 Gray's Inn Road, London, WC1X 8QZ

MACINTYRE STRATER INTERNATIONAL LTD ▼
46 Bedford Row, London, WC1R 4LR

MEHTA & TENGRA
24 Bedford Row, London, WC1R 4TQ

MORLEY AND SCOTT ◈
Lynton House, 7-12 Tavistock Square, London, WC1H 9LT
Tel: 020 7387 5868
Fax: 020 7388 3978
Email: ms@morleyandscott.co.uk
Website: http://www.morleyandscott.co.uk
Resident Partners/Directors: ICAEW Members
M J Bolton, T M Dharsi, P King
Resident Partners (Non-ICAEW Members):
R A Watson, S A Salter, D M Truman

Other Offices: Slough, Portsmouth, Solent
Registered by the ICAEW to carry out company audit work
Authorised and regulated by the Financial Services Authority for investment business

N. TYRRELL
3 Stedham Place, London, WC1A 1HU

NIGEL H. GILROY & CO
373 Russell Court, 3 Woburn Place, London, WC1H 0NH

OPUS HEALTH CAPITAL LTD
22a Theobalds Road, London, WC1X 8PF

OURY CLARK ◈
10 John Street, London, WC1N 2EB
Tel: 020 7067 4322
Resident Partners/Directors: ICAEW Members
J E Oury

P.S.J. ALEXANDER & CO
1 Doughty Street, London, WC1N 2PH

PATEL, SHAH & JOSHI
1 Doughty Street, London, WC1N 2PH

R.A. PICK & CO ◈
Cobham House, 9 Warwick Court, Grays Inn, London WC1R 5DJ
Tel: 020 7831 5399
Principal: ICAEW Member
R A Pick
Registered by the ICAEW to carry out company audit work
Regulated by the ICAEW for a range of investment business activities

RAYNER ESSEX LLP
Tavistock House South, Tavistock Square, London, WC1H 9LG
Tel: 020 7388 2641
Fax: 020 7387 8969
Email: th@rayneressex.com
Website: http://www.rayneressex.com
Other Offices: St Albans, Herts
Registered by the ICAEW to carry out company audit work
Authorised and regulated by the Financial Services Authority for investment business

SPECIALISATIONS – AUDIT & ASSURANCE

Audit

SPECIALISATIONS – BUSINESS & GENERAL ADVICE

Acquisitions and Mergers
Book-keeping
Company Formation

SPECIALISATIONS – FINANCIAL REPORTING

Accounts Preparation

SPECIALISATIONS – TAXATION

Investigations
Taxation

REEVE HEPBURN ◈
45 Bedford Row, London, WC1R 4LN
Tel: 020 7092 1761
Email: info@reeve-hepburn.co.uk
Principal: ICAEW Member
D R Willetts
Authorised and regulated by the Financial Services Authority for investment business

RHODES & RHODES ◈
42 Doughty Street, London, WC1N 2LY
Tel: 020 7831 1200
Resident Partners/Directors: ICAEW Members
J Katz, S A Levinson, G J West
Registered by the ICAEW to carry out company audit work
Regulated by the ICAEW for a range of investment business activities

RICHARD FREEMAN
3 Gray's Inn Square, London, WC1R 5AH

RICHARD JUNEMAN LTD
8 Great James Street, London, WC1N 3DF

S.G.BANISTER & CO
40 Great James Street, London, WC1N 3HB

SAFFERY CHAMPNESS ◈
Lion House, Red Lion Street, London, WC1R 4GB
Tel: 020 7841 4000
Fax: 020 7841 4100
Website: http://www.saffery.com
Training Contracts Available.
Resident Partners/Directors: ICAEW Members
P R N Adams, T P L Adams, A G D Arnott, C E Cromwell, M Di Leto, R T Elliott, D J Farnan, A J Fletcher, S J Garrard, A N Gaskell, T M T Gregory, G J Holbourn, P J Horsman, M P Johnson, D T Kakkad, N J Kelsey, P F Langdon, M G Lichten, M D McGarry, L G Mosca, C A H Nicholson, J R Shuffrey, C H M Simpson, J J Sykes, M E Webster
Resident Partners (Non-ICAEW Members):
M J Beattie, D G M Gordon, J J

continued

SAFFERY CHAMPNESS *cont*
Lane, R K Moore, M E G Burton, D L Bennett, J R Fox
Other Offices: Bournemouth, Bristol, Edinburgh, Geneva, Guernsey, Harrogate, High Wycombe, Inverness, Manchester, Peterborough
Registered by the ICAEW to carry out company audit work
Regulated by the ICAEW for a range of investment business activities
Authorised and regulated by the Financial Services Authority for investment business

INVESTOR IN PEOPLE

General Description: We are a top twenty firm providing expert advice to private clients and business owners.

SAMPSON WEST & CHRISTO
45 Doughty Street, London, WC1N 2LR

SAWIN & EDWARDS
15 Southampton Place, London, WC1A 2AJ

SHOOTER GREENE & CO
18 Hand Court, High Holborn, London, WC1V 6JF

SIMON COLES & CO
P O Box 600, London, WC1H 0XB
Tel: 020 7278 5447

SIMON COLES LTD
P O Box 600, London, WC1H 0XB
Tel: 020 7278 5447
Resident Partners/Directors: ICAEW Members
S G Coles

SONNEBORN & CO
High Holborn House, 52-54 High Holborn, London, WC1V 6RL

SOTERIOU BANERJI
253 Grays Inn Road, London, WC1X 8QT

WORKING FINANCE
127 Queen Alexandra Mansions, Tonbridge Street, London, WC1H 9DW

WORKING FINANCE LTD
127 Queen Alexandra Mansions, Tonbridge Street, London, WC1H 9DW

LONDON WC2

ACCOUNT ABILITY
Garden Studios, 11-15 Betterton Street, London, WC2H 9BP

ALLIOTTS ◈
Imperial House, 15 Kingsway, London, WC2B 6UN
Tel: 020 7240 9971
Email: london@alliotts.com
Website: http://www.alliotts.com
Resident Partners/Directors: ICAEW Members
N J Armstrong, C C Farmer, S Gupta, Y C Luk
Other Offices: Guildford, Harrow
Overseas Offices: Worldwide through Alliott Group
Registered by the ICAEW to carry out company audit work
Authorised and regulated by the Financial Services Authority for investment business

ARNOLD HILL & CO ◈
Craven House, 16 Northumberland Ave, London, WC2N 5AP
Tel: 020 7306 9100
Email: office@arnoldhill.co.uk
Website: http://www.arnoldhill.co.uk
Resident Partners/Directors: ICAEW Members
M J Bostelmann, L J Duncan, J M Moore, T J Straw, R J Usher-Somers
Registered by the ICAEW to carry out company audit work

SPECIALISATIONS – AUDIT & ASSURANCE
Audit

SPECIALISATIONS – BUSINESS & GENERAL ADVICE
Book-keeping
Management Advice to Business

SPECIALISATIONS – FINANCIAL REPORTING
Accounts Preparation

SPECIALISATIONS – TAXATION
Taxation
Trusteeship

General Description: The firm provides a bespoke service to substantial private companies, start-ups and private individuals. Its specialist trust department advises on trust creation and taxation, and manages trusts and estates on an on and off going basis. The firm has a large client base in the property sector, including non-resident landlords; other business sectors include financial services, publishing and manufacturing.

BAKER TILLY
Fourth Floor, 65 Kingsway, London, WC2B 6TD
Tel: 020 7413 5100
Resident Partners/Directors: ICAEW Members
M T F Belfourd, J S Blake, R J C Jones, A Richardson
Resident Partners (Non-ICAEW Members):
D Blacher

BAKER TILLY
Fourth Floor, 65 Kingsway, London, WC2B 6TD
Resident Partners/Directors: ICAEW Members
M T F Belfourd, J S Blake, K F Clark, R J C Jones, A Richardson, D J Searle
Resident Partners (Non-ICAEW Members):
D Blacher, G E Bull

BAKER TILLY
65 Kingsway, London, WC2B 6TD

BETRUSTTED
1 Embankment Place, London, WC2N 6RH

BOURNER BULLOCK
Sovereign House, 212-224 Shaftesbury Avenue, London, WC2H 8HQ
Tel: 020 7240 5821
Fax: 020 7240 5827
Email: bb@bournerbullock.co.uk
Website: http://www.bournerbullock.co.uk
Training Contracts Available.
Resident Partners/Directors: ICAEW Members
M S Brooks, D B Matkins, P J M Watts
Resident Partners (Non-ICAEW Members):
DP Wheeler
Other Offices: Chancery House, 199 Silbury Boulevard, Milton Keynes, MK9 1JL
Registered by the ICAEW to carry out company audit work
Regulated by the ICAEW for a range of investment business activities

SPECIALISATIONS – AUDIT & ASSURANCE
Assurance Services
Audit
Audit — Private Company

SPECIALISATIONS – BUSINESS & GENERAL ADVICE
Book-keeping Systems
Company Secretarial Service
Europe
Management Advice to Business
Management Consultancy

SPECIALISATIONS – FINANCIAL REPORTING
Accounts Preparation
Partnership/Sole Trader Accounts

SPECIALISATIONS – FORENSIC ACCOUNTING
Expert Witnesses in Litigation

SPECIALISATIONS – IT
Computer Consultants
Computer Systems and Consultancy
Information Technology

SPECIALISATIONS – SECTOR
Advertising/Design Agencies
Charities
Media
New Media
Property Development
Property Investment
Solicitors

SPECIALISATIONS – TAXATION
Estate Planning
Foreign Nationals in the UK
Payroll Service and Advice
Taxation
UK Subsidiaries of Overseas Multinationals

General Description: Bourner Bullock was founded in 1883. We provide professional services to a wide range of organisations and individuals. We are a member of the JPA International network of independent accountancy firms. We are also a member of the Added Value network of independent firms of accountants.
Languages Spoken:
French

CAVENDISH ★
61 Chandos Place, London, WC2N 4HG
Tel: 020 7836 4555
Resident Partners/Directors: ICAEW Members
S Henry, D I Lawrence

CHATRATH & CO
3rd Floor, 12/13 Little Newport Street, London, WC2H 7JJ

CHURCH & CO ◈
1st Floor, Burleigh House, 357 Strand, London WC2R 0HS

CONSTANTIN ★
Aldwych House, 81 Aldwych, London, WC2B 4HN

COPPARDS
Golden Cross House, 8 Duncannon Street, London, WC2N 4JF
Tel: 020 7484 5697
Email: david@coppards.co.uk
Resident Partners/Directors: ICAEW Members
D J Coppard
Registered by the ICAEW to carry out company audit work
Regulated by the ICAEW for a range of investment business activities

SPECIALISATIONS – SECTOR
Entertainers

DELOITTE & TOUCHE LLP ◈
180 Strand, London, WC2R 1BL

FERGUSON MAIDMENT & CO
Sardinia House, Sardinia Street, Lincolns Inn Fields, London WC2A 3LZ

FITZGERALD AND LAW LLP
8 Lincoln's Inn Fields, London, WC2A 3BP

GRAHAM WARD CBE
1 Embankment Place, London, WC2N 6RH
Tel: 020 7804 3101
Principal: ICAEW Member
G N C Ward

HENRY BACH & CO
Suite 2, 15 Broad Court, Covent Garden, London WC2B 5QN
Tel: 020 7240 2834
Principal: ICAEW Member
A R Bach

HENRY JARVIS FLEMING
First Floor, 74 Chancery Lane, London, WC2A 1AD
Tel: 020 7831 1097
Principal: ICAEW Member
R H Thistle

KERSHEN FAIRFAX
Beacon House, 113 Kingsway, London, WC2B 6PP
Tel: 020 7269 9559
Fax: 020 7269 9555
Email: profit@kershen-fairfax.com
Website: http://www.kershen-fairfax.com
Date Established: 1938
Resident Partners/Directors: ICAEW Members
P J Bentley, D G Hooper, D L Kershen-Fisher, A S Kirshen
Registered by the ICAEW to carry out company audit work
Regulated by the ICAEW for a range of investment business activities
General Description: A general practice offering a wide range of services to small and medium sized businesses and private clients. Providing a hands-on approach.

KERSHEN FAIRFAX LTD
Beacon House, 113 Kingsway, London, WC2B 6PP
Tel: 020 7269 9559
Resident Partners/Directors: ICAEW Members
P J Bentley, D G Hooper, D L Kershen-Fisher, A S Kirshen

KTNG
3rd Floor, 12-13 Little Newport Street, London, WC2H 7JJ

LUSTIG & CO
90 Long Acre, London, WC2E 9RZ

MABCO LTD
Russell Chambers, The Piazza, Covent Garden, London WC2E 8AA

MAN & CO (UK) LTD
3 Garrick House, 63 St Martin's Lane, London, WC2N 4JS
Tel: 020 7836 9188
Resident Partners/Directors: ICAEW Members
S Y Man

MITCHELLS GROUP LTD
40 Craven Street, London, WC2N 5NG

MITCHELLS (UK) LTD
40 Craven Street, London, WC2N 5NG

MORRIS & ASSOCIATES
1st Floor, 4 Henrietta Street, London, WC2E 8SF
Tel: 020 7379 7447
Principal: ICAEW Member
A H Morris

MUNSLOWS ★
2nd Floor, Manfield House, 1 Southampton Street, London WC2R 0LR

PETER LOBBENBERG & CO
74 Chancery Lane, London, WC2A 1AD
Tel: 020 7430 9300
Principal: ICAEW Member
J Peter Lobbenberg

PRAGER AND FENTON
8th Floor, Imperial House, 15-19 Kingsway, London WC2B 6UN

PRAGER AND FENTON LLP
Imperial House, 15-19 Kingsway, London, WC2B 6UN
Tel: 020 7632 1400
Fax: 020 7632 1401
Email: mgoldberg@pragerfenton.co.uk
Website: http://www.pragerfenton.com
Resident Partners/Directors: ICAEW Members
M L Goldberg, A K Jacobs
Resident Partners (Non-ICAEW Members):
M A Boomla

PRICEWATERHOUSE-COOPERS
80 Strand, London, WC2R 0AF

PRICEWATERHOUSE-COOPERS
1 Embankment Place, London, WC2N 6RH

PRICEWATERHOUSE-COOPERS AS LLP
1 Embankment Place, London, WC2N 6RH

PRICEWATERHOUSE-COOPERS LLP
1 Embankment Place, London, WC2N 6RH
Tel: 020 7583 5000
Resident Partners/Directors: ICAEW Members
V Abrams, P D Aitken, A Akdeniz, S Ali, S C Amiss, S Anderson, B R Andrews, G A Bagley, C J Baker, J K Baker, G A Barker, P A Barkus, L J Beal, A N Bell, A M Berridge, A J Bingham, D C Bishop, N G Blackwood, P Bloomfield, S H Boadle, J C Booker, A P Boucher, C E B Bowman, S A Bradley, J Burkitt, C J Burns, R W Burton, C J Buxton, N A V Campbell-Lambert, F P Canavan, A J L Casley, S J Cater, J W P Chalmers, I R Chambers, C S Clarke, P J Clokey, R D Collier-Keywood, A G Constantinidi, A D Cottis, D J Cox, E H L Cox, P R Cragg, S J Crosby, P C Cussons, S H Dale, M J Dawson, S Devenney, C M Dewar, J M S Dowty, I W Durrans, N R Edwards, A M Eldridge, J M Ellis, G W C Eversfield, N N Faquir, R J Farnsworth, P A F Figgis, J S J Fillingham, A W G Finn, K E Finn, N J Fletcher, N Freeman, S D A Friend, P R Galpin, M C J Gardiner, P D George, S R Gilder, M A Gill, A J Given, B B W Glass, C J Glazier, R J Gledhill, S W N Gleed, M T Grabowski, K D P Green, R J Green, N C Grimes, D P Guly, N C Hammans, K D Harrington, P S Harvey, S D Hasson, S J S Hawes, M T Heather, C F Hemmings, A J M Henderson, J Higgins, S Higgins, J P A Hines, A E Hodgson, M R Hodgson, R P Hodson, P Hogarth, P A Holgate, T E T Homer, J A Hook, L J Hooker, N Hopkin, N J Howlett, D N Hughes, M C Hughes, R W Hughes, Q C T Humberstone, R G Humphreys, R A Hunter, C J Jackson, P Jackson, W Jackson-Moore, P J Jacobs, D C Jenkins, A N Jones, C L Joseland, M B Karp, R A C Kaye, F E Kelsey, A C Kemp, V A Kerrigan, L C Kerswill, R J Keys, J S King, M A King, W H Kingsbury, F J Konings, A Lees, M J Legg, P J Lennon, A Levack, J S Liquorish, G S Lord, A.K.Mackeith, G A Mackichan, Viscount MacKintosh, J R Manning, K J Mansfield, Q Marikar, B J Marshall, P J McArdle, N R McChesney, A J McCrosson, A D McGill, C J A McLelland, R E Meakin, A G R Meeke, R J Milburn, P Mitchell, M C F Monfries, J G Mongan, J D Morgan, W J Morgan, K D Morris, S G Mount, Y M Munro, F P F Murphy, E L Myall-Schofield, S B Newman, U Newton, H M Nixseaman, S H J Pack, N R Page, S J Partridge, G S Pascoe, Z U Patel, A F C Paynter, C A Penwarden, S M Perry, D M H Phillips, M D R Phillips, J C Pickering, G K Pike, J M A Poirrette, T P Pope, A J Popham, I C Powell, K C Poynter, D T Prosser, M G Rajani, N J Ransome, J Ratcliffe, P S Rawlinson, N L S Rea, P G Rees, P F Rew, N H Reynolds, C D Richardson, J Richardson, R M Rollinshaw, A J B Rose, D A Russell, J E Ryan, G A Sanderson, J A Sansum, J M D Schofield, I M Selfridge, R G Sexton, S R Shah, J R Sheer, P A Shepherd, P Sheward, C J F Silcock, A E Simpson, D J A Skailes, A S M Skrzypecki, A J Smith, H K Smith, J M Smithies, D A Snell, J S Southgate, M K Speller, R J Spilsbury, R Sriskandan, L E Stapleton, J K Steveni, R D Stevens, J M Stevenson, P J A Stokes, W N Sutton, R J Sykes, C H Taylor, D Tecwyn, H Thomas, M C M Thomas, R Thomas, R C W Thompson, S J Thompson, K Tilson, C P Tompsett, T R Troubridge, G L Tucker, K L Turner, C E F Van Den Arend, R J Veysey, K N Walsh, S M Walton, G N C Ward, J M Waters, C D Watson, L J Watts, J T Wayman, R C G Weaver, J D Whitfield, D J Whiting, G T Williams, S Williams, I P J Wilson, R T G Winter, I M Wishart, P G Wood, N A Woodford, S L Woolfson, P D Wright, P L Wyman, C G Young

PRICEWATERHOUSE-COOPERS LLP
80 Strand, London, WC2R 0AF
Tel: 020 7583 5000
Resident Partners/Directors: ICAEW Members
D Allen, J R L Berriman, M R Cowan, R J H De Montfort, J Eilbeck, C M L Everest, C S M Hallett, S T Isted, J C Lloyd, R Mills, G S Oakland, R N Paterson, J L Smith, C M K Williams

RATCLIFFE & CO
74 Chancery Lane, London, WC2A 1AD
Tel: 020 7404 2600
Principal: ICAEW Member
A G Ratcliffe

SALTER & CO
120 Long Acre, London, WC2E 9ST

SHIPLEYS LLP
10 Orange Street, Haymarket, London, WC2H 7DQ
Tel: 020 7312 0000
Fax: 020 7312 0022
Email: advice@shipleys.com
Website: http://www.shipleys.com
Resident Partners/Directors: ICAEW Members
G N Fisher, S J Jeffcott, S A E Jell, S L Joberns, J Kinton, K S Roberts, S B Ryman, D Vassiliou, S M Whiting
Non-resident Partners (ICAEW Members):
J M A Henman, S W Robinson, A W Mein
Resident Partners (Non-ICAEW Members):
S G Moloney, B Bidnell, R Smailes, N Cruickshanks
Non-resident Partners (Non-ICAEW Members):

continued

SHIPLEYS LLP *cont*
G Haselton, M Luckett, S Foster

Other Offices: Godalming, Saffron Walden
Registered by the ICAEW to carry out company audit work
Regulated by the ICAEW for a range of investment business activities

SINGLA & CO
12 Devereaux Court, Strand, London, WC2R 3JL

SINGLA & CO LTD
12 Devereux Court, London, WC2R 3JL

SME CORPORATE FINANCE LTD
Floor 6, 456-458 Strand, London, WC2R 0DZ

STUART EDWARDS & CO
Garden Studios, 11-15 Betterton Street, London, WC2H 9BP

THORNE LANCASTER PARKER
8th Floor, Aldwych House, 81 Aldwych, London WC2B 4HN

VENTHAMS LTD
51 Lincolns Inn Fields, London, WC2A 3NA

WILSON WRIGHT & CO
71 Kingsway, London, WC2B 6ST
Tel: 020 7242 6506
Fax: 020 7404 0240
Email: wilco@wilsonwright.co.uk
Resident Partners/Directors: ICAEW Members
W Baker, B A Carmel, A P Cramer, M Lerner, I D Mablin
Resident Partners (Non-ICAEW Members):
K R J Maddison, J Grossman
Registered by the ICAEW to carry out company audit work
Regulated by the ICAEW for a range of investment business activities

THE OFFICIAL ICAEW DIRECTORY OF FIRMS 2009

ENGLAND

ABBOTS LANGLEY

G.J. BISHOP
16 Stewarts Close, Abbots Langley, WD5 0LU

T.D. BROOKS & CO
39 Margaret Close, Abbots Langley, WD5 0NW

ABINGDON

CRITCHLEYS ◈
Avalon House, Marcham Road, Abingdon, OX14 1UD

H.E. MIDWINTER FCA
13 St Peters Road, Abingdon, OX14 3SJ
Tel: 01235 522679
Principal: ICAEW Member
H E Midwinter

J. HINKINS
Acorn Cottage, Abingdon Road, Tubney, Abingdon OX13 5QQ

L J ACCOUNTANCY
7 Newman Lane, Drayton, Abingdon, OX14 4LP

LINDA GILES
12 The Gap, Marcham, Abingdon, OX13 6NJ
Tel: 01865 391063
Principal: ICAEW Member
L Giles

MARK G WELLS
84 Mill Street, Steventon, Abingdon, OX13 6SP

MARK WELLS CONSULTING LTD
84 Mill Street, Steventon, Abingdon, OX13 6SP
Tel: 01235 833949
Resident Partners/Directors: ICAEW Members
M G Wells

SPECIALISATIONS – BUSINESS & GENERAL ADVICE
Management Consultancy

SPECIALISATIONS – FINANCIAL REPORTING
Accounts Preparation
Limited Company Accounts
Partnership/Sole Trader Accounts

NOCKELS HORNSEY ◈
24 Bath Street, Abingdon, OX14 3QH
Tel: 01235 555315
Resident Partners/Directors: ICAEW Members
J R Hornsey, A G Nockels

R.J. HOLCOMBE & CO
Apple Tree Cottage, Church Street, Appleford, Abingdon OX14 4PA

TEASDALE & CO
1 Stert Street, Abingdon, OX14 3JF

WENN TOWNSEND
Victoria House, 10 Broad Street, Abingdon, OX14 3LH

ACCRINGTON

AINSWORTHS LTD
The Globe Centre, St James Square, Accrington, BB5 0RE
Tel: 01254 872737

C. CHAPLOW
32 Granville Road, Accrington, BB5 2LA

C P FUREY LTD
10 Larch Road, Oswaldtwistle, Accrington, BB5 3AN

D.H. SHARROCK & CO
30 St James Street, Accrington, BB5 1NT
Tel: 01254 384302
Principal: ICAEW Member
J R Marsden

D.J. DUCKWORTH LTD
20 Bank Street, Accrington, BB5 1HH
Tel: 01254 384527

DAVID S. SUTCLIFFE & CO
14 First Avenue, Church, Accrington, BB5 5EH

DEVEREUX ACCOUNTANTS LTD
Empire House, Edgar Street, Accrington, BB5 1PT

DPM ACCOUNTING SERVICES LTD
31 Coleridge Drive, Baxenden, Accrington, BB5 2PU

HAWORTHS LTD
The Old Tannery, Eastgate, Accrington, BB5 6PW
Tel: 01254 232521
Fax: 01254 872459
Email: enquiries@haworths.co.uk
Website: http://www.haworths.co.uk
Resident Partners (Non-ICAEW Members):
P Spencer
Other Offices:8 Station Road, Settle
(Tel: 01729 823755), 6 Station Road, Bentham
(Tel: 01524 261424)
Registered by the ICAEW to carry out company audit work
Authorised and regulated by the Financial Services Authority for investment business

SPECIALISATIONS – INVESTMENT BUSINESS
Financial Planning and Advice
Pensions Advice

SPECIALISATIONS – SECTOR
Agriculture
Doctors

MAYES BUSINESS PARTNERSHIP LTD
22-28 Willow Street, Accrington, BB5 1LP

ADDLESTONE

AIRDE ACCOUNTANCY
Brant House, 83 Church Road, Addlestone, KT15 1SF
Tel: 01932 848408
Fax: 01932 850984
Principal: ICAEW Member
R D Enticott

ANDREW E. BAIN
8 Scotland Bridge Road, New Haw, Addlestone, KT15 3HD

BRYANT & CO
3 Burcott Gardens, New Haw, Addlestone, KT15 2DE
Tel: 01932 857402
Principal: ICAEW Member
L M Bryant

D.J. WEAVER
4 Amis Avenue, New Haw, Addlestone, KT15 3ET

IAN KATTE & CO ◈
Lyndale House, 24 High Street, Addlestone, KT15 1TN
Tel: 01932 855385
Email: ian@iankatte.co.uk
Principal: ICAEW Member
I P Katte

S. COLLINS-DRYER
23 Millpond Court, Addlestone, KT15 2JY
Tel: 01932 820094
Principal: ICAEW Member
S J Collins-Dryer

ALCESTER

AIMS - NICK FROST ◈
1 The Maples, Great Alne, Alcester, B49 6HL
Tel: 01789 488131
Principal: ICAEW Member
N W Frost

ALAN G PIPE
3 Lower Cladswell Lane, Cookhill, Alcester, B49 5JY

BOLLANDS
Minerva Mill, Station Road, Alcester, B49 5ET
Tel: 01789 761377
Resident Partners/Directors: ICAEW Members
D E Delve
See display advertisement near this entry.

BOND PARTNERS LLP
Suite 2, 1st Floor Turnpike, Gate House, Birmingham Road, Alcester B49 5JG

THE CHILTERN PARTNERSHIP LTD
Grafton House, Bulls Head Yard, Alcester, B49 5BX
Tel: 01789 762831

MARTIN JONES
10 Seggs Lane, Alcester, B49 5HJ

REBECCA WILBER
63 Marleigh Road, Bidford-on-Avon, Alcester, B50 4EE

ALDERLEY EDGE

ABLETTS LTD
7A London Road, Alderley Edge, SK9 7JT
Tel: 01625 586137
Resident Partners/Directors: ICAEW Members
W J Ablett

P J MORGAN & CO LTD ◈
Long Acre, Horseshoe Lane, Alderley Edge, SK9 7QP

PICKERINGS ★
48 South Street, Alderley Edge, SK9 7ES

ALDERSHOT

AMAS
Suite 2, Wesley Chambers, Queens Road, Aldershot GU11 3JD

BRYANT & CO
35 Ashurst Road, Ash Vale, Aldershot, GU12 5AF
Tel: 01252 672874
Principal: ICAEW Member
P G Bryant

BUTCHER AND CO
3-7 Wyndham Street, Aldershot, GU12 4NY

GILROY & BROOKES
Ground Floor, Interpower House, Windsor Way, Aldershot GU11 1JG
Tel: 01252 320446
Fax: 01252 345195
Email: aldershot@gilroyandbrookes.co.uk
Resident Partners/Directors: ICAEW Members
B D Green, L J Powell

I.A.LANE
29 Highfield Avenue, Aldershot, GU11 3BZ

KEITH GRAHAM
Suite 2, Wesley Chambers, Queens Road, Aldershot GU11 3JD

P.G. THOMPSON & CO
3 Greyholme, 49 Victoria Road, Aldershot, GU11 1SJ

P.G. THOMPSON & CO
239b High Street, Aldershot, GU11 1TJ

RADFORD AND SERGEANT
73A High Street, Aldershot, GU11 1BY
Tel: 01252 324367
Principal: ICAEW Member
M Randall

SHORTLANDS LTD
Shortlands, Frimley Road, Ash Vale, Aldershot GU12 5PP

ALFRETON

BRADLEY & CO ◈
110 High Street, Alfreton, DE55 7HH
Tel: 01773 832121
Principal: ICAEW Member
J P Bradley

CEDAR & CO
8 Central Road, Alfreton, DE55 7BH

J.J. STANILAND
28 Peveril Drive, Riddings, Alfreton, DE55 4AP

SMITH COOPER ◈
Mansfield House, 57 Mansfield Road, Alfreton, DE55 7JJ
Tel: 01773 836666
Resident Partners/Directors: ICAEW Members
P W Duffin

ALNWICK

THE ALNWICK ACCOUNTANTS LTD
16 Bondgate Without, Alnwick, NE66 1PP
Tel: 01665 602457
Resident Partners/Directors: ICAEW Members
F Robson, J H Spowart

GREAVES GRINDLE ◈
Victoria House, Bondgate Within, Alnwick, NE66 1TA

JAMES LITTLE & CO
Leaside, Whittingham, Alnwick, NE66 4UP
Tel: 01665 574500
Principal: ICAEW Member
J Little

ALRESFORD

BUTLER & CO
Bowland House, West Street, Alresford, SO24 9AT
Tel: 01962 735544
Resident Partners/Directors: ICAEW Members
J M Butler

LOWNDES & CO
The Blackberry Patch, Parkstone Road, Ropley, Alresford SO24 0EP

MARK RAWLINGS ◈
Summerfield House, Upper Wield, Alresford, SO24 9RT
Tel: 01420 561204
Email: marawlings@aol.com
Principal: ICAEW Member
M A Rawlings

PRICE & CO
Meadsted House, 80 Jacklyns Lane, Alresford, SO24 9LJ

ROBIN ATKINS LTD
7 Lindley Gardens, Alresford, SO24 9PU

ALTON

B.L. SPICER FCA
3 Inwood Kilns, The Street, Binsted, Alton GU34 4PB

CERTAX ACCOUNTING
Charwell House Business Centre, Wilsom Road, Alton, GU34 2PP
Tel: 01420 86123
Principal: ICAEW Member
M J Lee

FOX & CO (ACCOUNTANTS) LTD
Atticus House, 2 The Windmills, Turk Street, Alton GU34 1EF
Tel: 01420 542444
Resident Partners/Directors: ICAEW Members
I Gilbert

GILROY & BROOKES
Lord Rodney House, 1 Normandy Street, Alton, GU34 1DD
Tel: 01420 82869
Fax: 01420 544934
Email: alton@gilroyandbrookes.co.uk

HAYES ACCOUNTANCY LTD
Sycamore House, Church Street, Bentworth, Alton GU34 5RB

HW
Berkeley House, Amery Street, Alton, GU34 1TH
Tel: 01420 86620
Resident Partners/Directors: ICAEW Members
A S Minifie, A J Parsons, B J Potter

INDIGO TAX & ACCOUNTANCY LTD
51 Queens Road, Alton, GU34 1JG

JOHN R. RISHWORTH
The Brackens, The Shrave, Four Marks, Alton GU34 5BJ

PKF (UK) LLP
Anstey Park House, Anstey Road, Alton, GU34 2RL
Tel: 01420 566800
Email: info.alton@uk.pkf.com
Website: http://www.pkf.co.uk
Resident Partners/Directors: ICAEW Members
D H Mead

SHEEN STICKLAND LLP ◈
4 High Street, Alton, GU34 1BU
Tel: 01420 83700
Fax: 01420 86020
Email: alton@sheen-stickland.co.uk
DX: 46909 ALTON
Website: http://www.sheen-stickland.co.uk
Date Established: 1944
Resident Partners/Directors: ICAEW Members
C A Matthissen, D A Sanders, P J Sharpe, C A Stephens
Other Offices: Chichester, West Sussex
Registered by the ICAEW to carry out company audit work
Regulated by the ICAEW for a range of investment business activities
SPECIALISATIONS – SECTOR

Agriculture
Charities
Church
Corporate
Dentists/Opticians
Doctors
Horticulture
Property
Solicitors

General Description: At Sheen Stickland LLP, we don't lose sight of the fact that every client is unique and deserves a first-class service tailored to their specific needs. We are able to take the stress out of personal tax returns, help plan for retirement and manage inheritance tax for families. For business clients we apply a calm, flexible and friendly approach to providing prompt and practical accounting, payroll, taxation and financial solutions. For a free introductory meeting please contact Philip Sharpe psharpe@sheen-stickland.co.uk or David Sanders dsanders@sheen-stickland.co.uk.

WHYTON ROBERTS
Clouds, Soldridge Road, Medstead, Alton GU34 5JF

ALTRINCHAM

ALLEN MILLS HOWARD LTD
56 Manchester Road, Altrincham, WA14 4PJ

ARTHUR GOW
21 Queens Road, Hale, Altrincham, WA15 9HE

ATHERDEN & CO
PO Box 660, Altrincham, WA14 3UZ
Tel: 0161 929 1616
Principal: ICAEW Member
J E Atherden

BEAUCHAMP CHARLES
145a Ashley Road, Hale, Altrincham, WA14 2UW

BEEVER AND STRUTHERS ◈
17 Stamford New Road, Altrincham, WA14 1BN

BERNARD ELLIOTT
56 Manchester Road, Altrincham, WA14 4PJ

BLAIR SHEPHERD
16a Regent Road, Altrincham, WA14 1RP
Tel: 0161 929 9909
Principal: ICAEW Member
S Shepherd

BRIAN LLOYD
Holly Cottage, Millington Lane, Millington, Altrincham WA14 3RR

CHRISTIAN DOUGLASS LLP
Ashley Hall, Ashley Road, Ashley, Altrincham WA14 3QA
Tel: 0161 236 6163

D. SWINDLEHURST
Flat 2, 67 Stockport Road, Timperley, Altrincham WA15 7LH

DHF ACCOUNTING LTD ◈
20 Market Street, Altrincham, WA14 1PF
Tel: 0161 927 3123
Email: frank.drainey@dhfaccounting.co.uk
Resident Partners/Directors: ICAEW Members
F G Drainey, H C Drainey

DOUBLE ESPRESSO & FRIENDS LTD
3 The Paddock, Timperley, Altrincham, WA15 7NR
Tel: 0161 980 8806
Resident Partners/Directors: ICAEW Members
D C Fletcher

E BARRY LIPKIN
Manor Lawn, 15 Normans Place, Altrincham, WA14 2AB

G.H. MURRAY & CO
St John's House, Barrington Road, Altrincham, WA14 1TJ

H. ROYCE
6 Filleigh, 2 Barry Rise, Bowdon, Altrincham WA14 3JS

HALSTEAD & CO
434 Hale Road, Hale Barns, Altrincham, WA15 8TH

HANLEYS LTD
Spring Court, Spring Road, Altrincham, WA14 2UQ

HODGSONS
1st Floor, Nelson House, Park Road, Timperley, Altrincham WA14 5BZ
Tel: 0161 969 2023
Website: http://www.hodgsons.co.uk
Resident Partners/Directors: ICAEW Members
D E M Mond

HW ◈
Bridge House, Ashley Road, Hale, Altrincham WA14 2UT
Tel: 0161 926 8558
Resident Partners/Directors: ICAEW Members
G C Fairclough, C A Graham, J L Whittick

JANE WAKSMAN ACA
1 Parkhill Road, Hale, Altrincham, WA15 9JX

JOHN SHEPPARD & CO LTD
Oak House, Barrington Road, Altrincham, WA14 1HZ

M S TWIST & CO
205a Ashley Road, Hale, Altrincham, WA15 9SQ

MARTIN T. MULLIN FCA ◈
120 Bloomsbury Lane, Timperley, Altrincham, WA15 6NT
Tel: 0161 980 0727
Principal: ICAEW Member
M T Mullin

MATRAVERS & CO ★ ◈
Bridgewater House, Century Park, Caspian Road, Altrincham WA14 5HH
Tel: 0161 927 7491
Fax: 0161 926 9947
Email: accountants@matravers.com
Website: http://www.matravers.com
Resident Partners/Directors: ICAEW Members
M D Matravers
Resident Partners (Non-ICAEW Members):
K Hughes, J Humphries
Registered by the ICAEW to carry out company audit work

MILNER BOARDMAN LTD
MBL House, 16 Edward Court, Altrincham Business Park, George Richards Way, Altrincham WA14 5GL
Tel: 0161 927 2727
Email: info@milnerb.co.uk
Website: http://www.milnerboardman.co.uk
Resident Partners/Directors: ICAEW Members
E E Jess, G R Mackridge
Resident Partners (Non-ICAEW Members):
A F C Collier
Registered by the ICAEW to carry out company audit work

MODIPLUS LTD
Paul House, Stockport Road, Timperley, Altrincham WA15 7UQ

PAYSTREAM ACCOUNTING SERVICES LTD
Mansion House, Manchester Road, Altrincham, WA14 4RW

PETER COOKSON & CO
18 Whalley Road, Hale, Altrincham, WA15 9DF

PETER M. RAVEN
The White House, 318 Manchester Road, West Timperley, Altrincham WA14 5NB
Tel: 0161 973 8699
Principal: ICAEW Member
P M Raven

PHILIP E KANAS
Downs Court, 29 The Downs, Altrincham, WA14 2QD
Tel: 0161 941 6162
Principal: ICAEW Member
P E Kanas

PHILIP SWALES LTD
16 Kingsway, Altrincham, WA14 1PJ
Tel: 0161 927 9282
Resident Partners/Directors: ICAEW Members
P H S G Swales

RICHARD RUSHTON
19 Queens Road, Hale, Altrincham, WA15 9HF

SIGNIA CORPORATE FINANCE
Browning House, 14 Barry Rise, Bowdon, Altrincham WA14 3JS

SIGNIA CORPORATE FINANCE LTD
Browning House, 14 Barry Rise, Bowdon, Altrincham WA14 3JS

STEPHEN HOBSON BA FCA
84 New Street, Altrincham, WA14 2QP
Tel: 0161 928 1128
Fax: 0161 941 3101
Email: stephen@stephenhobson.net
Mobile: 07973 293945
Principal: ICAEW Member
S Hobson
Registered by the ICAEW to carry out company audit work
Regulated by the ICAEW for a range of investment business activities

SPECIALISATIONS – AUDIT & ASSURANCE
Audit

SPECIALISATIONS – BUSINESS & GENERAL ADVICE
Book-keeping

SPECIALISATIONS – FINANCIAL REPORTING
Accounts Preparation
Limited Company Accounts
Partnership/Sole Trader Accounts

SPECIALISATIONS – TAXATION
Payroll Service and Advice
Taxation

continued

STEPHEN HOBSON BA FCA
cont
General Description: A high-tech but personal service.
Languages Spoken:
French
See display advertisement near this entry.

VINCERE PARTNERS LLP
The Corner House, 1 Aimson Road West, Timperley, Altrincham WA15 7XP
Tel: 0161 903 8319
Resident Partners/Directors:
ICAEW Members
T Lumb, S J Owers

W J SHEPHERD
33 West Road, Bowdon, Altrincham, WA14 2LA
Tel: 0161 941 5808
Principal: ICAEW Member
W J Shepherd

WALLA LEETE
The Mews, Northlands, Grey Road, Altrincham WA14 4BT
Tel: 0161 941 2233
Principal: ICAEW Member
R B Walla

WILLIAM A SANKEY FCA
10 Portland Road, Bowdon, Altrincham, WA14 2PA

YOUSHANI ◈
23 Stamford Street, Altrincham, WA14 1EX
Tel: 0161 929 1944
Principal: ICAEW Member
A Youshani

AMBLESIDE

SAINT & CO ▽ ◈
The Old Police Station, Church Street, Ambleside, LA22 0BT
Tel: 01539 433430
Email: ambleside@saint.co.uk
Website: http://www.saint.co.uk
Resident Partners/Directors:
ICAEW Members
I Thompson
Registered by the ICAEW to carry out company audit work
Authorised and regulated by the Financial Services Authority for investment business

WORDEN ASSOCIATES LTD
29 Fisherbeck Park, Ambleside, LA22 0AJ
Tel: 01539 432878
Resident Partners/Directors:
ICAEW Members
J R Brown

AMERSHAM

AIMS
Newhaven, Penn Street, Amersham, HP7 0PY

ATKINSONS ◈
The Red House, 10 Market Square, Amersham, HP7 0DQ
Tel: 01494 434830
Website: http://www.atkinsons-ca.co.uk
Principal: ICAEW Member
D N Atkinson
Registered by the ICAEW to carry out company audit work
Regulated by the ICAEW for a range of investment business activities

C D NASH LTD
1st Floor, 15a Hill Avenue, Amersham, HP6 5BD
Tel: 01494 727077
Resident Partners/Directors:
ICAEW Members
C D Nash

SPECIALISATIONS – SECTOR

Charities
Church
Doctors

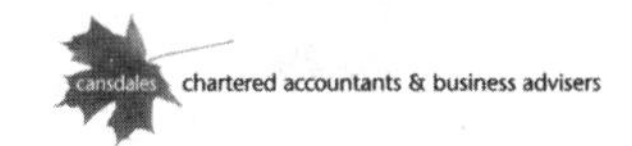

CANSDALES ◈
Bourbon Court, Nightingales Corner, Little Chalfont, Amersham HP7 9QS
Tel: 01494 765428
Fax: 01494 541803
Email: mailto@cansdales.co.uk
Website: http://www.cansdales.co.uk
Date Established: 1935
Training Contracts Available.
Resident Partners/Directors:
ICAEW Members
N S Evans, D J Stephenson

SPECIALISATIONS – AUDIT & ASSURANCE

Audit — Private Company
Internal Audit

SPECIALISATIONS – BUSINESS & GENERAL ADVICE

Company Formation
Management Accounting Consultancy
Management Advice to Business

SPECIALISATIONS – BUSINESS RECOVERY & INSOLVENCY

Reorganisations and Company Reconstructions

SPECIALISATIONS – FINANCIAL REPORTING

Limited Company Accounts
Limited Liability Partnership
Partnership/Sole Trader Accounts

SPECIALISATIONS – INVESTMENT BUSINESS

Financial Planning and Advice
Planning

SPECIALISATIONS – SECTOR

Agriculture
Artists/Graphic Designers
Charities
Church
Doctors
Housing Co-operatives
Leisure Industry
Manufacturing
Property Development
Property Investment
Registered Social Landlords
Retailers
Schools
Solicitors
Traders — General

SPECIALISATIONS – TAXATION

Back Duty
Estate Planning
Taxation
UK Subsidiaries of Overseas Multinationals
Value Added Tax

General Description: Chartered accountants, registered auditors and business advisers; 2 partners and 25 staff servicing businesses, charities and individuals countrywide especially in London, the Home Counties and the South. Services include financial and taxation planning, management and IT advice, audit, personal and corporate tax, book-keeping, VAT, payroll and a profit improvement service.
Languages Spoken:
French, German
See display advertisement near this entry.

CANSDALES
Bourbon Court, Nightingales Corner, Little Chalfont, Amersham HP7 9QS

CANSDALES LTD ◈
Bourbon Court, Nightingales Corner, Little Chalfont, Amersham HP7 9QS
Tel: 01494 765428
Fax: 01494 541800
Email: johnt@cansdales.co.uk
Website: http://www.cansdales.co.uk
Date Established: 2001
Resident Partners/Directors:
ICAEW Members
N S Evans, D J Stephenson
Authorised and regulated by the Financial Services Authority for investment business

SPECIALISATIONS – BUSINESS & GENERAL ADVICE

Investment Appraisal
Management Advice to Business

SPECIALISATIONS – INVESTMENT BUSINESS

Financial Planning and Advice
Pensions Advice
Planning

SPECIALISATIONS – SECTOR

FSA Members

SPECIALISATIONS – TAXATION

Estate and Inheritance
Estate Planning

General Description: Cansdales Ltd is owned by Cansdales Chartered Accountants and provides financial advice for wealth protection and creation. The company has 2 directors and 3 staff and is authorised and regulated by the Financial Services Authority.

CASEY LESTER
Equity House, 57 Hill Avenue, Amersham, HP6 5UN

CHILTERN ACCOUNTANCY SERVICES LTD
29 Highmoor, Amersham, HP7 9BU

D MCCOY BUSINESS CONSULTANCY
34 Long Park, Chesham Bois, Amersham, HP6 5LA

GG & CO
The Hide, 21 Clifton Road, Amersham, HP6 5PP

GILES & CO
7d Hill Avenue, Amersham, HP6 5BD

GILES ACCOUNTING SERVICES LTD
7d Hill Avenue, Amersham, HP6 5BD

J.R.ANTOINE & PARTNERS
75 Rickmansworth Road, Amersham, HP6 5JW
Tel: 01494 728777
Fax: 01494 728978
Email: info@antoines.co.uk
Website: http://www.antoines.co.uk
Resident Partners/Directors:
ICAEW Members
G J Hipgrave, R King
Registered by the ICAEW to carry out company audit work
Regulated by the ICAEW for a range of investment business activities

JOHN E. CURTIS
106 Bois Lane, Chesham Bois, Amersham, HP6 6DE
Tel: 01494 725249
Principal: ICAEW Member
J E Curtis

LINDA DUNNING
The Dormers, 92 Bell Lane, Amersham, HP6 6PG

MACKENZIE DODD CONSULTING LTD
St Marys Court, The Broadway, Amersham, HP7 0UT
Tel: 01494 772765
Resident Partners/Directors: ICAEW Members
J A Oxlade

N.S. LUCAS & CO ◈
The Courtyard, 80 High Street, Amersham, HP7 0DS

NICHOLAS GEE & CO
6 Devonshire Close, Amersham, HP6 5JG
Tel: 01494 434444
Principal: ICAEW Member
N Gee

NORMAN T. REA
41 Plantation Rd, Amersham, HP6 6HL

PHILIP PATTEN & CO
54 Oakington Avenue, Little Chalfont, Amersham, HP6 6ST
Tel: 01494 763179
Principal: ICAEW Member
B P Patten

ROSALIND GARRETT TAX SERVICES
Maple Lodge, Sycamore Close, Amersham, HP6 6BW
Tel: 01494 725590
Principal: ICAEW Member
R J Garrett-Bowes

SIMON HENNELL LTD
Newhaven, Penn Street, Amersham, HP7 0PY

W.L. BLAND & CO
141 High Street, Amersham, HP7 0DY

WILKINS KENNEDY ◈
Risborough House, 38-40 Sycamore Road, Amersham, HP6 5DZ
Tel: 01494 725544
Website: http://www.wilkinskennedy.com
Resident Partners/Directors: ICAEW Members
D Carey, S P Grant
Resident Partners (Non-ICAEW Members):
T E A Collerton
Other Offices: Ashford, Egham, Guildford, Hertford, London, Orpington, Reading Romsey, Southend, Winchester
Overseas Offices: Stanley, Falkland Islands
Registered by the ICAEW to carry out company audit work
Regulated by the ICAEW for a range of investment business activities
Individual(s) licensed for insolvency work by another RPB

SPECIALISATIONS – BUSINESS & GENERAL ADVICE
Acquisitions and Mergers
Disposal of Businesses
Outsourcing - Financial Services

SPECIALISATIONS – BUSINESS RECOVERY & INSOLVENCY
Bankruptcies
Corporate Recovery
Liquidations
Reorganisations and Company Reconstructions

SPECIALISATIONS – FORENSIC ACCOUNTING
Expert Witnesses in Litigation
Forensic Accounting

SPECIALISATIONS – SECTOR
Charities
Construction
Insurance Brokers
Property
Solicitors

ANDOVER

ALEXANDER VAUGHAN & CO
2nd Floor, Union House, Union Street, Andover SP10 1PA

BATAS LTD
Dunelm, Goodworth Clatford, Andover, SP11 7QX

BECK RANDALL & CARPENTER
Aldwych House, Winchester Street, Andover, SP10 2EA

BECK RANDALL & CARPENTER LTD
Aldwych House, Winchester Street, Andover, SP10 2EA

BRADY SCRACE LTD
Willowdale, 57 Rooksbury Road, Andover, SP10 2LP
Tel: 01264 350167
Resident Partners/Directors: ICAEW Members
E B Scrace

SPECIALISATIONS – TAXATION
Self Assessment Advice

CAROLE JUDD
82a Winchester Road, Andover, SP10 2ER

D. VELIDA & CO ◈
Centurion House, Central Way, Walworth Industrial Estate, Andover SP10 5AN
Tel: 01264 337695
Principal: ICAEW Member
D R W Velida

DICK GERMAIN
37 Springfield Close, Andover, SP10 2QR
Tel: 01264 324644
Principal: ICAEW Member
R M C Germain

DOMINIC MILLS
66b High Street, Black Swan Yard, Andover, SP10 1NG
Tel: 01264 337911
Principal: ICAEW Member
D Mills

HYSONS
14 London Street, Andover, SP10 2PA
Tel: 01264 323791
Principal: ICAEW Member
M E K Hyson

I.H. STEVENS & CO
14 Westover Farm, Goodworth Clatford, Andover, SP11 7LF
Tel: 01264 359837
Principal: ICAEW Member
I H Stevens

J.L. BAINES & CO
Chalklands, Hatherden, Andover, SP11 0HJ
Tel: 01264 735450
Principal: ICAEW Member
J L Baines

LANGDOWNS DFK LTD
8a Newbury Street, Andover, SP10 1DW
Tel: 01264 359333
Website: http://www.langdownsdfk.com

M.J. STARTUP & CO LTD
4 New Cottages, Furzedown Lane, Amport, Andover SP11 8BQ

SWIFT ACCOUNTING
Aldwych House, Winchester Street, Andover, SP10 2EA

TIMOTHY COOMER
3 Greenfields, Dunhills Lane, Enham Alamein, Andover SP11 6RB
Tel: 01264 334233
Principal: ICAEW Member
T Coomer

THE WOW COMPANY UK LTD
Samar House, North Way, Andover, SP10 5AZ
Tel: 0845 201 1582
Resident Partners/Directors: ICAEW Members
P D Croombs

ARLESEY

PHILIPPA VERZHBITSKAYA
1 Chancellors, Arlesey, SG15 6YB
Tel: 01462 731531
Principal: ICAEW Member
P H Verzhbitskaya

ARUNDEL

D MACDONALD & COMPANY LTD
The Old Stables, Arundel Road, Poling, Arundel BN18 9QA

THE MARTLET PARTNERSHIP LLP
The Old Stables, Arundel Road, Poling, Arundel BN18 9QA

W. WINWARD F.C.A
The Old Vicarage, North End Road, Yapton, Arundel BN18 0DT

ASCOT

A.C. WILSON
The Kingswood, Ridgemount Road, Ascot, SL5 9RW

BARRINGTON ZARACH & CO
23 Kings Road, Ascot, SL5 9AD
Tel: 01344 626458
Principal: ICAEW Member
B P Zarach

DAVIS BURTON SELLEK & CO ▽ ◈
The Galleries, Charters Road, Sunningdale, Ascot SL5 9QJ
Tel: 01344 620495
Website: http://www.dbsellek.co.uk
Resident Partners/Directors: ICAEW Members
G R Atkinson
Registered by the ICAEW to carry out company audit work
Regulated by the ICAEW for a range of investment business activities

GEOFFREY CARSON
Twin Pines, Devenish Road, Ascot, SL5 9PH
Tel: 01344 622927
Principal: ICAEW Member
G Carson

J.P. STEWART
Devenish Cottage, Devenish Road, Sunningdale, Ascot SL5 9QP

JACKSONS
The Old Bakehouse, Course Road, Ascot, SL5 7HL
Tel: 01344 874485
Principal: ICAEW Member
H Jackson

KIRK RICE ★
The Courtyard, High Street, Ascot, SL5 7HP
Tel: 01344 875000
Resident Partners/Directors: ICAEW Members
K A S Rice

KNIGHTS ◈
Baxter House, 48 Church Road, Ascot, SL5 8RR
Tel: 01344 891666
Principal: ICAEW Member
T Knight

MAURICE BRUNO LTD
Wyndham House, Sunning Avenue, Ascot, SL5 9PW
Tel: 01344 874921
Resident Partners/Directors:
ICAEW Members
M Bruno

SPOONER & CO
Mulberry, Shrubbs Hill Lane, Sunningdale, Ascot SL5 0LD

WENTWORTHS
White Hart House, Silwood Road, Ascot, SL5 0PY

ASHBOURNE

ALAN BAINES ◈
Church House, Thorpe, Ashbourne, DE6 2AW
Tel: 07785 283844
Principal: ICAEW Member
A L Baines

COATES AND PARTNERS LTD
51 St John Street, Ashbourne, DE6 1GP
Tel: 01335 301850
Fax: 01335 300315
Email: enquiries@coatesandpartners.co.uk
Website: http://www.coatesandpartners.co.uk
Resident Partners/Directors:
ICAEW Members
M I Blake, H H Bourchier, H Dowson
Resident Partners (Non-ICAEW Members):
K McKenzie

JOHN HAMILTON
Yew Tree House, Atlow, Ashbourne, DE6 1NT

R.C. TAYLOR
Brailsford Green, Church Lane, Brailsford, Ashbourne DE6 3BX

RADCLYFFE AND WOODROW LTD
52 St John Street, Ashbourne, DE6 1GH
Tel: 01335 342928
Resident Partners/Directors:
ICAEW Members
J R Woodrow

RICHARDSON NUTT LTD
Town Hall, Ashbourne, DE6 1ES

SMITH COOPER ◈
St John's House, 54 St John Street, Ashbourne, DE6 1GH
Tel: 01335 343141
Resident Partners/Directors:
ICAEW Members
B J Montgomery, S T Sread

WALKER SHARP & CO
15 Hillside Avenue, Ashbourne, DE6 1EG
Tel: 01335 300827
Principal: ICAEW Member
T C Walker-Sharp

ASHBY-DE-LA-ZOUCH

COUND & CO LLP
104/106 Market Street, Ashby-de-la-zouch, LE65 1AP

DEKM
Castle House, South Street, Ashby-De-La-Zouch, LE65 1BR

JOHNSON MURKETT & HURST
Rawdon House, Rawdon Terrace, Ashby-de-la-zouch, LE65 2GN
Tel: 01530 412877
Email: ashby@jmhaccounts.com
Website: http://www.jmhaccounts.co.uk
Resident Partners/Directors:
ICAEW Members
P J Nash, A W Stant, A J Turland
Other Offices:38 Millstone Lane, Leicester LE1 5JN
(Tel: 0116 262 7408)
Registered by the ICAEW to carry out company audit work
Regulated by the ICAEW for a range of investment business activities

NICK GERZIMBKE
25 Woodside, Ashby-De-La-Zouch, LE65 2NJ

PROGRESS ◈
6 Charter Point Way, Ashby Park, Ashby-De-La-Zouch, LE65 1NF

PROGRESS ACCOUNTANTS LLP ◈
6 Charter Point Way, Ashby Park, Ashby-De-La-Zouch, LE65 1NF

SANDERLINGS LLP
8 Derby Road, Ashby-De-La-Zouch, LE65 2HE

ASHFORD

AMT CONSULTING LTD
Pear Tree House, Maidstone Road, Hothfield, Ashford TN26 1AN

BRENDA MOONEY
The Oast House, The Street, Brook, Ashford TN25 5PG

BRIGHTLING & CO ◈
Brickyard Farm, Ashford Road, High Halden, Ashford TN26 3LJ

CALCUTT MATTHEWS
2nd Floor, Cardine House, 30 North Street, Ashford TN24 8JR

CALCUTT MATTHEWS LTD
2nd Floor, Cardine House, 30 North Street, Ashford TN24 8JR

CASSIDYS LTD ◈
South Stour Offices, Roman Road, Mersham, Ashford TN25 7HS
Tel: 01233 721555
Resident Partners/Directors:
ICAEW Members
S G Whorlow

CHAVEREYS
Cherry Court, Victoria Road, Ashford, TN23 7HE
Tel: 01233 610384
Email: admin@chavereys.co.uk
Website: http://www.chavereys.co.uk
Training Contracts Available.
Resident Partners/Directors:
ICAEW Members
M A Crawley, R J Davis, N Holmes
Other Offices:1 Penn Farm Studios Harston Road Haslingfield Cambridge CB23 1JZ
(Tel: 01223 874693)
Registered by the ICAEW to carry out company audit work
Regulated by the ICAEW for a range of investment business activities
SPECIALISATIONS – SECTOR

Agriculture
Horticulture

CHURCH & YOUNG
11 Station Road, Headcorn, Ashford, TN27 9SB
Tel: 01622 890779
Principal: ICAEW Member
W E Church

GERALD EDELMAN
Gateway House, Highpoint Business Village, Henwood, Ashford TN24 8DH

HMN ACCOUNTANTS LTD
Woodlands, Bourne Lane, Hamstreet, Ashford TN26 2HH

JUDY MUIR
2 Holmwood Cottages, Bonnington, Ashford, TN25 7AZ
Tel: 01233 720623

LARKINGS ◈
Strangford House, Church Road, Ashford, TN23 1RD
Tel: 01233 631062
Resident Partners/Directors:
ICAEW Members
A J Childs, S Coates

LARKINGS LTD ◈
Strangford House, Church Road, Ashford, TN23 1RD

MCCABE FORD WILLIAMS
Invicta Business Centre, Monument Way, Orbital Park, Ashford TN24 0HB
Tel: 01233 504954
Resident Partners/Directors:
ICAEW Members
D J Kendall, B Wright

MAGEE GAMMON
Henwood House, Henwood, Ashford, TN24 8DH

MAGEE GAMMON CORPORATE LTD
Henwood House, Henwood, Ashford, TN24 8DH
Tel: 01233 630000
Email: mg@mageegammon.com
Website: http://www.mageegammon.com
Resident Partners/Directors:
ICAEW Members
J M Gammon, A T D Tutt

MICHAEL WOOD ◈
22a Bank Street, Ashford, TN23 1BE
Tel: 01233 630027
Email: mw@mwca.biz
Principal: ICAEW Member
M A Wood
Registered by the ICAEW to carry out company audit work
Regulated by the ICAEW for a range of investment business activities

NETWORK 4M LTD ◈
Park Farm Barn, Brabourne, Ashford, TN25 6RG
Tel: 01303 812811
Resident Partners/Directors:
ICAEW Members
M G Ede, S J MacRae, T S Spencer

NICOLAOU DEARLE & CO (2005) LTD
13 Highpoint Business Village, Henwood, Ashford, TN24 8DH

NICOLAOU DEARLE (AUDIT) LLP
13 Highpoint Business Village, Henwood, Ashford, TN24 8DH

PETER S BENDALL LTD ◈
40 Park Road North, Ashford, TN24 8LY

R.K. RIDDLE
121 Imperial Way, Ashford, TN23 5HT
Tel: 01233 643808
Principal: ICAEW Member
R K Riddle

ROWAN & CO
4 Gibbs Hill, Headcorn, Ashford, TN27 9UD
Tel: 01622 891327
Principal: ICAEW Member
S M Rowan

TENBURY LTD ◈
Burleigh Road, School Road, Charing, Ashford TN27 0JW

W K FINN-KELCEY
Stourside Place, Station Road, Ashford, TN23 1PP
Tel: 01784 435561
Website: http://www.wilkinskennedy.com

continued

W K FINN-KELCEY *cont*
Other Offices:Amersham, Egham, Guildford, Hertford, London, Orpington, Reading, Romsey, Winchester, Southend
Overseas Offices: Stanley & Falkland Islands

W K FINN-KELCEY & CHAPMAN LTD
Stourside Place, 35-41 Station Road, Ashford, TN23 1PP

COLE & CO
6 Fordbridge Road, Ashford, TW15 2SG

GARDINER, HUNTER & CATT
13 Station Approach, Ashford, TW15 2GH

HAMISH CAMERON
17 Clifford Grove, Ashford, TW15 2JS

ASHINGTON

GREAVES & CO
41 North Seaton Rd, Ashington, NE63 0AG
Tel: 01670 812698
Principal: ICAEW Member
J Buckland

JONES BOYD
103 Station Road, Ashington, NE63 8RS

PETER WELDON & CO
87 Station Road, Ashington, NE63 8RS

T.W. TASKER
52a Station Rd, Ashington, NE63 9UJ
Tel: 01670 852342
Principal: ICAEW Member
T W Tasker

ASHTEAD

ALAN HOWELL
4 South View Road, Ashtead, KT21 2NB

ANTHONY R.J. CARTWRIGHT
16 Taleworth Park, Ashtead, KT21 2NH

DAVID BECKMAN & CO LTD ◈
62 The Street, Ashtead, KT21 1AT
Resident Partners/Directors:
ICAEW Members
D J Beckman
Authorised and regulated by the Financial Services Authority for investment business
SPECIALISATIONS – TAXATION
Personal

JOHN FENTON-JONES
50 Taleworth Road, Ashtead, KT21 2PY

LISA GADSBY BOOK KEEPING SERVICES
Barn Owl Cottage, 32 Agates Lane, Ashtead, KT21 2ND

TREVOR B. POOLE
109 Barnett Wood Lane, Ashtead, KT21 2LR

VA CORPORATE FINANCE
53 Leatherhead Road, Ashtead, KT21 2TP

ZIA MURSALEEN
53 Leatherhead Road, Ashtead, KT21 2TP

ASHTON-UNDER-LYNE

ALDERSONS
4 The Moorings, Mossley, Ashton-Under-Lyne, OL5 9BZ

ALLEN MILLS HOWARD & CO ★
23 Stockport Road, Ashton-under-lyne, OL7 0LA

BOLTON & CO ◈
14 Warrington Street, Ashton-under-lyne, OL6 6AS
Tel: 0161 343 1789
Principal: ICAEW Member
A K Bolton

CONNELLYS ◈
Trident House, 222 Katherine Street, Ashton-under-lyne, OL6 7AS
Tel: 0161 330 7152
Resident Partners/Directors:
ICAEW Members
D G Burton

D.A. WILLIAMSON & CO
14 Gorsey Way, Ashton-Under-Lyne, OL6 9HT

HANLEY & CO
18 Church Street, Ashton-Under-Lyne, OL6 6XE

HANLEY & CO LTD
18 Church Street, Ashton-Under-Lyne, OL6 6XE
Tel: 0161 339 7502
Resident Partners/Directors:
ICAEW Members
D R Logan

JOHN BEAUMONT & CO
230 Stamford Street, Ashton-under-lyne, OL6 7LJ

MOSS & WILLIAMSON ◈
Booth Street Chambers, Booth Street, Ashton-under-lyne, OL6 7LQ
Tel: 0161 330 2231
Resident Partners/Directors:
ICAEW Members
D Evans, M G Foote
See display advertisement near this entry.

STAUB & CO
3 Abbeydale Close, Ashton-under-lyne, OL6 9AS

ATHERSTONE

A. DAVID CONNER
9 Bishops Cleeve, Austrey, Atherstone, CV9 3EU
Tel: 01827 830310
Principal: ICAEW Member
A D Conner

HARRIS & SCREATON LTD
49 Station Street, Atherstone, CV9 1DB

SCREATON & CO
49 Station Street, Atherstone, CV9 1DB

WINCHESTERS
2 Kirtland Close, Austrey, Atherstone, CV9 3EZ

ATTLEBOROUGH

G M HOWARD & COMPANY LTD ◈
Bush House, Queens Square, Attleborough, NR17 2AF
Tel: 01953 455842

MARTIN & ACOCK
2 Cyprus Court, Queen's Square, Attleborough, NR17 2AE
Tel: 01953 452077
Website: http://www.martin-acock.com
Registered by the ICAEW to carry out company audit work

AXMINSTER

JOHN BUSE & CO
Shears Farmhouse, Umborne, Shute, Axminster EX13 7QL
Tel: 01297 552756
Principal: ICAEW Member
J A Buse

THOMAS WESTCOTT ★
Timberly, South Street, Axminster, EX13 5AD
Tel: 01297 33388
Resident Partners/Directors:
ICAEW Members
R Gillard, I McMurtry, N Smy

AYLESBURY

A D PARKS & CO
30 High Street, Wendover, Aylesbury, HP22 6EA

A W ACCOUNTING
31 Cumberland Close, Aylesbury, HP21 7HH

ACCURATE CONSULTING LTD
Oakfield Lodge, Main Street, Grendon Underwood, Aylesbury HP18 0SL
Tel: 01296 770877
Resident Partners/Directors: ICAEW Members
N M Hall

ALAN E. BUCKLE
39 The Croft, Haddenham, Aylesbury, HP17 8AS

ALAN GREEN & CO
Verna House, 9 Bicester Road, Aylesbury, HP19 9AG

ALISON J DODD
39 Rosebery Road, Aston Clinton, Aylesbury, HP22 5JY

AMINIAN & CO
Unit 2, Edison Business Centre, 52 Edison Road, Aylesbury, HP19 8TE
Tel: 01296 437521
Principal: ICAEW Member
M Aminian

ANGELL PINDER LTD ◈
24 Ripon Street, Aylesbury, HP20 2JP

C.R. TURNER & CO
15 Marroway, Weston Turville, Aylesbury, HP22 5TQ

CHATER FINANCIAL CONSULTANTS
Unit 8, Midshires Business Park, Smeaton Close, Aylesbury HP19 8HL

CLARKSON CLEAVER & BOWES LTD ◈
8A Wingbury Courtyard Business Village, Wingrave, Aylesbury, HP22 4LW
Tel: 01296 682575
Resident Partners/Directors: ICAEW Members
S J Clarkson

DAVID J. WATTS
White Wheels, Aston Abbotts, Aylesbury, HP22 4LU
Tel: 01396 681376
Principal: ICAEW Member
D J Watts

FEORE & CO
7 Ingram Avenue, Aylesbury, HP21 9DW
Tel: 01296 330049
Principal: ICAEW Member
A B Feore

FINANCIAL PROJECT CONSULTING
The Parlour, Manor Courtyard, Aston Sandford, Aylesbury HP17 8JB

GRASSO PARKER GREEN LLP
Nithsdale House, 159 Cambridge Street, Aylesbury, HP20 1BN

HILLIER HOPKINS LLP ◈
2a Alton House Office Park, Gatehouse Way, Aylesbury, HP19 8YF
Tel: 01296 484831
Email: info@hhllp.co.uk
Website: http://www.hillierhopkins.co.uk
Resident Partners/Directors: ICAEW Members
B L Anson, N Carter
Other Offices: Watford, Hemel Hempstead, London
Registered by the ICAEW to carry out company audit work
Authorised and regulated by the Financial Services Authority for investment business

INVESTOR IN PEOPLE

General Description: Chartered accountants and tax advisers.

HOW WALL MORRIS
Willow Corner, School Lane, Chearsley, Aylesbury HP18 0BT
Tel: 01844 202478
Principal: ICAEW Member
A L Wall Morris

J.H. THOMPSON & CO ◈
5 Burns Close, Long Crendon, Aylesbury, HP18 9BX
Tel: 01844 201401
Email: j.thompson@jhthompson.co.uk
Principal: ICAEW Member
J H Thompson
General Description: The enterprising choice. Specialising in SME business development.

LANCASTERS (ACCOUNTANTS) LTD
Manor Courtyard, Aston Sandford, Nr Haddenham, Aylesbury HP17 8JB

M J KERRIDGE & CO
Unit 8, Midshires Business Park, Smeaton Close, Aylesbury HP19 8HL

M.J. TOMPSETT
5 Hazeldene, Wendover, Aylesbury, HP22 6NG

MARY E. LOCKE
3 Flaxen Field, Weston Turville, Aylesbury, HP22 5GJ
Principal: ICAEW Member
M E Locke

MISS J.M. HACKING
5 Mill Mead, Wendover, Aylesbury, HP22 6BY
Tel: 01296 623618
Principal: ICAEW Member
J M Hacking

MULHALL & CO
2 Langdon Av, Aylesbury, HP21 9UX
Tel: 01296 486391
Principal: ICAEW Member
J B Mulhall

NEVILLE A. JOSEPH
Marlowe House, Hale Road, Wendover, Aylesbury HP22 6NE
Tel: 01296 623167
Principal: ICAEW Member
N A Joseph

NOTE FOR NOTE
15 Marroway, Weston Turville, Aylesbury, HP22 5TQ

NUMBERWORK UK LTD
8A Wingbury Courtyard Business Village, Wingrave, Aylesbury, HP22 4LW
Tel: 01296 689430
Resident Partners/Directors: ICAEW Members
S J Clarkson

NUNN HAYWARD
2nd Floor, Eastgate House, 46 Wedgewood Street, Aylesbury HP19 7HL
Tel: 01296 718500
Email: info@nunnhayward.com
Website: http://www.nunn-hayward.com
Resident Partners (Non-ICAEW Members):
D Butler
Registered by the ICAEW to carry out company audit work
Individual(s) licensed for insolvency work by another RPB

P.G.JEFFERY
84 Townside, Haddenham, Aylesbury, HP17 8AW
Tel: 01844 290050
Email: peter.jeffery.bucks@which.net

continued

P.G.JEFFERY *cont*
Date Established: 1984
Principal: ICAEW Member
P G Jeffery
SPECIALISATIONS – TAXATION
Personal
Self Assessment Advice
Small Traders

PENLEE CONSULTING LTD
32 Chiltern Road, Wendover, Aylesbury, HP22 6DA

PROBITTS & CO
No 1 Carrera House, Merlin Court, Gatehouse Close, Aylesbury HP19 8DP
Tel: 01296 484955
Website: http://www.probitts.co.uk
Principal: ICAEW Member
C M Probitts
See display advertisement near this entry.

PULSE
1a Carrera House, Gatehouse Close, Aylesbury, HP19 8DP

PULSE ACCOUNTANTS LTD
1a Carrera House, Gatehouse Close, Aylesbury, HP19 8DP

R.W. HONOUR
6 Slave Hill, Haddenham, Aylesbury, HP17 8AY

RFW
3 Church Street, Aylesbury, HP20 2QP

RUTHERFORDS
98 Walton Street, Aylesbury, HP21 7QP

SEDDON SMITH
Milton House, Gatehouse Road, Aylesbury, HP19 8EA

SEDDON SMITH LTD
Milton House, Gatehouse Road, Aylesbury, HP19 8EA

SMITHS ACCOUNTING & TAX
Milton House, Gatehouse Road, Aylesbury, HP19 8EA
Tel: 01296 422244

TAYLOR ROBERTS
Unit 9B, Wingbury Business Village, Upper Wingbury Farm, Aylesbury HP22 4LW

WITCHERT ASSOCIATES LTD
133 Sheerstock, Haddenham, Aylesbury, HP17 8EY
Tel: 01844 290585
Resident Partners/Directors: ICAEW Members
N G Pledger, K R Smith

AYLESFORD

ADRIAN JOHN
Belvedere, 20 Priestley Drive, Larkfield, Aylesford ME20 6TX

MCLEAN REID
1 Forstal Road, Aylesford, ME20 7AU

ZENON TAX LTD
51 The Stream, Ditton, Aylesford, ME20 6AG

ZENON TRAINING SERVICES LLP
51 The Stream, Ditton, Aylesford, ME20 6AG

ZENON TRANSACTION SERVICES LTD
51 The Stream, Ditton, Aylesford, ME20 6AG

ZENON TTAS LTD
51 The Stream, Ditton, Aylesford, ME20 6AG

BACUP

TENON LTD
7-9 Irwell Terrace, Bacup, OL13 9AJ
Tel: 01706 355505

BADMINTON

R.A. LESLIE & CO
The Old School House, Tormarton, Badminton, Gloucestershire GL9 1HZ

BAGSHOT

LORNA A GLENISTER ◈
5 The Square, Bagshot, GU19 5AX
Tel: 01276 452763
Website: http://www.lornaglenister.com
Principal: ICAEW Member
L A Glenister

MARTELL ASSOCIATES ★
28 Elizabeth Avenue, Bagshot, GU19 5NX

MORRIS & CO
Hartdene House, Bridge Road, Bagshot, GU19 5AT

MORRIS HARTDENE LTD
Hartdene House, Bridge Road, Bagshot, GU19 5AT

MOSSGROVES LLP
3 The Deans, Bridge Road, Bagshot, GU19 5AT
Tel: 01276 476733
Fax: 01276 476744
Email: contact@mossgrove-wells.co.uk
Resident Partners/Directors: ICAEW Members
J B Wells
Resident Partners (Non-ICAEW Members):
M C Crellin
Registered by the ICAEW to carry out company audit work
Regulated by the ICAEW for a range of investment business activities
See display advertisement near this entry.

PORTER GARLAND
Portland House, Park Street, Bagshot, GU19 5PG

PORTER GARLAND LTD
Portland House, Park Street, Bagshot, GU19 5PG
Tel: 01276 479100
Fax: 01276 479300
Email: info@portergarland.co.uk
Website: http://www.portergarland.co.uk
Resident Partners/Directors: ICAEW Members
P G Peel, T C A Pottinger, A Williams
Registered by the ICAEW to carry out company audit work
Regulated by the ICAEW for a range of investment business activities
See display advertisement near this entry.

BAKEWELL

ANDREW B SHARKEY LTD
Jasmine Cottage, Rowland, Bakewell, DE45 1NR

HARTINGTON ACCOUNTANCY SERVICES LTD
Upper Floor, Holme Court, Matlock Street, Bakewell DE45 1GQ

MARTIN JW VENNING
The Alma, School Lane, Baslow, Bakewell DE45 1RZ
Tel: 01433 583584
Principal: ICAEW Member
M J W Venning

R.W.MERCER & CO
Welford House, Matlock Street, Bakewell, DE45 1EE
Tel: 01629 812608
Principal: ICAEW Member
R W Mercer

SUSAN BARON
The Old School, School Lane, Over Haddon, Bakewell DE45 1JE

WEST & FOSTER ◈
Water Street, Bakewell, DE45 1EW
Tel: 01629 814606

BALDOCK

MICHAEL PLANT FCA
11 High Street, Baldock, SG7 6AZ
Tel: 01462 895737
Principal: ICAEW Member
Michael Plant

BAMPTON

BAMPTON ACCOUNTANCY SERVICES
The Old Dairy, Broad Street, Bampton, OX18 2LY

ROBERT WARNER
3 Aston Works, Back Lane, Aston, Bampton OX18 2DQ

BANBURY

AIMS - JEREMY EASTWOOD ACA
10 Broad Close, Barford St Michael, Banbury, OX15 0RW
Tel: 01869 337996
Principal: ICAEW Member
J C Eastwood

ANDREW DONALDSON
Oak Tree House, 17 Lake Walk, Adderbury, Banbury OX17 3PF

ANNE TUTT
Jasmine Cottage, The Green, Hook Norton, Banbury OX15 5LE

CHRISTOPHER DEAN & CO
Ivy Cottage, Bakers Lane, Tadmarton, Banbury OX15 5TB

COTTONS
Chiltern House, Waterperry Court, Middleton Road, Banbury OX16 4QG

CROSS & COMPANY BUSINESS DEVELOPMENT AND SUPPORT ◈
Grove End, Upper Brailes, Banbury, OX15 5BA

DAVID W GRAVES
Greenhill Farm, Sutton under Brailes, Banbury, OX15 5BE

EADIE YOUNG LTD
Chart House, Milton Road, Bloxham, Banbury OX15 4HD

ELLACOTTS LLP
Beechfield House, 38 West Bar, Banbury, OX16 9RX
Tel: 01295 250401
Fax: 01295 271375
Email: mail@ellacotts.co.uk
Training Contracts Available.
Resident Partners/Directors: ICAEW Members
P H Clayton, B A King, D B Saunders, J R S Thame

Registered by the ICAEW to carry out company audit work

Regulated by the ICAEW for a range of investment business activities

INVESTOR IN PEOPLE

EVERITT & CO ACCOUNTANCY & TAXATION SERVICES
The Squirrels, 14 Ironstone Hollow, Hook Norton, Banbury OX15 5NA

FAULKNER ASSOCIATES
The Maltings, 10 Beanacre, Hook Norton, Banbury OX15 5UA

FIDELIS LTD
Unit 103, The Colin Sanders Innovation Centre, Mewburn Road, Banbury OX16 9PA

G CAPSTICK & CO
Ashwood Lodge, Berry Hill Road, Adderbury, Banbury OX17 3HF

HILARY MAGUIRE LTD
Sunny Bank, Sibford Ferris, Banbury, OX15 5RG

HOLFORD TRAINING AND ACCOUNTANCY
5 Shutford Road, North Newington, Banbury, OX15 6AL

JOHN ROULSTONE
12 Silver Street, Chacombe, Banbury, OX17 2JR
Tel: 01295 710145
Principal: ICAEW Member
J A Roulstone

JONES BOUGHTON LTD
7 West Bar Street, Banbury, OX16 9SD
Tel: 01295 700081

KAREN MEADES
The Old Rectory, Chipping Warden, Banbury, OX17 1LR
Tel: 01295 660247
Principal: ICAEW Member
K L Meades

MCA BRESLINS
Greenway House, Sugarswell Business Park, Shenington, Banbury OX15 6HW

MCA BRESLINS BANBURY LTD
Greenway House, Sugarswell Business Park, Shenington, Banbury OX15 6HW

MAGUIRES
Sunny Bank, Sibford Ferris, Banbury, OX15 5RG

PAUL M TATE
3 Hanwell Court, Hanwell, Banbury, OX17 1HF

PETER E CAMPBELL & CO
9 The Rydes, Bodicote, Banbury, OX15 4EJ

PETER M. BOYCOTT & CO
Swalcliffe House, Swalcliffe, Banbury, OX15 5EY

PHIL THOMAS FCA
18 Home Close, Middleton Cheney, Banbury, OX17 2LD
Tel: 01295 712800
Principal: ICAEW Member
P S G Thomas

PHIPPS HENSON MCALLISTER
4 South Bar Street, Banbury, OX16 9AA
Tel: 01295 251589
Resident Partners/Directors: ICAEW Members
C Henson

PROFITRIGHT LTD
Greenhill Farm, Sutton under Brailes, Banbury, OX15 5BE

REAL ESTATE FINANCIAL SOLUTIONS LTD
3 Walnut Close, Culworth, Banbury, OX17 2BJ

RIDLEY MARRECO & CO LTD
Dove House, Mill Lane, Barford St Michael, Banbury OX15 0RH
Tel: 01869 337550
Resident Partners/Directors: ICAEW Members
S W Bunce

ROBERT A. ROWLETT
153 Bloxham Road, Banbury, OX16 9JU
Tel: 01295 273800
Principal: ICAEW Member
R A Rowlett

S.A. GALE
The Tile House, Marston St Lawrence, Banbury, OX17 2DA

S.J.E TUVEY
The Old Farmhouse, Chapel Lane, Shotteswell, Banbury OX17 1JB

SNOWDEN & CO ◈
Dial House, High Street, Hook Norton, Banbury OX15 5NQ

TUVEYS
The Old Farmhouse, Chapel Lane, Shotteswell, Banbury OX17 1JB

WELLERS ★
Kineton House, 31 Horse Fair, Banbury, OX16 0AE

WHITLEY STIMPSON ◈
Penrose House, 67 Hightown Road, Banbury, OX16 9BE
Tel: 01295 270200
Fax: 01295 271784
Email: admin@whitleystimpson.co.uk
Date Established: 1931
Training Contracts Available.
Resident Partners (Non-ICAEW Members):
V Buzzard, K Strrat, T Wallbank
Registered by the ICAEW to carry out company audit work
Regulated by the ICAEW for a range of investment business activities

WHITLEY STIMPSON LLP ◈
Penrose House, 67 Hightown Road, Banbury, OX16 9BE
Tel: 01295 270200
Fax: 01295 271784
Email: nickb@whitleystimpson.co.uk
Website: http://www.whitleystimpson.co.uk
Training Contracts Available.
Resident Partners/Directors:
ICAEW Members
M J Anson, N P R Bullen, M K Higgs, M Wyatt
Resident Partners (Non-ICAEW Members):
V Buzzard, T Wallbank, K Stirrat
Registered by the ICAEW to carry out company audit work
Regulated by the ICAEW for a range of investment business activities
General Description: Multi disciplinary practice offering full range of services in all key financial areas to wide range of clients from individuals to multi million pound international groups of companies.

BANSTEAD

A.R.SEAWARD
32 Palmersfield Road, Banstead, SM7 2LD
Tel: 01737 350356
Principal: ICAEW Member
A R Seaward

ARCHER HAYES ◈
Castle House, 39 Nork Way, Banstead, SM7 1PB

BENEDICT MACKENZIE
The Old Coach House, Croydon Lane, Banstead, SM7 3AT
Tel: 020 8661 7886
Individual(s) licensed for insolvency work by another RPB

BROOKS CARLING
Curzon House, 1st Floor, 24 High Street, Banstead SM7 2LJ
Tel: 01737 357283

BROOKS CARLING ACCOUNTANTS LTD
Curzon House, 1st Floor, 24 High Street, Banstead SM7 2LJ

K.J. BOWERS
25 Fiddicroft Avenue, Banstead, SM7 3AD

LANGDON WEST WILLIAMS PLC
Curzon House, 24 High Street, Banstead, SM7 2LJ
Tel: 01737 359242
Email: office@lwwplc.co.uk
Resident Partners/Directors:
ICAEW Members
K E Brickley, I S Watt
Authorised and regulated by the Financial Services Authority for investment business

PENDRAY & CO
The Hylands, 244 Chipstead Way, Woodmansterne, Banstead SM7 3LQ
Tel: 01737 358857
Principal: ICAEW Member
S E Pendray

PETER BAIKIE
21 Garrard Road, Banstead, SM7 2ER

PETER G STEWART
41 Warren Road, Banstead, SM7 1LG

RONALD B. CRONIN
2 Holly Hill Drive, Banstead, SM7 2BD
Tel: 01737 350690
Principal: ICAEW Member
R B Cronin

SERCO
133 Nork Way, Banstead, SM7 1HR

STEWARTS ACCOUNTANCY SERVICES
41 Warren Road, Banstead, SM7 1LG

TICKETT & CO
97 Wilmot Way, Banstead, SM7 2QA
Tel: 01737 356662
Principal: ICAEW Member
J Tickett

BANWELL

R&E CONSULTANTS
Stonebridge, Wolvershill Road, Banwell, Avon BS29 6DR

RICHARD ANNESLEY & CO
Stonebridge, Wolvershill Road, Banwell, Avon BS29 6DR

BARKING

GARROD, BECKETT & CO LTD
10 Town Quay Wharf, Abbey Road, Barking, IG11 7BZ

LAYTON TRAIN LTD
1 Town Quay Wharf, Abbey Road, Barking, IG11 7BZ
Tel: 020 8591 8555
Resident Partners/Directors:
ICAEW Members
T J Woolmer

BARNARD CASTLE

ADDISON & CO
Ebor House, 91 Galgate, Barnard Castle, DL12 8ES

ADDISON & CO (TEESDALE) LTD ◈
Ebor House, 91 Galgate, Barnard Castle, DL12 8ES
Tel: 01833 690202
Resident Partners/Directors:
ICAEW Members
D J Addison, R Tarn

ALLEN SYKES LTD
17 Galgate, Barnard Castle, DL12 8EQ
Tel: 01833 690474

NIGEL HERRING & CO
23 Market Place, Barnard Castle, DL12 8NB

PAUL & CO
35 Galgate, Barnard Castle, DL12 8EJ
Tel: 01833 690151

BARNET

A & L AUDIT SERVICES LTD ◈
Knight House, 27-31 East Barnet Road, Barnet, EN4 8RN
Tel: 0845 257 0040
Resident Partners/Directors:
ICAEW Members
A Panayiotou

A&L ◈
Knight House, 27-31 East Barnet Road, New Barnet, Barnet EN4 8RN
Tel: 0845 257 0040
Principal: ICAEW Member
A Panayiotou

ADEMA ASSOCIATES
Highstone House, 165 High Street, Barnet, EN5 5SU

ALAN K. JACKSON
63 Church Hill Road, East Barnet, Barnet, EN4 8SY
Tel: 020 8441 5564
Principal: ICAEW Member
A K Jackson

ALAN SACKS & CO
Little Red Court, 7 St Ronans Close, Hadley Wood, Barnet EN4 0JH

ASCA LTD
Little Red Court, 7 St Ronans Close, Hadley Wood, Barnet EN4 0JH

ASHINGS LTD ◈
Northside House, Mount Pleasant, Barnet, EN4 9LJ
Tel: 020 7117 0210
Resident Partners/Directors:
ICAEW Members
D D Ashing, N Kachwalla

B.V. PIGGOTT
Oakroyd, 1 Rowley Green Road, Arkley, Barnet EN5 3HH
Tel: 020 8440 4291
Principal: ICAEW Member
B V Piggott

BBK PARTNERSHIP
1 Beauchamp Court, Victors Way, Barnet, EN5 5TZ
Tel: 020 8446 6026
Fax: 020 8216 2521
Email: admin@bbkca.com
Website: http://www.bbkca.com
Resident Partners/Directors:
ICAEW Members
D M Beckwith, A D Kaye, S S Sahota
Other Offices:9 South Fens Business Centre, Fenton Way, Chatteris, Cambs PE16 6TT (Tel: 01354 707911)
Registered by the ICAEW to carry out company audit work
Regulated by the ICAEW for a range of investment business activities
Individual(s) licensed for insolvency work by the ICAEW

BRENNAN PEARSON & CO ◈
110-112 Lancaster Road, Barnet, EN4 8AL
Tel: 020 8440 3318
Fax: 020 8441 3775
Email: nah@brennanpearson.co.uk
Principal: ICAEW Member
N A Hewitt
Registered by the ICAEW to carry out company audit work
Regulated by the ICAEW for a range of investment business activities

BRYAL COMMERCIAL & FINANCIAL FACILITIES LTD
Flat 6, 71 Park Road, New Barnet, Barnet EN4 9QD
Tel: 020 8441 0649
Resident Partners/Directors:
ICAEW Members
A Shanson

CARTWRIGHTS
Regency House, 33 Wood Street, Barnet, EN5 4BE

CHRISTOPHER GOLDIE & CO
11 Kings Road, Barnet, EN5 4EF

CHRISTOPHER GOLDIE & CO LTD
11 Kings Road, Barnet, EN5 4EF

COLIN D LUKE & CO
79 Northumberland Road, New Barnet, Barnet, EN5 1EB
Tel: 020 8275 8818
Email: colin@colinluke.co.uk
Principal: ICAEW Member
C D Luke
Registered by the ICAEW to carry out company audit work

COLLIER & CO
9 Knoll Lodge, Lyonsdown Road, Barnet, EN5 1RZ

CONROY & LERMER
42 Lytton Road, New Barnet, Barnet, EN5 5BY

CROFTUS LTD
34 Crescent West, Hadley Wood, Barnet, EN4 0EJ

D.C. PRICE & CO
63 Wood Street, Barnet, EN5 4BT

DAVID JOSEPH & CO LTD
2 Wardrew Court, Lyonsdown Road, New Barnet, Barnet EN5 1JA

DAVIS BONLEY
Northside House, Mount Pleasant, Barnet, EN4 9EE
Tel: 020 8216 2100
Resident Partners/Directors: ICAEW Members
D Daniels, A S Davis

DEBSON & CO
Galley House, Second Floor, Moon Lane, Barnet EN5 5YL
Tel: 020 8440 1059
Email: info@debsonandco.co.uk
Date Established: 1979
Principal: ICAEW Member
J G Debson
Registered by the ICAEW to carry out company audit work
Regulated by the ICAEW for a range of investment business activities

SPECIALISATIONS – FINANCIAL REPORTING
Limited Company Accounts
Partnership/Sole Trader Accounts

SPECIALISATIONS – SECTOR
Charities
Solicitors

SPECIALISATIONS – TAXATION
Foreign Nationals in the UK
Offshore Companies
Taxation

Languages Spoken:
French

EVANS MOCKLER
Highstone House, 165 High Street, Barnet, EN5 5SU

EVANS MOCKLER LTD
Highstone House, 165 High Street, Barnet, EN5 5SU
Fax: 020 8447 1512
DX: 130037 BARNET 3
Resident Partners/Directors: ICAEW Members
M Evans
Resident Partners (Non-ICAEW Members):
M Mockler, S Toghill

F L CONSULTANCY LTD
29 Greenhill Park, New Barnet, Barnet, EN5 1HQ

FINANCIAL KNOW HOW LTD
13 St Albans Road, Barnet, EN5 4LN

FLC
29 Greenhill Park, New Barnet, Barnet, EN5 1HQ

FRANK NEWMAN & CO
106 Church Hill Road, Barnet, EN4 8XB

GALLAGHER & BROCKLEHURST
4 Plantagenet Road, Barnet, EN5 5JQ
Tel: 020 8441 1998
Fax: 020 8441 1585
Email: london@g-b.co.uk
Resident Partners/Directors: ICAEW Members
S E Brocklehurst, J E M Gallagher
Registered by the ICAEW to carry out company audit work

THE GREENE PARTNERSHIP ★
Durkan House, 5th Floor, 155 East Barnet Road, Barnet EN4 8QZ
Tel: 020 8275 8484
Resident Partners/Directors: ICAEW Members
G M Greene

H. GUDERLEY & CO
67 Lancaster Avenue, Barnet, EN4 0ER

IKF BUSINESS SERVICES LTD
84 Crescent Road, Barnet, EN4 9RJ

IOANNOU & CO
13-15 High Street, Barnet, EN5 5UJ

J.B. COOKE & CO
11 Calton Road, New Barnet, Barnet, EN5 1BY

J.S. ROSE & CO ◈
Fiosam House, 25 Station Road, New Barnet, Barnet EN5 1PH
Tel: 020 8364 8866
Email: jsrose@jsrose.co.uk
Principal: ICAEW Member
J S Rose
Registered by the ICAEW to carry out company audit work
Regulated by the ICAEW for a range of investment business activities

JEFF LERMER AND ASSOCIATES
42 Lytton Road, New Barnet, Barnet, EN5 5BY

THE KELMANSON PARTNERSHIP ★
Avco House, 6 Albert Road, Barnet, EN4 9SH

LAKERS
3 Galley House, Moon Lane, Barnet, EN5 5YL

LAWRENCE, NUDDS & CO
Alpha House, 176a High Street, Barnet, EN5 5SZ
Tel: 020 8449 5625
Email: lnandco@aol.com
Resident Partners/Directors: ICAEW Members
J D Lawrence, T R Nudds
Registered by the ICAEW to carry out company audit work

LAWRENCE PHILLIPS & CO
36 Woodville Road, Barnet, EN5 5HA

LEONARD MOGILNER & CO ◈
30 Leys Gardens, Cockfosters, Barnet, EN4 9NA
Tel: 020 8441 2100
Fax: 020 8449 4743
Email: lm@mogilner.co.uk
Website: http://www.mogilner.co.uk
Principal: ICAEW Member
L Mogilner
Registered by the ICAEW to carry out company audit work

MCGOVERNS
24 Westpole Avenue, Cockfosters, Barnet, EN4 0AY

NEW THINKING LEADERS LTD
42 Lytton Road, New Barnet, Barnet, EN5 5BY

NEWMAN RAPHAEL LTD
106 Church Hill Road, Barnet, EN4 8XB

NICHOLAS PETERS & CO
7b High Street, Barnet, EN5 5UE

NOVITT BAMFORD LTD
4 Corbar Close, Barnet, EN4 0JL
Tel: 020 8440 5020
Resident Partners/Directors: ICAEW Members
B Novitt

P R WILBY
13 Alan Drive, Barnet, EN5 2PP

PARIS & CO UK LTD
9 Leys Gardens, Cockfosters, Barnet, EN4 9NA

PARKSIDE
12 Stuart Road, Barnet, EN4 8XG

PETROU & CO
4 Heddon Court, Cockfosters Road, Barnet, EN4 0DE
Tel: 020 8364 9918
Principal: ICAEW Member
S Petrou

R. HERBERT & CO
27 Newmans Way, Hadley Wood, Barnet, EN4 0LR

R M SARGEANT
13 Fairgreen, Cockfosters, Barnet, EN4 0QS

RAJ SHAH & CO
46 Heddon Court Avenue, Barnet, EN4 9NG

RAMM LOUIS & CO
Fifth Floor, Kingmaker House, Station Road, New Barnet, Barnet EN5 1NZ

ROLT HARRISON & HEWITT ◈
110/112 Lancaster Road, Barnet, EN4 8AL
Tel: 020 8441 9649
Fax: 020 8441 3775
Email: nah@rolts.co.uk
Date Established: 1921
Resident Partners/Directors: ICAEW Members
N A Hewitt, H E A Rolt
Other Offices: Huntingdon (Kimbolton)
Registered by the ICAEW to carry out company audit work
Regulated by the ICAEW for a range of investment business activities

STANTON PARTNERS
Warren House, Carrington Close, Arkley, Barnet EN5 3NA
Tel: 020 8441 1779
Principal: ICAEW Member
S D Stanton

TAYLORS
Battle House, 1 East Barnet Road, Barnet, EN4 8RR
Tel: 020 8449 8297
Principal: ICAEW Member
R Gulabivala

THEMIS & CO ◈
80 Lyonsdown Road, Barnet, EN5 1JL
Tel: 020 8441 7362
Principal: ICAEW Member
T Themistocli

THERESA M. BOLTON
32 Granville Road, Barnet, EN5 4DS

WOLFF & CO
7 Kenerne Drive, Barnet, EN5 2NW

BARNOLDSWICK

WINDLE & BOWKER LTD
Croft House, Station Road, Barnoldswick, BB18 5NA
Tel: 01282 813031
Resident Partners/Directors: ICAEW Members
S T Briggs, E R Hargreaves, M C Heming

BARNSLEY

ANGUS NORDON & CO ★
194 Pontefract Road, Cudworth, Barnsley, S72 8AF

ASHWORTH BAILEY LTD
20a Racecommon Road, Barnsley, S70 1BH

CINDERHALL LTD
Moor End, Silkstone Common, Barnsley, S75 7RA

DEB ◈
DEB House, 19 Middleswood Way, Wharncliffe Business Park, Carlton, Barnsley S71 3HR

GIBSON BOOTH
12 Victoria Road, Barnsley, S70 2BB
Tel: 01226 213131
Resident Partners/Directors: ICAEW Members
G Dickinson, S P Mell, D J Paget, I Walker, R I Watson, E C Wetton
Resident Partners (Non-ICAEW Members):
R W Quarton
Individual(s) licensed for insolvency work by the ICAEW

HARRIS & CO ◈
Marland House, 13 Huddersfield Road, Barnsley, S70 2LW
Tel: 01226 282461

HARRISACCOUNTS LLP ◈
Marland House, 13 Huddersfield Road, Barnsley, S70 2LW
Tel: 01226 282461
Resident Partners/Directors: ICAEW Members
M A Barratt, R A Cave, T I Garner, P Hinchliffe

HART MOSS DOYLE LTD
69 High Street, Dodworth, Barnsley, S75 3RQ

HEWITT & CO
50 Hoyland Road, Hoyland Common, Barnsley, S74 OPB
Tel: 01226 744522
Principal: ICAEW Member
N J Smith

MELVYN LUNN
49 Church Street, Darton, Barnsley, S75 5HF

R.E. NEEDS
42 Huddersfield Road, Barnsley, S75 1DW
Tel: 01226 282692

R.E. NEEDS LTD
42 Huddersfield Road, Barnsley, S75 1DW
Tel: 01226 282692
Resident Partners/Directors: ICAEW Members
R E Needs

SUGDENS
Unit 20, Zenith Park, Whaley Road, Barnsley S75 1HT
Tel: 01226 771206
Principal: ICAEW Member
A B Sugden

TENON LTD
Sterling House, Maple Court, Tankersley, Barnsley S75 3DP
Tel: 01226 232924

THORNTONS ACCOUNTING LTD
176/178 Pontefract Road, Cudworth, Barnsley, S72 8BE

WHITEHILL COMMUNICATIONS LTD
11 Tivy Dale Close, Cawthorne, Barnsley, S75 4ER

BARNSTAPLE

BULLIMORES ◈
3 Boutport Street, Barnstaple, EX31 1RH

CRICK & CO
15a Silver Street, Barnstaple, EX32 8HR

DAVISONS LTD
31 Queen Street, Barnstaple, EX32 8HQ

ELIZABETH PALETHORPE
39 Ashleigh Road, Barnstaple, EX32 8JY

GLOVER STANBURY & CO ◈
30 Bear Street, Barnstaple, EX32 7DD
Tel: 01271 375271
Email: info@gloverstanbury.co.uk
Website: http://www.gloverstanbury.co.uk
Resident Partners/Directors: ICAEW Members
N A Bennett, S D Pearce, B C Ross, K N Salter, M R Shute

LARGE
13 Silver Street, Barnstaple, EX32 8HR

PERRINS LTD
Custom House, The Strand, Barnstaple, EX31 1EU

RICHARD TARR & CO
Wood Park, East Down, Barnstaple, EX31 4LZ

SIMPKINS EDWARDS
21 Boutport Street, Barnstaple, EX31 1RP
Tel: 01271 342233
Email: Barnstaple@SimpkinsEdwards.co.uk
Website: http://www.simpkinsedwards.co.uk
Resident Partners/Directors: ICAEW Members
D G Clapp, I A Huggett
Registered by the ICAEW to carry out company audit work
Regulated by the ICAEW for a range of investment business activities

STEVENS & WILLEY ★
Grenville House, 9 Boutport Street, Barnstaple, EX31 1TZ
Tel: 01271 321621
Website: http://www.stevensandwilley.co.uk
Resident Partners/Directors: ICAEW Members
H L Mansford

THOMAS WESTCOTT ★
47 Boutport Street, Barnstaple, EX31 1SQ
Tel: 01271 374138
Resident Partners/Directors: ICAEW Members
P B Petrides

BARROW-IN-FURNESS

CLARKE JEFFERIES
105 Duke Street, Barrow-in-Furness, LA14 1RH

G. MOON & CO
74 Duke Street, Barrow-in-Furness, LA14 1RX
Tel: 01229 811808
Principal: ICAEW Member
G Moon

J.L. WINDER & CO ★ ◈
125 Ramsden Square, Barrow-in-furness, LA14 1XA
Tel: 01229 820390
Fax: 01229 870595
Email: enquiries@jlwinder.co.uk
Website: http://www.jlwinder.co.uk
Resident Partners/Directors: ICAEW Members
G M Haythornthwaite, S J Roberts, G Smith, J L Winder
Resident Partners (Non-ICAEW Members):
S M Leonard
Registered by the ICAEW to carry out company audit work

KNOX ACCOUNTING
Waterside House, Bridge Approach, Barrow-in-Furness, LA14 2HE

MELVILLE & CO ◈
Unit 17/18, Trinity Enterprise Centre, Furness Business Park, Ironworks Road, Barrow-in-Furness LA14 2PN
Tel: 01229 434000
Fax: 01229 434044
Email: info@melville18.co.uk
Resident Partners/Directors: ICAEW Members
J R Goffe, R D Longton
Registered by the ICAEW to carry out company audit work
Regulated by the ICAEW for a range of investment business activities
SPECIALISATIONS – SECTOR

Charities
See display advertisement near this entry.

R.F. MILLER & CO
102 Duke Street, Barrow-in-furness, LA14 1RD
Tel: 01229 820003
Resident Partners (Non-ICAEW Members):
E M Harris

WINDER (IFA) LTD
125 Ramsden Square, Barrow-in-furness, LA14 1XA
Tel: 01229 820390
Resident Partners/Directors: ICAEW Members
G M Haythornthwaite, G Smith

BARROW-UPON-HUMBER

ACARA ACCOUNTANCY
Hadley Ridge, North End, Goxhill, Barrow-upon-humber, SOUTH HUMBERSIDE DN19 7JX
Tel: 01469 530363
Principal: ICAEW Member
R H Guggiari

BARTON-UPON-HUMBER

STEPHENSON, SMART & CO ◈
41 High Street, Barton-upon-humber, DN18 5PD

BASILDON

BROWN & CO
2 Lords Court, Cricketers Way, Basildon, SS13 1SS

BROWN & CO AUDIT LTD
2 Lords Court, Cricketers Way, Basildon, SS13 1SS

BROWN & CO LLP
2 Lords Court, Cricketers Way, Basildon, SS13 1SS

DAGAS LTD ◈
1 Gate Lodge Way, Laindon, Basildon, SS15 4AR
Tel: 01268 532797
Resident Partners/Directors: ICAEW Members
D G Sunderland

ELLIOTT, MORTLOCK BUSBY & CO ★
Abacus House, 7 Argent Court, Sylvan Way, Southfields Business Park, Basildon SS15 6TH
Tel: 01268 492724
Fax: 01268 492726
Website: http://www.emb-accountants.co.uk
Resident Partners/Directors: ICAEW Members
A G Busby
Resident Partners (Non-ICAEW Members):
A R Wenden
Registered by the ICAEW to carry out company audit work
Regulated by the ICAEW for a range of investment business activities

F. PITTOCK & CO
Tremlett Villa, London Road, Pitsea, Basildon SS13 2DB
Tel: 01268 553014
Principal: ICAEW Member
F Pittock

JOHN COWLING & CO
1 Britten Close, Great Berry, Langdon Hills, Basildon SS16 6TB
Tel: 01268 410037
Principal: ICAEW Member
J H Cowling

MGI RICKARD KEEN LLP ◈
Glenny House, Fenton Way, Southfields Business Park, Basildon SS15 6TD
Tel: 01268 548127
Website: http://www.rickardkeen.co.uk
Training Contracts Available.
Resident Partners/Directors: ICAEW Members
K E Davies, N C Kelleway
Other Offices:7-11 Nelson Street, Southend-on-Sea, SS1 1EH
Registered by the ICAEW to carry out company audit work
Regulated by the ICAEW for a range of investment business activities

INVESTOR IN PEOPLE

SUNDERLAND & CO ◈
1 Gate Lodge Way, Laindon, Basildon, SS15 4AR
Tel: 01268 532797

BASINGSTOKE

2COOKES LTD
1 Cranesfield, Sherborne St John, Basingstoke, RG24 9LN

A.E. DOWD
Roentgen Court, Roentgen Road, Daneshill, Basingstoke RG24 8NT
Tel: 01256 325337
Principal: ICAEW Member
A E Dowd
Registered by the ICAEW to carry out company audit work

AIMS - NIGEL TAYLOR
Lower Farm, Green Lane, Ellisfield, Basingstoke RG25 2QL

ASHLEY DOGGETT & CO
5 Crossborough Gardens, Crossborough Hill, Basingstoke, RG21 4LB

B.A.T.S
5 Crossborough Gardens, Basingstoke, RG21 4LB

BAKER TILLY
Spring Park House, Basing View, Basingstoke, RG21 4HG
Tel: 01256 486800
Resident Partners/Directors: ICAEW Members
K A Barwick, R W Fisher

BAKER TILLY
2nd Floor, Spring Park House, Basing View, Basingstoke RG21 4HG

BAKER TILLY TAX AND ADVISORY SERVICES LLP
Spring Park House, Basing View, Basingstoke, RG21 4HG
Tel: 01256 486800
Resident Partners/Directors: ICAEW Members
K A Barwick, M L I Blain, R W Fisher, J F Thompson
Resident Partners (Non-ICAEW Members):
T J Smith

BARRIE M. SMITH ◈
10a Winchester Street, Basingstoke, RG21 7DY
Tel: 01256 357642
Principal: ICAEW Member
B M Smith

BATS LTD
5 Crossborough Gardens, Basingstoke, RG21 4LB

CHRIS BAWTREE FCA
8 Kingsmill Road, Basingstoke, RG21 3JJ
Tel: 01256 325898
Principal: ICAEW Member
C O Bawtree

COOKE, COOKE & CO
1 Cranesfield, Sherborne St John, Basingstoke, RG24 9LN

CRANLEYS ◈
Winton House, Winton Square, Basingstoke, RG21 8EN

EDWIN G. MONGER
49 West End, Sherborne St John, Basingstoke, RG24 9LE
Tel: 01256 850545
Principal: ICAEW Member
E G Monger

EUROFIN TAXATION SERVICES LTD
Telford House, Hamilton Close, Basingstoke, RG21 6YT

HW
Viewpoint, Basing View, Basingstoke, RG21 4RG
Tel: 01256 840414

JOHN & ANNE HUDSON ◈
15 Neville Close, Basingstoke, RG21 3HG
Tel: 01256 411588
Resident Partners/Directors: ICAEW Members
A E Hudson, J C M Hudson

JP ASSOCIATES ◈
Burley Wood, Ashe, Basingstoke, RG25 3AG
Tel: 07771 968620
Principal: ICAEW Member
Sir Jonathan Portal

KAY LINNELL & CO
Brick Kiln Cottage, Avenue Road, Herriard, Basingstoke RG25 2PR
Tel: 01256 381301
Principal: ICAEW Member
K C S H Linnell

LANE MONNINGTON WELTON
Riverside View, Basing Road, Old Basing, Basingstoke RG24 7AL

LIFELINE ACCOUNTANCY SERVICES
12 Ferguson Close, Basingstoke, RG21 3JA

MARSHALL KEEN
Pinewood, Crockford Lane, Chineham, Basingstoke RG24 8AL

MARSHALL KEEN LTD
Pinewood, Crockford Lane, Chineham, Basingstoke RG24 8AL

NEWMAN THORPE LTD
179a Pack Lane, Basingstoke, RG22 5HW

PAUL DAVIS
27 Hill Road, Oakley, Basingstoke, RG23 7HS
Tel: 01256 782545
Principal: ICAEW Member
P A Davis
General Description: Accounts, tax, training.

PIPER THOMPSON
62/64 New Road, Basingstoke, RG21 7PW

R.A. RANDALL
166 Kempshott Lane, Kempshott, Basingstoke, RG22 5LA

ROGER YEATES
4 Petrel Croft, Kempshott, Basingstoke, RG22 5JY
Tel: 01256 359287
Principal: ICAEW Member
R Yeates

TENON
Clifton House, Bunnian Place, Basingstoke, RG21 7JE
Tel: 01256 370370

TENON AUDIT LTD
Clifton House, Bunnian Place, Basingstoke, RG21 7JE
Tel: 01256 370370
Resident Partners/Directors: ICAEW Members
C S Cairns

TERRY MARSH
Barley Mow House, Woods Lane, Cliddesden, Basingstoke RG25 2JG
Tel: 01256 461903
Principal: ICAEW Member
T G Marsh

WELLER MACKRILL
South Building, Upper Farm, Wootton St Lawrence, Basingstoke RG23 8PE
Tel: 01256 782059

WELLER MACKRILL LTD
South Building, Upper Farm, Wootton St Lawrence, Basingstoke RG23 8PE
Tel: 01256 782059
Resident Partners/Directors: ICAEW Members
L J Mackrill

WELLS & CO
Telford House, Hamilton Close, Basingstoke, RG21 6YT
Tel: 01256 816236
Principal: ICAEW Member
T A Wells
Registered by the ICAEW to carry out company audit work

BATH

1ST CONSULT LTD ◈
Rowley Stables, Combe Hay, Bath, BA2 7EF
Tel: 01225 830353
Resident Partners/Directors: ICAEW Members
P F Mills

ACCOUNTANCY, BUSINESS AND TAXATION SERVICES LTD
Flat 2, Cathcart House, Snow Hill, Bath BA1 6DL

ADVANCE BUSINESS CONSULTANTS LTD
Courtyard Mews, Piccadilly Place, London Road, Bath BA1 6PL

AK ACCOUNTANCY LTD
23 Denmark Road, Bath, BA2 3RE
Tel: 01225 400106

ALAN C GARRETT
5 Garstons, Bathford, Bath, BA1 7TE

AM PITT MA FCA
14 Queen Square, Bath, BA1 2HN

ANDREW MULLETT FCA
10 Highbury Place, Camden, Bath, BA1 2JW

APODI LTD
Horsecombe Grange, Horsecombe Vale, Bath, BA2 5QR

BERKELEY BATE ◈
27-28 Monmouth Street, Bath, BA1 2AP
Tel: 01225 445196
Email: mail@b-bate.co.uk
Principal: ICAEW Member
J S Bate
Regulated by the ICAEW for a range of investment business activities
SPECIALISATIONS – FINANCIAL REPORTING
Limited Company Accounts
Partnership/Sole Trader Accounts
SPECIALISATIONS – TAXATION
Partnerships and Sole Traders
Personal

BERKELEY HALL MARSHALL LTD
6 Charlotte Street, Bath, BA1 2NE

BOND PARTNERS LLP
201 Newbridge Road, Bath, BA1 3HH

CLASSIC FINANCIAL SOLUTIONS LLP
17 St Peters Terrace, Lower Bristol Road, Bath, BA2 3BT
Tel: 01225 319371
Fax: 01225 480278
Email: info@cfsca.com
Website: http://www.cfsca.com
Date Established: 2005
Non-resident Partners (ICAEW Members):
J S H Ingram-Johnson, K B Haines
Non-resident Partners (Non-ICAEW Members):
P Trevenna
Other Offices: Cheltenham

CREW & HAMMOND ★
4/5 Bridge Street, Bath, BA2 4AP

D C HUGHESDON
165 Newbridge Hill, Bath, BA1 3PX
Tel: 01225 442788
Principal: ICAEW Member
D C Hughesdon

DAVID TAYLOR ◈
31 Sion Hill, Bath, BA1 2UW

DAWN MINERS
34 Fairfield Avenue, Bath, BA1 6NH

DELOITTE & TOUCHE LLP ◈
20 Manvers Street, Bath, BA1 1PX
Tel: 01225 44700
Website: http://www.deloitte.co.uk

FULLER
4/5 Bridge Street, Bath, BA2 4AS

FULLER CHF LLP
4/5 Bridge Street, Bath, BA2 4AP

G.C. BARBER
Westcross House, 73 Midford Road, Bath, BA2 5RT
Tel: 01225 837711
Fax: 01225 833661
Email: graham@gcbarber.co.uk
Website: http://www.gcbarber.co.uk
Date Established: 1992
Principal: ICAEW Member
G C Barber
Regulated by the ICAEW for a range of investment business activities

GRAHAM BROWN & CO
2 Bathwick Terrace, Bathwick Hill, Bath, BA2 4EL

JOHN FOSTER & CO
Office Four, 3 Edgar Buildings, Bath, BA1 2FJ

JOHN YALLOP
8 Richmond Heights, Bath, BA1 5QJ

KEN FRYER ◈
8 Coronation Road, Bath, BA1 3BH
Tel: 07041 492171
Website: http://www.kenfryer.co.uk
Principal: ICAEW Member
K W Fryer
Registered by the ICAEW to carry out company audit work
Regulated by the ICAEW for a range of investment business activities

LESLIE, WARD & DREW
Kingston House, Pierrepont Street, Bath, BA1 1LA
Tel: 01225 420508
Email: mail@lesliewardanddrew.co.uk
Resident Partners/Directors: ICAEW Members
J A Drew, H E Ward
Registered by the ICAEW to carry out company audit work

LEWIS & CO
Walden, Widcombe Hill, Bath, BA2 6ED

LONDON & BATH LTD
14 Queen Square, Bath, BA1 2HN

MARK GARRETT
1st Floor, 11 Laura Place, Bath, BA2 4BL

MARY WISKER ACCOUNTANCY SERVICES
91 Penn Hill Road, Bath, BA1 3RT

MONAHANS
3 Pierrepont Street, Bath, BA1 1LB

MONAHANS LTD
Lennox House, 3 Pierrepont Street, Bath, BA1 1LB
Tel: 01249 766966
Resident Partners/Directors: ICAEW Members
L Boss, H M Hilliard, M J Longmore

MOORE STEPHENS
30 Gay Street, Bath, BA1 2PA
Tel: 01225 486100
Email: bath@moorestephens.com
Training Contracts Available.
Resident Partners/Directors: ICAEW Members
R J Branch, M P Burnett, V E Davies, A J Vince
Resident Partners (Non-ICAEW Members):
A D Turner
Registered by the ICAEW to carry out company audit work

O'HARA WOOD
29 Gay Street, Bath, BA1 2NT

PATMORE & CO ◈
Isabella Mews, The Avenue, Combe Down, Bath BA2 5EH
Tel: 01225 832121
Principal: ICAEW Member
A W Patmore

PEARSON MAY ◈
37 Great Pulteney Street, Bath, BA2 4DA

PEOPLE AND BUSINESS
Lawrence House, Lower Bristol Road, Bath, BA2 9ET

PETHERICKS & GILLARD LTD ◈
124 High Street, Midsomer Norton, Bath, BA3 2DA

PURCELLS UK LTD
342 Bloomfield Road, Bath, BA2 2PB

R.D. OWEN & CO ◈
18a Queen Square, Bath, BA1 2HR
Tel: 01225 422183
Resident Partners/Directors: ICAEW Members
R N Browning, C R Sullivan

R D OWEN SERVICES LTD
Queen Caroline House, 18a Queen Square, Bath, BA1 2HR

richardsongroves

Accountants, Business and Tax Consultants

RICHARDSON GROVES ◈
Cleveland House, Sydney Road, Bath, BA2 6NR
Tel: 01225 443014
Email: marketing@richardsongroves.com
Resident Partners/Directors: ICAEW Members
P J Groves, M T Richardson

ROBSON TAYLOR
Charter House, The Square, Lower Bristol Road, Bath BA2 3BH

ROBSON TAYLOR LLP ◈
Charter House, The Square, Lower Bristol Road, Bath BA2 3BH

ROLAND J. ADAMSON
1 North Parade Passage, Bath, BA1 1NX
Tel: 01225 446661
Email: accounts@ra-bath.freeserve.co.uk
Principal: ICAEW Member
R J Adamson

SPECIALISATIONS – TAXATION

Personal

STEVE JONES
74 Newbridge Road, Bath, BA1 3LA
Tel: 01225 331432
Principal: ICAEW Member
S L Jones

T O SYLVESTER
87 Winsley Hill, Limpley Stoke, Bath, Wiltshire BA2 7FA
Tel: 01225 722776
Principal: ICAEW Member
T O Sylvester

TARGET
Lawrence House, Lower Bristol Road, Bath, BA2 9ET

TARGET CONSULTING LTD
Lawrence House, Lower Bristol Road, Bath, BA2 9ET
Tel: 01225 486300
Fax: 01225 486310
Email: target@target-accountants.com
Website: http://www.target-accountants.com
Date Established: 1998
Resident Partners/Directors: ICAEW Members
A L Bennett, A P Sandiford, K Seeley
Resident Partners (Non-ICAEW Members):
M Harman, G Lenthall

Registered by the ICAEW to carry out company audit work

Regulated by the ICAEW for a range of investment business activities

General Description: A leading business and accountancy firm with offices in Bath, Reading, Rugby and London. Authorised provision of financial services.

TARGET CONSULTING GROUP LTD
Lawrence House, Lower Bristol Road, Bath, BA2 9ET

TARGET WINTERS
Lawrence House, Lower Bristol Road, Bath, BA2 9ET

TARGET WINTERS LTD
Lawrence House, Lower Bristol Road, Bath, BA2 9ET

TERRY BICKENSON
96 Broadmoor Lane, Bath, BA1 4LB

THORSTEN ORR
Flat 7, 5 Little Stanhope Street, Bath, BA1 2BH

BATLEY

ACCOUNTANCY SERVICES (BATLEY) LTD
21 Henrietta Street, Batley, WF17 5DN

CHRIS SINCLAIR ACCOUNTANTS LTD ◈
17 Upper Batley Low Lane, Batley, WF17 0AP
Tel: 01924 479232
Resident Partners/Directors: ICAEW Members
C G Sinclair

K.E. MATHERS & CO
Nethercroft, Upper Batley Lane, Batley, WF17 0AR

SUTCLIFFE & CO
3 Branch Road, Batley, WF17 5RY
Tel: 01924 472350
Principal: ICAEW Member
S G Sutcliffe

BATTLE

B.A. KHAN & CO
Parkgate Manor, Catsfield, Battle, TN33 9DT

BROWN RUSSELL LTD
The Watch Oak, Chain Lane, Battle, TN33 0YD

D H COUPEE
Holmes House, The Green, Sedlescombe, Battle TN33 0QA
Tel: 01424 870450
Principal: ICAEW Member
D H Coupee

MCPHERSON & PARTNERS
26 High Street, Battle, TN33 0EA

MCPHERSON & PARTNERS (BATTLE) LLP
26 High Street, Battle, TN33 0EA

MALCOLM F. TEGG
The Old Gun House, Sedlescombe, Battle, TN33 0QJ
Tel: 01424 870345
Fax: 01424 871011
Email: clergycare@aol.com
Principal: ICAEW Member
M F Tegg

General Description: Specialist in taxation and financial management for the clergy.

MANNINGTONS
39 High Street, Battle, TN33 0EE
Tel: 01424 774447
Resident Partners/Directors: ICAEW Members
R F Dennard

ROBERT DUFFILL LTD
3 Mount Street, Battle, TN33 0EG
Tel: 01424 773123
Resident Partners/Directors: ICAEW Members
R F Duffill

BEACONSFIELD

A J FRALL
Braemar, 19 Long Grove, Seer Green, Beaconsfield HP9 2YN
Tel: 01494 675996
Principal: ICAEW Member
A J Frall

ACCOUNTS & MORE LTD
10 Copperfields, Beaconsfield, HP9 2NS

AJCK LTD
29 Eghams Wood Road, Beaconsfield, HP9 1JU

ANDERTONS
Hytec House, 27 Burgess Wood Road South, Beaconsfield, HP9 1EX

CASSERLY ACCOUNTING
16 Tilsworth Road, Beaconsfield, HP9 1TR

CHARTERHOUSE (ACCOUNTANTS) LLP
Clarendon House, 20-22 Aylesbury End, Beaconsfield, HP9 1LW
Tel: 01494 680068
Fax: 01494 674436
Email: info@charter-house.net
Website: http://www.charter-house.net
Resident Partners (Non-ICAEW Members):
D White

FOSTER PESCHARDT
C/O H. Johnston, 7 Manor Farm Way, Seer Green, Beaconsfield HP9 2YD

harwoodhutton

HARWOOD HUTTON ◈
22 Wycombe End, Beaconsfield, HP9 1NB
Tel: 01494 739500
Fax: 01494 739555
Email: info@harwoodhutton.co.uk
DX: 34504 BEACONSFIELD
Website: http://www.harwoodhutton.co.uk
Date Established: 1957
Training Contracts Available.
Resident Partners/Directors: ICAEW Members
J C Cable, G Corney, R J Hutton, D E Jones, A J Stronach
Resident Partners (Non-ICAEW Members):
J R S Brace, P D Agius

Registered by the ICAEW to carry out company audit work
Licensed by another DPB to carry on investment business

INVESTOR IN PEOPLE

General Description: Business advisers, accountants, tax consultants, registered auditors, forensic specialists, corporate finance, private client advisers.

Languages Spoken:
Spanish, Portuguese, French, German, Hindi, Gujarati, Swahili, Polish, Punjabi, Bengali

HLB VANTIS AUDIT PLC
55 Station Road, Beaconsfield, HP9 1QL
Tel: 01494 675321
Website: http://www.hlbvantisaudit.com
Training Contracts Available.

Registered by the ICAEW to carry out company audit work

Regulated by the ICAEW for a range of investment business activities

SPECIALISATIONS – AUDIT & ASSURANCE

Audit
Audit — Private Company
Audit — Public Company

continued

HLB VANTIS AUDIT PLC
cont
SPECIALISATIONS – FINANCIAL REPORTING
Audit Exemption Report

I.A. MACHIN
19 Seer Mead, Seer Green, Beaconsfield, HP9 2QL
Tel: 01494 676321
Principal: ICAEW Member
I A Machin

J J DRURY
65 Wattleton Road, Beaconsfield, HP9 1RY

K.M.ELLIOTT
8 The Spinney, Beaconsfield, HP9 1SB
Tel: 01494 671481
Principal: ICAEW Member
K M Elliott

MACHIN & CO ◈
19 Seer Mead, Seer Green, Beaconsfield, HP9 2QL
Tel: 01494 671366
Fax: 01494 676321
Email: howard.machin@machinandco.com
Principal: ICAEW Member
H N Machin
Registered by the ICAEW to carry out company audit work

MK CLIFFORD -KING
29 Eghams Wood Road, Beaconsfield, HP9 1JU

POULTON & CO
15 Oakdene, Beaconsfield, HP9 2BZ

STANWORTH & CO
15 Ledborough Wood, Beaconsfield, HP9 2DJ

VANTIS GROUP LTD
55 Station Road, Beaconsfield, HP9 1QL
Tel: 01494 675321
Website: http://www.vantisplc.com/beaconsfield
Resident Partners/Directors: ICAEW Members
N A Relph
General Description: ICAEW Registered.

BEAMINSTER

BROWN FIELD BOYER
3 Manor Vale, Mosterton, Beaminster, DT8 3LF

BROWN FIELD BOYER LTD
3 Manor Vale, Mosterton, Beaminster, DT8 3LF
Tel: 01308 867528
Resident Partners/Directors: ICAEW Members
S J Brown, M D Field

BROWN AND CO (SW) LTD
Brown & Co, 3 Manor Vale, Mosterton, Beaminster DT8 3LF

GARRATT WATTS
24 Chard Road, Drimpton, Beaminster, DT8 3RF
Tel: 01308 867758
Principal: ICAEW Member
J G Watts

SARUM MANAGEMENT SERVICES LTD Ⓜ
24 Chard Road, Drimpton, Beaminster, DT8 3RF
Tel: 01308 867758
Resident Partners/Directors: ICAEW Members
J G Watts
SPECIALISATIONS – SECTOR
Hotels/Public Houses

BECCLES

DAVID WHITTLE & CO
5 The Walk, Beccles, NR34 9AJ

N.J. LIDDELL & CO
Moor Farm, Kings Lane, Sotherton, Beccles NR34 8AF
Tel: 01986 872540
Principal: ICAEW Member
N J Liddell

NEWMAN & CO ◈
7 Hungate, Beccles, NR34 9TT
Tel: 01502 711356
Fax: 01502 711627
Email: beccles@newmans-online.co.uk
Other Offices: Diss

BECKENHAM

ADAM & CO
8 St Clare Court, Foxgrove Avenue, Beckenham, BR3 5BG

ADRIAN ANDREWS ◈
42 Bushey Way, Beckenham, BR3 6TB

ANTHONY R VINCENT BSC FCA FCIE
79 Foxgrove Road, Beckenham, BR3 5BB
Tel: 020 7007 0819
Resident Partners/Directors: ICAEW Members
A R Vincent

BAHRAMS LTD
46 Bushey Way, Park Langley, Beckenham, BR3 6TB

BECKENHAM BUSINESS SERVICES LTD
3 Mackenzie Road, Beckenham, BR3 4RT

CARON M KEHOE
53 Brabourne Rise, Park Langley, Beckenham, BR3 6SD

CONSTANT & CO ACCOUNTANCY SERVICES LTD
80 Croydon Road, Beckenham, BR3 4DF
Tel: 020 8663 4877
Resident Partners/Directors: ICAEW Members
C Constantinou

D.N.ELDRIDGE
26 Eden Way, Eden Park, Beckenham, BR3 3DJ

D. STOKER & CO ★
Abacus House, 367 Blandford Road, Beckenham, BR3 4NW

E J BUTLER ◈
Manor Road House, 42 Manor Road, Beckenham, BR3 5LE
Tel: 020 8658 8623
Principal: ICAEW Member
E J Butler

ECLIPSE CONSULTANCY LTD
9 Limes Road, Beckenham, BR3 6NS

EDWARDS
409-411 Croydon Road, Beckenham, BR3 3PP
Tel: 020 8658 2288
Principal: ICAEW Member
J Duggan

G.ILIFFE
6 Greystoke Court, 29 Albemarle Road, Beckenham, BR3 5HL
Tel: 020 8650 4953
Principal: ICAEW Member
G C Iliffe

G P IVORY & CO LTD
80 Croydon Road, Beckenham, BR3 4DF
Tel: 020 8663 4877
Resident Partners/Directors: ICAEW Members
G Ivory

GEORGE JOHNSON
50 Oakwood Avenue, Beckenham, BR3 6PJ
Tel: 020 8658 1442
Principal: ICAEW Member
G L Johnson

GYRO LTD
Tarn House, 58 Kelsey Lane, Beckenham, BR3 3NE

HAMMONDS
Burnhill Business Centre, Provident House, Burrell Row, Beckenham BR3 1AT
Tel: 020 8249 6328
Fax: 020 8249 6329
Email: info@hammondsaccountants.co.uk
Website: http://www.hammondsaccountants.co.uk
Principal: ICAEW Member
G W Miles
Registered by the ICAEW to carry out company audit work
SPECIALISATIONS – AUDIT & ASSURANCE
Audit
SPECIALISATIONS – BUSINESS & GENERAL ADVICE
Book-keeping
Company Secretarial Service
Management Advice to Business
Management Consultancy
SPECIALISATIONS – FINANCIAL REPORTING
Accounts Preparation
Limited Company Accounts
Partnership/Sole Trader Accounts
SPECIALISATIONS – TAXATION
Payroll Service and Advice
Taxation

HELEN GARRETT ACA
17 St James's Avenue, Beckenham, BR3 4HF

J W H MARTIN
1 Cherry Tree Walk, Beckenham, BR3 3PF

JAMES G RUDDOCK-BROYD
2 Mayfield Lodge, 28 Brackley Road, Beckenham, BR3 1RQ

MELVYN DAVIES & CO
9 Limes Road, Beckenham, BR3 6NS
Tel: 020 8663 3332
Principal: ICAEW Member
J M Davies

PATSON & CO ◈
9 Limes Road, Beckenham, BR3 6NS

PHILIP JONES & CO
Oak Cottage, Walled Garden Close, Beckenham, BR3 3GN

R HOYLE
51 Oakwood Avenue, Beckenham, BR3 6PT

R.K. BALL
42 Downs Hill, Beckenham, BR3 5HB
Tel: 020 8658 0172
Principal: ICAEW Member
R K Ball

RICHARD DOVEY & CO
61 Malmains Way, Beckenham, BR3 6SB

ROBERT W BELCHER
County House, 221-241 Beckenham Road, Beckenham, BR3 4UF

ROBERT W. BELCHER ◈
County House, 221-241 Beckenham Road, Beckenham, BR3 4UF
Tel: 020 8778 1119
Principal: ICAEW Member
R W Belcher
Registered by the ICAEW to carry out company audit work

SILVER, SEVKET & CO ★
16 Bromley Road, Beckenham, BR3 5JE

STIDDARD MATHERS LTD
Kent CCC, Worsley Bridge Road, Beckenham, BR3 1RL

BEDALE

GMC ACCOUNTANCY LTD ◈
18 North End, Bedale, DL8 1AB
Tel: 01677 424077
Resident Partners/Directors: ICAEW Members
G M Chipp

KENNETH EASBY LLP
Oak House, 35 North End, Bedale, DL8 1AQ
Tel: 01677 422188
Fax: 01677 428941
Email: bedale@kennetheasby.co.uk
Website: http://www.kennetheasby.co.uk
Resident Partners/Directors: ICAEW Members
R W Dunning, C Hutson, S J Rainbow
Other Offices: Oak Mount, Standard Way, Northallerton, N Yorks DL6 2XQ, Victoria Buildings, Rear 15 Victoria Rd, Darlington, Co Durham DL1 5RB

Registered by the ICAEW to carry out company audit work

Regulated by the ICAEW for a range of investment business activities

BEDFORD

80K LTD
45 Days Lane, Biddenham, Bedford, MK40 4AE

AIMS - TIM KEMP
Top Barn, Rectory Road, Steppingley, Bedford MK45 5AT

BAKER NOEL LTD
45A Station Road, Willington, Bedford, MK44 3QL

BELL & CO
64 Harpur Street, Bedford, MK40 2ST

BRIDGE BUSINESS RECOVERY LLP
King William House, 46 Harpur Street, Bedford, MK40 2QT
Tel: 01234 330444

CAMFIELD CHAPMAN LOWE LTD
39 Parmiter Way, Ampthill, Bedford, MK45 2RG

COOMBS (BEDFORD) LTD
164 Bedford Road, Kempston, Bedford, MK42 8BH

COWLEY HOLMES ACCOUNTANTS LLP ◈
9 Goldington Road, Bedford, MK40 3JY
Tel: 01234 355300
Email: mail@cowleyholmes.co.uk
Resident Partners/Directors: ICAEW Members
B D Cowley

COX & CO
The Granary, High Street, Bedford, MK43 8DB
Tel: 01234 888703
Principal: ICAEW Member
D A Cox

DAVID YOUNG
12 Charlbury Court, Merton Road, Bedford, MK40 3AE
Tel: 01234 272110
Principal: ICAEW Member
D G M Young

DEREK A PARRY ◈
82 Tyne Crescent, Brickhill, Bedford, MK41 7UL
Tel: 01234 346407
Email: derek@parry12.fsnet.co.uk
Principal: ICAEW Member
D A Parry

SPECIALISATIONS – FORENSIC ACCOUNTING

Expert Witnesses in Litigation
Forensic Accounting

EVERITT, JAMES & CO
7 Ison Close, Biddenham, Bedford, MK40 4BH

FAST ACCOUNTING SERVICES LTD
PO Box 803, Ampthill, Bedford, MK45 9AJ

UHY GEORGE HAY ◈
Bedford I Lab, Stannard Way, Priory Business Park, Bedford MK44 3RZ

GKP LTD ◈
First Floor, 5 Doolittle Yard, Froghall Road, Ampthill, Bedford MK45 2NW

GODFREY LAWS & CO LTD ◈
1 Doolittle Yard, Froghall Road, Ampthill, Bedford MK45 2NW
Tel: 01525 716668

GREGORY WILDMAN ◈
The Granary, Crowhill Farm, Ravensden Road, Wilden, Bedford MK44 2QS
Tel: 0845 644 9955
Fax: 0845 644 9277
Email: info@gregwild.co.uk
Website: http://www.gregwild.co.uk
Resident Partners/Directors: ICAEW Members
L C Gregory, H A Jones, D M Lewsley
Resident Partners (Non-ICAEW Members):
A S Mitchell

Registered by the ICAEW to carry out company audit work

Regulated by the ICAEW for a range of investment business activities

SPECIALISATIONS – AUDIT & ASSURANCE

Audit

SPECIALISATIONS – BUSINESS & GENERAL ADVICE

Acquisitions and Mergers
Book-keeping
Company Formation
Data Processing Services
Management Advice to Business

SPECIALISATIONS – FINANCIAL REPORTING

Limited Company Accounts
Partnership/Sole Trader Accounts

SPECIALISATIONS – IT

Computerised Accounting Systems

SPECIALISATIONS – TAXATION

Payroll Service and Advice
Taxation
UK Subsidiaries of Overseas Multinationals

General Description: Tailor their service to you dependent on your goals and ambitions, then work with you to achieve these objectives using their expertise in finance, data analysis, IT, tax planning and decision making.

HILL DAY
Wayside House, Bedford Road, Ravensden, Bedford MK44 2RA

HW
136-140 Bedford Road, Kempston, Bedford, MK42 8BH
Tel: 01234 841842
Email: bedford@hwca.com
Resident Partners/Directors: ICAEW Members
R Hammond, A S Minifie
Resident Partners (Non-ICAEW Members):
E Di-Lorenzo

Registered by the ICAEW to carry out company audit work

Regulated by the ICAEW for a range of investment business activities

General Description: A general practice providing accounting services, payroll and tax advice to owner managed businesses.

HW PRESCOTT GENDY ASLAM LTD
42 High Street, Flitwick, Bedford, MK45 1DU
Tel: 01525 717424
Resident Partners/Directors: ICAEW Members
G J Goss, R Hammond, A S Minifie

IAN S DUNCAN LTD
68 Brecon Way, Bedford, MK41 8DE
Tel: 01234 351160
Resident Partners/Directors: ICAEW Members
I S Duncan

JANET TURLEY FCA
7 Lucas Court, Biddenham, Bedford, MK40 4RN

JENNINGS & CO
Room G12, Bedford i-lab, Priory Business Park, Stannard Way, Bedford MK44 3RZ

JOHN DAUNCEY FCA
New Farm, Colesden, Bedford, MK44 3DB

JOHN WILDMAN
15 Grove Place, Bedford, MK40 3JJ
Tel: 01234 358800
Fax: 01234 358830
Website: http://www.jwaccounts.com
Principal: ICAEW Member
J D Wildman

JONATHAN VOWLES
114 High Street, Cranfield, Bedford, MK43 0DG
Tel: 01234 752566
Principal: ICAEW Member
J C Vowles

KEENS SHAY KEENS LTD ◈
2nd Floor, Exchange Building, 16 St Cuthberts Street, Bedford MK40 3JG
Tel: 01234 301000
Fax: 01234 301001
Email: bedford@ksk.co.uk
Website: http://www.ksk.co.uk
Resident Partners/Directors: ICAEW Members
C W Little

Registered by the ICAEW to carry out company audit work

Regulated by the ICAEW for a range of investment business activities

SPECIALISATIONS – FINANCIAL REPORTING

Foreign Subsidiary Companies

SPECIALISATIONS – SECTOR

Barristers

LIBERTY FINANCIAL SOLUTIONS GROUP LTD
Cranfield Innovation Centre, University Way, Cranfield Technology Park, Cranfield, Bedford MK43 0BT

MACINTYRE HUDSON LLP ◈
Equipoise House, Grove Place, Bedford, MK40 3LE
Tel: 01234 268761
Website: http://www.macintyrehudson.co.uk
Resident Partners/Directors: ICAEW Members
M J Darvell, B N Richens, R W Trunchion
Resident Partners (Non-ICAEW Members):
M Grech-Marguerat, A Kariya

Regulated by the ICAEW for a range of investment business activities

MARTIN TELFER
5 Brookfields, Pavenham, Bedford, MK43 7QA

MAZARS CORPORATE FINANCE LTD ◈
19 Goldington Road, Bedford, MK40 3JY
Tel: 01234 402000

MAZARS LLP ◈
19 Goldington Road, Bedford, MK40 3JY
Tel: 01234 402000
Resident Partners/Directors: ICAEW Members
D C Birch, S N Monico
Registered by the ICAEW to carry out company audit work
Authorised and regulated by the Financial Services Authority for investment business

MD ACCOUNTING LTD
53 Irwin Road, Bedford, MK40 3UN

MILLER & CO
17 Grove Place, Bedford, MK40 3JJ
Tel: 01234 364181
Principal: ICAEW Member
L D Miller

MORGAN-JONES & CO
Wychwood Cottage, 38 High Street, Riseley, Bedford MK44 1DX

MORRISONS
7 Grove Place, Bedford, MK40 3JJ
Tel: 01234 218833
Principal: ICAEW Member
K S Morrison

MORRISONS BUSINESS ADVISERS ★
7 Grove Place, Bedford, MK40 3JJ
Tel: 01234 218832
Resident Partners/Directors: ICAEW Members
K S Morrison

N H ACCOUNTANTS LTD
6 Bedford Road, Barton-le-Clay, Bedford, MK45 4JU

NEIL CLARK ◈
394 Goldington Road, Bedford, MK41 9NT

PA GREGORY FCA
150B Clophill Road, Maulden, Bedford, MK45 2AE

PENTAGON FINANCIAL LTD
Priory Business Park, Bedford, MK44 3WH

PETER J. MONAHAN & CO
26 Grove Place, Bedford, MK40 3JJ
Tel: 01234 352668
Principal: ICAEW Member
P J Monahan

PETER L HOOD
20 Neville Crescent, Bromham, Bedford, MK43 8JE

R THOMPSON & CO LTD
Sterling Offices, 30a Mill Street, Bedford, MK40 3HD

RAWLINSON PRYDE LTD
Argent House, 5 Goldington Road, Bedford, MK40 3JY
Tel: 01234 300500
Resident Partners/Directors: ICAEW Members
G Pryde, D J Rawlinson

RAWLINSON PRYDE & PARTNERS ★
Argent House, 5 Goldington Road, Bedford, MK40 3JY

RODNEY B TAYLOR
119 Norman Road, Barton-le-Clay, Bedford, MK45 4QG

THOMPSON & CO
30A Mill Street, Bedford, MK40 3HD

THOMPSONS
1 Grove Place, Bedford, MK40 3JJ

THOMPSONS ACCOUNTANTS AND ADVISORS LTD
1 Grove Place, Bedford, MK40 3JJ

WHITTAKER & COMPANY LTD
13 Doolittle Mill, Froghall Road, Ampthill, Bedford MK45 2ND

WHITTAKER FINANCIALS
13 Doolittle Mill, Froghall Road, Ampthill, Bedford MK45 2ND

WMW CONSULTANTS
The Granary, Warren Farm, Warren Lane, Clophill, Bedford MK45 4AS

WMW CONSULTANTS
27 St Cuthberts Street, Bedford, MK40 3JG

WRIGHT CONNECTIONS LTD
Bedford Business Centre, 61-63 St Peters Street, Bedford, MK40 2PR

BEDWORTH

BISHOP SIMMONS
Mitre House, School Road, Bulkington, Bedworth CV12 9JB

BISHOP SIMMONS LTD
Mitre House, School Road, Bulkington, Bedworth CV12 9JB

LEONARD WILSON & CO
Colinton House, Leicester Road, Bedworth, CV12 8AB

BELPER

DAVID WALKER
6 The Pastures, Duffield, Belper, DE56 4EX

HUNTER JONES ALTON
36 Bridge Street, Belper, DE56 1AX
Tel: 01773 825661
Resident Partners/Directors: ICAEW Members
A G R Alton, F E C Alton

JOHN AYRE LTD
29a Shaw Lane, Holbrook, Belper, DE56 0TG

K.W. SEEDS
3 Leche Croft, Belper, DE56 0DD
Tel: 01773 829940
Principal: ICAEW Member
K W Seeds

NICHOLSON BLYTHE
36 Market Place, Belper, DE56 1FZ

WILLIS COOPER
Upper Floor, Old Mill House, Bridgefoot, Belper DE56 2UA

WILLIS COOPER LTD
Upper Floor, Old Mill House, East Mill, Belper DE56 2UA

BELVEDERE

HLM LLP
108 Parsonage Manorway, Belvedere, DA17 6LY

BENFLEET

BROOMS
Broom House, 39-43 London Road, Hadleigh, Benfleet SS7 2QL

BROOMS PROFESSIONAL SERVICES LTD
Broom House, 39-43 London Road, Hadleigh, Benfleet SS7 2QL

DANIEL A NICE BA ACA
56 Hall Farm Road, Benfleet, SS7 5JS

DAVID NORTHFIELD
412 Daws Heath Road, Benfleet, SS7 2UD

K.V. LADEN
7 St Marys Road, Benfleet, SS7 1NR
Tel: 01268 751513
Principal: ICAEW Member
K V Laden

KEITH COLLINS
7 Sidwell Park, Benfleet, SS7 1LQ
Tel: 01268 794299
Principal: ICAEW Member
N K Collins

MASONS
4 Hadleigh Business Centre, 351 London Road, Hadleigh, Benfleet SS7 2BT

MASONS AUDIT LTD ◈
4 Hadleigh Business Centre, 351 London Road, Hadleigh, Benfleet SS7 2BT
Tel: 01702 426770
Fax: 01702 556386
Email: admin@masons.u-net.com

TAYLORS ◈
203 London Road, Hadleigh, Benfleet, SS7 2RD
Tel: 01702 552008
Principal: ICAEW Member
C R N Taylor

THOMAS EDWARD DIXON & CO ◈
376 London Road, Hadleigh, Benfleet, SS7 2DA
Tel: 01702 552929
Resident Partners/Directors: ICAEW Members
I D Francis, R J Wells

BERKHAMSTED

ALL ABOUT BUSINESS LTD
Audley House, North Bridge Road, Berkhamsted, HP4 1EH

ALL ABOUT NUMBERS LTD
Audley House, North Bridge Road, Berkhamsted, HP4 1EH

BRYAN L WALLS
14a Coram Close, Berkhamsted, HP4 2JG
Tel: 07714 484842
Principal: ICAEW Member
B L Walls

CHARLES A ROBERTS
41 Broadwater, Lower Kings Road, Berkhamsted, HP4 2AH
Tel: 01442 872205
Fax: 01442 872205
Email: charles.a.roberts4@btopenworld.com
Principal: ICAEW Member
C A Roberts

CHRIS SWINSON
Roseheath Wood, Bullbeggars Lane, Berkhamsted, HP4 2RS

COLE & CO
15 Emperor Close, Berkhamsted, HP4 1TD

COLIN GRAY & CO
26 Lower Kings Road, Berkhamsted, HP4 2AB

COLIN GRAY & CO
26 Lower Kings Road, Berkhamsted, HP4 2AB

COLIN GRAY & CO LTD
26 Lower Kings Road, Berkhamsted, HP4 2AB

D.T. RODGERS
3 Ruscote, Cross Oak Road, Berkhamsted, HP4 3NA
Tel: 01442 864793
Fax: 01442 879910
Email: derrick.rodgers@btconnect.com

Principal: ICAEW Member
D T Rodgers
Regulated by the ICAEW for a range of investment business activities

F.W.P. LEA & CO
129 High Street, Berkhamsted, HP4 2DJ
Tel: 01442 870358
Email: plea@fwplea.co.uk
Principal: ICAEW Member
F W P Lea

GANT MASSINGALE
Fairlight, Meadway, Berkhamsted, HP4 2PN
Tel: 01442 873619
Resident Partners/Directors: ICAEW Members
J F Gant, M Massingale

GRIFFITHS PRESTON
Aldbury House, Dower Mews, 108 High Street, Berkhamsted HP4 2BL
Tel: 01442 870277
Email: clive@g-paccounts.co.uk
Principal: ICAEW Member
A C J Preston

HARRIS & CO ◈
Audley House, North Bridge Road, Berkhamsted, HP4 1EH
Tel: 01442 872878

HARTS
3 Churchgates, The Wilderness, Berkhamsted, HP4 2UB
Tel: 01442 874038
Email: office@harts.co.uk
Website: http://www.harts.co.uk
Date Established: 1987
Principal: ICAEW Member
J M Hart

SPECIALISATIONS – AUDIT & ASSURANCE
Audit — Private Company

SPECIALISATIONS – FINANCIAL REPORTING
Limited Companies

SPECIALISATIONS – TAXATION
Partnerships and Sole Traders
Payroll Service and Advice
Personal
Self Assessment Advice
Small Traders
UK Subsidiaries of Overseas Multinationals
See display advertisement near this entry.

JOHN COSSINS & CO ◈
Mulberry House, 11 Oxfield Close, Berkhamsted, HP4 3NE
Tel: 01442 863231
Principal: ICAEW Member
J C Cossins

PETER HARRIS & CO
Audley House, Northbridge Road, Berkhamsted, HP4 1EH

PETER HARRIS & CO
Audley House, Northbridge Road, Berkhamsted, HP4 1EH

ROBINSON
21 Holly Drive, Berkhamsted, HP4 2JR

STEWARTS ACCOUNTANTS LTD
271 High Street, Berkhamsted, HP4 1AA

BERWICK-UPON-TWEED

GREAVES WEST & AYRE ▽
1-3 Sandgate, Berwick-upon-tweed, TD15 1EW
Tel: 01289 306688
Email: reception@gwayre.co.uk
Website: http://www.greaveswestayre.co.uk
Resident Partners/Directors: ICAEW Members
A N Ayre, P B Ayre, R H Dalgleish, A J Patterson
Resident Partners (Non-ICAEW Members):
J H Coats, S W Allister, C Frame, S A F Faed, C G Little
Registered by the ICAEW to carry out company audit work
Authorised and regulated by the Financial Services Authority for investment business

J.H. GREENWOOD & CO
Ava Lodge, Castle Terrace, Berwick-upon-tweed, TD15 1NP
Tel: 01289 302463
Principal: ICAEW Member
J H Greenwood

JAMES H. GREENWOOD & CO LTD
Ava Lodge, Castle Terrace, Berwick-upon-tweed, TD15 1NP
Tel: 01289 302463
Resident Partners/Directors: ICAEW Members
J H Greenwood

LAURENCE J. PEARSON
5 Tweed Street, Berwick-upon-tweed, TD15 1NG

SIMON BEVAN
Cheviot View, Holy Island, Berwick-upon-tweed, TD15 2SQ
Tel: 01289 389317
Principal: ICAEW Member
S J P Bevan

BETCHWORTH

BRAIDWOOD & CO
Willow Grange, The Street, Betchworth, RH3 7DJ
Tel: 01737 843034
Email: chrisbraidwood@aol.com
Principal: ICAEW Member
C E Braidwood

PHILIP HAYNES FCA
Briarsmead, Old Road, Buckland, Betchworth RH3 7DU

BEVERLEY

AIC ACCOUNTANCY
97 Normandy Avenue, Beverley, HU17 8PR

CBA FINANCIAL SERVICES LTD
72 Lairgate, Beverley, HU17 8EU

THE CBA PARTNERSHIP ◈
72 Lairgate, Beverley, HU17 8EU

CHRISTOPHER J. SNAITH ◈
Tarn House, 55 The Meadows, Leven, Beverley HU17 5LX
Tel: 01964 542095
Principal: ICAEW Member
C J Snaith

JACKSON ROBSON LICENCE LTD ◈
49a Saturday Market Place, Beverley, HU17 8AA
Tel: 01482 870055

JANET COISH
2 Paradise Square, Beverley, HU17 0HG
Tel: 01482 888534
Principal: ICAEW Member
J A Coish

RICHARD L HUDSON FCA
The Elms, 29 North Bar Without, Beverley, HU17 7AG
Tel: 01482 881408
Principal: ICAEW Member
R L Hudson

ROBSON & CO LTD ◈
Sigma House, Beverley Business Park, Oldbeck Road, Beverley HU17 0JS
Tel: 01482 889400
Resident Partners/Directors: ICAEW Members
I P Robson, S J Smale, R G Worthington

ROBSONS ◈
Sigma House, Beverley Business Park, Oldbeck Road, Beverley HU17 0JS
Tel: 01482 889400
See display advertisement near this entry.

SOWERBY FRS
Beckside Court, Annie Reed Road, Beverley, HU17 0LF

SOWERBY FRS LLP ◈
Beckside Court, Annie Reed Road, Beverley, HU17 0LF
Tel: 01482 888820
Resident Partners/Directors: ICAEW Members
A M Allen, J C Hackney

BEWDLEY

ANDREW WATSON CONSULTING LTD
Lane Cottage, Pound Green, Arley, Bewdley DY12 3LF
Tel: 01299 404911
Resident Partners/Directors: ICAEW Members
A Watson

DHJH
Springhill House, 94-98 Kidderminster Road, Bewdley, DY12 1DQ

DHJH LTD ◈
Springhill House, 94-98 Kidderminster Road, Bewdley, DY12 1DQ
Tel: 01299 403503
Resident Partners/Directors: ICAEW Members
N C Danks, P T Johnston

BEXHILL-ON-SEA

ASHDOWN HURREY LLP ◈
28 Wilton Road, Bexhill-On-Sea, TN40 1EZ
Tel: 01424 730300
Resident Partners/Directors: ICAEW Members
P A Bradbury

GIBBONS MANNINGTON
20-22 Eversley Road, Bexhill-On-Sea, TN40 1HE

HONEY BARRETT LTD
48 St Leonards Road, Bexhill-On-Sea, TN40 1JB
Tel: 01424 730345
Resident Partners/Directors: ICAEW Members
G W Coleman, E H Densley
Registered by the ICAEW to carry out company audit work
Regulated by the ICAEW for a range of investment business activities
SPECIALISATIONS – SECTOR

Doctors

IMG
The Studio, Worsham Farmhouse, Worsham Lane, Bexhill-On-Sea TN40 2QP
Tel: 0845 200 9856
Principal: ICAEW Member
I R Goad

KEVAN DUNN
18 Clavering Walk, Bexhill-on-sea, TN39 4TN

MCPHERSON & PARTNERS
23 St Leonards Road, Bexhill-On-Sea, TN40 1HH
Tel: 01424 730000

MCPHERSON & PARTNERS LLP ◈
23 St Leonards Road, Bexhill-On-Sea, TN40 1HH
Tel: 01424 730000
Email: bexhill@mcphersons.co.uk
Website: http://www.mcphersons.co.uk
Resident Partners/Directors: ICAEW Members
A Buontempo, M Finch, A Gill, K McPherson

ROBERT K. BENDELL
10 Holmesdale Road, Bexhill-on-sea, TN39 3QE
Tel: 01424 225245
Principal: ICAEW Member
R K Bendell

BEXLEY

A.N.J. SULLIVAN
10 Dukes Orchard, Bexley, DA5 2DU

APC INTERIM SOLUTIONS LTD
30 Parkhurst Road, Bexley, DA5 1AR

C. MITCHELL & CO
Deremar, 33 Faesten Way, Bexley, DA5 2JB

CHAPPELL COLE & CO
Heritage House, 34 North Cray Road, Bexley, DA5 3LZ

CHAPPELL COLE & CO LTD
Heritage House, 34 North Cray Road, Bexley, DA5 3LZ

CONRAD RUFFONI
Suite 14, Kent House, Old Bexley Business Park, 19 Bourne Road, Bexley DA5 1LR
Tel: 01322 310610
Principal: ICAEW Member
P C Ruffoni

DHILLONS
139 Blendon Road, Bexley, DA5 1BT
Tel: 020 8301 5400
Fax: 0870 056 9045
Email: office@dhillons.org
Website: http://www.dhillons.org
Principal: ICAEW Member
A A Dhillon

KISHENS
3 Montpelier Avenue, Bexley, DA5 3AP

KISHENS LTD
3 Montpelier Avenue, Bexley, DA5 3AP

LEVETT, CHARLES & CO
Abacus House, 70-72 High Street, Bexley, DA5 1AJ
Tel: 01322 528185
Principal: ICAEW Member
T C Clark
Registered by the ICAEW to carry out company audit work
Regulated by the ICAEW for a range of investment business activities

MORRIS & ASSOCIATES
38 Steynton Ave, Bexley, DA5 3HG
Tel: 020 8302 7614

ONLINE FINANCIAL & ACCOUNTANCY LTD
71 Bexley High Street, Bexley, DA5 1AA

THE SMALL ACCOUNTS CO
3 Nutmead Close, Bexley, DA5 2DT

THE SMALL ACCOUNTS COMPANY LTD
3 Nutmead Close, Bexley, DA5 2DT

BEXLEYHEATH

ADAMS ACCOUNTANCY SERVICES LTD
24 Inglewood Road, Barnehurst, Bexleyheath, DA7 6JS

MRS SARAH KEEBLE BA(HONS) ACA CTA
51 Pembury Road, Bexleyheath, DA7 5LN

PERRYS
273 Broadway, Bexleyheath, DA6 8DG

RICHARD KEMP & CO
33a Crook Log, Bexleyheath, DA6 8EB

BICESTER

A S HOWES & CO LTD
Unit 3a, Minton Place, Victoria Road, Bicester OX26 6QB

BAXTER PAYNE & HAIGH ★
Claremont House, Deans Court, Bicester, OX26 6BW
Tel: 01869 252151
Resident Partners/Directors: ICAEW Members
S P Baxter, P J Parmar, S V Payne

BEADMAN & CO
Maple Lodge, Paines Hill, Steeple Aston, Bicester OX25 4SQ
Tel: 01869 347650
Principal: ICAEW Member
P M F Beadman

C.J. LEECH & CO
88 Sheep Street, Bicester, OX26 6LP
Tel: 01869 244414
Principal: ICAEW Member
C J Leech

CLARK HOWES AUDITING SOLUTIONS LTD
2 Minton Place, Victoria Road, Bicester, OX26 6QB

DAVID WILKINS
25a Market Square, Bicester, OX26 6AD
Tel: 01869 241782
Principal: ICAEW Member
D E Wilkins

MIKE BLACK
9 Crockwell Close, Bicester, OX26 2HG
Tel: 01869 325757
Principal: ICAEW Member
M A Black

PAYNE & PAYNE LTD
14 Kennedy Road, Bicester, OX26 2BG

DAVID PEAKE LTD
11 Siskin Road, Bicester, OX26 6UD

TITCHENERS LTD
Deans Court, 1-3 London Road, Bicester, OX26 6BU
Tel: 01869 242595
Resident Partners/Directors: ICAEW Members
N T Oakey
See display advertisement near this entry.

VINE & CO
Beyond The Pond, 1 Bicester Road, Marsh Gibbon, Bicester OX27 0EU
Tel: 01869 278800
Principal: ICAEW Member
G Vine

BIDEFORD

DAVISONS LTD
41-42 High Street, Bideford, EX39 3AA

GLOVER STANBURY & CO ◈
27 Bridgeland Street, Bideford, EX39 2PZ
Tel: 01237 471881
Email: info@gloverstanbury.co.uk
Website: http://www.gloverstanbury.co.uk
Resident Partners/Directors: ICAEW Members
M J Chance

MARTIN J. FISHLEIGH
Mount Cottage, Mount Pleasant, Westleigh, Bideford EX39 4LJ

MAYNARD JOHNS
12 Chingswell Street, Bideford, EX39 2NF
Tel: 01237 472071

R T MARKE & CO LTD
69 High Street, Bideford, EX39 2AT

SULLY & CO ◈
Sully House, 7 Clovelly Road Industrial Estate, Bideford, EX39 3HN
Tel: 01237 471736
Fax: 01237 476440
Email: post@sullyandco.co.uk
Website: http://www.sullyandco.co.uk
Principal: ICAEW Member
J B Edwards

THOMAS WESTCOTT ★
64 High Street, Bideford, EX39 2AN
Tel: 01237 472725
Resident Partners/Directors: ICAEW Members
K J Berry, J S Poyner

BIGGLESWADE

UHY GEORGE HAY ◈
Brigham House, High Street, Biggleswade, SG18 0LD
Tel: 01767 315010
Email: biggleswade@georgehay.co.uk
Website: http://www.georgehay.co.uk
Resident Partners/Directors: ICAEW Members
J L Horsley
Resident Partners (Non-ICAEW Members):
C E Fuller, A P Newman
Registered by the ICAEW to carry out company audit work

KEENS SHAY KEENS LTD ◈
Victoria House, 42-44 Shortmead Street, Biggleswade, SG18 0AP
Tel: 01767 221000
Email: bwade@ksk.co.uk
Website: http://www.ksk.co.uk
Resident Partners/Directors: ICAEW Members
W R Kingston

MARTIN FOSTER & CO LTD
Unit 3, Manor Farm, Lower Caldecote, Biggleswade SG18 9BB
Tel: 01767 601103
Resident Partners/Directors: ICAEW Members
M Foster

SMYTH & CO
4 High Street, Langford, Biggleswade, SG18 9RR
Tel: 01767 220214

BILLERICAY

AIMS - CHRISTOPHER VAN VEEN
420 Outwood Common Road, Billericay, CM11 1ET
Tel: 01277 624100
Fax: 01277 624100
Email: chrisv@aims.co.uk
Website: http://www.aims.co.uk
Principal: ICAEW Member
C W Van Veen

B. FLEETWOOD
62 Chapel Street, Billericay, CM12 9LS
Tel: 01277 652444
Principal: ICAEW Member
B Fleetwood

D & L ACCOUNTANCY SERVICES
11 Burleigh Close, Billericay, CM12 0YG

FIRST CALL ACCOUNTING
50 Church Road, Ramsden Heath, Billericay, CM11 1PA

KEITH WRIGHT FCA
5 Stock Road, Billericay, CM12 0AD

MONK & CO
114 Stock Road, Billericay, CM12 0RT
Tel: 01277 655563
Principal: ICAEW Member
K Monk

THE MUDD PARTNERSHIP
Lakeview House, 4 Woodbrook Crescent, Billericay, CM12 0EQ
Tel: 01277 630999
Resident Partners/Directors: ICAEW Members
P Alexandrou, C M Jones, G T McGhie, J A Stanley, C Walby

BILLINGHAM

AIMS - SIMON GOLDSTRONG ACA
55 Heaton Road, Grange Park, Billingham, TS23 3GP

JONES HARPER ★
25 Roseberry Road, Billingham, TS23 2SD

BILLINGSHURST

C J D STOKES
29 Carpenters, Billingshurst, RH14 9RA

HILTON SHARP & CLARKE
Atlantic House, Jengers Mead, Billingshurst, RH14 9PB
Tel: 01403 786788

R E GREATOREX FCA
Beeches Brook, Wisborough Green, Billingshurst, RH14 0HP
Tel: 01403 700796
Principal: ICAEW Member
R E Greatorex

TIM FOX
Pawlies Farm, Loxwood, Billingshurst, RH14 0QN

BILSTON

D. YARSLEY
Office 5, Wellington House, Bean Road, Bilston WV14 9EE
Tel: 01902 675444
Principal: ICAEW Member
D Yarsley

HARRIS & CO ◈
Rooms 1-8, First Floor Offices, 1-6 Mount Pleasant, Bilston WV14 7LJ

LANCASTER CLEMENTS LTD
Stanley House, 27 Wellington Road, Bilston, WV14 6AH

BINGLEY

CHRISTOPHER MASLEN
Old Tan House, Cottingley Bridge, Bingley, BD16 1NB
Tel: 01274 569962
Principal: ICAEW Member
C J Maslen

CLARKE DOWZALL & BALDING
6 Old Main Street, Bingley, BD16 2RH
Tel: 01535 275722
Fax: 01274 562491
Email: info@cdbaccountants.co.uk
Website: http://www.cdbaccountants.co.uk
Principal: ICAEW Member
C L Balding
Registered by the ICAEW to carry out company audit work

LONG & CO
PO Box 109, Bingley, BD16 1ZQ
Tel: 01535 275346
Principal: ICAEW Member
J B Whitaker

MUGGLESTON & CO
50 Southway, Eldwick, Bingley, BD16 3DT

PARAGON FINANCIAL MANAGEMENT LTD ◈
11 Ferrands Close, Harden, Bingley, BD16 1JA

W. CRAWFORD
38 Oak Avenue, Bingley, BD16 1ES

W.J.WHITLEY & CO
Skipton Chambers, Chapel Lane, Bingley, BD16 2NG

WILKINSON AND PARTNERS ★
Victoria Mews, 19 Mill Field Road, Cottingley Business Park, Cottingley, Bingley BD16 1PY
Tel: 01274 518200
Resident Partners/Directors: ICAEW Members
P Raistrick, D Wilkinson

BIRCHINGTON

HILARY ADAMS LTD
30 The Square, Birchington, CT7 9AB
Tel: 01843 845141
Email: hilary@hilaryadams.co.uk
Website: http://www.hilaryadams.co.uk
Other Offices:158 High Street, Herme Bay, Unit 5, Anthony's Way, Medway City Estate, Rochester

RICHARD FLOYD & CO
38 Station Road, Birchington, CT7 9DQ
Tel: 020 8858 9157

SPURLING CANNON LTD
194 Canterbury Road, Birchington, CT7 9AQ

BIRKENHEAD

ALAN GLAZIER & CO ◈
36 Upton Road, Claughton, Birkenhead, CH41 0DF
Tel: 0151 653 6007
Principal: ICAEW Member
A Glazier

BLEASE, LLOYD & CO
Hamilton House, 56 Hamilton Street, Birkenhead, CH41 5HZ
Tel: 0151 647 9581
Fax: 0151 666 2163
Email: admin@bleaselloyd.co.uk
Resident Partners/Directors: ICAEW Members
P B Bowler, J C Hughes
Registered by the ICAEW to carry out company audit work
Regulated by the ICAEW for a range of investment business activities
General Description: A full range of accountancy, audit and taxation services provided on a personal basis.

DENISONS
116 Chester Street, Birkenhead, CH41 5DL

LERMAN QUAILE
56 Hamilton Square, Birkenhead, CH41 5AS

MCLINTOCKS LTD
56 Hamilton Street, Birkenhead, CH41 5HZ

MCLINTOCKS BLEASE LLOYD
Hamilton House, 56 Hamilton Street, Birkenhead, CH41 5HZ

P.M. DODD & CO
58 Osmaston Road, Prenton, Birkenhead, CH42 8LL

PRIORY PRACTICE LTD
1 Abbots Quay, Monks Ferry, Birkenhead, CH41 5LH

ROBERT S. BOYS & CO
28-30 Grange Road West, Birkenhead, CH41 4DA

BIRMINGHAM

A.C. LUCKMAN & CO
5 Hollybank Road, Birmingham, B13 0RF

A.K. HAWKINS & CO
Lehing Farm, Headley Heath Lane, Headley Heath, Birmingham B38 0DH

A.K. PATEL & CO ◈
1 Coton Lane, Erdington, Birmingham, B23 6TP
Tel: 0121 373 7370
Principal: ICAEW Member
U A Patel
Registered by the ICAEW to carry out company audit work
Regulated by the ICAEW for a range of investment business activities
SPECIALISATIONS – AUDIT & ASSURANCE
Audit — Private Company
SPECIALISATIONS – BUSINESS & GENERAL ADVICE
Book-keeping
SPECIALISATIONS – FINANCIAL REPORTING
Accounts Preparation
Audit Exemption Report
Limited Companies
Limited Company Accounts
Partnership/Sole Trader Accounts
SPECIALISATIONS – SECTOR
Dentists/Opticians
Doctors
SPECIALISATIONS – TAXATION
Capital Gains — Limited Companies
Capital Gains — Personal
Partnerships and Sole Traders
Payroll Service and Advice
Personal
Self Assessment Advice
Small Traders
Taxation
Value Added Tax

A L GOLDMAN
8 Malmesbury Park, 263 Harborne Road, Edgbaston, Birmingham B15 3JA

ABBEY MOUNT ACCOUNTANCY SERVICES
44 High House Drive, Lickey, Birmingham, B45 8ET

ABERCROMBIE & CO
1325A Stratford Road, Hall Green, Birmingham, B28 9HL

AD PATEL & CO LTD ◈
3 Cromer Road, Birmingham, B12 9QP
Tel: 0121 440 0441
Resident Partners/Directors: ICAEW Members
A D Patel

ADVANCE CORPORATE SERVICES ◈
Concorde House, Trinity Park, Solihull, Birmingham B37 7UQ
Tel: 0121 635 5090
Principal: ICAEW Member
I R Thornton

ADVANTIS SERVICES LTD
Somerville House, 20-22 Harborne Road, Edgbaston, Birmingham B15 3AA

AIMS ACCOUNTANTS FOR BUSINESS
10 Denise Drive, Harborne, Birmingham, B17 0BN

AIMS HELEN PALMER
22 Croftdown Road, Birmingham, B17 8RB

AKA
803 Stratford Road, Springfield, Birmingham, B11 4DA

AKBER & CO
451 Moseley Road, Birmingham, B12 9BX
Tel: 0121 440 7862
Fax: 0121 440 7863
Email: akberalifazel@aol.com
Principal: ICAEW Member
A F Somji
Registered by the ICAEW to carry out company audit work
See display advertisement near this entry.

ALHAMBRA ACCOUNTING LTD
Crown House, 28 George Street, Balsall Heath, Birmingham B12 9RG

ANDERSONS KBS LTD
The Old Guild House, 1 New Market Street, Birmingham, B3 2NH

ANDREW YULE & CO
1564 Pershore Road, Stirchley, Birmingham, B30 2NL

ANIL K. BHAGI
91 Soho Hill, Hockley, Birmingham, B19 1AY

ANTHONY G. FINE
9 The Regents, Norfolk Road, Birmingham, B15 3PP

ANTHONY TAYLOR & CO
25 Lordswood Road, Harborne, Birmingham, B17 9RP
Tel: 0121 428 2717
Principal: ICAEW Member
A C Taylor

ARK ASSOCIATES
50 Newhall Street, Birmingham, B3 3QE
Tel: 0121 248 8448

ARK ASSOCIATES LTD
50 Newhall Street, Birmingham, B3 3QE

ASSERTA
25 Pear Tree Drive, Great Barr, Birmingham, B43 6HR

AVICENNA CONSULTING
535 Coventry Road, Small Heath, Birmingham, B10 0LL

AVICENNA CONSULTING LTD
535 Coventry Road, Small Heath, Birmingham, B10 0LL

B.A. RUDGE & CO
Bordesley Hall, The Holloway, Alvechurch, Birmingham B48 7QB
Tel: 01527 597400
Principal: ICAEW Member
P A Rudge

B.N. PATTNI
75 The Parklands, Erdington, Birmingham, B23 6LA
Tel: 0121 350 3676
Principal: ICAEW Member
B N Pattni

BAKER TILLY
St Philips Point, Temple Row, Birmingham, B2 5AF
Tel: 0121 214 3100
Resident Partners/Directors: ICAEW Members
S J Chapman, C R Fray, M A Huggins, P R Johnson, N H Weston

BAKER TILLY
St Philips Point, Temple Row, Birmingham, B2 5AF
Tel: 0121 214 3100
Resident Partners/Directors: ICAEW Members
J C Bleach, W S Devitt, C R Fray, M A Huggins, G K Moreton
Resident Partners (Non-ICAEW Members):
G S Grewal, S A Hart, P A Oxtoby

BAKER TILLY
St Philips Point, Temple Row, Birmingham, B2 5AF

BAKER TILLY RESTRUCTURING AND RECOVERY LLP
St Philips Point, Temple Row, Birmingham, B2 5AF
Tel: 0121 214 3100
Resident Partners/Directors: ICAEW Members
P H Allen, G E B Mander
Resident Partners (Non-ICAEW Members):
L R Bailey

BAKER TILLY TAX AND ADVISORY SERVICES LLP
St Philips Point, Temple Row, Birmingham, B2 5AF
Tel: 0121 214 3100
Resident Partners/Directors: ICAEW Members
J C Bleach, S J Chapman, J J W Conlan, W S Devitt, C R Fray, D Green, M A Huggins, P R Johnson, G E B Mander, G K Moreton, N H Weston
Resident Partners (Non-ICAEW Members):
L R Bailey, G S Grewal, S A Hart, S T Hodgetts, W A Longe, P A Oxtoby, M Taylor

BARNETT RAVENSCROFT LLP
13 Portland Road, Edgbaston, Birmingham, B16 9HN
Tel: 0121 454 7241
Resident Partners/Directors: ICAEW Members
P A Barnett, R H D Gold

BARRON & CO
175 Cole Valley Road, Hall Green, Birmingham, B28 0DG
Tel: 0121 325 6921
Principal: ICAEW Member
J D Barron

BAYLISS & CO
25 Lordswood Road, Harborne, Birmingham, B17 9RP

BDO STOY HAYWARD LLP
125 Colmore Row, Birmingham, B3 3SD
Tel: 0121 352 6200
Fax: 0121 352 6222
Resident Partners/Directors: ICAEW Members
M A Anslow, I J Curtis, K J Ellis, G S Elsworth, A Lee Jones, A L Jones, T W Lawton, T A Macintosh, S S Plaha, C K Rayment, D G Rogers, R Rose, J A Stephan, R P Turton, S B Ward, D R Wells, G A Whittaker
Resident Partners (Non-ICAEW Members):
N R Buckley, M K Jones, M J Palmer, D T Pooler, S Hopper

BEGBIES TRAYNOR LTD
Newater House, 11 Newhall Street, Birmingham, B3 3NY
Tel: 0121 200 8150
Website: http://www.begbies-traynor.com
Resident Partners/Directors: ICAEW Members
W J Kelly, I J Lownes

SPECIALISATIONS – BUSINESS & GENERAL ADVICE
Acquisitions and Mergers
Disposal of Businesses

SPECIALISATIONS – BUSINESS RECOVERY & INSOLVENCY
Bankruptcies
Corporate Recovery
Liquidations

BJ ◈
Charterhouse, Legge Street, Birmingham, B4 7EU
Tel: 0121 333 3100
Fax: 0121 359 1848
Email: alan.webb@rsmbentleyjennison.com
Website: http://www.rsmbentleyjennison.com
Resident Partners/Directors: ICAEW Members
J M C Bowes, M J T Crooks, J F Hodgson, J A Jennison, K L Malyn, R C Meek, S A Newman, A D Pym, A P Warrilow, A J Webb, P Whitehead
Registered by the ICAEW to carry out company audit work

BLOOMER HEAVEN ◈
33 Lionel Street, Birmingham, B3 1AB

BLOOMER HEAVEN LTD ◈
33 Lionel Street, Birmingham, B3 1AB
Tel: 0121 236 0465
Resident Partners/Directors: ICAEW Members
P B Jones, S E Law, C M Stephen-Haynes
Resident Partners (Non-ICAEW Members):
J Boyce, C S Barlow
Registered by the ICAEW to carry out company audit work

BLOOMER HEAVEN PAYROLL
33 Lionel Street, Birmingham, B3 1AB

BRESLINS ◈
Albion Court, 18-20 Frederick Street, Birmingham, B1 3HE

BRESLINS BIRMINGHAM LTD
Albion Court, 18-20 Frederick Street, Birmingham, B1 3HE

BRIAN MOGFORD & CO
Crossways House, 1199 Stratford Road, Hall Green, Birmingham B28 8BU

BRIANTS
111 Hagley Road, Birmingham, B16 8LB

BRINDLEYS
2 Wheeleys Road, Edgbaston, Birmingham, B15 2LD

BRINDLEYS LTD
2 Wheeleys Road, Edgbaston, Birmingham, B15 2LD

CAIRNS BAILEY & CO ★ ◈
3 Beacon Court, Birmingham Road, Great Barr, Birmingham B43 6NN
Tel: 0121 358 2286
Fax: 0121 358 8140
Email: enquiries@cairnsbailey.co.uk
Resident Partners/Directors: ICAEW Members
J C Cairns, M A Cairns
Resident Partners (Non-ICAEW Members):
I A Bailey
Registered by the ICAEW to carry out company audit work
SPECIALISATIONS – SECTOR
Clubs/Associations

CATALYST CORPORATE FINANCE LLP
9th Floor, Bank House, 8 Cherry Street, Birmingham B2 5AC

CATTANEO LLP
1 Victoria Square, Birmingham, B1 1BD

CHADSWORTH LTD
Unit 3A, Wing Yip Centre, 278 Thimble Mill Lane, Nechells, Birmingham B7 5HD

CHARTS ◈
17-19 Church Road, Northfield, Birmingham, B31 2JZ
Tel: 0121 477 3533
Principal: ICAEW Member
M A Brown

CHEW
Second Floor, Cathay Building, 86 Holloway Head, Birmingham B1 1NB

CLARK & DEEN LLP ◈
Benson House, Suite D, 98-104 Lombard Street, Digbeth, Birmingham B12 0QR
Tel: 0845 310 3108
Resident Partners/Directors: ICAEW Members
P G Salisbury-Jones

CLEARLINE BUSINESS CONSULTANTS
552-554 Bristol Road, Selly Oak, Birmingham, B29 6BD

CLEARWATER CORPORATE FINANCE LLP
75-77 Colmore Row, Birmingham, B3 2AP

CLEMENT KEYS
39/40 Calthorpe Road, Edgbaston, Birmingham, B15 1TS
Tel: 0121 456 4456
Fax: 0121 456 4510
Email: client@clementkeys.co.uk
Website: http://www.clementkeys.co.uk
Date Established: 1885
Training Contracts Available.
Resident Partners/Directors: ICAEW Members
S Atkins, J R Bates, R A Cocker, P T Cook, S M Cutler, D A McNab, M T Meakin, R J Parsons, A T Robertson, G C Whitehouse, I S Yorke
Resident Partners (Non-ICAEW Members):
M S Sahota
Registered by the ICAEW to carry out company audit work
Regulated by the ICAEW for a range of investment business activities

INVESTOR IN PEOPLE

SPECIALISATIONS – BUSINESS & GENERAL ADVICE
Acquisitions and Mergers
Divorce/Matrimonial

SPECIALISATIONS – FORENSIC ACCOUNTING
Expert Witnesses in Litigation
Forensic Accounting

SPECIALISATIONS – SECTOR
Charities
Doctors
Entertainers
Media
Solicitors

SPECIALISATIONS – TAXATION
Estate and Inheritance
Investigations
Payroll Service and Advice
Taxation
Trusts
Value Added Tax

CLIVE SHEDD & CO ◈
232 Sladepool Farm Road, Highters Heath, Birmingham, B14 5EE

COLLINSON LONG LLP
55 Newhall Street, Birmingham, B3 3RB

COLLINSONS
55 Newhall Street, Birmingham, B3 3RB

D.E. PALFREYMAN
176 Leach Green Lane, Rednal, Birmingham, B45 8EH

D. SEELEY & CO
40 Bear Hill, Alvechurch, Birmingham, B48 7JX
Tel: 0121 445 2445
Principal: ICAEW Member
D W Seeley
Registered by the ICAEW to carry out company audit work

DAINS LLP
Unit 306, Third Floor, Fort Dunlop, Fort Parkway, Birmingham B24 9FD
Tel: 0845 555 8844
Fax: 0845 555 8811
Email: birmingham@dains.com
Website: http://www.dains.com
Date Established: 1926
Resident Partners/Directors: ICAEW Members
P D Bradshaw, A R Massey, A P Morris, S G Wright
Non-resident Partners (ICAEW Members):
N D Smith, M F P Smith, H M P Reynolds
Non-resident Partners (Non-ICAEW Members):
M Castree, N Hawksley, A McQuillan, R C McNeilly, S C Bursell
Other Offices: Burton, Lichfield, Rugeley, Swadlincote, Coleshill
Registered by the ICAEW to carry out company audit work
Regulated by the ICAEW for a range of investment business activities

DAINS LLP
138 High Street, Coleshill, Birmingham, B46 3BJ
Tel: 0845 555 8844
Fax: 01675 464994
Email: coleshill@dains.com
Website: http://www.dains.com
Date Established: 1926
Resident Partners/Directors: ICAEW Members
C J Windsor
Non-resident Partners (ICAEW Members):
N D Smith, S G Wright, M F P Smith, A R Massey, H M P Reynolds, P D Bradshaw, A Morris
Non-resident Partners (Non-ICAEW Members):
M Castree, N Hawksley, A McQuillan, R McNeilly, S C Bursell
Other Offices: Burton, Lichfield, Rugeley, Swadlincote, Birmingham
Registered by the ICAEW to carry out company audit work
Regulated by the ICAEW for a range of investment business activities

DAVID P. PEARSON
24 St Mary's Road, Harborne, Birmingham, B17 0HA
Tel: 0121 681 0151
Principal: ICAEW Member
D P Pearson

DAVIS & CO ◈
2 Plantagenet Buildings, 98 Spencer Street, Hockley, Birmingham B18 6DB
Tel: 0121 683 0232
Email: davischartac@hotmail.com
Principal: ICAEW Member
S M Chilton

DELOITTE & TOUCHE LLP ◈
Four Brindleyplace, Birmingham, B1 2HZ
Tel: 0121 632 6000
Website: http://www.deloitte.co.uk
Resident Partners/Directors: ICAEW Members
S G Austin, D N Boocock, H W Campion, T G M Downing, R D Edwards, P C Gallimore, S Griggs, D Hall, C W Hindle, A C Howl, N A Johnson, M W Jones, N G Jones, J A Lodge, A L Marks, C G Oswald, M D Perkins, A P Peters, P N Pickard, C D Robertson, A Smith, G M Thomas, N F Tratalos, G B Whitefoot, J Whitlock, D L Z Wong

DELTA ACCOUNTANCY SERVICES
57 Stotfold Road, Maypole, Birmingham, B14 5JD

DIXIE ASSOCIATES LTD
34 Swarthmore Road, Selly Oak, Birmingham, B29 4JS

DIXIE ASSOCIATES LTD
AIMS Accountants for Business, 34 Swarthmore Road, Selly Oak, Birmingham B29 4JS

DTE CORPORATE RECOVERY AND INSOLVENCY SERVICES LTD
85-89 Colmore Row, Birmingham, B3 2BB

ELIZABETH A. JOHNSON
5 Lee Road, Hollywood, Birmingham, B47 5NY
Tel: 01564 823792
Principal: ICAEW Member
E A Johnson

ERNST & YOUNG LLP
One Colmore Square, Birmingham, B4 6HQ
Tel: 0121 535 2000
Resident Partners/Directors: ICAEW Members
I Best, M J Carter, C H H Cowling, A J Dale, D K Duggins, S A Fowler, J A Houlden, J Hughes, S P Lucey, T Lukic, L Marston-Weston, N J Meredith, J W Middup, B Morton, S D O'Neill, C A Oates, M D G Upton, C J Voogd, A Ward, N G Woodward

EXACTAX ACCOUNTS SOLUTIONS
491a Alum Rock Road, Alum Rock, Birmingham, B8 3EA

FAIRWEATHER & CO
Montan House, 36 Calthorpe Road, Birmingham, B15 1TS

FARMILOES LLP
Winston Churchill House, Ethel Street, Birmingham, B2 4BG
Tel: 0121 643 7951
Resident Partners/Directors: ICAEW Members
R D Long, C R Osborn, S Y C Poon, D K Purser, D R T Sara
Registered by the ICAEW to carry out company audit work
Regulated by the ICAEW for a range of investment business activities

FELTONS
8 Sovereign Court, 8 Graham Street, Birmingham, B1 3JR

FELTONS (BHAM) LTD
8 Sovereign Court, 8 Graham Street, Birmingham, B1 3JR

FINNIESTON BERRY PARTNERSHIP LTD ◈
Europa House, 72-74 Northwood Street, Birmingham, B3 1TT
Tel: 0121 262 6420
Resident Partners/Directors: ICAEW Members
E L Berry, C M Finnieston

FLINT & THOMPSON
1325a Stratford Road, Hall Green, Birmingham, B28 9HL

FLINT & THOMPSON LTD
1325A Stratford Road, Hall Green, Birmingham, B28 9HL
Tel: 0121 777 7171
Resident Partners/Directors: ICAEW Members
D H Neville, M D Williams

FRIEND LLP
Quayside, 252-260 Broad Street, Birmingham, B1 2HF

G.P. HOLLAND
44 Rowney Croft, Hall Green, Birmingham, B28 0PL
Tel: 0121 744 7620
Principal: ICAEW Member
G P Holland

GLYN PREECE ASSOCIATES
Phoenix House, 12 Phoenix Green, Edgbaston, Birmingham B15 3NR
Tel: 0121 454 7099
Email: glyn.preece@gmail.com
Resident Partners/Directors: ICAEW Members
G Preece

GODWIN HARBY
Grays Court, 5 Nursery Road, Birmingham, B15 3JX

GOPAL & CO
349 Hagley Rd, Edgbaston, Birmingham, B17 8DL
Tel: 0121 434 4404
Principal: ICAEW Member
G S Iyengar

GRANT THORNTON UK LLP
Centre City Tower, 7 Hill Street, Birmingham, B5 4UU
Tel: 0121 697 6000
Resident Partners/Directors: ICAEW Members
R Hale, C Key, D P Munton, M Pilley, M D Sheppard, G C Smith
Resident Partners (Non-ICAEW Members):
Y M Redfern, J Roberts

GRANT THORNTON UK LLP
Enterprise House, 115 Edmund Street, Birmingham, B3 2HJ
Tel: 0121 212 4000
Resident Partners/Directors: ICAEW Members
C E Cattaneo, K M Godfree, R Hale, J F Hardbattle, D W Jewkes, W R Kerr, C Key, S P Line, D P Munton, M Pilley, A Roberts, M D Sheppard, G C Smith, M A Taylor, R Welsby, D P White, J N Whitfield
Resident Partners (Non-ICAEW Members):
A M Dunn, A M Menzies, N Tombs, E Williams, Y M Redfern, D P Hartland

H. ASHLEY
9 Allcock Street, Birmingham, B9 4DY

H. GOSRANI
12 Blakesley Road, Yardley, Birmingham, B25 8XU

HARBEN BARKER LTD
112 High Street, Coleshill, Birmingham, B46 3BL
Tel: 01675 466344
Resident Partners/Directors: ICAEW Members
P Scott

HARTMANS
Trenleigh House, 3 Woodbridge Road, Moseley, Birmingham B13 8EH

HASMUK PATEL & CO
Lalita Buildings, 378 Walsall Road, Perry Barr, Birmingham B42 2LX
Tel: 0121 356 2999
Principal: ICAEW Member
H Patel

HEATHCOTE & COLEMAN LLP ◈
Heathcote House, 136 Hagley Road, Birmingham, B16 9PN

HORVATH ACCOUNTANTS
26 Knighton Road, Bournville, Birmingham, B31 2EH

HW ◈
Sterling House, 71 Francis Road, Birmingham, B16 8SP
Tel: 0121 456 1613
Resident Partners/Directors: ICAEW Members
F H Briggs, D J Holdway

IAN TODD & CO ◈
4200 Waterside Centre, Birmingham Business Park, Birmingham, B37 7YN
Tel: 0121 717 4735
Email: ian@iantodd.com
Principal: ICAEW Member
I D E Todd
Registered by the ICAEW to carry out company audit work
Regulated by the ICAEW for a range of investment business activities

J.D. SMALL
7 Niall Close, Edgbaston, Birmingham, B15 3LU

J.E. ELLIOTT
63 Greenhill Road, Moseley, Birmingham, B13 9SU

J.G. THORNTON
Elfrey, 157 Holly Lane, Erdington, Birmingham B24 9LA
Tel: 0121 373 8213
Principal: ICAEW Member
J G Thornton

J. RAINE
25 Barlows Road, Edgbaston, Birmingham, B15 2PN

J SMITH
51 Ascot Road, Moseley, Birmingham, B13 9EN
Tel: 0121 449 3942
Principal: ICAEW Member
J C Smith

J W HINKS
19 Highfield Road, Edgbaston, Birmingham, B15 3BH
Tel: 0121 456 0190
Email: info@jwhinks.co.uk
Resident Partners/Directors: ICAEW Members
R R Barnes, J A Bomber, B D Hadfield, P O H Jones, D J Thursfield
Resident Partners (Non-ICAEW Members):
N A Aston

J W SCRIVENS & CO LTD
Grays Court, 5 Nursery Road, Edgbaston, Birmingham B15 3JX
Tel: 0121 428 4334
Fax: 0121 428 1383
Email: info@jwscrivens.co.uk
Website: http://www.jwscrivens.co.uk
Date Established: 1924
Resident Partners/Directors: ICAEW Members
G Litherland
Registered by the ICAEW to carry out company audit work
Regulated by the ICAEW for a range of investment business activities

SPECIALISATIONS – FINANCIAL REPORTING
Limited Company Accounts
Partnership/Sole Trader Accounts

SPECIALISATIONS – SECTOR
Barristers
Dentists/Opticians
Doctors
Solicitors

SPECIALISATIONS – TAXATION
Payroll Service and Advice
Taxation

JAMES SMALL
7 Niall Close, Edgbaston, Birmingham, B15 3LU

JAMES, STANLEY & CO
1733 Coventry Road, South Yardley, Birmingham, B26 1DT
Tel: 0121 706 8585
Email: andrew@jamesstanley.co.uk
Website: http://www.jamesstanley.co.uk
Date Established: 1922
Principal: ICAEW Member
A E S James

SPECIALISATIONS – AUDIT & ASSURANCE
Audit — Private Company

SPECIALISATIONS – BUSINESS & GENERAL ADVICE
Management Accounting Consultancy

SPECIALISATIONS – FINANCIAL REPORTING
Accounts Preparation

SPECIALISATIONS – TAXATION
Taxation

JASPER CORPORATE FINANCE LLP
Baskerville House, Centenary Square, Birmingham, B1 2ND

JASSAL & CO
829 Stratford Road, Springfield, Birmingham, B11 4DA

JAVED & CO ◈
109 Hagley Road, Edgbaston, Birmingham, B16 8LA
Tel: 0121 687 7000
Fax: 0121 687 7001
Email: mail@javed.co.uk
Website: http://www.javed.co.uk
Date Established: 1978
Training Contracts Available.
Resident Partners/Directors: ICAEW Members
Z Haq, R Javed, M A A Nomani
Registered by the ICAEW to carry out company audit work

continued

JAVED & CO *cont*
Authorised and regulated by the Financial Services Authority for investment business

INVESTOR IN PEOPLE

Languages Spoken:
Punjabi, Urdu

JEAN POWELL & CO
53 Monsal Road, Great Barr, Birmingham, B42 2DE

JOHN E. KIRKPATRICK
502 Lickey Road, Rednal, Birmingham, B45 8UU

JOHN ELLIS & CO
The Barn, 173 Church Road, Northfield, Birmingham B31 2LX
Tel: 0121 478 1964
Resident Partners/Directors: ICAEW Members
K J Chester, J G Ellis

JOHNSON & CO
239 Moor End Lane, Birmingham, B24 9DS
Tel: 07971 173370
Email: andrew@johnsonca.co.uk
Principal: ICAEW Member
A A M Johnson

JRW
36A Wake Green Road, Moseley, Birmingham, B13 9PE

JUDITH MILLWARD
31 Augustus Road, Edgbaston, Birmingham, B15 3PQ

K S SAWHNEY ◈
104 Britannic Park, 15 Yew Tree Road, Moseley, Birmingham B13 8NF
Tel: 07973 286601
Principal: ICAEW Member
K S Sawhney

KAS & CO (UK) LTD ◈
95 Vivian Road, Birmingham, B17 0DR
Tel: 0121 628 9696
Resident Partners/Directors: ICAEW Members
K Sodha
Registered by the ICAEW to carry out company audit work

KELMSCOTT CONSULTING LTD
43 Kelmscott Road, Harborne, Birmingham, B17 8QW

KHANNA & CO
6 Vicarage Road, Edgbaston, Birmingham, B15 3ES

KHANNA & CO LTD
6 Vicarage Road, Edgbaston, Birmingham, B15 3ES

KIRTLEY QURESHI & CO
221 Lady Pool Road, Birmingham, B12 8LG

KNIGHT-GREGSON
40 Kingsmere Close, Birmingham, B24 8QL
Tel: 0121 350 8212
Principal: ICAEW Member
M D Knight-Gregson

KPMG LLP
2 Cornwall Street, Birmingham, B3 2DL
Tel: 0121 232 3000
Resident Partners/Directors: ICAEW Members
K R Anderson, A I Argyle, J P Brittain, G M Collins, S H Craik, K P Edge, M J Egglenton, R J Fenton, G W Frith, M C Froom, A W Graham, I G Greaves, J A Hendley, S P Hollis, M T Hopton, S L Jonsson, J D Leech, J A Lovell, P N Meehan, N D Meredith, J J Morgan, G Neale, W P J O'Reilly, N Paul, S Purkess, M R Rahman, M J Rowley, I M Starkey, M A Steventon, D K Turner, G A Watts, R J West, R C Widdowson
Resident Partners (Non-ICAEW Members):
D J Fripp, C A Gumn, G S Hayre, R Higgins, A Hine, C W Hudson, C R Knowles, M A McDonagh, A D McLeish, R Nixon, M J Orton

L Y Y N
65 Lower Essex Street, Birmingham, B5 6SN
Tel: 0121 622 2277

L Y Y NG ACCOUNTING SERVICES LTD
65 Lower Essex Street, Birmingham, B5 6SN
Tel: 0121 622 2277
Resident Partners/Directors: ICAEW Members
L Y Y Ng

LAW & CO ◈
Pool House, Arran Close, 106 Birmingham Road, Great Barr, Birmingham B43 7AD

LAWRENCE & CO
8 Greenfield Crescent, Birmingham, B15 3BE

LOWE MCTERNAN LTD
Highcroft House, 81-85 New Road, Rubery, Rednal, Birmingham B45 9JR
Tel: 0121 457 6400
Fax: 0121 457 6457
Email: thebusiness@lmct.co.uk
Website: http://www.lmct.co.uk
Resident Partners/Directors: ICAEW Members
S C Peachey, C S Williams
Resident Partners (Non-ICAEW Members):
D P Wright
Registered by the ICAEW to carry out company audit work
Regulated by the ICAEW for a range of investment business activities

LOWSON WARD ◈
292 Wake Green Road, Birmingham, B13 9QP
Tel: 0121 778 6278

LOWSON WARD LTD ◈
292 Wake Green Road, Birmingham, B13 9QP
Tel: 0121 778 6278
Resident Partners/Directors: ICAEW Members
P R Ward

M A EDWARDS ACCOUNTANTS LTD ◈
30a The Green, Kings Norton, Birmingham, B38 8SD
Tel: 0121 459 6623
Resident Partners/Directors: ICAEW Members
M A Edwards

M & J LAWRENCE BUSINESS SERVICES
39 Chester Road, Castle Bromwich, Birmingham, B36 9DL

M.F. KHAN & CO
25 Parkdale Close, Erdington, Birmingham, B24 8JU
Tel: 0121 766 5715
Principal: ICAEW Member
N S Khan

M.H. JONES & CO
Stuart House, Valepits Road, Garretts Green, Birmingham B33 0TD

M LAWRENCE & CO
213 Station Road, Stechford, Birmingham, B33 8BB

M.R. WATSON & CO
122 Northfield Road, Kings Norton, Birmingham, B30 1DX

MAINSTREAM ACCOUNTANCY SERVICES
9 Crondal Place, Edgbaston, Birmingham, B15 2LB

MALCOLM PIPER & CO LTD
Business Services Centre, 446-450 Kingstanding Road, Birmingham, B44 9SA

MALLETT, JONES & CO
Lee House, 6a Highfield Road, Edgbaston, Birmingham B15 3ED
Tel: 0121 454 7387
Principal: ICAEW Member
D M Mason
Registered by the ICAEW to carry out company audit work

MARCUS & CO
Bank House, 36-38 Bristol Street, Birmingham, B5 7AA
Tel: 0121 622 3633
Resident Partners/Directors: ICAEW Members
D Markou

MARK GIBBON
74 Park Hill Road, Harborne, Birmingham, B17 9HJ

MASON + CO
Somerville House, 20-22 Harborne Road, Edgbaston, Birmingham B15 3AA

MASON LAW LLP
9 Frederick Road, Edgbaston, Birmingham, B15 1TW
Tel: 0121 248 7248
Email: accounts@masonlawllp.com
Resident Partners/Directors: ICAEW Members
D S Fisher, R E Law

SPECIALISATIONS – AUDIT & ASSURANCE
Pension Scheme Auditors

SPECIALISATIONS – FINANCIAL REPORTING
Accounts Preparation

SPECIALISATIONS – INVESTMENT BUSINESS
Financial Planning and Advice

SPECIALISATIONS – TAXATION
Estate and Inheritance

MAZARS CORPORATE FINANCE LTD ◈
Lancaster House, 67 Newhall Street, Birmingham, B3 1NG

MAZARS LLP ◈
Lancaster House, 67 Newhall Street, Birmingham, B3 1NG
Tel: 0121 212 4579
Resident Partners/Directors: ICAEW Members
L Cartwright, S J Lewis, A J Millington, A S Wood
Resident Partners (Non-ICAEW Members):
S D Chandler, T G Davies
Registered by the ICAEW to carry out company audit work
Authorised and regulated by the Financial Services Authority for investment business
Individual(s) licensed for insolvency work by the ICAEW

MDP
61 Charlotte Street, St Paul's Square, Birmingham, B3 1PX

MEAGER WOOD LOCKE & CO
123 Hagley Road, Edgbaston, Birmingham, B16 8LD
Tel: 0121 450 4900
Resident Partners/Directors: ICAEW Members
C B Locke, C G Meager

MGI WENHAM MAJOR ★
89 Cornwall Street, Birmingham, B3 3BY

MICHAEL DUFTY PARTNERSHIP LTD
61 Charlotte Street, St Paul's Square, Birmingham, B3 1PX
Tel: 0121 233 0222
Resident Partners/Directors: ICAEW Members
D V Payne

MICHAEL HEAVEN & ASSOCIATES LTD
Quadrant Court, 48 Calthorpe Road, Edgbaston, Birmingham B15 1TH

MICHAEL KAY & CO
2 Water Court, Water Street, Birmingham, B3 1HP
Tel: 0121 236 0060
Principal: ICAEW Member
M H P Daly, M Kay

MOORE STEPHENS LLP ◈
Beaufort House, 94-96 Newhall Street, Birmingham, B3 1PB

MRS M FEATHERSTONE ACA
13 Wentworth Road, Harborne, Birmingham, B17 9SH

MSGEE
1022-1028 Coventry Road, Birmingham, B25 8DP

MSGEE INTERNATIONAL LTD
1022-1028 Coventry Road, Birmingham, B25 8DP

N J KHAN & CO
Unit Two, The Boxworks, Carver Street, Jewellery Quarter, Birmingham B1 3AP

N T CHEW
2nd Floor Cathay Building, 86 Holloway Head, Birmingham, B1 1NB

NASIM AHMAD & CO
48 Woodend, Handsworth Wood, Birmingham, B20 1EN
Tel: 0121 357 6987
Principal: ICAEW Member
N Ahmad

NORRIS-SMALL ◈
2 Camino Road, Harborne, Birmingham, B32 3XE
Tel: 0121 693 7878
Principal: ICAEW Member
L E Norris-Small

NOTTINGHAM WATSON LTD
15 Highfield Road, Hall Green, Birmingham, B28 0EL

ORBIS PARTNERS LLP
134 Edmund Street, Birmingham, B3 2ES
Tel: 0121 234 6070
Resident Partners/Directors: ICAEW Members
G D Ecob, C Gregory, S Zaki

P.J. DOYLE & CO
45 Heather Drive, Rednal, Birmingham, B45 9RA
Tel: 0121 453 0107
Principal: ICAEW Member
P J Doyle

PALMERMOORE
Kings Chambers, 201 Streetly Road, Birmingham, B23 7AJ

PARKER BUSINESS DEVELOPMENT LTD ◈
1192 Warwick Road, Acocks Green, Birmingham, B27 6BT
Tel: 0121 333 4949
Email: info@parkerbd.co.uk
Website: http://www.parkerbd.co.uk
Resident Partners/Directors: ICAEW Members
A G Parker

PARKES & CO ◈
5 Crondal Place, Edgbaston, Birmingham, B15 2LB
Tel: 0121 440 2460
Principal: ICAEW Member
L E Parkes

PATRICIA A JONES
316 Bristol Road, Edgbaston, Birmingham, B5 7SN

PAUL TRODDEN & CO
30 St Mary's Row, Moseley, Birmingham, B13 8JG
Tel: 0121 449 8121
Principal: ICAEW Member
P J Trodden

PAYNE & CO
76 Grove Vale Avenue, Great Barr, Birmingham, B43 6BZ
Tel: 0121 357 8386
Principal: ICAEW Member
S A Allen

PHILIP DAVIES
3 Park Hall Crescent, Castle Bromwich, Birmingham, B36 9SN

PHILIP J. COOKE
Hollyoak, 1 White House Drive, Barnt Green, Birmingham B45 8HF

PKF (UK) LLP
New Guild House, 45 Great Charles Street, Birmingham, B3 2LX
Tel: 0121 212 2222
Email: info.birmingham@uk.pkf.com
Website: http://www.pkf.co.uk
Resident Partners/Directors: ICAEW Members
S H Beavan, M R G Cook, R L F Hudson, D G Liddell, S Littlejohns, T R Stephenson, H G Voisey
Resident Partners (Non-ICAEW Members):
I J Gould

PLANNING & CONTROL SOLUTIONS LTD ◈
17 Beachburn Way, Handsworth Wood, Birmingham, B20 2AU

POPPLETON AND APPLEBY ★
35 Ludgate Hill, Birmingham, B3 1EH

PRICEWATERHOUSE-COOPERS
Temple Court, 35 Bull Street, Birmingham, B4 6JT

PRICEWATERHOUSE-COOPERS
Cornwall Court, 19 Cornwall Street, Birmingham, B3 2DT

PRICEWATERHOUSE-COOPERS LLP
Cornwall Court, 19 Cornwall Street, Birmingham, B3 2DT
Tel: 0121 265 5000
Resident Partners/Directors: ICAEW Members
L K Anderson, R S Auluk, J S Bourdeaux, I F Dykes, S C Fairchild, I L Gardner, J A Hare, C D Hibbs, R J Hunt, D C John, S Kentish, P J Millward, J E B Minards, A C Morris, M R Mullins, A Parker, R J Porter, S M Rissbrook, G E Roberts, M W Robinson, C D Romans, S Rowe, E M Shires, J Singh, M L Smith, G A Telford, J N C Titcomb, A Wiggins, R P Worrall

R.A. LEA & CO
St Helens House, 23-31 Vittoria Street, Birmingham, B1 3ND

R.A. LEA & CO LTD
St Helens House, 23-31 Vittoria Street, Birmingham, B1 3ND
Tel: 0121 236 3317

R.J. TAYLOR & CO
Unit A2, Imex Business Park, Flaxley Road, Birmingham B33 9AL
Tel: 0121 783 1300
Principal: ICAEW Member
R J Taylor

R. PYATT
10 Friary Close, Hamstead Hall Road, Handsworth Wood, Birmingham B20 1HP

RBC
1 Victoria Square, Birmingham, B1 1BD
Tel: 0121 236 2252
Principal: ICAEW Member
R W Brown

ROBERT M W WOOD
27 Silver Birch Drive, Hollywood, Birmingham, B47 5RB

ROCHESTERS
3 Caroline Court, Caroline Street, St Paul's Square, Birmingham B3 1TR

ROLLASON ACCOUNTANCY ◈
37 Wood Lane, Harborne, Birmingham, B17 9AY

RSW ◈
Unit 6-17, 17 Thorp Street, Birmingham, B5 4AT
Tel: 0121 622 4762
Principal: ICAEW Member
R C H Wong

RUDGE & CO
Bordesley Hall, The Holloway, Alvechurch, Birmingham B48 7QA

RUDGE & CO LTD
Bordesley Hall, The Holloway, Alvechurch, Birmingham B48 7QA

RUS
1190a - 1192 Stratford Road, Hall Green, Birmingham, B28 8AB
Tel: 0121 777 1200

RWTA LTD
118 Hampton Court Road, Harborne, Birmingham, B17 9AG

S. SYEDAIN & CO ★
119 Pershore Road, Birmingham, B5 7NX

SADLER SAMSON
Sadler Samson Business Centre, 195 Church Road, Yardley, Birmingham B25 8UR
Tel: 0121 784 5818
Resident Partners/Directors: ICAEW Members
I D Barnett, K T Pym

SANDERLINGS LLP
Sanderling House, 1071 Warwick Road, Acocks Green, Birmingham B27 6QT

SHAREEF & CO LTD
18-22 Stoney Lane, Yardley, Birmingham, B25 8YP
Tel: 0121 783 5555
Resident Partners/Directors: ICAEW Members
N M Shareef

SHOESMITHS
Suites 1 & 2, Ground Floor, 54 Hagley Road, Edgbasten, Birmingham B16 8PE
Tel: 0121 454 5825
Fax: 0121 452 1554
Email: edg@shoesmiths.net
Website: http://www.shoesmiths.net
Resident Partners/Directors: ICAEW Members
G W Cross, E R Shoesmith
Registered by the ICAEW to carry out company audit work
Regulated by the ICAEW for a range of investment business activities

SIDNEY A. BEALE & CO
338 Yardley Road, Yardley, Birmingham, B25 8LT

SIGMA
Crown House, 28 George Street, Birmingham, B12 9RG

SINCLAIR & CO (ACCOUNTANTS) LTD
7 Portland Road, Edgbaston, Birmingham, B16 9HN

SKN
9 Lozells Road, Birmingham, B19 2TN

SKN SERVICES LTD
9 Lozells Road, Birmingham, B19 2TN

SMITH COOPER ◈
The Old Guild House, 1 New Market Street, Birmingham, B3 2NH
Tel: 0121 222 4150

SPRINGBOARD CORPORATE FINANCE LTD ◈
Three Brindley Place, Birmingham, B1 2JB

STANLEY YULE
79 Church Hill, Northfield, Birmingham, B31 3UB
Tel: 0121 411 1446
Fax: 0121 411 1457
Email: info@stanleyyule.co.uk
Website: http://www.stanleyyule.com
Resident Partners (Non-ICAEW Members):
B Saunders, J Mankoo
Other Offices: Walsall
Registered by the ICAEW to carry out company audit work
Languages Spoken:
German, Swahili, Punjabi

STUCKEYS
8 Greenfield Crescent, Edgbaston, Birmingham, B15 3AU

SYEDAIN & CO ◈
119 Pershore Road, Edgbaston, Birmingham, B5 7NX
Tel: 0121 440 4242
Resident Partners/Directors:
ICAEW Members
M I Asif
SPECIALISATIONS – FINANCIAL REPORTING
Accounts Preparation

T CHEUNG & CO
Unit 3A, Wing Yip Centre, 278 Thimble Mill Lane, Nechells, Birmingham B7 5HD

T CHEW & CO LTD
Second Floor, Cathay Building, 86 Holloway Head, Birmingham B1 1NB

T S PATARA & CO LTD
Financial House, 352 Bearwood Road, Bearwood, Birmingham B66 4ET
Tel: 0121 434 4747
Resident Partners/Directors:
ICAEW Members
T S Patara

T WOOD & CO (BIRMINGHAM) LTD
129 Hazelhurst Road, Kings Heath, Birmingham, B14 6AG

TANIA OXLEY
10 Denise Drive, Harborne, Birmingham, B17 0BN
Tel: 0121 426 5612
Email: tania.oxley@aims.co.uk
Principal: ICAEW Member
T K V Oxley

TAXCARE
Bank House, 36-38 Bristol Street, Birmingham, B5 7AA
Tel: 0121 622 3633

TAXCARE LTD
Bank House, 36-38 Bristol Street, Birmingham, B5 7AA
Tel: 0121 622 3633
SPECIALISATIONS – SECTOR
Corporate

TENON LTD
6th Floor, The White House, 111 New Street, Birmingham B2 4EU
Tel: 0121 616 6790
Resident Partners/Directors:
ICAEW Members
A Appleyard

THAPERS
Harpal House, 14 Holyhead Road, Handsworth, Birmingham B21 0LT

TRAFALGAR ACCOUNTANCY & TAX LTD
Trafalgar House, 261 Alcester Road South, Birmingham, B14 6DT

TREVOR JONES & CO ▽
Old Bank Chambers, 582-586 Kingsbury Road, Erdington, Birmingham B24 9ND

TWAMLEY AND CO ◈
80 High Street, Coleshill, Birmingham, B46 3AH

UNADKAT & CO
12 The Wharf, Bridge Street, Birmingham, B1 2JS

UNADKAT & CO LTD
12 The Wharf, Bridge Street, Birmingham, B1 2JS

VANTIS BUSINESS RECOVERY SERVICES
104-106 Colmore Row, Birmingham, B3 3AG
Tel: 0121 710 1680
Website: http://www.vantisplc.com/businessrecovery
Principal: ICAEW Member
B J Marsh
Individual(s) licensed for insolvency work by another RPB
SPECIALISATIONS – BUSINESS RECOVERY & INSOLVENCY
Bankruptcies
Corporate Recovery
Liquidations

W H HOOPER
1st Floor Offices, 167 Sutton Road, Wylde Green, Birmingham B23 5TN

WATSON ASSOCIATES
First Floor, 15 Highfield Road, Hall Green, Birmingham B28 0EL

WEBSTERS
65 Church Street, Birmingham, B3 2DP

WH PARKER ★
174 High Street, Harborne, Birmingham, B17 9PP
Tel: 0121 428 6300
Resident Partners/Directors:
ICAEW Members
R J Sarjeant, N F Williams

WHALLEY & CO
Whalley & Co, 29 Chester Road, Castle Bromwich, Birmingham B36 9DA

YASBAR SERVICES LTD
2220 Coventry Road, Sheldon, Birmingham, B26 3JH

YOUNIS BHATTI & CO LTD
1st Floor, 93 Broad Street, Birmingham, B15 1AU

BIRTLEY

APPLAUSE ACCOUNTANCY SERVICES
60 Beamish View, Birtley, DH3 1RS

BISHOP AUCKLAND

ALLEN SYKES LTD
5 Henson Close, South Church Enterprise Park, Bishop Auckland, DL14 6WA
Tel: 01388 777877
Resident Partners/Directors:
ICAEW Members
G R Herbert, J F Hindmarsh, P Lamb, D Stanwix

ALLEN SYKES LTD
Unit 1C, Castle Gardens, Stanhope, Bishop Auckland DL13 2FJ
Tel: 01388 526408

CHIPCHASE NELSON ★ ◈
Bank Chambers, 5 Kensington, Cockton Hill Road, Bishop Auckland DL14 6HX
Tel: 01388 661414

JACKSON ANDERSON LTD
5 Victoria Avenue, Bishop Auckland, DL14 7JH

MITCHELLS GRIEVSON
Kensington House, 3 Kensington, Bishop Auckland, DL14 6HX

MITCHELLS GRIEVSON LTD
Kensington House, 3 Kensington, Bishop Auckland, DL14 6HX

BISHOP'S STORTFORD

BARROW & CO ★ ◈
Rae House, Dane Street, Bishop's Stortford, CM23 3BT
Tel: 01279 656667

COOK & PARTNERS LTD
5 The Chantry, Hadham Road, Bishop's Stortford, CM23 2QR

DAVID J. TRILL
Thorley Houses Farm, Thorley Lane West, Bishop's Stortford, CM23 4BN
Tel: 01279 758377
Principal: ICAEW Member
D J Trill
SPECIALISATIONS – TAXATION
Taxation
General Description: Taxation consultancy.

GERRY DESLER
Stonebridge House, Chelmsford Road, Hatfield Heath, Bishop's Stortford CM22 7BD

MAGI ASSOCIATES
Holly Cottage, Berden, Bishop's Stortford, CM23 1AE

MICHAEL J. SCOTT
68 Heath Row, Bishop's Stortford, CM23 5DF
Tel: 01279 757419
Principal: ICAEW Member
M J Scott

MONTPELIER AUDIT LTD
23 Hockerill Court, London Road, Bishop's Stortford, CM23 5SB

MONTPELIER PROFESSIONAL (HERTS) LTD
23 Hockerill Court, London Road, Bishop's Stortford, CM23 5SB

MORRIS WHEELER & CO
26 Church Street, Bishop's Stortford, CM23 2LY

MORRIS WHEELER & CO LTD
26 Church Street, Bishop's Stortford, CM23 2LY
Tel: 01279 464400
Resident Partners/Directors:
ICAEW Members
M S Burrows, P C Morris, P A Wheeler

THE OAKLEY PARTNERSHIP ★
25 Warwick Road, Bishop's Stortford, CM23 5NH

PB FINANCIAL PLANNING LTD
Causeway House, 1 Dane Street, Bishop's Stortford, CM23 3BT

PETER JENSEN
5 Bridge Street, Bishop's Stortford, CM23 2JU
Tel: 01279 504254
Principal: ICAEW Member
P A Jensen

PRICE BAILEY
Causeway House, 1 Dane Street, Bishop's Stortford, CM23 3BT

PRICE BAILEY LLP ◈
Causeway House, 1 Dane Street, Bishop's Stortford, CM23 3BT

PRICE BAILEY PRIVATE CLIENT LLP
Causeway House, 1 Dane Street, Bishop's Stortford, CM23 3BT
Tel: 01279 755888
Website: http://www.pricebailey.co.uk
Resident Partners/Directors: ICAEW Members
S Brook, P G Martin, N Mayhew
Resident Partners (Non-ICAEW Members):
P Dearsley
Authorised and regulated by the Financial Services Authority for investment business
Individual(s) licensed for insolvency work by the ICAEW

TONY HINE & CO
Herne House, 68 Birchanger Lane, Birchanger, Bishop's Stortford CM23 5QA
Tel: 01279 647292
Principal: ICAEW Member
A Hine

WALTON & CO
1 Northgate End, Bishop's Stortford, CM23 2ET
Tel: 01279 465974
Email: info@waltonandco.com
Principal: ICAEW Member
D A Walton
Registered by the ICAEW to carry out company audit work

SPECIALISATIONS – AUDIT & ASSURANCE
Audit
Pension Scheme Auditors

SPECIALISATIONS – BUSINESS & GENERAL ADVICE
Company Formation

SPECIALISATIONS – FINANCIAL REPORTING
Limited Company Accounts
Partnership/Sole Trader Accounts

SPECIALISATIONS – SECTOR
Charities
General Description:
Specialists in pension fund auditing.

WILLIAM GEORGE
3 Maple Spring, Bishop's Stortford, CM23 2PU

BISHOPS CASTLE

D.R.E. & CO
45 Church Street, Bishops Castle, SY9 5AD

DRE & CO LTD
45 Church Street, Bishops Castle, SY9 5AD

PETER GEARY & CO
31 Church Street, Bishops Castle, SY9 5AD

PETER GEARY & CO LTD
31 Church Street, Bishops Castle, SY9 5AD

SYKES & CO ★
1st Floor, The Old Primary School, Bishops Castle, SY9 5AE
Tel: 01588 638426

BLACKBURN

ALASTAIR WALMSLEY CONSULTING LTD ◈
12 Yew Tree Close, Clayton le Dale, Blackburn, BB1 9HP
Tel: 01254 249123
Resident Partners/Directors: ICAEW Members
A S Walmsley

BISHOP & PARTNERS LTD
Phoenix Park, Blakewater Road, Blackburn, BB1 5BG

BOWLAND ATLANTIC
3 Salisbury Street, Great Harwood, Blackburn, BB6 7SJ
Tel: 01254 619639
Principal: ICAEW Member
C J Smith

C T JONES & CO
Suite 108A, Glenfield Park, Philips Road, Blackburn BB1 5PF

DOUGLASS GRANGE ◈
Stanley House, Phoenix Park, Blakewater Road, Blackburn BB1 5RW
Tel: 01254 665655
Resident Partners/Directors: ICAEW Members
I Douglass, A J Grange

DTE CORPORATE RECOVERY AND INSOLVENCY SERVICES LTD
24 Wellington Street, St Johns, Blackburn, BB1 8AF

EGAN ROBERTS LTD
Glenfield House, Philips Road, Blackburn, BB1 5PF
Tel: 01254 583515
Resident Partners/Directors: ICAEW Members
K Roberts

EGAN ROBERTS LTD
Glenfield House, Philips Road, Blackburn, BB1 5PF
Tel: 01254 583515
Fax: 01254 263561
Email: accounts@egan.co.uk
Website: http://www.egan.co.uk

FORREST & CO ★
30 Heron Close, Blackburn, BB1 8NU

HAYES & CO
4 St Andrews Place, Off Wellington Street, St Johns, Blackburn BB1 8AL

HOWARD & CO ◈
10-12 Wellington Street, (St Johns), Blackburn, BB1 8AG
Tel: 01254 662414
Resident Partners/Directors: ICAEW Members
M T Forshaw, N J Howard

J SIMON WESTHEAD & ASSOCIATES
The White House, 37 Mellor Brow, Mellor, Blackburn BB2 7EX

MENSIS LTD
6 Watling Gate, Brockhall Village, Old Langho, Blackburn BB6 8BN

MICHAEL F. ATHERTON
12 Hollies Close, Feniscowles, Blackburn, BB2 5AJ

MWI
9-11 St Andrews Street, Blackburn, BB1 8AE

P.R. MOSS
12 Hawkshaw Bank Road, Blackburn, BB1 8JS
Tel: 01254 670756
Principal: ICAEW Member
P R Moss

PIERCE C A LTD ◈
Mentor House, Ainsworth Street, Blackburn, BB1 6AY
Tel: 01254 688100
Email: info@pierce.co.uk
Website: http://www.pierce.co.uk
Resident Partners/Directors: ICAEW Members
S J Baxendale, G G Boyes, J D Green, M Maden-Wilkinson, T E Nutter, P Warren
Resident Partners (Non-ICAEW Members):
N T Hussain

PM & M CORPORATE FINANCE LTD ◈
Oakmount, 6 East Park Road, Blackburn, BB1 8BW
Tel: 01254 679131
Fax: 01254 681759
Email: blackburn@pmm.co.uk
Website: http://www.pmm.co.uk
Resident Partners/Directors: ICAEW Members
R A Ainscough, J E Akrill, S M Anderson, M Battersby, D P Bradley, A R Brierley, R L Cornes, D L Eatough, L E Parry, A Tinker

SPECIALISATIONS – SECTOR
Advertising/Design Agencies
Agriculture
Architects/Surveyors
Catering/Restaurants
Charities
Clothing/Textiles
Corporate
Dentists/Opticians
Doctors
Engineers
Food Industry
Hotels/Public Houses
Leisure Industry
Manufacturing
Nursing Homes/Clinics
Property
Property Development
Property Investment
Road Haulage and Distribution
Solicitors
Travel Industry
General Description:
Associated with Praxity.

PM&M SOLUTIONS FOR BUSINESS LLP ◈
Oakmount, 6 East Park Road, Blackburn, BB1 8BW
Tel: 01254 679131
Fax: 01254 681759
Email: blackburn@pmm.co.uk
Website: http://www.pmm.co.uk
Training Contracts Available.
Resident Partners/Directors: ICAEW Members
R A Ainscough, S M Anderson, A R Brierley, D L Eatough, L E Parry, A Tinker
Other Offices: 34 Wellgate, Clitheroe BB7 2DP, 83 Bank Parade, Burnley BB11 1UG
Registered by the ICAEW to carry out company audit work

INVESTOR IN PEOPLE

RIDEHALGH LTD
Guardian House, 42 Preston New Road, Blackburn, BB2 6AH
Tel: 01254 52414

continued

RIDEHALGH LTD *cont*
Resident Partners/Directors: ICAEW Members
S Henry
Registered by the ICAEW to carry out company audit work

TURPIN LUCAS LEES
440 Whalley New Road, Roe Lee, Blackburn, BB1 9SL

WATERWORTHS ◈
Central Buildings, Richmond Terrace, Blackburn, BB1 7AP
Tel: 01254 686600
Fax: 01254 682483
Email: info@waterworths.co.uk
Website: http://www.waterworths.co.uk
Date Established: 1881
Resident Partners/Directors: ICAEW Members
P J Bridge, L Bury, W J Campbell, S L Lomax, A T Rowntree, A S B Thom, G Wilson
Registered by the ICAEW to carry out company audit work
Regulated by the ICAEW for a range of investment business activities

BLACKPOOL

BRIAN BEWICK
Office No 2, Bispham Market Building, Bispham Market 220 Red Bank Road, Bispham, Blackpool FY2 0HJ

CAMPBELL CROSSLEY & DAVIS
348/350 Lytham Road, Blackpool, FY4 1DW
Tel: 01253 349331
Fax: 01253 348434
Website: http://www.campbell-crossley-davis.co.uk
Resident Partners/Directors: ICAEW Members
S D Mondy, P G C Riley, P Swarbrick, R I Williamson, I M Wroe
Individual(s) licensed for insolvency work by the ICAEW

CCW
295/297 Church Street, Blackpool, FY1 3PJ

CHAMPION ACCOUNTANTS LLP
54 Caunce Street, Blackpool, FY1 3LJ

CHAMPION HAWARTH MOORE LTD
54 Caunce Street, Blackpool, FY1 3LJ
Tel: 01253 621512
Fax: 01253 752576
Email: blackpool@champion-accountants.co.uk
Website: http://www.champion-accountants.co.uk
Resident Partners/Directors: ICAEW Members
G Cosgrove, S J Crilley, D L Thorn
Other Offices: Manchester, Chester, Preston, Southport

COOPE, BADMAN & CO
209 Church Street, Blackpool, FY1 3TE

COX
192 West Park Drive, Blackpool, FY3 9LW

CROSSLEY & DAVIS
348-350 Lytham Road, Blackpool, FY4 1DW

D.S. RIDING & CO
Sherwood House, Division Lane, Blackpool, FY4 5DZ

EDWARD BRIDGE AND CO
205/207 Church Street, Blackpool, FY1 3PA

GOORNEY & TAYLOR
14 Abingdon Street, Blackpool, FY1 1PY
Tel: 01253 620112
Resident Partners/Directors: ICAEW Members
R G Taylor, P G Wigan

HARK GRIMLEY & CO
89-91 Marsden Road, Blackpool, FY4 3BY
Tel: 01253 405125
Fax: 01253 341561
Email: office@harkgrimley.co.uk
Principal: ICAEW Member
A W Keenan
Registered by the ICAEW to carry out company audit work

HORNE BROOKE SHENTON
21 Caunce Street, Blackpool, FY1 3LA

JOHN POTTER & HARRISON
112-114 Whitegate Drive, Blackpool, FY3 9XH

JPH LTD
112-114 Whitegate Drive, Blackpool, FY3 9XH

M.B. WORMLEIGHTON & CO
341 Lytham Road, Blackpool, FY4 1DS
Tel: 01253 347017
Principal: ICAEW Member
M B Wormleighton

M.BARNFATHER & CO
16 Birley Street, Blackpool, FY1 1DU

MITCHELL RAMSDEN ◈
132 Highfield Road, Blackpool, FY4 2HH
Tel: 01253 345444
Resident Partners/Directors: ICAEW Members
M Muschamp, B H Taylor
See display advertisement near this entry.

MOORE & SMALLEY LLP
Fylde House, Skyways Commercial Campus, Amy Johnson Way, Blackpool FY4 2RP

RAWCLIFFE & CO ◈
West Park House, 7/9 Wilkinson Avenue, Blackpool, FY3 9XG
Tel: 01253 798812
Resident Partners/Directors: ICAEW Members
D A Harben, C J Harrison

STANLEY WILKINSON & CO
139 Red Bank Road, Bispham, Blackpool, FY2 9HZ
Tel: 01253 622324
Principal: ICAEW Member
S Wilkinson

WILLIAM HARLING & CO ◈
23 Abingdon Street, Blackpool, FY1 1DG

WISEMANS
255 Church Street, Blackpool, FY1 3PB
Tel: 01253 628936
Resident Partners/Directors: ICAEW Members
P H Payne, G S White

BLANDFORD FORUM

PETER MARSH
14 Upper School Lane, Blandford St Mary, Blandford Forum, DT11 9QG
Tel: 01258 455887
Principal: ICAEW Member
P Marsh

THE TAX PARTNERSHIP ★
Westbury Cottage, Tarrant Gunville, Blandford Forum, DT11 8JN
Tel: 01258 830268
Resident Partners/Directors: ICAEW Members
T C Heaton

BLYTH

ERIC BONE
Offshore House, Euroseas Centre, Albert Street, Blyth NE24 1LZ
Tel: 01670 541538
Principal: ICAEW Member
E Bone

G D HAKIN & CO
9 Stanley Street, Blyth, NE24 2BS
Tel: 01670 352474
Fax: 01670 367422

Resident Partners/Directors: ICAEW Members
R B Gibson, T J Herbert
Registered by the ICAEW to carry out company audit work

SPECIALISATIONS – AUDIT & ASSURANCE
Audit

SPECIALISATIONS – FINANCIAL REPORTING
Accounts Preparation

SPECIALISATIONS – TAXATION
Taxation

NICHOL GOODWILL BROWN LTD
18 Stanley Street, Blyth, NE24 2BU

BODMIN

BENNETT JONES & CO
94 Fore Street, Bodmin, PL31 2HR
Tel: 01208 78266
Resident Partners/Directors: ICAEW Members
R J Healey, M S Spence

CORNISH ACCOUNTING SOLUTIONS ◈
20 Crockwell Street, Bodmin, PL31 2DS

DEREK COUSENS LTD
58 Kestell Parc, Bodmin, PL31 1HP

NASH & CO
77 Fore Street, Bodmin, PL31 2JB
Tel: 01208 77977
Principal: ICAEW Member
J A Luker

BOGNOR REGIS

AVN PETERSONS LTD
Church House, 94 Felpham Road, Bognor Regis, PO22 7PG

BENNETT & CO
10 Normanton Avenue, Bognor Regis, PO21 2TX

BROMLEY CLACKETT
76 Aldwick Road, Bognor Regis, PO21 2PE

BROMLEY CLACKETT LTD
76 Aldwick Road, Bognor Regis, PO21 2PE

DAVID BOWDEN & CO
19 Den Avenue, Bognor Regis, PO21 1HE
Tel: 01243 823011
Principal: ICAEW Member
D M A Brownrigg

DAVID CROOK & CO
6 Martineau Close, Bognor Regis, PO21 4BT
Tel: 01243 268468
Principal: ICAEW Member
D F Crook

M E FREDRICKS LTD
98 London Road, Bognor Regis, PO21 1DD

P.L DOWNS
Michaelmas Cottage, Roundle Square Road, Felpham, Bognor Regis PO22 8JX

PETERSONS
Church House, 94 Felpham Road, Bognor Regis, PO22 7PG

ROSE GREEN CONSULTANCY LTD
26 Blondell Drive, Aldwick, Bognor Regis, PO21 4BQ

SAMANTHA THOMPSON
Westside, 1 Halliford Drive, Barnham, Bognor Regis PO22 0AB

WINDELL & CO
Westering, 45 Downview Road, Barnham, Bognor Regis PO22 0EF
Tel: 01243 553804
Resident Partners/Directors: ICAEW Members
D M Windell, S P Windell

WINDELL & CO ACCOUNTANTS LTD
45 Downview Road, Barnham, Bognor Regis, PO22 0EF
Tel: 01243 553804
Resident Partners/Directors: ICAEW Members
D M Windell

BOLTON

AIMS
44 Dale Lee, Westhoughton, Bolton, BL5 3YE
Tel: 01942 842345

APPLEBY & WOOD
Bolton Enterprise Centre, Washington Street, Bolton, BL3 5EY

BARLOW ANDREWS ◈
Carlyle House, 78 Chorley New Road, Bolton, BL1 4BY
Tel: 01204 527451
Training Contracts Available.
Resident Partners/Directors: ICAEW Members
J D Barden, D A Kay, G W Leigh, M J Pearson, P A Riding, M R C Sheen, A G Smith

INVESTOR IN PEOPLE

SPECIALISATIONS – AUDIT & ASSURANCE
Audit — Private Company

SPECIALISATIONS – BUSINESS & GENERAL ADVICE
Outsourcing - Financial Services

SPECIALISATIONS – SECTOR
Property Investment

SPECIALISATIONS – TAXATION
Capital Gains — Limited Companies
Estate and Inheritance

BENTLEYS
Hazlemere, 70 Chorley New Road, Bolton, BL1 4BY
Tel: 01204 388675
Resident Partners/Directors: ICAEW Members
K L Acton, R Darby, J C Hargraves, J J Shaw, M A Turner

SPECIALISATIONS – AUDIT & ASSURANCE
Audit

SPECIALISATIONS – FINANCIAL REPORTING
Accounts Preparation

SPECIALISATIONS – FORENSIC ACCOUNTING
Forensic Accounting

SPECIALISATIONS – INVESTMENT BUSINESS
Planning

SPECIALISATIONS – SECTOR
Charities

SPECIALISATIONS – TAXATION
Taxation
Value Added Tax

BILL THOMAS & CO
58 France Street, Westhoughton, Bolton, BL5 2HP
Tel: 01942 815290
Principal: ICAEW Member
W E L Thomas

C.D. HINDLEY & CO
29 Captain Lees Garden, Westhoughton, Bolton, BL5 3YF
Tel: 01942 813681
Principal: ICAEW Member
C D Hindley

CLB COOPERS ★ ◈
Laurel House, 173 Chorley New Road, Bolton, BL1 4QZ
Tel: 01204 551100
Fax: 01204 551101
Email: bolton@clbcoopers.co.uk
Website: http://www.clbcoopers.co.uk
Training Contracts Available.
Resident Partners/Directors: ICAEW Members
I T Smethurst, M D Worsley
Registered by the ICAEW to carry out company audit work
Regulated by the ICAEW for a range of investment business activities
General Description: CLB Coopers - Delivering solutions through excellence.

COWGILL HOLLOWAY
Regency House, 45-51 Chorley New Road, Bolton, BL1 4QR

COWGILL HOLLOWAY LLP
Regency House, 45-51 Chorley New Road, Bolton, BL1 4QR
Tel: 01204 414243
Resident Partners/Directors: ICAEW Members
A J Ball, P A Cowgill, J Marshall, M J Murphy, P Stansfield, S P Stead

CROSSLEY & DAVIS
52 Chorley New Road, Bolton, BL1 4AP

DAVID CAMPBELL & CO
8 New Heys Way, Bradshaw, Bolton, BL2 4AR
Tel: 01204 308396
Fax: 01204 602657
Principal: ICAEW Member
D Campbell

DEBTMATTERS LTD
Mansell House, Aspinall Way, Middlebrook Business Park, Bolton BL6 6QQ

DJ LATHAM
70 Newbrook Road, Over Hulton, Bolton, BL5 1ET
Tel: 01204 655914
Principal: ICAEW Member
D J Latham

DONNELLYS
Peel House, 2 Chorley Old Road, Bolton, BL1 3AA
Tel: 01204 369200
Resident Partners/Directors: ICAEW Members
N L Baxendale, A J Donohoe

G L RAMSBOTTOM & CO LTD
Kenmore, Bolton Road, Bradshaw, Bolton BL2 3EU
Tel: 01204 596604
Resident Partners/Directors: ICAEW Members
G L Ramsbottom

HALL ROBINSON
25 Teak Drive, Kearsley, Bolton, BL4 8RR

HALL ROBINSON LTD
25 Teak Drive, Kearsley, Bolton, BL4 8RR
Tel: 0161 728 3599
Resident Partners/Directors: ICAEW Members
G W Midgley

HAYWOOD & CO LLP
Kevan Pilling House, 1 Myrtle Street, Bolton, BL1 3AH

HIGSONS
93 Market Street, Farnworth, Bolton, BL4 7NS
Tel: 01204 861772
Fax: 01204 572753
Email: admin@higsons.co.uk
Website: http:/

continued

HIGSONS *cont*
www.higsons.co.uk
Resident Partners/Directors: ICAEW Members
K Higson
Resident Partners (Non-ICAEW Members):
A Barlow
Registered by the ICAEW to carry out company audit work
Regulated by the ICAEW for a range of investment business activities

HILL ECKERSLEY & CO
62 Chorley New Road, Bolton, BL1 4BY

HINDLEY & CO
733 Manchester Road, Over Hulton, Bolton, BL5 1BA

HUNTER & CO
415 Blackburn Road, Bolton, BL1 8NJ

J.F. BALSHAW FCA
20 Old Kiln Lane, Heaton, Bolton, BL1 5PD
Tel: 01204 840472
Principal: ICAEW Member
J F Balshaw

J. HALL & CO LTD
255 Breightmet Fold Lane, Bolton, BL2 5NB
Tel: 01204 391630
Resident Partners/Directors: ICAEW Members
J Hall

MARK HASLAM, SONS & CO
17 Wood Street, Bolton, BL1 1EB
Tel: 01204 525211
Resident Partners/Directors: ICAEW Members
C Haslam, C A Haslam

MARK LOMAX
Canmore, 90 Chapeltown Road, Bromley Cross, Bolton BL7 9ND

MICHAEL SOHOR & CO ◈
74 St George's Road, Bolton, BL1 2DD
Tel: 01204 391505
Email: michael.sohor@btinternet.com
Website: http://www.michaelsohor.co.uk
Principal: ICAEW Member
M E Sohor
Registered by the ICAEW to carry out company audit work

MIKE EGAN & CO
168 Lee Lane, Horwich, Bolton, BL6 7AF

MURPHY & CO
The Coach House, 24b Park Hill Street, Bolton, BL1 4AR

NEIL HOOTON ACCOUNTANCY SERVICES LTD ◈
Old Bank Chambers, 99 Market Street, Farnworth, Bolton BL4 7NS
Tel: 01204 791978
Resident Partners/Directors: ICAEW Members
N E Hooton

NEIL HOOTON ACCOUNTANCY SERVICES LTD
660 Plodder Lane, Farnworth, Bolton, BL4 0LG

NICHOLAS HADJINICOLAOU
151 Longsight, Harwood, Bolton, BL2 3JE

NICK HULME CORPORATE FINANCE ◈
Atria, Spa Road, Bolton, BL1 4AG
Tel: 0845 644 2664
Principal: ICAEW Member
N A Hulme

NIGEL WHITTLE
Parkside House, 167 Chorley New Road, Bolton, BL1 4RA
Tel: 01204 370200
Principal: ICAEW Member
N J Whittle

P A HULL & CO
365 Tonge Moor Road, Bolton, BL2 2JR

P.B. SYDDALL & CO ◈
Grafton House, 81 Chorley Old Road, Bolton, BL1 3AJ
Tel: 01204 380038
Resident Partners/Directors: ICAEW Members
N W Polding, J Ridings, P B Syddall

PETER WILSON
Suite 6, Rockfield House, 512 Darwen Road, Bromley Cross, Bolton BL7 9DX
Tel: 01204 309761
Fax: 01204 309524
Email: peter@peterwilsonfca.co.uk
Mobile: 07970 192338
Date Established: 1990
Principal: ICAEW Member
P Wilson
General Description: We specialise in the preparation of accounts and online tax returns with the use of the newest technology available.

R.D. HILL ASSOCIATES
5 Whinslee Drive, Lostock, Bolton, BL6 4NB

R P SMITH & CO
71 Chorley Old Road, Bolton, BL13AJ

R P SMITH & CO LTD
71 Chorley Old Road, Bolton, BL13AJ

R.P. SMITH & CO ◈
71 Chorley Old Road, Bolton, BL1 3AJ
Tel: 01204 534421
Resident Partners/Directors: ICAEW Members
P H Lowe

RAJA & CO
Aknam, 56 Chorley New Road, Bolton, BL1 4AP

RYANS ◈
67 Chorley Old Road, Bolton, BL1 3AJ
Tel: 01204 523263
Resident Partners/Directors: ICAEW Members
K R Bell, C A Chisnall

S C HOSKER & CO LTD
Endeavour House, 98 Waters Meeting Road, Navigation Business Park, The Valley, Bolton BL1 8SW

SHAFIQ & CO
1 Lark Street, Bolton, BL1 2UA

STAFFORD & CO
Nelson Mill, Gaskell Street, Bolton, BL1 2QS
Tel: 0845 330 0103
Fax: 0845 330 5023
Email: info@staffordandcompany.co.uk
Website: http://www.staffordandcompany.co.uk
Resident Partners/Directors: ICAEW Members
K J Stafford, R J Stafford
Resident Partners (Non-ICAEW Members):
S E Harrison
Registered by the ICAEW to carry out company audit work

STEGGLES & CO
2a Peel Street, Farnworth, Bolton, BL4 8AA
Tel: 01204 792182
Principal: ICAEW Member
A Steggles

STEVE ASTBURY LTD
379 Stitch-Mi-Lane, Harwood, Bolton, BL2 3PR

TENON LTD
Clive House, Clive Street, Bolton, BL1 1ET
Tel: 01204 395000

TENON AUDIT LTD
Clive House, Clive Street, Bolton, BL1 1ET
Tel: 01204 395000
Resident Partners/Directors: ICAEW Members
P Draper

TREVOR COX
3 Greenleas, Lostock, Bolton, BL6 4PL

UNIQUE BUSINESS FINANCE LTD
Mansell House, Aspinall Close, Horwich, Bolton BL6 6QQ

WARINGS
Bedford House, 60 Chorley New Road, Bolton, BL1 4DA
Tel: 01204 534031
Website: http://www.warings.co.uk
Resident Partners/Directors: ICAEW Members
H Chambers, P A Lydon, R J Massey
Resident Partners (Non-ICAEW Members):
N Crookall

WILLIAM WETTON & CO
3 Greenleas, Lostock, Bolton, BL6 4PL

WRAGGE AND LEE
Minerva House, 5 Chorley New Road, Bolton, BL1 4QR
Tel: 01204 521080
Resident Partners/Directors: ICAEW Members
F T Berry, D F Morlidge

BOOTLE

61 STANLEY ROAD LTD
61 Stanley Road, Bootle, L20 7BZ

ANDREW D. KILSHAW
99 Stanley Road, Bootle, L20 7DA

ERIC N. JONES & CO ◈
Stratford House, 149 Stanley Rd, Bootle, L20 3DL
Tel: 0151 933 6997
Principal: ICAEW Member
E N Jones

PEERS & SMITH
Mast House, Derby Road, Bootle, L20 1EA

SATTERTHWAITE BROOKS & POMFRET LLP
Oriel House, 2-8 Oriel Road, Bootle, L20 7EP

BORDON

A.J. CHARIK & CO ◈
24 Churchill Crescent, Headley, Bordon, GU35 8ND
Tel: 01428 712437
Principal: ICAEW Member
A J Charik

ANTHONY J WILLIAMS
27 Forest Centre, Pinehill Road, Bordon, GU35 0TN

CREDOR POINT LTD
Arford Lodge, Bowcott Hill, Headley, Bordon GU35 8DF

E-PRACTICE
The Studio, Drift Road, Bordon, GU35 9DZ

JOHN HOLDAWAY
Plum Cottage, Honeysuckle Lane, Headley Down, Bordon GU35 8JA

N J CHARMAN
The Lodge, Mount Pleasant Road, Lindford, Bordon GU35 0PR

SWC
Hollywood, Furze Vale Road, Headley Down, Bordon GU35 8EP
Tel: 07765 253329
Principal: ICAEW Member
S W Crew

BOREHAMWOOD

BEHRMAN SWINDELL & CO
4b Shenley Road, Borehamwood, WD6 1DL

CARTER BACKER WINTER
Devonshire Business Park, Chester Road, Borehamwood, WD6 1NA

DAVID A. ROSE & CO
39 Deacons Hill Road, Elstree, Borehamwood, WD6 3HZ

DKS
The Kinnetic Business Centre, Theobald Street, Borehamwood, WD6 4PJ

DUBELL & CO
16 Hartfield Avenue, Elstree, Borehamwood, WD6 3JE

E.H. COHEN & CO
58 Anthony Road, Borehamwood, WD6 4NG

GILL PEER & COMPANY LTD
13 Alwyn Close, Elstree, Borehamwood, WD6 3LF

GOODIER, SMITH AND WATTS LTD
Devonshire House, Manor Way, Borehamwood, WD6 1QQ

HURSHENS
14 Theobald Street, Borehamwood, WD6 4SE

HURSHENS LTD
14 Theobald Street, Borehamwood, WD6 4SE

HUTSKALL LTD
5 Theobald Court, Theobald Street, Borehamwood, WD6 4RN

I.J. BROWNSTEIN & CO
59 Deacons Hill Road, Elstree, Borehamwood, WD6 3HZ
Tel: 020 8953 3808
Principal: ICAEW Member
I J Brownstein

IAN SEGAL & CO
5 Theobald Court, Theobald Street, Borehamwood, WD6 4RN

INIMEX ASSOCIATES LTD
33 Anthony Road, Borehamwood, WD6 4NF
Tel: 020 8953 9840
Principal: ICAEW Member
H J Osper

IVAN SOPHER & CO ◈
5 Elstree Gate, Elstree Way, Borehamwood, WD6 1JD
Tel: 020 8207 0602
Principal: ICAEW Member
I Sopher

J BROWN & CO
9 Beechfield Close, Borehamwood, WD6 4NT
Tel: 020 8207 6666
Principal: ICAEW Member
J Robertson

JUPPS ◈
30 Grosvenor Road, Borehamwood, WD6 1BT
Tel: 020 8953 2470
Principal: ICAEW Member
N G A Jupp

KEN FREEDMAN & CO
7 Ascot Close, Elstree, Borehamwood, WD6 3JH

LAURENCE A COHEN
25 Hartfield Avenue, Elstree, Borehamwood, WD6 3JB
Tel: 020 8953 0901
Principal: ICAEW Member
L A Cohen

LAURENCE BENSON & CO
39 Links Drive, Elstree, Borehamwood, WD6 3PP
Tel: 020 8905 1404
Principal: ICAEW Member
L M Benson

LERMAN JACOBS DAVIS
Roman House, 13 High Street, Elstree, Borehamwood WD6 3EP

LERMAN JACOBS DAVIS LLP
13 High Street, Elstree, Borehamwood, WD6 3EP

MARK SASSOON
8 Sheraton Close, Elstree, Borehamwood, WD6 3PZ

NEVILLE LEVY & CO
26 Gables Avenue, Borehamwood, WD6 4SP

NEWMAN BROWN
Kinetic Centre, Theobald Street, Borehamwood, WD6 4BA

NORMAN STANLEY ◈
Suite 1R10, Elstree Business Centre, Elstree Way, Borehamwood WD6 1RX

REEVE-YOUNG & CO
Silverbirch Cottage, Watford Road, Elstree, Borehamwood WD6 3BE
Tel: 020 8207 1413
Principal: ICAEW Member
H D R Young

RICKMAN
31 Croxdale Road, Borehamwood, WD6 4QA
Tel: 020 8953 3426
Principal: ICAEW Member
L Rickman

S. KAPUR & CO
6 Hartfield Close, Elstree, Borehamwood, WD6 3JD

SAGER & CO
7 Water End Close, Borehamwood, WD6 4PW
Tel: 020 8953 9700
Principal: ICAEW Member
A M Sager

SINI
Timbers, St Nicholas Close, Elstree, Borehamwood WD6 3EW

BOSTON

BOND PARTNERS LLP
Chapel House, Cowbridge, Boston, PE22 7AX

BRIAN JAMES
45 Wide Bargate, Boston, PE21 6SH
Tel: 01205 362900
Email: brianrjames@btinternet.com
Principal: ICAEW Member
B R James

DEXTER & SHARPE ★
The Old Vicarage, Church Close, Boston, PE21 6NE

DUNCAN & TOPLIS
5 Resolution Close, Endeavour Park, Boston, PE21 7TT
Tel: 01205 310250
Fax: 01205 365405
Email: info@boston.duntop.co.uk
Website: http://www.duntop.co.uk
Resident Partners/Directors: ICAEW Members
T G Godson, J R Hodson, A N Reynolds
Resident Partners (Non-ICAEW Members):
C Newitt
Registered by the ICAEW to carry out company audit work
Regulated by the ICAEW for a range of investment business activities
General Description: Other offices please see Grantham.

HAMSHAW & CO
100 Wide Bargate, Boston, PE21 6SE

MARTIN, NYE & CO ★
Enterprise House, Priory Road, Freiston, Boston PE22 0JZ

RICHARD WOODS & CO
Southwold House, Boston Road, Swineshead, Boston PE20 3HB
Tel: 020 7828 9853
Principal: ICAEW Member
R L Woods

TENON LTD
4 Red Lion Street, Boston, PE21 6NY
Tel: 01205 357114

BOURNE

ACCOUNTANCY CONSULTANTS EAST ◈
58 North Street, Bourne, PE10 9AB
Tel: 01778 423777
Principal: ICAEW Member
C E Glithero

DEXTER & SHARPE ★
Commerce House, 18 West Street, Bourne, PE10 9NE

GRAHAM ANDERSON
Holwell, Stainfield Road, Kirkby Underwood, Bourne PE10 0SG

REBBECK & CO
Bramley Cottage, 45 Haconby Lane, Morton, Bourne PE10 0NP

BOURNE END

M R SALVAGE LLP
7/8 Eghams Court, Boston Drive, Bourne End, SL8 5YS
Tel: 01628 522773
Email: info@mrsalvage.co.uk
Website: http://www.mrsalvage.co.uk
Resident Partners/Directors: ICAEW Members
R Davies, M E Field, A L Horton, M R Salvage, G R Sutton, J Taylor
Registered by the ICAEW to carry out company audit work
Regulated by the ICAEW for a range of investment business activities

R. G. BURNAND & CO
Suite 4, Thamesbourne Lodge, Station Road, Bourne End SL8 5QH

SUSAN CHURCH ACCOUNTANCY SERVICES
8 Dandridge Drive, Bourne End, SL8 5UW

WILKINS & CO
36 Chalklands, Bourne End, SL8 5TJ

BOURNEMOUTH

THE ACCOUNTANCY FELLOWSHIP LTD
9 Queens Road, Bournemouth, BH2 6BA
Tel: 01202 757385
Resident Partners/Directors: ICAEW Members
W G Belcher

ALAN W SIMONS & CO
Hillview Business Centre, 2 Leybourne Avenue, Bournemouth, BH10 6HF
Tel: 01202 523446
Principal: ICAEW Member
A W Simons

ALLAN G. WHITTLE & CO ★ ◈
Alum House, 5 Alum Chine Road, Westbourne, Bournemouth BH4 8DT
Tel: 01202 761341
Resident Partners/Directors:
ICAEW Members
G T Ferguson

ASHLEIGH ACCOUNTANCY LTD
1 Ashleigh Rise, Bournemouth, BH10 4FB
Tel: 01202 779952
Resident Partners/Directors:
ICAEW Members
P P Hampton

B N JACKSON NORTON ★
2nd Floor, Bristol & West House, Post Office Road, Bournemouth BH1 1BL

B.S. ROSE & CO
Milford Lodge, 38a Talbot Avenue, Talbot Woods, Bournemouth BH3 7HZ
Tel: 07772 761839
Principal: ICAEW Member
B S Rose

BUCHANANS LTD
1123a Christchurch Road, Boscombe East, Bournemouth, BH7 6BQ

CARTER & COLEY
3 Durrant Road, Bournemouth, BH2 6NE
Tel: 01202 786600
Resident Partners/Directors:
ICAEW Members
A A Clark, A Cooke, R Smedley

CONTINUUM LTD
Gild House, 66 Norwich Avenue West, Bournemouth, BH2 6AW

D. R. J. BELBIN
78 Brackendale Road, Queen's Park, Bournemouth, BH8 9HZ

DAFFURN & CO LTD ◈
No 1 Fiscal House, 834 Christchurch Road, Bournemouth, BH7 6DQ
Tel: 01202 421209
Resident Partners/Directors:
ICAEW Members
P R Daffurn
Registered by the ICAEW to carry out company audit work

DEAVIN & CO
3 Russell-Cotes Road, Bournemouth, BH1 3AB

DEVCOMP LTD
36 Markham Avenue, Northbourne, Bournemouth, BH10 7HN

FINDLAY JAMES
898-902 Winbourne Road, Moordown, Bournemouth, BH9 2BJ

HARRISONS ◈
4 Brackley Close, South East Sector, Bournemouth International Airport, Bournemouth BH23 6SE
Tel: 01202 590596
Resident Partners/Directors:
ICAEW Members
N G Depper, M R G Magrath

HIXSONS LTD ◈
24 Cecil Avenue, Bournemouth, BH8 9EJ
Tel: 01202 520010
Resident Partners/Directors:
ICAEW Members
N V Hixson

HOWARD COHEN
Tall Trees, 15a Dean Park Road, Bournemouth, BH1 1HU

IAN DEVERILL
36 Markham Avenue, Northbourne, Bournemouth, BH10 7HN

IAN SAINSBURY
62 Branksome Hill Road, Bournemouth, BH4 9LG

J. S. BELT & CO
82 Castle Lane West, Bournemouth, BH9 3JU

J. S. BELT & CO LTD
82 Castle Lane West, Bournemouth, BH9 3JU
Tel: 01202 540538
Resident Partners/Directors:
ICAEW Members
J S Belt

JEAN G. BUTLER
29 Darracott Rd, Bournemouth, BH5 2AY

LEVYS
Number One Trinity, 161 Old Christchurch Road, Bournemouth, BH1 1JU

M J RHODES & CO ◈
First Floor, 8 Poole Hill, Bournemouth, BH2 5PS
Tel: 01202 469375
Principal: ICAEW Member
M J Rhodes

MARTIN AND CO
158 Richmond Park Road, Bournemouth, BH8 8TW

N.R. SHARLAND & CO ◈
First Floor, Austin House, 43 Poole Road, Bournemouth BH4 9DN
Tel: 01202 761888
Principal: ICAEW Member
N R Sharland

PETER R. DENNIS
37 Saxonbury Road, Southbourne, Bournemouth, BH6 5NB

POTTER & POLLARD ◈
Richmond Court, 216 Capstone Road, Bournemouth, BH8 8RX
Tel: 01202 526677

POTTER & POLLARD LTD ◈
Richmond Court, 216 Capstone Road, Bournemouth, BH8 8RX
Tel: 01202 526677
Resident Partners/Directors:
ICAEW Members
R E Bagshawe

PRICEWATERHOUSE-COOPERS
Hill House, Richmond Hill, Bournemouth, BH2 6HR

PRICEWATERHOUSE-COOPERS LLP
Hill House, 41 Richmond Hill, Bournemouth, BH2 6HR
Tel: 01202 294621

R & L GILES LTD
21 St Ives Gardens, Bournemouth, BH2 6NS
Tel: 01202 295735
Resident Partners/Directors:
ICAEW Members
L A Giles, R E Giles

R. BRUCE BINGHAM & CO
12 Camelford Court, 15 Marlborough Road, Bournemouth, BH4 8DD

R E LOCK
41 Leven Avenue, Talbot Woods, Bournemouth, BH4 9LJ
Tel: 01202 769321
Principal: ICAEW Member
R E Lock

RAY COCKREM ACA
38 Elmgate Drive, Littledown, Bournemouth, BH7 7EG

RICHARD DUNFORD & CO
118 Norton Road, Bournemouth, BH9 2QB
Tel: 01202 535087
Principal: ICAEW Member
R J Dunford

RICHARD DUNFORD LTD
118 Norton Road, Bournemouth, BH9 2QB

RJ TAX MANAGEMENT LTD
2 Lansdowne Crescent, Bournemouth, BH1 1SA
Tel: 01202 719082
Website: http://www.rjtm.co.uk
Resident Partners/Directors:
ICAEW Members
R R Jennings

ROTHMAN PANTALL & CO
1123 Christchurch Road, Boscombe East, Bournemouth, BH7 6BQ

SAFFERY CHAMPNESS ◈
1 St Stephens Court, St Stephens Road, Bournemouth, BH2 6LA
Tel: 01202 294281
Fax: 01202 290 759
Website: http://www.saffery.com
Training Contracts Available.
Resident Partners/Directors:
ICAEW Members
E Brierley, N F Fernyhough, C W D Macey
Other Offices: Bristol, Edinburgh, Geneva, Guernsey, Harrogate, High Wycombe, Inverness, Manchester, London, Peterborough
Registered by the ICAEW to carry out company audit work
Regulated by the ICAEW for a range of investment business activities

INVESTOR IN PEOPLE

General Description: See London office entry.

SCHOFIELDS ★
6th Floor, Dean Park House, 8-10 Dean Park Crescent, Bournemouth BH1 1PL
Tel: 01202 555785
Fax: 01202 290644
Email: enquiries@schofieldsonline.co.uk
DX: 7625 BOURNEMOUTH 1
Website: http://www.schofieldsonline.co.uk
Date Established: 1936
Training Contracts Available.
Resident Partners/Directors:
ICAEW Members
P J Schofield
Resident Partners (Non-ICAEW Members):
C Prett
Registered by the ICAEW to carry out company audit work
Authorised and regulated by the Financial Services Authority for investment business

THE SOLUTIONS CENTRE LTD
218 Malvern Road, Bournemouth, BH9 3BX
Tel: 01202 526711
Resident Partners/Directors:
ICAEW Members
M Davis

SPW (UK) LLP
Cranbourne Chambers, The Square, Bournemouth, BH2 5AQ

STEPHEN PENNY AND PARTNERS ★ ◈
898/902 Wimborne Road, Moordown, Bournemouth, BH9 2DW
Tel: 01202 526522
Fax: 01202 535793
Email: accountants@sp-partners.co.uk
Resident Partners/Directors: ICAEW Members
R E Bagshawe
Resident Partners (Non-ICAEW Members):
S A J Penny
Registered by the ICAEW to carry out company audit work
Regulated by the ICAEW for a range of investment business activities

INVESTOR IN PEOPLE

STEPHENSON & CO
Ground Floor, Austin House, 43 Poole Road, Westbourne, Bournemouth BH4 9DN
Tel: 01202 769881
Resident Partners/Directors: ICAEW Members
C K Bailey, M R Smith

STEWART & CO ★ ◈
Ebenezer House, 5a Poole Road, Bournemouth, BH2 5QJ
Tel: 01202 312345
Resident Partners/Directors: ICAEW Members
C J Stewart

TAYLOR RAE ACCOUNTANCY LTD ◈
426-428 Holdenhurst Road, Bournemouth, BH8 9AA
Tel: 01202 398923
Resident Partners/Directors: ICAEW Members
M W Farley, R.V.T. Mitchell-Fox

TENON LTD
30 Christchurch Road, Bournemouth, BH1 3PD
Tel: 01202 554456

TENON AUDIT LTD
30 Christchurch Road, Bournemouth, BH1 3PD
Tel: 01202 554456

W.G. BELCHER & CO
9 Queens Road, Westbourne, Bournemouth, BH2 6BA
Tel: 01202 757385
Principal: ICAEW Member
W G Belcher

BRACKLEY

UPSTONE BLENCOWE
15 High Street, Brackley, NN13 7DH

BRACKNELL

BERKELEY-TAX LTD
Berkeley House, 5 Roman Way, Bracknell, RG42 7UT

INVEST IN UK LTD
Forest House, 3-5 Horndean Road, Bracknell, RG12 0XQ
Tel: 01344 305244
Email: kevin.beare@kevinbeare.com
Website: http://www.kevinbeare.com
Resident Partners/Directors: ICAEW Members
K L Beare
Other Offices:88 Wood Street, London, EC2V 7RS

SPECIALISATIONS – FINANCIAL REPORTING
Foreign Subsidiary Companies

SPECIALISATIONS – TAXATION
Payroll Service and Advice

JAN L. JALOVY
15 Redditch, Bracknell, RG12 0TT

KAR ACCOUNTANCY & BUSINESS SOLUTIONS
11 Benedict Green, Warfield, Bracknell, RG42 3DW
Tel: 01344 482558
Principal: ICAEW Member
K A Roberts

KEVIN BEARE & CO
Forest House, 3-5 Horndean Road, Bracknell, RG12 0XQ

MARK SELDON & CO
10 Sherwood Close, Lily Hill, Bracknell, RG12 2SB

MIAN & MALIK
28 Sarum, Roman Wood, Bracknell, RG12 8XZ

WARD WILLIAMS
Arlington Court, Venture House, 2 Arlington Square, Downshire Way, Bracknell RG12 1WA

BRADFORD

A.K. BIGGIN & CO
Bantams Business Centre, Valley Parade, Bradford, BD8 7DY
Tel: 01274 673642

ADVANTAGE
240 Gain Lane, Bradford, BD3 7DW

ALAN DAVID ARTHUR BSC (ECON) ◈
76 Hallowes Park Road, Cullingworth, Bradford, BD13 5AR

ANDREW S. PARKER ◈
2 Meadow Court, Allerton, Bradford, BD15 9JZ
Tel: 01274 544737
Email: andrew@asparker.co.uk
Principal: ICAEW Member
A S Parker
Registered by the ICAEW to carry out company audit work

SPECIALISATIONS – AUDIT & ASSURANCE
Audit

SPECIALISATIONS – FINANCIAL REPORTING
Accounts Preparation
Limited Company Accounts
Partnership/Sole Trader Accounts

SPECIALISATIONS – SECTOR
Corporate

SPECIALISATIONS – TAXATION
Personal
Taxation

ASHFORDS ACCOUNTANTS LTD
1378 Leeds Road, Bradford, BD3 8NE
Tel: 01274 661556
Resident Partners/Directors: ICAEW Members
S A Shah

AUKER RHODES LTD ◈
Royd House, 286 Manningham Lane, Bradford, BD8 7BP
Tel: 01274 548000
Resident Partners/Directors: ICAEW Members
D H Akester, R H Doyle, R J Kenyon, J A Pedley, G A Rudloff

AVIACCS LTD
29 Moor Close Lane, Queensbury, Bradford, BD13 2NS
Tel: 01274 412441
Resident Partners/Directors: ICAEW Members
Y A Evans

BAKER TILLY
Horwath Clark Whitehill, Pelican House, 10 Currer Street, Bradford BD1 5BA

BAKER TILLY TAX AND ADVISORY SERVICES LLP
Pelican House, Little Germany, Bradford, BD1 5BA
Tel: 01274 732522
Resident Partners/Directors: ICAEW Members
S M Brown, R Clark, P W Geldeard, K R Hillam

BAKER TILLY UK AUDIT LLP
Pelican House, Little Germany, Bradford, BD1 5BA
Tel: 01274 732522
Resident Partners/Directors: ICAEW Members
R Clark, K R Hillam

BOSTOCKS, BOYCE WELCH
Black Dyke House, High Street, Queensbury, Bradford BD13 2PA
Tel: 01274 673642

CHARLES E. COFFEY & CO
Unicredit House, Irwell Street Entrance, 16 Paley Road, Bradford BD4 7EJ

CHARLES E.COFFEY & CO LTD
Unicredit House, Irwell Street Entrance, 16 Paley Road, Bradford BD4 7EJ

CLARKSON & CO
Jubilee Mill, Suite 9, North Street, Bradford BD1 4EW
Tel: 01274 224313
Principal: ICAEW Member
R H Clarkson
Registered by the ICAEW to carry out company audit work
Regulated by the ICAEW for a range of investment business activities

COMPANY SOLUTIONS LTD ◈
Velocity Business & Innovation Centre, Angel Way, Bradford, BD7 1BX
Tel: 01274 841401
Website: http://www.companysolutions.co.uk
Resident Partners/Directors: ICAEW Members
R Beattie
General Description: Design and implementation of employee share schemes, corporate governance and company secretarial consultancy.

D.H.SHAW
7 Chapel Row, Wilsden, Bradford, BD15 0EQ

DAVID ALLEN ASSOCIATES
122 Hill Top Road, Thornton, Bradford, BD13 3QX
Tel: 01274 835435
Mobile: 07970 542850
Principal: ICAEW Member
D S Allen

SPECIALISATIONS – BUSINESS & GENERAL ADVICE
Book-keeping

SPECIALISATIONS – FINANCIAL REPORTING
Accounts Preparation

SPECIALISATIONS – TAXATION
Personal
Trusts

DAVID BOLDY
6 Spring Farm Mews, Wilsden, Bradford, BD15 0EF

DAVID M. PULLAN
Highfield House, Highfield Road, Idle, Bradford BD10 8QY

DAVID WILES ASSOCIATES
The Coach House, 7 Carlton Drive, Heaton, Bradford BD9 4DL
Tel: 01274 541871
Principal: ICAEW Member
D P Wiles

DONALD STOKES ◈
33 Mossy Bank Close, Queensbury, Bradford, BD13 1PX
Tel: 01274 817414
Principal: ICAEW Member
D C Stokes

FEARNSIDE MARSHALL
Eldon Chambers, 6 Eldon Place, Bradford, BD1 3TH

FIRTH PARISH
5 Eldon Place, Bradford, BD1 3AU
Tel: 01274 727767
Fax: 01274 308313
Email: info@firth-parish.com
Website: http://www.firth-parish.com
Training Contracts Available.
Resident Partners/Directors: ICAEW Members
G Beaumont, L R Brain, S Hudson
Registered by the ICAEW to carry out company audit work
Regulated by the ICAEW for a range of investment business activities

FLETCHER GREENWOOD & CO ◈
11/13 Broad Street, Manor Row, Bradford, BD1 4QT
Tel: 01274 729178
Resident Partners/Directors: ICAEW Members
I J Fletcher, A D Simpson

H.V.BAMFORD & CO
99 Main Street, Wilsden, Bradford, BD15 0DZ
Tel: 01535 272963
Principal: ICAEW Member
M O Bamford

HEATON, LUMB, LISLE ◈
12 Albion Road, Idle, Bradford, BD10 9PY
Tel: 01274 611510

KAREN MOUNTAIN
4/6 Royd View, Windy Bank Lane, Amblerthorn, Queensbury, Bradford BD13 2NW
Tel: 01274 817802
Principal: ICAEW Member
K J Mountain

MGI WATSON BUCKLE ◈
York House, Cottingley Business Park, Bradford, BD16 1PE
Tel: 01274 516700

MGI WATSON BUCKLE LLP
York House, Cottingley Business Park, Bradford, BD16 1PE
Tel: 01274 516700
Resident Partners/Directors: ICAEW Members
C R Padgett, S M Sedgwick, A W Thornton, D K Warren

NAYLOR WINTERSGILL
Carlton House, Grammar School Street, Bradford, BD1 4NS

NAZMAN ◈
Valley Point, Forster Square, Bradford, BD1 4AA

R.D. SUTTON & CO
544 Leeds Road, Thackley, Bradford, BD10 8JH
Tel: 01274 617174
Principal: ICAEW Member
R D Sutton

RAWSE, VARLEY & CO ◈
Lloyds Bank Chambers, Hustlergate, Bradford, BD1 1UQ

S M SMITH
7 Slingsby Close, Apperley Bridge, Bradford, BD10 0UJ

S M SMITH LTD
7 Slingsby Close, Apperley Bridge, Bradford, BD10 0UJ

STUART B. LODGE & CO
44 Bradford Road, Idle, Bradford, BD10 9PE
Tel: 01274 414134
Principal: ICAEW Member
S B Lodge

T. NAWAZ & CO
Cambridge House, 66 Little Horton Lane, Bradford, BD5 0HX

THOMPSONS
4 Bradford Road, Idle, Bradford, BD10 9PP

TOREVELL DENT (BRADFORD) LLP ★
4th Floor, 153/155 Sunbridge Road, Bradford, BD1 2NU

WALTER DAWSON & SON
Apex House, 38 Little Horton Lane, Bradford, BD5 0AL
Tel: 01274 722354
Resident Partners/Directors: ICAEW Members
J Hall

BRADFORD-ON-AVON

LAMEY & CO
Old Nursery House, Masons Lane, Bradford-On-Avon, BA15 1QN

R.N. THOMAS & CO
31 Silver Street, Bradford-on-avon, BA15 1JX

TRIPP & CO
The Old Brewery, Newtown, Bradford-On-Avon, BA15 1NF
Tel: 01225 869109

TRIPP ACCOUNTANCY LTD
The Old Brewery, Newtown, Bradford-On-Avon, BA15 1NF
Tel: 01225 869109
Resident Partners/Directors: ICAEW Members
M B Tripp

BRAINTREE

A W. BECKINSALE & CO
1 St Peters Road, Braintree, CM7 9AN

BAKER CHAPMAN & BUSSEY
Braintree House, 18 Bocking End, Braintree, CM7 9AA
Tel: 01376 559000
Email: mail@bakerchapman.co.uk
Website: http://www.bakerchapman.co.uk
Registered by the ICAEW to carry out company audit work
Regulated by the ICAEW for a range of investment business activities

DAVID REID AUDIT AND ACCOUNTANCY LTD ◈
Unit 4, The Bardfield Centre, Braintree Road, Great Bardfield, Braintree CM7 4SL
Tel: 01371 811093
Fax: 01371 811318
Resident Partners/Directors: ICAEW Members
D M Reid

J.T. WHALLEY & CO
8 Bridport Way, Braintree, CM7 9FJ

JAYNES & CO
20 New Street, Braintree, CM7 1ES
Tel: 01376 321140
Email: mail@jaynesandco.com
Website: http://www.jaynesandco.com
Principal: ICAEW Member
E J Coeshall
Registered by the ICAEW to carry out company audit work

SPECIALISATIONS – AUDIT & ASSURANCE
Audit — Private Company

SPECIALISATIONS – BUSINESS & GENERAL ADVICE
Management Advice to Business

SPECIALISATIONS – FINANCIAL REPORTING
Limited Companies
Limited Company Accounts
Partnership/Sole Trader Accounts

SPECIALISATIONS – SECTOR
Clubs/Associations

SPECIALISATIONS – TAXATION
Executorship
Self Assessment Advice

JOANNE OLLEY
31 Denton Crescent, Black Notley, Braintree, CM77 8ZZ

LAMBERT CHAPMAN LLP ◈
3 Warners Mill, Silks Way, Braintree, CM7 3GB
Tel: 01376 326266
Email: braintree@lambert-chapman.co.uk
Website: http://www.lambert-chapman.co.uk
Resident Partners/Directors: ICAEW Members
N Forsyth, P R Short, N A Whittle
Resident Partners (Non-ICAEW Members):
L Potter, C Harman
Other Offices: Chelmsford, Maldon
Registered by the ICAEW to carry out company audit work

SPECIALISATIONS – AUDIT & ASSURANCE
Audit — Private Company

SPECIALISATIONS – BUSINESS & GENERAL ADVICE
Acquisitions and Mergers
Management Advice to Business

SPECIALISATIONS – FINANCIAL REPORTING
Accounts Preparation

SPECIALISATIONS – FORENSIC ACCOUNTING
Expert Witnesses in Litigation

SPECIALISATIONS – SECTOR
Agriculture
Construction

SPECIALISATIONS – TAXATION
Estate and Inheritance
Payroll Service and Advice
Taxation
Trusts

General Description: An approachable independent firm of Chartered Accountants, operating in Essex and surrounding counties to include the City of London, offering a comprehensive service to owner managed businesses and private clients.

BRAMPTON

1.2.1 ACCOUNTANCY SERVICES
4 Railway Cottages, Low Row, Brampton, CA8 2LG

G. MADDOX
Rosslyn, 9 Oak Park, Brampton, CA8 1TP

GN EMERSON LTD
Common House, Gelt Road, Brampton, CA8 1QQ
Tel: 01697 73362
Resident Partners/Directors: ICAEW Members
C Emerson

PAGE MADDOX LTD
Rosslyn, 9 Oak Park, Brampton, CA8 1TP

BRENTFORD

RIZVI & CO
1 York Parade, Great West Road, Brentford, TW8 9AA

SIVA PALAN & CO
59-75 Boston Manor Road, Brentford, TW8 9JJ

BRENTWOOD

757 LTD
123 Priests Lane, Shenfield, Brentwood, CM15 8HJ

A M ROBINSON
3 Hospital Cottages, Crescent Road, Brentwood, CM14 5JA
Tel: 01277 220271
Principal: ICAEW Member
A M Robinson

ALDINGTON NAVESEY & CO LTD
19 Billericay Road, Herongate, Brentwood, CM13 3PS

ANSONS
Parker House, 104a Hutton Road, Shenfield, Brentwood CM15 8NB

B W CHATTEN LLP
Room 44, Millfield Business Centre, Ashwells Road, Brentwood CM15 9ST
Tel: 01277 372298
Resident Partners/Directors: ICAEW Members
B W Chatten

BERKELEY TOWNSEND ◈
Hunter House, 150 Hutton Road, Shenfield, Brentwood CM15 8NL
Tel: 01277 227070
Email: welcome@berkeleytownsend.com
Website: http://www.berkeleytownsend.com
Resident Partners/Directors: ICAEW Members
D J Aquino
Resident Partners (Non-ICAEW Members):
L Ogden
Registered by the ICAEW to carry out company audit work
Authorised and regulated by the Financial Services Authority for investment business
General Description: We are a professional firm providing an efficient and focused service.

MAURICE J. BUSHELL & CO
8 High Street, Brentwood, CM14 4AB

MICHAEL E GREENE
48 Western Road, Brentwood, CM14 4SS

MOULTON JOHNSON
25a Crown Street, Brentwood, CM14 4BA
Tel: 01277 228444
Resident Partners/Directors: ICAEW Members
I K Johnson

NW CONSULTANTS LTD
Fairbourne, The Close, Rose Valley, Brentwood CM14 4JA

PETERS & WRIGHT
387 Ongar Road, Pilgrim's Hatch, Brentwood, CM15 9JA

STERLINGS ACCOUNTANCY SOLUTIONS LTD
18 Springfield Avenue, Hutton, Brentwood, CM13 1RE
Tel: 01277 200018
Resident Partners/Directors: ICAEW Members
D J Parker

TIFFIN GREEN ★
11 Queens Road, Brentwood, CM14 4HE
Tel: 01277 224422
Resident Partners/Directors: ICAEW Members
N O Tidbury

BRIDGNORTH

A C RALPH LTD
c/o The Old Grammar School, St Leonards Close, Bridgnorth, WV16 4EJ

F.T. PICKFORD & CO
12 Northgate, Bridgnorth, WV16 4ER

F.T. PICKFORD & CO LTD
12 Northgate, Bridgnorth, WV16 4ER

J.A. HEMMING
Unit 9a, High Grosvenor, Worfield, Bridgnorth WV15 5PN
Tel: 01746 710001
Principal: ICAEW Member
J A Hemming

MHA FIELDINGS
The Post House, Astley Abbotts, Bridgnorth, WV16 4SW

PINNER DARLINGTON
HSBC Bank Chambers, Listley St, Bridgnorth, WV16 4AW
Tel: 01746 762345
Resident Partners/Directors: ICAEW Members
K Fullerton

SILVER & CO ◈
The Hollies, 16 St Johns Street, Bridgnorth, WV15 6AG

STANTON RALPH & CO
The Old Grammar School, St Leonard's Close, Bridgnorth, WV16 4EJ

TURNER PEACHEY ◈
12 West Castle Street, Bridgnorth, WV16 4AB
Tel: 01746 762589
Email: bridgnorth@turner-peachey.co.uk
Website: http://www.turner-peachey.co.uk
Non-resident Partners (ICAEW Members):
S Allum, C R Hemming
Other Offices: Oswestry,Telford, Welshpool
Registered by the ICAEW to carry out company audit work
Regulated by the ICAEW for a range of investment business activities

WALLACE CROOKE & CO
College House, St Leonards Close, Bridgnorth, WV16 4EJ

BRIDGWATER

A.C. MOLE & SONS ◈
Riverside House, Riverside Business Park, Wylds Road, Bridgwater TA6 4BH
Tel: 01278 446088
Fax: 01278 450027
Email: stevegolby@acmole.co.uk
Website: http://www.acmole.co.uk
Date Established: 1902
Resident Partners/Directors: ICAEW Members
S Golby, P A Kingdom
Registered by the ICAEW to carry out company audit work
Regulated by the ICAEW for a range of investment business activities

AIMS - M J GORDON
57 Taunton Road, Bridgwater, TA6 3LP

ALBERT GOODMAN
Unit 2.2 Sedgemoor Auction Centre, Huntworth Business Park, North Petherton, Bridgwater TA6 6TS

ASPEN-WAITE
Rubis House, 15 Friarn Street, Bridgwater, TA6 3LH
Tel: 01278 445 151
Resident Partners/Directors: ICAEW Members
A N Fox, R M L Lytton-Bernard, P D Waite

BUTTERWORTH JONES ◈
7 Castle St, Bridgwater, TA6 3DT
Tel: 01278 458251
Fax: 01278 428358
Email: bridgwater@butterworthjones.co.uk
Resident Partners/Directors: ICAEW Members
P J Butterworth, N C F Miles
Resident Partners (Non-ICAEW Members):
R W Symons
Registered by the ICAEW to carry out company audit work
Regulated by the ICAEW for a range of investment business activities

C.J. POTTS
44 Chapel Road, Pawlett, Bridgwater, TA6 4SH

CLIVE STEWARD LTD
7 Spoonbill Road, Bridgwater, TA6 5QZ
Tel: 01278 457455
Resident Partners/Directors: ICAEW Members
C J Steward

DOUCE & CO
5 Castle Street, Bridgwater, TA6 3DD
Tel: 01278 446340
Principal: ICAEW Member
J T Douce

JAMES SOUTAR & CO
Firland, High Street, Othery, Bridgwater TA7 0QA
Tel: 01823 698385
Principal: ICAEW Member
J Soutar

MAXWELLS ◈
4 King Square, Bridgwater, TA6 3YF
Tel: 01278 423008
Fax: 01278 450624
Email: steve@maxwellsaccountants.co.uk
Training Contracts Available.
Resident Partners/Directors: ICAEW Members
S T L Ball, M R Berry, N Blannin, C N Hall-Tomkin, P J Littler, A W Turrell, D A Villis
Resident Partners (Non-ICAEW Members):
S M Lake
Registered by the ICAEW to carry out company audit work
Regulated by the ICAEW for a range of investment business activities
Individual(s) licensed for insolvency work by the ICAEW

MICHAEL J DODDEN & CO
34 & 38 North Street, Bridgwater, TA6 3YD

SULLY & CO
18-22 Angel Crescent, Bridgwater, TA6 3AL

BRIDLINGTON

ATKINSONS
Eagle Manor, 12 Quay Road, Bridlington, YO15 2AD

CHARLES A WOOD & CO
14 Wellington Road, Bridlington, YO15 2BH

CHARLES A WOOD & CO LTD
14 Wellington Road, Bridlington, YO15 2BH

HOPSON & CO
Hopson & Co Ltd, 138 Quay Road, Bridlington, YO16 4JB

HOPSON & CO LTD
138 Quay Road, Bridlington, YO16 4JB

JACKSON ROBSON LICENCE LTD ◈
2/4 Wellington Road, Bridlington, YO15 2BN
Tel: 01262 672905

JH BOSTON & CO LTD
Ebor Cottage, 80 High Street, Bempton, Bridlington YO15 1HP

LLOYD DOWSON & CO
Medina House, 2 Station Avenue, Bridlington, YO16 4LZ

LLOYD DOWSON LTD
Medina House, 2 Station Avenue, Bridlington, YO16 4LZ

WINN & CO (YORKSHIRE) LTD
7 Manor Street, Bridlington, YO15 2SA

BRIDPORT

ANTHONY ALFORD
Shepherd's Crook, Netherbury, Bridport, DT6 5LY
Tel: 01308 488319
Principal: ICAEW Member
A P R Alford

BIBBY & LEGGE LTD
Unit 3D, Dreadnought Trading Estate, Magdalen Lane, Bridport DT6 5BU
Tel: 01308 459662
Resident Partners/Directors: ICAEW Members
R N Bibby

CHRIS LAVIS & CO ◈
Pineapple Business Park, Salway Ash, Bridport, DT6 5DB
Tel: 01308 488100
Principal: ICAEW Member
C A Lavis

CHRISTOPHER NORMAN
1 Manor Cottages, Symondsbury, Bridport, DT6 6HB

KEITH AUCKLAND ACA
Guppys Lodge, Fishpond Bottom, Bridport, DT6 6NN

M.W. BURROUGH & CO ◈
10 South St, Bridport, DT6 3NJ
Tel: 01308 422224
Principal: ICAEW Member
S Dorrington-Ward

MARTIN & COMPANY (BRIDPORT) LTD
2 Victoria Grove, Bridport, DT6 3AA
Registered by the ICAEW to carry out company audit work

ROSS MARTIN TAX CONSULTANCY LTD
The Roost, The Orchard, Uploders, Bridport DT6 4PF

SCOTT VEVERS
65 East Street, Bridport, DT6 3LB
Tel: 01308 423237
Principal: ICAEW Member
J Scott

SIMON JOHN CHRISTOPHER LTD
Hawthorne, Whitchurch Canonicorum, Bridport, DT6 6RH
Tel: 07798 833715

BRIERLEY HILL

M T MANLEY & CO LTD
1 Charnwood Close, Lakeside, Brierley Hill, DY5 3UE

PETER NEALE ACCOUNTANCY SERVICES
6 Sandringham Way, Brierley Hill, DY5 3JR

THOMAS NOCK MARTIN
5 Hagley Court South, The Waterfront, Brierley Hill, DY5 1XE

BRIGG

B H.J. FRENCH ◈
Ancholme house, Hall Lane, Elsham, Brigg DN20 0SX
Tel: 01652 680719
Principal: ICAEW Member
B H J French

CLAIRE MOSEY ACA
Woodstock, Bigby Road, Brigg, DN20 8HN

HW
40 Bigby Street, Brigg, DN20 8EF

P A HUTCHINSON & CO LTD ◈
Old Courts Road, Brigg, Lincolnshire, DN20 8JD
Tel: 01652 650440
Resident Partners/Directors: ICAEW Members
P A Hutchinson

R.N. STORE & CO ◈
The Poplars, Bridge Street, Brigg, DN20 8NQ
Tel: 01625 655111
Resident Partners/Directors: ICAEW Members
J R Bletcher, R J Haslehurst, A Ingleton

STEPHENSON, SMART & CO ★ ◈
Barclays Bank Chambers, 9a Market Place, Brigg, DN20 8ES

VS CONSULTANCY
Ley Mons, Melton Road, Wrawby, Brigg DN20 8SL

VS CONSULTANCY LTD
Ley Mons, Melton Road, Wrawby, Brigg DN20 8SL

BRIGHOUSE

ARMITAGES LTD ◈
9 Archbell Avenue, Brighouse, HD6 3SU

BROSNANS
Birkby House, Bailiff Bridge, Brighouse, HD6 4JJ

BROSNANS LTD
Birkby House, Bailiff Bridge, Brighouse, HD6 4JJ

J.F. BANKS & CO
76 Huddersfield Road, Brighouse, HD6 3RD
Tel: 01484 718183
Principal: ICAEW Member
J F Banks

PETER STABLES
77 Smith House Lane, Brighouse, HD6 2LF

SLEIGH STORY
46b Bradford Road, Brighouse, HD6 1RY

STEPHEN A THORNTON
Southroyd, 165A Halifax Road, Brighouse, HD6 2EQ
Tel: 01484 712929
Principal: ICAEW Member
S A Thornton

TOWNE & CO
208 Towngate, Brighouse, HD6 4HH

BRIGHTON

STYLE ACCOUNTANTS LTD
Bank House, Southwick Square, Southwick, Brighton BN42 4FN

ALAN R. MOYSE
12 Shepherds Croft, Withdean, Brighton, BN1 5JF

ANTRAMS ★
44-46 Old Steine, Brighton, BN1 1NH
Tel: 01273 328907
Fax: 01273 220025
Email: sa@antrams.com
Website: http://www.antrams.com
Resident Partners/Directors: ICAEW Members
D E Brown, A L Henton
Resident Partners (Non-ICAEW Members):
S J Antram
Registered by the ICAEW to carry out company audit work
SPECIALISATIONS – AUDIT & ASSURANCE
Audit
SPECIALISATIONS – FINANCIAL REPORTING
Limited Company Accounts
Partnership/Sole Trader Accounts
SPECIALISATIONS – TAXATION
Payroll Service and Advice
Taxation

BAKER TILLY
International House, First Floor, Queens Road, Brighton BN1 3XE
Tel: 01273 223400
Resident Partners/Directors: ICAEW Members
J A H Killick, D B Knapp

BAKER TILLY
International House, First Floor, Queens Road, Brighton BN1 3XE
Tel: 01273 223400
Resident Partners/Directors: ICAEW Members
P G Beckett, K A Lickorish

BAKER TILLY
1st Floor International House, Queens Road, Brighton, BN1 3XE

BAKER TILLY RESTRUCTURING AND RECOVERY LLP
International House, First Floor, Queens Road, Brighton BN1 3XE
Tel: 0845 037 0700
Resident Partners (Non-ICAEW Members):
S A Maund, A White

BAKER TILLY REVAS LTD
International House, Queens Road, Brighton, BN1 3XE

BAKER TILLY TAX AND ADVISORY SERVICES LLP
International House, First Floor, Queens Road, Brighton BN1 3XE
Tel: 01273 223400
Resident Partners/Directors: ICAEW Members
P G Beckett, J A H Killick, D B Knapp, K A Lickorish, W Telford, C J Warne
Resident Partners (Non-ICAEW Members):
S A Maund, A White, R J Mitchell

BARRY HILL & CO
The Brighton Forum, 95 Ditchling Road, Brighton, BN1 4ST

BAXTER SMITH PARKER
30 New Road, Brighton, BN1 1BN

BEGBIES TRAYNOR LTD
2/3 Pavilion Buildings, Brighton, BN1 1EE
Tel: 01273 747847
Fax: 01273 747743
Website: http://www.begbies-traynor.com
Resident Partners/Directors: ICAEW Members
G W Rhodes
Resident Partners (Non-ICAEW Members):
I P Sykes
Individual(s) licensed for insolvency work by the ICAEW
Individual(s) licensed for insolvency work by another RPB
SPECIALISATIONS – BUSINESS RECOVERY & INSOLVENCY
Bankruptcies
Corporate Recovery
Liquidations
Reorganisations and Company Reconstructions
General Description: A long established practice specialising in insolvency and related matters for companies, partnerships and individuals.

BREEZE & ASSOCIATES LTD
6 Marlborough Place, Brighton, BN1 1UB
Tel: 01273 573590
Website: http://www.breezeassociates.com

CARLTON HAINES LTD
Carlton House, 28/29 Carlton Terrace, Portslade, Brighton BN41 1XF

CHARIOT HOUSE LTD
48 Highdown Road, Brighton, BN3 6ED

CHISNALL COMER ISMAIL & CO ★
Maria House, 35 Millers Road, Brighton, BN1 5NP
Tel: 01273 502788
Email: cci@cciaccountants.com
Resident Partners/Directors: ICAEW Members
H F Chisnall, R Gibb
Registered by the ICAEW to carry out company audit work
Regulated by the ICAEW for a range of investment business activities

CLAMP GOGARTY LTD
Bank House, Southwick Square, Southwick, Brighton BN42 4FN

CLARKE WALKER ◈
Montpelier House, Third Floor, 99 Montpelier Road, Brighton BN1 3BE
Tel: 01273 820920
Email: mail@clarke-walker.com
Website: http://www.clarke-walker.com
Principal: ICAEW Member
B C Aukett

CLARKE WALKER LTD
Montpelier House, Third Floor, 99 Montpelier Road, Brighton BN1 3BE
Tel: 01273 820920
Resident Partners/Directors: ICAEW Members
B C Aukett

COHEN DAVIDSON LTD
68 Trafalgar Street, Brighton, BN1 4EB

DAVID C GORROD
68 Ship Street, Brighton, BN1 1AE

FEIST HEDGETHORNE
Preston Park House, South Road, Brighton, BN1 6SB

FEIST HEDGETHORNE LTD ◈
Preston Park House, South Road, Brighton, BN1 6SB
Tel: 01273 701200
Fax: 01273 701300
Email: admin@feist-hedgethorne.co.uk
Website: http://www.feist-hedgethorne.co.uk
Resident Partners/Directors: ICAEW Members
P R Feist, K R Hall, P J Hedgethorne
Registered by the ICAEW to carry out company audit work
Regulated by the ICAEW for a range of investment business activities
SPECIALISATIONS – IT
Computer Consultants
SPECIALISATIONS – SECTOR
Artists/Graphic Designers
Doctors
Entertainers
Property

FINANCIAL FORENSICS LLP
Brighton Forum, 95 Ditchling Road, Brighton, BN1 4ST
Tel: 01273 705878
Email: ros.stow@financial-forensics.co.uk
Other Offices: The Brighton Forum, 95 Ditchling Rd, Brighton, BN1 4ST (Tel: 01273 705878)
SPECIALISATIONS – FORENSIC ACCOUNTING
Forensic Accounting

FRIEND-JAMES ★ ◈
169 Preston Road, Brighton, BN1 6AG
Tel: 01273 562563
Email: stewart@friend-james.co.uk
Training Contracts Available.
Resident Partners/Directors: ICAEW Members
J S Forster, J D Warner
Authorised and regulated by the Financial Services Authority for investment business

GHIACI GOODHAND SMITH LTD
12a Marlborough Place, Brighton, BN1 1WN

GIBSON APPLEBY
2nd Floor, Blenheim House, 120 Church Street, Brighton, BN1 1AU

GRANT THORNTON UK LLP
Lees House, 21 Dyke Road, Brighton, BN1 3GD
Tel: 01293 583471

GROSVENOR PARTNERS LLP
First Floor, 3 Queens Road, Brighton, BN1 3WA

HARTLEY FOWLER LLP ◈
Pavilion View, 19 New Road, Brighton, BN1 1EY
Tel: 01273 202311
Fax: 01273 206496
Email: info.btn@hartleyfowler.com
Website: http://www.hartleyfowler.com
Training Contracts Available.
Resident Partners/Directors: ICAEW Members
D M Fennell-Crouch, G C Rolliston
Registered by the ICAEW to carry out company audit work
Regulated by the ICAEW for a range of investment business activities
SPECIALISATIONS – FORENSIC ACCOUNTING
Expert Witnesses in Litigation
Forensic Accounting

HILTON SHARP & CLARKE ◈
30 New Road, Brighton, BN1 1BN
Tel: 01273 324163
Fax: 01273 323983
Email: help@hsc.uk.net
DX: 36699 BRIGHTON 2
Website: http://www.hsc.uk.net
Training Contracts Available.
Resident Partners/Directors: ICAEW Members
D G Bishop, M L Faull, R K Moore, F C Roberts, D J B Shinn, M W Tickel, C S Young
Resident Partners (Non-ICAEW Members):
S E Smith
Other Offices: Billingshurst, RH14 9BP
(Tel: 01403 786788)

J.E. BORRETT
Flat 1, 28 Lewes Crescent, Brighton, BN2 1GB

JEREMY KNIGHT & CO
68 Ship Street, Brighton, BN1 1AE
Tel: 01273 203654
Website: http://www.jeremyknight.co.uk
Principal: ICAEW Member
W J J Knight
Other Offices: Croydon
Individual(s) licensed for insolvency work by another RPB

SPECIALISATIONS – BUSINESS RECOVERY & INSOLVENCY
Bankruptcies
Corporate Recovery
Liquidations
Reorganisations and Company Reconstructions

JL ◈
26 St Vincents Court, The Strand, Brighton Marina Village, Brighton BN2 5XJ
Tel: 01273 607200
Principal: ICAEW Member
J D Lopez

JOHN A. TUFFIN & CO
12-13 Ship Street, Brighton, BN1 1AD
Tel: 01273 202071
Resident Partners/Directors: ICAEW Members
P J Tuffin, R Q A Tuffin

JOHN E. POWELL
24 Colebrook Road, Brighton, BN1 5JH

LEIGH MARX
11 Kensington Place, Brighton, BN1 4EJ
Tel: 01273 670934
Principal: ICAEW Member
B M Leigh

LUCRAFT, HODGSON & DAWES ◈
Ground Floor, 19 New Road, Brighton, BN1 1UF
Tel: 01273 321526
Fax: 01273 321565
Email: enquiries@lucrafts.co.uk
Website: http://www.lucrafts.co.uk
Training Contracts Available.
Resident Partners/Directors: ICAEW Members
C J Ford, S B Samuels, W Taylor
Non-resident Partners (ICAEW Members):
P J Everest, G M Butterworth
Other Offices:2/4 Ash Lane, Rustington, West Sussex BN16 3BZ
(Tel: 01903 772244)
(Fax: 01903 771071)

SPECIALISATIONS – AUDIT & ASSURANCE
Audit — Private Company
Pension Scheme Auditors

SPECIALISATIONS – BUSINESS & GENERAL ADVICE
Book-keeping
Company Formation
Company Secretarial Service
Management Advice to Business

SPECIALISATIONS – FINANCIAL REPORTING
Accounts Preparation
Limited Company Accounts
Partnership/Sole Trader Accounts

SPECIALISATIONS – TAXATION
Payroll Service and Advice
Taxation

See display advertisement near this entry.

MCPHERSONS LTD
Montpelier House, 99 Montpelier Road, Brighton, BN1 3BE
Tel: 01273 206445
Resident Partners/Directors: ICAEW Members
G J Tait

MARKS & CO
100 Church St, Brighton, BN1 1UJ

MAZARS CORPORATE FINANCE LTD ◈
37 Frederick Place, Brighton, BN1 4EA

MAZARS LLP ◈
37 Frederick Place, Brighton, BN1 4EA
Tel: 01273 206788
Resident Partners/Directors: ICAEW Members
A J Alexander, R A Hopkins, D W Martin
Registered by the ICAEW to carry out company audit work
Authorised and regulated by the Financial Services Authority for investment business

OMNI MANAGEMENT LTD
Blenheim House, 56 The Steine, Brighton, BN1 1NH

ONE
3 Elms Lea Avenue, Brighton, BN1 6UG

PAUL R BOWES
57 Centurion Road, Brighton, BN1 3LN

PETER AUGUSTE & CO ◈
1 Dukes Passage, Off Duke Street, Brighton, BN1 1BS

PLUMMER PARSONS ◈
2 Frederick Terrace, Frederick Place, Brighton, BN1 1AX
Resident Partners/Directors: ICAEW Members
K L McCurdy

PLUMMER PARSONS ACCOUNTANTS LTD ◈
2 Frederick Terrace, Frederick Place, Brighton, BN1 1AX
Tel: 01273 725123
Resident Partners/Directors: ICAEW Members
K L McCurdy

ROBGOG LTD ◈
Bank House, Southwick Square, Southwick, Brighton BN42 4FN
Tel: 01273 596970
Resident Partners/Directors: ICAEW Members
R J Gogarty

RODNEY STEPHENSON LTD
40 Henge Way, Portslade, Brighton, BN41 2EP

SPOFFORTHS LLP
One Jubilee Street, Brighton, BN1 1GE
Tel: 01273 811000
Resident Partners/Directors: ICAEW Members
C H Eve, A J F Jones, S P J Kirkham

SRC
Blenheim House, 56 The Steine, Brighton, BN1 1NH

TENON LTD
3rd Floor, Lyndean House, 43-46 Queens Road, Brighton BN1 3XB
Tel: 01273 725566

THE WALKER BROWN PARTNERSHIP LLP
32 Trafalgar Road, Portslade, Brighton, BN41 1LD

THE WALKER BROWN PARTNERSHIP LLP
27 Balsdean Road, Woodingdean, Brighton, BN2 6PG

WILSON SANDFORD (BRIGHTON) LTD ◈
97 Church Street, Brighton, BN1 1UJ
Tel: 01273 728441
Fax: 01273 326715
Email: info@wilsonsandford.co.uk
Website: http://www.wilsonsandford.co.uk
Date Established: 1982
Resident Partners/Directors: ICAEW Members
A C Sandford, R F S Wilson
Resident Partners (Non-ICAEW Members):
C Sandford
Registered by the ICAEW to carry out company audit work
Regulated by the ICAEW for a range of investment business activities

SPECIALISATIONS – BUSINESS & GENERAL ADVICE
Company Formation

SPECIALISATIONS – FINANCIAL REPORTING
Accounts Preparation

SPECIALISATIONS – TAXATION
Payroll Service and Advice
Taxation

General Description: Members of UK200 Group.

WYNMOORE LTD
3 Elms Lea Avenue, Brighton, BN1 6UG

BRISTOL

A.D.G. JONES
Osmunda, Wells Road, Hallatrow, Bristol BS39 6EJ

A.D. NOYES
30 Queen Square, Bristol, BS1 4ND

A.J. BINLEY
44 Hill Grove, Henleaze, Bristol, BS9 4RQ

ACKLANDS ◈
Waterloo House, Waterloo Street, Clifton, Bristol BS8 4BT
Tel: 0117 923 7788
Website: http://www.acklands.co.uk
Registered by the ICAEW to carry out company audit work
Regulated by the ICAEW for a range of investment business activities

ACKLANDS LTD ◈
Waterloo House, Waterloo Street, Clifton, Bristol BS8 4BT
Tel: 0117 923 7788
Fax: 0117 923 8123
Website: http://www.acklands.co.uk
Resident Partners/Directors: ICAEW Members
T E O'Keefe

ADAMS ROOT & ASSOCIATES LTD
80 Shirehampton Road, Stoke Bishop, Bristol, BS9 2DR

AIMS - COLIN PEARSON
10 The Rowans, St Mary's Park, Portishead, Bristol BS20 6SR

AK ACCOUNTANCY LTD
64 Coronation Road, Downend, Bristol, BS16 5SL
Tel: 0117 957 3393
Resident Partners/Directors: ICAEW Members
A K Green

ANDREW SLADE
Trym Lodge, 1 Henbury Road, Westbury-on-Trym, Bristol BS9 3HQ
Tel: 0117 310 1284
Principal: ICAEW Member
A R Slade

ANDREW WATERS & ASSOCIATES LTD ◈
16 Westfield Road, Westbury-On-Trym, Bristol, BS9 3HG
Tel: 0117 904 7872
Email: aw@awatersassociates.co.uk
Resident Partners/Directors:
ICAEW Members
A F Waters

SPECIALISATIONS – SECTOR

Construction
Property Development

ANNING AND CO
5 High Street, Westbury-On-Trym, Bristol, BS9 3BY

B N JACKSON NORTON ★
14 Orchard Street, Bristol, BS1 5EH

BAKER & CO
Golden Meadow, 21 Dennyview Road, Abbots Leigh, Bristol BS8 3RD

BAKER TILLY
Hartwell House, 55-61 Victoria Street, Bristol, BS1 6AD
Resident Partners/Directors:
ICAEW Members
J P Banks

BAKER TILLY
Hartwell House, 55-61 Victoria Street, Bristol, BS1 6AD

BAKER TILLY RESTRUCTURING AND RECOVERY LLP
Hartwell House, 55-61 Victoria Street, Bristol, BS1 6AD
Tel: 0117 945 2000
Resident Partners (Non-ICAEW Members):
A M Sheridan

BAKER TILLY TAX AND ADVISORY SERVICES LLP
Hartwell House, 55-61 Victoria Street, Bristol, BS1 6AD
Resident Partners/Directors:
ICAEW Members
A P Allchin, J P Banks, E J Corrigan, A Farquhar, N J Hardy, H J Wheelhouse
Resident Partners (Non-ICAEW Members):
A M Sheridan

BAKER TILLY UK AUDIT LLP
Hartwell House, 55-61 Victoria Street, Bristol, BS1 6AD
Resident Partners/Directors:
ICAEW Members
A P Allchin, N J Hardy, D E Simpson-Price, H J Wheelhouse

BALES ◈
15 Cheddar Close, Nailsea, Bristol, BS48 4YA
Tel: 01275 854237
Email: c.bales@bales.uk.com
Website: http://www.bales.uk.com
Principal: ICAEW Member
C R Bales

BARNES HUNTER
3 Kings Court, Little King Street, Bristol, BS1 4HW
Tel: 0117 930 0061
Resident Partners/Directors:
ICAEW Members
C Barnes, D M Hunter

BDO STOY HAYWARD LLP
Fourth Floor, One Victoria Street, Bristol, BS1 6AA
Tel: 0117 930 1500
Fax: 0117 930 1505
Resident Partners/Directors:
ICAEW Members
J L H Brown, S E J Girling, P A Jelley, M Joy
Resident Partners (Non-ICAEW Members):
G D Randall

BEGBIES TRAYNOR
Harbourside House, 4-5 The Grove, Bristol, BS1 4QZ
Tel: 0117 937 7130
Website: http://www.begbies-traynor.com

SPECIALISATIONS – BUSINESS RECOVERY & INSOLVENCY

Bankruptcies
Corporate Recovery
Liquidations

BELHUS LTD
14 Dublin Crescent, Henleaze, Bristol, BS9 4NA
Tel: 0117 962 4100
Resident Partners/Directors:
ICAEW Members
D J Orr

BENEDICT MACKENZIE
Citypoint, Temple Gate, Bristol, BS1 6PL
Tel: 0117 373 6222

BER ACCOUNTING LTD
30 Old Sneed Avenue, Stoke Bishop, Bristol, BS9 1SE

BERNARD ATKINS
205 Wells Road, Knowle, Bristol, BS4 2DF

BERWELL CONSULTANCY
Bowbridge House, 23 Kings Drive, Bishopston, Bristol BS7 8JW
Tel: 0117 942 7204
Principal: ICAEW Member
C Bamber

BISHOP FLEMING
16 Queen Square, Bristol, BS1 4NT
Tel: 0117 910 0250
Website: http://www.bishopfleming.co.uk
Resident Partners/Directors:
ICAEW Members
M D Lee, J H Scaife, J M Williams

BLACKMORE & CO
Pier Cottage, Pier Road, Portishead, Bristol BS20 7HG

BLENHEIM CONSULTING LTD ◈
PO Box 464, Bristol, BS34 8SE

BLENHEIM CONSULTING LTD
3 Brins Close, Stoke Gifford, Bristol, BS34 8XU

BRIAN E HAWTHORN
12 Cotham Road, Bristol, BS6 6DR

BRIAN E RAY
30 Old Sneed Avenue, Stoke Bishop, Bristol, BS9 1SE

BRISTOL TAX SHOP
118 High Street, Staple Hill, Bristol, BS16 5HH

BURNSIDE
8 Pipe Lane, St Augustines, Bristol, BS1 5AJ

BURNSIDE (BRISTOL) LTD
8 Pipe Lane, Bristol, BS1 5AJ

BURTON SWEET ◈
Thornton House, Richmond Hill, Clifton, Bristol BS8 1AT
Tel: 0117 973 8441
Email: clifton@burton-sweet.co.uk
Website: http://www.burton-sweet.co.uk
Resident Partners/Directors:
ICAEW Members
D Biddel, T M Williams

Registered by the ICAEW to carry out company audit work

Regulated by the ICAEW for a range of investment business activities

BURTON SWEET ◈
Cornerstone House, Midland Way, Thornbury, Bristol BS35 2BS
Tel: 01454 415645

BURTON SWEET CORPORATE FINANCE
Thornton House, Richmond Hill, Clifton, Bristol BS8 1AT

BURTON SWEET CORPORATE FINANCE LTD
Thornton House, Richmond Hill, Clifton, Bristol BS8 1AT

BUTTERWORTH JONES ◈
Old Bank, The Triangle, Paulton, Bristol BS39 7LE
Tel: 01761 417414
Fax: 01761 417268
Email: paulton@butterworthjones.co.uk

Registered by the ICAEW to carry out company audit work

Regulated by the ICAEW for a range of investment business activities

C.C. WILLIAMS & CO
38 High Street, Yatton, Bristol, BS49 4JA

C.D. HUNT & CO
18 Little Stoke Road, Stoke Bishop, Bristol, BS9 1HQ
Tel: 0117 968 2019
Principal: ICAEW Member
C D Hunt

C.J. FISHER & CO
11 Oakwood Road, Henleaze, Bristol, BS9 4NP

C&M SERVICES (BRISTOL) LTD
19 The Park, Bristol, BS32 0AP
Tel: 07743 767687
Resident Partners/Directors:
ICAEW Members
K Docherty

C.V. MITCHELL & CO
4 Cranleigh Gardens, Stoke Bishop, Bristol, BS9 1HD
Tel: 0117 968 8813
Principal: ICAEW Member
C V Mitchell

CALLEN CONSULTANTS LTD
146 Bath Road, Longwell Green, Bristol, BS30 9DB

CARTER & CO
7 Downs Road, Westbury-on-Trym, Bristol, BS9 3TX
Tel: 0117 962 4926
Resident Partners/Directors:
ICAEW Members
G M Carter

CASTLE CORPORATE FINANCE LTD
Flat 505, Thomas Court, Three Queens Lane, Bristol BS1 6LF

CHRISTOPHER G. BROWN & CO
Cooks, Broad Street, Wrington, Bristol BS40 5LD
Tel: 01934 863386
Principal: ICAEW Member
C G Brown

CLARK & CO
22 Leaman Close, Chipping Sodbury, Bristol, BS37 6HA
Tel: 01454 317222
Principal: ICAEW Member
D Clark

CLEVERDON & CO ◈
82a High Street, Nailsea, Bristol, BS48 1AS
Tel: 01275 854961
Email: info@cleverdon.biz
Website: http://www.cleverdon.biz

CONWAY & CO
Glen Yeo House, Station Road, Congresbury, Bristol BS49 5DY

COPSON GRANDFIELD LTD ◈
30-31 St James Place, Mangotsfield, Bristol, BS16 9JB
Tel: 0117 956 1067
Resident Partners/Directors: ICAEW Members
S Copson

CUE & CO
6 Stanley Terrace, Bristol, BS3 3PJ

CUE & CO LTD ◈
6 Stanley Terrace, Bristol, BS3 3PJ

D.I. GARLAND
7 Highlands Road, Long Ashton, Bristol, BS41 9EN

D P HOWELL
33 Grove Road, Coombe Dingle, Bristol, BS9 2RJ

DAVID A. WILSON
5 Passage Road, Westbury On Trym, Bristol, BS9 3HN
Tel: 0117 950 9977
Principal: ICAEW Member
D A Wilson

DAVID BUNKER
3-8 Redcliffe Parade West, Bristol, BS1 6SP

DAVID COTTRELL & CO ◈
The Old Bakery, 11a Canford Lane, Westbury-on-Trym, Bristol BS9 3DE
Tel: 0117 950 5148
Principal: ICAEW Member
D Cottrell

DAVID ELLIOTT & CO
Southdown, 59 Grove Road, Coombe Dingle, Bristol BS9 2RT

DAVID EXELL ASSOCIATES
PO Box 1601, Broad Street, Wrington, Bristol BS40 5WA

DAVID S M ELLIOTT & COMPANY LTD
Southdown, 59 Grove Road, Coombe Dingle, Bristol BS9 2RT
Tel: 0117 968 5476
Resident Partners/Directors: ICAEW Members
D S M Elliott

DELOITTE & TOUCHE LLP ◈
3 Rivergate, Temple Quay, Bristol, BS1 6GD
Tel: 0117 921 1622
Website: http://www.deloitte.co.uk
Resident Partners/Directors: ICAEW Members
S L Cleveland, M Gregory, D Hedditch, M P Hill, A P M Jones, M P McQueen, I M Stone, S L Sturt, S N Woodward

DEREK J. STENNER LTD ◈
The Mews, Hounds Road, Chipping Sodbury, Bristol BS37 6EE
Tel: 01454 329100
Resident Partners/Directors: ICAEW Members
D J Stenner

DSL ACCOUNTANCY LTD
3 Ridgeview, Long Ashton, Bristol, BS41 9EQ

DUGGAN WOOD ▽
2 Westbury Mews, Westbury Hill, Westbury-on-Trym, Bristol BS9 3QA

DUNKLEY & CO
4 The Courtyard, Woodlands, Bradley Stoke, Bristol BS32 4NB

DUNKLEY & CO LTD
Woodlands Grange, Woodlands Lane, Bradley Stoke, Bristol BS32 4JY

DURY & CO
14 Fairfield Road, Montpellier, Bristol, BS6 5JP

EDWIN FUSSELL & CO
111 High Street, Hanham, Bristol, BS15 3QG

EDZELL LINDSAY LTD
8 Ashgrove Road, Redland, Bristol, BS6 6LY

ELLIOTT BUNKER LTD
3-8 Redcliffe Parade West, Bristol, BS1 6SP
Tel: 0117 929 9931
Resident Partners/Directors: ICAEW Members
P Cridland, N Michael

ERNST & YOUNG LLP
One Bridewell Street, Bristol, BS1 2AA
Tel: 0117 981 2050
Resident Partners/Directors: ICAEW Members
T Denny, S J Gratton, B Hadfield, R P Jones

EVANS & PARTNERS ◈
9 Bank Road, Kingswood, Bristol, BS15 8LS
Tel: 0117 967 5215
Fax: 0117 935 2116
Email: ep@evanspartners.co.uk
Website: http://www.evanspartners.co.uk
Date Established: 1943
Resident Partners/Directors: ICAEW Members
M R Evans, O J Evans, D Morland
Registered by the ICAEW to carry out company audit work

SPECIALISATIONS – AUDIT & ASSURANCE
Audit

SPECIALISATIONS – FINANCIAL REPORTING
Accounts Preparation

SPECIALISATIONS – SECTOR
Dentists/Opticians

SPECIALISATIONS – TAXATION
Investigations
Payroll Service and Advice
Taxation

EVANS & PARTNERS ◈
36 North Street, Bedminster, Bristol, BS3 1HW
Tel: 0117 963 5088
Email: ep@evanspartners.co.uk
Website: http://www.evanspartners.co.uk

SPECIALISATIONS – AUDIT & ASSURANCE
Audit

SPECIALISATIONS – FINANCIAL REPORTING
Accounts Preparation

SPECIALISATIONS – TAXATION
Back Duty
Payroll Service and Advice
Taxation

F.G. DAYER
9 Beaufort Road, Frampton Cotterell, Bristol, BS36 2AD

F.P.LEACH & CO
Northumbria House, 62/64 Northumbria Drive, Henleaze, Bristol BS9 4HW

F. PAYNE ◈
9 Christmas Steps, Bristol, BS1 5BS
Tel: 0117 925 3260
Principal: ICAEW Member
F Payne

FLAT MANAGEMENT CO ACCOUNTS LTD
50 Downend Road, Downend, Bristol, BS16 5UE

FORD & CO
6 Cleeve Lodge Road, Downend, Bristol, BS16 6AG

FORENSIC ACCOUNTING SERVICES
1st Floor, Aztec Centre, Aztec West, Almondsbury, Bristol BS32 4TD

G J HARBOUR
1 Windrush Road, Keynsham, Bristol, BS31 1QL

GEOFF GOLLOP & CO LTD ◈
St Brandon's House, 29 Great George Street, Bristol, BS1 5QT
Tel: 0117 920 0066
Email: gg@geoffgollop.co.uk
Resident Partners/Directors: ICAEW Members
G R Gollop
Registered by the ICAEW to carry out company audit work

SPECIALISATIONS – SECTOR
FSA Members

SPECIALISATIONS – TAXATION
Estate Planning

GILES
32 High Street, Winterbourne, Bristol, BS36 1JN

GOLDSMITHS BAYLEY LTD
7 Glentworth Road, Clifton, Bristol, BS8 4TB

GOLDWYNS (BRISTOL) LTD
9 Portland Square, Bristol, BS2 8ST
Tel: 01179 232080

GORDON A. SMITH
The Gables, 14 Beech Road, Saltford, Bristol BS31 3BE
Tel: 01225 872941
Principal: ICAEW Member
G A Smith

GORDON WOOD, SCOTT & PARTNERS
Dean House, 94 Whiteladies Road, Clifton, Bristol BS8 2QX
Tel: 0117 946 6149
Resident Partners/Directors: ICAEW Members
J D Moorcraft, R J Williams, E G Winstone

GRANT THORNTON UK LLP
Hartwell House, 55-61 Victoria Street, Bristol, BS1 6AD
Tel: 0117 926 8901
Resident Partners/Directors: ICAEW Members
M L Aldridge, P T J Brooke, R Dooley, M P Gerrard, J C Golding, P A Gourd, H R H Gregory, N Morrison, M B Warburton, P L Woodall
Non-resident Partners (ICAEW Members):
J G Davies, W H W Davies, M B Warburton
Resident Partners (Non-ICAEW Members):
L E Evans, R L Pritchard

GREENMAN FRENCH LTD
Byways, The Batch, Bishop Sutton, Bristol BS39 5US
Tel: 01275 332150
Resident Partners/Directors: ICAEW Members
S K French

HARWOOD LANE & CO ◈
1-4 Crossley Farm Business Centre, Swan Lane, Winterbourne, Bristol BS36 1RH
Tel: 01454 772727
Fax: 01454 773737
Email: mail@harwoodlane.co.uk
Website: http://www.harwoodlane.co.uk
Resident Partners/Directors: ICAEW Members
R C Cook, D C Cox
Registered by the ICAEW to carry out company audit work
Regulated by the ICAEW for a range of investment business activities
See display advertisement near this entry.

HENRY AND BANWELL LTD
26 Berkeley Square, Clifton, Bristol, BS8 1HP

HOLLINGDALE POOLEY
Bramford House, 23 Westfield Park, Clifton, Bristol BS6 6LT

HOLLINGDALE POOLEY LTD
Bramford House, 23 Westfield Park, Clifton, Bristol BS6 6LT

HOUGHTON STONE ★
The Conifers, Filton Road, Hambrook, Bristol BS16 1QG

HW BRISTOL LTD
174 Whiteladies Road, Clifton, Bristol, BS8 2XU
Tel: 0117 974 2569
Resident Partners/Directors: ICAEW Members
M J Bracher, G C Fairclough, A S Minifie, D E Seabright

HWCA LTD ◈
174 Whiteladies Road, Bristol, Gloucestershire, BS8 2XU
Tel: 0117 974 2569
Resident Partners/Directors: ICAEW Members
M J Bracher

IAIN S.E. WILTSHIRE
111 High Street, Hanham, Bristol, BS15 3QG
Tel: 0117 967 7788
Principal: ICAEW Member
I S E Wiltshire

IAIN S.E. WILTSHIRE LTD
111 High Street, Hanham, Bristol, BS15 3QG
Tel: 0117 967 7788
Resident Partners/Directors: ICAEW Members
I S E Wiltshire

IAN F CONWAY & CO ◈
The Gatehouse, 9 Farleigh Court, Old Weston Road, Flax Bourton, Bristol BS48 1UR

ICON CORPORATE FINANCE ◈
5 Kings Court, Little King Street, Bristol, BS1 4HW
Tel: 0117 922 0505

INNISFREE 2000 LTD
Charnwood House, Marsh Road, Ashton, Bristol BS3 2NA
Tel: 0117 962 8889
Resident Partners/Directors: ICAEW Members
R A Stone

J. BRAIN
8 Whitegates, Shopping Centre, Flaxpits Lane, Winterbourne, Bristol BS36 1JX

J.I.COLLINSON
12 Windsor Place, Mangotsfield, Bristol, BS16 9DD
Tel: 0117 956 2997
Principal: ICAEW Member
J I Collinson

J.L. WHITE & CO
46 Engine Lane, Nailsea, Bristol, BS48 4RL

J. PEARSON & CO ◈
Patch Elm House, Patch Elm Lane, Rangeworthy, Bristol BS37 7LT

J. WHITE & CO
46 Engine Lane, Nailsea, Bristol BS48 4RL

JAMES
6 Beaconsfield Road, Clifton, Bristol, BS8 2TS
Tel: 0117 973 9517
Email: james_accountants@blueyonder.co.uk
Principal: ICAEW Member
C L Bettridge
Registered by the ICAEW to carry out company audit work

JAMES & CO
15 Queens Walk, Thornbury, Bristol, BS35 1SR
Tel: 01454 885452
Principal: ICAEW Member
A R James

JAMES H.P. MCLAUGHLIN
34 Ludlow Close, Willsbridge, Bristol, BS30 6EB

JANET ESSEX
Saville Court, 11 Saville Place, Clifton, Bristol BS8 4EJ

JEREMY WINDOWS
5 Beauley Road, Bristol, BS3 1PX

JEREMY WINDOWS LTD
5 Beauley Road, Bristol, BS3 1PX

JM MUSE FCA
38 Lawrence Weston Road, Bristol, BS11 0PR

JOANNE BELLEW
1 Pier Close, Portishead, Bristol, BS20 7BU

JOHN DAVIS & CO ★
172 Gloucester Road, Bristol, BS7 8NU

JULIE WAKEFORD
7 The Lawns, Yatton, Bristol, BS49 4BG
Tel: 01934 834969
Principal: ICAEW Member
J C Wakeford

K.M. VICKERS & CO LTD
Avon Court, 82-84 Hotwell Road, Hotwells, Bristol BS8 4UB

KAREN BABER
24 Long Thorn, Backwell, Bristol, BS48 3GY
Tel: 01275 461065
Principal: ICAEW Member
K S Baber

KELLER & CO
367b Church Road, Frampton Cotterell, Bristol, BS36 2AQ

KELLER ACCOUNTANCY SERVICES LTD
367b Church Road, Frampton Cotterell, Bristol, BS36 2AQ

KLG ASSOCIATES LTD
66B Cleeve Hill, Downend, Bristol, BS16 6HQ

KPMG LLP
100 Temple Street, Bristol, BS1 6AG
Tel: 0117 905 4000
Resident Partners/Directors: ICAEW Members
A Antonius, D R Burgess, C M Casey, D P Clifford, M J Cockwell, D J Crawshaw, R S Gaunt, R J Hill, A J Hodgson, P F Spicer, S A Tharani
Resident Partners (Non-ICAEW Members):
A Campbell-Orde, N Hopkins

KPS
6 Cleeve Lodge Road, Downend, Bristol, BS16 6AG

LATRIGG LTD
Latrigg, The Glen, Saltford, Bristol BS31 3JP
Tel: 01225 400237
Resident Partners/Directors: ICAEW Members
H E Grist

LAWES & CO UK LTD
Boyces Building, 42 Regent Street, Clifton, Bristol BS8 4HU
Tel: 0117 974 5221
Resident Partners/Directors: ICAEW Members
K L Lawes
Registered by the ICAEW to carry out company audit work

continued

LAWES & CO UK LTD *cont*
Authorised and regulated by the Financial Services Authority for investment business

LIONEL C HARBER
37 Charnhill Drive, Mangotsfield, Bristol, BS16 9JR

LLOYDBOTTOMS
118 High Street, Staple Hill, Bristol, BS16 5HH
Tel: 0117 957 3537
Website: http://www.lloydbottoms.co.uk
Regulated by the ICAEW for a range of investment business activities

LLOYDBOTTOMS LTD
118 High Street, Staple Hill, Bristol, BS16 5HH

LYONS & CO
18 Barn Owl Way, Stoke Gifford, Bristol, BS34 8RZ
Tel: 0117 983 0042
Principal: ICAEW Member
C J Lyons

M J COOMBS
Ty Nant, Rotcombe Lane, High Littleton, Bristol BS39 6JP

M.R COOPER
1 Cheddar Close, Nailsea, Bristol, BS48 4YA

M W MEDICAL ▽
2 Westbury Mews, Westbury Hill, Westbury-on-Trym, Bristol BS9 3QA

MANSON BOXA LTD ◈
8 Kings Road, Clifton, Bristol, BS8 4AB
Tel: 0845 054 5559
Website: http://www.mansonboxa.co.uk
Resident Partners/Directors: ICAEW Members
J Manson

MARGARET MUNDY ACA
5 Beauley Road, Bristol, BS3 1PX

MARY ASFOUR
21 Fremantle Road, Bristol, BS6 5SY
Tel: 0117 924 6760
Principal: ICAEW Member
T M Asfour

MATRIX ACCOUNTING AND TAXATION SOLUTIONS
4 The Courtyard, Woodlands, Bradley Stoke, Bristol BS32 4NB

MATTHEWS ACCOUNTING
125 Cranbrook Road, Redland, Bristol, BS6 7DE

MAZARS CORPORATE FINANCE LTD ◈
Clifton Down House, Beaufort Buildings, Clifton, Bristol BS8 4AN

MAZARS LLP ◈
Clifton Down House, Beaufort Buildings, Clifton Down, Clifton, Bristol BS8 4AN
Tel: 0117 973 4481
Resident Partners/Directors: ICAEW Members
T C H Ball, D R A Bott, A T H Edwards, M A Stewart
Registered by the ICAEW to carry out company audit work
Authorised and regulated by the Financial Services Authority for investment business
Individual(s) licensed for insolvency work by the ICAEW

MBA MICHAEL BISHOP & ASSOCIATES
Elderns, 19b Kings Weston Road, Henbury, Bristol BS10 7QT

MENSIS LTD ◈
8 The Plain, Thornbury, Bristol, BS35 2AG
Tel: 01454 417300
Email: info@mensis.co.uk
Date Established: 1995

SPECIALISATIONS – BUSINESS & GENERAL ADVICE

Book-keeping
Company Formation
Company Secretarial Service
Data Processing Services
Management Accounting Consultancy
Management Advice to Business

SPECIALISATIONS – FINANCIAL REPORTING

Accounts Preparation
Limited Companies
Limited Company Accounts
Partnership/Sole Trader Accounts

SPECIALISATIONS – TAXATION

Capital Gains — Limited Companies
Capital Gains — Personal
Customs Duty
National Insurance Advice
Partnerships and Sole Traders
PAYE Advice
Payroll Service and Advice
Personal
Self Assessment Advice
Small Traders
UK Nationals Overseas
Value Added Tax

General Description: Pro-active accountancy and taxation support throughout the year.
See display advertisement near this entry.

MICHAEL J. COOMBS
Ty Nant, Rotcombe Lane, High Littleton, Bristol BS39 6JP

MILES CMC
Stanley House, 33-35 West Hill, Portishead, Bristol BS20 6LG
Tel: 01275 848550
Website: http://www.milescmc.co.uk
Principal: ICAEW Member
C J Miles
Registered by the ICAEW to carry out company audit work

MILLENER DAVIES
Southfield House, Southfield Road, Westbury On Trym, Bristol BS9 3BH
Tel: 0117 962 1110
Fax: 0117 962 1400
Email: md@millener-davies.co.uk
Resident Partners/Directors: ICAEW Members
G E Davies, P A Millener
Registered by the ICAEW to carry out company audit work
Authorised and regulated by the Financial Services Authority for investment business

MILSTED LANGDON LLP
1 Redcliff Street, Bristol, BS1 6NP
Tel: 0117 9452 500
Resident Partners/Directors: ICAEW Members
N P Belletty, R A S Isaacs, D S Jacobs, S R Jenkins

MONICA C.A. JAMES
2 Scots Cottages, Kington, Thornbury, Bristol BS35 1NF

MOONEY WILLIAMS MAY LTD
11 Great George Street, Bristol, BS1 5RR
Tel: 0117 929 2393
Resident Partners/Directors: ICAEW Members
M T Mooney, C G Williams

MOORE STEPHENS LLP
1-2 Little King Street, Bristol, BS1 4HW

NAYLOR WILLIS
Redland House, 157 Redland Road, Bristol, BS6 6YE

NEIL ELLIS CONSULTING
18 Imperial Walk, Bristol, BS14 9AE

NEXIA SMITH & WILLIAMSON AUDIT LTD
Portwall Place, Portwall Lane, Bristol, BS1 6NA

NEXIA SMITH & WILLIAMSON LLP
Portwall Place, Portwall Lane, Bristol, BS1 6NA
Tel: 0117 376 2000

NICHOLAS WELLS
7 Fenbrook Close, Hambrook, Bristol, BS16 1QJ

NICK JAMES
Yew Tree Cottage, Scot Lane, Chew Stoke, Bristol BS40 8UW

NIGEL D. SARA
12 Paulton Drive, Bishopston, Bristol, BS7 8JJ

ONE 2 ONE ACCOUNTANTS LTD
108 Bedminster Down Road, Bristol, BS13 7AF
Tel: 0117 9663 121
Resident Partners/Directors: ICAEW Members
M J Richards

P.A.P. LEACH
14 Manilla Rd, Clifton, Bristol, BS8 4ED

PARRY BUSINESS SERVICES LTD
28 Briarwood, Westbury on Trym, Bristol, BS9 3SS
Tel: 0117 962 8120
Email: info@parrybsl.com
Resident Partners/Directors: ICAEW Members
S M Parry
General Description: Accounting & tax advice for SMEs.

PATRICK O'CONOR BSC FCA ◈
51 Downs Park West, Westbury Park, Bristol, BS6 7QL

PAUL CROWDY PARTNERSHIP LTD
Redmayne House, 4 Whiteladies Road, Clifton, Bristol BS8 1PD

PAUL FORD & CO
26 Cherwell Road, Keynsham, Bristol, BS31 1QT

PAYNE & CO
Holly Cottage, Over Lane, Almondsbury, Bristol BS32 4DF

PAYNE & CO ACCOUNTANTS LTD
Holly Cottage, Over Lane, Almondsbury, Bristol BS32 4DF

PETER HAIGH ◈
The Old Estate Office, Westway Farm, Bishop Sutton, Bristol BS39 5XP
Tel: 01275 334296
Principal: ICAEW Member
P J Haigh

PETER J. BALL
25 Kersteman Road, Bristol, BS6 7BX
Tel: 0117 924 5358
Principal: ICAEW Member
P J Ball

PETER S. WHITFIELD
13 Briarwood, Westbury on Trym, Bristol, BS9 3SS
Tel: 0117 962 9297
Principal: ICAEW Member
P S Whitfield

PETER SMITH LTD
50 Downend Road, Downend, Bristol, BS16 5UE

PETER SMITH FCA
50 Downend Road, Downend, Bristol, BS16 5UE

PHILIP WALKER
Anthony's Well, Chew Stoke, Bristol, BS40 8XG

PHILLIP CORBIN
Trym Lodge, 1 Henbury Road, Westbury-on-Trym, Bristol BS9 3HQ
Tel: 0845 226 6962
Website: http://www.phillipcorbin.co.uk
Principal: ICAEW Member
P A Corbin
SPECIALISATIONS – TAXATION
Capital Gains — Limited Companies
Capital Gains — Personal
Self Assessment Advice
Taxation
General Description: Taking the trouble out of tax.

PICKLED PARSNIP LTD
236 Henleaze Road, Henleaze, Bristol, BS9 4NG

PJE
3 Oakfield Court, Oakfield Road, Clifton, Bristol BS8 2BD

PKF (UK) LLP
Pannell House, 6-7 Litfield Place, Clifton, Bristol BS8 3LX
Tel: 0117 906 4000
Email: info.bristol@uk.pkf.com
Website: http://www.pkf.co.uk
Resident Partners/Directors: ICAEW Members
N J Buxton, N E S Dimes, A D J Lloyd

POLLARD GOODMAN
49 High Street, Westbury on Trym, Bristol, BS9 3ED
Tel: 0117 959 0599
Resident Partners/Directors: ICAEW Members
C V Pollard

PREMIER FINANCIAL DIRECTION LTD ◈
Mead Court, Stock Lane, Langford, Bristol BS40 5EU
Tel: 01934 853388
Resident Partners/Directors: ICAEW Members
C J Gahagan

PRICEWATERHOUSE-COOPERS
31 Great George Street, Bristol, BS1 5QD

PRICEWATERHOUSE-COOPERS LLP
31 Great George Street, Bristol, BS1 5QD
Tel: 0117 929 1500
Resident Partners/Directors: ICAEW Members
R F Bacon, C A Bates, K A Beaumont, T N Bentham, P F Bonvoisin, S J Chapman, D L Charles, T J Coyle, A B Elgood, S J Fish, C G Gentle, S W Harrison, A J Hemus, D A Howell, R N Lewis

PROPHET & COLLINSON
Leicester House, 116A Station Road, Yate, Bristol BS37 4PQ

PROWTING & PARTNERS LTD
6 West Park, Clifton, Bristol, BS8 2LT

R G HOLDER & CO LTD
Whetcombe Whey, Ropers Lane, Wrington, Bristol BS40 5NH

R.S. PORTER & CO
77/81 Alma Rd, Clifton, Bristol, BS8 2DP

RAYMARSH
6 Cleeve Lodge Road, Downend, Bristol, BS16 6AG

RAYMARSH FORD LTD
6 Cleeve Lodge Road, Downend, Bristol, BS16 6AG

REDLAND BUSINESS CONSULTANCY LTD
4 Branksome Road, Redland, Bristol, BS6 7LL
Tel: 0117 924 8312
Resident Partners/Directors: ICAEW Members
F E Small

RICHARDSON WHITBY SMITH LTD
137a Shirehampton Road, Sea Mills, Bristol, BS9 2EA

RICHARDSON WHITBY SMITH LTD
53 High Street, Keynsham, Bristol, BS31 1DS

ROBERT BROWN & CO ◈
6 Clanage Road, Bower Ashton, Bristol, BS3 2JX
Tel: 0117 966 4578
Email: robert@rtbrown.co.uk
Website: http://www.rtbrown.co.uk
Principal: ICAEW Member
R T Brown
Registered by the ICAEW to carry out company audit work

ROBERT M. WALTERS
5 Glen Drive, Stoke Bishop, Bristol, BS9 1SA

ROBERTS & CO (BRISTOL) LTD
24 High Street, Chipping Sodbury, Bristol, BS37 6AH

ROBSON TAYLOR LLP ◈
Froomsgate House, Rupert Street, Bristol, BS1 2QJ

ROGER C. OATEN
First Floor, 23 Westfield Park, Redland, Bristol BS6 6LT

ROGERS EVANS
Suite B1, White House Business Centre, Forest Road, Kingswood, Bristol BS15 8NH

ROGERS PAULLEY
Arclight House, 3 Unity Street, Bristol, BS1 5HH
Tel: 0117 930 8700

ROGERS PAULLEY LTD
Arclight House, 3 Unity Street, Bristol, BS1 5HH
Tel: 0117 930 8700
Resident Partners/Directors: ICAEW Members
C S Rogers

ROSSITER SMITH & CO
Bank House, 1 Burlington Road, Bristol, BS6 6TJ

ROY MACFARLANE
Saville Court, Saville Place, Clifton, Bristol BS8 4EJ

RSM BENTLEY JENNISON ◈
Third Floor Howard House, Queens Avenue, Clifton, Bristol BS8 1QT
Tel: 0117 925 9255
Fax: 0117 980 6900
Email: geoff.speirs@rsmbentleyjennison.com
Website: http://www.rsmbentleyjennison.com
Resident Partners/Directors: ICAEW Members
D R Cook, A J Hards, G M Sinkinson, G P Speirs, A J Wood
Registered by the ICAEW to carry out company audit work

S.M. JAUFURAULLY
122 Northover Road, Westbury On Trym, Bristol, BS9 3LG

SAFFERY CHAMPNESS ◈
Beaufort House, 2 Beaufort Road, Clifton, Bristol BS8 2AE
Tel: 0117 915 1617
Fax: 0117 915 1618
Website: http://www.saffery.com
Training Contracts Available.
Resident Partners/Directors: ICAEW Members
J Barnes, D Lemon, D C Wragg
Resident Partners (Non-ICAEW Members):
R J Cartwright
Other Offices: Bournemouth, Edinburgh, Geneva, Guernsey, Harrogate, High Wycombe, Inverness, Manchester, London, Peterborough

continued

SAFFERY CHAMPNESS *cont*

Registered by the ICAEW to carry out company audit work

Regulated by the ICAEW for a range of investment business activities

Authorised and regulated by the Financial Services Authority for investment business

INVESTOR IN PEOPLE

General Description: See London office entry.

SALLY MORRIS ACCOUNTANCY
15 Broadway Road, Bishopston, Bristol, BS7 8ES
Tel: 0117 942 2128
Email: sally.morris@smaccountancy.co.uk
Website: http://www.smaccountancy.co.uk
Resident Partners/Directors: ICAEW Members
S E Morris

SAM BINKS
Coombe Farm Cottage, Canford Lane, Bristol, BS9 3PE

SAYER VINCENT
King's House, Orchard Street, Bristol, BS1 5EH

AERO ACCOUNTANCY SERVICES LTD
43 William Street, Totterdown, Bristol, BS3 4TY

SIMON STORVIK & COMPANY LTD
7 Rockleaze Avenue, Bristol, BS9 1NG

SIRI PERERA
6 Seymour Avenue, Bishopston, Bristol, BS7 9HJ

NEXIA SMITH & WILLIAMSON AUDIT (BRISTOL) LLP
Portwall Place, Portwall Lane, Bristol, BS1 6NA

SMITH & WILLIAMSON (BRISTOL) LLP
Portwall Place, Portwall Lane, Bristol, BS1 6NA

SMITH & WILLIAMSON LLP
Oakfield House, Oakfield Grove, Clifton, Bristol BS8 2BN

SMITH & WILLIAMSON SOLOMON HARE
Oakfield House, 15-23 Oakfield Grove, Bristol, BS8 2BN
Tel: 0117 933 3000
Resident Partners/Directors: ICAEW Members
M D Lea, P E Moody, D W Roper
General Description: Smith and Williamson is an independent professional and financial services group employing over 1400 people. We are leading providers of investment management, financial advisory and accountancy services to private clients, professional practices and mid-sized companies. Nexia Smith & Williamson Audit (Bristol) LLP provides audit services to complement the specialist financial advisory services provided by Smith & Williamson.

SOPHIE TRAFFORD
Church Lodge, Station Road, Wrington, Bristol BS40 5LG

SPARKES & CO
Tarquin, Brinsea Road, Congresbury, Bristol BS49 5JF
Tel: 01934 833141
Principal: ICAEW Member
R E Sparkes

STANLEY JOSEPH LTD
The Clock Tower, Farleigh Court, Old Weston Road, Flax Bourton, Bristol BS48 1UR

STEVEN WAINWRIGHT FCA
11 Sandling Avenue, Horfield, Bristol, BS7 0HS
Tel: 07811 182629
Principal: ICAEW Member
S R Wainwright

STONE & PARTNERS
571 Fishponds Road, Fishponds, Bristol, BS16 3AF

STUART A. GRIGGS
99 High Street, Yatton, Bristol, BS49 4DR

SULLY PARTNERSHIP
8 Unity Street, College Green, Bristol, BS1 5HH
Tel: 0117 317 7000
Resident Partners/Directors: ICAEW Members
I C Bascombe, N J Chivers

TAX PARTNER LTD
21 Dennyview Road, Abbots Leigh, Bristol, BS8 3RD

TONY DICKER LTD
29 Courtenay Road, Keynsham, Bristol, BS31 1JU
Tel: 0117 330 8501

TRENFIELD WILLIAMS
The Old Railway Station, Sea Mills Lane, Stoke Bishop, Bristol BS9 1FF

TYLER & CO
3 Home Farm Way, Easter Compton, Bristol, BS35 5SE

TYRRELL'S
69 Princess Victoria Street, Clifton, Bristol, BS8 4DD

WALBROOK BUREAU SERVICES LTD
34 High Street, Westbury-on-Trym, Bristol, BS9 3DZ

WARREN & CO BUSINESS CONSULTANCY LTD
Meadhaven, Church Lane, Flax Bourton, Bristol BS48 3QF
Tel: 01275 464444
Resident Partners/Directors: ICAEW Members
C R Warren, L J Warren

WARREN & CO (PARTNERSHIP)
Meadhaven, Church Lane, Flax Bourton, Bristol BS48 3QF
Tel: 01275 464444
Resident Partners/Directors: ICAEW Members
C R Warren, L J Warren

WEST COUNTRY ACCOUNTING SERVICES LTD
D2 White House Business Centre, House Forest Road, Kingswood, Bristol BS15 8DH
Tel: 0117 980 5960
Resident Partners/Directors: ICAEW Members
L J Levan

WESTCAS
D2 White House Buisness Centre, Forest Road, Kingswood, Bristol BS15 8DH

WHITTAKER GREGORY & CO
Brick House, 21 Horse Street, Chipping Sodbury, Bristol BS37 6DA
Tel: 01454 318191
Resident Partners/Directors: ICAEW Members
M C Gregory, C D Whittaker

WHYATT PAKEMAN PARTNERS
Colkin House, 16 Oakfield Rd, Clifton, Bristol BS8 2AP
Tel: 0117 973 0294
Fax: 0117 923 8249
Email: wpp@wpp.uk.com
Website: http://www.wpp.uk.com
Resident Partners/Directors: ICAEW Members
D K Golledge, P Hemmings, R Pimblett, P G Tyler

Registered by the ICAEW to carry out company audit work

Regulated by the ICAEW for a range of investment business activities

General Description: Long established independent practice with commitment and enthusiasm to work closely with, and guide clients through, the challenges and opportunities they face in today's business environment. Services include audit, tax planning and compliance, business start up and accounts preparation, management advice and forecasts, computer consultancy and payroll bureau.

WILLIAM PRICE & CO
Westbury Court, Church Road, Westbury-on-Trym, Bristol BS9 3EF

WINTERS CONSULTING
59A North Street, Nailsea, Bristol, BS48 4BS

WORMALD & PARTNERS ★ ◈
Redland House, 157 Redland Road, Bristol, BS6 6YE
Tel: 0117 973 6856
Resident Partners/Directors: ICAEW Members
N A Dando, D R Patel

YAQUB & CO
274 Stapleton Road, Easton, Bristol, BS5 0NW

YAQUB & CO LTD
274 Stapleton Road, Easton, Bristol, BS5 0NW

BRIXHAM

JAMES KNIGHTON
2 Copythorne Road, Brixham, TQ5 8QQ

PETER RILEY
21 New Road, Brixham, TQ5 8NB
Tel: 01803 858912
Principal: ICAEW Member
P W Riley

WILLIAM OXLEY
6 The Mount, Furzeham, Brixham, TQ5 8QY

BROADSTAIRS

FOWLES W.J.
12 Waldron Road, Broadstairs, CT10 1TB
Tel: 01843 863639
Principal: ICAEW Member
W J Fowles

J CLEVERDON LTD
7 The Broadway, Broadstairs, CT10 2AD

KEMPS ◈
84 High Street, Broadstairs, CT10 1JJ

KEMPS ACCOUNTING SOLUTIONS LTD
84 High Street, Broadstairs, CT10 1JJ

LEVICKS
Station Gates, 3 Lloyd Road, Broadstairs, CT10 1HY
Tel: 01843 862716
Resident Partners/Directors: ICAEW Members
M A Collier, M J Hurdman

SEWELL & CO ◈
Rafters, 31 Luton Avenue, Broadstairs, CT10 2DH

SPURLING CANNON LTD
45a High Street, Broadstairs, CT10 1JP

W.J. FOWLES F.C.A.
12 Waldron Road, Broadstairs, CT10 1TB

BROADSTONE

BURTON PIPER & CO
12 Sorrel Gardens, Broadstone, BH18 9WA
Tel: 07906 520384
Principal: ICAEW Member
T M B Piper

CHRISTOPHER J. ADAMS
5 Portmore Close, Broadstone, BH18 8BZ
Tel: 01202 605556
Email: info@christopher-adams.co.uk
Principal: ICAEW Member
C J Adams

DAVID ENDICOTT
47 Ashwood Drive, Broadstone, BH18 8LN

DAVID J PAYNE LTD
Room 5, 13b Moor Road, Broadstone, BH18 8AZ

DAVID RIDLEY ASSOCIATES
Manor House, 1 Macaulay Road, Broadstone, BH18 8AS

HELEN PHENIX & CO
61 Greensleeves Avenue, Broadstone, BH18 8BJ
Tel: 01202 604562
Principal: ICAEW Member
H L Phenix

LAMBERT MANN LTD
33 Corfe Way, Broadstone, BH18 9ND
Tel: 01202 250900
Resident Partners/Directors: ICAEW Members
K P F Mann

NEWTON MAGNUS LTD ◈
Arrowsmith Court, Station Approach, Broadstone, BH18 8AT
Tel: 01202 697611
Resident Partners/Directors: ICAEW Members
S I Magnus

THOMAS HARVEY
11a Upper Golf Links Road, Broadstone, BH18 8BT

BROADWAY

ALPHA ACCOUNTANCY EVESHAM LTD
35 Badsey Road, Willersey, Broadway, WR12 7PR

LINDSAY BECKMAN & CO
8 Bloxham Road, Broadway, WR12 7EU
Tel: 01386 853653
Principal: ICAEW Member
L Beckman

LINDSAY BECKMAN & CO LTD
8 Bloxham Road, Broadway, WR12 7EU
Tel: 01386 853653
Resident Partners/Directors: ICAEW Members
L Beckman

BROCKENHURST

DAVID GRIFFITHS ◈
Westville, Ober Road, Brockenhurst, SO42 7ST
Tel: 01590 623487
Principal: ICAEW Member
D Griffiths

NICHOLAS FILOSE
Greenmead, Waters Grn, Brockenhurst, SO42 7RG

TAX & ACCOUNTS SOLUTIONS LTD
2 Garland Cottage, Lyndhurst Road, Brockenhurst, SO42 7RH

BROMLEY

AIMS - ANDREW MACKAY FCA
39 Hillbrow Road, Bromley, BR1 4JL

BAKER TILLY
Lancaster House, 7 Elmfield Road, Bromley, BR1 1LT
Tel: 020 8461 8000
Resident Partners/Directors: ICAEW Members
H L Arthurs, A Hollands, I E Stewart
Resident Partners (Non-ICAEW Members):
A F Lovett

BAKER TILLY
Lancaster House, 7 Elmfield Road, Bromley, BR1 1LT

BAKER TILLY TAX AND ADVISORY SERVICES LLP
Lancaster House, 7 Elmfield Road, Bromley, BR1 1LT
Tel: 020 8461 8000
Resident Partners/Directors: ICAEW Members
H L Arthurs, R F Cornish, M B Hearne, A Hollands, S J Robb, I E Stewart
Resident Partners (Non-ICAEW Members):
A F Lovett

BRIDGE GADHOK & CO
12 Homefield Road, Bromley, BR1 3AL

BRYAN BURR
9 Waverley Close, Bromley, BR2 9SW

C. BAJARIA & CO
42 Bromley Common, Bromley, BR2 9PD

CKP
141 Queen Anne Avenue, Bromley, BR2 0SH

CRANE & PARTNERS
Sussex House, 8-10 Homesdale Road, Bromley, BR2 9LZ
Tel: 020 8464 0131
Fax: 020 8464 6018
Email: info@craneandpartners.com
Website: http://www.craneandpartners.com
Resident Partners/Directors: ICAEW Members
G Atkin, G A Collett, R T McDonagh

Registered by the ICAEW to carry out company audit work

Authorised and regulated by the Financial Services Authority for investment business
Individual(s) licensed for insolvency work by another RPB

D.P. MARSHALL ★
25 Highfield Road, Bickley, Bromley, BR1 2JN
Tel: 020 8467 4072
Resident Partners/Directors: ICAEW Members
D P Marshall

DALY MANDEL
105 Southlands Road, Bromley, BR2 9QT
Tel: 020 8466 0771
Principal: ICAEW Member
P W B Mandel

DAVID CLARK
Broadway House, 3 High Street, Bromley, BR1 1LF

DAVID PAUL
5 Aldermary Road, Bromley, BR1 3PH
Tel: 020 8466 7695
Principal: ICAEW Member
D J Paul

ENTERPRISE SOLUTIONS (ENGLAND) LTD
Findings, Woodlands Close, Bromley, BR1 2BD

F.W. BERRINGER & CO ◈
Lygon House, 50 London Road, Bromley, BR1 3RA
Tel: 020 8290 1113
Fax: 020 8461 6950
Email: info@fwberringer.co.uk
Resident Partners/Directors: ICAEW Members
P Allan, J Cardnell, C J Raven, P Tymms
Resident Partners (Non-ICAEW Members):
Y M Mantle

Registered by the ICAEW to carry out company audit work

Regulated by the ICAEW for a range of investment business activities

FOXWELL & CO
12 The Dale, Keston, BR2 6HW
Tel: 01689 860588
Principal: ICAEW Member
A G Foxwell

GRUGEON REYNOLDS LTD
Rutland House, 44 Masons Hill, Bromley, BR2 9JG
Tel: 020 8460 0543
Email: info@grugeonreynolds.co.uk
Website: http://www.grugeonreynolds.co.uk
Resident Partners/Directors: ICAEW Members
K Cheeseman, M J Porter, A Roberts

HARRISON HILL CASTLE & CO
Melbury House, 34 Southborough Road, Bickley, Bromley BR1 2EB

HEATHER M GOULD FCA
51 Lakes Road, Keston, BR2 6BN
Tel: 07890 852547
Principal: ICAEW Member
H M Gould

J.S. TIDMARSH
121 Durham Road, Bromley, BR2 0SP

J.S. TILEY
Spignalls, Woodlands Road, Bromley, BR1 2AE

KELLEDY & CO
4 Cecil Way, Hayes, Bromley, BR2 7JU
Tel: 020 8462 1982
Principal: ICAEW Member
D A Kelledy

KEMPTON, EMSDEN & CO
34 Napier Road, Bromley, BR2 9JA
Tel: 020 8460 7295
Principal: ICAEW Member
T D Wingham

PAUL CRAIK
51 Mead Way, Bromley, BR2 9ER

PAULINE LONSDALE
Broadway House, 3 High Street, Bromley, BR1 1LF
Tel: 020 8228 1207
Email: pauline.lonsdale@lineone.net
Website: http://www.paulinelonsdale.co.uk
Principal: ICAEW Member
P A Lonsdale

Regulated by the ICAEW for a range of investment business activities

SPECIALISATIONS – TAXATION

Capital Gains — Personal
Employee
Estate and Inheritance

continued

PAULINE LONSDALE *cont*
Executorship
Foreign Nationals in the UK
Personal
Trusts
UK Nationals Overseas
General Description: Member of the Society of Trust and Estate Practitioners. Services to professional firms and individuals. Accountancy and taxation support to solicitors in probate, trust and family matters.

PBMC
Westcliff House, 106 Southlands Road, Bromley, BR2 9QY

PHILIP S. COOPER
22 Mays Hill Road, Shortlands, Bromley, BR2 0HN
Tel: 020 8466 8424
Principal: ICAEW Member
P S Cooper

STERLING HAY
Kingfisher House, 21-23 Elmfield Road, Bromley, BR1 1LT

SUSAN ATKINS
Yew House, Barnet Wood Road, Bromley, BR2 8HJ

WINTER & CO
Melbury House, 34 Southborough Road, Bickley, Bromley BR1 2EB

BROMSGROVE

BATTLEFIELD LTD ◈
Battlefield House, Kidderminster Road, Dodford, Bromsgrove B61 9AD

CURO
Curo House, Greenbox, Westonhall Road, Stoke Prior, Bromsgrove B60 4AL

CURO PROFESSIONAL SERVICES LTD
Curo House, Greenbox, Westonhall Road, Stoke Prior, Bromsgrove B60 4AL
Tel: 0870 428 9482
Resident Partners/Directors: ICAEW Members
A Madden, J A Whelan

FULLARD DUFFILL
106 Birmingham Road, Bromsgrove, B61 0DF

HARRISON, PRIDDEY & CO
22 St John Street, Bromsgrove, B61 8QY

J.L. WYATT & CO
6 College Road, Bromsgrove, B60 2NE
Tel: 01527 871532
Principal: ICAEW Member
J L Wyatt

JOHN E. LAVENDER
4 Fox Lane, Bromsgrove, B61 7NL

JOHN H SMITH ◈
Little Acre, Perryfields Road, Bromsgrove, B61 8QW
Tel: 01527 875277
Principal: ICAEW Member
J H Smith

KAVANAGH LTD
Battlefield House, Kidderminster Road, Dodford, Bromsgrove B61 9AD
Tel: 01527 559203
Website: http://www.kavanaghco.com
Resident Partners/Directors: ICAEW Members
P J Kavanagh
Registered by the ICAEW to carry out company audit work

KENNETH H. BLEARS
Church Green, 4 Church Lane, Bromsgrove, B61 8RB

KENNETH MORRIS LTD
9-11 New Road, Bromsgrove, B60 2JF
Tel: 01527 872888
Email: mail@kennethmorris.co.uk
Website: http://www.kennethmorris.co.uk
Resident Partners (Non-ICAEW Members):
T J Ford
Regulated by the ICAEW for a range of investment business activities

PINFIELDS LTD
George House, 2A Worcester Road, Bromsgrove, B61 7AB

S & J ACCOUNTANTS ★
27 Wildmoor Lane, Catshill, Bromsgrove, B61 0NT

SHERWOOD HARBORNE LTD
Sherwood House, 548 Birmingham Road, Lydiate Ash, Bromsgrove B61 0HT

BROMYARD

ANDREW WINTERBURN LTD
Lloyds Bank Chambers, 17 Broad Street, Bromyard, HR7 4BT
Tel: 01885 488 990
Fax: 01885 488809
Resident Partners/Directors: ICAEW Members
A S Winterburn

COLE BISHOP & CO
Market Square Chambers, Bromyard, HR7 4BP

COLE BISHOP & CO LTD
Market Square Chambers, Bromyard, HR7 4BP
Tel: 01885 483268
Resident Partners/Directors: ICAEW Members
M Bishop

HOYLE & CO
Wootton Farm, Pencombe, Bromyard, HR7 4RR
Tel: 01885 400775
Principal: ICAEW Member
J A Hoyle

BROUGH

BLUESKY CORPORATE FINANCE LTD
Milestone Farm, 56-58 Westgate, North Cave, Brough HU15 2NJ

CLIFFORD DAY
21 Pinfold, South Cave, Brough, HU15 2HE
Tel: 01430 423572
Principal: ICAEW Member
C Day

JOHNSON & CO
Hawthorn House, 28 Cowgate, Welton, Brough HU15 1NB

TINA WAKELING FCA
25 Southcote Close, South Cave, Brough, HU15 2BQ

TWS
25 Southcote Close, South Cave, Brough, HU15 2BQ

BROUGHTON-IN-FURNESS

ACCOUNTING EVIDENCE LTD
Well House, Broughton-in-Furness, LA20 6HS
Tel: 01229 716651
Email: info@accountingevidence.com
Website: http://www.accountingevidence.com
Mobile: 07816 767154

SPECIALISATIONS – FORENSIC ACCOUNTING
Expert Witnesses in Litigation
Forensic Accounting

General Description: Accounting Evidence Ltd are forensic accountants specialising in crime and proceeds of crime including restraint, confiscation and civil recovery proceedings under the Proceeds of Crime Act 2002 and earlier legislation. The firm are chartered accountants and the director, David Winch, is an accredited expert witness and well respected speaker and writer, noted for his depth of accounting and legal knowledge of proceeds of crime and money laundering issues. The firm acts in cases throughout the United Kingdom.

BRYAN REDHEAD & CO
Market Street, Broughton-in-furness, LA20 6HP
Tel: 01229 716778
Principal: ICAEW Member
B B Redhead

BROXBOURNE

CRM
33 New Road, Broxbourne, EN10 7LN

DAVID M. WALLIS & CO
10 Badminton Place, Broxbourne, EN10 7PA
Tel: 01992 465598
Principal: ICAEW Member
D M Wallis

HOWARTH ARMSBY
23 Monson Road, Broxbourne, EN10 7DY

KEMP & CO ◈
5 Eaton Gardens, Broxbourne, EN10 6SA
Tel: 01992 462752
Principal: ICAEW Member
D A Kemp

P R HORNSBY & CO
The Old Mustard Pot, 99 High Road, Broxbourne, EN10 7BN

P R HORNSBY & COMPANY LTD
The Old Mustard pot, 99 High Road, Broxbourne, EN10 7BN

V. ACQUISTO
5 Stafford Drive, Broxbourne, EN10 7JT
Tel: 01992 464321
Principal: ICAEW Member
V Acquisto

BUCKFASTLEIGH

LANGFORD SYKES LTD
Cullaford House, Lower Coombe, Buckfastleigh, TQ11 0HT
Tel: 01364 643415
Resident Partners/Directors: ICAEW Members
F M L Sykes

BUCKHURST HILL

DUTCHMANS ◈
3 Station Parade, Cherry Tree Rise, Buckhurst Hill, IG9 6EU
Tel: 020 8559 7799
Fax: 020 8559 7790
Email: mailbox@dutchmans.co.uk
Website: http://www.dutchmans.co.uk
Principal: ICAEW Member
M A Poile
Registered by the ICAEW to carry out company audit work
Authorised and regulated by the Financial Services Authority for investment business

SPECIALISATIONS – AUDIT & ASSURANCE
Audit

SPECIALISATIONS – FINANCIAL REPORTING
Accounts Preparation

SPECIALISATIONS – INVESTMENT BUSINESS
Financial Planning and Advice
SPECIALISATIONS – SECTOR
Charities
Doctors
Solicitors
SPECIALISATIONS – TAXATION
Estate Planning
Executorship
Payroll Service and Advice
Personal
Taxation

LISA DARBY ACA
18 Church Road, Buckhurst Hill, IG9 5RU

M J ROBERTS ASSOCIATES LTD
Regency House, Kings Place, Buckhurst Hill, IG9 5EB

P.R. ADAMS & CO
Astra Chambers, Church Road, Buckhurst Hill, IG9 5TZ

PETER ANGEL & CO
Finance House, 77 Queens Road, Buckhurst Hill, IG9 5BW
Tel: 020 8504 6611

PETER ANGEL & CO LTD
Finance House, 77 Queens Road, Buckhurst Hill, IG9 5BW

R.J.BRADSHAW & CO
98 Westbury Lane, Buckhurst Hill, IG9 5PW

ROGER D. NEVILLE
97 Rous Road, Buckhurst Hill, IG9 6BU
Tel: 07973 414657
Principal: ICAEW Member
R D Neville

BUCKINGHAM

AH ACCOUNTING LTD ◈
41 Kingfisher Road, Buckingham, MK18 7EX
Tel: 01280 814049
Resident Partners/Directors: ICAEW Members
A Heath

AJR & CO LTD ◈
1 Sandhill Farm, Middle Claydon, Buckingham, MK18 2LD
Tel: 01296 738668
Principal: ICAEW Member
A J G Richardson

ANTHISTLE CRAVEN
Moreton House, 31 High Street, Buckingham, MK18 1NU
Tel: 01280 813208
Fax: 01280 824902
Email: mail@anthistlecraven.co.uk
Website: http://www.anthistlecraven.co.uk
Resident Partners/Directors: ICAEW Members
M P Anthistle
Resident Partners (Non-ICAEW Members):
S Craven
Registered by the ICAEW to carry out company audit work

BUCKINGHAMS
Top Floor, 24a West Street, Buckingham, MK18 1HE

BUCKINGHAMS (ACCOUNTANTS) LTD
Top Floor, Hampden House, 24a West Street, Buckingham MK18 1HE

CAMFIELD CHAPMAN LOWE LTD ◈
17a Sheep Street, Winslow, Buckingham, MK18 3HL

COPPERS & CO
Green End Farmhouse, 22 Green End, Granborough, Buckingham MK18 3NT

GRIFFITHS PRESTON
Botolph Farmhouse, Botolph Claydon, Buckingham, MK18 2LR
Tel: 01296 714075

I 4 BUSINESS LTD
4 The Close, Leckhampstead Road, Akeley, Buckingham MK18 5HD

J.P. THORNTON & CO
The Old Dairy, Adstockfields, Adstock, Buckingham MK18 2JE
Tel: 01296 714886
Principal: ICAEW Member
J P Thornton

MARTIN, NYE & CO ★
186 High Street, Winslow, Buckingham, MK18 3DQ

N.A. NORMAN & CO
31 High Street, Winslow, Buckingham, MK18 3HE

TAX FORM SOLUTIONS LTD
186 High Street, Winslow, Buckingham, MK18 3DQ

TEARLE & CARVER
Chandos House, School Lane, Buckingham, MK18 1HD
Tel: 01280 823904
Resident Partners/Directors: ICAEW Members
A Carver

TRICOM SERVICES LTD
22 High Street, Buckingham, MK18 1NU
Tel: 01280 821466
Resident Partners/Directors: ICAEW Members
D Sinnett

BUDE

A.M. FANSON
Trelawney Court, 25a Lynstone Road, Bude, EX23 8LR

CRANE, COX & CO
Hele Farmhouse, Hele Road, Marhamchurch, Bude EX23 0JB
Tel: 01288 361191
Principal: ICAEW Member
M R Crane

METHERELL GARD LTD ◈
Burn View, Bude, EX23 8BX
Tel: 01288 352381
Resident Partners/Directors: ICAEW Members
D N Cox, P L Mead

NEIL DAVIES ASSOCIATES ◈
Bude Business Centre, Kings Hill Industrial Estate, Bude, EX23 8QN

BUDLEIGH SALTERTON

R.M. WALMSLEY
21 Clinton Terrace, Budleigh Salterton, EX9 6RY
Tel: 01395 445409
Principal: ICAEW Member
R M Walmsley

SAXBY & SINDEN LTD ◈
18 High Street, Budleigh Salterton, EX9 6LQ
Tel: 01395 443766
Resident Partners/Directors: ICAEW Members
A J Sinden

BUNGAY

ANTHONY ABBOTT & CO
48 St Marys Street, Bungay, NR35 1AX

ANTHONY ABBOTT LTD
48 St Marys Street, Bungay, NR35 1AX

LARKING GOWEN ◈
6 St Mary's Street, Bungay, NR35 1AX
Tel: 01986 895317
Non-resident Partners (ICAEW Members):
G S Pilcher

BUNTINGFORD

BOND PARTNERS LLP
Bay House, Horse Shoe Hill, Great Hormead, Buntingford SG9 0NL

JOHN D KILBY & CO LTD
Mutfords, Hare Street, Buntingford, SG9 0ED
Tel: 01763 289466
Resident Partners/Directors: ICAEW Members
J D Kilby

BURFORD

N J BOWMAN LTD
Bowman & Hillier Building, The Old Brewery, Priory Lane, Burford OX18 4SG

THOMAS BELL-RICHARDS LTD
Bowman & Hillier Building, The Old Brewery, Priory Lane, Burford OX18 4SG
Tel: 01993 823999
Resident Partners/Directors: ICAEW Members
T A M Bell-Richards

BURGESS HILL

CLIFFORD SHARP & CO
42 Park Road, Burgess Hill, RH15 8ET

GEORGE T. EHLERS
Trendlewood, Ditchling Common, Burgess Hill, RH15 0SE
Tel: 01444 254246
Principal: ICAEW Member
G T Ehlers

HOWARD ATTREE SMITH & CO
12 Park Court, Park Road, Burgess Hill, RH15 8EY
Tel: 01444 235350
Principal: ICAEW Member
A H Attree

K-C ACCOUNTS
4 Chilcomb, Burgess Hill, RH15 0DJ

KAY CHEAL
4 Chilcomb, Burgess Hill, RH15 0DJ
Tel: 01444 257530
Principal: ICAEW Member
K E Cheal

KEYMER HASLAM & CO ◈
4/6 Church Road, Burgess Hill, RH15 9AE

MANSER HUNOT
Highland House, Albert Drive, Burgess Hill, RH15 9TN

PENFOLD SCUTT ◈
30-32 Station Road, Burgess Hill, RH15 9DS

WILDER COE ◈
Gloucester House, Church Walk, Burgess Hill, RH15 9AS
Tel: 01444 245258
Resident Partners/Directors: ICAEW Members
C J Rebbetts

BURNHAM-ON-CROUCH

ELLIOTT & CO
15 Dragon Close, Burnham-on-crouch, CM0 8PW
Tel: 01621 784683
Principal: ICAEW Member
P G L Elliott

BURNHAM-ON-SEA

BUTTERWORTH JONES ◈

80 Oxford St, Burnham-on-sea, TA8 1EF
Tel: 01278 783861
Fax: 01278 792160
Email: burnham@butterworthjones.co.uk
Resident Partners/Directors: ICAEW Members
D R John, S R Pegler
Registered by the ICAEW to carry out company audit work
Regulated by the ICAEW for a range of investment business activities

T P LEWIS & PARTNERS (BOS) LTD

3/5 College Street, Burnham-on-Sea, TA8 1AR
Tel: 01278 788 071
Email: mail@tplewis.co.uk
Website: http://www.tplewis.co.uk
Resident Partners/Directors: ICAEW Members
J R Boswell, P K Ison, T P Lewis

BURNLEY

ALAN CRABTREE

Braeside, 6 Scott Park Road, Burnley, BB11 4JN
Tel: 01282 429898
Principal: ICAEW Member
A C Crabtree

ASHWORTH MOULDS

11 Nicholas Street, Burnley, BB11 2AL
Tel: 01282 432171
Fax: 01282 412510
Email: accountants@ashworthmoulds.co.uk
Website: http://www.ashworthmoulds.co.uk
Resident Partners/Directors: ICAEW Members
M Holmes, D A Pickles, J Roberts
Other Offices:1 Grange Crescent, Rawtenstall BB4 7QT
Registered by the ICAEW to carry out company audit work

SPECIALISATIONS – BUSINESS & GENERAL ADVICE

Acquisitions and Mergers
Disposal of Businesses
Management Advice to Business

SPECIALISATIONS – SECTOR

Charities
Dentists/Opticians
Doctors
Entertainers
Insurance Brokers
Manufacturing
Solicitors
Travel Industry

SPECIALISATIONS – TAXATION

Back Duty
Estate Planning
Executorship
Taxation

BOARDWELL & CO

Oakdene, Barrowford Road, Burnley, BB12 9AT

K M BUSINESS SOLUTIONS LTD ◈

4-6 Grimshaw Street, Burnley, BB11 2AZ
Tel: 01282 426331
Email: info@kmaccountants.co.uk
Website: http://www.kmaccountants.co.uk
Resident Partners/Directors: ICAEW Members
S Heap, G D Porter, R S Rothwell
Resident Partners (Non-ICAEW Members):
M Heaton
Registered by the ICAEW to carry out company audit work
Regulated by the ICAEW for a range of investment business activities

SPECIALISATIONS – AUDIT & ASSURANCE

Audit

SPECIALISATIONS – BUSINESS & GENERAL ADVICE

Book-keeping Systems
Company Formation
Management Advice to Business

SPECIALISATIONS – FINANCIAL REPORTING

Accounts Preparation

SPECIALISATIONS – IT

Computerised Accounting Systems

SPECIALISATIONS – SECTOR

Charities
Doctors
Manufacturing
Retailers
Solicitors

SPECIALISATIONS – TAXATION

Payroll Service and Advice
Taxation

KM

4-6 Grimshaw Street, Burnley, BB11 2AZ

MACMAHON LEGGATE LTD

Charter House, 18-20 Finsley Gate, Burnley, BB11 2HA

PM&M SOLUTIONS FOR BUSINESS LLP

83 Bank Parade, Burnley, BB11 1UG
Tel: 01282 438035
Fax: 01282 427021
Email: burnley@pmm.co.uk
Website: http://www.pmm.co.uk
Resident Partners/Directors: ICAEW Members
M Battersby, D P Bradley, R L Cornes
Registered by the ICAEW to carry out company audit work

W G CHADWICK

1 Yorke Street, Burnley, BB11 1HD

W.G. CHADWICK LTD

1 Yorke Street, Burnley, BB11 1HD
Tel: 01282 450636
Resident Partners/Directors: ICAEW Members
W G Chadwick

BURNTWOOD

J. BLATHERWICK

132 Ogley Hay Road, Chase Terrace, Burntwood, WS7 2HX

BURTON-ON-TRENT

APAZ LTD

Gretton House, Waterside Court, Third Avenue, Centrum 100, Burton-On-Trent DE14 2WQ

BOURNE & CO ◈

6 Lichfield Street, Burton-on-trent, DE14 3RD
Tel: 01283 568912
Resident Partners/Directors: ICAEW Members
M J Edwards, D Meadows, M R Nutt

BUCKLER SPENCER

128 New Street, Burton-on-trent, DE14 3QW

THE CHARTWELL PRACTICE ◈

Chartwell House, 4 St Pauls Square, Burton-On-Trent, DE14 2EF

DAINS LLP

1st Floor, Gibraltar House, First Avenue, Burton-On-Trent DE14 2WE
Tel: 0845 555 8844
Fax: 01283 507969
Email: burton@dains.com
Website: http://www.dains.com
Date Established: 1926
Non-resident Partners (ICAEW Members):
A R Massey, H M P Reynolds, M F P Smith, N D Smith, S G Wright, P D Bradshaw, A P Morris
Resident Partners (Non-ICAEW Members):
A McQuillan, R C McNeilly, S C Bursell
Non-resident Partners (Non-ICAEW Members):
M Castree , N Hawksley
Other Offices: Coleshill, Lichfield, Rugeley, Swadlincote, Birmingham
Registered by the ICAEW to carry out company audit work
Regulated by the ICAEW for a range of investment business activities

FINANCIAL PLANNERS CO UK LTD

Gretton House, Waterside Court, Third Avenue Centrum 100, Burton-on-trent DE14 2WQ

GREENHALGH BUSINESS SERVICES LTD

240 Branston Road, Burton-On-Trent, DE14 3BT
Tel: 01283 531711
Fax: 01283 510825
Email: burton@greenhalghco.net
Website: http://www.greenhalghco.net
Resident Partners/Directors: ICAEW Members
G Brockway
Non-resident Partners (ICAEW Members):
C Peacock, P A Handley, M Henshaw
Resident Partners (Non-ICAEW Members):
N P Shaw
Non-resident Partners (Non-ICAEW Members):
G Brockway
Other Offices: Nottingham, Uttoxeter
Registered by the ICAEW to carry out company audit work

JOHN CANNON & CO

The Gables, 47 Efflinch Lane, Barton-under-Needwood, Burton-On-Trent DE13 8EU

JS SHERWOOD

West Cottage, Newborough End, Newborough, Burton-On-Trent DE13 8SR

MATTHEWS & CO

40 Ferrers Road, Yoxall, Burton-on-trent, DE13 8PS
Tel: 01543 472096
Principal: ICAEW Member
D G Matthews

NICHOLSON BLYTHE LTD ◈

Claremont House, 223 Branston Road, Burton-On-Trent, DE14 3BT
Tel: 01283 545 888
Website: http://www.nicholsonblythe.co.uk
Resident Partners/Directors: ICAEW Members
J J Nicholson, A J Stebbings
Other Offices:36 Market Place, Belper, Derby

SPECIALISATIONS – TAXATION

Capital Gains — Personal
Personal
Small Traders

PEACH & CO

115 Byrkley Street, Burton-on-trent, DE14 2EG
Tel: 01283 566441
Principal: ICAEW Member
S L Hall
Registered by the ICAEW to carry out company audit work

SMITH COOPER ◈
Bermuda House, Crown Square, First Avenue, Burton-on-trent DE14 2TB
Tel: 01283 561621
Resident Partners/Directors: ICAEW Members
C L Beachell, R G Hives

TIM SMITH
14 Newton Park, Newton Solney, Burton-on-trent, DE15 0SX
Tel: 01283 702390
Principal: ICAEW Member
T R Smith

WHALE & CO
Suite 2, Worthington House, 146 High Street, Burton-On-Trent DE14 1JE
Tel: 01283 544732
Email: enquiries@whaleandco.co.uk
Website: http://www.whaleandco.co.uk

BURY

AJP CORPORATE ACCOUNTANTS LTD
Unit 9, Brenton Business Complex, Bond Street, Bury BL9 7BE

ANTHONY MARSHALL LTD
70 Market Street, Tottington, Bury, BL8 3LJ
Tel: 01204 888651
Resident Partners/Directors: ICAEW Members
A Marshall

ATS ASSOCIATES - ROGER HARRIS
Denebank, 117 Bolton Road, Hawkshaw, Bury BL8 4JF

B.H. KWAN
16 Pontinscale Close, Leigh Lane Walshaw, Bury, BL8 1RL

B.J. ROTH ◈
10 Whitby Close, Bury, BL8 2TX
Tel: 0161 761 2544
Principal: ICAEW Member
B J Roth

BARCROFTS
157 Bolton Road, Bury, BL8 2NW
Tel: 0161 797 2782
Principal: ICAEW Member
S J Barcroft

COLIN BARKER
11 Felton Close, Hollins, Bury, BL9 8BJ

CONNOR RICHARDSON ◈
Victoria Buildings, 9 Silver Street, Bury, BL9 0EU
Tel: 0161 764 1069
Principal: ICAEW Member
I R M Connor

COWGILL HOLLOWAY & CO
10 Bolton Street, Ramsbottom, Bury, BL0 9HX
Tel: 01706 822918
Resident Partners/Directors: ICAEW Members
P A Cowgill, M J Murphy, P Stansfield

DAVID J CONWAY & CO ◈
Unit 24, Bury Business Centre, Kay Street, Bury BL9 6BU
Tel: 0161 764 7332

DTE
DTE Business Advisory Services Ltd, DTE House, Hollins Mount, Hollins Lane, Bury BL9 8AT

DTE BUSINESS ADVISORY SERVICES ◈
D T E House, Hollins Mount, Unsworth, Bury BL9 8AT

DTE BUSINESS ADVISORY SERVICES LTD ◈
DTE House, Hollins Mount, Hollins Lane, Bury BL9 8AT

DTE CORPORATE RECOVERY AND INSOLVENCY SERVICES LTD
D T E House, Hollins Mount, Bury, BL9 8AT

DTE LEONARD CURTIS
D T E House, Hollins Lane, Bury, BL9 8AT

E.A.LITTLE
Larkmount, Walmersley, Bury, BL9 6TD
Tel: 0161 764 1784
Principal: ICAEW Member
E A Little

GAFFNEYS
2 Longsight Road, Holcombe Brook, Bury, BL0 9TD

GMCL
21 Kenmor Avenue, Bury, BL8 2DY

HORSFIELD & SMITH ◈
Tower House, 269 Walmersley Road, Bury, BL9 6NX
Tel: 0161 761 5231
Fax: 0161 761 3001
Email: post@horsfield-smith.co.uk
Website: http://www.horsfield-smith.co.uk
Resident Partners/Directors: ICAEW Members
S F Collier, P G Nicol, C A Nuttall, J Staples
Registered by the ICAEW to carry out company audit work
Regulated by the ICAEW for a range of investment business activities

HORSFIELDS ★
Belgrave Place, 8 Manchester Rd, Bury, BL9 0ED

J.S. MARTIN
495 Bolton Road West, Holcombe Brook, Bury, BL0 9RN

JOHN C. EMERY & CO ★
20 Bodiam Road, Greenmount, Bury, BL8 4DW
Tel: 07708 459931
Resident Partners/Directors: ICAEW Members
J C Emery
See display advertisement near this entry.

MARSDEN & CO
41 Knowsley Street, Bury, BL9 0ST
Tel: 0161 705 1888
Resident Partners/Directors: ICAEW Members
P M Mendelson, M B Rostron

METCALFES ★ ◈
1-3 St Marys Place, Bury, BL9 0DZ
Tel: 0161 764 7440
Fax: 0161 764 8874
Email: info@metcalfesplus.com
Website: http://www.metcalfesplus.com
Resident Partners/Directors: ICAEW Members
H Marsh
Resident Partners (Non-ICAEW Members):
D Stott
Registered by the ICAEW to carry out company audit work

MOSLEY & CO ◈
14 Market Place, Ramsbottom, Bury, BL0 9HT

NEAL FRAIN
Rochebury House, 27 Knowsley Street, Bury, BL9 0ST

STEPHEN HARRIS & CO
Belgrave Place, 8 Manchester Road, Bury, BL9 0ED

T.S. HOPE & CO
56a Bury Road, Edenfield, Ramsbottom, Bury BL0 0ET
Tel: 01706 824333
Principal: ICAEW Member
T S Hope

THOMPSON JONES LLP
2 Heap Bridge, Bury, BL9 7HR
Tel: 0161 272 0022
Resident Partners/Directors: ICAEW Members
P Boddis, P D Carlin, D Emery, J K Stone

VARDEN NUTTALL LTD
Crown House, Heap Bridge, Bury, BL9 7JR
Tel: 0870 977 8100
Fax: 0870 977 8101
Email: phil.nuttall@vardennuttall.co.uk

continued

VARDEN NUTTALL LTD *cont*
Resident Partners/Directors: ICAEW Members
P A Nuttall
Individual(s) licensed for insolvency work by the ICAEW
General Description:
Specialists in IVAs.

BURY ST. EDMUNDS

ANTHONY MILLS
5 Fox & Hounds Close, Thurston, Bury St. Edmunds, IP31 3NS

BAKER TILLY
Abbottsgate House, Hollow Road, Bury St. Edmunds, IP32 7FA
Tel: 01284 763311
Resident Partners/Directors: ICAEW Members
S J Orriss
Resident Partners (Non-ICAEW Members):
D J B Coventry

BAKER TILLY
Abbottsgate House, Hollow Road, Bury St. Edmunds, IP32 7FA
Tel: 01284 763311
Resident Partners/Directors: ICAEW Members
P A B Howard, D A Locke, C Sutherland, C L Wash
Resident Partners (Non-ICAEW Members):
D J B Coventry, C L Harrall

BAKER TILLY
Abbotsgate House, Hollow Road, Bury St. Edmunds, IP32 7FA

BAKER TILLY RESTRUCTURING AND RECOVERY LLP
Abbottsgate House, Hollow Road, Bury St. Edmunds, IP32 7FA
Tel: 01284 763311
Resident Partners/Directors: ICAEW Members
N Millar

BAKER TILLY TAX AND ADVISORY SERVICES LLP
Abbottsgate House, Hollow Road, Bury St. Edmunds, IP32 7FA
Tel: 01284 763311
Resident Partners/Directors: ICAEW Members
C L Devlin, P A B Howard, D A Locke, N Millar, M Z Orriss, S J Orriss, J H Penn, A J C Sandbach, C Sutherland, D C W Unwin, C L Wash, M G Watkins
Resident Partners (Non-ICAEW Members):
D J B Coventry, S M Duffety, C L Harrall

COLIN TIFFIN FCA
Oak Lodge, Livermere Road, Great Barton, Bury St. Edmunds IP31 2RZ
Tel: 01284 787398
Principal: ICAEW Member
C M Tiffin

DAVID ROBERTON & CO ★
84 Whiting Street, Bury St Edmunds, IP33 1NZ
Tel: 01284 760383
Resident Partners/Directors: ICAEW Members
S J Cook

EASTER GREEN PARTNERSHIP
Office A, Hoste House, Whiting Street, Bury St. Edmunds IP33 1NR

ENSORS ◈
Saxon House, Moseleys Farm, Business Centre, Fornham All Saints, Bury St. Edmunds IP28 6JY
Tel: 01284 722300
Resident Partners/Directors: ICAEW Members
I C Brookman, R W Hatch, G D Page

FINANCE ASSURE LTD ◈
The Lowe, Fen Road, Pakenham, Bury St. Edmunds IP31 2JS

G M HOWARD & COMPANY LTD ◈
Unit 17, Park Farm Business Centre, Fornham St Genevieve, Bury St. Edmunds IP28 6TS
Tel: 01284 704363
Resident Partners/Directors: ICAEW Members
G M Howard

GASCOYNES LTD
15 Whiting Street, Bury St. Edmunds, IP33 1NX
Tel: 01284 755956
Email: info@gascoynes.co.uk
Website: http://www.gascoynes.co.uk
Resident Partners/Directors: ICAEW Members
B Gascoyne

GEOFF MITCHELL
Morleys House, 7a St Martins Street, Bury St Edmunds, IP33 1JL

GRAHAME ISARD
20a Hatter Street, Bury St. Edmunds, IP33 1NE
Tel: 01284 761914
Principal: ICAEW Member
G R H Isard

GRANT THORNTON UK LLP
18 Langton Place, Bury St. Edmunds, IP33 1NE
Tel: 01284 701271
Non-resident Partners (ICAEW Members):
R J Chaplin
Non-resident Partners (Non-ICAEW Members):
G J Markham

GRAY & CO
Springvale, Police Station Square, Mildenhall, Bury St Edmunds IP28 7ER
Tel: 01638 715534
Principal: ICAEW Member
I S Gray
Registered by the ICAEW to carry out company audit work

HOWARD & CO ◈
Unit 17, Park Farm Business Centre, Fornham Park, Fornham St Genevieve, Bury St. Edmunds IP28 6TS
Tel: 01284 704363

IS BUSINESS LTD
59 Abbeygate Street, Bury St. Edmunds, IP33 1LB

JACOBS ALLEN
59 Abbeygate Street, Bury St. Edmunds, IP33 1LB

JOHN MARTYN LTD
Cages Farm, Tuffields Road, Whepstead, Bury St. Edmunds IP29 4TL

KNIGHTS LOWE
Eldo House, Kempson Way, Suffolk Business Park, Bury St Edmunds IP32 7AR
Tel: 01284 701300
Principal: ICAEW Member
P A Knights

MICHAEL E. BREWSTER
April Cottage, Green Road, Woolpit, Bury St. Edmunds IP30 9RF
Tel: 01359 241199
Principal: ICAEW Member
M E Brewster

NICHOLAS BROOKS BA FCA
10 School Road, Elmswell, Bury St. Edmunds, IP30 9EQ

NORTH & CO
The Old Rectory, The Street, Worlington, Bury St. Edmunds IP28 8RU
Tel: 01638 711642
Principal: ICAEW Member
E K Klingaman

PLUSHCOURT ESTATES LTD ◈
2 The Estate Yard, Ixworth, Bury St. Edmunds, IP31 2HE
Resident Partners/Directors: ICAEW Members
J R Chenery

ROBERTSON REID
Mitchery Farmhouse, Rattlesden, Bury St. Edmunds, IP30 0SS

S.E.S. CONSULTANCY LTD
6 Fallowfield, Beyton, Bury St. Edmunds, IP30 9BN

SPIRE ACCOUNTANCY SERVICES LTD
The Old Rectory, Worlington, Bury St. Edmunds, IP28 8RU
Tel: 01638 711642
Resident Partners/Directors: ICAEW Members
E K Klingaman

STACEY & PARTNERS ◈
87 Whiting Street, Bury St. Edmunds, IP33 1PD
Tel: 01284 773400
Website: http://www.staceys.co.uk
Resident Partners/Directors: ICAEW Members
M A Wallace
Registered by the ICAEW to carry out company audit work
Regulated by the ICAEW for a range of investment business activities

STACEY & PARTNERS LTD
87 Whiting Street, Bury St. Edmunds, IP33 1PD

T.J.M. DOUGHERTY
7 The Coppice, Great Barton, Bury St. Edmunds, IP31 2TT
Tel: 01284 788440
Principal: ICAEW Member
T J Dougherty

WALLER WILSON & CO
The Forge Cottage, 2 High Street, Mildenhall, Bury St Edmunds IP28 7EJ

WHITING & PARTNERS ◈
Garland House, Garland Street, Bury St. Edmunds, IP33 1EZ
Tel: 01553 774745
Resident Partners/Directors: ICAEW Members
M Caddock, C Kelly, T J Nunn, P M Peters, P N Tatum, S Taylor, A Winearls

WHITING & PARTNERS ◈
Willow House, 46 St Andrews Street, Mildenhall, IP28 7HB
Tel: 01638 712267
Resident Partners/Directors: ICAEW Members
B J Nudds, J W Planton

BUSHEY

A MILLER & CO
58 High Road, Bushey Heath, Bushey, WD23 1SF

ALAN SEARS
2 Hartsbourne Park, 180 High Road, Bushey Heath, Bushey WD23 1SD

BETTER BOOKKEEPING
34 Rutherford Way, Bushey Heath, Bushey, WD23 1NJ

BRAHAMS & CO
43 Wren Crescent, Bushey, WD23 1AN

D. HARROD
14 Woodstock Road, Bushey Heath, Bushey, WD23 1PH

GREENE MILLER & CO
14 Woburn Close, Bushey, WD23 4XA
Tel: 020 8950 3995
Principal: ICAEW Member
L Greene

HADLEIGHS
Sai Krupa, 27 Beechcroft Road, Bushey, WD23 2JU

J B DAVERN & CO
149-151 Sparrows Herne, Bushey, WD23 1AQ

J.M. SANDERS & CO
Badgers Croft, Hive Road, Bushey Heath, Bushey WD23 1JG

LEIWY SHERMAN & CO ★ ◈
19 Downalong, Bushey, WD23 1HZ
Tel: 020 8950 7668
Resident Partners/Directors: ICAEW Members
D H A Leiwy

LESLIE WOOLFSON & CO
Profex House, 25 School Lane, Bushey, WD23 1SS

M.S.ALINEK
7 Upton Lodge Close, Bushey, WD23 1AG
Tel: 020 8950 4209
Principal: ICAEW Member
M S Alinek

NR PULVER & CO
191 Sparrows Herne, Bushey, WD23 1AJ

REISMAN & CO
63 High Road, Bushey Heath, Bushey, WD23 1EE

ROBSON & CO
51 Wayside Avenue, Bushey Heath, Bushey, WD23 4SH

RONALD ELLIOTT & CO
26 Catsey Woods, Bushey Heath, Bushey, WD23 4HS
Tel: 020 8950 4049
Principal: ICAEW Member
R Elliott

RONALD HENDON & CO
16 The Callenders, Heathbourne Road, Bushey Heath, WD23 1PU

SHASENS & RE10 (SOUTH EAST) LTD
18 Vale Road, Bushey, WD23 2HE

SIMONS, KAPLIN & CO
10 Lower Tub, Bushey, WD23 4SN

BUXTON

ABC ACCOUNTANTS
28a Hardwick Street, Buxton, SK17 6DH
Tel: 01298 72243
Email: abcaccountants@btconnect.com
Date Established: 1981

SPECIALISATIONS – BUSINESS & GENERAL ADVICE
Book-keeping
Management Advice to Business

SPECIALISATIONS – FINANCIAL REPORTING
Accounts Preparation

SPECIALISATIONS – SECTOR
Dentists/Opticians

SPECIALISATIONS – TAXATION
Payroll Service and Advice
Taxation

EW ACCOUNTANCY PRACTICE LTD
28a Hardwick Street, Buxton, SK17 6DH

GUTHRIE ACCOUNTANCY SERVICES LTD ◈
Unit 1, 11 Eagle Parade, Buxton, SK17 6EQ
Tel: 01298 71110

LAYTON LEE
6 Manchester Road, Buxton, SK17 6SB

LOMAS & CO
28a Hardwick Street, Buxton, SK17 6DH
Tel: 01298 25585
Resident Partners/Directors: ICAEW Members
A Lomas, M E Percival

PHILIP J. WARHURST
37 Brown Edge Road, Buxton, SK17 7AG

SMITH COOPER ◈
2A Grove Parade, Buxton, SK17 6AJ
Tel: 01298 24536

WJ & JA FRISBY ★
27a Park Road, Buxton, SK17 6SG

CALLINGTON

H.M.C. ASSOCIATES LTD
9 Guipavas Road, Callington, PL17 7PL
Tel: 01579 382675
Resident Partners/Directors: ICAEW Members
S W McGuire

HMC ASSOCIATES
9 Guipavas Road, Callington, PL17 7PL

CALNE

JAMES NEVE & CO LTD
5 Wessington Court, Calne, SN11 0SS

CAMBERLEY

A.P. JONES
19 Tekels Avenue, Camberley, GU15 2LA

ABACUS BUSINESS STRATEGIES LTD
13 Fairway Heights, Camberley, GU15 1NJ

ARLENE CASTLE LTD
31 Redcrest Gardens, Camberley, GU15 2DU

B. BLEWETT
13 Cedar Avenue, Blackwater, Camberley, GU17 0JE

BUTT, MILLER & CO ◈
92 Park Street, Camberley, GU15 3NY
Tel: 01276 25542
Fax: 01276 686441
Email: mailroom@buttmiller.co.uk
Website: http://www.buttmiller.co.uk
Date Established: 1982
Resident Partners/Directors: ICAEW Members
N B Butt, D Miller
Resident Partners (Non-ICAEW Members):
P R G Male
Registered by the ICAEW to carry out company audit work

C B HUNT
52 Roundway, Camberley, GU15 1NU

COULTHARDS MACKENZIE
17 Park Street, Camberley, GU15 3PQ
Tel: 01276 65470
Resident Partners/Directors: ICAEW Members
M J Church

DAVID J MILLER
8 Savoy Grove, Blackwater, Camberley, GU17 9JW

EDEN OUTSOURCING LTD
Tuscam House, Trafalgar Way, Camberley, GU15 3BN
Tel: 0870 066 7112
Resident Partners/Directors: ICAEW Members
P J Giltrap

GPB ASSOCIATES
Quatro House, Lyon Way, Camberley, GU16 7ER
Tel: 01276 692205
Principal: ICAEW Member
G P Broad

HARDING ACCOUNTANTS LTD
23 Frogmore Park Drive, Blackwater, Camberley, GU17 0PG
Tel: 01276 33028
Resident Partners/Directors: ICAEW Members
B R Harding

HAWKINS SCOTT
Wyvern House, 55-61 Frimley High Street, Frimley, Camberley GU16 7HJ

J.N.VICKERY
2 Quebec Gardens, Blackwater, Camberley, GU17 9DE

JOHN J MAY ◈
2 Belmont Mews, Camberley, GU15 2PH
Tel: 01276 61579
Fax: 01276 61579
Email: john@jjmay.co.uk
Mobile: 07860 715075
Principal: ICAEW Member
J J May

SPECIALISATIONS – BUSINESS & GENERAL ADVICE
Management Advice to Business

JOHN WESTON
Rhodenwood, 40 Hillcrest Road, Camberley, GU15 1LG

MAY ASSOCIATES ◈
2 Belmont Mews, Camberley, GU15 2PH

MILLER & CO
2 The Pavilions End, Camberley, GU15 2LD

MITCHELL & CO ◈
13 Verran Road, Watchetts Lake, Camberley, GU15 2ND
Tel: 01276 682802
Principal: ICAEW Member
A R Mitchell

MRS MARY OSBORNE
6 Russet Gardens, Camberley, GU15 2LG
Tel: 01276 21623
Principal: ICAEW Member
M Osborne

NFW ACCOUNTING SERVICES LTD
1 Bailey Close, Frimley, Camberley, GU16 7EN
Tel: 07747 616424
Resident Partners/Directors: ICAEW Members
N F West

R.J.W. ASSOCIATES
High Copse, Pinemount Road, Camberley, GU15 2LU

ROBERT I.K. DUROE
4 Lansdowne Road, Frimley, Camberley, GU16 9UW

ROBERT P.C. GODDARD
42 Theobalds Way, Frimley, Camberley, GU16 9RF
Tel: 01276 20718
Principal: ICAEW Member
R P C Goddard

RSH ACCOUNTING
Waters Edge, 4 Sydney Loader Place, Darby Green, Camberley GU17 0AF
Tel: 01252 877347
Email: rshaccounting@yahoo.co.uk
Resident Partners/Directors: ICAEW Members
R S Hunt

SPECIALISATIONS – BUSINESS & GENERAL ADVICE
Book-keeping
Management Accounting
Consultancy

SPECIALISATIONS – FINANCIAL REPORTING
Accounts Preparation

SPECIALISATIONS – SECTOR
Property Investment

SHEARER ACCOUNTING
10 Evergreen Road, Frimley, Camberley, GU16 8PU
Tel: 07933 910959
Resident Partners/Directors: ICAEW Members
S E Shearer

SOWERBUTTS & CO LTD
Fiscal House, 367 London Road, Camberley, GU15 3HQ
Tel: 01276 61164
Resident Partners/Directors: ICAEW Members
L G Sowerbutts, S R Sowerbutts

STEWART & CO
Knoll House, Knoll Road, Camberley, GU15 3SY
Tel: 01276 61203
Fax: 01276 25450
Email: action@stewartco.co.uk
Website: http://www.stewartco.co.uk
Date Established: 1958
Resident Partners/Directors: ICAEW Members
P J Clennell, A N Cousins, D A Hartley, D A McCusker
Registered by the ICAEW to carry out company audit work

SYKES, DALBY & TRUELOVE ◈
5 Green Lane, Blackwater, Camberley, GU17 9DG

TURNER & CO
10A White Hart Parade, London Road, Blackwater, Camberley GU17 9AD
Tel: 01276 38982
Principal: ICAEW Member
M Turner

CAMBORNE

BRIANTS ◈
Market Square House, Commercial Street, Camborne, TR14 8JY
Tel: 01209 716671
Principal: ICAEW Member
T A C Briant

JOHN ASHLEY
Chy Rose, 1a Roskear Villas, Camborne, TR14 8DF

KELSALL STEELE
20 Chapel Street, Camborne, TR14 8ED

LACEY & CO
Fiveways, 1 South Terrace, Camborne, TR14 8SS

CAMBRIDGE

AC
23 Brownlow Road, Cambridge, CB4 3NG

ACCOUNTING ANGELS
10 Brewers Close, Longstanton, Cambridge, CB24 3BY

AGM PARTNERS LLP ◈
St Johns Innovation Centre, Cowley Road, Cambridge, CB4 0WS

AIMS
33 Dunstal Field, Cottenham, Cambridge, CB24 8UH

AIMS - DAVID SEELY FCA
33 Dunstal Field, Cottenham, Cambridge, CB24 8UH

AIMS - GREGORY WALKER
Yew Tree Farmhouse, Linton Road, Hadstock, Cambridge CB21 4NU

AIMS - GREGORY WALKER FCA
Yew Tree Farmhouse, Linton Road, Hadstock, Cambridge CB1 6NU

ALAN S. KINDRED
Normans Corner, 41 Church Lane, Fulbourn, Cambridge CB21 5EP

ANDERSON & CO
Sumpter House, 8 Station Road, Histon, Cambridge CB24 9LQ
Tel: 01223 236277
Resident Partners/Directors: ICAEW Members
F J H Anderson, A R Doggett

ANDREW R SHAW
Windsmoor, School Lane, Chittering, Cambridge CB25 9PW

ANDY CLARKE MOTOR LTD
23 Brownlow Road, Cambridge, CB4 3NG

ASHCROFT ANTHONY
The Cottages, Grange Road, Duxford, Cambridge CB22 4WF

ASHCROFT ANTHONY LTD
The Cottages, Grange Farm, Grange Road, Duxford, Cambridge CB22 4WF
Tel: 01763 209113
Resident Partners/Directors: ICAEW Members
R C S J Percy
See display advertisement near this entry.

ASTRACON LTD
2 The Firs, Moorfield Road, Duxford, Cambridge CB2 4PY

BDO STOY HAYWARD LLP
First Floor, Clarendon House, Clarendon Road, Cambridge CB2 8FH
Tel: 01223 535000
Fax: 01223 535001
Resident Partners/Directors: ICAEW Members
G E Hanson, I C A Northen

BERNARD HAWES
52 Maids Causeway, Cambridge, CB5 8DD
Tel: 01223 354376
Principal: ICAEW Member
B H Hawes

BRIANT, ELMORE & CO
155 Station Road, Histon, Impington, Cambridge CB24 9NP
Tel: 01223 233207
Fax: 01223 233208
Email: david@briantelmore.co.uk
Principal: ICAEW Member
D J Elmore

BROWN MCLEOD & BERRIE
12 Spring Lane, Bottisham, Cambridge, CB25 9BL

BURCHILL & CO
Reed House, 16 High Street, West Wratting, Cambridge CB21 5LU

C.S. WONG
118 High Street, Sawston, Cambridge, CB22 3HJ
Tel: 01223 701922
Principal: ICAEW Member
C S Wong

CHATER ALLAN LLP
Beech House, 4a Newmarket Road, Cambridge, CB5 8DT

CHAVEREYS
1 Penn Farm Studios, Harston Road, Haslingfield, Cambridge CB3 7JZ

CKL GOLDING
6 Tunbridge Court, Tunbridge Lane, Bottisham, Cambridge CB25 9TU

CKL GOLDING LTD
Quy Court, Colliers Lane, Stow-cum-Quy, Cambridge CB25 9AU
Tel: 01223 810100
Resident Partners/Directors: ICAEW Members
S Cronk, L J Golding, P N Howard-Jones

COLIN C ANDREWS LTD
10 Cockle Close, Newton, Cambridge, CB22 7TW

COLIN FAIERS
4 Elm Way, Willingham, Cambridge, CB24 5JS

DAVID HOLLINGSBEE LTD
59 Sedgwick Street, Cambridge, CB1 3AJ

DBA GROUP LTD ◈
2 Oakington Business Park, Dry Drayton Road, Oakington, Cambridge CB24 3DQ
Tel: 01223 202166
Resident Partners/Directors: ICAEW Members
D M Blair

DELOITTE & TOUCHE LLP ◈
City House, 126-130 Hills Road, Cambridge, CB2 1RY
Tel: 01223 460222
Website: http://www.deloitte.co.uk
Resident Partners/Directors: ICAEW Members
M Baines, R J Blackwell, W R T Crane, D E M Halstead, S J B Henderson, R C Knights, A T Swarbrick

DENNIS CROSS
Sycamore House, 5 Vine Close, Stapleford, Cambridge CB22 5BZ

ENSORS ◈
Anglia House, 285 Milton Road, Cambridge, CB4 1XQ
Tel: 01223 420721
Resident Partners/Directors: ICAEW Members
D Gorman, P Williams

ERNST & YOUNG LLP
Compass House, 80 Newmarket Road, Cambridge, CB5 8DZ
Tel: 01223 557000

G.H.W.ASHMAN
09a North Street, Burwell, Cambridge, CB25 0BB

GH BUSINESS & ACCOUNTANCY SERVICES
47a Lambs Lane, Cottenham, Cambridge, CB24 8TB

GILLIAN SMITH
25 Tavistock Road, Cambridge, CB4 3NB
Tel: 01223 365376
Principal: ICAEW Member
G Smith

GRANT THORNTON UK LLP
Byron House, Cambridge Business Park, Cowley Road, Cambridge CB4 0WZ
Tel: 01223 225600
Resident Partners/Directors: ICAEW Members
I S Carr, J Corbishley, M J Hughes, L A Jeanroy, A D Seekings
Non-resident Partners (ICAEW Members):
K A Gale, A G O'Rourke, S J Robinson
Resident Partners (Non-ICAEW Members):
K S Mitchell, N M E Dixon, G P Davies

HARDCASTLE BURTON ◈
St Johns Innovation Centre, Cowley Road, Cambridge, CB4 0WS
Tel: 01223 420252

HILARY SEAWARD LTD
9 Sherlock Road, Cambridge, CB3 0HR

JASANI & CO
380 Cherry Hinton Road, Cambridge, CB1 8BA
Tel: 01223 245551
Principal: ICAEW Member
M A M Jasani

JEFFERYS, HOUGHTON & CO
The Commercial Centre, 6 Green End, Comberton, Cambridge CB23 7DY
Tel: 01223 262128
Fax: 01223 262287
Email: jennifer@jefferys-houghton.freeserve.co.uk
Website: http://www.jefferys-houghton.co.uk
Date Established: 1986
Principal: ICAEW Member
J K Houghton

JULIAN CHILVERS ◈
72 Cavendish Avenue, Cambridge, CB1 7UT
Tel: 01223 501393
Principal: ICAEW Member
J D J Chilvers

KEMPSTERS
The Coach House, Fen Road, Lode, Cambridge CB25 9HD

KPMG LLP
37 Hills Road, Cambridge, CB2 1XL
Tel: 01223 366692
Resident Partners/Directors: ICAEW Members
R F Ferguson, H K Sant

KRAILING & CO
48 High Street, West Wratting, Cambridge, CB21 5LU

LAKIN ROSE
Pioneer House, Vision Park, Histon, Cambridge CB24 9NL

LAKIN ROSE LTD ◈
Pioneer House, Vision Park, Histon, Cambridge CB24 9NL
Tel: 01223 235707
Training Contracts Available.
Resident Partners/Directors: ICAEW Members
C Beaumont, C P J Dougherty, S P Rose
Resident Partners (Non-ICAEW Members):
C Barnes

Registered by the ICAEW to carry out company audit work

Regulated by the ICAEW for a range of investment business activities

LAST & CO
269 Newmarket Road, Cambridge, CB5 8JE
Tel: 01223 315155
Principal: ICAEW Member
P F Last

LEONARD FREEMAN FCA
Regus Centre, Cambourne Business Park, Cambridge, CB23 6DP

M H D O'CALLAGHAN
36 Seymour Street, Cambridge, CB1 3DQ

M. HOLROYD
11 Headley Gardens, Great Shelford, Cambridge, CB22 5JZ

MACGILLIVRAY & CO
1 Coniston Road, Cambridge, CB1 7BZ
Tel: 01223 246470
Principal: ICAEW Member
A.D.MacGillivray

MCKAY & CO
5 Quidditch Lane, Cambourne, Cambridge, CB3 6DD

MCTEAR WILLIAMS & WOOD ★ ◈
Sheraton House, Castle Park, Cambridge, CB3 0AX
Tel: 01223 370115

MARKLEY DAVIS
31 Edinburgh Avenue, Sawston, Cambridge, CB22 3DW
Tel: 01223 701617
Principal: ICAEW Member
L A Davis

MARY DEEMING
34 Queensway, Sawston, Cambridge, CB22 3DJ
Tel: 01223 834033
Principal: ICAEW Member
M J Deeming

MICHAEL LEWIS AUDIT LTD
William James House, Cowley Road, Cambridge, CB4 0WX

MONKS
Abacus House, Castle Park, Cambridge, CB3 0AN

NICHOLAS CLIFFE & CO LTD ◈
Mill House, Mill Court, Great Shelford, Cambridge CB22 5LD
Tel: 01223 471576
Email: enquiries@nicholas-cliffe.co.uk
Website: http://www.nicholas-cliffe.co.uk
Mobile: 07885 407658
Date Established: 2002
Resident Partners/Directors: ICAEW Members
A N Cliffe

Registered by the ICAEW to carry out company audit work

Regulated by the ICAEW for a range of investment business activities

Languages Spoken:
French, German

P A BECK
41 Kingston Street, Cambridge, CB1 2NU

P W ACCOUNTANTS LTD
82b High Street, Sawston, Cambridge, CB22 3HJ
Tel: 01223 830020
Resident Partners/Directors: ICAEW Members
P E Whitmell

PAMELA STONEY
61 Earith Road, Willingham, Cambridge, CB24 5LS

PAUL CHAPPELL
2 The Firs, Moorfield Road, Duxford, Cambridge CB22 4PY

PB FINANCIAL PLANNING LTD
The Quorum, Barnwell Road, Cambridge, CB5 8RE

PB FINANCIAL PLANNING LTD
Chequers House, 77-81 Newmarket Road, Cambridge, CB5 8EU

PEM TECHNOLOGY
St Johns Innovation Centre, Cowley Road, Cambridge, CB4 0WS

PETER WATTS & CO
14 Alms Hill, Bourn, Cambridge, CB23 2SH

PETERS ELWORTHY & MOORE ◈
Salisbury House, Station Road, Cambridge, CB1 2LA
Tel: 01223 728222
Fax: 01223 461424
Email: pem@pem.co.uk

continued

PETERS ELWORTHY & MOORE *cont*
Website: http://www.pem.co.uk
Date Established: 1875
Resident Partners/Directors: ICAEW Members
P Chapman, A J Counsell, R D C Guthrie, J A Lettice, J H Parry, S M Peak, C Walklett, R Webster, P H F Wilsdon
Resident Partners (Non-ICAEW Members):
A E Dewey, D Carr, S W Norris
Registered by the ICAEW to carry out company audit work
Authorised and regulated by the Financial Services Authority for investment business
Individual(s) licensed for insolvency work by another RPB

PRENTIS & CO LLP
115c Milton Road, Cambridge, CB4 1XE

PRICE BAILEY LLP ◈
The Quorum, Barnwell Road, Cambridge, CB5 8RE
Tel: 01223 565035
Resident Partners/Directors: ICAEW Members
L R Bailey, M Clapson, S R Everall, A J Hulme, C W Olley, D J Robinson
Non-resident Partners (Non-ICAEW Members):
P N Cullen
Registered by the ICAEW to carry out company audit work
Authorised and regulated by the Financial Services Authority for investment business
Individual(s) licensed for insolvency work by the ICAEW

PRICE BAILEY PRIVATE CLIENT LLP
The Quorum, Barnwell Road, Cambridge, CB5 8RE

PRICEWATERHOUSE-COOPERS
Abacus House, Castle Park, Cambridge, CB3 0AN

PRICEWATERHOUSE-COOPERS LLP
Abacus House, Castle Park, Cambridge, CB3 0AN
Tel: 01223 460055
Resident Partners/Directors: ICAEW Members
C H W Birch, D C Gibbs, S D M Tapping

R.G. JENYNS
Bottisham Hall, Bottisham, Cambridge, CB5 9ED

R P IMRAY
6 The Old Maltings, 135 Ditton Walk, Cambridge, CB5 8PY
Tel: 01223 411141
Principal: ICAEW Member
R P Imray

RABROOKES & CO
95 St Matthews Gardens, Cambridge, CB1 2PH

REAL ESTATE FINANCIAL SOLUTIONS LTD
25 Edis Way, Foxton, Cambridge, CB22 6RW
Tel: 01223 871504
Resident Partners/Directors: ICAEW Members
J M Tauwhare

REARDON & CO LTD
Ash House, Breckenwood Road, Fulbourn, Cambridge CB21 5DQ

RESOLVE BUSINESS SOLUTIONS
2 High Street, Histon, Cambridge, CB24 9LG

RESOLVE CAMBRIDGE LTD
2 High Street, Histon, Cambridge, CB4 9LG

ROMSEY CAPITAL LTD
121 Catharine Street, Cambridge, CB1 3AP

S.C. TWEEDIE-WAGGOTT & CO
46 Thornton Court, Girton, Cambridge, CB3 0NS
Tel: 01223 277363
Principal: ICAEW Member
S C Tweedie-Waggott

STAFFORDS
CPC1, Capital Park, Fulbourn, Cambridge CB21 5XE

STAFFORDS CAMBRIDGE LLP
CPC1, Capital Park, Fulbourn, Cambridge CB21 5XE

STANES RAND & CO
10 Jesus Lane, Cambridge, CB5 8BA

STANES RAND LLP
10 Jesus Lane, Cambridge, CB5 8BA

STREETS WHITMARSH STERLAND AUDIT
62- 64 Hills Road, Cambridge, CB2 1LA

STREETS WHITMARSH STERLAND LLP
62-64 Hills Road, Cambridge, CB2 1LA
Tel: 01223 570000
Email: info@streetsweb.co.uk
Website: http://www.streetsweb.co.uk

STUART ARRANDALE
23-25 Gwydir Street, Cambridge, CB1 2LG

SUSAN J ROYCE
14 Lady Jane Court, Cavendish Avenue, Cambridge, CB1 7UW

T.D MARCUSON
15 West Hill Road, Foxton, Cambridge, CB22 6SZ

TAYABALI TOMLIN & WHITE
5 High Green, Great Shelford, Cambridge, CB22 5EG

TRACY NEWMAN & CO LTD
Trinity House, Cambridge Business Park, Cowley Road, Cambridge CB4 0WZ

TRAFALGAR ACCOUNTING AND TAXATION SERVICES LLP
8 Emsons Close, Linton, Cambridge, CB21 4NB
Tel: 01223 897930
Resident Partners/Directors: ICAEW Members
T J Richardson

TT&W LTD
5 High Green, Great Shelford, Cambridge, CB22 5EG

WHITMARSH STERLAND
62 Hills Road, Cambridge, CB2 1LA

WKH
4 Newmarket Road, Cambridge, CB5 8DT

YOUNGMAN & CO ◈
163 Mill Road, Cambridge, CB1 3AN
Tel: 01223 242948

CAMELFORD

BARKERS
Council Offices, College Road, Camelford, PL32 9TL

CANNOCK

ACCOUNTANCY 4 GROWTH LTD ◈
33 Wolverhampton Road, Cannock, WS11 1AP

DJW ACCOUNTANCY SERVICES ◈
5 Robin Close, Huntington, Cannock, WS12 4PQ
Tel: 01543 502381
Principal: ICAEW Member
D J Wheatley

K L RICHARDSON & CO
20 South Close, Cannock, WS11 1EH

LINDLEY & CO ★
Unit 2, Waterside Business Park, Wolverhampton Road, Cannock WS11 1SN

OAKWOODS ACCOUNTANCY LTD
8 Morston Court, Kingswood Lake, Cannock, WS11 8JB

RICE & CO
Bank House, Mill Street, Cannock, WS11 0DW

ROSTANCE EDWARDS LTD ◈
5 Chase House, Park Plaza, Hayes Way, Cannock WS12 2DD
Tel: 01543 570222
Resident Partners/Directors: ICAEW Members
D A Rostance

SHELVOKE, PICKERING, JANNEY & CO
57-61 Market Place, Cannock, WS11 1BP
Tel: 01543 571174
Fax: 01543 502658
Email: sandyhough@shelvokes.co.uk
Date Established: 1937
Resident Partners/Directors: ICAEW Members
A G Hough, B Matthews
Authorised and regulated by the Financial Services Authority for investment business

SPECIALISATIONS – AUDIT & ASSURANCE
Audit

SPECIALISATIONS – BUSINESS & GENERAL ADVICE
Book-keeping
Company Formation

SPECIALISATIONS – FINANCIAL REPORTING
Accounts Preparation
Partnership/Sole Trader Accounts

SPECIALISATIONS – INVESTMENT BUSINESS
Financial Planning and Advice
Pensions Advice

SPECIALISATIONS – SECTOR
Corporate

SPECIALISATIONS – TAXATION
Back Duty
Partnerships and Sole Traders
Payroll Service and Advice
Personal
Self Assessment Advice
Taxation
Value Added Tax

SILVER & CO ◈
25 Park Road, Cannock, WS11 1JN

THOMPSON ACCOUNTANCY LTD
2 Gloucester Way, Heath Hayes, Cannock, WS11 7YN
Tel: 01543 459123
Resident Partners/Directors: ICAEW Members
L F Thompson

CANTERBURY

A.J. WELCH
30 St George's Place, Canterbury, CT1 1UT

AIMS - COLIN ELLIOTT
The Paddock, Bishopsbourne, Canterbury, CT4 5HT

ALAN RATFORD & CO
7 Mill Road, Sturry, Canterbury, CT2 0AJ

ANDREW WEBSTER
48 St Martins Hill, Canterbury, CT1 1PP

BURGESS HODGSON
Camburgh House, 27 New Dover Road, Canterbury, CT1 3DN
Tel: 01227 454627
Training Contracts Available.
Resident Partners/Directors: ICAEW Members
P Gatland, K Jones, K C May, A R Miles, C S Reid, C D Slater, R C Stewart, S M Sutton
Resident Partners (Non-ICAEW Members):
M D Laughton, M J Horne
Registered by the ICAEW to carry out company audit work
Regulated by the ICAEW for a range of investment business activities

BURNS WARING ◈
Roper Yard, Roper Road, Canterbury, CT2 7EX
Tel: 01227 766666
Resident Partners/Directors: ICAEW Members
S J T Askew, R J Calderwood
Registered by the ICAEW to carry out company audit work
Regulated by the ICAEW for a range of investment business activities

BURNS WARING & PARTNERS LTD
Roper Yard, Canterbury, CT2 7EX

F. WHITTEN
29 High Street, Bridge, Canterbury, CT4 5JZ

FINDLAY JAMES
31 St Georges Place, Canterbury, CT1 1XD

GEARY & CO
Church Hill Farm, Elmstone, Canterbury, CT3 1HN

GRAHAM J. CRYER
3 Humpty Dumpty Meadow, St Thomas Hill, Canterbury, CT2 8HN

JAKE DAVIES & CO
Haleswood, 2 The Crescent, St Stephens, Canterbury CT2 7AG

JOHN SUDWORTH
5 The Street, Molash, Canterbury, CT4 8HH

JOHN WILLIAM HALEY ◈
Hame, Stodmarsh Road, Canterbury, CT3 4AP
Tel: 01227 764207
Principal: ICAEW Member
J W Haley

LAKIN CLARK
Delandale House, 37 Old Dover Road, Canterbury, CT1 3JF
Tel: 01227 454861
Resident Partners/Directors: ICAEW Members
D N G Adam, A R Amlot

LEVICKS
12 Dover Street, Canterbury, CT1 3HD
Tel: 01227 455183
Email: enquiries@levicksaccountants.co.uk
Non-resident Partners (Non-ICAEW Members):
T Pearcy

N TATE & CO LTD
6F Thomas Way, Lakesview Business Park, Canterbury, CT3 4JZ
Tel: 01227 713787
Resident Partners/Directors: ICAEW Members
N L Tate

NICHOLAS CHARLES LEWIS & CO
5 Leycroft Close, Canterbury, CT2 7LD
Tel: 01227 459867
Principal: ICAEW Member
N C Lewis

PENTINS
Lullingstone House, 5 Castle Street, Canterbury, CT1 2FG

PETER BRUFF & CO
Cherry Court, 5 Cherry Orchard, Littlebourne, Canterbury CT3 1QG
Tel: 01227 722822
Principal: ICAEW Member
P F J Bruff

REEVES+NEYLAN LLP
37 St Margarets Street, Canterbury, CT1 2TU
Tel: 01227 768231
Fax: 01227 458383
Email: canterbury@reeves-neylan.com
Website: http://www.reeves-neylan.com
Resident Partners/Directors: ICAEW Members
N J Alder, D J Ashman, M M Connolly, M K R Dyer, R W Heasman, G H Jones, S J Ledger, P A R Manser, T Mills, C N Relf, R M Sutton, M C W Terry, A C J Tinham, P N Wood
Resident Partners (Non-ICAEW Members):
N Fright
Registered by the ICAEW to carry out company audit work
Regulated by the ICAEW for a range of investment business activities

RICHARDS & CO
The Dormer House, 159 Rough Common Road, Canterbury, CT2 9BS
Tel: 01227 462576
Principal: ICAEW Member
T R Richards

SPAIN BROTHERS & CO ◈
Westgate House, 87 St Dunstan's Street, Canterbury, CT2 8AE
Tel: 01227 769321
Fax: 01227 464169
Email: canterbury@spainbrothers.co.uk
Resident Partners/Directors: ICAEW Members
P H Cheshire, A J Dixon, P A Flood
Registered by the ICAEW to carry out company audit work
Regulated by the ICAEW for a range of investment business activities

TIMOTHY P. BOLTON
Latchmere House, Watling Street, Canterbury, CT1 2UD

CANVEY ISLAND

J. GRIFFITHS & CO
75 Steli Avenue, Canvey Island, SS8 9QF

MAYNARD HEADY ◈
Matrix House, 12-16 Lionel Road, Canvey Island, SS8 9DE
Tel: 01268 680702
Fax: 01268 694326
Email: info@maynard-heady.co.uk
Website: http://www.maynard-heady.co.uk
Training Contracts Available.
Resident Partners/Directors: ICAEW Members
R J Baines, N J Bragg, S J Caten, D Datson, R M Port, D J Smith
Other Offices:40-42 High Street, Maldon, Essex
Registered by the ICAEW to carry out company audit work

S.R. ANTHONY
26 Beachway, Canvey Island, SS8 0BD

TOUMBAS & CO
5 Long Road, Canvey Island, SS8 0JA
Tel: 01268 695676
Principal: ICAEW Member
P G Toumbas

CARLISLE

ARMSTRONG WATSON ◈
15 Victoria Place, Carlisle, CA1 1EW
Tel: 01228 553333
Resident Partners/Directors: ICAEW Members
S C Kirkham, A M Taylor

ARMSTRONG WATSON ◈
Bute House, Montgomery Way, Rosehill, Carlisle CA1 2RW
Tel: 01228 690000
Resident Partners/Directors: ICAEW Members
A Harrington, K J Johnston, G W Sewell

ARMSTRONG WATSON ◈
Fairview House, Victoria Place, Carlisle, CA1 1HP
Tel: 01228 591000
Fax: 01228 591822
Email: clientservice@armstrongwatson.co.uk
Website: http://www.armstrongwatson.co.uk
Resident Partners/Directors: ICAEW Members
J E Carroll, A J Johnston, D Warwick, A J Watts
General Description:
Accountants & financial advisers. 35 partners. Ranked 26th in a survey of UK Accountancy profession. Specialises in: corporate accounts; business services; corporate finance; financial planning & wealth management; payroll services; computer solutions; insolvency & corporate recovery.

BARRETT & CO (CARLISLE) LTD
56 Warwick Road, Carlisle, CA1 1DR

MIKE BARRETT
56 Warwick Road, Carlisle, CA1 1DR

BUTLER ACCOUNTANCY SERVICES LTD
Suite 1 Telford House, Riverside, Warwick Road, Carlisle CA1 2BT

CHRISTIAN DOUGLASS LLP
14 Clifford Court, Cooper Way, Parkhouse Business Park, Carlisle CA3 0JG

DAVID ALLEN & CO ◈
Dalmar House, Barras Lane Estate, Dalston, Carlisle CA5 7NY
Tel: 01228 711888
Fax: 01228 711826
Email: mail@david-allen.co.uk
Website: http://www.david-allen.co.uk
Principal: ICAEW Member
S D Allen
Registered by the ICAEW to
continued

DAVID ALLEN & CO *cont*
carry out company audit work
Regulated by the ICAEW for a range of investment business activities

DAVID RAY
Woodlands, Southwaite, Carlisle, CA4 0NB

DODD & CO
Fifteen Rosehill, Montgomery Way, Rosehill Estate, Carlisle CA1 2RW
Tel: 01228 530913
Resident Partners/Directors: ICAEW Members
I W Brown, A M Johnston, D Johnston, M S Ward, R M Wharton

E.J. WILLIAMS & CO
4 Brunswick Street, Carlisle, CA1 1PP

GORDON CONSULTANCY LTD
Hamilton, 13 The Nurseries, Linstock, Carlisle CA6 4RR
Tel: 01228 539158
Resident Partners/Directors: ICAEW Members
R W Gordon

JAMES WA CRUICKSHANK & CO ◈
Inglewood, Wreay, Carlisle, CA4 0RL

LAMONT PRIDMORE ◈
Bourne House, Milbourne Street, Carlisle, CA2 5XF
Tel: 01228 401400
Website: http://www.lamontpridmore.co.uk

LAMONT PRIDMORE LTD
Arkle House, 31 Lonsdale Street, Carlisle, CA1 1BJ

LITTLE ACCOUNTING SOLUTIONS
16 Mill Street, Longtown, Carlisle, CA6 5TF

MONTPELIER PROFESSIONAL (BORDERS) LTD
Gelt Suite, Coulton House, Harraby Green Business Park, Carlisle CA1 2NU

N.B. LANCASTER & CO
5 Cecil Street, Carlisle, CA1 1NL

N.K. PHILLIPS
2 Ferguson Road, Carlisle, CA2 6EP
Tel: 01228 532555
Principal: ICAEW Member
N K Phillips

O'REILLY ◈
6 Brunswick Street, Carlisle, CA1 1PN
Tel: 01228 528081
Resident Partners/Directors: ICAEW Members
A Little, J F McLaren

P. FURMSTON & CO
Longburgh Farmhouse, Burgh by Sands, Carlisle, CA5 6AF
Tel: 01228 576865
Principal: ICAEW Member
P Willis

PHILIP JONES CONSULTING LTD ◈
5 Fisher Street, Carlisle, CA3 8RR
Tel: 01228 611651
Resident Partners/Directors: ICAEW Members
P D Jones

RS LIDDELL CONSULTING LTD
Treyarnon, Lonning Foot, Rockcliffe, Carlisle CA6 4AB
Tel: 01228 674420
Resident Partners/Directors: ICAEW Members
R S Liddell

SAINT & CO ▽ ◈
Sterling House, Wavell Drive, Rosehill, Carlisle CA1 2SA
Tel: 01228 534371
Email: advice@saint.co.uk
Website: http://www.saint.co.uk
Resident Partners/Directors: ICAEW Members
P A J Boothroyd, P R Dhillon, L M Farrer, S Farrer, J Little
Registered by the ICAEW to carry out company audit work
Authorised and regulated by the Financial Services Authority for investment business
Individual(s) licensed for insolvency work by the ICAEW
SPECIALISATIONS – SECTOR

Hotels/Public Houses

SHEPHERD & CO
1st Floor, 4 Fisher Street, Carlisle, CA3 8RN
Tel: 01228 510661
Principal: ICAEW Member
W R Shepherd

STEELES SUPPORT SERVICES ◈
c/o Stoneleigh, 6 Carlton Gardens, Stanwix, Carlisle CA3 9NP
Tel: 01228 527554
Principal: ICAEW Member
R J Steele

CARNFORTH

ALAN MOULSDALE LTD
Dale House, Tewitfield, Carnforth, LA6 1JH

BURTON DAVY
Silverdale Suite, Clawthorpe Hale Business Centre, Burton, Carnforth LA6 1NU

DUDLEY & CO ★
33 New Street, Carnforth, LA5 9BX
Tel: 01524 732988
Resident Partners/Directors: ICAEW Members
J C Thompson

J.R. MAYOR ◈
39 Pear Tree Park, Holme, Carnforth, LA6 1SD
Tel: 01524 782013
Principal: ICAEW Member
J R Mayor

KNEILL & CO
Mayfield, Back Gate, Ingleton, Carnforth LA6 3BT
Tel: 01524 241877
Principal: ICAEW Member
M A Kneill

THOMPSON & CO
33 New Street, Carnforth, LA5 9BX
Tel: 01524 732988
Principal: ICAEW Member
J C Thompson

TRIGITAL CONSULTANTS LTD
Jingling Barn, Jingling Lane, Kirkby Lonsdale, Carnforth LA6 2AW

CARSHALTON

B.M. MAY & CO
41 Salisbury Road, Carshalton, SM5 3HA
Tel: 020 8647 0135
Principal: ICAEW Member
B M May

LINKS ACCOUNTANCY & MORTGAGE SERVICES LTD
7 Rotherfield Road, Carshalton, SM5 3DN

MICHAEL E. BLAKE & CO
Evans Corner, Woodmansterne Lane, Carshalton, SM5 4DQ

MORGANS ◈
86 High Street, Carshalton, SM5 3AE
Tel: 020 8773 4466
Principal: ICAEW Member
R J C Morgan
See display advertisement near this entry.

SKINGLE HELPS & CO
28 Southway, Carshalton Beeches, Carshalton, SM5 4HW
Tel: 020 8770 1095
Principal: ICAEW Member
J V R Helps

VIJAY SHAH & CO
5 The Parade, Pound Street, Carshalton, SM5 3RJ

CASTLE CARY

COLIN ILLINGWORTH-KAY
4 Castle Rise, Castle Cary, BA7 7ND

CASTLEFORD

D'ARCY HOWARD CASTLEFORD LTD ◈
7A Pontefract Road, Castleford, WF10 4JE
Tel: 01977 557669
Resident Partners/Directors: ICAEW Members
B F Martyn

HANSONS
St Oswald House, St Oswald Street, Castleford, WF10 1DH
Tel: 01977 552881
Website: http://www.hansons.uk.com

PGU ACCOUNTING LTD
St Oswald House, St Oswald Street, Castleford, WF10 1DH

R.G. HILTON & CO
10a Bank Street, Castleford, WF10 1HZ

CATERHAM

AML
Maybrook House, 97 Godstone Road, Caterham, CR3 6RE

AMLBENSON LTD
AML Maybrook House, 97 Godstone Road, Caterham, CR3 6RE

BARBER TOUCAN LTD
1 The Crescent, Station Road, Woldingham, Caterham CR3 7DB
Tel: 01883 653530
Resident Partners/Directors: ICAEW Members
D H Mole

D.V. UDALL & CO
Dukes Edge, Lunghurst Road, Woldingham, Caterham CR3 7HE

DM ASSOCIATES
1 The Crescent, Station Road, Woldingham, Caterham CR3 7DB

G.R. POTTON & CO
2 Harestone Valley Road, Caterham, CR3 6HB
Tel: 01883 348222
Fax: 01883 348717
Email: grahampotton@aol.com
Principal: ICAEW Member
G R Potton
Registered by the ICAEW to carry out company audit work

KEITH TOWERS
Greensleeves, 65 Harestone Lane, Caterham, CR3 6AL

M. GODDARD & CO
69 Tupwood Lane, Caterham, CR3 6DD
Tel: 01883 341101
Resident Partners/Directors: ICAEW Members
M P Goddard

M T BUCKLEY & CO
2 Beulah Walk, Woldingham, Caterham, CR3 7LL

MALCOLM PRIOR & CO ◈
4 Timber Lane, Caterham, CR3 6LZ
Tel: 01883 340086
Principal: ICAEW Member
M B C Prior
Registered by the ICAEW to carry out company audit work
Regulated by the ICAEW for a range of investment business activities

P.L.T. MAW & CO
192 Harestone Valley Road, Caterham, CR3 6BT

PEACHEY & CO (ACCOUNTANTS) LTD
4 Sunny Rise, Chaldon, Caterham, CR3 5PR
Tel: 01883 340999
Resident Partners/Directors: ICAEW Members
D Peachey

PETER HOSKIN LTD
Chadley, Park View Road, Woldingham, Caterham CR3 7DJ
Tel: 01883 653116
Resident Partners/Directors: ICAEW Members
P J M Hoskin

PETERS & CO ★
1 Park Road, Caterham, CR3 5TB

ROGER LUGG & CO
12/14 High Street, Caterham, CR3 5UA
Tel: 01883 349211
Resident Partners/Directors: ICAEW Members
H D Barrett, B W Chapman, R B Lugg

S NUNN & CO LTD
Unit 2, Guards Avenue, The Village, Caterham CR3 5XL

UPTON NEENAN LEES
6a Croydon Road, Caterham, CR3 6QB

CHALFONT ST. GILES

CHENERY & CO
36 Palliser Road, Chalfont St Giles, HP8 4DL

DAVID CORNISH
Marlins, Back Lane, Chalfont St Giles, HP8 4PF

KATE BERRYMAN
Micklebeck, Burtons Lane, Chalfont St. Giles, HP8 4BN

LAWSON & CO ◈
Little Hide, 18 The Lagger, Chalfont St Giles, HP8 4DG
Tel: 01494 873545
Fax: 01494 873545
Email: mail@lawsonsaccountants.co.uk
Date Established: 1991
Principal: ICAEW Member
T H Lawson
Registered by the ICAEW to carry out company audit work

SPECIALISATIONS – AUDIT & ASSURANCE
Audit

SPECIALISATIONS – FINANCIAL REPORTING
Limited Company Accounts
Partnership/Sole Trader Accounts

SPECIALISATIONS – TAXATION
Capital Gains — Personal
Investigations
Partnerships and Sole Traders
Self Assessment Advice

RICHARD J GOWER
Redferns, 35 The Lagger, Chalfont St. Giles, HP8 4DH

CHARD

ALBERT GOODMAN
Essex House, 47 Fore Street, Chard, TA20 1QA

LENTELLS
Catford House, 26 Fore Street, Chard, TA20 1PT
Tel: 01460 64441

LENTELLS LTD
26 Fore Street, Chard, TA20 1PT

NEELD WELLINGS ◈
Rawlings Barn, Wambrook, Chard, TA20 3DF
Tel: 01460 66353
Principal: ICAEW Member
A N Wellings

THOMAS LANE
Little Hill Cottage, Buckland St Mary, Chard, TA20 3SS

CHATHAM

BEAK KEMMENOE ◈
1-3 Manor Road, Chatham, ME4 6AE
Tel: 01634 830100
Resident Partners/Directors: ICAEW Members
J H Kemmenoe, R D Price, M J Samways

CAS
346c High Street, Chatham, ME4 4NP

CAS HOUSE LTD
346c High Street, Chatham, ME4 4NP

GOLDBLATTS LTD
Victoria House, 14 New Road Avenue, Chatham, ME4 6BA

GRAEME M. PIKE LTD
48 Prince Charles Avenue, Chatham, ME5 8EY
Tel: 01634 862286
Resident Partners/Directors: ICAEW Members
G M Pike

HURKAN SAYMAN & CO ★
2D Luton Road, Chatham, ME4 5AA

MACKINLAY
8 Manor Road, Chatham, ME4 6AG

MOORE STEPHENS LLP
Victory House, Quayside, Chatham Maritime, Chatham ME4 4QU

PETER MORLEY
15 Pinewood Drive, Lordswood, Chatham, ME5 8XU

REEVES+NEYLAN LLP
Montague Place, Quayside, Chatham Maritime, Chatham ME4 4QU
Tel: 01634 899800
Resident Partners/Directors: ICAEW Members
A J Q Griggs, T P W Levey, S M Robinson, C R Stevens
Resident Partners (Non-ICAEW Members):
D R Turner
Registered by the ICAEW to carry out company audit work
Regulated by the ICAEW for a range of investment business activities

CHATTERIS

BBK PARTNERSHIP
9 South Fens Business Centre, Fenton Way, Chatteris, PE16 6TT

BRIAN COX & CO
Crown Buildings, 18 Market Hill, Chatteris, PE16 6BA
Tel: 01354 693542
Principal: ICAEW Member
B J Cox

EDWARDS ★
Bank House, 2 Park Street, Chatteris, PE16 6AE

CHEADLE

BORDERBAY LTD
13 Rushside Road, Cheadle Hulme, Cheadle, SK8 6NW
Tel: 0161 485 7136
Resident Partners/Directors: ICAEW Members
A J P Bebbington

CAROLE A BARTON FCA
5 Grange Park Road, Cheadle, SK8 1HQ

CHANDLEY ROBINSON LTD
33 Church Road, Gatley, Cheadle, SK8 4NG

CHANDLEY ROBISON
33 Church Road, Gatley, Cheadle, SK8 4NG

CHD ASSOCIATES LLP
Ground Floor, Eden Point, Three Acres Lane, Cheadle Hulme, Cheadle SK8 6RL
Tel: 0161 488 3381
Resident Partners/Directors: ICAEW Members
D J Evans-Dudley

CONNOR RICHARDSON ◈
23 Mellor Road, Cheadle Hulme, Cheadle, SK8 5AT
Tel: 0161 485 7575

CRAWLEY
23 Keswick Avenue, Gatley, Cheadle, SK8 4LE

D M JONES
2 Burnside Road, Gatley, Cheadle, SK8 4NA

DAVID STONEFIELD & COMPANY LTD
70 Grasmere Road, Gatley, Cheadle, SK8 4RS

G. KRYSTEK & CO
Portwood House, 2 Brooklyn Road, Cheadle, SK8 1BS

GHATAN & CO
4 Park Lodge Close, Cheadle, SK8 1HU
Tel: 0161 832 9447
Principal: ICAEW Member
N Ghatan

HARROP MARSHALL ◈
Strathblane House, Ashfield Road, Cheadle, SK8 1BB
Tel: 0161 608 1666
Email: advice@harropmarshall.co.uk
Website: http://www.harropmarshall.co.uk
Resident Partners/Directors: ICAEW Members
T G Bowler, C J Westbury
Registered by the ICAEW to carry out company audit work
General Description: Pro-active advice for growing your business.

LANDSMAN
1 Arlington Road, Cheadle, SK8 1LW

LANGER & CO
8-10 Gatley Road, Cheadle, SK8 1PY

LANGER & CO LTD
8-10 Gatley Road, Cheadle, SK8 1PY

LANGERS
8-10 Gatley Road, Cheadle, SK8 1PY

LUCAS REIS LTD
Landmark House, Station Road, Cheadle Hulme, Cheadle SK8 7BS
Tel: 0161 486 3304
Resident Partners/Directors: ICAEW Members
S F Reis

MOSS & WILLIAMSON
3 Mellor Road, Cheadle Hulme, Cheadle, SK8 5AT
Tel: 0161 488 4458
Resident Partners/Directors: ICAEW Members
A E Booth, C H McLean

P.R. WHITTAKER
49 Woodfield Road, Cheadle Hulme, Cheadle, SK8 7JT
Tel: 0161 485 1189
Principal: ICAEW Member
P R Whittaker

PHILIP GABBIE LTD
28 Park Lodge Close, Cheadle, SK8 1HU

RACHEL LANDSMAN
1 Arlington Road, Cheadle, SK8 1LW

ROSH FD LTD ◈
49 Springfield Road, Gatley, Cheadle, SK8 4PF
Tel: 07734 212648
Resident Partners/Directors: ICAEW Members
M B Hyman

SOLAR ACCOUNTANTS
No 1 Lakeside, Cheadle Royal Business Park, Cheadle, SK8 3GB

STEVEN GLICHER & CO ◈
Fin House, 1 Oakwater Avenue, Cheadle Royal, Cheadle SK8 3SR
Tel: 0161 495 4302
Principal: ICAEW Member
S V Glicher

THOMAS GARE
44 Ramillies Avenue, Cheadle Hulme, Cheadle, SK8 7AL

TUSSIES LTD
31 Wilmslow Road, Cheadle Hulme, Cheadle, SK8 1DR

CHEAM

THP LTD
Century House, Station Way, Cheam, SM3 8SW

CHEDDAR

HELEN BARDLE
7 Cliff Street, Cheddar, BS27 3PT
Tel: 01934 744333
Principal: ICAEW Member
H L Bardle

T P LEWIS & PARTNERS
Bath Street, Cheddar, BS27 3AA
Tel: 01934 743274
Email: mail@tplewis.co.uk

CHELMSFORD

ABILITY ACCOUNTING SERVICES LTD
11 Westbourne Grove, Chelmsford, CM2 9RT
Tel: 01245 611429
Resident Partners/Directors: ICAEW Members
J E Fall

ANNE CORFIELD
15 Curzon Way, Chelmer Village, Chelmsford, CM2 6PF

APPERLEY ROWLEY & CO ★
Bell House, Bell Street, Great Baddow, Chelmsford CM2 7JS

AUDIT ENGLAND
23 Oaklands Crescent, Old Moulsham, Chelmsford, CM2 9PP

AUDIT ENGLAND LTD
23 Oaklands Crescent, Old Moulsham, Chelmsford, CM2 9PP

BAKER TILLY
Marlborough House, Victoria Road South, Chelmsford, CM1 1LN
Tel: 01245 354402
Resident Partners/Directors: ICAEW Members
P H Chamberlain

BAKER TILLY
Marlborough House, Victoria Road South, Chelmsford, CM1 1LN
Tel: 01245 354402
Resident Partners/Directors: ICAEW Members
D Bardell
Resident Partners (Non-ICAEW Members):
J R Marchant

BAKER TILLY
Marlborough House, Victoria Road South, Chelmsford, CM1 1LN

BAKER TILLY TAX AND ADVISORY SERVICES LLP
Marlborough House, Victoria Road South, Chelmsford, CM1 1LN
Tel: 01245 354402
Resident Partners/Directors: ICAEW Members
D Bardell, J T Barnes, P H Chamberlain, I F Cruse, R Harvey
Resident Partners (Non-ICAEW Members):
J T Barnes, J R Marchant

BARRY WATKINSON & CO
Moulsham Mill, Parkway, Chelmsford, CM2 7PX

BARRY WATKINSON & CO LTD
Moulsham Mill, Parkway, Chelmsford, CM2 7PX

BDO STOY HAYWARD LLP
66 Broomfield Road, Chelmsford, CM1 1SW
Tel: 01245 264644
Fax: 01245 490682
Resident Partners/Directors: ICAEW Members
R D Adams, G W Miller

BERKE FINE FUSSELL LTD ◈
Beren Court, Newney Green, Chelmsford, CM1 3SQ
Tel: 01245 249060
Resident Partners/Directors: ICAEW Members
S R Fussell

BIRD LUCKIN LTD ◈
Aquila House, Waterloo Lane, Chelmsford, CM1 1BN
Tel: 01245 254200
Fax: 01245 254254
Email: enquiries@bird-luckin.co.uk
Website: http://www.bird-luckin.co.uk
Resident Partners/Directors: ICAEW Members
G A L Adams, D F P Enser, D P Huggins, J Osborne, C Pardoe, I J Plunkett, G A Smith, K P Thomas
Resident Partners (Non-ICAEW Members):
P A Warren
Other Offices: Dunmow

Registered by the ICAEW to carry out company audit work

INVESTOR IN PEOPLE

SPECIALISATIONS – AUDIT & ASSURANCE
Assurance Services
Audit

SPECIALISATIONS – BUSINESS & GENERAL ADVICE
Acquisitions and Mergers
Book-keeping
Company Secretarial Service

Management Accounting Consultancy
Management Consultancy

SPECIALISATIONS – FINANCIAL REPORTING
Accounts Preparation

SPECIALISATIONS – IT
Computer Systems and Consultancy

SPECIALISATIONS – SECTOR
Corporate

SPECIALISATIONS – TAXATION
Payroll Service and Advice
Taxation
Trusts
Value Added Tax

General Description: One of the largest independent Essex-based firms with a wide range of general and specialist directors and team members offering clients a first class personal service.

BRIAN PAYNE & CO ◈
16 Anchor Street, Chelmsford, CM2 0JY

C & M TRAMONTINI LTD ◈
Bruce House, 15 The Street, Hatfield Peverel, Chelmsford CM3 2DP
Tel: 01245 381929
Resident Partners/Directors: ICAEW Members
C Tramontini

CARLTON BAKER CLARKE LLP
Carlton House, 101 New London Road, Chelmsford, CM2 0PP

CHARLTON BAKER CLARKE
Carlton House, 101 New London Road, Chelmsford, CM2 0PP

DAVID SARJANT & CO
16 Anchor Street, Chelmsford, CM2 0JY
Tel: 01245 354967
Email: davidsarjantandco@eclipse.co.uk
Principal: ICAEW Member
D Sarjant

EDMUND CARR
146 New London Road, Chelmsford, CM2 0AW

EDMUND CARR LLP
146 New London Road, Chelmsford, CM2 0AW

FASB CONSULTANTS Ⓜ ◈
P.O. Box 3757, (13 Howard Drive), Chelmsford, CM1 6NZ
Tel: 07860 844808
Resident Partners/Directors: ICAEW Members
D A Clarke

FISHER MICHAEL
Boundary House, 4 County Place, New London Road, Chelmsford CM2 0RE
Tel: 01245 358955
Email: ask@fisher-michael.co.uk
Resident Partners/Directors: ICAEW Members
N Carpenter, N Shaw
Resident Partners (Non-ICAEW Members):
A Kaley
Registered by the ICAEW to carry out company audit work
See display advertisement near this entry.

G LUNT
9 Gordon Road, Chelmsford, CM2 9LL

JIM CARPENTER
12 Juniper Road, Boreham, Chelmsford, CM3 3DB
Tel: 01245 468160
Principal: ICAEW Member
J J Carpenter

LAMBERT CHAPMAN LLP ◈
Kensal House, 77 Springfield Road, Chelmsford, CM2 6JG
Tel: 01245 216800
Email: chelmsford@lambert-chapman.co.uk
Website: http://www.lambert-chapman.co.uk
Resident Partners/Directors: ICAEW Members
M N P A Atkinson, B A Hill
Other Offices: Braintree, Maldon
Registered by the ICAEW to carry out company audit work

SPECIALISATIONS – AUDIT & ASSURANCE
Audit — Private Company

SPECIALISATIONS – BUSINESS & GENERAL ADVICE
Disposal of Businesses
Management Advice to Business

SPECIALISATIONS – FINANCIAL REPORTING
Accounts Preparation

SPECIALISATIONS – SECTOR
Agriculture
Charities
Construction
Human Resources
Property Development
Schools

SPECIALISATIONS – TAXATION
Taxation

LB GROUP
129 New London Road, Chelmsford, CM2 0QT

LEGGATT BELL
14 Railway Street, Chelmsford, CM1 1QS
Tel: 01245 353347
Resident Partners/Directors: ICAEW Members
P J Reeve, D V Thomason

M HARCOURT WILLIAMS & CO
The Old Forge, East Hanningfield, Chelmsford, CM3 8AA
Tel: 01245 400362
Principal: ICAEW Member
M F Harcourt Williams

M.J. WHELAN
85 Lime Walk, Moulsham Lodge, Chelmsford, CM2 9NJ
Tel: 01245 263529
Principal: ICAEW Member
M J Whelan

MACINTYRE HUDSON LLP ◈
Moulsham Court, 39 Moulsham Street, Chelmsford, CM2 0HY
Tel: 01245 353177
Website: http://www.macintyrehudson.co.uk
Resident Partners/Directors: ICAEW Members
I M Bray, J S D Cope, D P Nicholas, L M Waghorn
Resident Partners (Non-ICAEW Members):
A Snowdon, L Waghorn
Regulated by the ICAEW for a range of investment business activities

MCTEAR WILLIAMS & WOOD ★ ◈
The Waterhouse Business Centre, Cromar Way, Chelmsford, CM1 2QE
Tel: 01245 396812

MARTIN C COOK & CO
2nd Floor, Raeburn House, 2 Baron Road, South Woodham Ferrers, Chelmsford CM3 5XQ
Tel: 01245 322929

MARTIN C COOK & CO LTD
Raeburn House, 2 Baron Road, South Woodham Ferrers, Chelmsford CM3 5XQ
Tel: 01245 322929
Resident Partners/Directors: ICAEW Members
M C Cook

MOULSHAM AUDITS LTD
Moulsham Mill, Parkway, Chelmsford, CM2 7PX

N.J. HICKLING
75 First Avenue, Chelmsford, CM1 1RX

OCTOBER MARKETING LTD
17 Cawkwell Close, Chelmsford, CM2 6SG

OSBORNE FORBES LTD
9-11 Stortford Road, Great Dunford, Chelmsford, CM6 1DA

PEATY & CO
163 - 164 Moulsham Street, Chelmsford, CM2 0LD
Tel: 01245 350707
Principal: ICAEW Member
Gerald Peaty

PETER THORN
38 Greenways, Chelmsford, CM1 4EF

QUANTIC ACCOUNTANCY ◈
Malus, Appletree Corner, Hartford End, Chelmsford, CM3 1LE
Tel: 01245 237361

RODERICKS & CO
Sworders Farm, Pleshey, Chelmsford, CM3 1HU

S.L. SCOTT
235 New London Road, Chelmsford, CM2 9AA
Tel: 01245 357211
Principal: ICAEW Member
S L Scott

SEAN ROWE LTD
169 New London Road, Chelmsford, CM2 0AE

SEGRAVE & POCKNELL
46 Hullbridge Road, South Woodham Ferrers, Chelmsford, CM3 5NG

SHAPIRO DYMANT & CO
17 Cawkwell Close, Chelmsford, CM2 6SG

SPENCER FELLOWS & CO
169 New London Road, Chelmsford, CM2 0AE

TENON LTD
Moriston House, 75 Springfield Road, Chelmsford, CM2 6JB
Tel: 01245 348337

THP LTD
Shalford Court, 95 Springfield Road, Chelmsford, CM2 6JL

WALTERS AND TUFNELL
122 New London Road, Chelmsford, CM2 0RG

WALTERS AND TUFNELL LTD
122 New London Road, Chelmsford, CM2 0RG

WATERSHEDS LTD ◈
2 St John's Court, Moulsham Street, Chelmsford, CM2 0JD
Tel: 01245 257301

WILLIAM EVANS & PARTNERS
165 New London Road, Chelmsford, CM2 0AD

CHELTENHAM

A.E. MITCHELL & CO
The Coach House, Fields Road, Chedworth, Cheltenham GL54 4NQ

ACCOUNTSOLVE LTD
7 Woodgate Close, Charlton Kings, Cheltenham, GL52 6UW

ANDERSON GRIFFIN LTD
Rotunda Buildings, Montpellier Street, Cheltenham, GL50 1SX

ANDORRAN LTD ◈
6 Manor Park Business Centre, Mackenzie Way, Cheltenham, GL51 9TX
Tel: 01242 244856
Resident Partners/Directors: ICAEW Members
R F Downes, S E Garside

ANDREW PIGGOTT
10 Station Close, Leckhampton, Cheltenham, GL53 0AB

ANGELA PAULL & CO
1 New Barn, Manor Farm Courtyard, Southam, Cheltenham GL52 3PB
Tel: 01242 221477
Principal: ICAEW Member
A M Webb

B & P ACCOUNTING
Kingsley House, Church Lane, Shurdington, Cheltenham GL51 4TQ

B & P ACCOUNTING PARTNERSHIP
Kingsley House, Church Lane, Shurdington, Cheltenham GL51 5TQ

BPC PARTNERS LTD
7 Imperial Square, Cheltenham, GL50 1QB
Tel: 01242 226789
Email: info@bpcpartners.co.uk
Website: http://www.bpcpartners.co.uk
Resident Partners/Directors: ICAEW Members
M A G Bull, P K Cadbury
Registered by the ICAEW to carry out company audit work
General Description: See website for our services.

BROWN & CO
The Bramery, 44 Alstone Lane, Cheltenham, GL51 8HE

CECIL SANDERSON
4 Lansdown Parade, Cheltenham, GL50 2LH

CHANDLER ASSOCIATES LTD
Grange Farm House, Brockhampton, Cheltenham, GL54 5XQ
Tel: 01242 820629
Resident Partners/Directors: ICAEW Members
R C Chandler

CHARGROVE BUSINESS SERVICES LTD ◈
Chargrove House, Main Road, Shurdington, Cheltenham GL51 4GA

CLASSIC FINANCIAL SOLUTIONS ◈
79 Promenade, Cheltenham, GL50 1PJ
Tel: 01242 548600
Fax: 01242 548605
Email: info@cfsca.com
Website: http://www.cfsca.com
Resident Partners (Non-ICAEW Members):
T D Farley, P Trevanna
Other Offices: Bath

CLASSIC FINANCIAL SOLUTIONS LLP
79 Promenade, Cheltenham, GL50 1PJ

CLIVE THOMAS
16 Quat Goose Lane, Swindon Village, Cheltenham, GL51 9RX

COLIN F HARWOOD
4 Keynsham Street, Cheltenham, GL52 6EJ
Tel: 01242 511181
Principal: ICAEW Member
C F Harwood

CROSSLEY & CO ◈
Oriel Lodge, Oriel Road, Cheltenham, GL50 1XN
Tel: 01242 677722
Principal: ICAEW Member
N R C Standeven

CURTIS & CO
1 Imperial Square, Cheltenham, GL50 1QB
Tel: 01242 571727
Principal: ICAEW Member
R W H Curtis

DAVID KEFFLER & CO
30 Greenway Lane, Charlton Kings, Cheltenham, GL52 6LB
Tel: 07714 209078
Principal: ICAEW Member
D P Keffler

DAVIES MAYERS BARNETT LLP ◈
Pillar House, 113-115 Bath Road, Cheltenham, GL53 7LS
Tel: 01242 252555
Resident Partners/Directors: ICAEW Members
T G Davies, N J Mayers, M A Minchella, N S Smith

FINDLAY JAMES
Saxon House, Saxon Way, Cheltenham, GL52 6QX

FINNEMORES
10 St Edwards Walk, Charlton Kings, Cheltenham, GL53 7RS
Tel: 01242 263274
Principal: ICAEW Member
J M Finnemore

FINNEMORES LTD
10 St Edwards Walk, Charlton Kings, Cheltenham, GL53 7RS
Tel: 01242 263274
Resident Partners/Directors: ICAEW Members
J M Finnemore

FRANCIS & CO ◈
Festival House, Jessop Avenue, Cheltenham, GL50 3SH
Tel: 01242 633744

FRASER & ASSOCIATES ◈
1 Imperial Square, Cheltenham, GL50 1QB

GARDNER BROWN
Calderwood House, 7 Montpellier Parade, Cheltenham, GL50 1UA

GITTINS & CO
3 Tebbit Mews, Winchcombe Street, Cheltenham, GL52 2NF
Tel: 01452 813689
Principal: ICAEW Member
C D Gittins

GRANT & CO (ACCOUNTANTS) LTD ◈
7 Manor Park Business Centre, Mackenzie Way, Cheltenham, GL51 9TX
Tel: 01242 223160
Resident Partners/Directors: ICAEW Members
M G Gray

HARPERSHELDON ◈
The Old School House, Leckhampton Road, Cheltenham, GL53 0AX
Tel: 01242 513232
Resident Partners/Directors: ICAEW Members
J Harper, S Sheldon

HAZLEWOODS LLP
Windsor House, Bayshill Road, Cheltenham, GL50 3AT
Tel: 01242 237661
Website: http://www.hazlewoods.co.uk
Resident Partners/Directors: ICAEW Members
A W Brookes, N M Haines, P A

Kinahan, S M Lawrence, A E Randle
Resident Partners (Non-ICAEW Members):
N L Webber, J Cartwright

SPECIALISATIONS – SECTOR

Nursing Homes/Clinics
Solicitors

HAZLEWOODS LLP

Staverton Court, Staverton, Cheltenham, GL51 0UX
Tel: 01242 680000
Website: http://www.hazlewoods.co.uk
Resident Partners/Directors: ICAEW Members
N F Dee, D R Pierce, G T Rew, P A Swan
Resident Partners (Non-ICAEW Members):
A D Flambard, M E Beaney

SPECIALISATIONS – SECTOR

Agriculture
Dentists/Opticians

HOOPER & CO

Little Shipton, London Road, Charlton Kings, Cheltenham GL52 6YU

HORWATH CLARK WHITEHILL LLP

Carrick House, Lypiatt Road, Cheltenham, GL50 2QJ
Tel: 01242 234421
Resident Partners/Directors: ICAEW Members
N M Denniss, M A Hall, M A Hunt, M Regan, S S Russell

HORWATH SMALL BUSINESS CENTRE

William Burford House, 27 Lansdown Place Lane, Cheltenham, GL50 2LB

KINGSCOTT DIX

Malvern View Business Park, Stella Way, Bishops Cleeve, Cheltenham GL52 7DQ
Tel: 01242 679099
Fax: 01242 679199
Email: kdc@kingscottdix.co.uk
Website: http://www.kingscott-dix.co.uk
Date Established: 1992
Resident Partners/Directors: ICAEW Members
S W Fullard, G Wala

Registered by the ICAEW to carry out company audit work

Regulated by the ICAEW for a range of investment business activities

MICHAEL J. MITCHELL

11 Chestnut Terrace, Charlton Kings, Cheltenham, GL53 8JQ
Tel: 01242 572810
Principal: ICAEW Member
M J Mitchell
General Description:
Specialises in one-to-one service to sole traders and people starting in business.
See display advertisement near this entry.

MITCHELL GLANVILLE LTD ◈

41 Rodney Road, Cheltenham, GL50 1HX
Tel: 01242 260066
Resident Partners/Directors: ICAEW Members
J R D Glanville, N J Mitchell

MORETON & CO

Armscote House, Upper Dowdeswell, Andoversford, Cheltenham GL54 4LU

NICHOLAS TEE FCA

The Parsonage, Shipton Oliffe, Cheltenham, GL54 4HU

ORIEL ACCOUNTING LTD

Cheltenham House, Clarence Street, Cheltenham, GL50 3JR
Tel: 0845 226 1839
Resident Partners/Directors: ICAEW Members
B P Pursey

PHILIP COLLINS

37 Carmarthen Road, Up Hatherley, Cheltenham, GL51 3JZ

POPE & CO

1 Drayton Close, Swindon Village, Cheltenham, GL51 9QB

R.F. CAREY

5 Courtrai, Lansdown Castle Drive, Cheltenham, GL51 7AF

ROBERT COOMBES

6 Smith Barry Circus, Upper Rissington, Cheltenham, GL54 2NQ

SJD (SOUTH WEST) LTD

17 Royal Crescent, Cheltenham, GL50 3DA
Tel: 01242 282901
Resident Partners/Directors: ICAEW Members
P J R Morris

STEWART AYLWARD FCA

Isbourne, Chandos Street, Winchcombe, Cheltenham GL54 5HX

THOMAS & CO

Collane, 261 Hatherley Road, Cheltenham, GL51 6HF

W FRANCIS & CO LTD ◈

Festival House, Jessop Avenue, Cheltenham, GL50 3SH

WARNER & CO

Lowe House, 55 Townsend Street, Cheltenham, GL51 9HA

WILLIAM HINTON

Ross House, The Square, Stow on the Wold, Cheltenham GL54 1AF
Tel: 01451 831130

WILLIAM HINTON LTD ◈

Ross House, The Square, Stow on the Wold, Cheltenham GL54 1AF
Tel: 01451 831130
Fax: 01451 832233
Email: enquiries@williamhinton.co.uk
Website: http://www.williamhinton.co.uk
Training Contracts Available.
Resident Partners/Directors: ICAEW Members
C W K Hinton

Registered by the ICAEW to carry out company audit work

Regulated by the ICAEW for a range of investment business activities

SPECIALISATIONS – AUDIT & ASSURANCE

Audit

SPECIALISATIONS – FINANCIAL REPORTING

Accounts Preparation
Limited Companies
Limited Company Accounts
Partnership/Sole Trader Accounts

SPECIALISATIONS – TAXATION

Partnerships and Sole Traders
Payroll Service and Advice
Personal
Taxation

General Description: "Making Business Better" - see our website for details.
See display advertisement near this entry.

WILSHAW & ELLIS

Westcote, Sherborne, Cheltenham, GL54 3DU

CHERTSEY

DRAKE & CO
Drake House, 80 Guildford Street, Chertsey, KT16 9AD
Tel: 01932 562676
Principal: ICAEW Member
R J Drake

FULLER HARVEY LTD ◈
Mill House, 58 Guildford Street, Chertsey, KT16 9BE
Tel: 01932 564098
Resident Partners/Directors: ICAEW Members
M T C Harvey, S M Keane

FULLER SPURLING & CO
Mill House, 58 Guildford Street, Chertsey, KT16 9BE

H.G.FIELD & CO ★ ◈
2 Guildford Street, Chertsey, KT16 9BQ
Tel: 01932 563404
Resident Partners/Directors: ICAEW Members
J A Ensor, A Rodrigues

KEITH SAUNDERS
Fairview, 22 Ottershaw Park, Ottershaw, Chertsey KT16 0QG
Tel: 01932 872498
Principal: ICAEW Member
K A Saunders

CHESHAM

ELIZABETH POOLEY
Norfolk House, Station Road, Chesham, HP5 1DH
Tel: 01494 791012
Principal: ICAEW Member
E A Pooley

FRANCIS & HOWE LTD ◈
Botley House, East Street, Chesham, HP5 1DQ

FRANCIS AND HOWE ASSOCIATES ◈
Botley House, East Street, Chesham, HP5 1DQ
Tel: 01494 782 541
Fax: 01494 400119
Email: info@francisandhowe.com
Website: http://francisandhowe.com
Registered by another RSB to carry out company audit work
Regulated by the ICAEW for a range of investment business activities

GOLDING WEST & CO LTD
16 Station Road, Chesham, HP5 1DH

IAN WALTER
9 Holly Tree Close, Ley Hill, Chesham, HP5 3QT
Tel: 01494 784406
Principal: ICAEW Member
I A Walter

J.W. RIDGEWAY & CO
106a High Street, Chesham, HP5 1EB
Tel: 01494 774077
Principal: ICAEW Member
J W Ridgeway
Registered by the ICAEW to carry out company audit work

JACQUARDS ◈
2 Wannions Close, Chesham, HP5 1YA
Tel: 0845 055 5551

JACQUARDS LTD ◈
2 Wannions Close, Chesham, HP5 1YA
Tel: 0845 055 5551
Resident Partners/Directors: ICAEW Members
J Patel

JEAN INGRAM
106a High Street, Chesham, HP5 1EB
Tel: 01494 792038
Principal: ICAEW Member
J P Ingram

MICHAEL HARDMAN
Oak House, Botley Road, Chesham, HP5 1XG
Tel: 07771 561783
Principal: ICAEW Member
M R Hardman

MURRAY ACCOUNTING SERVICES LTD
Mead Court, 10 The Mead Business Centre, 176-178 Berkhamstead Road, Chesham HP5 3EE
Tel: 01494 792792
Resident Partners/Directors: ICAEW Members
I F C Murray

RICHARD WYATT & CO
109c High Street, Chesham, HP5 1DE

SHARP CONSULTING (UK) LTD
182 White Hill, Chesham, HP5 1AZ
Tel: 01494 786182
Resident Partners/Directors: ICAEW Members
J C Sharp

TONY EGINTON & CO
1 Upper Gladstone Road, Chesham, HP5 3AF
Tel: 01494 792557
Principal: ICAEW Member
A C T Eginton

CHESSINGTON

CHARTERHOUSE & CO ◈
Unit 15D, Oakcroft Road, Chessington, KT9 1RH

H. GRAHAM KING & CO ◈
Southernhay, Suite 7, 207 Hook Road, Chessington, KT9 1HJ
Tel: 020 8391 2266
Principal: ICAEW Member
K Holden

KAMAL J. CHOPRA
46 Drake Road, Chessington, KT9 1LW
Tel: 020 8391 1418
Principal: ICAEW Member
K J Chopra

CHESTER

AGP
1st Floor, 2 City Road, Chester, CH1 3AE
Tel: 01244 325511
Fax: 01928 718806
Email: runcorn@agp-accountants.co.uk
Website: http://www.agp-accountants.co.uk
Training Contracts Available.
Resident Partners/Directors: ICAEW Members
R S Gamwell, R K Lloyd, S A McLean
Non-resident Partners (ICAEW Members):
P Chesters, I A Black
Non-resident Partners (Non-ICAEW Members):
L C Thomas
Other Offices: Chester, Warrington
Registered by the ICAEW to carry out company audit work
Regulated by the ICAEW for a range of investment business activities

AIMS ACCOUNTANTS FOR BUSINESS
19 St Christophers Close, Upton, Chester, CH2 1EJ

AIMS - CRAIG WYNNE FCA ◈
29 Meadowcroft, Higher Kinnerton, Chester, CH4 9AY
Tel: 01244 661859
Principal: ICAEW Member
E C Wynne

AIMS - DAVID MATHER
19 St Christophers Close, Upton, Chester, CH2 1EJ

ANDREW CABELLO
27 Edwards Road, Chester, CH4 8HW

ARGOED BUSINESS SERVICES LTD ◈
5 St Johns Court, Vicars Lane, Chester, CH1 1QE

BAKER TILLY
Steam Mill, Steam Mill Street, Chester, CH3 5AN
Tel: 01244 505100
Resident Partners/Directors: ICAEW Members
R M Davies, S M Harris, J M Jones

BAKER TILLY
The Steam Mill, Steam Mill Street, Chester, CH3 5AN

BAKER TILLY TAX AND ADVISORY SERVICES LLP
Steam Mill, Steam Mill Street, Chester, CH3 5AN
Tel: 01244 505100
Resident Partners/Directors: ICAEW Members
R M Davies, S M Harris, J M Jones, G Potts
Resident Partners (Non-ICAEW Members):
G Garner-Jones

BAKEWELL ACCOUNTANCY SERVICES
4 Coed Terfyn, Penymynydd, Chester, CH4 0XB

BELLANCO LTD
32 The Yonne, Chester, CH1 2NH

BENSON FLYNN
4 Abbey Square, Chester, CH1 2HU
Tel: 01244 320300
Principal: ICAEW Member
A J Flynn

BRADSHAWS
Charter Court, 2 Well House Barns, Chester Road, Bretton, Chester CH4 0DH

CHAMPION ◈
Refuge House, 33-37 Watergate Row South, Chester, CH1 2LE

CHAMPION ACCOUNTANTS LLP
Refuge House, 33-37 Watergate Row South, Chester, CH1 2LE

CHAMPION ALLWOODS LTD
Refuge House, 33-37 Watergate Row South, Chester, CH1 2LE
Tel: 01244 312351
Fax: 01244 404440
Email: chester@champion-accountants.co.uk
Website: http://www.champion-accountants.co.uk
Resident Partners/Directors: ICAEW Members
G Cosgrove, M P Jackson, N P D Jackson
Other Offices: Manchester, Southport, Preston, Blackpool

CHRISTOPHER D JONES
Strawberry Cottage, Strawberry Lane, Mollington, Chester CH1 6LL
Tel: 01244 851893
Principal: ICAEW Member
C D Jones

COPPLESTONE UNSWORTH & CO
9 Abbey Square, Chester, CH1 2HU

D.& I. WALTON ◈
17 Lancaster Drive, Vicars Cross, Chester, CH3 5JW
Tel: 01244 318946
Principal: ICAEW Member
I Walton

DAVID WHARRIE & CO
Woodside House, Ashton, Chester, CH3 8AE

DEBT ASSIST DIRECT LTD
24 Nicholas Street, Chester, CH1 2AU

EDWARD ROBINSON & CO
Suite S1, Chester Enterprise Centre, Hoole Bridge, Chester CH2 3NE

ELLIS & CO ◈
114/120 Northgate Street, Chester, CH1 2HT
Tel: 01244 343504
Email: info@ellis-uk.com
Website: http://www.ellis-uk.com
Principal: ICAEW Member
C R Ellis

FOUNTAIN ACCOUNTANCY LTD
Curzon Chambers, 1 Curzon Street, Saltney, Chester CH4 8BP
Tel: 01244 689930
Resident Partners/Directors: ICAEW Members
R D P Jones, D G Roberts

HALL LIVESEY BROWN ◈
10 Nicholas Street, Chester, CH1 2NX

HARGREAVES & WOODS
Richmond Place, 127 Boughton, Chester, CH3 5BH
Tel: 01244 400219
Fax: 01244 400385
Email: post@hargreaveswoods.co.uk
Website: http://www.hargreaveswoods.co.uk

JEFFCOTT'S ◈
5 St Johns Court, Vicars Lane, Chester, CH1 1QP

KAVANAGH KNIGHT & CO LTD
Chaldean House, 7 Chandos Close, Chester, CH4 7BJ
Tel: 01244 679912
Resident Partners/Directors: ICAEW Members
M L Wright

L J O'BRIEN
Hawthorne Farmhouse, Ince Lane, Wimbolds Trafford, Chester CH2 4JP
Tel: 01244 301062
Principal: ICAEW Member
L J O'Brien

LAURA DAVEY BOOKKEEPING & BUSINESS SERVICES
6 Lime Grove, Elton, Chester, CH2 4PX

MCALEAVY & CO ◈
Riverside House, River Lane, Saltney, Chester CH4 8RQ

MCLINTOCKS ◈
2 Hilliards Court, Chester Business Park, Chester, CH4 9PX
Tel: 01244 680780
Resident Partners/Directors: ICAEW Members
M W Caputo, J A McLintock, T J Mitchell
Resident Partners (Non-ICAEW Members):
D J McLaughlin, C Blake

MARTIN WILLIAMS & CO
1st Floor Great Western House, Boundary Lane, Saltney, Chester CH4 8RD

MEACHER-JONES ◈
Bowman House, Bold Square, Chester, CH1 3LZ

MEACHER-JONES & COMPANY LTD ◈
Bowman House, Bold Square, Chester, CH1 3LZ
Tel: 01244 401001
Website: http://www.meacher-jones.com
Resident Partners/Directors: ICAEW Members
D R Meacher-Jones
Registered by the ICAEW to carry out company audit work
Languages Spoken:
Polish

MILITARY HOUSE LTD
Military House, 24 Castle Street, Chester, CH1 2DS

MILNE THOMAS & CO
27 Seller Street, Chester, CH1 3NA
Tel: 01244 321105
Resident Partners/Directors: ICAEW Members
A M Milne, S V Thomas

MITCHELL CHARLESWORTH ◈
24 Nicholas Street, Chester, CH1 2AU
Tel: 01244 323051
Resident Partners/Directors: ICAEW Members
R J Hall, R A K Hoppins

MORRIS & CO
1 Heritage Court, Lower Bridge Street, Chester, CH1 1RD
Tel: 01244 328301
Fax: 01244 313626
Email: mail@moco.co.uk
Website: http://www.moco.co.uk
Resident Partners/Directors: ICAEW Members
A Bailey, S Barker, W O R Benoy, J M Carr, E W Greeves, N O Ledingham
Other Offices: Ashton House, Chadwick Street, Moreton, Wirral CH46 7TE (Tel: 0151 678 7979)
Registered by the ICAEW to carry out company audit work
Regulated by the ICAEW for a range of investment business activities
SPECIALISATIONS – BUSINESS & GENERAL ADVICE
Franchising
SPECIALISATIONS – FORENSIC ACCOUNTING
Expert Witnesses in Litigation
SPECIALISATIONS – SECTOR
Charities
Dentists/Opticians
Doctors
General Description: Specialists in new small, family and expanding businesses as well as acting for dentists.

P.R. BATEMAN
9 Pembroke Close, Chester, CH4 7BS

P.R. BATEMAN QUTERIM FINANCIAL MANAGEMENT
9 Pembroke Close, Chester, CH4 7BS

PARKIN S. BOOTH & CO ★
2 City Road, Chester, CH1 3AE

PRIORY PRACTICE LTD
3 Hunter Street, Chester, CH1 2AR

PURSGLOVE & BROWN
Military House, 24 Castle Street, Chester, CH1 2DS

PURSGLOVE & BROWN
Military House, 24 Castle Street, Chester, CH1 2DS

RATIOCINATOR LTD
Richmond Place, 127 Boughton, Chester, CH3 5BH

ROBERT A. LEWIS & CO
Manor Farm, West End, Ashton, Chester CH3 8DG

SHAW AUSTIN LTD ◈
2 White Friars, Chester, CH1 1NZ
Tel: 01244 400244
Resident Partners/Directors: ICAEW Members
C A Goy, D H Shaw

STEPHEN R FOX ACA
20 Waverton Mill Quays, Waverton, Chester, CH3 7PX

SULLIVAN & CO ◈
7 Newry Park, Chester, CH2 2AR
Tel: 01244 378719
Email: sullivanchartacc@aol.com
Resident Partners/Directors: ICAEW Members
N J A Sullivan
SPECIALISATIONS – BUSINESS & GENERAL ADVICE
Management Consultancy
SPECIALISATIONS – FORENSIC ACCOUNTING
Forensic Accounting
SPECIALISATIONS – TAXATION
Taxation

SUZANNE HILL & CO
Rose Cottage, Cross Lanes, Oscroft, Tarvin, Chester CH3 8NQ

SUZANNE HILL & CO LTD
Rose Cottage, Cross Lanes, Oscroft, Tarvin, Chester CH3 8NQ
Tel: 01829 740515
Resident Partners/Directors: ICAEW Members
S M Hill

UHY HACKER YOUNG
St John's Chambers, Love Street, Chester, CH1 1QN
Tel: 01244 320532
Fax: 01244 505930
Email: office@uhy-chester.com
Website: http://www.uhy-uk.com
Resident Partners/Directors: ICAEW Members
J G Ierston, N S Jenkins
Overseas Offices: Via UHY International - 49 Countries
Registered by the ICAEW to carry out company audit work
Authorised and regulated by the Financial Services Authority for investment business
Languages Spoken:
Welsh, Russian

CHESTER LE STREET

B J STRAUGHAN & PARTNERS
Epworth House, 7 Lucy Street, Chester Le Street, DH3 3UP

BIRTLEY BUSINESS SERVICES
27 Durham Road, Birtley, Chester Le Street, DH3 2QG

GILPIN AND HARDING
15 St Johns Place, Birtley, Chester Le Street, DH3 2PW

ROWLANDS
Rowlands House, Portobello Road, Birtley, Chester Le Street DH3 2RY
Tel: 0191 411 2468
Fax: 0191 411 2460
Email: alan.hynd@rowlandsaccountants.co.uk
Website: http://www.rowlandsaccountants.co.uk
Resident Partners/Directors: ICAEW Members
E Brannigan, C Chater, E C Glover, D Nairn, D G Waugh
Non-resident Partners (ICAEW Members):
D T Taylor, D Coates
Resident Partners (Non-ICAEW Members):
A Hynd
Non-resident Partners (Non-ICAEW Members):
J H Madden
Other Offices:5-7 Eastgate, Hexham, Northumberland NE46 1BH, 17A Belle Villas, Ponteland, Newcastle upon Tyne NE20 9BD, Gladstone House, Gladstone Street, Crook, Co Durham DL15 9ED, 8 High Street, Yarm, Cleveland TS15 9AE
Registered by the ICAEW to carry out company audit work
Regulated by the ICAEW for a range of investment business activities
General Description: Delivering our brand of "excellence" to owner managed business.

STRAUGHANS
Hadrian House, Front Street, Chester Le Street, DH3 3DB

STRAUGHANS LTD
Hadrian House, Front Street, Chester Le Street, DH3 3DB
Tel: 0191 388 3377
Fax: 0191 387 1745
Email: straughans@straughans.co.uk
Website: http://www.straughans.co.uk
Resident Partners/Directors: ICAEW Members
M J H Tait
Resident Partners (Non-ICAEW Members):
M Fleming
SPECIALISATIONS – TAXATION
Investigations
Trusts

TORBITT & CO LTD ◈
27 Durham Road, Birtley, Chester Le Street, DH3 2QG
Tel: 0191 410 8300
Email: geoff@torbitt.co.uk
Resident Partners/Directors: ICAEW Members
G C Torbitt
Registered by the ICAEW to carry out company audit work
General Description: Small local firm giving personal service to the small business.

CHESTERFIELD

A C DRENNAN
73 Ashgate Avenue, Chesterfield, S40 1JD
Tel: 01246 222987
Principal: ICAEW Member
A C Drennan

BARBER HARRISON & PLATT ◈
57/59 Saltergate, Chesterfield, S40 1UL

CHRIS EDWARDS
Clamarpen, 17 Napier Court, Gander Lane, Barlborough, Chesterfield S43 4PZ

DAVID KIRK LTD
94-96 Saltergate, Chesterfield, S40 1LG

DEY & CO ◈
Brookdale, 41 Clarence Road, Chesterfield, S40 1LH
Tel: 01246 234777
Principal: ICAEW Member
J W Dey

GRS ACCOUNTING LTD
17 Birley Brook Drive, Newbold, Chesterfield, S41 8XN

HADFIELDS
Commerce House, 658B Chatsworth Road, Chesterfield, S40 3JZ

JOHN A. ROBERTS & CO ◈
42 Sheffield Road, Chesterfield, S41 7LL

LYNN M HOUGHTON
2 Dunston Place, Dunston Road, Chesterfield, S41 8NL
Tel: 01246 269900
Principal: ICAEW Member
L M Houghton
Individual(s) licensed for insolvency work by the ICAEW

MCABA LTD
91-97 Saltergate, Chesterfield, S40 1LA

MARTIN BRUNO
94-96 Saltergate, Chesterfield, S40 1LG

MILLAR & CO
17 Farm View, Tupton, Chesterfield, S42 6BD
Tel: 01246 250106
Principal: ICAEW Member
I D G Millar

MITCHELLS
91-97 Saltergate, Chesterfield, S40 1LA

MODIRI ◈
Tapton Park Innovation Centre, Brimington Road, Tapton, Chesterfield S41 0TZ
Tel: 01246 541923

MODIRI & CO ◈
Tapton Park Innovation Centre, Brimington Road, Tapton, Chesterfield S41 0TZ
Tel: 01246 541923
Principal: ICAEW Member
M Modiri Hamedan

P & L ACCOUNTANCY LTD
Future House, South Place, Beetwell Street, Chesterfield S40 1SZ

PRESTONS
Berry Hill House, 1 Cross Street, Chesterfield, S40 4TT

SHORTS ◈
6 Fairfield Road, Chesterfield, S40 4TP
Tel: 01246 208282
Fax: 01246 201618
Email: accounts@shortsaccountants.co.uk
Date Established: 1890
Resident Partners/Directors: ICAEW Members
P D Beeson, J A Bown, J A Brier, H K Freeman, P E Freeman
Resident Partners (Non-ICAEW Members):
C J Chambers, P N Varley, A J Irvine
Other Offices:912 Ecclesall Road, Sheffield S11 8TR
Registered by the ICAEW to carry out company audit work

SHORTS
Westfield House, 2 Ashgate Road, Chesterfield, S40 4AA

SMITH CRAVEN
18 South Street, Chesterfield, S40 1QX

STEPHEN C HUDSON
24 Westfield Close, Brampton, Chesterfield, S40 3RS

SUTTON MCGRATH LTD ◈
4 Royal Court, Basil Close, Chesterfield, S41 7SL

WALL GREEN
119 High Street, Clay Cross, Chesterfield, S45 9DZ
Tel: 01246 865825
Principal: ICAEW Member
G S Wall

CHICHESTER

BENSON & HINCHLIFFE ★
138A High Street, Selsey, Chichester, PO20 0QE

BUCHANANS LTD
4 Dukes Court, Bognor Road, Chichester, PO19 8FX

CABLE FINANCIAL DIRECTIONS LTD ◈
5 Downs Road, West Stoke, Chichester, PO18 9BQ
Tel: 07748 986619
Resident Partners/Directors: ICAEW Members
J E Cable

CFO SOLUTIONS LTD
47 Maplehurst Road, Chichester, PO19 6QL

CHARLES BROWNLEE
11 Graffham Close, Chichester, PO19 5AW

COBRA MANAGEMENT CONSULTANTS LTD
Inglenook, Main Road, Nutbourne, Chichester PO18 8RR

DAVID EXELL ASSOCIATES
Huntlands, Birdham, Chichester, PO20 7BY

DAVID MOATE
Woodlands, Batchmere Road, Batchmere, Chichester PO20 7LH

DAVID NASON
1 St Richards Walk, Canon Lane, Chichester, PO19 1QA
Tel: 01243 775615
Principal: ICAEW Member
T D Nason

ELLIOTT & PARTNERS
City Gates, 2/4 Southgate, Chichester, PO19 8DJ
Tel: 01243 780761
Fax: 01243 785503
Resident Partners/Directors: ICAEW Members
L J Elliott, R Spedding
Registered by the ICAEW to carry out company audit work

EVANS, WEIR
The Victoria, 25 St Pancras, Chichester, PO19 7LT
Tel: 01243 787751
Fax: 01243 779755
Email: accountancy@evansweir.co.uk
Principal: ICAEW Member
R Swaffield
Regulated by the ICAEW for a range of investment business activities

HWCA LTD ◈
Cawley Priory, South Pallant, Chichester, PO19 1SY
Tel: 01243 781234
Resident Partners/Directors: ICAEW Members
C S Homan, J C Ragg, S J Scurr

J CASEY & CO
Forum House, Stirling Road, Chichester, PO19 7DN

JAMES TODD & CO
Nos 1 & 2 The Barn, Oldwick, West Stoke Road, Lavant, Chichester PO18 9AA

JONES AVENS LTD
Jones Avens, Piper House, 4 Dukes Court, Bognor Road, Chichester PO19 8FX

LAWSONS
Keyham, Runcton Lane, Runcton, Chichester PO20 1LT

LEWIS BROWNLEE SHERLOCK
Avenue House, Southgate, Chichester, PO19 1ES
Tel: 01243 782423
Fax: 01243 528918
Email: info@lewisbrownleesherlock.co.uk
Website: http://www.lewisbrownleesherlock.co.uk
Training Contracts Available.
Resident Partners/Directors: ICAEW Members
A J R Lewis, M Merritt, W J C Neville
Resident Partners (Non-ICAEW Members):
S J Burns, S M Alexander
Registered by the ICAEW to carry out company audit work
Authorised and regulated by the Financial Services Authority for investment business
Languages Spoken:
French, Spanish

LINDA GIBSON
44 Hillfield Road, Selsey, Chichester, PO20 0LF

M. YARR
105 Cedar Drive, Parklands, Chichester, PO19 3EL

MCEWEN & CO LTD
21 St Martins Square, Chichester, PO19 1NR
Tel: 01243 788600
Resident Partners/Directors: ICAEW Members
L M J McEwen

MICHAEL DONNELY & CO
Clevelands, Fordwater Road, Chichester, PO19 6PS
Tel: 01243 533835
Principal: ICAEW Member
M Donnely

MOORE STEPHENS
3 East Pallant, Chichester, PO19 1TR
Tel: 01243 531800

MOORE STEPHENS (SOUTH) LLP
3 East Pallant, Chichester, PO19 1TR
Tel: 01243 531600
Fax: 01243 520637
Email: michaelscott@cbsouthern.co.uk
Website: http://www.moorestephens.co.uk
Training Contracts Available.
Resident Partners/Directors: ICAEW Members
G J Francis, A D Henshaw, M J Scott, M I Wakeford, M F J Weil, A S Wulff
Other Offices: Salisbury, Isle of Wight, Southampton
Overseas Offices: Member of Moore Stephens (International) Limited with 621 offices in 95 Countries

INVESTOR IN PEOPLE

R.D. WORTHINGTON
Arden Cottage, The Drive, Bosham, Chichester PO18 8JQ

R S HALL AND CO
Dragon's Lair, 27 Belle Meade Close, Woodgate, Chichester PO20 3YD

ROBERT SADLER & CO
30b Southgate, Chichester, PO19 1DP

ROWDENS
Lyndale, Mill Lane, Runcton, Chichester PO20 1PP

ROWDENS LTD
Lyndale, Mill Lane, Runcton, Chichester PO20 1PP
Tel: 01243 776088
Resident Partners/Directors: ICAEW Members
J B Rowden, P A Rowden

SHEEN STICKLAND LLP ◈
7 East Pallant, Chichester, PO19 1TR

SPOFFORTHS LLP
9 Donnington Park, 85 Birdham Road, Chichester, PO20 7AJ
Tel: 01243 787627
Resident Partners/Directors: ICAEW Members
R A Dunlop, A J Pearce, A J Spofforth, D M Spofforth

STONHAM.CO

STONHAM.CO
1 Market Avenue, Chichester, PO19 1JU
Tel: 01243 839000
Fax: 01243 839901
Email: mail@stonham.co.uk
Website: http://www.stonham.co.uk
Principal: ICAEW Member
E J Stonham
Other Offices: London, Southampton, Guildford, Bristol, Exeter, Witney, Redruth
Individual(s) licensed for insolvency work by the ICAEW

SPECIALISATIONS – BUSINESS & GENERAL ADVICE

Debt Counselling

SPECIALISATIONS – BUSINESS RECOVERY & INSOLVENCY

Bankruptcies
Corporate Recovery
Liquidations

SPECIALISATIONS – FORENSIC ACCOUNTING

Forensic Accounting

SPECIALISATIONS – SECTOR

Agriculture
Architects/Surveyors
Barristers
Charities
Church
Construction
Electronics
Engineers
Estate Agents
FSA Members
Horticulture
Hotels/Public Houses
Insurance Brokers
Lloyds Underwriters
Manufacturing
Nursing Homes/Clinics
Paper/Printing/Publishing
Property Development
Road Haulage and Distribution
Solicitors
Traders — General

General Description: Business rescue specialists.
Languages Spoken:
Spanish, French, Polish

CHIGWELL

A.K. VALERA
Sai Kutir, 28 Brook Way, Chigwell, IG7 6AW

DAVID CRAMMER & CO
20 Courtland Drive, Chigwell, IG7 6PW
Tel: 020 8500 2236
Principal: ICAEW Member
D J Crammer

ENGELSMAN & CO ★
The Estate House, 201 High Road, Chigwell, IG7 5BJ

HAMPTON WELLS
2 Woolhampton Way, Chigwell, IG7 4QH

PUGH CLARKE & CO
175 Manor Road, Chigwell, IG7 5QB

CHIPPENHAM

BOWEN MAY LLP ◈
Griffon House, Seagry Heath, Great Somerford, Chippenham SN15 5EN
Tel: 01249 720341
Website: http://www.bowen-may.co.uk
Resident Partners/Directors: ICAEW Members
W C R Bowen, J May

CARTER DUTTON
65 St Mary Street, Chippenham, SN15 3JF

CARTER DUTTON LLP
65 St Mary Street, Chippenham, SN15 3JF
Tel: 01249 650441
Resident Partners/Directors: ICAEW Members
J M Duffill, R W Dutton, R L Mander
Registered by the ICAEW to carry out company audit work
Regulated by the ICAEW for a range of investment business activities

INVESTOR IN PEOPLE

CHARLES TYE
Somerford House, 12 The Causeway, Chippenham, SN15 3BT

DAVID C KING ◈
The Old King William, Nettleton, Chippenham, SN14 7NW

GOODWIN SHAW ◈
39 Market Place, Chippenham, SN15 3HT

GORDON LAWRENCE ◈
30 The Pound, Bromham, Chippenham, SN15 2HE
Tel: 01380 850294
Principal: ICAEW Member
G C Lawrence

THE HANSON PARTNERSHIP LLP
Brinkworth House, Brinkworth, Chippenham, SN15 5DF

J.W.SWALES & CO LTD
The Grange, Yatton Keynell, Chippenham, SN14 7BA

KAREN CRAWFORD LTD ◈
2 Highbank, Slaughterford, Chippenham, SN14 8RG
Tel: 01249 783217
Resident Partners/Directors: ICAEW Members
K L Crawford

KAREN SAYERS LTD
29 Silver Street, Colerne, Chippenham, SN14 8DY
Tel: 01255 744355
Resident Partners/Directors: ICAEW Members
K P Sayers

LINDSEYTYE LTD
The Stables, Manor Farm Drive, Sutton Benger, Chippenham SN15 4RW

LM WOOD
22 John Aubrey Close, Yatton Keynell, Chippenham, SN14 7EG

MENZIES CAMERON & CO
Rowden House, 25 Rowden Hill, Chippenham, SN15 2AQ

MONAHANS
Bewley House, Marshfield Road, Chippenham, SN15 1JW
Tel: 01249 766966

MONAHANS ◈
Bewley House, Marshfield Road, Chippenham, SN15 1JW
Tel: 01249 766966
Resident Partners/Directors: ICAEW Members
S M Cooper

PEARSON MAY
67/68 St Mary Street, Chippenham, SN15 3JF

SILBURY BUSINESS ADVISERS LTD
Venture House, Calne Road, Lyneham, Chippenham SN15 4PP
Tel: 01249 891440

THOMAS CHIPPENDALE
39 Market Place, Chippenham, SN15 3HT

TIM CHAPPLE
10 St Mellion Close, Monkton Park, Chippenham, SN15 3XN

CHIPPING CAMPDEN

MARK KIRKBRIDE & CO LTD ★
Greenbanks, Hoo Lane, Chipping Campden, GL55 6AZ

MICHAEL LINDNER
The Gallery Room, The Old Police Station, High Street, Chipping Campden GL55 6HB

P.B. REAST
78 Cedar Road, Mickleton, Chipping Campden, GL55 6SZ
Tel: 01386 430001
Principal: ICAEW Member
P B Reast

ROSEMARY TOMLINSON
2 Bank Farm Cottages, Bran Mill Lane, Paxford, Chipping Campden GL55 6XJ
Tel: 01386 593526
Principal: ICAEW Member
R O Tomlinson

CHIPPING NORTON

BRONSENS
Hillside, Albion Street, Chipping Norton, OX7 5BH
Tel: 01608 641702

EDWARD J. BAKER LTD
Badgers Bank, Hastings Hill, Churchill, Chipping Norton OX7 6NA
Tel: 01608 659683
Email: e.baker@virgin.net
Resident Partners/Directors: ICAEW Members
E J Baker

LAKIN & CO
Rest Hill House, Over Worton, Chipping Norton, OX7 7EN
Tel: 01608 683867
Principal: ICAEW Member
M P Lakin

M R THOMAS
5 Church Meadow, Milton-under-Wychwood, Chipping Norton, OX7 6JG

MARK O'BRIEN & CO
22 New Street, Chipping Norton, OX7 5LJ

POTTS & CO ★
6 Jacobs Yard, Middle Barton, Chipping Norton, OX7 7BY

RICHARD FLOYD & CO
Midland Bank Chambers, Market Place, Chipping Norton, OX7 5NA
Tel: 01483 302782

THE SOUTHILL PARTNERSHIP ◈
6 Southill, Cornbury Park, Charlbury, Chipping Norton OX7 3EW
Tel: 01608 811533
Resident Partners/Directors: ICAEW Members
K E Gooding, M Leggett

TITCHENERS LTD
Midland Bank Chambers, Market Place, Chipping Norton, OX7 5NA
Tel: 01608 642570
See display advertisement near this entry.

V.M. MURPHY & CO
Finsbury House, New Street, Chipping Norton, OX7 5LL
Tel: 01608 641041
Principal: ICAEW Member
V M Murphy

CHISLEHURST

A.C. FLETCHER ◈
4 Copperfield Way, Chislehurst, BR7 6RY
Tel: 020 8467 5314
Principal: ICAEW Member
A C Fletcher

BIDDLE MATTHEWS
Mulberry House, 18a Ashfield Lane, Chislehurst, BR7 6LQ

FLETCHER NAESSENS ◈
4 Copperfield Way, Chislehurst, BR7 6RY
Tel: 020 8467 5314
Principal: ICAEW Member
A C Fletcher

G R GADSBY
The Orchard, Manor Park, Chislehurst, BR7 5QE

G.S. WEST & CO
2 Inglewood, Kemnal Road, Chislehurst, BR7 6NF

GILLMORE F.C. & CO
198 Leesons Hill, Chislehurst, BR7 6QH

L.J. CHRISFIELD
29 The Meadow, Chislehurst, BR7 6AA
Tel: 020 8468 7730
Principal: ICAEW Member
L J Chrisfield

MARATEA LTD
19 Holbrook Lane, Chislehurst, BR7 6PE

MATTISON & CO
10A Royal Parade, Chislehurst, BR7 6NR
Tel: 020 8295 3987
Resident Partners/Directors: ICAEW Members
S A Hanrahan, J Mattison
Resident Partners (Non-ICAEW Members):
S A Hipwell

R.L. VAUGHAN & CO
71/75 High Street, Chislehurst, BR7 5AG

WHEAT & BUTLER
19 Holbrook Lane, Chislehurst, BR7 6PE

YEUNG & CO
14 Grange Drive, Chislehurst, BR7 5ES

CHORLEY

ABRAMS ASHTON
41 St Thomas's Road, Chorley, PR7 1JE

ABRAMS ECOB LTD ◈
41 St Thomas's Road, Chorley, PR7 1JE

AMANDA STEAD
Weavers Cottage, Holt Lane, Brindle, Chorley PR6 8NE

AMANDA STEAD LTD
Weavers Cottage, Holt Lane, Brindle, Chorley PR6 8NE

APL ACCOUNTANTS LLP ◈
9 St Georges Street, Chorley, PR7 2AA
Tel: 01257 231640
Resident Partners/Directors: ICAEW Members
P Hodges, S L Jeffries

C MARSDEN CONSULTANCY LTD
Mount View, 3 Wigan Lane, Heath Charnock, Chorley PR7 4DD

CLARE & CO
Bannisters, Chorley Road, Withnell, Chorley PR6 8BG
Tel: 01254 832426
Principal: ICAEW Member
J Clare

DEBT FREE DIRECT LTD
Fairclough House, Church Street, Adlington, Chorley PR7 4EX

E HEYS & CO
229 Coppull Moor Lane, Coppull, Chorley, PR7 5JA

HODGSON ACCOUNTANCY AND BUSINESS SERVICES LTD
73 The Farthings, Astley Village, Chorley, PR7 1SH

JOHN A. EDGAR & CO
7 Merefield, Astley Village, Chorley, PR7 1UP
Tel: 01257 268373
Principal: ICAEW Member
R D Lonsdale

JOHN GOULDING & CO LTD
4 Southport Road, Chorley, PR7 1LD
Tel: 01257 260366
Resident Partners/Directors: ICAEW Members
S Gardiner, A Hilton, B A Rigby

JUSTIN COLLIGHAN ACA
5 Farm House Close, Whittle-le-Woods, Chorley, PR6 7QN

M.H.C.LUNT
Ashburn, Woodhart Lane, Eccleston, Chorley PR7 5TB
Tel: 01257 450279
Principal: ICAEW Member
M H C Lunt

MCMILLAN & CO ◈
28 Eaton Avenue, Matrix Office Park, Buckshaw Village, Chorley PR7 7NA
Tel: 01772 299888
Website: http://www.mcmillanaccountants.com
Resident Partners/Directors: ICAEW Members
A B McLaughlin, J F D McMillan

MCMILLAN & CO LTD
28 Eaton Avenue, Matrix Office Park, Buckshaw Village, Chorley PR7 7NA
Tel: 01772 299888
Resident Partners/Directors: ICAEW Members
A B McLaughlin, J F D McMillan
Resident Partners (Non-ICAEW Members):
T A Reynolds

R.P. SMITH & CO ◈
28 St Thomas's Rd, Chorley, PR7 1HX
Tel: 01257 263015
Resident Partners/Directors: ICAEW Members
D P Abbott, K M Brophy, S J Worswick

ROTHERHAM TAYLOR LTD ◈
1 Church Street, Adlington, Chorley, PR7 4EX
Tel: 01257 480597
Resident Partners/Directors: ICAEW Members
M W Barton

ROY D. BROWN
13 Mountain Road, Coppull, Chorley, PR7 5EL
Tel: 01257 793160
Principal: ICAEW Member
R D Brown

STEPHEN THOMAS
Greenlands, Parkside Drive, Whittle-Le Woods, Chorley PR6 7PH

TENON LTD
Sumner House, St Thomas's Rd, Chorley, PR7 1HP
Tel: 01257 518000

TENON AUDIT LTD
Sumner House, St Thomas's Road, Chorley, PR7 1HP
Tel: 01257 518000

CHRISTCHURCH

AIMS - ROBERT W FIELD BSC ACA
9 Hinton Wood Avenue, Christchurch, BH23 5AB

CAMERON CAVEY CONSULTING LTD
97 Bargates, Christchurch, BH23 1QQ

DAVID EXELL ASSOCIATES
3 Miller Road, Christchurch, BH23 3SX

FILER KNAPPER LLP ◈
10 Bridge Street, Christchurch, BH23 1EF
Tel: 01202 483341
Fax: 01202 483550
Email: info@filerknapper.co.uk
Website: http://www.filerknapper.co.uk
Resident Partners/Directors: ICAEW Members
S Ellson, L J Filer, J Sparkes
Resident Partners (Non-ICAEW Members):
C B Ratcliffe
Registered by the ICAEW to carry out company audit work
Regulated by the ICAEW for a range of investment business activities

HOWARD BAKER LTD
280a Lymington Road, Highcliffe, Christchurch, BH23 5ET

J. AUBIN LTD
4 Old Barn Close, Christchurch, BH23 2QZ
Tel: 01202 480810
Resident Partners/Directors: ICAEW Members
D J H Aubin

K.E. LUDFORD
17 Stibbs Way, Bransgore, Christchurch, BH23 8HG

LEWIS BALL & CO
William House, 32 Bargates, Christchurch, BH23 1QL

LEWIS BALL & CO LTD
William House, 32 Bargates, Christchurch, BH23 1QL

MARSHALL BEAVEN
Christchurch Business Centre, Grange Road, Christchurch, BH23 4JD
Tel: 01425 274923
Fax: 01425 272435
Principal: ICAEW Member
P F Beaven

P.D. ROOT
95 Jumpers Road, Christchurch, BH23 2JS
Tel: 01202 473471
Principal: ICAEW Member
P D Root

RICHARD MANN & CO LTD
294a Lymington Road, Highcliffe, Christchurch, BH23 5ET
Tel: 01425 277033

ROGERS EVANS
Druitt Buildings, High Street, Christchurch, BH23 1AW

SARON RUSDEN
3 The Paddock, 73a Mudeford, Christchurch, BH23 3NJ

CHURCH STRETTON

JAMES HOLYOAK & PARKER LTD
32 Sandford Avenue, Church Stretton, SY6 6EN
Tel: 01743 355022

CIRENCESTER

ANDREW MILLER & CO
The Mews, Stratton Cleeve, Cheltenham Road, Cirencester GL7 2JD
Tel: 01285 640649
Website: http://www.milleraccountants.co.uk
Principal: ICAEW Member
A G Miller

EMMA VEELENTURF BSC ACA
Cancourt Cottage, Ampney St Peter, Cirencester, GL7 5SH

GLAISTER JONES & CO
1a The Wool Market, Dyer Street, Cirencester, GL7 2PR
Tel: 01285 640101
Principal: ICAEW Member
R J Jones

HEYDON & CO
6 Templar Mews, Black Jack Street, Cirencester, GL7 2AA

J D FROST ACCOUNTANTS
7 Links View, Cirencester, GL7 2NF
Tel: 01285 652208
Resident Partners/Directors: ICAEW Members
J D Frost

MACCALLUM SLATOR ◈
Claverton House, Love Lane, Cirencester, GL7 1YG
Tel: 01285 659929
Principal: ICAEW Member
T Slator
Regulated by the ICAEW for a range of investment business activities
Individual(s) licensed for insolvency work by the ICAEW

MCGILLS
Oakley House, Tetbury Road, Cirencester, GL7 1US
Tel: 01285 652128
Resident Partners/Directors: ICAEW Members
S G Nuttall, A I Palmer

MARK TUFNELL
The Old Forge, Calmsden, Cirencester, GL7 5ET

MORRIS OWEN ◈
Dyer House, Dyer Street, Cirencester, GL7 2PP
Tel: 01285 642677
Registered by the ICAEW to carry out company audit work
Authorised and regulated by the Financial Services Authority for investment business

SHEPHERD SMAIL
Northway House, The Forum, Cirencester, GL7 2QY

WENN TOWNSEND
Gosditch House, 5 Gosditch Street, Cirencester, GL7 2AG
Tel: 01285 659778
Fax: 01285 641265
Email: partners@wenntownsend.net
Website: http://www.wenntownsend.co.uk
Resident Partners/Directors: ICAEW Members
S M Shelley
Resident Partners (Non-ICAEW Members):
R L Herbert
Other Offices: Oxford, Abingdon
Registered by the ICAEW to carry out company audit work

INVESTOR IN PEOPLE

WOODWARD HALE ★
38 Dollar Street, Cirencester, GL7 2AN
Tel: 01285 659341
Website: http://www.woodwardhale.co.uk
Resident Partners/Directors: ICAEW Members
V E Cowling, R K Hale, M J Hewlett
Resident Partners (Non-ICAEW Members):
V L Oliver
Registered by the ICAEW to carry out company audit work
Regulated by the ICAEW for a range of investment business activities

CLACTON-ON-SEA

D.S BOOTH & CO
19 Tower Estate, Point Clear, St Osyth, Clacton-on-Sea CO16 8NG
Tel: 01255 821808
Principal: ICAEW Member
D S Booth

THE JAMESONS PARTNERSHIP LTD
92 Station Road, Clacton-on-sea, CO15 1SG
Tel: 01255 220044
Fax: 01255 220999
Email: mail@jamesons.net
Website: http://www.jamesons.net
Training Contracts Available.
Resident Partners/Directors: ICAEW Members
A D Brown, J Short, W J Wilson
Registered by the ICAEW to carry out company audit work
Regulated by the ICAEW for a range of investment business activities

JEREMY WEBSTER
The White House, Beaumont-cum-Moze, Clacton-on-sea, CO16 0AU

THE PRICE CONSULTANCY
8 The Acorns, Jaywick, Clacton-on-Sea, CO15 2QW
Tel: 01255 433469

YOUNG & CO
Church Farm House, Lodge Lane, Tendring, Clacton-on-Sea CO16 0BS
Tel: 01255 831191
Principal: ICAEW Member
T Layland

CLECKHEATON

CALVERT DAWSON LLP
288 Oxford Road, Gomersal, Cleckheaton, BD19 4PY
Tel: 01274 851770
Resident Partners/Directors: ICAEW Members
P A Calvert, B Dawson

CLOUGH BUSINESS DEVELOPMENT
New Chartford House, Centurion Way, Cleckheaton, BD19 3QB

CLOUGH & COMPANY LLP
New Chartford House, Centurion Way, Cleckheaton, BD19 3QB
Tel: 01274 876333
Email: cloughs@clough.co.uk
Resident Partners/Directors: ICAEW Members
N C Bullas, N Gash, S Gash, L A Kendrew, R H Thompson
Resident Partners (Non-ICAEW Members):
M S Khan

CLOUGH MANAGEMENT SERVICES
New Chartford House, Centurion Way, Cleckheaton, BD19 3QB

CLOUGH MANAGEMENT SERVICES LLP
New Chartford House, Centurion Way, Cleckheaton, BD19 3QB

CLOUGH PRIESTLEY
New Chartford House, Centurion Way, Cleckheaton, BD19 3QB

CLOUGH PRIESTLEY LTD
New Chartford House, Centurion Way, Cleckheaton, BD19 3QB

CORPORATE FINANCE SERVICES
New Chartford House, Centurion Way, Cleckheaton, BD19 3QB

CORPORATE FINANCE SERVICES LLP
New Chartford House, Centurion Way, Cleckheaton, BD19 3QB

DAVID MILNES LTD
Premier House, Bradford Road, Cleckheaton, BD19 3TT
Tel: 01274 870511
Resident Partners/Directors: ICAEW Members
D J Milnes

FERGUSSON & CO LTD
5-7 Northgate, Cleckheaton, BD19 4LE
Tel: 01274 876644
Resident Partners/Directors: ICAEW Members
M E Fergusson
Individual(s) licensed for insolvency work by another RPB

FINANCE DIRECTORS (YORKSHIRE) LTD ◈
Premier House, Bradford Road, Cleckheaton, BD19 3TT
Tel: 01274 876822
Resident Partners/Directors: ICAEW Members
J H G Holliss

GREENWOOD, BARTON & CO
Barclays Bank Chambers, 2 Northgate, Cleckheaton, BD19 5AA

HUQUE CHAUDHRY ASSOCIATES LTD
Network House, West 26, Cleckheaton, BD19 4TT

JOHN HOLLISS & CO ◈
Premier House, Bradford Road, Cleckheaton, BD19 3TT
Tel: 01274 615475
Principal: ICAEW Member
J H G Holliss

JOHN MANNERS
3 Field Hurst, Scholes Lane, Scholes, Cleckheaton, BD19 6NG
Tel: 01274 869876
Principal: ICAEW Member
J M Manners

KILNER JOHNSON ASSOCIATES
Network House, West 26, Cleckheaton, BD19 4TT

KJA ASSOCIATES LTD
Network House, West 26, Cleckheaton, BD19 4TT

KJA DAWSON BROWN LTD
Network House, West 26, Cleckheaton, BD19 4TT

M I PETTY
4-6 Upper Green Avenue, Scholes, Cleckheaton, BD19 6PD
Tel: 01274 851897
Principal: ICAEW Member
M I Petty

YORKSHIRE AUDIT BUREAU
Network House, West 26, Cleckheaton, BD19 4TT

YORKSHIRE AUDIT BUREAU LTD
Network House, West 26, Cleckheaton, BD19 4TT

CLEETHORPES

BLOW ABBOTT LTD
36 High Street, Cleethorpes, DN35 8JN

CARR JEMMETT LTD
66 St Peters Avenue, Cleethorpes, DN35 8HP

CARR JEMMETT (CLEETHORPES) LTD
66 St Peters Avenue, Cleethorpes, DN35 8HP

CLEETHORPES ACCOUNTANCY LTD ◈
3 Wardall Street, Cleethorpes, DN35 8HA
Tel: 01472 290444
Resident Partners/Directors: ICAEW Members
P J Curtis, D H Tuck

CLEVEDON

C.G. WALTON
The Tynings, Ham Lane, Kingston Seymour, Clevedon BS21 6XE

CHRIS MADGE & CO
The Stables, Clevedon Hall, Clevedon, Avon BS21 7SJ
Tel: 01275 872888
Website: http://www.chris-madge.co.uk
Principal: ICAEW Member
C B Madge

SPECIALISATIONS – FORENSIC ACCOUNTING

Expert Witnesses in Litigation
Forensic Accounting

SPECIALISATIONS – TAXATION

Back Duty
Customs Duty
Investigations
PAYE Advice
Value Added Tax

CHRISTOPHER R. BROWN LTD ◈
24 Albert Road, Clevedon, BS21 7RR
Tel: 01275 341174
Resident Partners/Directors: ICAEW Members
C R Brown

J.& A.W. SULLY & CO ◈
Paramount House, 2 Concorde Drive, Clevedon, Avon BS21 6UH
Tel: 01275 879179
Principal: ICAEW Member
S R Allan

JADE
2 Tone Road, Clevedon, Avon, BS21 6LG

JADE FINANCIAL MANAGEMENT LTD
2 Tone Road, Clevedon, Avon, BS21 6LG

MISS PATRICIA LEWIS FCA
207 Clevedon Road, Tickenham, Clevedon, Avon BS21 6RX

NEWSHAM, HANSON & CO
1-5 Bellevue Road, Clevedon, Avon, BS21 7NP
Tel: 01275 873269
Resident Partners/Directors: ICAEW Members
D R Hanson

STONHAM.CO
Tickton Lodge, 8 Bellevue Road, Clevedon, Avon BS21 7NR

TAX INVESTIGATION SERVICES
The Stables, Clevedon Hall, Clevedon, BS21 7SJ
Tel: 01275 872888

CLITHEROE

ADAMS & CO ACCOUNTANTS LTD
36 York Street, Clitheroe, BB7 2DL

DAVID H EVANS LTD ◈
Unit 2, The Old Sawmill, Shaw Bridge Street, Clitheroe BB7 1LY
Tel: 01200 428460
Website: http://www.evansaccountants.com
Resident Partners/Directors: ICAEW Members
D H Evans

GRAHAM SHAW
2 St Paul's Close, Clitheroe, BB7 2NA
Tel: 01200 424026
Email: gshawfca@btconnect.com
Website: http://www.grahamshaw.co.uk
Principal: ICAEW Member
G Shaw

HUMPHREY JOHNSON FCA
53 Edisford Road, Clitheroe, BB7 3LA

MAGNET ASSOCIATES LTD
4 Brookes Lane, Whalley, Clitheroe, BB7 9RG

REDMAYNE & CO ◈
The Old Bank House, Harris Court, Wellgate, Clitheroe BB7 2DP
Tel: 01200 453200

TOWERS & GORNALL ★
Suites 5 & 6, The Printworks, Hey Road, Barrow, Clitheroe BB7 9WB

COALVILLE

COALRAVEN ★
127 Station Road, Hugglescote, Coalville, LE67 2GD

ELVERSTONE TOMLIN
16a Belvoir Road, Coalville, LE67 3QE

GEORGINA RAFFLE
Warringtons, Gelsmoor Road, Coleorton, Coalville LE67 8JF
Tel: 01530 222954
Principal: ICAEW Member
G Raffle

HELEN HUGHES
1a Main Street, Thornton, Coalville, LE67 1AF
Tel: 07785 727947
Resident Partners/Directors: ICAEW Members
H L Hughes

HENSTOCK SHOOTER
Unit 6, Cartwright Court, Cartwright Way, Bardon Hill, Coalville LE67 1UE

W D ALLSOPP
7 Daisy Close, Bagworth, Coalville, LE67 1HP
Tel: 01530 230360
Principal: ICAEW Member
W D Allsopp

COBHAM

02VIE LTD
43 Oxshott Way, Cobham, KT11 2RU

CAMBUS CONSULTING LTD
24 Lodge Close, Cobham, KT11 2SQ

FRANACCOUNTS
78 Portsmouth Road, Cobham, KT11 1PP

J.D.G. HOLME
40 Littleheath Lane, Cobham, KT11 2QN

S.I. GOMPELS & CO
7 Heathfield, Stoke D'Abernon, Cobham, KT11 2QY
Tel: 01372 843668
Principal: ICAEW Member
S I Gompels

SIMON GRANGER ◈
Little Mede, Blundel Lane, Stoke D'Abernon, Cobham KT11 2SF

TAXDORE
Collingwood, 8 Oxshott Rise, Cobham, KT11 2RN

TIM DRAKE ◈
Garden Cottage Ockham Lane, Hatchford, Cobham, KT11 1LP
Tel: 01932 863443
Principal: ICAEW Member
T W Drake

WELLDEN TURNBULL LLP ◈
78 Portsmouth Road, Cobham, KT11 1PP
Tel: 01932 868444
Training Contracts Available.
Resident Partners/Directors: ICAEW Members
R W John, S A Spevack
Registered by the ICAEW to carry out company audit work
Regulated by the ICAEW for a range of investment business activities
SPECIALISATIONS – BUSINESS & GENERAL ADVICE
Divorce/Matrimonial
SPECIALISATIONS – SECTOR
Solicitors
SPECIALISATIONS – TAXATION
Foreign Nationals in the UK
UK Subsidiaries of Overseas Multinationals

WT ACCOUNTANTS LTD
78 Portsmouth Road, Cobham, KT11 1PP

COCKERMOUTH

GIBBONS & CO
Lakeland Office, 2 Europe Way, Cockermouth, CA13 0RJ

JOHN BELFORD & CO LTD
14a Main Street, Cockermouth, CA13 9LQ

SAINT & CO ▽ ◈
Unit 3, Lakeland Business Park, Lamplugh Road, Cockermouth CA13 0QT
Tel: 01900 824118
Email: cockermouth@saint.co.uk
Website: http://www.saint.co.uk
Resident Partners/Directors: ICAEW Members
D E Johnson
Registered by the ICAEW to carry out company audit work
Authorised and regulated by the Financial Services Authority for investment business
Individual(s) licensed for insolvency work by the ICAEW

WOOD BERRY & CO
5 Anderson Court, Sullart Street, Cockermouth, CA13 0EB

COLCHESTER

AIMS - TIM CARNEY
Tudor House, The Green, Great Bentley, Colchester CO7 8PG

ANDREW COLBECK
313a Ipswich Road, Colchester, CO4 0HN

ANTHONY RUSSEL LTD
1 Market Hill, Coggeshall, Colchester, CO6 1TS

ASAP ACCOUNTING SERVICES LTD
The Old Cartlodge, Warrens Farm, Great Tey, Colchester CO6 1AJ

BAKER CHAPMAN & BUSSEY
Magnet House, 3 North Hill, Colchester, CO1 1DZ
Tel: 01206 715000
Email: mail@bakerchapman.co.uk
Website: http://www.bakerchapman.co.uk
Resident Partners/Directors: ICAEW Members
A B S Bussey, J Frost, V Jones, A C Taylor
Registered by the ICAEW to carry out company audit work
Regulated by the ICAEW for a range of investment business activities

BAVERSTOCKS LTD
Lawley House, Butt Road, Colchester, CO3 3DG

BEAUMONT SEYMOUR ★ ◈
47 Butt Road, Colchester, CO3 3BZ

BLACKWATER BOOKKEEPING
62 Firs Road, West Mersea, Colchester, CO5 8NL

BRANNANS ★
Stane House, Salmon's Corner, Near Coggeshall, Colchester C06 1RX

BUTT COZENS ◈
Town Wall House, Balkerne Hill, Colchester, CO3 3AD
Tel: 01206 549303
Fax: 01206 763386
Email: info@buttcozens.co.uk
Website: http://www.buttcozens.co.uk
Resident Partners/Directors: ICAEW Members
P E Gardiner, D T Lay-Flurrie, M J Simpson
Registered by the ICAEW to carry out company audit work
Regulated by the ICAEW for a range of investment business activities
SPECIALISATIONS – AUDIT & ASSURANCE
Audit
SPECIALISATIONS – BUSINESS & GENERAL ADVICE
Feasibility Studies
Management Accounting Consultancy
Management Advice to Business
SPECIALISATIONS – BUSINESS RECOVERY & INSOLVENCY
Reorganisations and Company Reconstructions
SPECIALISATIONS – INVESTMENT BUSINESS
Planning
SPECIALISATIONS – SECTOR
Corporate
SPECIALISATIONS – TAXATION
Investigations

CLARENDONS
Beaver House, Plough Road, Great Bentley, Colchester CO7 8LG

CLIFFORD C. PALMER & CO
61-67 Rectory Road, Wivenhoe, Colchester, CO7 9ES
Tel: 01206 827770
Email: office@ccpalmer.eclipse.co.uk
Date Established: 1935
Principal: ICAEW Member
C J Pilgrim

ELIZABETH BURDEN ◈
254 Coggeshall Road, Little Tey, Colchester, CO6 1HT
Tel: 01206 211890
Principal: ICAEW Member
E J Burden
Registered by the ICAEW to carry out company audit work
SPECIALISATIONS – AUDIT & ASSURANCE
Audit
SPECIALISATIONS – FINANCIAL REPORTING
Accounts Preparation
SPECIALISATIONS – TAXATION
Payroll Service and Advice
Taxation

GEORGE PEARCE & CO ◈
The Forge, Langham, Colchester, CO4 5PX
Tel: 01206 322826
Principal: ICAEW Member
G A Pearce

GRANITE MORGAN SMITH ★ ◈
122 Feering Hill, Feering, Colchester, CO5 9PY
Tel: 01376 574848
Website: http://www.granitemorgansmith.co.uk
Resident Partners/Directors: ICAEW Members
C J Smith
Resident Partners (Non-ICAEW Members):
D R L Morgan

GRIFFIN CHAPMAN ◈
Blackburn House, 32a Crouch Street, Colchester, CO3 3HH

HOLM LUCKING
Graphic House, 11 Magdalen Street, Colchester, CO1 2JT
Tel: 01206 767007
Resident Partners/Directors: ICAEW Members
D T Holm, W Lucking

HOOPER & CO
5 Marlowe Way, Colchester, CO3 4JP

HOOPER & CO (FINANCIAL MANAGEMENT) LTD
5 Marlowe Way, Colchester, CO3 4JP

HOWLETT'S
50 Elmcroft, Elmstead Market, Colchester, CO7 7YZ
Tel: 01206 826434
Principal: ICAEW Member
S O Howlett

HUBBARD LLOYD
2 The Atrium, Phoenix Square, Wyncolls Road, Colchester CO4 9PE
Tel: 01206 843999
Email: info@hubbardlloyd.co.uk
Resident Partners/Directors: ICAEW Members
D S Hubbard

INGRAM ACCOUNTANCY SERVICES LTD
29 Wellesley Road, Colchester, CO3 3HE

J A CHARTERS & CO LTD
1 Chapel Street North, Colchester, CO2 7AT

J.D. LANCASTER
Tenpenny House, Colchester Main Road, Alresford, Colchester CO7 8DJ

J.KIRKWOOD & CO
Braefoot, Fox Street, Ardleigh, Colchester CO7 7PS
Tel: 01206 860680
Email: jakaco@btopenworld.com
Date Established: 1970
Principal: ICAEW Member
J Kirkwood
SPECIALISATIONS – FINANCIAL REPORTING
Accounts Preparation
SPECIALISATIONS – TAXATION
Self Assessment Advice
Taxation

JOHN WOODMAN
3 Cadman House, Off Peartree Road, Colchester, CO3 0NW
Tel: 01206 561086
Principal: ICAEW Member
J Woodman

KIRBY ROOKYARD LTD
1 Castle Court, St Peters Street, Colchester, CO1 1EW

LARKING GOWEN ◈
892 The Crescent, Colchester Business Park, Colchester, CO4 9YQ
Tel: 01206 222277
Resident Partners/Directors: ICAEW Members
J R Tucker

LB GROUP
82 East Hill, Colchester,
CO1 2QW

LB GROUP LTD
82 East Hill, Colchester,
CO1 2QW

MARTIN BECK
7 Hurnard Drive, Colchester,
CO3 3SH
Tel: 07775 573820
Principal: ICAEW Member
M W Beck

MARTYN LEWIS
1 Brewery House, Brook Street,
Wivenhoe, Colchester CO7 9DS
Tel: 01206 823835
Principal: ICAEW Member
M L Lewis

N.W. RIVETT
41 Thompson Avenue,
Colchester, CO3 4HW
Tel: 01206 525648
Email: n.rivett@ntlworld.com
Mobile: 07709 441139
Principal: ICAEW Member
N W Rivett

NICHOLAS J. GRIMES
Spindrift, 39 Dunthorne Road,
Colchester, CO4 0HZ
Tel: 01206 870446
Principal: ICAEW Member
N J Grimes

PACE
3 The Retreat, Glebe Lane,
Abberton, Colchester CO5 7NW
Tel: 08707 477236
Website: http://
www.pacecharteredaccountants.c
o.uk

PASSMORE WEEKS & RICHARDSON
Unit 2, Beacon End Courtyard,
London Road, Stanway,
Colchester CO3 0NU

PETER FEDARB & CO
22 President Road, Lexden,
Colchester, CO3 9ED

PETER FITT
7 Coast Road, West Mersea,
Colchester, CO5 8QE

PEYTON TYLER MEARS
Middleborough House, 16
Middleborough, Colchester,
CO1 1QT

REVILL PEARCE
Stane House, Salmons Corner,
Nr. Coggeshall, Colchester
CO6 1RX
Tel: 01206 212115
Principal: ICAEW Member
A J Prevett

RICHARD SEXTON & CO
St Margaret's, 3 Manor Road,
Colchester, CO3 3LU

SCRUTTON BLAND
820 The Crescent, Colchester
Business Park, Colchester,
CO4 9YQ
Tel: 01206 838400
Fax: 01206 838401
Email: mail@
scruttonbland.co.uk
Website: http://
www.scruttonbland.co.uk
Resident Partners/Directors: ICAEW Members
A P Strickland, E R Twinn
Resident Partners (Non-ICAEW Members):
T Mulley, T E O'Connor, G
Bradley
Registered by the ICAEW to carry out company audit work
Regulated by the ICAEW for a range of investment business activities
General Description: We have 12 partners and 2 offices in the area and can provide a full range of services to our clients. We are pleased to be members of Nexia International.

SJB & CO
8 Barnfield, Feering, Colchester,
CO5 9HP
Tel: 01376 571358
Principal: ICAEW Member
S J Bell

TAYLOR AND DAVIS LTD
The Causeway, Great Horkesley,
Colchester, CO6 4EJ

TAYLOR DAVIS
The Causeway, Great Horkesley,
Colchester, CO6 4EJ

TILE & CO
Warden House, 37 Manor Road,
Colchester, CO3 3LX

TILMAN & CO
15 Searle Way, Eight Ash Green,
Colchester, CO6 3QS
Tel: 01206 547785
Principal: ICAEW Member
J A Tilman

WHITTLE & CO ◈
Century House South, North
Station Road, Colchester,
CO1 1RE
Tel: 01206 762200
Email: mail@whittles.co.uk
Website: http://
www.whittles.co.uk
Resident Partners/Directors: ICAEW Members
T M Moriarty, R M Skells, R
Ward, P J Whittle
Registered by the ICAEW to carry out company audit work
Regulated by the ICAEW for a range of investment business activities

SPECIALISATIONS – AUDIT & ASSURANCE
Audit

SPECIALISATIONS – SECTOR
Charities

SPECIALISATIONS – TAXATION
Estate and Inheritance

WHITTLE & CO ◈
15 High Street, West Mersea,
Colchester, CO5 8QA
Tel: 01206 385049

WOOD & DISNEY LTD ◈
1 Lodge Court, Lodge Lane,
Langham, Colchester CO4 5NE
Tel: 01206 233170
Fax: 01206 233170
Email: info@wood-disney.co.uk
Website: http://www.wood-
disney.co.uk
Resident Partners/Directors: ICAEW Members
P Disney
Registered by the ICAEW to carry out company audit work

SPECIALISATIONS – BUSINESS & GENERAL ADVICE
Management Advice to Business

COLEFORD

DOUGLAS E.H. SMITH
The Buckstone House, Staunton,
Coleford, GL16 8PD

COLNE

AIMS - DAVID F HODGSON ◈
7 School Lane, Laneshawbridge,
Colne, BB8 7JB
Tel: 01282 869049
Principal: ICAEW Member
D F Hodgson

BIRKETT, TOMLINSON & CO ◈
Regency House, 67 Albert Road,
Colne, BB8 0BP
Tel: 01282 864684
Principal: ICAEW Member
R D Dingwall

BLACKBURN & BLACKBURN LTD
Glenroyd, Keighley Road, Colne,
BB8 7HF

BLACKBURN & BLACKBURN LTD
Linden House, 49 Albert Road,
Colne, BB8 0BP

HARGREAVES,BROWN & BENSON
1 Bond Street, Colne, BB8 9DG

CONGLETON

CS LAWRENCE & CO LTD
2 Martins Court, West Street,
Congleton, CW12 1JR

HAMMOND MCNULTY ★
Bank House, Market Square,
Congleton, CW12 1ET

JACOB & CO LTD
94 Mill Street, Congleton,
CW12 1AG
Tel: 01260 276295
Resident Partners/Directors: ICAEW Members
C Jacob

MITTEN CLARKE LTD
The Post House, Mill Street,
Congleton, CW12 1AB

PAUL AUSTEN ASSOCIATES ◈
Charter House, 7-9 Wagg Street,
Congleton, CW12 4BA
Tel: 01260 281106
Principal: ICAEW Member
P J Austen

R H FROOM BBS FCA
93 Mill Green, Congleton,
CW12 1GD

STEVEN ELLWOOD
94 Biddulph Road, Congleton,
CW12 3LY

CONSETT

AIMS - NICHOLAS COTTAM
Burn Cottage, Front Street,
Ebchester, Consett DH8 0PJ

CHAPMAN & CHAPMAN
Unit 30a, Werdohl Business
Park, 1 Industrial Estate, Consett
DH8 6TJ

JOHN ALDERDICE & SON ◈
21 Sherburn Terrace, Consett,
DH8 6ND
Tel: 01207 503817
Resident Partners/Directors: ICAEW Members
M Brolly, J N Straughan

JONES BOYD
63 Medomsley Road, Consett,
DH8 5HQ

MCMANUS HALL
Office One Steel House, Ponds
Court Business Park, Genesis
Way, Consett DH8 5XP

MURRAY & LAMB ACCOUNTANTS LTD ◈
25-27 Medomsley Road,
Consett, DH8 5HE
Tel: 01207 581599
Resident Partners/Directors: ICAEW Members
S Lamb, G S Murray

CORBRIDGE

ARTHUR WAPPAT
The Old Granary, Dilston
Steadings, Corbridge, NE45 5RF

JOHN L. HINKLEY
Corbridge Business Centre, Tinklers Bank, Corbridge, NE45 5SB
Tel: 01434 634212
Principal: ICAEW Member
J L Hinkley

CORBY

A PLUS ACCOUNTANTS LTD
48A Arnhill Road, Gretton, Corby, NN17 3DN

HWCA LTD ◈
44 High Street, Corby, NN17 1UU
Tel: 01536 409494

J.D. GARDINER & CO
Chisholm House, 9 Queens Square, Corby, NN17 1PD
Tel: 01536 201019
Principal: ICAEW Member
J D Gardiner

J.D. GARDINER CO
Chisholm House, 9 Queens Square, Corby, NN17 1PD
Tel: 01536 201019
Principal: ICAEW Member
J D Gardiner

MARRAY & MCINTYRE ★
Hawthorn House, 1 Medlicott Close, Corby, NN18 9NF

MOORE STEPHENS ◈
Stuart House, Elizabeth Street, Corby, NN17 1SE

CORSHAM

CLEAR VISION ACCOUNTANCY LTD
1 Abacus House, Newlands Road, Corsham, SN13 0BH
Tel: 01249 712074
Fax: 01249 716242
Resident Partners/Directors: ICAEW Members
R D Walsh

SPECIALISATIONS – SECTOR

Dentists/Opticians

CLEAR VISION ACCOUNTANCY GROUP LTD
1 Abacus House, Newlands Road, Corsham, SN13 0BH

DODSON LIFFORD HALL ★
87 Pickwick Road, Corsham, SN13 9BY

COTTINGHAM

ACCOUNTANCY & SECRETARIAL SERVICES LTD ★
217 Hallgate, Cottingham, HU16 4BG
Tel: 01482 845212
Resident Partners/Directors: ICAEW Members
C S Wright

BRISTON JOHNSON & CO
8 Carrington Avenue, Cottingham, HU16 4DU
Tel: 01482 844474
Principal: ICAEW Member
E C Johnson

C.A.TICHIAS
Eastwood, 22 The Wolds, Cottingham, HU16 5LF

CHRIS WRIGHT & CO LTD
217 Hallgate, Cottingham, HU16 4BG
Tel: 01482 845212
Resident Partners/Directors: ICAEW Members
C S Wright

EAST RIDING ACCOUNTS
48 New Village Road, Cottingham, HU16 4NA

G.C. REID & CO ◈
57 Hull Road, Cottingham, HU16 4PT
Tel: 01482 845925
Principal: ICAEW Member
G C Reid

P.H. CROOK
Bradavon, 45 The Dales, Cottingham, HU16 5JS
Tel: 01482 844505
Principal: ICAEW Member
P H Crook

COULSDON

ACORNES
83 Chipstead Valley Road, Coulsdon, CR5 3BP

AIMS - SEAMUS CLARKE ACA
87a Bradmore Way, Coulsdon, CR5 1PE

ALAN CORNEFERT
83 Chipstead Valley Road, Coulsdon, CR5 3BP

AVERILLO CORFIELD
24 Keston Avenue, Coulsdon, CR5 1HL

C.A. EVANS & CO
122 St Andrews Road, Coulsdon, CR5 3HD
Tel: 020 8660 0560
Date Established: 1999
Principal: ICAEW Member
C A Evans

GLM GHEST LLOYD LTD
103-105 Brighton Road, Coulsdon, CR5 2NG

LLOYD & CO
103-105 Brighton Road, Coulsdon, CR5 2NG
Tel: 020 8668 0500
Fax: 020 8668 0900
Email: mail@lloydandco.net
Date Established: 1987
Resident Partners/Directors: ICAEW Members
M R Lloyd, M L Martin
Registered by the ICAEW to carry out company audit work

M SOMERS & CO
37a Chipstead Valley Road, Coulsdon, CR5 2RB

PALMERS
28 Chipstead Station Parade, Chipstead, Coulsdon, CR5 3TF
Tel: 01737 557546
Email: advice@palmersca.co.uk
Principal: ICAEW Member
C M J Palmer
Registered by the ICAEW to carry out company audit work

PC & CHAN LTD
14 The Village Square, Netherne on the Hill, Coulsdon, CR5 1LZ
Tel: 01737 550946
Email: pcchanltd@yahoo.co.uk
Resident Partners/Directors: ICAEW Members
P W K Chan

SHERIDAN BROOKS LTD
176 Brighton Road, Coulsdon, CR5 2NF
Tel: 020 8763 8835
Resident Partners/Directors: ICAEW Members
S S Jackson, A P Sheridan
Registered by the ICAEW to carry out company audit work

WILLIAM KYNE ◈
13 Chaldon Way, Coulsdon, CR5 1DG

COVENTRY

A.J. THACKER & CO ◈
22 Queens Road, Coventry, CV1 3EG

ACCUMEN BUSINESS CONSULTANCY LTD ◈
The Quadrant Business Centre, 3 The Quadrant, Coventry, CV1 2DY
Tel: 02476 243613
Resident Partners/Directors: ICAEW Members
T S Saran

AMBER
12 Greenfield Avenue, Balsall Common, Coventry, CV7 7UG

AMBER ADVISORY LTD
12 Greenfield Avenue, Balsall Common, Coventry, CV7 7UG

ARMSTRONGS
Sovereign House, 12 Warwick Street, Earlsdon, Coventry CV5 6ET

ARMSTRONGS ACCOUNTANCY LTD
Sovereign House, 12 Warwick Street, Earlsdon, Coventry CV5 6ET
Tel: 02476 715111
Email: info@armstrongs-accountancy.co.uk
Resident Partners/Directors: ICAEW Members
J R M Armstrong, P Georgiades

BOND & CO
110 Kenilworth Road, Coventry, CV4 7AH
Tel: 02476 693007
Principal: ICAEW Member
P R Bond

BRESLINS BIRMINGHAM LTD
The Innovation Centre, Binley Business Park, Coventry, CV3 2TX

BURROWS SCARBOROUGH
Sovereign House, 12 Warwick Street, Coventry, CV5 6ET

BURROWS SCARBOROUGH SILK LTD
Sovereign House, 12 Warwick Street, Earlsdon, Coventry CV5 6ET
Tel: 02476 717633
Resident Partners/Directors: ICAEW Members
N J Burrows

CATALYST BUSINESS SUPPORT LTD
Victoria House, 44-45 Queens Road, Coventry, CV1 3EH

CROMPTON & CO
42 Queens Road, Coventry, CV1 3DX

CROMPTON & CO FINANCIAL SOLUTIONS LTD
42 Queens Road, Coventry, CV1 3DX

CROMWELL ACCOUNTING SERVICES
Unit 1, 15 Allesley Old Road, Coventry, CV5 8BU

CRYSTAL BUSINESS SERVICES LTD ◈
264 Stoney Stanton Road, Coventry, CV1 4FP
Tel: 02476 525369
Resident Partners/Directors: ICAEW Members
A Dedat

D.B. JONES & CO
14 Providence Street, Earlsdon, Coventry, West Midlands CV5 6ED

DAFFERNS LLP
Queens House, Queens Road, Coventry, CV1 3DR
Tel: 02476 221046
Fax: 02476 631702
Email: cov@dafferns.com
Website: http://www.dafferns.com
Resident Partners/Directors: ICAEW Members
G R Cox, A C Jones, B C Jukes, R J Miller
Resident Partners (Non-ICAEW Members):
M J Gibbs

Other Offices: Warwick House, 32 Clarendon Street, Leamington Spa
Registered by the ICAEW to carry out company audit work
Regulated by the ICAEW for a range of investment business activities

DAVID CLEAVER & CO
25 Heycroft, Coventry, CV4 7HE
Tel: 02476 417010
Principal: ICAEW Member
D K Cleaver

FOX EVANS
Abbey House, 7 Manor Road, Coventry, CV1 2FW

FOX EVANS LTD
Abbey House, 7 Manor Road, Coventry, CV1 2FW
Tel: 02476 257317
Email: enq@foxevans.co.uk
Website: http://www.foxevans.co.uk
Resident Partners/Directors: ICAEW Members
R Anderson, J A Banbrook, J M Higgitt

FRANCIS WEBBS ◈
Melrose House, 53 Walsgrave Road, Coventry, CV2 4HE

G.L. ASTON
23 Church Lane, Old Arley, Coventry, CV7 8FW

HARRISON BEALE & OWEN LTD ◈
15 Queens Road, Coventry, CV1 3DE
Tel: 02476 631303
Resident Partners/Directors: ICAEW Members
P G Ewing

I 4 BUSINESS LTD
Bank House, 23 Warwick Road, Coventry, CV1 2EW

JAMES KENNEY & CO
202-204 Swan Lane, Coventry, CV2 4GD
Tel: 02476 257165
Resident Partners/Directors: ICAEW Members
G H G Hayward, J Kenney

JOHN D. HARRIS
108 Main Street, Wolston, Coventry, CV8 3HP
Tel: 02476 544341
Principal: ICAEW Member
J D Harris

JOHN G. JONES
8 Briars Close, Coventry, CV2 5JR
Tel: 02476 441503
Principal: ICAEW Member
J G Jones

K LINDSAY & CO LTD
11 Asthill Grove, Styvechale, Coventry, CV3 6HN

LDP FINANCIAL SERVICES LTD
Victoria House, 44-45 Queens Road, Coventry, CV1 3EH

LUCKMANS DUCKETT PARKER
44-45 Queens Road, Coventry, CV1 3EH

M J CALDERBANK LTD
Rustic Ridge, Benton Green Lane, Berkswell, Coventry CV7 7DB
Tel: 07711 552291
Resident Partners/Directors: ICAEW Members
M J Calderbank

M.J. CURTIS & CO
11 Farcroft Avenue, Broad Lane, Coventry, CV5 7DU

M.J. CURTIS & CO
222 Broadgate House, Broadgate, Coventry, CV1 1NG

MCCRANOR KIRBY HILL LTD
Clifford House, 38-44 Binley Road, Coventry, CV3 1JA
Tel: 02476 258621
Email: enquiries@mkhonline.co.uk
Website: http://www.mkhonline.co.uk
Resident Partners/Directors: ICAEW Members
P R Chapman, R Perry, C J Squire
Resident Partners (Non-ICAEW Members):
A T Hall, P West
Registered by the ICAEW to carry out company audit work

MISTRY & CO
89 B & C Far Gosford Street, Gosford Green, Coventry, CV1 5EA

MISTRY ACCOUNTANTS LTD
89 B & C Far Gosford Street, Gosford Green, Coventry, CV1 5EA
Tel: 02476 227004
Resident Partners/Directors: ICAEW Members
G Mistry

P.J.WILLIAMS
45 Baginton Road, Styvechale, Coventry, CV3 6JX
Tel: 02476 414811
Principal: ICAEW Member
P J Williams

PRIME
29 Warwick Road, Coventry, CV1 2ES

PRIME ACCOUNTANTS GROUP LTD ◈
29 Warwick Road, Coventry, CV1 2ES
Tel: 02476 220208
Email: coventry@primeaccountants.co.uk
DX: 11221 COVENTRY
Website: http://www.primeaccountants.co.uk
Resident Partners (Non-ICAEW Members):
J B Skelding
SPECIALISATIONS – FORENSIC ACCOUNTING
Forensic Accounting

PRIME COVENTRY LLP
29 Warwick Road, Coventry, CV1 2ES

ROGER EDMONDS
18 Bradley Croft, Balsall Common, Coventry, CV7 7PZ

SACHDEVS ◈
63 Cromwell Lane, Westwood Heath, Coventry, CV4 8AQ

SHENSTONES LTD
1a Needlers End Lane, Balsall Common, Coventry, CV7 7AF

SHETH & CO ◈
270-272 Radford Road, Coventry, CV6 3BU
Tel: 02476 601099
Email: advice@sheth.co.uk
Website: http://www.sheth.co.uk
Principal: ICAEW Member
V P Sheth
Registered by the ICAEW to carry out company audit work
SPECIALISATIONS – AUDIT & ASSURANCE
Audit
SPECIALISATIONS – FINANCIAL REPORTING
Accounts Preparation
Limited Company Accounts
SPECIALISATIONS – SECTOR
Corporate
SPECIALISATIONS – TAXATION
Taxation
See display advertisement near this entry.

SOHALS
16 Binley Road, Gosford Green, Coventry, CV3 1HZ

SOHALS LTD
16 Binley Road, Gosford Green, Coventry, CV3 1HZ

SPENCER GARDNER DICKINS ◈
3 Coventry Innovation Village, Cheetah Road, Coventry, CV1 2TL
Tel: 02476 257481

SPENCER GARDNER DICKINS LTD ◈
3 Coventry Innovation Village, Cheetah Road, Coventry, CV1 2TL
Tel: 02476 25481
Resident Partners/Directors: ICAEW Members
D Burton, P V R Dickins, D S Thomas
Resident Partners (Non-ICAEW Members):
B J Gardner, P B Spencer

SPENCER GARDNER DICKINS LLP
Unit 3, Coventry Innovation Village, Cheetah Road, Coventry CV1 2TL

SUMUP LTD
28 Pangfield Park, Allesley Park, Coventry, CV5 9NL

TUDOR & CO
21 Heycroft, Gibbet Hill, Coventry, CV4 7HE

WEAVER BUCKWORTH & PARTNERS ◈
18 Queens Road, Coventry, CV1 3EG
Tel: 02476 227755
Resident Partners/Directors: ICAEW Members
E W Buckworth, G J Holt

WILSON DURRANT
2 The Quadrant, Coventry, CV1 2DX

CRADLEY HEATH

COURTS
3 Hayseech, Cradley Heath, B64 7JL

GRIFFITHS & PEGG
42-43 Reddal Hill Road, Cradley Heath, B64 5JS
Tel: 01384 566188
Fax: 01384 566700
Email: enquiries@griffiths-pegg.co.uk
Website: http://www.griffiths-pegg.co.uk
Date Established: 1948
Resident Partners/Directors: ICAEW Members
B F Arch, A A B Grainger
Registered by the ICAEW to carry out company audit work
Regulated by the ICAEW for a range of investment business activities

MICHAEL WARNES
2a High Haden Road, Cradley Heath, B64 7PE

STEVE SMITH
38 Timbertree Road, Cradley Heath, B64 7LE
Tel: 01384 565367
Principal: ICAEW Member
S P Smith

CRAMLINGTON

N. ELLIOTT & CO
2 Gilsland Grove, Northburn Vale, Cramlington, NE23 3SY

CRANBROOK

CRESTEN PREDDY - AIMS ACCOUNTANTS FOR BUSINESS
Firle Cottage, Chapel Lane, Iden Green, Cranbrook TN17 4HQ
Tel: 01580 240 698
Principal: ICAEW Member
A C Preddy

D T S BOLTON
Laurels Back Lane, Goudhurst, Cranbrook, TN17 1AN
Tel: 01580 211731
Principal: ICAEW Member
D T S Bolton

DUNCOMBE & CO ◈
Beech Hill, Glassenbury Road, Cranbrook, TN17 2QJ
Tel: 01580 720330
Principal: ICAEW Member
J R Duncombe

K.J. VAN-DOREN
The Northdown, Cranbrook Road, Goudhurst, Cranbrook TN17 1DP
Tel: 01580 212850
Principal: ICAEW Member
K J Van-Doren

MCCABE FORD WILLIAMS
Bank Chambers, High Street, Cranbrook, TN17 3EG
Tel: 01580 714111
Email: cranbrook@mfw.co.uk
Website: http://www.mfw.co.uk
Resident Partners/Directors: ICAEW Members
D N A Boobbyer, N R Hayward
Resident Partners (Non-ICAEW Members):
M G Humphreys
Registered by the ICAEW to carry out company audit work

MORGAN & CO
Cockshott Farmhouse, Highgate Hill, Hawkhurst, Cranbrook TN18 4LS

MORRISON GOVAN
Bull Farm Barn, Hartley, Cranbrook, TN17 3QE

PLAYFOOT & CO
Old Printers House, Stone Street, Cranbrook, TN17 3HF
Tel: 01580 713055
Resident Partners/Directors: ICAEW Members
D J Playfoot, N J Playfoot

WEST, WAKE, PRICE & CO
Abacus House, Cranbrook Road, Hawkhurst, Cranbrook TN18 4AR

CRANLEIGH

A.R. ROSENBERG
Square Leg Cottage, The Green, Ewhurst, Cranleigh GU6 7RR

AIMS - DAVID SMITH
3 Bank Buildings, 149 High Street, Cranleigh, GU6 8BB
Tel: 01483 267205

COOKS ACCOUNTANCY SERVICES
28 Clappers Meadow, Alfold, Cranleigh, GU6 8HH

COOKS ACCOUNTANCY SERVICES LTD
28 Clappers Meadow, Alfold, Cranleigh, GU6 8HH

COUNSELLS
Smithbrook Kilns, Cranleigh, GU6 8JJ
Tel: 01483 277891
Principal: ICAEW Member
D J Counsell
Registered by the ICAEW to carry out company audit work
Regulated by the ICAEW for a range of investment business activities

IAN E. TOMLINSON
11 Hitherwood, Cranleigh, GU6 8BW
Tel: 01483 271205
Principal: ICAEW Member
I E Tomlinson

LINDA KOSCIA LTD
Wedgewood, Mapledrakes Road, Ewhurst, Cranleigh GU6 7QW

RICHARD GREEN
Smithwood Farmhouse, Smithwood Common, Cranleigh, GU6 8QY

CRAVEN ARMS

A.F.R. BENSON
The Racehouse, Aston Munslow, Craven Arms, SY7 9EN

DYKE RUSCOE & HAYES LTD ◈
St Matthews House, Craven Arms, SY7 9NN
Tel: 01588 672776

JEAN M. CARLESS
Tudor Cottage, Leamoor Common, Wistanstow, Craven Arms SY7 8DN

CRAWLEY

AESICA CONSULTING
4 Gregory Close, Maidenbower, Crawley, RH10 7LB
Tel: 01293 881879
Resident Partners/Directors: ICAEW Members
K M Tonkin

ATHERTON BAILEY LLP ◈
Arundel House, 1 Amberley Court, Whitworth Road, Crawley RH11 7XL
Tel: 01293 410333
Resident Partners/Directors: ICAEW Members
M P Fillmore, N T Paul

BAKER TILLY
12 Gleneagles Court, Brighton Road, Crawley, RH10 6AD
Tel: 01293 565165
Resident Partners/Directors: ICAEW Members
J E Bugden, D G McCulloch, J D Warner

BAKER TILLY
12 Gleneagles Court, Brighton Road, Crawley, RH10 6AD
Tel: 01293 565165
Resident Partners/Directors: ICAEW Members
I A Bell, J E Bugden, J W Dent, J M Ericson, A A Holmes, R J Hymas, E W Jarvis, J D Warner

BAKER TILLY
12 Gleneagles Court, Brighton Road, Crawley, RH10 6AD

BAKER TILLY RESTRUCTURING AND RECOVERY LLP
12 Gleneagles Court, Brighton Road, Crawley, RH10 6AD
Tel: 0845 057 0700
Resident Partners/Directors: ICAEW Members
J D Ariel, J E Bugden

BAKER TILLY TAX AND ACCOUNTING LTD
12 Gleneagles Court, Brighton Road, Crawley, RH10 6AD

BAKER TILLY TAX AND ADVISORY SERVICES LLP
12 Gleneagles Court, Brighton Road, Crawley, RH10 6AD
Tel: 01293 565165
Resident Partners/Directors: ICAEW Members
J D Ariel, I A Bell, J E Bugden, J W Dent, J M Ericson, A A Holmes, R J Hymas, E W Jarvis, D G McCulloch, D A Payne, J D Warner
Resident Partners (Non-ICAEW Members):
S M R Harding-Rolls

DELOITTE & TOUCHE LLP ◈
Global House, High Street, Crawley, RH10 1DL
Tel: 01293 533493
Website: http://www.deloitte.co.uk
Resident Partners/Directors: ICAEW Members
E L S Bairstow, S D Burnhope, N R Harris, D S Longley, G C Pickett

GRANT THORNTON UK LLP
The Explorer Building, Fleming Way, Manor Royal, Crawley RH10 9GT
Tel: 01293 554130
Resident Partners/Directors: ICAEW Members
P G C Carne, T E Lewin, P Owen, S P S Weatherseed
Resident Partners (Non-ICAEW Members):
E T Walsh

I.D. HOLLAND
Bailiffs Cottage, Hophurst Lane, Crawley, RH10 4LN

J.R. WINSLET
Windyridge, Borers Arms Road, Copthorne, Crawley RH10 3LJ
Tel: 01342 712030
Principal: ICAEW Member
J R Winslet

KPMG LLP
1 Forest Gate, Brighton Road, Crawley, RH11 9PT
Tel: 01293 652000
Resident Partners/Directors: ICAEW Members
P R Gresham, N C Standen, M K G Stevens, S J Whitmore

LANDLORDS TAX SERVICES LTD
Shaw House, Pegler Way, Crawley, RH11 7AF

LEWIS ROWELL
20 Springfield Road, Crawley, RH11 8AD

MAURICE PATRY
Shaw House, Pegler Way, Crawley, RH11 7AF

MILLARD & CO
18 Stace Way, Worth, Crawley, RH10 7YW

NICHOLAS HILL
Oak Tree Cottage, Rusper Road, Ifield, Crawley RH11 0HU

P.K. MANKELOW & CO
P.O.Box 45, Crawley, RH10 3YP
Tel: 01342 717233
Principal: ICAEW Member
P K Mankelow

RICHARD PLACE DOBSON SERVICES LTD ◈
29 High Street, Crawley, RH10 1BQ
Tel: 01293 521191
Resident Partners/Directors: ICAEW Members
M N Frost, P R Hayden, M R Tyson

TAX CONSULTING SOLUTIONS
53 The Business Centre, Metcalf Way, Crawley, RH11 7XX

TYAS & CO ◈
5 East Park, Crawley, RH10 6AN

CREDITON

J.N. WILSON
Meadow View, Cheriton Fitzpaine, Crediton, EX17 4BB
Tel: 01363 866423

J.T. STAPLETON & CO
4 Market Street, Crediton, EX17 2AJ
Tel: 01363 773191
Fax: 01363 772195
Website: http://www.jtstapletonandco.co.uk
Resident Partners/Directors: ICAEW Members
C P Bird, J T Stapleton
See display advertisement near this entry.

PRUE STOPFORD FCA
Pilgrim Cottage, Polson Hill, Morchard Bishop, Crediton EX17 6SD
Tel: 01363 877240
Principal: ICAEW Member
P J L Stopford

R BOARD ACCOUNTING SERVICES
39 Barnfield, Crediton, EX17 3HS

ROBERT LYNN FCA
1 Pitt Court, Nymet Rowland, Crediton, EX17 6AN
Tel: 01363 83383
Principal: ICAEW Member
R Lynn

THOMAS WESTCOTT ★
96 High Street, Crediton, EX17 3LB
Tel: 01363 775426

WORTHAM JAQUES ◈
130a High Street, Crediton, EX17 3LQ
Tel: 01392 774593
Resident Partners/Directors: ICAEW Members
D G Wortham

CREWE

A.D.SMITH & CO
205a Nantwich Road, Crewe, CW2 6DD

AJH
10 Westgate Park, Hough, Crewe, CW2 5GY
Tel: 01270 842173
Principal: ICAEW Member
A J Hardy

AJH ACCOUNTANCY
10 Westgate Park, Hough, Crewe, CW2 5GY

ALEXANDER LAYTON
130-132 Nantwich Road, Crewe, CW2 6AZ

ALEXTRA ACCOUNTANTS LTD
Units 12-14 Macon Court, Herald Drive, Crewe, CW1 6EA

BANKS SHERIDAN
Datum House, Electra Way, Crewe, CW1 6ZF

BANKS SHERIDAN LTD ◈
Datum House, Electra Way, Crewe, CW1 6ZF
Tel: 01270 530970
Resident Partners/Directors: ICAEW Members
S P Banks

BROOKES O'HARA LTD
Old Hall Farmhouse, Barthomley, Crewe, CW2 5PE

C.J. O'BRIEN & CO
25 Station Road, Goostrey, Crewe, CW4 8PJ

CHRIS HAWORTH & CO
The Gables, Goostrey Lane, Twemlow Green, Holmes Chapel, Crewe CW4 8BH
Tel: 01477 534911
Principal: ICAEW Member
C G T Haworth

DAVID ALLMAN & CO
70 Nantwich Road, Crewe, CW2 6AL

DAVID C CLEAVER
Blackden Heath Farm, Blackden Lane, Holmes Chapel, Crewe CW4 8DG
Tel: 01477 571677
Principal: ICAEW Member
D C Cleaver

DAVID RODICK ◈
259 Edleston Road, Crewe, CW2 7EA
Tel: 01270 849111
Principal: ICAEW Member
D J Rodick

DAVID SHAW
9 Gorsty Hill Close, Balterley, Crewe, CW2 5QS

HAMMOND MCNULTY ★
8 Mallard Court, Mallard Way, Crewe Buisness Park, Crewe CW1 6ZQ

JOHN ROGER MURRAY ROACH
1 St Andrew's Drive, Holmes Chapel, Crewe, CW4 7DN

K.B. JONES
6 Strathmore Close, Holmes Chapel, Crewe, CW4 7PP
Tel: 01477 535809
Principal: ICAEW Member
K B Jones

SYNERGY ACCOUNTANCY AND TAX SOLUTIONS LTD ◈
70 Nantwich Road, Crewe, CW2 6AL
Tel: 01270 509900
Resident Partners/Directors: ICAEW Members
D M Allman

TAXASSIST ACCOUNTANTS
259 Edleston Road, Crewe, CW2 7EA

CREWKERNE

CHALMERS & CO (SW) LTD ◈
6 Linen Yard, South Street, Crewkerne, TA18 8AB
Tel: 01460 279000
Fax: 01460 279009
Email: crewkerne@chalmers.org.uk
Resident Partners/Directors: ICAEW Members
S M Bachrach, D N Parsons, H E Tayler, R S Wigley
Other Offices: Yeovil, Somerset
Registered by the ICAEW to carry out company audit work
Regulated by the ICAEW for a range of investment business activities

CROMER

BARBER & CO
12 Church Street, Cromer, NR27 9ER
Tel: 01263 513971
Principal: ICAEW Member
I Barber

LARKING GOWEN ◈
Bellamy House, 13 West Street, Cromer, NR27 9HZ
Tel: 01263 512907
Resident Partners/Directors: ICAEW Members
P J Moy

CROOK

ROWLANDS
Gladstone House, Gladstone Street, Crook, DL15 9ED
Tel: 01388 762478
Fax: 01388 762695
Email: don.taylor@rowlandsofcrook.co.uk
Resident Partners/Directors: ICAEW Members
D T Taylor
Other Offices: Chester-le-Street, Yarm, Hexham, Ponteland
Registered by the ICAEW to carry out company audit work
Regulated by the ICAEW for a range of investment business activities

CROWBOROUGH

AH PARTNERSHIP
1st Floor, Crowton House, The Broadway, Crowborough TN6 1DA

ALAN J. FELLS
Beverley Barne, Goldsmiths Avenue, Crowborough, TN6 1RH

DAVID A ACOTT
12 The Farthings, Crowborough, TN6 2TW

IAIN MURRAY
Crowborough Hall, Uckfield Road, Crowborough, TN6 3SU

JD BUSINESS SOLUTIONS LTD
1 Manor Way, Crowborough, TN6 1LS

JENNY DINNAGE
1 Manor Way, Crowborough, TN6 1LS

KEMP ACCOUNTANTS ★
Little Compton, Rannoch Road, Crowborough, TN6 1RB
Tel: 01892 668324
Resident Partners/Directors: ICAEW Members
S M Kemp

NUMIS LTD
1st Floor, Brook House, Mount Pleasant, Crowborough TN6 2NE
Tel: 01892 664020
Resident Partners/Directors: ICAEW Members
T I Skittles, K Wells
Registered by the ICAEW to carry out company audit work

PDH ACCOUNTANTS LTD
Timbers, Southview Road, Crowborough, TN6 1HW

REDSHIELD ACCOUNTANCY SERVICES
New Oaks, Southview Close, Southview Road, Crowborough TN6 1HH
Tel: 01892 667606
Principal: ICAEW Member
J S A Morris

REEDS
Copperfields, Mount Pleasant, Crowborough, TN6 2NF
Tel: 01892 668676
Principal: ICAEW Member
C R Reed

ROBERT W BELCHER LTD
Park Grove, Lye Green, Crowborough, TN6 1UU

VINCENT BLAKE
The Old Farmhouse, Town Row Green, Crowborough, TN6 3QU

WILLIAMS & CO
Bramley Cottage, Town Row Green, Rotherfield, Crowborough TN6 3QU

CROWTHORNE

ACT
Crowthorne Enterprise Centre, Crowthorne Business Estate, Old Wokingham Road, Crowthorne RG45 6AW

ATKINSON HUNTER & CO
Talbot House, High Street, Crowthorne, RG45 7AQ

DURRANTS
24 Wellington Business Park, Dukes Ride, Crowthorne, RG45 6LS

HERBERT J. MOORE
35 Edgcumbe Park Drive, Crowthorne, RG45 6HU

JADIR & CO LTD
23 Parkway, Crowthorne, RG45 6EP
Tel: 01344 777122
Resident Partners/Directors: ICAEW Members
R A Al Jadir

PKB
Beechey House, 87 Church Street, Crowthorne, RG45 7AW

R C BARRETT & CO
Stratfield House, 265 High Street, Crowthorne, RG45 7AH

R C BARRETT & CO (WOKINGHAM) LTD
Stratfield House, 265 High Street, Crowthorne, RG45 7AH

RICE ASSOCIATES
Sherwood House, 104 High Street, Crowthorne, RG45 7AX
Tel: 01344 761415
Resident Partners/Directors: ICAEW Members
D Rice, S E Wildey
See display advertisement near this entry.

WILDER JAYAKAR & CO
15 Heathermount Gardens, Crowthorne, RG45 6HW

CROYDON

ANDREW THURBURN & CO
38 Tamworth Road, Croydon, CR0 1XU
Tel: 020 8680 8586
Principal: ICAEW Member
A J Thurburn

ASH & CO ACCOUNTANTS LTD
Acorn House, 74-94 Cherry Orchard Road, Croydon, CR9 6DA

AVERILLO & ASSOCIATES
16 South End, Croydon, CR0 1DN

AYNESLEY WALTERS COHEN LTD ◈
16 South End, Croydon, CR0 1DN
Tel: 020 8686 4488
Resident Partners/Directors: ICAEW Members
G Cohen

B N JACKSON NORTON ★
22 Laud Street, Croydon, CR0 1SU

BARKER HIBBERT & CO
133 Cherry Orchard Road, Croydon, CR0 6BE
Tel: 020 8681 1951
Resident Partners/Directors: ICAEW Members
C J Brockwell, R S Clarke

BRITT & KEEHAN ◈
60 Fitzjames Avenue, Croydon, CR0 5DD
Tel: 020 8654 1020
Email: jill.keehan@brittandkeehan.co.uk
Resident Partners/Directors: ICAEW Members
M Britt, J Keehan
Registered by the ICAEW to carry out company audit work

SPECIALISATIONS – SECTOR

Charities

BRUCE M.L. GRAY
Suite 122, Airport House, Purley Way, Croydon CR0 0XZ

BRYDEN JOHNSON ◈
1-4 Kings Parade, Lower Coombe Street, Croydon, CR0 1AA
Tel: 020 8686 0255
Resident Partners/Directors: ICAEW Members
G R Bull, N F K Johnson
Non-resident Partners (Non-ICAEW Members):
J K Wilding

C.G.HARWOOD
2 Rochester Gardens, Croydon, CR0 5NN

C.R.S. LINK
3 Waldegrove, Croydon, CR0 5JX

CHANTREY VELLACOTT DFK LLP
Corinthian House, 17 Lansdowne Road, Croydon, CR0 2BX
Tel: 020 8686 3915
Fax: 020 8681 4063
Email: info@cvdfk.com
Website: http://www.cvdfk.com
Resident Partners/Directors: ICAEW Members
M F R Cooper, M E Gillett, S R Levine, A K Syrocki, R J Willis
Resident Partners (Non-ICAEW Members):
S I Corrall, G A Hacker
Other Offices: Brighton & Hove, Colchester, Leicester, London, Northampton, Reading, Stevenage, Watford
Registered by the ICAEW to carry out company audit work
Regulated by the ICAEW for a range of investment business activities
Individual(s) licensed for insolvency work by the ICAEW

INVESTOR IN PEOPLE

CRANFIELDS
3 Church Rd, Croydon, CR0 1SG

CROYDON BUSINESS CENTRE LTD
16 South End, Croydon, CR0 1DN
Tel: 020 8686 4488
Resident Partners/Directors: ICAEW Members
G Cohen

CTM PARTNERSHIP LTD
838 Wickham Road, Croydon, CR0 8ED

D.S. & CO
DS House, 306 High Street, Croydon, CR0 1NG
Tel: 020 8686 7757
Fax: 020 8760 0498
Email: dhiraj@dsandco.com
Website: http://www.dsandco.com
Mobile: 07831 288660
Principal: ICAEW Member
D F Shah
Registered by the ICAEW to carry out company audit work
Regulated by the ICAEW for a range of investment business activities

SPECIALISATIONS – AUDIT & ASSURANCE

Audit

SPECIALISATIONS – BUSINESS & GENERAL ADVICE

Book-keeping
Management Advice to Business
Management Consultancy

SPECIALISATIONS – FINANCIAL REPORTING

Accounts Preparation
Limited Company Accounts
Partnership/Sole Trader Accounts

SPECIALISATIONS – INVESTMENT BUSINESS

Planning

SPECIALISATIONS – IT

Computer Consultants
Computer Systems and Consultancy

SPECIALISATIONS – SECTOR

Corporate
Property Development
Property Investment

SPECIALISATIONS – TAXATION

Back Duty
Capital Gains — Limited Companies
Capital Gains — Personal
Investigations
National Insurance Advice
Partnerships and Sole Traders
PAYE Advice
Payroll Service and Advice
Personal
Taxation

DAECHE DUBOIS & PLINSTON
Mansfield House, 139 Shirley Road, Croydon, CR0 7LR
Tel: 020 8662 1313
Fax: 020 8654 7642
Email: johnplinston@btinternet.com
Principal: ICAEW Member
J A Plinston

ECA ACCOUNTING SERVICES
78 Shirley Way, Shirley, Croydon, CR0 8PB

FITZGERALD MITHIA ★
Newgate House, 431 London Road, Croydon, CR0 3PF

FLEMMINGS
76 Canterbury Road, Croydon, CR0 3HA
Tel: 020 8665 7050
Resident Partners/Directors: ICAEW Members
H C Shah, S Shah, S P Shah

GRAHAM COHEN & CO ◈
16 South End, Croydon, CR0 1DN
Tel: 020 8686 4488

GRAHAM COHEN & CO LTD ◈
16 South End, Croydon, CR0 1DN
Tel: 020 8686 4488
Resident Partners/Directors: ICAEW Members
G Cohen

HAINES WATTS ★
Airport House, Purley Way, Croydon, CR0 0XZ

HAMILTON-EDDY & CO ▽
39 Tamworth Road, Croydon, CR0 1XU
Tel: 020 8688 9264
Fax: 020 8688 5292
Email: all@hamilton-eddy.co.uk
Website: http://www.hamilton-eddy.co.uk
Resident Partners/Directors: ICAEW Members
D W Weeden
Resident Partners (Non-ICAEW Members):
P I Charles

continued

HAMILTON-EDDY & CO*cont*
Registered by another RSB to carry out company audit work
Licensed by another DPB to carry on investment business
SPECIALISATIONS – AUDIT & ASSURANCE
Audit
SPECIALISATIONS – BUSINESS & GENERAL ADVICE
Company Secretarial Service
SPECIALISATIONS – FINANCIAL REPORTING
Accounts Preparation
Partnership/Sole Trader Accounts
SPECIALISATIONS – INVESTMENT BUSINESS
Financial Planning and Advice
SPECIALISATIONS – TAXATION
Taxation
Trusteeship

HOWARD LONG
41 St Peters Road, Croydon, CR0 1HN

INGLE BHATTI & CO
RAB House, 102-104 Park Lane, Croydon, CR0 1JB

J.C. JENNER
52 Friars Wood, Pixton Way, Forestdale, Croydon, CR0 9JP

JEFFREY ALTMAN & CO ◈
Wayman House, 141 Wickham Road, Shirley, Croydon
CR0 8TE

JEREMY KNIGHT & CO
75 Park Lane, Croydon, CR9 1XS
Tel: 020 8686 4274
Individual(s) licensed for insolvency work by another RPB

JOHNSON & CO
318A Stafford Road, Croydon, CR0 4NH
Tel: 020 8681 1236
Principal: ICAEW Member
D V Johnson

KEYTE & CO ACCOUNTANTS LTD
Coombe Avenue, Croydon, CR0 5SD

KHMM
18 Wing Yip Business Centre, 544 Purley Way, Croydon, CR0 4NZ

THE KINGS MILL PARTNERSHIP
75 Park Lane, Croydon, CR9 1XS
Tel: 020 8686 7942
Fax: 020 8667 0909
Email: enquiries@kingsmill.co.uk
Resident Partners/Directors: ICAEW Members
D J Mitchell, P A Taylor

Resident Partners (Non-ICAEW Members):
D L Day
Other Offices: Ashdown House, High Street, Cross-in-Hand, Heathfield, East Sussex TN21 0SR
Registered by the ICAEW to carry out company audit work

LESLIE BURGESS
87 Shirley Avenue, Croydon, CR0 8SP
Tel: 020 8654 1221
Principal: ICAEW Member
L Burgess

M I HASAN
Beechwood, 25 Upper Shirley Road, Shirley, Croydon
CR0 5EB

M. LILANI & CO
1c Church Road, Croydon, CR0 1SG
Tel: 020 8253 8003
Principal: ICAEW Member
M N Lilani

THE MCCAY PARTNERSHIP
Financial House, 14 Barclay Road, Croydon, CR0 1JN
Tel: 020 8681 0090
Fax: 020 8680 2113
Email: info@mccays.co.uk
Website: http://www.mccays.co.uk
Resident Partners/Directors: ICAEW Members
J B McCay, J Mon
Registered by the ICAEW to carry out company audit work
SPECIALISATIONS – AUDIT & ASSURANCE
Audit
SPECIALISATIONS – BUSINESS & GENERAL ADVICE
Book-keeping
Company Formation
Company Secretarial Service
SPECIALISATIONS – FINANCIAL REPORTING
Accounts Preparation
Limited Company Accounts
Partnership/Sole Trader Accounts
SPECIALISATIONS – TAXATION
Payroll Service and Advice
Taxation

MASON DHARSI LTD ◈
29 Cuthbert Road, Croydon, CR0 3RB
Tel: 020 8686 5283
Resident Partners/Directors: ICAEW Members
C J S Mason

PALMER MCCARTHY ★
Toronto House, 49a South End, Croydon, CR9 1LT

REYNOLDS & CO
Charter House, 29A London Road, Croydon, CR0 2RE
Tel: 020 8760 9929
Principal: ICAEW Member
R J Reynolds

RICHARD TOZER LLP
Berkeley House, 62 Hartland Way, Croydon, CR0 8RF

RICHARD W. WESLEY & CO
68 Waddon Court Road, Croydon, CR0 4AJ

SALEEMI ASSOCIATES ◈
792 Wickham Road, Croydon, CR0 8EA
Tel: 020 8777 3055
Website: http://www.saleemiassociates.com
Principal: ICAEW Member
M A Saleemi

Registered by the ICAEW to carry out company audit work
SPECIALISATIONS – AUDIT & ASSURANCE
Audit
SPECIALISATIONS – BUSINESS & GENERAL ADVICE
Book-keeping
SPECIALISATIONS – FINANCIAL REPORTING
Accounts Preparation
SPECIALISATIONS – SECTOR
Dentists/Opticians
Doctors
Property
Retailers
SPECIALISATIONS – TAXATION
Payroll Service and Advice
Taxation

SELF & CO
HCL House, Beddington Farm Road, Croydon, CR0 4XB

SHAIKH & CO
174 Canterbury Road, Croydon, CR0 3HE
Tel: 020 86841321
Principal: ICAEW Member
M Shaikh

SHERWOODS
30 Addiscombe Grove, Croydon, CR9 5AY

SIBA & CO
308 High Street, Croydon, CR0 1NG
Tel: 020 8680 7796
Principal: ICAEW Member
M Siba

SIMPSON WREFORD & PARTNERS ◈
Suffolk House, George Street, Croydon, CR0 0YN
Tel: 020 8681 5500
Fax: 020 8681 8926
Email: info@simpsonwreford.com
Website: http://www.simpsonwreford.com
Resident Partners/Directors: ICAEW Members
C J Atkinson, N Hunwick, T P Lindfield, A Weaks, D J Wilkes
General Description: For all your business and tax solutions. Four hundred yards from East Croydon station, we are a team of twenty five professionals who will advise on all tax and accounting matters for the individual, his business and family.

SINCLAIR & CO
10 Colson Road, Croydon, CR0 6UA
Tel: 020 8681 1003
Fax: 020 8680 8369
Principal: ICAEW Member
D A P Sinclair

SOMERTON & CO
Challenge House, 616 Mitcham Road, Croydon, CR0 3AA

STEWARD & PELLANT LLP ◈
Marco Polo House, 3-5 Lansdowne Road, Croydon, CR0 2BX

TENON LTD
The Lansdowne Building, Lansdowne Road, Croydon, CR9 2ER
Tel: 020 8263 6061

VKM ACCOUNTANTS LTD
106 Orchard Way, Croydon, CR0 7NN

WANDLE HOUSE ASSOCIATES
Wandle House, 47 Wandle Road, Croydon, CR0 1DF

CULLOMPTON

ACCOUNTING ASSOCIATES LTD
4 Luxton Court, Cockpit Hill, Cullompton, EX15 1FJ

JULIET MACKIE
Hill View, Cornhill, Hemyock, Cullompton EX15 3RQ
Tel: 01823 680733
Principal: ICAEW Member
J Mackie

SANDRA ALDWORTH
The School House, Clayhidon, Cullompton, EX15 3PL
Tel: 01823 680671
Principal: ICAEW Member
S Aldworth

DARLINGTON

C P WAITES
24 St Cuthberts Way, Darlington, DL1 1GB
Tel: 01325 354440
Principal: ICAEW Member
N S Waites

CHRIS HOPE
Roselea, 82 Cleveland Avenue, Darlington, DL3 7BE

CHRIS SKINNER
27 Albatross Way, Darlington, DL1 1DN

CHRISTIE PROUD THOMPSON ★
64 Duke Street, Darlington, DL3 7AN
Tel: 01325 360773
Fax: 01325 468688
Email: lbc@cpt-online.co.uk
Resident Partners/Directors: ICAEW Members
L B Christie

CLIVE OWEN & CO LLP ◈
140 Coniscliffe Road, Darlington, DL3 7RT
Tel: 01325 349700
Resident Partners/Directors: ICAEW Members
A I Allan, N Baldry, C P Beaumont, P A Hogan, A W Luckett, C F Owen

COAD & CO LTD
32 Houndgate, Darlington, DL1 5RH

EURA AUDIT UK
Burden Chambers, 73 Duke Street, Darlington, DL3 7SD

EURA AUDIT UK ★
Burden Chanmbers, 73 Duke Street, Darlington, DL3 7SD

FINDLAY JAMES
140 Coniscliffe Road, Darlington, DL3 7RT

HUNTON & CO
23 Rossway, Darlington, DL1 3RD

HUNTON BROS LTD
23 Rossway, Darlington, DL1 3RD

HW ◈
Sterling House, 22 St Cuthberts Way, Darlington, DL1 1GB
Tel: 01325 254700
Resident Partners/Directors: ICAEW Members
P Collingwood, C G Dedman, D H Maultby, J C Scott

ICS(NORTH EAST) LTD
49 Duke Street, Darlington, DL3 7SD

J P WALTERS & CO
67 Duke Street, Darlington, DL3 7SD

JANE PALMER ◈
18 Exeter Drive, Haughton Grange, Darlington, DL1 2SE
Tel: 01325 284206
Principal: ICAEW Member
J I Palmer

KENNETH EASBY LLP
Victoria Buildings, Rear 15 Victoria Road, Darlington, DL1 5RB
Tel: 01325 489921
Resident Partners/Directors: ICAEW Members
C D Syers

KING, HOPE & CO
31 Victoria Road, Darlington, DL1 5SB
Tel: 01325 469188
Resident Partners/Directors: ICAEW Members
P J Bramwell

MALCOLM CLARK & CO
39 Grange Road, Darlington, DL1 5NB

MITCHELL GORDON
43 Coniscliffe Road, Darlington, DL3 7EH
Tel: 01325 368000

MITCHELL GORDON LTD ◈
43 Coniscliffe Road, Darlington, DL3 7EH
Tel: 01325 368000
Resident Partners/Directors: ICAEW Members
M D Gordon, N A Vassilounis

MOLLART & CO ★
39 Grange Road, Darlington, DL1 5NB

NIGEL HERRING & CO
21 Coniscliffe Road, Darlington, DL3 7EE

PAUL VARTY
24 St Cuthberts Way, Darlington, DL1 1GB
Tel: 01325 481681
Principal: ICAEW Member
P A Varty

ROB BARRIGAN CONSULTING
Stoer House, 1 Polam Road, Darlington, DL1 5NW
Tel: 01325 285 577
Principal: ICAEW Member
R Barrigan

ROBSON SCOTT ASSOCIATES
ICS(North East) limited, 49 Duke Street, Darlington, DL3 7SD

SANDERS SWINBANK LTD ◈
7 Victoria Road, Darlington, DL1 5SN
Tel: 01325 382828
Resident Partners/Directors: ICAEW Members
D Sanders, S M A Swinbank

TOM HARRISON INSOLVENCY SERVICES
17 Victoria Road, Darlington, DL1 5SF

VANTIS GROUP LTD ◈
1st Floor North Point, Faverdale North, Faverdale Industrial Estate, Darlington DL3 0PH
Tel: 01325 382 323
Website: http://www.vantisplc.com/darlington
General Description: ICAEW Registered.

DARTFORD

AARDVARK TAXATION SERVICES LTD
Benvenuti, 61 Norfield Road, Dartford, DA2 7NY

ALLENDALE HARVEY & CO
Summit House, 2-2A Highfield Road, Dartford, DA1 2JY

BARNES ROFFE LLP
16-19 Copperfields, Spital Street, Dartford, DA1 2DE
Tel: 01322 275335
Resident Partners/Directors: ICAEW Members
M P Cientanni, K J Mason, D Stannett

CALDWELL & BRAHAM ▽
Westgate House, Spital Street, Dartford, DA1 2EH

CONRADI MORRISON & CO ◈
4 Summerhill Road, Dartford, DA1 2LP
Tel: 01322 278188

COULSON & CO
Benvenuti, 61 Norfield Road, Dartford, DA2 7NY

DONAL LUCEY LAWLOR ◈
43 Highfield Road, Dartford, DA1 2JS
Tel: 01322 277725
Principal: ICAEW Member
P J Lawlor

HEDLEY DUNK
Trinity House, 3 Bullace Lane, Dartford, DA1 1BB

HEDLEY DUNK LTD
Trinity House, 3 Bullace Lane, Dartford, DA1 1BB

J ROBINSON & CO
West Hill House, West Hill, Dartford, DA1 2EU

KEITH COULSON & CO LTD
Benvenuti, 61 Norfield Road, Dartford, DA2 7NY

KENT ACCOUNTANCY LTD
Regus House, Victory Way, Admiral Park, Crossway, Dartford DA2 6QD

MACK BUSINESS SERVICES LTD
36A Gordon Road, Dartford, DA1 2LQ
Tel: 01322 271184
Resident Partners/Directors: ICAEW Members
A Grant

MICHAEL WATTS & CO
Ostler's Lodge, 70 Oakfield Lane, Dartford, DA1 2SY
Tel: 01322 222344
Principal: ICAEW Member
M D Watts

S&J ACCOUNTING SERVICES LTD
65 Chestnut Grove, Wilmington, Dartford, DA2 7PQ

SADLER DAVIES & CO
25A Essex Road, Dartford, DA1 2AU
Tel: 01322 271617
Fax: 01322 223222
Email: info@sadlerdavies.co.uk
Website: http://www.sadlerdavies.co.uk
Mobile: 07850 142732
Date Established: 1986
Principal: ICAEW Member
G E J Sadler
See display advertisement near this entry.

SAZAN & CO
93 Crayford Road, Crayford, Dartford, DA1 4AS

STEPHEN M FRYER
First Floor, Westgate House, Spital Street, Dartford DA1 2EH
Tel: 01322 288277
Principal: ICAEW Member
S M Fryer

STRACHAN & CO
Summerhill Cottage, 9 Summerhill Road, Dartford, DA1 2LP

WERNHAM WALLACE SKINNER & CO
Summit House, 2A Highfield Road, Dartford, DA1 2JY
Tel: 01322 222106
Resident Partners/Directors: ICAEW Members
D J Skinner, F Wernham

DARTMOUTH

DAVID J. BEENY & CO
36 Victoria Road, Dartmouth, TQ6 9SB
Tel: 01803 832361
Fax: 01803 835361
Email: office@davidjbeeny.co.uk
Website: http://www.davidjbeeny.co.uk
Principal: ICAEW Member
D J Beeny
Registered by the ICAEW to carry out company audit work
See display advertisement near this entry.

DARWEN

BARLOW ANDREWS
Bank Chambers, Belgrave Square, Darwen, BB3 1BU

HINDLE & JEPSON
10 Borough Rd, Darwen, BB3 1PL
Tel: 01254 702111
Fax: 01254 706837
Email: info@hindleandjepson.co.uk
Website: http://www.hindleandjepson.co.uk
Training Contracts Available.
Resident Partners/Directors: ICAEW Members
D W Wilson
Resident Partners (Non-ICAEW Members):
C A Smith
Registered by the ICAEW to carry out company audit work

JENNINGS & CO ★
159/163 Blackburn Road, Hollins Grove, Darwen, BB3 1ET
Tel: 01254 774013
Resident Partners/Directors: ICAEW Members
T A Gilchreaste

JENNINGS & GILCHREASTE ★
159/163 Blackburn Road, Hollins Grove, Darwen, BB3 1ET
Tel: 01254 774013
Resident Partners/Directors: ICAEW Members
T A Gilchreaste

LEN ENTWISTLE ◈
290 Blackburn Road, Lynwood, Darwen, BB3 0AA
Tel: 01254 708881
Principal: ICAEW Member
L Entwistle

WALKDEN I.J.
Lower Hill Farm, Tockholes, Darwen, BB3 0NF

DAVENTRY

ANTHONY BLACKSTOCK LTD
37 High Street, Eydon, Daventry, NN11 3PP

COTTONS
The Stables, Church Walk, Daventry, NN11 4BL

DELYTH BENDING ACCOUNTANCY LTD ◈
4 The Paddock, Lower Boddington, Daventry, NN11 6YF
Tel: 01327 264380
Resident Partners/Directors: ICAEW Members
D C Bending

DNG DOVE NAISH ◈
14 Cottesbrooke Park, Heartlands Business Park, Daventry, NN11 8YL
Tel: 01604 657200
Resident Partners/Directors: ICAEW Members
R M Burkimsher, I C Robson

DRAKE FLETCHER & CO
Sheaf House, 1-3 Sheaf Street, Daventry, NN11 4AA

MERRYHILL ACCOUNTANCY SERVICES LTD
73 High Street, Braunston, Daventry, NN11 7HS

STEPHEN FRANKLIN FCA CTA
45 Membris Way, Woodford Halse, Daventry, NN11 3QZ
Tel: 01327 261098
Email: franklin.fca@which.net
Principal: ICAEW Member
S Franklin

SPECIALISATIONS – FINANCIAL REPORTING
Partnership/Sole Trader Accounts

SPECIALISATIONS – TAXATION
Capital Gains — Personal
Estate and Inheritance
Partnerships and Sole Traders
Personal
Self Assessment Advice
Small Traders
Trusts

WILSONS ACCOUNTING SERVICES
10 The Glebe, Badby, Daventry, NN11 3AZ
Tel: 01327 700157
Principal: ICAEW Member
S Wilson

DEAL

COLEMAN & CO
8A Alfred Square, Deal, CT14 6LU

HIGSON & CO ◈
45 Queen Street, Deal, CT14 6EY
Tel: 01304 381542
Principal: ICAEW Member
P J L Higson

HIGSON APS LTD ◈
45 Queen Street, Deal, CT14 6EY
Tel: 01304 381542
Resident Partners/Directors: ICAEW Members
P J L Higson

DERBY

A.J. PEARSON
1 Packington Hill, Kegworth, Derby, DE74 2DF

AIMS - DAVID GOULD ◈
7 Montpelier, Quarndon, Derby, DE22 5JW
Tel: 01332 541111
Principal: ICAEW Member
D C Gould
Registered by the ICAEW to carry out company audit work

AIMS - GRAHAM EARDLEY
17 Wilsthorpe Road, Breaston, Derby, DE72 3EA

AIMS - RICHARD WHITEHEAD
8 Buxton Drive, Little Eaton, Derby, DE21 5AN

ANDERSONS ACCOUNTANTS LTD
Bank Chambers, Market Place, Melbourne, Derby DE73 8DS

ANDERSONS ACCOUNTANTS AND BUSINESS ADVISORS
Bank Chambers, 39 Market Place, Melbourne, Derby DE73 8DS

ARMITAGE - WINTER
15 Vernon Street, Derby, DE1 1FT

ARMITAGE - WINTER LTD
15 Vernon Street, Derby, DE1 1FT
Tel: 01332 292948
Email: info@armitagewinter.co.uk
Resident Partners/Directors: ICAEW Members
J R Armitage

ASHGATES ★ ◈
5 Prospect Place, Millennium Way, Pride Park, Derby DE24 8HG

ASHGATES CORPORATE SERVICES LTD
5 Prospect Place, Millennium Way, Pride Park, Derby DE24 8HG

ASTACX LTD
Longcroft Farmhouse, 31 Derby Road, Aston-on-Trent, Derby DE72 2AE

BATES WESTON
The Mills, Canal Street, Derby, DE1 2RJ
Tel: 01332 365855
Email: enquiries@batesweston.co.uk
Website: http://www.batesweston.co.uk
Individual(s) licensed for insolvency work by another RPB

BLYTHE SQUIRES WILSON ◈
1-2 Vernon Street, Derby, DE1 1FR
Tel: 01332 360676
Fax: 01332 294363
Email: info@blythesquireswilson.co.uk
Website: http://www.blythesquireswilson.co.uk
Resident Partners/Directors: ICAEW Members
A D Castledine, R G Squires, J H Wilson
Registered by the ICAEW to carry out company audit work
Regulated by the ICAEW for a range of investment business activities
Languages Spoken:
French

BOURNE & CO ◈
3 Charnwood Street, Derby, DE1 2GY
Tel: 01332 340159
Resident Partners/Directors: ICAEW Members
J J Delaney, N D Gale, I Hill

BW BUSINESS SERVICES LTD ◈
The Mill, Canal Street, Derby, DE1 2RJ
Tel: 01332 365855
Email: enquiries@batesweston.co.uk
Website: http://www.batesweston.co.uk
Training Contracts Available.
Resident Partners/Directors: ICAEW Members
R J Carman, G Evans, I K Neal, R J Smith, W D Thomas
Registered by the ICAEW to carry out company audit work
Regulated by the ICAEW for a range of investment business activities
Authorised and regulated by the Financial Services Authority for investment business

INVESTOR IN PEOPLE

CAMERON HUGHES LTD ◈
16 Jubilee Parkway, Jubilee Business Park, Derby, DE21 4BJ
Tel: 01332 204777
Resident Partners/Directors: ICAEW Members
G S Gilbert, M Hayton

CAMPAGNA-SMITH
Fernleigh House, 10 Uttoxeter Road, Mickleover, Derby DE3 0DA
Tel: 01332 521323
Resident Partners/Directors: ICAEW Members
G Campagna, M J Smith

CEDAR & CO
Lucre House, 106-108 Ashbourne Road, Derby, DE22 3AG

CEDAR ASSOCIATES (UK) LTD
Lucre House, 108 Ashbourne Road, Derby, DE22 3AG

CEDAR AUDIT LTD
106-108 Ashbourne Road, Derby, DE22 3AG

CLIPPER ACCOUNTING LTD
PO Box 5503, 11 Derwent Street, Draycott, Derby DE72 3ZH
Tel: 01332 870123
Resident Partners/Directors: ICAEW Members
N S Wallis
Languages Spoken:
German

COOPER PARRY LLP ◈
3 Centro Place, Pride Park, Derby, DE24 8RF
Tel: 01332 295544
Fax: 01332 295600
Email: advice@cooperparry.com
Website: http://www.cooperparry.com
Resident Partners/Directors: ICAEW Members
J J Bowler, A P Cheatham, R E Farmer, K Francis, A Honarmand, J P N Martin, P D Rowley, P R Sterling

DAVID WILLIAMS & CO ◈
66 Belper Road, Derby, DE1 3EN
Tel: 01332 345713
Principal: ICAEW Member
D H A Williams

DEKM
5 Trinity Terrace, London Road, Derby, DE1 2QS
Tel: 01332 293396
Fax: 01332 291513
Email: info@dekm.co.uk
Website: http://www.dekm.co.uk
Resident Partners/Directors: ICAEW Members
P E Bradley, J H Downes
Other Offices: Ashby De La Zouch (Tel: 01530 416667)
Registered by the ICAEW to carry out company audit work
Regulated by the ICAEW for a range of investment business activities

E.H. WOODWARD
Hall Farm, Risley, Derby, DE72 3TT
Tel: 0115 939 7307
Principal: ICAEW Member
E H Woodward

FLANDERS & CO
Bunkers, 8 Ladycroft Paddock, Allestree, Derby DE22 2GA
Tel: 01332 258700
Principal: ICAEW Member
J B Flanders

FOX ASSOCIATE
2nd Floor, Saxon House, Heritage Gate, Friary Street, Derby DE1 1NL

HAINES WATTS (EAST MIDLANDS) LTD ◈
10 Stadium Business Court, Millennium Way, Pride Park, Derby DE24 8HP
Tel: 01332 258700
Resident Partners/Directors: ICAEW Members
M J Bowles, T Clewes, A S Minifie, R W Willcox

HIGHGROVE ACCOUNTANTS
1st Floor, Unit 13, Victoria Way, Pride Park, Derby DE24 8AN

HSKS & CO
18 St Christophers Way, Pride Park, Derby, DE24 8JY
Tel: 01332 200105

HSKS LTD ◈
18 St Christophers Way, Pride Park, Derby, DE24 8JY

ICA
183 Normanton Road, Derby, DE23 6US
Tel: 01332 294888
Principal: ICAEW Member
I Younus

JOHN V. WOODWARD
28 Friar Gate, Derby, DE1 1BX
Tel: 01332 291313
Email: john.v.woodward@btconnect.com
Principal: ICAEW Member
J V Woodward

continued

JOHN V. WOODWARD *cont*

SPECIALISATIONS – TAXATION

Taxation

JOHNSON TIDSALL ◈

81 Burton Road, Derby, DE1 1TJ
Tel: 01332 363116
Fax: 01332 349984
Email: general@johnsontidsall.co.uk
Website: http://www.johnsontidsall.co.uk
Resident Partners/Directors: ICAEW Members
D Hobbs, D J Mellor, R E Minns, S P Robotham, B A Scott

Registered by the ICAEW to carry out company audit work

Regulated by the ICAEW for a range of investment business activities

SPECIALISATIONS – AUDIT & ASSURANCE

Audit

SPECIALISATIONS – BUSINESS & GENERAL ADVICE

Management Advice to Business

SPECIALISATIONS – BUSINESS RECOVERY & INSOLVENCY

Liquidations

SPECIALISATIONS – TAXATION

Taxation

KEITH GREGORY

26 Barley Close, Little Eaton, Derby, DE21 5DJ

L.W. RILEY

68 Moor End, Spondon, Derby, DE21 7EE

LIGHTLINK LTD

15 Kingston Street, Derby, DE1 3EZ
Tel: 01332 361326
Resident Partners/Directors: ICAEW Members
A Fowler-Colwell

LINGS ◈

Provident House, 51 Wardwick, Derby, DE1 1HN
Tel: 01332 346605
Fax: 01332 291399
Email: mail@lings-accountants.co.uk
Website: http://www.lings-accountants.co.uk
Resident Partners/Directors: ICAEW Members
C L Howard, F J Marson, R Ransom, A Smith, M Wragg

Registered by the ICAEW to carry out company audit work

Regulated by the ICAEW for a range of investment business activities

M J SHAPCOTT & COMPANY LTD ◈

Charter House, Wyvern Court, Stanier Way, Wyvern Business Park, Derby DE21 6BF

M.S. CAISTER & CO LTD

Prosperity House, 121 Green Lane, Derby, DE1 1RZ

MABE ALLEN LLP ◈

50 Osmaston Road, Derby, DE1 2HU
Tel: 01332 345265
Resident Partners/Directors: ICAEW Members
J P Allen, K Slack

MCGREGORS CORPORATE

11 Melbourne Court, Pride Park, Derby, DE24 3LZ

MAURICE EDWARD GRANGER

143 Burley Lane, Quarndon, Derby, DE22 5JS
Tel: 01332 550477
Principal: ICAEW Member
M E Granger

MOORE STEPHENS LLP

Rooms 105 & 106, The Old Courthouse, 18-20 St Peters Churchyard, Derby DE1 1NN

P J FINNEGAN ◈

10 Rutland Drive, Mickleover, Derby, DE3 9FW
Tel: 01332 512933
Principal: ICAEW Member
P J Finnegan

PARKINSON MATTHEWS LLP ◈

Cedar House, 35 Ashbourne Road, Derby, DE22 3FS
Tel: 01332 360808
Fax: 01332 384801
Email: enquiries@pmllp.co.uk
Resident Partners/Directors: ICAEW Members
R J Matthews, K Parkinson

See display advertisement near this entry.

PAUL BRAMMAN LTD

7 Radstone Close, Oakwood, Derby, DE21 2PT
Tel: 01332 662369
Resident Partners/Directors: ICAEW Members
P F Bramman

PEARSONS

20 Irongate, Derby, DE1 3GP
Tel: 01332 364299
Principal: ICAEW Member
A Pearson

PKF (UK) LLP
Century House, St James Court, Friar Court, Derby DE1 1BT
Tel: 01332 372936
Email: info.derby@uk.pkf.com
Website: http://www.pkf.co.uk
Resident Partners/Directors: ICAEW Members
J A Thompson
Resident Partners (Non-ICAEW Members):
M Plampin

POTTER & CO
79 Friar Gate, Derby, DE1 1FL
Tel: 01332 343709
Resident Partners/Directors: ICAEW Members
R J Potter, W S Potter

PRICEWATERHOUSE-COOPERS LLP
Donington Court, Pegasus Business Park, Castle Donington, Derby DE74 2UZ
Tel: 01509 604000
Resident Partners/Directors: ICAEW Members
P R Harrold, T Kachhela, A J Lyon, S D Maddison, A McMurdo, B K Smith, R W Tandy

R.V. HOAD & CO
Suite 11, Keynes House, Chester Park, Alfreton Road, Derby DE21 4AS
Tel: 01332 344086
Fax: 01332 295046
Email: victor@rvhoad.co.uk
Principal: ICAEW Member
R V Hoad
Registered by the ICAEW to carry out company audit work

SPECIALISATIONS – AUDIT & ASSURANCE
Audit

SPECIALISATIONS – BUSINESS & GENERAL ADVICE
Book-keeping
Company Formation

SPECIALISATIONS – FINANCIAL REPORTING
Accounts Preparation
Limited Company Accounts
Partnership/Sole Trader Accounts

SPECIALISATIONS – TAXATION
Small Traders
Taxation

RAYMOND M. GREEN
25 Croft Close, Spondon, Derby, DE21 7EF

RICHARDSON NUTT LTD
Unit 7, Stadium Business Court, Millennium Way, Pride Park, Derby DE24 8HP
Tel: 01332 342385
Fax: 01332 382130
Resident Partners/Directors: ICAEW Members
P B Hilton, D Sisson
General Description: General practice.

ROBERT J GILL FCA
4 Rutland Drive, Mickleover, Derby, DE3 9FW

S 9
18 Merlin Way, Mickleover, Derby, DE3 0SL

S 9 LTD
18 Merlin Way, Mickleover, Derby, DE3 0SL

SIBBALDS LTD ◈
41 St Mary's Gate, Derby, DE1 3JX

SMITH COOPER ◈
Wilmot House, St James Court, Friar Gate, Derby DE1 1BT
Tel: 01332 332021
Resident Partners/Directors: ICAEW Members
A R Delve, A M Durbin, J P Farnsworth, J Morgan

TAX INVESTIGATION SERVICES
Longcroft Farmhouse, 31 Derby Road, Aston-on-Trent, Derby DE72 2AE
Tel: 01332 799815
Fax: 01332 799815
Email: help@taxtis.co.uk
Website: http://www.taxtis.co.uk

SPECIALISATIONS – TAXATION
Back Duty
Investigations

General Description: We specialise in HMRC enquiries - local compliance, special civil investigations, civil investigation of fraud, etc.

TOM DAY
Ashleigh, Barton Blount, Church Broughton, Derby DE65 5AP

V.G. CUNDY & CO
175 Ladybank Road, Mickleover, Derby, DE3 0QF
Tel: 01332 510718
Principal: ICAEW Member
V G Cundy

WILCOX & CO ◈
Smithy Farm, Twyford, Barrow on Trent, Derby DE73 7HJ

DEREHAM

BAXTERS
Mill Road Farmhouse, Low Road, North Tuddenham, Dereham NR20 3AB

HAWORTH & CO LTD
21 Market Place, Dereham, NR19 2AX
Tel: 01362 690022
Resident Partners/Directors: ICAEW Members
P J Haworth

HODGES & CO
62 Norwich Street, Dereham, NR19 1AD

JEMMETT FOX
The White House, High Street, Dereham, NR19 1DR

JEMMETT FOX ANGLIA LTD
The White House, High Street, Dereham, NR19 1DR
Tel: 01362 851118
Resident Partners/Directors: ICAEW Members
A M Fox

JEMMETT FOX (UK) LTD
The White House, High Street, Dereham, NR19 1DR

LARKING GOWEN ◈
1 Tavern Lane, Dereham, NR19 1PX
Tel: 01362 693318
Resident Partners/Directors: ICAEW Members
C J Greeves, S G Rudd

ROGER CLAXTON
2 The Glebe, Hockering, Dereham, NR20 3TX

WAYNE FLEMING ASSOCIATES LTD
Greenfields, Swanton Road, Dereham, NR20 4PS
Tel: 01362 852168
Resident Partners/Directors: ICAEW Members
W P Fleming

WILLIAM DANN & CO ◈
30-32 Norwich Street, Dereham, NR19 1BX

DEVIZES

CHARLTON BAKER
6/7 Market Place, Devizes, SN10 1HT

DAVID OWEN & CO
17 Market Place, Devizes, SN10 1BA
Tel: 01380 722211
Fax: 01380 729524
Email: accountants@dowen.com
Website: http://www.dowen.com
Resident Partners/Directors: ICAEW Members
P Bennett, M E Buckland, D Head, D Wiltshire
Non-resident Partners (ICAEW Members):
N J Gamage
Resident Partners (Non-ICAEW Members):
A M Coombes
Non-resident Partners (Non-ICAEW Members):
T A Roberts
Other Offices: 126 High Street, Marlborough
Registered by the ICAEW to carry out company audit work
Regulated by the ICAEW for a range of investment business activities
General Description: Established for over 100 years. Great emphasis is placed on partner contact and quality of service.

L E BULL & CO ★
Greystone House, 14 High Street, Devizes, SN10 1AY
Tel: 01380 723496
Resident Partners/Directors: ICAEW Members
J E Smith

DEWSBURY

FORREST BURLINSON
20 Owl Lane, Dewsbury, WF12 7RQ

NICHOLAS & CO
The Barn, 1 Nook Green, Thornhill, Dewsbury WF12 0BJ

WALTER DAWSON & SON
7 Wellington Road East, Dewsbury, WF13 1HF
Tel: 01924 462493
Fax: 01924 465389
Email: info@walterdawson.co.uk
Website: http://www.walterdawson.co.uk
Date Established: 1886
Resident Partners/Directors: ICAEW Members
G D Atkinson
Other Offices: 38 Little Horton Lane, Bradford BD5 0AL, Revenue Chambers, St Peter's Street, Huddersfield HD1 1DL, 9 Kerry Street, Horsforth, LS18 4AW
Registered by the ICAEW to carry out company audit work
Regulated by the ICAEW for a range of investment business activities

DIDCOT

J.R. HOWLAND
15 Bear Lane, North Moreton, Didcot, OX11 9AS

MARCHWOODS
3 Berry Lane, Blewbury, Didcot, OX11 9QJ

DISS

ANDREW BAGNALL
Wyndham House, The Street, Market Weston, Diss IP22 2NZ

CATE ALLWOOD
12 Church Close, Pulham St Mary, Diss, Norfolk IP21 4RR

DERRICK SHEPPARD & CO
Orchard House, Back Lane, Garboldisham, Diss IP22 2SD

HAINES WATTS ◈
8 Hopper Way, Diss Business Park, Diss, IP22 4GT
Tel: 01379 640555
Resident Partners/Directors: ICAEW Members
G M Laughton, A S Minifie, M Neale, P D Sumpter

KEITH S CHAPMAN
15A Market Place, Diss, IP22 4AB
Tel: 01379 641885
Principal: ICAEW Member
K S Chapman

LARKING GOWEN ◈
Faiers House, Gilray Road, Diss, IP22 4WR
Tel: 01379 651067
Resident Partners/Directors: ICAEW Members
G S Pilcher, I S Webster

LOVEWELL BLAKE ◈
Durrants, 19 St Nicholas Street, Diss, IP22 4LB
Tel: 01379 640343
Email: pdy@lovewell-blake.co.uk
Website: http://www.lovewell-blake.co.uk
Non-resident Partners (ICAEW Members):
P D Young
General Description: The practice has 21 partners and our other offices are listed under our Norwich entry.

ROWAN BLAXLAND
Grove Lodge, Grove Road, Brockdish, Diss IP21 4JP

WAVENEY ACCOUNTANTS LTD ◈
4b Church Street, Diss, IP22 4DD
Tel: 01379 640640
Fax: 01379 650459
Email: diss@newmans-online.co.uk
Resident Partners/Directors: ICAEW Members
L R Newman
Other Offices: Beccles

DONCASTER

ALAN HOLLOWAY
18 Lumley Drive, Tickhill, Doncaster, DN11 9QE

ALAN ROBERTS & COMPANY LTD ◈
Chartered Chambers, 294 Balby Road, Balby, Doncaster DN4 0QF
Tel: 01302 311777
Resident Partners/Directors: ICAEW Members
A Roberts

ALLOTTS
Sidings Court, Lakeside, Doncaster, DN4 5NU
Tel: 01302 349218
Website: http://www.allotts.co.uk
Resident Partners/Directors: ICAEW Members
S Pepper
Resident Partners (Non-ICAEW Members):
K Williamson

ARTHUR WIGGLESWORTH & CO LTD
1-2 Albion Place, Doncaster, DN1 2EG
Tel: 01302 364011
Resident Partners/Directors: ICAEW Members
A Wigglesworth

BLAND & CO ◈
70 Balby Road, Doncaster, DN4 0JL
Tel: 01302 730800
Principal: ICAEW Member
D V Bland

BLENKINSOP & CO
1 Shardlow Gardens, Bessacarr, Doncaster, DN4 6UB

BOND PARTNERS LLP
Unit 1 Farriers Court, Horse Fair Green, Thorne, Doncaster DN8 5EE

BRODERICKS GBC ★
Melbourne House, 27 Thorne Road, Doncaster, DN1 2EZ

CERTAX ACCOUNTING (DONCASTER)
117 Wivelsfield Road, Doncaster, DN4 0UY

CROZIER JONES & CO ★
5 Thorne Road, Doncaster, DN1 2HJ

D & J RANDLES LTD
203 Askern Road, Bentley, Doncaster, DN5 OJR

D.C. BROWN
48 Airedale Avenue, Tickhill, Doncaster, DN11 9UD

D.V. BLAND LTD ◈
70 Balby Road, Doncaster, DN4 0JL
Tel: 01302 730800
Resident Partners/Directors: ICAEW Members
D V Bland

DAVID KIRK & CO
2 Crompton Road, Crompton Business Park, Doncaster, DN2 4PJ
Tel: 01302 767461
Principal: ICAEW Member
D G Kirk

GILDERSON & CO
Hawthorn House, High Levels, Sandtoft, Doncaster DN8 5SJ
Tel: 01777 249144
Principal: ICAEW Member
J E Gilderson

GLOVER & CO
13/15 Netherhall Road, Doncaster, DN1 2PH
Tel: 01302 340800
Fax: 01302 340888
Email: info@gloverandco.com
Website: http://www.gloverandco.com
Date Established: 1886
Resident Partners/Directors: ICAEW Members
P S Mellor, N A Williams

GLOVER & CO ◈
22 High Street, Epworth, Doncaster, DN9 1ET
Tel: 01427 872303

HAWSONS
5 Sidings Court, White Rose Way, Doncaster, DN4 5NU

CHUA LOWE & CO
5 Crookhill Road, Conisbrough, Doncaster, DN12 2AD

CHUA LOWE & CO
5 Crookhill Road, Conisbrough, Doncaster, DN12 2AD

CHUA LOWE (JB) LTD
5 Crookhill Road, Conisbrough, Doncaster, DN12 2AD
Tel: 01709 868864
Resident Partners/Directors: ICAEW Members
L L Lowe

MICHAEL D. JONES
Chelwood, Carrhouse Road, Belton, Doncaster DN9 1PG

MICHAEL FENTON & CO LTD
1 Railway Court, Ten Pound Walk, Doncaster, DN4 5FB

ROYSTON PARKIN ★ ◈
5 Railway Court, Ten Pound Walk, Doncaster, DN4 5FB
Tel: 01302 320444
Fax: 01302 342604
Email: doncaster@roystonparkin.co.uk
Resident Partners/Directors: ICAEW Members
L C Pridmore
Registered by another RSB to carry out company audit work
Licensed by another DPB to carry on investment business

SPECIALISATIONS – SECTOR

Construction
Dentists/Opticians
Retailers

General Description: We are a small but expanding firm specialising in general practice and business advice.

SMITH CRAVEN
Kelham House, Kelham Street, Doncaster, DN1 3RE

TENON LTD
Richmonds House, White Rose Way, Doncaster, DN4 5JH
Tel: 01302 762839

W. BRIAN COPLEY
Barn Cottage, 7 Castlegate, Tickhill, Doncaster DN11 9QP
Tel: 01302 759429
Principal: ICAEW Member
W B Copley

WWW ATKINSONCOCOM LTD
5 Mill Lane, Warmsworth, Doncaster, DN4 9RG

DORCHESTER

COLIN MOREY
Flat 3, Herrison House, Charlton Down, Dorchester DT2 9XA
Tel: 01305 259792
Principal: ICAEW Member
C Morey

COYNE BUTTERWORTH & CHALMERS
48 High West Street, Dorchester, DT1 1UT

COYNE BUTTERWORTH REID LTD
48 High West Street, Dorchester, DT1 1UT
Tel: 01305 263000
Resident Partners/Directors: ICAEW Members
D R Gordon-Smith, T Houlberg, D C W Reid

EDWARDS & KEEPING ◈
Unity Chambers, 34 High East Street, Dorchester, DT1 1HA
Tel: 01305 251333
Email: office@edwardsandkeeping.co.uk
Website: http://www.edwardsandkeeping.co.uk
Training Contracts Available.
Resident Partners/Directors: ICAEW Members
I M Carrington, R J A Edwards, K Hobbs, M L Meyers
Resident Partners (Non-ICAEW Members):
R J Upshall
Registered by the ICAEW to carry out company audit work
Regulated by the ICAEW for a range of investment business activities

INVESTOR IN PEOPLE

SPECIALISATIONS – SECTOR

Agriculture

General Description: A long established Dorset firm providing a personal service to a wide range of personal and business clients.

J.S. PHILLIPS
Mill House, Dewlish, Dorchester, DT2 7LT

JOY, LANE & CO ◈
4 South Terrace, South Street, Dorchester, DT1 1DE
Tel: 01305 262293
Principal: ICAEW Member
T R Stockley

LOFTS & CO ◈
6 South Terrace, South Street, Dorchester, DT1 1DE
Tel: 01305 250502
Principal: ICAEW Member
M C Lofts

M.W. DALE
10 Hillfort Close, Dorchester, DT1 2QT

NIGEL WOODRUFF
24 Cornwall Road, Dorchester, DT1 1RX

PERKS SIMM
The Old Rectory, South Walks Road, Dorchester, DT1 1DT

PUGSLEY REVILL ★
18 High West Street, Dorchester, DT1 1UW

READ WOODRUFF ★
24 Cornwall Road, Dorchester, DT1 1RX

DORKING

ACCOUNTING & BUSINESS LTD
Barn Studios, Gaterounds, Parkgate Road, Newdigate, Dorking RH5 5AJ

ACQUIS LTD
The Bell House, 57 West Street, Dorking, RH4 1BS

BARRY MCCANN
Westfield, 10 Westfield Gardens, Westcott Road, Dorking RH4 3DX

BULLIMORES LLP ◈
Old Printers Yard, 156 South Street, Dorking, RH4 2HF
Tel: 01306 880880
Fax: 01306 889281
Email: partners@bullimores.co.uk
Website: http://www.bullimores.co.uk
Resident Partners/Directors: ICAEW Members
N Boot, M J Brett, T Edwards
Registered by the ICAEW to carry out company audit work
Regulated by the ICAEW for a range of investment business activities

C.J. TANNER
6 Rose Hill, Dorking, RH4 2EG

C K SPELLER ◈
2 Claremont Court, Rose Hill, Dorking, RH4 2EE
Tel: 01306 502625
Principal: ICAEW Member
C K Speller

COOKSEY PERRY & CO
Wayside, Old Horsham Road, Beare Green, Dorking RH5 4RB

D.R. ANDREWS
Northacre, Deerleap Road, Westcott, Dorking RH4 3LE

ELLIS ATKINS
1 Paper Mews, 330 High Street, Dorking, RH4 2TU

H.K. DAY & CO
83 South Street, Dorking, RH4 2JU
Tel: 01306 886456
Principal: ICAEW Member
H K Day

JAMES HARMAN & CO
The Atrium, Curtis Road, Dorking, RH4 1XA
Tel: 01306 646484
Resident Partners/Directors: ICAEW Members
H J W Harman

JOHN WHITEHOUSE FCA
The Brown House, Holmbury St Mary, Dorking, RH5 6PF

LANGLEY ASSOCIATES
Milton Heath House, Westcott Road, Dorking, RH4 3NB

LLOYD ACCOUNTING
Chapel Cottage, Chapel Lane, Westhumble, Dorking RH5 6AY
Tel: 01306 741949
Principal: ICAEW Member
G A Lloyd

M.J. PINCHES
3 Rose Hill Arch Mews, Rose Hill, Dorking, RH4 2ER
Tel: 01306 877565
Principal: ICAEW Member
M J Pinches

MAPPERSON PRICE
286a High Street, Dorking, RH4 1QT

NEWTON & CO ◈
Ranmore House, 19 Ranmore Road, Dorking, RH4 1HE
Tel: 01306 884208
Fax: 01306 882877
Email: newton-co@tiscali.co.uk
Date Established: 1972
Principal: ICAEW Member
D H Jennings
Registered by the ICAEW to carry out company audit work
Regulated by the ICAEW for a range of investment business activities

REED & CO
Hallings Hatch, Parkgate Road, Newdigate, Dorking RH5 5DY

REED ACCOUNTS & TAX LTD
Hallings Hatch, Parkgate Road, Newdigate, Dorking RH5 5DY

RICHARD MATTHEW LTD
17 Broomfield Park, Westcott, Dorking, RH4 3QQ

RM PROFESSIONAL PRACTICE LTD
Forge House, Ansell Road, Dorking, RH4 1UN
Tel: 01306 885024
Resident Partners/Directors: ICAEW Members
S R M Knights

SIMON D H PULLAR
Monks Tower, Honeywood Lane, Okewood Hill, Dorking RH5 5PZ

STONE R. DUNCAN & CO
Sunrise House, Newdigate Road, Beare Green, Dorking RH5 4QD
Tel: 01306 713172
Principal: ICAEW Member
R D Stone

STONEBRIDGE PARTNERSHIP
1 Chalkpit Terrace, Dorking, RH4 1HX

THE STONEBRIDGE PARTNERSHIP LTD
1 Chalkpit Terrace, Dorking, RH4 1HX
Tel: 01306 640605
Resident Partners/Directors: ICAEW Members
N K Privett

TANNER & CO
6 Rose Hill, Dorking, RH4 2EG

TATTERSALLS
Concept House, 3 Dene Street, Dorking, RH4 2DR
Tel: 01306 889910

TJS CONSULTANTS
Ridgeway, Westfield, Hoe Lane, Abinger Hammer, Dorking RH5 6RS

WHITTINGTON & CO
83 South Street, Dorking, RH4 2JU
Tel: 01306 743326
Principal: ICAEW Member
C C Whittington

DOVER

BEVERTON & CO
3 The Old Print House, Russell Street, Dover, CT16 1PX

G.R. WEBB
17 Bernard Gardens, Shepherdswell, Dover, CT15 7PH

MCCABE FORD WILLIAMS
Charlton House, Dour Street, Dover, CT16 1BL
Tel: 01304 204006
Resident Partners/Directors: ICAEW Members
I D Pascall, J D Sheather, T J Shipley

R.F. BAVINGTON-JONES
1 Oak Cottages, Cox Hill, Shepherdswell, Dover CT15 7NB
Tel: 01304 832228
Principal: ICAEW Member
R.F. Bavington-Jones

REEVES+NEYLAN LLP
77 Biggin Street, Dover, CT16 1BB

SPAIN BROTHERS & CO ◈
5 St James's Street, Dover, CT16 1QD
Tel: 01304 201994
Fax: 01304 240117
Email: mminus@spainbrothers.co.uk
Resident Partners/Directors: ICAEW Members
M E J Minus
Registered by the ICAEW to carry out company audit work

SUSAN KING ACA
Hazlemere, 115 London Road, Temple Ewell, Dover CT16 3BY
Tel: 01304 820753
Principal: ICAEW Member
Susan King

DOWNHAM MARKET

FULCRUM
The Old Orchard, Bexwell Road, Downham Market, PE38 9LJ

MAPUS-SMITH & LEMMON LLP
23 London Road, Downham Market, PE38 9BJ
Tel: 01366 383300
Website: http://www.mapus.co.uk
Resident Partners/Directors: ICAEW Members
P E Farrow
Registered by the ICAEW to carry out company audit work
Regulated by the ICAEW for a range of investment business activities

MELLOR BELLAMY ★
27/29 Bridge Street, Downham Market, PE38 9DW

DRIFFIELD

BLYTH & CO CORPORATE SERVICES LTD
Church View Cottage, Fordon Road, Burton Fleming, Driffield YO25 3PS
Tel: 01262 470566
Resident Partners/Directors: ICAEW Members
C R Blyth

HOWARD WALKER
Ivy House, Goodmanham Road, Middleton on the Wolds, Driffield YO25 9DE

JACKSON ROBSON LICENCE LTD ◈
33/35 Exchange Street, Driffield, YO25 6LL
Tel: 01377 252195
Resident Partners/Directors: ICAEW Members
A C Ludlam, R M Miles, G R Mountain, P M Robson, A R Wilson

REDMAN NICHOLS
Maclaren House, Skerne Road, Driffield, YO25 6PN
Tel: 01377 257788
Principal: ICAEW Member
A J Nichols

ULLYOTT
6 George Street, Driffield, YO25 6RA
Tel: 01377 272341

ULLYOTT LTD
6 George Street, Driffield, YO25 6RA
Tel: 01377 272341
Resident Partners/Directors: ICAEW Members
S J Ullyott

DROITWICH

BALLARD DALE SYREE WATSON LLP
Oakmoore Court, Kingswood Road, Hampton Lovett, Droitwich WR9 0QH
Tel: 01905 794504
Fax: 01905 795281
Resident Partners/Directors: ICAEW Members
G W Ballard, D B Dale, E H Peters, J A Syree, M A Watson

JOHN A.L.CARSLAKE
The Old Thatch, Sale Green, Droitwich, WR9 7LP
Tel: 01905 391639
Principal: ICAEW Member
J A L Carslake

ORMEROD RUTTER LTD
The Oakley, Kidderminster Road, Droitwich, WR9 9AY
Tel: 01905 777600
Fax: 01905 778584
Email: mail@ormerodrutter.co.uk
Website: http://www.ormerodrutter.co.uk
Resident Partners/Directors: ICAEW Members
C A McGrory

SPECIALISATIONS – FORENSIC ACCOUNTING

Expert Witnesses in Litigation
Forensic Accounting

PAUL ALTON ◈
Admin House, 6 North Street, Droitwich, WR9 8JB
Tel: 0121 453 5432
Website: http://www.paulalton.co.uk
Principal: ICAEW Member
Paul Alton

PRICE PEARSON WHEATLEY
Clarendon House, 14 St Andrews Street, Droitwich, WR9 8DY
Tel: 01905 773143
Resident Partners/Directors: ICAEW Members
J S Wheatley

R.T BRIGHTON ◈
12 Wensleydale, Droitwich, WR9 8PF
Tel: 01905 775395

R.T BRIGHTON LTD ◈
12 Wensleydale, Droitwich, WR9 8PF
Tel: 01905 775395
Resident Partners/Directors: ICAEW Members
R T Brighton

RICHARD SHAW
24 Bagehott Road, Droitwich, WR9 8UH

DRONFIELD

D M LINELL & CO
Design House, 27 Chesterfield Road, Dronfield, Derbyshire S18 2XA

D M LINELL & CO LTD
Design House, 27 Chesterfield Road, Dronfield, Derbyshire S18 2WZ

IAN R. COLLINS & CO
The Bridge House, Mill Lane, Dronfield, S18 2XL

J.E.S. DUNN
Yew Tree Cottage, Unthank Lane, Holmesfield, Dronfield S18 7WF
Tel: 0114 289 0684
Principal: ICAEW Member
J E S Dunn

JOHN S DANSON & CO
35 Salisbury Road, Dronfield, Derbyshire, S18 1UG

DUDLEY

AGS ACCOUNTANTS AND BUSINESS ADVISORS LTD
Castle Court 2, Castlegate Way, Dudley, DY1 4RH

CK
Castle Court 2, Castlegate Way, Dudley, DY1 4RH

CK ACCOUNTING SERVICES
Castle Court 2, Castlegate Way, Dudley, DY1 4RH

CK AUDIT
Castle Court 2, Castlegate Way, Dudley, DY1 4RH

CK CORPORATE FINANCE
Castle Court 2, Castlegate Way, Dudley, DY1 4RH
Tel: 01384 245200

G.P. BROOKES
24 Abbotsford Drive, Dudley, DY1 2HD
Tel: 01384 233813
Email: garybrookes@blueyonder.co.uk
Principal: ICAEW Member
G P Brookes
Registered by the ICAEW to carry out company audit work

SPECIALISATIONS – SECTOR

Charities
Church

General Description: Specialist in all aspects of not-for-profit sector.

GIBBENS WATERFIELD LTD
Priory House, 2 Priory Road, Dudley, DY1 1HH

HOMER KNOTT & CO
Hawthorne House, Charlotte Street, Dudley, DY1 1TD

JOHN D CAPEWELL
47 Hockley Lane, Netherton, Dudley, DY2 0JW

MANEX ACCOUNTANTS LTD
8 Castle Court 2, Castle Gate Way, Dudley, DY1 4RA
Tel: 0845 408 5151
Resident Partners/Directors: ICAEW Members
C J Meehan

MAZARS CORPORATE FINANCE LTD ◈
The Broadway, Dudley, DY1 4PY

MAZARS LLP ◈
The Broadway, Dudley, DY1 4PY
Tel: 01384 230432
Resident Partners/Directors: ICAEW Members
D G Chapman, I G M Holder, G B Jones, P M Lucas, P Waller
Registered by the ICAEW to carry out company audit work

Authorised and regulated by the Financial Services Authority for investment business

NEIL WESTWOOD & CO
101 Dixons Green Road, Dudley, DY2 7DJ
Tel: 01384 253232
Principal: ICAEW Member
N A Westwood
See display advertisement near this entry.

PINNER DARLINGTON
Broughton House, 187 Wolverhampton Street, Dudley, DY1 3AD
Tel: 01384 254207
Resident Partners/Directors: ICAEW Members
R Pinner

POOLE WATERFIELD ★ ◈
Priory House, Priory Road, Dudley, DY1 1HH

PPG ACCOUNTANTS LTD
Ferndale House, 3 Firs Street, Dudley, DY2 7DN

PRICE PEARSON ◈
Finch House, 28-30 Wolverhampton Street, Dudley, DY1 1DB
Tel: 01384 456780
Fax: 01384 455991
Email: info@pricepearson.com
Website: http://www.pricepearson.com
Training Contracts Available.
Resident Partners/Directors: ICAEW Members
V Brassington, N C Davis, A J Homer, F J McKay, D E Price, K A Turner, A Williams
Resident Partners (Non-ICAEW Members):
J N Lucas, R M Burrows, P Y Cox
Non-resident Partners (Non-ICAEW Members):
S Garrington, C Cooper
Other Offices:6 Church Street, Kidderminster
(Tel: 01562 744444)
Registered by the ICAEW to carry out company audit work
Regulated by the ICAEW for a range of investment business activities

SPECIALISATIONS – AUDIT & ASSURANCE

Audit — Private Company

SPECIALISATIONS – BUSINESS & GENERAL ADVICE

Acquisitions and Mergers
Disposal of Businesses

SPECIALISATIONS – TAXATION

Back Duty

PRIDE
Polymer Court, Hope Street, Dudley, DY2 8RS

ROBERT BROWN & CO
21 Westley Street, Dudley, DY1 1TS
Tel: 01384 213868
Email: enquiries@robert-brown.co.uk
Website: http://www.robert-brown.co.uk
Principal: ICAEW Member
R W I Brown
Registered by the ICAEW to carry out company audit work

RONALD SHAW & CO
Ashford House, 95 Dixons Green, Dudley, DY2 7DJ

SAXON & CO
Kings Chambers, Queens Cross, Dudley, DY1 1QT

TAXWISE
Finch House, 28-30 Wolverhampton Street, Dudley, DY1 1DB

WALKER HUBBLE
5 Parsons Street, Dudley, DY1 1JJ

WORTON ROCK LTD ◈
Churchfield House, 36 Vicar Street, Dudley, DY2 8RG
Tel: 01384 254453
Fax: 01384 456218
Email: dudley@wortonrock.co.uk
Website: http://www.wortonrock.co.uk
Resident Partners (Non-ICAEW Members):
W D Chinn

INVESTOR IN PEOPLE

YATES & CO
Grazebrook House, Peartree Lane, Dudley, DY2 0XW

DUKINFIELD

FLETCHERS ◈
Albion House, 163-167 King Street, Dukinfield, SK16 4LF

GILLIAN TAYLOR
56 Salisbury Drive, Dukinfield, SK16 5DL

J W WALSH ACCOUNTANTS LTD ◈
Albion House, 163-167 King Street, Dukinfield, SK16 4LF
Tel: 0161 339 7007
Resident Partners/Directors: ICAEW Members
J W Walsh

DULVERTON

CATHERINE YANDLE
9 Amory Road, Dulverton, TA22 9DY

DUNMOW

ALISON WHITE FCA
Combe Cottage, Stortford Road, Leaden Roding, Dunmow CM6 1RB

BIRD LUCKIN LTD
Gateway House, 42 High Street, Dunmow, CM6 1AH
Tel: 01371 873873
Fax: 01371 876401
Email: enquiries@bird-luckin.co.uk
Website: http://www.bird-luckin.co.uk
Resident Partners/Directors: ICAEW Members
A Barnwell, J Gallant, A L Meakin
Other Offices: Chelmsford
Registered by the ICAEW to carry out company audit work

SPECIALISATIONS – AUDIT & ASSURANCE

Assurance Services
Audit

SPECIALISATIONS – BUSINESS & GENERAL ADVICE

Company Secretarial Service
Management Accounting Consultancy

SPECIALISATIONS – FINANCIAL REPORTING

Accounts Preparation

SPECIALISATIONS – IT

Computer Systems and Consultancy

SPECIALISATIONS – SECTOR

Corporate

SPECIALISATIONS – TAXATION

Payroll Service and Advice
Taxation

C.RENGERT & CO
Chequers, Watling Lane, Thaxted, Dunmow CM6 2QY
Tel: 01371 830500
Principal: ICAEW Member
C Rengert

FORBES
Taylors Piece, 9-11 Stortford Road, Great Dunmow, Dunmow CM6 1DA

FORBES LTD
Taylors Piece, 9-11 Stortford Road, Great Dunmow, Dunmow CM6 1DA

IAN SHAW
Mandalay, Chelmsford Road, Felsted, Dunmow CM6 3EP

J ALLEN & CO
Clayton House, 12 High Street, Dunmow, CM6 1AG

M.P. CURTIS
New Barn Farm, Lindsell, Dunmow, CM6 3QH

ROWLAND COWEN & CO
1 Holders Meadows, Holders Green, Lindsell, Dunmow CM6 3QQ

DUNSTABLE

A.B. DEVITT
39 Westoning Road, Harlington, Dunstable, LU5 6PB

ANGELL PINDER LTD ◈
1 Victoria Street, Dunstable, LU6 3AZ
Tel: 01582 600048
Resident Partners/Directors: ICAEW Members
M Angell, S J Pinder

CLIFFORD BYGRAVE
The Rustlings, Valley Close, Studham, Dunstable LU6 2QN
Tel: 01582 872070
Principal: ICAEW Member
C Bygrave

G.J. TAYLOR
31a Evelyn Road, Dunstable, LU5 4NG
Tel: 01582 668620
Principal: ICAEW Member
G J Taylor

HIGGINSON & CO (UK) LTD
3 Kensworth Gate, 200-204 High Street South, Dunstable, LU6 3HS

LANDERS
Church View Chambers, 38 Market Square, Toddington, Dunstable LU5 6BS

LANDERS ACCOUNTANTS LTD
Church View Chambers, 38 Market Square, Toddington, Dunstable LU5 6BS
Tel: 01525 873922
Resident Partners/Directors: ICAEW Members
R Brown

LESLIE E. CASTON
8 Bower Close, Eaton Bray, Dunstable, LU6 2DU

M.A. SUTCLIFFE
213 Castle Hill Road, Totternhoe, Dunstable, LU6 2DA

MINNEY & CO
59 Union Street, Dunstable, LU6 1EX

N.R.DUNCOMBE
Green Spinney, Oldhill Wood, Studham, Dunstable LU6 2NF
Tel: 01582 872786
Principal: ICAEW Member
N R Duncombe

PROFIT PLUS (UK) LTD
Queens Chambers, Eleanors Cross, Dunstable, LU6 1SU

ROGERS
20 St Georges Close, Toddington, LU5 6AT
Tel: 01525 872675
Resident Partners/Directors: ICAEW Members
F J Rogers

STOTEN GILLAM LTD ◈
Alban House, 99 High Street South, Dunstable, LU6 3SF
Tel: 01582 608601
Resident Partners/Directors: ICAEW Members
M L McLaren, C J Trevor, J Wright

SUZANNE SPICER
7 Keswick Close, Dunstable, LU6 3AW
Tel: 01582 662815
Principal: ICAEW Member
S Spicer

THATCHERS ◈
13 Dunstable Road, Studham, Dunstable, LU6 2QG
Tel: 01582 873111
Principal: ICAEW Member
J E Bassil

DURHAM

AJD ACCOUNTING
17 Apperley Avenue, High Shincliffe, Durham, DH1 2TY

BARBARA EWIN LTD
Pear Tree Cottage, Old Durham, Durham, DH1 2RY
Tel: 0191 386 1791
Resident Partners/Directors: ICAEW Members
B A Ewin

CHIPCHASE, ROBSON & CO
3 Springfield Park, Durham, DH1 4LS
Tel: 0191 386 8172
Principal: ICAEW Member
R E Robson

CLIVE OWEN & CO LLP ◈
Aire House, Mandale Business Park, Belmont Ind Estate, Durham DH1 1TH

J.N STRAUGHAN & CO
Fram Well House, Framwelgate, Durham, DH1 5SU
Tel: 0191 384 7783
Resident Partners/Directors: ICAEW Members
P R Craig, W H Sawyer

JANE ASCROFT ACCOUNTANCY LTD
Farfalls House, New Brancepeth, Durham, DH7 7HP
Tel: 0191 373 3290
Resident Partners/Directors: ICAEW Members
J Ascroft

SPECIALISATIONS – SECTOR

Charities

JOHN E GAYER LTD ◈
Hall Farm, Mordon, Durham, TS21 2EY
Tel: 01740 620324
Resident Partners/Directors: ICAEW Members
J E Gayer

JONES BOYD
16/17 Marshall Terrace, Gilesgate Moor, Durham, DH1 2HX

M.L. PEARSON
Duncruachan House, Potters Bank, Durham, DH1 3RR

N.I. COULTHARD ◈
47 Lindisfarne Road, Newton Hall, Durham, DH1 5YH
Tel: 0191 384 3403
Principal: ICAEW Member
N I Coulthard

PULLAN BARNES
49 Front Street, Framwellgate Moor, Durham, DH1 5BL

RIBCHESTERS ◈
67 Saddler Street, Durham, DH1 3NP
Tel: 0191 384 8581
Resident Partners/Directors: ICAEW Members
D M Armstrong, J D Holloway, A Ribchester

DURSLEY

BURTON SWEET ◈
Prospect House, 5 May Lane, Dursley, GL11 4JH
Tel: 01453 542483
Resident Partners/Directors: ICAEW Members
N M Kingston

THE HANSON PARTNERSHIP LLP
Unit 3, Wick Business Centre, Upper Wick, Dursley GL11 6DE

EAST BOLDON

BOND PARTNERS LLP
5A Station Terrence, East Boldon, NE36 0ED

BREWSTER & CO
5a Station Terrace, East Boldon, NE36 0LJ
Tel: 0191 519 3979
Principal: ICAEW Member
C T Brewster

EAST GRINSTEAD

AIMS - SIMON FISHBURN FCA
10 The Old Convent, East Grinstead, RH19 3RS

ALEXANDRA DURRANT
10A/12A High Street, East Grinstead, RH19 3AW
Tel: 01342 311133
Fax: 01342 311135
Email: alexandra@alexandra-durrant.co.uk
Principal: ICAEW Member
A B Durrant
Registered by the ICAEW to carry out company audit work
General Description: Sole Practitioner, from May 1993, specialising in small business, partnership, sole traders, limited companies with particular skills in PAYE/NI advice. Lecturer and author on payroll and PAYE/NI matters.

ANTHONY MUNDY & CO
14 High Street, East Grinstead, RH19 3AW

ANTHONY MUNDY & CO LTD
14 High Street, East Grinstead, RH19 3AW

BEECHCROFT ASSOCIATES LTD
The Barn, Park Farm, Woodcock Hill, Felbridge, East Grinstead RH19 2RB

BROOKS & CO
Hampton House, High Street, East Grinstead, RH19 3AW
Tel: 01342 317789
Email: mharding@brooksand.co.uk
Resident Partners/Directors: ICAEW Members
K J Dixon
Non-resident Partners (ICAEW Members):
R Ferris, M J Harding
Resident Partners (Non-ICAEW Members):
F Down
Non-resident Partners (Non-ICAEW Members):
S A Sundaran
Other Offices: Sutton
Registered by the ICAEW to carry out company audit work
Regulated by the ICAEW for a range of investment business activities

SPECIALISATIONS – IT

Computerised Accounting Systems

Languages Spoken:
French

DEREK FIELD & CO ★
2nd Floor, Crown House, 37 High Street, East Grinstead RH19 3AF

HOCKLEY WRIGHT & CO LTD
Berkeley House, 18 Station Road, East Grinstead, RH19 1DJ
Tel: 01342 301099
Resident Partners/Directors: ICAEW Members
J A Pinard, J H Wright, K D H Wright

JOHN F HALLMARK
Moonrakers, 29 Overton Shaw, East Grinstead, RH19 2HN

LINGFIELD PARTNERS LLP
The Barn, Park Farm, Felbridge, East Grinstead RH19 2RB

LITHGOW, NELSON & CO
Moor Hall, Sandhawes Hill, East Grinstead, RH19 3NR

MICHAEL J DIEBEL
Dalsland, Sandy Lane, East Grinstead, RH19 3LP

MICHAEL W I WHYKE
20 Marlpit Road, Sharpthorne, East Grinstead, RH19 4PD

MONTGOMERY MCNALLY & CO
4 Greenstede Avenue, East Grinstead, RH19 3HZ
Principal: ICAEW Member
A C Pope

PLACE CAMPBELL ★
Wilmington House, High Street, East Grinstead, RH19 3AU
Tel: 01342 324321
Fax: 01342 316106
Email: mail@placecampbell.com
DX: 300219 EAST GRINSTEAD
Website: http://www.placecampbell.com
Resident Partners/Directors: ICAEW Members
N J Avis, R G C Bridger, E A Monk, M D Watkins
Resident Partners (Non-ICAEW Members):
J J Lawrence, J A Constantine

SPECIALISATIONS – SECTOR

Barristers

PLACE FLIGHT
Montrose House, 22 Christopher Road, East Grinstead, RH19 3BT
Tel: 01342 319333
Fax: 01342 317966
Email: placeflight@pavilion.co.uk
Principal: ICAEW Member
G L Flight
Registered by the ICAEW to carry out company audit work
Regulated by the ICAEW for a range of investment business activities

S.E.WOOD
Fieldings, 6 Wheelers Way, Felbridge, East Grinstead RH19 2QJ
Tel: 01342 325273
Principal: ICAEW Member
S E Wood

EAST MOLESEY

CHRISTIE BUCHANAN
Bridge House, 11 Creek Road, East Molesey, KT8 9BE
Tel: 020 8783 1000
Principal: ICAEW Member
H A Adamjee

SPECIALISATIONS – BUSINESS & GENERAL ADVICE

Outsourcing - Financial Services

SPECIALISATIONS – SECTOR

Schools

SPECIALISATIONS – TAXATION

Payroll Service and Advice

HUGHES COLLETT LTD
Bridge House, 11 Creek Road, East Molesey, KT8 9BE

NEWBY CROUCH
Ember House, 35-37 Creek Road, East Molesey, KT8 9BE

OXLEY & CO
17 Manor Road, East Molesey, KT8 9JU

EASTBOURNE

ADVANTA
29 Gildredge Road, Eastbourne, BN21 4RU
Tel: 01323 411222

ADVANTA BUSINESS SERVICES LTD
29 Gildredge Road, Eastbourne, BN21 4RU
Tel: 01323 411222
Email: info@advanta-ca.com
Website: http://www.advanta-ca.com
Resident Partners/Directors: ICAEW Members
P Diomedou, M S Toghill

AUKETT & CO
Gildredge House, 5 Gildredge Road, Eastbourne, BN21 4RB
Tel: 01323 646548
Principal: ICAEW Member
D R Aukett

BREEZE & ASSOCIATES LTD
5 Cornfield Terrace, Eastbourne, BN21 4NN
Tel: 01323 411416
Resident Partners/Directors: ICAEW Members
A L Breeze, C K Marsh, G A Pengelly

BREWER & CO
1 Abbotsleigh House, 3 Dalton Road, Eastbourne, BN20 7NP

BREWER & COMPANY LTD
1 Abbotsleigh House, 3 Dalton Road, Eastbourne, BN20 7NP

BRIAN R. ETHERIDGE
3 Mountney Road, Eastbourne, BN21 1RJ
Tel: 01323 730053
Principal: ICAEW Member
B R Etheridge

CLIFTON PAGE WOOD ◈
11a Gildredge Road, Eastbourne, BN21 4RB
Tel: 01323 640338
Principal: ICAEW Member
I P J Clifton
Registered by the ICAEW to carry out company audit work

COLIN F LUCK
105 Baldwin Avenue, Eastbourne, BN21 1UL
Tel: 01323 641134
Principal: ICAEW Member
C F Luck

DAVID C MERRICK & CO
11 Glebe Close, Old Town, Eastbourne, BN20 8AW

DDR SECURITIES LTD ◈
22 New Upperton Road, Eastbourne, BN2 1NU
Tel: 0845 130 4385
Resident Partners/Directors: ICAEW Members
D C Rose

DOMINIC HILL ASSOCIATES LTD ◈
Archer House, Britland Estate, Northbourne Road, Eastbourne BN22 8PW
Tel: 01323 649509
Resident Partners/Directors: ICAEW Members
P D Hill

FINDLAY JAMES
21 Gardner Close, Eastbourne, BN23 6DQ

FREARSON & CO ◈
187 Ringwood Road, Eastbourne, BN22 8UW

GEORGE SCURRY & CO ◈
Westmead, 8 Warren Close, Eastbourne, BN20 7TY
Tel: 01323 641966
Principal: ICAEW Member
G M Scurry

HONEY BARRETT LTD ◈
53 Gildredge Road, Eastbourne, BN21 4SF
Tel: 01323 412277
Resident Partners/Directors: ICAEW Members
P A J Knight
Resident Partners (Non-ICAEW Members):
C E Cole
Registered by the ICAEW to carry out company audit work
Regulated by the ICAEW for a range of investment business activities
Languages Spoken:
French

HUMPHREY & CO ◈
7-9 The Avenue, Eastbourne, BN21 3YA
Tel: 01323 730631
Website: http://www.humph.co.uk
Training Contracts Available.
Resident Partners/Directors: ICAEW Members
N D Ellison, E W Hylton, M J Macefield, R J F McTear, C P Potter, A M Robinson, P G Skilbeck, A G Smith
Other Offices: Curtis House, 34 Third Avenue, Hove, East Sussex BN3 2PD

JOHN CONNELL & CO
39 Park Lane, Eastbourne, BN21 2UY
Tel: 01323 502935
Principal: ICAEW Member
J C S Connell

JOHN F.D. ASHBY
Braeside, 39 Silverdale Road, Eastbourne, BN20 7AT

KENNETH M. BRADSHAW
44 Pashley Road, Eastbourne, BN20 8EA
Tel: 01323 411243
Fax: 01323 725991
Email: kenmbrad@yahoo.co.uk
Principal: ICAEW Member
K M Bradshaw

SPECIALISATIONS – FINANCIAL REPORTING

Accounts Preparation

SPECIALISATIONS – TAXATION

Taxation

LMDB LTD ◈
Railview Lofts, 19c Commercial Road, Eastbourne, BN21 3XE
Tel: 01323 732748
Resident Partners/Directors: ICAEW Members
R M S Booth, S Diomedou

LMDB ACCOUNTANTS ◈
Railview Lofts, 19c Commercial Road, Eastbourne, BN21 3XE
Tel: 01323 732748

OBC
2 Upperton Gardens, Eastbourne, BN21 2AH

OBC THE ACCOUNTANTS LTD ◈
2 Upperton Gardens, Eastbourne, BN21 2AH
Tel: 01323 720555
Resident Partners/Directors: ICAEW Members
A P Hill, M J D Ogilvie

PERKINS COPELAND
15 Gildredge Rd, Eastbourne, BN21 4RA
Tel: 01323 411019
Email: info@perkinscopeland.co.uk
Resident Partners/Directors: ICAEW Members
C P Freeman, S A Gausden
Registered by the ICAEW to carry out company audit work
Regulated by the ICAEW for a range of investment business activities

PLUMMER PARSONS ◈
18 Hyde Gardens, Eastbourne, BN21 4PT
Tel: 01323 431200
Resident Partners/Directors: ICAEW Members
N C Beckhurst, N J H Brown, C J Burgess, S J Griffen

PLUMMER PARSONS ACCOUNTANTS LTD
18 Hyde Gardens, Eastbourne, BN21 4PT
Tel: 01323 431200
Resident Partners/Directors: ICAEW Members
N C Beckhurst, N J H Brown, C J Burgess, S J Griffen

PRICE & CO ▽ ◈
30/32 Gildredge Road, Eastbourne, BN21 4SH
Tel: 01323 639661
Fax: 01323 738198
Email: advice@price.co.uk
Website: http://www.price.co.uk
Date Established: 1963
Resident Partners/Directors: ICAEW Members
M J Neilan, M Preece, S Wood
Resident Partners (Non-ICAEW Members):
K T Macdonald
Registered by the ICAEW to carry out company audit work
Regulated by the ICAEW for a range of investment business activities

ROGERS & CO
Suite E, 102A Longstone Road, Eastbourne, BN21 3SJ
Tel: 01323 416442
Principal: ICAEW Member
N D Rogers

SOVEREIGN BUSINESS SERVICES
2 Upperton Gardens, Eastbourne, BN21 2AH

T.D.M. CREES
29 Summerdown Lane, East Dean, Eastbourne, BN20 0LE

EASTLEIGH

ATHERTON BAILEY LLP
99 Leigh Road, Eastleigh, SO50 9DR
Tel: 02380 651441

ATKINSONS
32 Hiltingbury Road, Eastleigh, SO53 5SS

BOND & CO ◈
59B Leigh Road, Eastleigh, SO50 9DF
Tel: 02380 611389
Resident Partners/Directors: ICAEW Members
P A Bond, B Venney

COLLINSON & CO
130 Bournemouth Road, Chandler's Ford, Eastleigh, SO53 3AL

COLLINSON & CO (ACCOUNTANTS) LTD
130 Bournemouth Road, Chandler's Ford, Eastleigh, SO53 3AL

CROWCROFT & CROWCROFT
12 The Drove, Horton Heath, Eastleigh, SO50 7NW
Tel: 02380 694705
Resident Partners/Directors: ICAEW Members
C R Crowcroft, G Crowcroft

CW FELLOWES LTD
Templars House, Lulworth Close, Chandlers Ford, Eastleigh SO53 3TL
Tel: 02380 247070
Website: http://www.cwfellows.com
Resident Partners/Directors: ICAEW Members
K M G Beazley, W J Cuthbert, B A Elkins, R L Green-Wilkinson, C A E Spencer, A R N Wilson
Resident Partners (Non-ICAEW Members):
M Wright-Green
Other Offices: Carnac Place, Cams Hall Estate, Fareham, PO16 8UY
Registered by the ICAEW to carry out company audit work
Regulated by the ICAEW for a range of investment business activities

INVESTOR IN PEOPLE

DAVID EARLEY LTD
Ketts House, Winchester Road, Chandler's Ford, Eastleigh SO53 2FZ

EASTLEIGH ACCOUNTANTS LTD
89 Leigh Road, Eastleigh, SO50 9DQ

G.W BUTLER
5 Rothsbury Drive, Valley Park, Chandlers Ford, Eastleigh SO53 4QQ

GRAHAM MARTIN & CO
89 Leigh Road, Eastleigh, SO50 9DQ

HOWSON-GREEN & CO
Ashton House, 12 The Precinct, Winchester Road, Chandler's Ford, Eastleigh SO53 2GB

HWB
Highland House, Mayflower Close, Chandler's Ford, Eastleigh SO53 4AR

HWB HOLDINGS LTD
Highland House, Mayflower Close, Chandler's Ford, Eastleigh SO53 4AR

JOHN SNELL LTD
302 Hursley Road, Chandlers Ford, Eastleigh, SO53 5PF

KNIGHT GOODHEAD
7 Bournemouth Road, Chandler's Ford, Eastleigh, SO53 3DA

KNIGHT GOODHEAD LTD
7 Bournemouth Road, Chandler's Ford, Eastleigh, SO53 3DA

Langdowns DFK

LANGDOWNS DFK LTD
Flemming Court, Leigh Road, Eastleigh, SO50 9PD
Tel: 02380 613000
Website: http://www.langdownsdfk.com
Resident Partners/Directors: ICAEW Members
D J Ings, R P Law, G E Taylor, R Warwick

MICHAEL ALAN NORTHOVER
130 Bournemouth Road, Chandler's Ford, Eastleigh, SO53 3AL
Tel: 02380 255520
Principal: ICAEW Member
M A Northover

NEWMAN THORPE LTD
11 Fleming Court Business Centre, Leigh Road, Eastleigh, SO50 9PD
Tel: 02380 649689
Resident Partners/Directors: ICAEW Members
C S Thorpe-Manley

P G & S A WATSON LTD
Denstone, 6 Park Road, Chandlers Ford, Eastleigh SO53 2EU

PETER DEANE & CO ★
21 Guildford Drive, Chandlers Ford, Eastleigh, SO53 3PR
Tel: 02380 276252
Resident Partners/Directors: ICAEW Members
P M Deane

PLAYTER & CO
18 Stinchar Drive, Badgers Copse, Chandlers Ford, Eastleigh SO53 4QH

RICHARD JUETT
2 St Mary's Road, Bishopstoke, Eastleigh, SO50 6BP

RICHARD SMALL & CO ◈
24 Central Precinct, Winchester Road, Chandlers Ford, Eastleigh SO53 2GA
Tel: 02380 253848
Principal: ICAEW Member
R E Small

ROBERT ANTHONY
36 Merdon Avenue, Chandlers Ford, Eastleigh, SO53 1EP
Tel: 02380 253960
Principal: ICAEW Member
R N Anthony

ROMERIL MARTIN
9 Medway Drive, Chandlers Ford, Eastleigh, SO53 4SR
Tel: 02380 271767
Email: alison.romeril@which.net
Principal: ICAEW Member
A M Romeril
Regulated by the ICAEW for a range of investment business activities

SPECIALISATIONS – TAXATION

Capital Gains — Personal
Estate and Inheritance
Personal
Trusts

ROTHMAN PANTALL & CO ◈
10 Romsey Road, Eastleigh, SO50 9AL
Tel: 02380 614555
Fax: 02380 616558
Email: eastleigh@rothman-pantall.co.uk
Website: http://www.rp-eastleigh.co.uk
Resident Partners/Directors: ICAEW Members
C S Cox, R D L Showan

SPECIALISATIONS – FORENSIC ACCOUNTING

Expert Witnesses in Litigation

SPECIALISATIONS – INVESTMENT BUSINESS

Financial Planning and Advice
Pensions Advice

SPECIALISATIONS – SECTOR

Charities
Clubs/Associations
Hotels/Public Houses
Insurance Brokers
Property Development
Property Investment

SPECIALISATIONS – TAXATION

Estate and Inheritance
Executorship
Trusteeship
Trusts
Value Added Tax

General Description: A personal service for both personal and business clients.

ROTHMAN PANTALL & CO
Fryern House, 125 Winchester Road, Chandlers Ford, Eastleigh SO53 2DR
Tel: 02380 265550
Fax: 02380 258700
Email: chandlers-ford@rothman-pantall.co.uk
Website: http://www.rothman-pantall.co.uk
Resident Partners/Directors: ICAEW Members
A W Bennett, A R Johnson, A J Perriam, D M Smyth

S.B.T.S LTD
72a Thornbury Wood, Chandler's Ford, Eastleigh, SO53 5DQ

STONE OSMOND LTD
75 Bournemouth Road, Chandlers Ford, Eastleigh, SO53 3AP

TENON LTD
Highfield Court, Tollgate, Chandler's Ford, Eastleigh SO53 3TY
Tel: 02380 646464
Resident Partners/Directors: ICAEW Members
C S Jackson

TENON AUDIT LTD
Highfield Court, Tollgate, Chandlers Ford, Eastleigh SO53 3TY
Tel: 02380 646464

THOMAS R. LAYZELL & CO
185 Winchester Road, Chandlers Ford, Eastleigh, SO53 2DU

UNDERWOOD BARRON ★
Monks Brook House, 13/17 Hursley Road, Chandlers Ford, Eastleigh SO53 2FW

WALJI & CO
Reza Hooda, Prospect House, 50 Leigh Road, Eastleigh SO50 9DT

WALJI & CO
Prospect House, 50 Leigh Road, Eastleigh, SO50 9DT

WALJI & CO PRIVATE CLIENTS LTD
Prospect House, 50 Leigh Road, Eastleigh, SO50 9DT
Tel: 02380 610573
Fax: 02380 613901
Email: info@walji.uk.com
Resident Partners/Directors: ICAEW Members
R Hooda, S M H Walji

SPECIALISATIONS – AUDIT & ASSURANCE

Audit

SPECIALISATIONS – FINANCIAL REPORTING

Accounts Preparation

SPECIALISATIONS – INVESTMENT BUSINESS
Financial Planning and Advice
SPECIALISATIONS – TAXATION
Taxation

WALJI & CO (UK) LLP
Prospect House, 50 Leigh Road, Eastleigh, SO50 9DT

EDENBRIDGE

BARRY COMPTON & CO
South Barn, Crockham Park, Crockham Hill, Edenbridge TN8 6SR
Tel: 01732 860380
Email: bcccompton@aol.com
Principal: ICAEW Member
B C C Compton

GEOFFREY PECK
PO Box 3, Edenbridge, TN8 5ZF

GP TAX LTD
Edenbridge House, 128 High Street, Edenbridge, TN8 5AY

JOHN W. PACK
3 Leydens Court, Hartfield Road, Edenbridge, TN8 5NH

M.A. WAKELING
Picketts Mead, High Street, Cowden, Edenbridge TN8 7JH
Tel: 01342 850580
Principal: ICAEW Member
M A Wakeling

P.R. WILLANS & CO
Edenbridge House, 128 High Street, Edenbridge, TN8 5AY
Tel: 020 8467 6860
Principal: ICAEW Member
P R Willans

RICHARD P G LEWIS
Little Lewins, Spout Lane, Crockham Hill, Edenbridge TN8 6RT

SOUTHWORTH & CO LTD
Woodlea, Four Elms, Edenbridge, TN8 6NE

WBD ACCOUNTANTS LTD
Norton House, Fircroft Way, Edenbridge, TN8 6EJ
Tel: 01732 865965
Website: http://www.wbdaccountants.com
Resident Partners (Non-ICAEW Members):
K G Wood
Registered by the ICAEW to carry out company audit work
Regulated by the ICAEW for a range of investment business activities

EDGWARE

A.U. CHAUHAN & CO
A.U. Chauhan & Co, 108a High Street, Edgware, HA8 7HF
Tel: 020 8905 6262
Principal: ICAEW Member
A U Chauhan

ACCOUNTPRO SERVICES LTD ◈
Premier House, 112 Station Road, Edgware, HA8 7BJ
Tel: 020 8952 3337
Resident Partners/Directors: ICAEW Members
P Udani

AHL LTD
Chartwell House, 292-294 Hale Lane, Edgware, HA8 8NP

ALBECK LTD
112 Green Lane, Edgware, HA8 8EJ

ALTMAN, BLANE & CO
Middlesex House, 29/45 High Street, Edgware, HA8 7LH

ANDREW M SHERLING FCA
100 Green Lane, Edgware, HA8 8EJ
Tel: 020 8238 2779
Principal: ICAEW Member
A M Sherling

APPLEDAY ASSOCIATES LTD
Premier House, 112-114 Station Road, Edgware, HA8 7BJ
Tel: 020 8952 7646
Resident Partners/Directors: ICAEW Members
A V Malde

ARNOLD WINTER
13 Glendale Avenue, Edgware, HA8 8HF

BARRY P. BENNIS & CO
9 Chilton Road, Edgware, HA8 7NJ
Tel: 020 8952 8476
Principal: ICAEW Member
B P Benveniste

BLANDFORDS & CO LTD
116 Edgware Way, Edgware, HA8 8JT

CAMROSE CONSULTING LTD
61 St Margarets Road, Edgware, HA8 9UT

CANN POLUS
Premier House, 112 Station Road, Edgware, HA8 7AQ

CMEASY LTD
Anglo Dal House, 5 Spring Villa Park, Edgware, HA8 7EB

D. GUPTA & CO
88 Howberry Road, Edgware, HA8 6SY

DBS ACCOUNTING SERVICES LTD
Premier House, 112 Station road, Edgware, HA8 7BJ

DEITCH COOPER ★
54-58 High Street, Edgware, HA8 7EJ
Tel: 020 8951 4346
Resident Partners/Directors: ICAEW Members
K K Shah

DIONG & CO
20 Mowbray Road, Edgware, HA8 8JQ

EDGAR ELIAS & CO
Trinominis House, First Floor, 125-129 High Street, Edgware HA8 7DB
Tel: 020 8905 7557
Principal: ICAEW Member
E Elias

ELLIOT, WOOLFE & ROSE
Equity House, 128-136 High Street, Edgware, HA8 7TT
Tel: 020 8952 0707
Fax: 020 8952 2332
Email: advice@ewr.co.uk
Website: http://www.ewr.co.uk
Date Established: 1975
Resident Partners/Directors: ICAEW Members
M P Horsnell, M L Rose, S N Seifert, F S Waxman
Resident Partners (Non-ICAEW Members):
N M Freedman
Registered by the ICAEW to carry out company audit work
Regulated by the ICAEW for a range of investment business activities
Individual(s) licensed for insolvency work by the ICAEW

F.S. DALAL & CO
116 Edgware Way, Edgware, HA8 8JT

FINER HEYMANN LLP
Premier House, 112 Station Road, Edgware, HA8 7BJ
Tel: 020 8381 2111
Resident Partners/Directors: ICAEW Members
I M Finer, R Heymann

GILLESPIE INVERARITY & CO ★
9a North Parade, Mollison Way, Edgware, HA8 5QH

H SUMMERS LTD
26 Lake View, Edgware, HA8 7RU
Tel: 020 8958 4505
Resident Partners/Directors: ICAEW Members
H Summers

HAIDER NAQVI & CO ◈
Concept House, 225 Hale Lane, Edgware, HA8 9QF
Tel: 020 8958 8015
Principal: ICAEW Member
S Z H H Naqvi

HARRIS KAFTON ★
Ground Floor, Elizabeth House, 54-58 High Street, Edgware HA8 7EJ
Tel: 020 8381 3770
Fax: 020 8381 3470
Website: http://www.harriskafton.co.uk
Resident Partners/Directors: ICAEW Members
D N Thakrar
Resident Partners (Non-ICAEW Members):
F P Flourentzou
Registered by the ICAEW to carry out company audit work
Regulated by the ICAEW for a range of investment business activities
SPECIALISATIONS – AUDIT & ASSURANCE
Audit
SPECIALISATIONS – FINANCIAL REPORTING
Accounts Preparation
SPECIALISATIONS – TAXATION
Self Assessment Advice
Taxation

HINDOCHA & CO
34 Queensbury Station Parade, Edgware, HA8 5NN

HINDOCHA & CO LTD
34 Queensbury Station Parade, Edgware, HA8 5NN

IFIELD KEENE ASSOCIATES
11 Whitchurch Parade, Whitchurch Lane, Edgware, HA8 6LR

J.H.COWAN & CO
3 Handel Close, Canons Drive, Edgware, HA8 7QZ
Tel: 020 8952 3501
Principal: ICAEW Member
J H Cowan

JOSEPH GOH & CO ◈
Charlene House, 44 St Margarets Road, Edgware, HA8 9UU
Tel: 020 8958 8027
Principal: ICAEW Member
S C Goh

KARIM & CO
142 Edgware Way, Edgware, HA8 8JY

KI TOB
125 Wolmer Garden, Edgware, HA8 8QF
Tel: 020 8238 2534
Principal: ICAEW Member
J Wahnon
Registered by the ICAEW to carry out company audit work
Regulated by the ICAEW for a range of investment business activities

LAURENCE TAYLOR
9 Handel Close, Edgware, HA8 7QZ

LAWRENCE BRAHAM & CO
18 The Rise, Edgware, HA8 8NR

LUSTIGMAN & COMPANY LTD
27 Manor Park Crescent, Edgware, HA8 7NH

M. BOLTSA
Premier House, 112-114 Station Road, Edgware, HA8 7BJ

M. RABIN & CO
22 Hillcrest Avenue, Edgware, HA8 8PA

MALCOLM PAGET LTD
117 Whitchurch Gardens, Edgware, HA8 6PG

MARTIN BRIGGS & CO
Banbury House, 121 Stonegrove, Edgware, HA8 7TJ
Tel: 020 8905 3400
Principal: ICAEW Member
M S Briggs

MARTIN TIANO & CO ◈
2nd Floor, Highview House, 165-167 Station Road, Edgware HA8 7JU
Tel: 020 8905 6611
Principal: ICAEW Member
M Tiano

MICHAEL J. PERRY & CO
Premier House, 112 Station Road, Edgware, HA8 7BJ
Tel: 020 8952 4055
Principal: ICAEW Member
M J Perry

MILSTON & CO
57 Wolmer Gardens, Edgware, HA8 8QB

MOUKTARIS & CO ◈
156A Burnt Oak Broadway, Edgware, HA8 0AX

NAREN UNADKAT & CO
50 Wychwood Avenue, Edgware, HA8 6TH

PACKMAN, LESLIE & CO
Gresham House, 144 High Street, Edgware, HA8 7EZ
Tel: 020 8951 4141
Fax: 020 8951 4992
Email: plc@packman.co.uk
Resident Partners/Directors: ICAEW Members
J D Packman
Resident Partners (Non-ICAEW Members):
S A Lindsey
Registered by the ICAEW to carry out company audit work
Regulated by the ICAEW for a range of investment business activities

PARIS PARTNERSHIP
Russell House, 140 High Street, Edgware, HA8 7LW

PASSER, CHEVERN & CO
5 Spring Villa Road, Edgware, HA8 7EB

PATMANS
94 Brinkburn Gardens, Edgware, HA8 5PP
Tel: 020 8951 3355
Principal: ICAEW Member
R Patel

PINNICK LEWIS ★
Handel House, 95 High Street, Edgware, HA8 7DB

REED TAYLOR BENEDICT
First Floor, Trinominis House, 125-129 High Street, Edgware HA8 7DB

RICHARD JOSEPH & CO ◈
2nd Floor, 65 Station Road, Edgware, HA8 7HX
Tel: 020 8952 5407
Principal: ICAEW Member
R L Joseph

ROBERT E. LONG
21 Gresham Road, Edgware, HA8 6NU

S.A. MANN
4 Canons Close, Edgware, HA8 7QR

S.H. BETTANEY
78 Harrowes Meade, Edgware, HA8 8RP
Tel: 020 8958 9806
Principal: ICAEW Member
S H Bettaney

S.N. BARTARYA
Chartwell House, 1st Floor, 292 Hale Lane, Edgware, HA8 8NP

S. SHAH & CO
17 Lovatt Close, Edgware, HA8 9XG
Tel: 020 8958 2253
Principal: ICAEW Member
S Z Shah

SEAFIELDS
50 Bullescroft Road, Edgware, HA8 8RW
Tel: 020 8958 4562
Fax: 020 8958 6157
Email: seafields@onetel.com
Mobile: 07802 743194
Principal: ICAEW Member
N B Shah

SPECIALISATIONS – BUSINESS & GENERAL ADVICE
Book-keeping
Company Formation

SPECIALISATIONS – FINANCIAL REPORTING
Accounts Preparation
Limited Company Accounts

Partnership/Sole Trader Accounts

SPECIALISATIONS – TAXATION

Payroll Service and Advice
Taxation

See display advertisement near this entry.

SHEARS & PARTNERS LTD
88 Edgware Way, Edgware, HA8 8JS

STEPHEN DEUTSCH
102 Green Lane, Edgware, HA8 8EJ

STRAUSS PHILLIPS & CO
PO Box 585, Edgware, HA8 4DU

SUSAN GOLDSMITH LTD
3 Kings Drive, Edgware, HA8 8EB

SYDNEY PARKER & CO
Parke House, 77 Edgwarebury Lane, Edgware, HA8 8NJ
Tel: 020 8905 4466
Principal: ICAEW Member
S S Parker

Registered by the ICAEW to carry out company audit work

Regulated by the ICAEW for a range of investment business activities

TEAMWORK FINANCIAL SERVICES LTD
31 Cheyneys Avenue, Edgware, HA8 6SA

V. MISTRY & CO
Premier House, 112 Station Road, Edgware, HA8 7BJ
Tel: 020 8907 4757
Principal: ICAEW Member
V Mistry

VINSHAW & CO
1 Promenade Chambers, 1-8 Edgwarebury Lane, Edgware, HA8 7JZ

VINSHAW LTD
1 Promenade Chambers, 1-8 Edwarebury Lane, Edgware, HA8 7JZ

WISTERIA ◈
Cavendish House, 369 Burnt Oak Broadway, Edgware, HA8 5AW

WISTERIA LTD
Ground Floor, Cavendish House, 369 Burnt Oak Broadway, Edgware HA8 5AW

EGHAM

MENZIES LLP ◈
Heathrow Business Centre, 65 High Street, Egham, TW20 9EY

THE SURREY PRACTICE LTD ◈
Tara, Tite Hill, Englefield Green, Egham TW20 0NH
Tel: 01784 435001
Resident Partners/Directors: ICAEW Members
J P Chittock

WILKINS KENNEDY ◈
Gladstone House, 77-79 High Street, Egham, TW20 9HY
Tel: 01784 435561
Website: http://www.wilkinskennedy.com
Resident Partners/Directors: ICAEW Members
R W Williams
Resident Partners (Non-ICAEW Members):
K J T Walmsley, K A Stevens, M Hall
Other Offices: Amersham, Ashford, Guildford, Hertford, London, Orpington, Reading, Romsey, Southend, Winchester
Overseas Offices: Stanley, Falkland Islands

Registered by the ICAEW to carry out company audit work

Regulated by the ICAEW for a range of investment business activities
Individual(s) licensed for insolvency work by another RPB

SPECIALISATIONS – BUSINESS & GENERAL ADVICE

Acquisitions and Mergers
Disposal of Businesses
Outsourcing - Financial Services

SPECIALISATIONS – BUSINESS RECOVERY & INSOLVENCY

Bankruptcies
Corporate Recovery
Liquidations
Reorganisations and Company Reconstructions

SPECIALISATIONS – FORENSIC ACCOUNTING

Expert Witnesses in Litigation

SPECIALISATIONS – SECTOR

Charities
Construction
Dentists/Opticians
FSA Members
Insurance Brokers
Property
Solicitors

ELLAND

PEEL WALKER
11 Victoria Rd, Elland, HX5 0AE
Tel: 01422 372475
Resident Partners/Directors: ICAEW Members
S Cousen, P A Nutton

ELLESMERE

MORRIS COOK ◈
3-5 Watergate Street, Ellesmere, SY12 0EX
Tel: 01691 622098
Resident Partners/Directors: ICAEW Members
M A Jones

ELLESMERE PORT

ELAINE M HULSE
6 Manor Park Drive, Great Sutton, Ellesmere Port, CH66 2ET
Tel: 0151 339 4224
Principal: ICAEW Member
E M Hulse

JOHNSTONE, HOWELL & CO
Fairfield House, 104 Whitby Road, Ellesmere Port, CH65 0AB
Tel: 01513 561496
Resident Partners/Directors: ICAEW Members
A M Bagnall, L Glasman, A F Watson

LERMAN QUAILE
First Floor, 80 Whitby Road, Ellesmere Port, Ellesmere Port CH65 0AA

ELY

ANDREW BORLAND
75 Newnham Street, Ely, CB7 4PQ
Tel: 01353 665545
Principal: ICAEW Member
A H Borland

BRIAN MARSTON ACCOUNTANCY & TAXATION SERVICES LTD
2 Chapel Close, Little Thetford, Ely, CB6 3HS
Tel: 01353 649488
Resident Partners/Directors: ICAEW Members
B Marston

C.R.DYER & CO
3 Elmfield, Ely, CB6 1BE

FINDLAY JAMES
30 Hasse Road, Soham, Ely, CB7 5UW

FLETCHER THOMPSON ◈
Mill House, 21 High Street, Wicken, Ely CB7 5XR
Tel: 01353 727766
Principal: ICAEW Member
K J Fletcher

GEOFF SPURR & CO
41 Fore Hill, Ely, CB7 4AA
Tel: 01353 666002
Principal: ICAEW Member
G S Spurr

MOORE & CO
36 High Street, Soham, Ely, CB7 5HE

PRICE BAILEY LLP ◈
Richmond House, 16 - 18 Broad Street, Ely, CB7 4AH
Tel: 01353 662892
Website: http://www.pricebailey.co.uk
Resident Partners/Directors: ICAEW Members
T J Smith
Resident Partners (Non-ICAEW Members):
N G Pollington

Registered by the ICAEW to carry out company audit work

Authorised and regulated by the Financial Services Authority for investment business
Individual(s) licensed for insolvency work by the ICAEW

PRICE BAILEY PRIVATE CLIENT LLP
Richmond House, Broad Street, Ely, CB7 4AH

TONY EVERITT
3a Northfield Road, Soham, Ely, CB7 5UE
Tel: 01353 722617
Principal: ICAEW Member
T K Everitt

TRACY NEWMAN & CO LTD
14 High Street, Wilburton, Ely, CB6 3RB
Tel: 01353 749661
Resident Partners/Directors: ICAEW Members
T L Newman

TSW INTERNATIONAL TAXATION CONSULTING
Lower Floor, 41 Forehill, Ely, CB7 4AA

WHITING & PARTNERS ◈
41 St Marys Street, Ely, CB7 4HF
Tel: 01353 662595
Website: http://www.whitingandpartners.co.uk
Resident Partners/Directors: ICAEW Members
I G C Piper, C E Sprague, R J Tyler

YOUNGMAN & CO ◈
11 Lynn Road, Ely, CB7 4EG
Tel: 01353 662447
Principal: ICAEW Member
B J Youngman
Other Offices:163 Mill Road, Cambridge, Cambs CB1 3AN
Registered by the ICAEW to carry out company audit work

SPECIALISATIONS – AUDIT & ASSURANCE

Audit

SPECIALISATIONS – FINANCIAL REPORTING

Accounts Preparation

EMSWORTH

DYER-SMITH & CO ◈
7A High Street, Emsworth, PO10 7AQ
Tel: 01243 377037
Email: chris@italladdsup.co.uk
Date Established: 1984
Principal: ICAEW Member
C S P Dyer-Smith
Registered by the ICAEW to carry out company audit work

GOFF AND CO
89 Havant Road, Emsworth, PO10 7LF

P.R. STRATTON
2 Butlers Yard, 7 Main Road, Emsworth, PO10 8AP
Tel: 01243 377149
Principal: ICAEW Member
P R Stratton

RICHARD SHEARS
The Old Flour Mill, Queen Street, Emsworth, PO10 7BT
Tel: 01243 378727
Principal: ICAEW Member
R J Shears

TITCHENERS LTD
The Old Flour Mill, Queen Street, Emsworth, PO10 7BT
Tel: 01243 378727
See display advertisement near this entry.

ENFIELD

A. R. HUNT & CO
50 Ridge Crest, Enfield, EN2 8JX
Tel: 020 8366 7563
Principal: ICAEW Member
A R Hunt

ANDREW J. GEARY
2nd Floor, 159a Chase Side, Enfield, EN2 0PW
Tel: 020 8363 8121
Email: andrew.j.geary@btconnect.com
Website: http://www.andrewjgeary.co.uk
Principal: ICAEW Member
A J Geary
Registered by the ICAEW to carry out company audit work

ANDREW LIM
111 Parsonage Lane, Enfield, EN2 0AB

ANDY BELEJ
75c Chase Side, Enfield, EN2 6NL

ANTHONY H LUSMAN & CO
20 John Keats Lodge, Chase Side Crescent, Enfield, EN2 0JZ
Tel: 020 8363 4545
Principal: ICAEW Member
A H Lusman

AUGMENTURE LTD
20 Links Side, Enfield, EN2 7QZ
Tel: 07958 560791
Resident Partners/Directors: ICAEW Members
M Di Franco

B. WRIGHT & CO ◈
28 Byculla Avenue, Enfield, EN2 8DN
Tel: 020 8363 5502
Email: brian@wrightaccounts.co.uk
Website: http://www.wrightaccounts.co.uk
Principal: ICAEW Member
B Wright

SPECIALISATIONS – FINANCIAL REPORTING

Accounts Preparation

SPECIALISATIONS – TAXATION

Taxation

BRIAN PAUL LTD
Chase Green House, 42 Chase Side, Enfield, EN2 6NF
Tel: 020 8366 4200
Resident Partners/Directors: ICAEW Members
B.M. O'Leary, P J Phillips

CAROL LE GRYS
19 Amberley Road, Bush Hill Park, Enfield, EN1 2QX
Tel: 020 8360 7258
Principal: ICAEW Member
C.A. Le Grys

CHRIS MARSH
3 Sherringham Court, 13 The Ridgeway, Enfield, EN2 8NS

CLIVE PARKER & CO
70 Graeme Road, Enfield, EN1 3UT
Tel: 020 8364 6152
Principal: ICAEW Member
C W Parker

DAVID WARREN & CO
32 Phipps Hatch Lane, Enfield, EN2 0HN

DAVID WARREN & CO LTD
32 Phipps Hatch Lane, Enfield, EN2 0HN

GEO LITTLE SEBIRE & CO
Oliver House, 19-23 Windmill Hill, Enfield, EN2 7AB
Tel: 020 8367 1313
Email: post@gls.co.uk
Website: http://www.gls-online.co.uk
Resident Partners/Directors: ICAEW Members
G A Cleaver, R J Crawley, P J Moston
Resident Partners (Non-ICAEW Members):
L McAuby
Registered by the ICAEW to carry out company audit work
Authorised and regulated by the Financial Services Authority for investment business

GEORGE ACHILLEA LTD ◈
49 Ash Grove, Bush Hill Park, Enfield, EN1 2LB
Tel: 020 8351 7457
Resident Partners/Directors: ICAEW Members
George Achillea

GERALD BERLYN FCA
Flat 10, Elderberry Court, 39b Bycullah Road, Enfield, EN2 8FF
Tel: 020 8367 5200
Principal: ICAEW Member
G Berlyn

H. AMARA MAKALANDA
11 Drapers Road, Enfield, EN2 8LT
Tel: 020 8366 5743
Principal: ICAEW Member
H A Makalanda

HOWARD, WADE & JACOB
197/205 High Street, Ponders End, Enfield, EN3 4DZ

IMN & CO
53 Queen Annes Grove, Bush Hill Park, Enfield, EN1 2JS

J DANIELS & CO
1 Chase Side Crescent, Enfield, EN2 0JA

J.E. PALLACE
19 Private Road, Enfield, EN1 2EH

LAURIE COWAN
4 Chase Side, Enfield, EN2 6NF

MOORE STEPHENS LLP ◈
57 London Road, Enfield, EN2 6SW

NORTH LONDON ACCOUNTANCY SERVICES
369 Hertford Road, Enfield, EN3 5JW

OWEN BUSINESS SOLUTIONS LTD
1 Cobham Close, Enfield, EN1 3SD

PETER DUFFELL
32 The Ridgeway, Enfield, EN2 8QH
Tel: 020 8363 2879
Principal: ICAEW Member
P M Duffell

REX HARROLD & CO
The Old Coach House, Theobalds Park Road, Enfield, EN2 9BD

SONAM FRASI & CO
256a Ladysmith Road, Enfield, EN1 3AF

T.J. WALKER
173 Wellington Road, Bush Hill Park, Enfield, EN1 2RL

W ACCOUNTANCY LTD
369 Hertford Road, Enfield, EN3 5JW

EPPING

FGS ACCOUNTANCY & TAXATION
39 Woodland Way, Theydon Bois, Epping, CM16 7DY

GANE JACKSON SCOTT ★
144 High Street, Epping, CM16 4AS
Tel: 01992 574224
Resident Partners/Directors: ICAEW Members
G.R. O'Malley

J.B. DALE ◈
The Black Cottage, Bell Common, Epping, CM16 4DZ
Tel: 01992 550836
Principal: ICAEW Member
J B Dale

JOHN T. NOBLE
273 High Street, Epping, CM16 4DA
Tel: 01992 565504
Principal: ICAEW Member
J T Noble

MARSDENS
Tudor House, High Road, Thornwood, Epping CM16 6LT

MARSDENS LTD
Tudor House, High Road, Thornwood, Epping CM16 6LT

P.T. LOOKER & CO
3 Stonards Hill, Epping, CM16 4QE

RICHARD S HARRIS & CO LTD
45 Bell Common, Epping, CM16 4DY

S. COBBIN & CO
The Old Surgery, 15a Station Road, Epping, CM16 4HG
Tel: 01992 560007
Principal: ICAEW Member
S Cobbin

EPSOM

B.A.GEE
30 Sandown Lodge, Avenue Road, Epsom, KT18 7QX
Tel: 01372 720473
Principal: ICAEW Member
B A Gee

BDO STOY HAYWARD LLP
Emerald House, East Street, Epsom, KT17 1HS
Tel: 01372 734300
Fax: 01372 734301
Resident Partners/Directors: ICAEW Members
J Aston, D E Bawtree, S D Bosley, N F Burbidge, K R Cook, K J Davies, D M Eagle, R E Hawkins, S Hill, R L Miller, P D Rego, A J Stickland, L J Wills
Resident Partners (Non-ICAEW Members):
A J Conley, R C Field

BEVIS & CO
Apex House, 6 West Street, Epsom, KT18 7RG
Tel: 01372 840280
Fax: 01372 840282
Email: chris@bevisandco.co.uk
Website: http://www.bevisandco.co.uk
Mobile: 07917 165546
Principal: ICAEW Member
C J Bevis
Registered by the ICAEW to carry out company audit work

SPECIALISATIONS – SECTOR

Entertainers
Media

General Description: Commercially experienced accountants with extensive music industry knowledge, royalty audits and catalogue valuations carried out.

CLAIRE SMITH ACA ACCOUNTANCY SERVICES
77 Rosebery Road, Langley Vale, Epsom, KT18 6AB

COLIN ANDERSON FCA
41 Manor Green Road, Epsom, KT19 8RN

COOPER DAWN JERROM LTD
Effra House, 34 High Street, Ewell, Epsom KT17 1RW

CWM
1a High Street, Epsom, KT19 8DA

DAVID CANN
22 Chartwell Place, Epsom, KT18 5JH

DAVID PAYNE
60 The Green, Epsom, KT17 3JJ

DAVIES GIMBER BROWN LLP
Ryebrook Studios, Woodcote Side, Epsom, KT18 7HD

EPSOM ACCOUNTING LTD
93 High Street, Epsom, KT19 8DR
Tel: 01372 726406
Resident Partners/Directors: ICAEW Members
D C Shepherd

G.V. FISHER FCA
Flint House, 58 Worple Road, Epsom, KT18 5EL
Tel: 01372 720241
Principal: ICAEW Member
G V Fisher

HAKIM FRY ◈
69-71 East Street, Epsom, KT17 1BP
Tel: 01372 748798
Fax: 01372 748801
Email: admin@hakimfry.co.uk
Resident Partners/Directors: ICAEW Members
J P Hakim, N C Patel, D Witham

SPECIALISATIONS – TAXATION

UK Nationals Overseas

HLB VANTIS AUDIT PLC
The White Cottage, 19 West Street, Epsom, KT18 7BS
Tel: 01372 743 816
Website: http://www.hlbvantisaudit.com
Training Contracts Available.
Registered by the ICAEW to carry out company audit work
Regulated by the ICAEW for a range of investment business activities

SPECIALISATIONS – AUDIT & ASSURANCE

Audit
Audit — Private Company
Audit — Public Company

SPECIALISATIONS – FINANCIAL REPORTING

Audit Exemption Report

J.F. MALLABAR & CO
24a West Street, Epsom, KT18 7RJ
Tel: 01372 745111
Principal: ICAEW Member
A M Ridge

KENNY & CO
39 Wallace Fields, Ewell, Epsom, KT17 3AX

KEVIN A. MALLETT
18 The Broadway, Stoneleigh, Ewell, Epsom, KT17 2HU

KINGS ACCOUNTING HOUSE LTD
37 Gayfere Road, Epsom, KT17 2JY

M.E. BALL & ASSOCIATES LTD
Global House, 1 Ashley Avenue, Epsom, KT18 5AD

M.R. EVANS & CO
Birchwood, 5 Castle Way, Ewell, Epsom KT17 2PG

MICHAEL W.J. LINNEY
17 Church Street, Epsom, KT17 4PF

MORGAN CORPORATE FINANCE LTD
Thw White Cottage, 19 West Street, Epsom, KT19 7BS

P.O'N. CARDEN
1st Floor (Rear Suite), 56-58 High Street, Ewell, Epsom KT17 1RW
Tel: 020 8394 2957
Principal: ICAEW Member
P O Carden

RAWLINSON & HUNTER★ ◈
Lower Mill, Kingston Road, Ewell, Epsom KT17 2AE
Tel: 020 7842 2000
Fax: 020 7842 2080
Email: firstname.lastname@rawlinson-hunter.com
Website: http://www.rawlinson-hunter.com
Resident Partners/Directors: ICAEW Members
M Harris, K S Nagra, P M Prettejohn, F J Stephens
Non-resident Partners (ICAEW Members):
C J A Bliss, R Drennan, S P Jennings, R B Melling, P A Baker, D C Rawlings, A Shilling, J C Kelly
Non-resident Partners (Non-ICAEW Members):
D G Barker, S Ousley
Overseas Offices: Australia, Bermuda, British Virgin Islands, Cayman Islands, Guernsey, Jersey, Monaco, London, New Zealand, Switzerland
Registered by the ICAEW to carry out company audit work
Regulated by the ICAEW for a range of investment business activities
General Description: For a full description of our services, see our head office entry under London EC4.
Languages Spoken:
French, German, Spanish

RICHARD RAMALINGUM & CO
30 West Gardens, Ewell Village, Epsom, KT17 1NE
Tel: 020 8143 1821
Principal: ICAEW Member
R Ramalingum

TUDOR JOHN
Nightingale House, 46/48 East Street, Epsom, KT17 1HQ

TUDOR JOHN LTD
Nightingale House, 46-48 East Street, Epsom, KT17 1HQ

VANTIS FINANCIAL MANAGEMENT LTD
The White Cottage, 19 West Street, Epsom, KT18 7BS
Tel: 01372 743 816
Website: http://www.vantisplc.com/financialmanagement
Authorised and regulated by the Financial Services Authority for investment business

continued

VANTIS FINANCIAL MANAGEMENT LTD *cont*

SPECIALISATIONS – INVESTMENT BUSINESS

Financial Planning and Advice
Pensions Advice
Planning

VANTIS GROUP LTD
The White Cottage, 19 West Street, Epsom, KT18 7BS
Tel: 01372 743 816
Website: http://www.vantisplc.com/epsom
Resident Partners/Directors: ICAEW Members
T B F Bain
General Description: ICAEW Registered.

WILLIAM B. PRESTON
1 Montrouge Crescent, Epsom, KT17 3PB

WILLIAMS & CO
8-10 South Street, Epsom, KT18 7PF
Tel: 01372 741163
Resident Partners/Directors: ICAEW Members
P Smith, M Williams

ERITH

CKR ★ ◈
74-76 West Street, Erith, DA8 1AF
Tel: 01322 445200
Email: ckr@accountant.com
Resident Partners/Directors: ICAEW Members
D C Williams

DOUGLAS COLMER & CO
Orwell Lodge, 13 Lesney Park Road, Erith, DA8 3DQ
Tel: 01322 337795
Principal: ICAEW Member
D J Colmer

R.K. LAWRENCE & CO
94 Brook Street, Erith, DA8 1JF

T. KING & CO
72 Mill Road, Erith, DA8 1HN

ESHER

BELL DINWIDDIE & CO
Glenavon House, 39 Common Road, Claygate, Esher KT10 0HG
Tel: 01372 470313
Principal: ICAEW Member
P J Bell

BODY DUBOIS
The Bellbourne, 103 High Street, Esher, KT10 9QE
Tel: 01372 469888

BODY DUBOIS LTD ◈
The Bellbourne, 103 High Street, Esher, KT10 9QE
Tel: 01372 469888
Resident Partners/Directors: ICAEW Members
R Amin, J Dubois

BODY DUBOIS ASSOCIATES LLP
The Bellbourne, 103 High Street, Esher, KT10 9QE
Tel: 01372 469888

DIXCART
Hillbrow House, Hillbrow Road, Esher, KT10 9NW

DIXCART INTERNATIONAL LTD
Hillbrow House, Hillbrow Road, Esher, KT10 9NW

H. BAUJI
Summerhill, Hunting Close, Esher, KT10 8PB

HOLMES & CO
10 Torrington Road, Claygate, Esher, KT10 0SA
Tel: 01372 465378
Fax: 01372 464539
Email: holmes_and_co@hotmail.com
Date Established: 1992
Principal: ICAEW Member
J R Holmes
Regulated by the ICAEW for a range of investment business activities

SPECIALISATIONS – FINANCIAL REPORTING

Limited Companies

SPECIALISATIONS – SECTOR

Charities

SPECIALISATIONS – TAXATION

Partnerships and Sole Traders
Self Assessment Advice
Small Traders

LAURENCE TANNER
9 Grove Way, Esher, KT10 8HH

MICHAEL BURKE & COMPANY LTD
Brooklawn, 12 Littleworth Road, Esher, KT10 9PD

MICHAEL GEORGE & CO LTD
Dawes Court House, High Street, Esher, KT10 9QD
Tel: 01372 469939
Resident Partners/Directors: ICAEW Members
M R George

MOLE VALLEY ACCOUNTANTS LTD
Windrush, 25 Riverside Drive, Esher, KT10 8PG
Tel: 01372 469926
Resident Partners/Directors: ICAEW Members
J M Stadius

NOEL M. PERITON
14 Claremont Avenue, Esher, KT10 9JD

R.A. ELLIS & CO
9 The Elms, Church Road, Claygate, Esher KT10 0JT
Tel: 01372 465025
Principal: ICAEW Member
R A Ellis
Individual(s) licensed for insolvency work by the ICAEW

RICHES & CO ★
42-46 High Street, Esher, KT10 9QY
Tel: 01372 460760
Resident Partners/Directors: ICAEW Members
R G Bolton, N J Caso, J N Reed
See display advertisement near this entry.

ROBERT J SMITH
17 Meadow Close, Hinchley Wood, Esher, KT10 0AY

STEDMAN & CO
Cassel, 33 Foley Road, Claygate, Esher KT10 0LU
Tel: 01372 811663
Principal: ICAEW Member
J F Stedman

STEEDS & CO ◈
1 Littleworth Avenue, Esher, KT10 9PB
Tel: 01372 465909
Principal: ICAEW Member
D W H Steeds

T.J. RIDER & CO
36 Oaken Lane, Claygate, Esher, KT10 0RG
Tel: 01372 464145
Principal: ICAEW Member
T J Rider

TIMOTHY JONES & CO ◈
1 Arbrook Lane, Esher, KT10 9EG
Tel: 01372 464549
Principal: ICAEW Member
T S Jones

WOOLFORD & CO
Hillbrow House, Hillbrow Road, Esher, KT10 9NW

WOOLFORD & CO LLP
Hillbrow House, Hillbrow Road, Esher, KT10 9NW
Tel: 01372 471117
Email: peter.wilman@woolford.co.uk
Website: http://www.woolford.co.uk
Resident Partners/Directors: ICAEW Members
L Binge, J C Dunne, P Wilman

ETCHINGHAM

NIGEL WEST & CO
18 Rother View, Burwash, Etchingham, TN19 7BN
Tel: 01435 883505
Principal: ICAEW Member
N R S West

EVESHAM

ALLCHURCH BAILEY LTD
Almswood House, 93 High Street, Evesham, WR11 4DU

BARBARA ROWLAND LTD
Summer House, Knowle Hill, Evesham, WR11 7EL

C.M. DALBY
18 Merstow Green, Evesham, WR11 4BD
Tel: 01386 45979
Principal: ICAEW Member
C M Dalby

CLEMENT RABJOHNS
111-113 High Street, Evesham, WR11 4XP

MARK SATTERLEY
58 Clyde Avenue, Evesham, WR11 3FE

EXETER

AAAH ACCOUNTANTS FOR US LTD ◈
Sweet Meadows, Clifford Bridge, Drewsteignton, Exeter EX6 6QB

ALEXANDER MAITLAND LTD
50 Cowick Street, St Thomas, Exeter, EX4 1AP

BEGBIES TRAYNOR LTD
Balliol House, Southernhay Gardens, Exeter, EX1 1NP
Tel: 01392 260800
Resident Partners/Directors: ICAEW Members
I E Walker
SPECIALISATIONS – BUSINESS RECOVERY & INSOLVENCY
Bankruptcies
Corporate Recovery
Liquidations

BICK PARTNERSHIP ◈
Hampton Place, 52 Longbrook Street, Exeter, EX4 6AH

BISHOP FLEMING ◈
Stratus House, Emperor Way, Exeter Business Park, Exeter EX1 3QS
Tel: 01392 448800
Website: http://www.bishopfleming.co.uk
Resident Partners/Directors: ICAEW Members
R E T Borton, B G Payne, D C Savill

BRITAC LTD
10 Highcroft, Exeter, EX4 4JQ
Tel: 01392 877706
Resident Partners/Directors: ICAEW Members
S J Bright

BUSH & CO ◈
2 Barnfield Crescent, Exeter, EX1 1QT
Tel: 01392 432525
Resident Partners/Directors: ICAEW Members
N Bamber, R P Carne, I E Powell, S Truran

BUSINESS SUPPORT MATTERS LTD ◈
Glenacre, Newton St Cyres, Exeter, EX5 5AW

CLARKSON MAYER LTD
11 Church Road, Silverton, Exeter, EX5 4HS
Tel: 01392 873768
Resident Partners/Directors: ICAEW Members
T J Bates

COLLINS DAVIES
19 Bettysmead, Exeter, EX4 8LN
Tel: 01392 217112
Resident Partners/Directors: ICAEW Members
D H Davies

COOKS
32 Argyll Road, Pennsylvania, Exeter, EX4 4RY
Tel: 01392 666766
Principal: ICAEW Member
P A R Cook

DAVID EXELL ASSOCIATES
3 Alphinbrook Court, Alphinbrook Road, Marsh Barton, Exeter EX2 8QR

DAVID FRUMIN & ASSOCIATES ◈
48 Queen Street, Exeter, EX4 3SR
Tel: 01392 493394
Fax: 01392 493394
Email: Frumind@aol.com
Mobile: 07831 446551
Date Established: 1993
Regulated by the ICAEW for a range of investment business activities

E J CAMDEN
3 Trews Weir Court, Trews Weir Reach, Exeter, EX2 4JS

E.J. COCHRANE
35 Thornton Hill, Exeter, EX4 4NR

ERNST & YOUNG LLP
Broadwalk House, Southernhay West, Exeter, EX1 1LF
Tel: 01392 284300
Resident Partners/Directors: ICAEW Members
J H Johns

FRANCIS CLARK ◈
Vantage Point, Wood Water Park, Pynes Hill, Exeter EX2 5FD
Tel: 01392 667000
Website: http://www.francisclark.co.uk
Resident Partners/Directors: ICAEW Members
L J Banfield, M S Clark, C G Cooke, P D Egan, S A Grinsted, S J Hobson, A H Richards, P Serjeant
Resident Partners (Non-ICAEW Members):
S K Austen
Authorised and regulated by the Financial Services Authority for investment business
Individual(s) licensed for insolvency work by the ICAEW
General Description: Largest independent firm in the South West, with particular strengths in taxation, VAT, corporate finance, financial planning, forensic accounting, IT and insolvency.

GERARD KIRK
5 Barnfield Crescent, Exeter, EX1 1RF

HAY AUDIT LTD
Berkeley House, Dix's Field, Exeter, EX1 1PZ
Tel: 01392 215522
Resident Partners/Directors: ICAEW Members
L D F Hill

HAY TAX LTD
Berkeley House, Dix's Field, Exeter, EX1 1PZ
Tel: 01392 215522
Resident Partners/Directors: ICAEW Members
L D F Hill

HWCA LTD
3 Southernhay West, Exeter, EX1 1JG
Tel: 01392 260310
Fax: 01392 421475
DX: 8317 EXETER
Website: http://www.hwca.com
Training Contracts Available.
Resident Partners/Directors: ICAEW Members
D J Barnes, B De Cruz, C S Thomas
Resident Partners (Non-ICAEW Members):
M Harris

IAN ROPER & CO
Alphinbrook Court, Alphinbrook Road, Marsh Barton, Exeter EX2 8QR

JANE COCHRANE
35 Thornton Hill, Exeter, EX4 4NN

JANE MINERS
2 Turlake Mews, Cowley, Exeter, EX5 5ER

JOHN ADCOCK & CO
7 Marlborough Road, Exeter, EX2 4TJ

K.R.HAM
Brambles, Noman's Chapel, Thorverton, Exeter EX5 5JP

KIRK HILLS
5 Barnfield Crescent, Exeter, EX1 1RF

LEWIS KNIGHT ◈
Suite D, Pinbrook Court, Venny Bridge, Pinhoe, Exeter EX4 8JQ
Tel: 01392 206444
Resident Partners/Directors: ICAEW Members
P M A Bartlett, A T Knight

M J SMITH & CO LTD
Woodbury House, Green Lane, Exton, Exeter EX3 0PW
Tel: 01392 875391
Resident Partners/Directors: ICAEW Members
M J Smith

MAITLAND WRIGHT LTD
Trelissa, Old Winslade, Clyst St Mary, Exeter EX5 1AS

MANAGEMENT ACCOUNTING SOLUTIONS
New Nutwalls, Aylesbeare, Exeter, EX5 2JL

MARGARET THOMSON
6 Broadpark, Brampford Speke, Exeter, EX5 5HP

MERLIN ACCOUNTANCY SERVICES LTD
4 Charnley Avenue, Redhills, Exeter, EX4 1RE

MICHAEL GASKELL
1 Woods Cottage, Farringdon, Exeter, EX5 2HY
Tel: 01395 232829
Principal: ICAEW Member
M A Gaskell

THE MILL CONSULTANCY ◈
3 Barnfield Crescent, Exeter, EX1 1QT
Tel: 01392 432654
Principal: ICAEW Member
J R Davison

OCEAN CONSULTANCY LTD ◈
14 Chitterley Business Centre, Silverton, Exeter, EX5 4DB
Tel: 01392 861282
Resident Partners/Directors: ICAEW Members
D J Park

PEPLOWS ◈
2 Cranmere Court, Lustleigh Close, Matford Business Park, Exeter EX2 8PW
Tel: 01392 223930
Email: enquiries@peplows.co.uk
Website: http://www.peplows.co.uk
Resident Partners/Directors: ICAEW Members
P Guest
Other Offices: Newton Abbot, Torquay
Registered by the ICAEW to carry out company audit work
Regulated by the ICAEW for a range of investment business activities

R.E. COATES
48 Countess Wear Road, Exeter, EX2 6LR

RICHARD THOMAS
26-28 Southernhay East, Exeter, EX1 1NS

ROBINSON STOPFORD LTD
30 West Avenue, Exeter, EX4 4SE
Tel: 01392 274894
Resident Partners/Directors: ICAEW Members
D R Robinson, P J L Stopford

ROGER GUILLEBAUD & CO ◈
Sweet Meadows, Clifford Bridge, Drewsteignton, Exeter EX6 6QB

SHEPPARD ROCKEY & WILLIAMS LTD
Sannerville Chase, Exminster, Exeter, EX6 8AT
Tel: 01392 824777
Website: http://www.srwaccountants.co.uk
Resident Partners/Directors: ICAEW Members
E T Rockey, S L Williams

SIDAWAYS LTD
20 North Street, Exeter, EX4 3QS

SIMPKINS EDWARDS
Michael House, Castle Street, Exeter, EX4 3LQ
Tel: 01392 211233
Email: exeter@simpkinsedwards.co.uk
Website: http://www.simpkinsedwards.co.uk
Resident Partners/Directors: ICAEW Members
J L Coombs, C J Nightingale, L Sommerville-Woodward
Resident Partners (Non-ICAEW Members):
C Bowker, M J Campbell
Registered by the ICAEW to carry out company audit work
Regulated by the ICAEW for a range of investment business activities

SIMPKINS EDWARDS
Unit 19, Exeter Livestock Centre, Marsh Barton, Exeter EX2 8FD
Tel: 01392 211233

STEINER & CO
50 Cowick Street, Exeter, EX4 1AP

STEPHEN J. BRIGHT
10 High Croft, Lower Argyll Road, Exeter, EX4 4JQ
Tel: 01392 877706
Principal: ICAEW Member
S J Bright

STONHAM.CO
4 Barnfield Crescent, Exeter, EX1 1QT

TENON LTD
2nd Floor Berkeley House, Dix's Field, Exeter, EX1 1PZ

THOMAS WESTCOTT ★
26-28 Southernhay East, Exeter, EX1 1NS
Tel: 01392 208150
Resident Partners/Directors: ICAEW Members
J Flood, M J Marsh, J Potter, D H Simpson, R B Thomas

THOMPSON JENNER ◈
1 Colleton Crescent, Exeter, EX2 4DG
Tel: 01392 258553
Email: enquiries@tjexeter.co.uk
Website: http://www.thompson-jenner.co.uk
Resident Partners/Directors: ICAEW Members
M Hart, A P Walmsley, J P Westley
Resident Partners (Non-ICAEW Members):
G J Salter
Registered by the ICAEW to carry out company audit work
Regulated by the ICAEW for a range of investment business activities

WHEELERS
6 Providence Court, Pynes Hill, Exeter, EX2 5JL

WHEELERS (2020) LTD
6 Providence Court, Pynes Hill, Exeter, EX2 5JL

WILKINSONS ◈
Little Churchill, Whimple, Exeter, EX5 2PE
Tel: 01404 822073
Principal: ICAEW Member
F H Wilkinson

EXMOUTH

BICK PARTNERSHIP ◈
18A Littleham Road, Exmouth, EX8 2QG

BRIAN D. WATSON
1A Windsor Sq, Exmouth, EX8 1JU
Tel: 01395 271772
Principal: ICAEW Member
B D Watson

COLLINS DAVIES
371 Exeter Road, Exmouth, EX8 3NS
Tel: 01395 225307
Resident Partners/Directors: ICAEW Members
R H Collins

DAVID J. GINGELL
15 Raddenstile Lane, Exmouth, EX8 2JL

J. W. C. A LTD ◈
1 Victoria Road, Exmouth, EX8 1DL
Tel: 01395 227322
Resident Partners/Directors: ICAEW Members
J R Wheeler

JOHN WHEELER ◈
Suite 1C, 1 Victoria Road, Exmouth, EX8 1DL
Tel: 01395 227332
Fax: 01395 272825
Email: advice@jwheeler.co.uk
Regulated by the ICAEW for a range of investment business activities

SPECIALISATIONS – BUSINESS & GENERAL ADVICE
Data Processing Services
Management Advice to Business

SPECIALISATIONS – FINANCIAL REPORTING
Accounts Preparation

SPECIALISATIONS – TAXATION
Taxation

JON RANSOM
4 Pound Lane Office Suites, Unit 1, Pound Lane Trading Estate, Exmouth EX8 4NP
Tel: 01395 222210
Principal: ICAEW Member
J P Ransom

SOUTHON & CO
6 The Parade, Exmouth, EX8 1RL

TANDY & CO
Little Foxholes, Foxholes Hill, Exmouth, EX8 2DF
Tel: 01395 222209
Principal: ICAEW Member
E H Tandy

SPECIALISATIONS – FORENSIC ACCOUNTING
Forensic Accounting

THOMPSON JENNER
28 Alexandra Terrace, Exmouth, EX8 1BD

EYE

PASSMORE WEEKS & RICHARDSON
36 Church Street, Stradbroke, Eye, IP21 5HS

FAIRFORD

PHILIP NICKSON & CO LTD
10 Lancaster Road, Kempsford, Fairford, GL7 4DW

FAKENHAM

HARRIS KAFTON
11a Norwich Street, Fakenham, NR21 9AF
Tel: 01328 851306
Resident Partners/Directors: ICAEW Members
M Halford, M B Harris

LARKING GOWEN ◈
Summerhill House, 1 Sculthorpe Road, Fakenham, NR21 9HA
Tel: 01328 863121
Resident Partners/Directors: ICAEW Members
D C Missen
Non-resident Partners (ICAEW Members):
C G Greeves

M.C. BUXTON
2 Green Farm Barns, Little Snoring, Fakenham, NR21 0JW

STEPHENSON SMART ★
Connaught House, 11 Oak Street, Fakenham, NR21 9DX
Tel: 01328 863318
Email: nigel.ward@stephenson-smart.com
Resident Partners/Directors: ICAEW Members
N R Ward

W.R. KEWLEY & CO
The Old Post Office, The Street, West Raynham, Fakenham NR21 7AD
Tel: 01328 838611
Principal: ICAEW Member
J Massingberd-Mundy

FALMOUTH

A.J. EVANS
186 Longfield, Falmouth, TR11 4ST
Tel: 01326 212600
Principal: ICAEW Member
A J Evans

BOADENS ★ ◈
59/61 Killigrew Street, Falmouth, TR11 3PF
Tel: 01326 312119
Resident Partners/Directors: ICAEW Members
S A Tregenza-Hall

CAROLE J. BARNETT
102 Kimberley Park Road, Falmouth, TR11 2DQ
Tel: 01326 315422
Principal: ICAEW Member
C J Barnett

CLARK JENNER ◈
Porth Gwyn, Avenue Road, Falmouth, TR11 4AY
Tel: 01326 211550
Principal: ICAEW Member
C W Jenner

CLIVE BOWYER LTD
Admiralty House, 2 Bank Place, Falmouth, TR11 4AT
Tel: 01326 376115
Principal: ICAEW Member
D C Bowyer

GLYNIS TYRRELL
1a Berkeley Court, Berkeley Vale, Falmouth, TR11 3PB
Tel: 01326 319191
Principal: ICAEW Member
G Tyrrell

HODGSONS ◈
48 Arwenack Street, Falmouth, TR11 3JH
Tel: 01326 317785
Fax: 01326 211975
Email: falmouth@hodgsons.uk.com
Website: http://www.hodgsons.uk.com
Resident Partners/Directors: ICAEW Members
J P D Hodgson
Non-resident Partners (ICAEW Members):
P J D Hodgson, P J M Stevenson
Non-resident Partners (Non-ICAEW Members):
P C Sanderson
Registered by the ICAEW to carry out company audit work
Regulated by the ICAEW for a range of investment business activities

MATTHEWS COOPER ◈
52 Killigrew Street, Falmouth, TR11 3PP
Tel: 01326 211113
Principal: ICAEW Member
N G Matthews

PAUL & MAUNDRELL ◈
The Athenaeum, Kimberley Place, Falmouth, TR11 3QL
Tel: 01326 313451
Principal: ICAEW Member
C N Maundrell

FAREHAM

A&N ACCOUNTANCY SERVICES
27 Sorrel Drive, Whiteley, Fareham, PO15 7JL

ABA
49 Park Lane, Fareham, PO16 7LE

AD ACCOUNTANCY
1 Fitzwilliam Avenue, Hill Head, Fareham, PO14 3SD
Tel: 01329 510496
Principal: ICAEW Member
A J Davidson

ALEXANDER VAUGHAN & CO
The Old Laundry, Bridge Street, Southwick, Fareham PO17 6DZ

ALLIOTT WINGHAM LTD ◈
Kintyre House, 70 High Street, Fareham, PO16 7BB
Tel: 01329 822232
Resident Partners/Directors: ICAEW Members
M J Nolan, M Wingham

ARTHUR DANIELS & CO★ ◈
227a West Street, Fareham, PO16 0HZ
Tel: 01329 280056
Email: mail@arthurdaniels.co.uk
Website: http://www.arthurdaniels.co.uk
Resident Partners/Directors: ICAEW Members
R E Madden, B K Plumb
Resident Partners (Non-ICAEW Members):
I S Lindsey
Authorised and regulated by the Financial Services Authority for investment business

AVENUE BUSINESS SERVICES
1 Silvertrees, Lady Bettys Drive, Titchfield, Fareham PO15 6RJ

CASSON BECKMAN
Murrills House, 48 East Street, Portchester, Fareham PO16 9XS

CASSON BECKMAN BUSINESS AND TAX ADVISERS LTD
Murrills House, 48 East Street, Portchester, Fareham PO16 9XS

CHARLES MARCUS LTD
Cams Hall, Cams Hill, Fareham, PO16 8AB

COMPASS ACCOUNTANTS LTD
Venture House, The Tanneries, East Street, Titchfield, Fareham PO14 4AR

D V MARLOW & CO LTD
72 West Street, Portchester, Fareham, PO16 9UN
Tel: 02392 200270
Website: http://www.dvm.co.uk
Resident Partners/Directors: ICAEW Members
D V Marlow
Registered by the ICAEW to carry out company audit work

D.V. MARLOW & CO
72 West Street, Portchester, Fareham, PO16 9UN

DHB FELLOWES
Carnac Place, Cams Hall Estate, Fareham, PO16 8UY

G R STONE
1 Union Street, Fareham, PO16 7XX
Tel: 01329 828115

G R STONE LTD
1 Union Street, Fareham, PO16 7XX

LAWRENCE PHILLIPS & CO
42 Lipizzaner Fields, Whiteley, Fareham, PO15 7BH

MFA ◈
6a The Gardens, Fareham, PO16 8SS

MFA ACCOUNTANTS LTD
6A The Gardens, Fareham, PO16 8SS

morleyandscott
accounting

MORLEY AND SCOTT ◈
Wentworth House, 4400 Parkway, Whiteley, Fareham PO15 7FJ
Tel: 01489 566700
Fax: 01489 588099
Email: ms@morleyandscott.co.uk
Website: http://www.morleyandscott.co.uk
Resident Partners/Directors: ICAEW Members
A B Cole, M A Perrin, A Price
Resident Partners (Non-ICAEW Members):
S Howard, D Gosling, J Foundling
Other Offices: London, Slough, Portsmouth
Registered by the ICAEW to carry out company audit work
Authorised and regulated by the Financial Services Authority for investment business

PALMER, RILEY & CO ◈
First Floor, Wallington Court, Fareham Heights, Standard Way, Fareham PO16 8XT
Tel: 01329 288511
Principal: ICAEW Member
J Metherell
Authorised and regulated by the Financial Services Authority for investment business
Languages Spoken:
French, German, Spanish
See display advertisement near this entry.

R.J.G. PALMER GARDNER ◈
Norgar House, 10 East Street, Fareham, PO16 0BN
Tel: 01329 282222
Resident Partners/Directors: ICAEW Members
S J L Gardner

ROTHMAN PANTALL & CO
229 West Street, Fareham, PO16 0HZ

ROTHMAN PANTALL & CO
16 Little Park Farm Road, Segensworth West, Fareham, PO15 5TD

RSM BENTLEY JENNISON ◈
Unit 1, Manor Court, Barnes Wallis Road, Fareham PO15 5TH
Tel: 01489 566000
Registered by the ICAEW to carry out company audit work

THE TAX SHOP OF FAREHAM ◈
Kintyre House, 70 High Street, Fareham, PO16 7BB
Tel: 01329 231706

THOMAS & WOOLVEN ★
Town Quay House, 99 Gosport Road, Fareham, PO16 0PY

WARD & CO
Wallington Cottage, Drift Road, Fareham, PO16 8SY

FARINGDON

INFINITUDE SERVICES LTD
24 Fernham Road, Faringdon, SN7 7LB

PETER J. THOMPSON
Selwood Cottage, Littleworth, Faringdon, SN7 8ED

FARNBOROUGH

ASHDOWN PRICE
Sheiling House, Invincible Road, Farnborough, GU14 7QU

DAVIDSONS ★
23 Comfrey Close, Farnborough, GU14 9XX

FLAXMAN ACCOUNTING SERVICES LTD
Rushmoor Business Centre, Kingsmead, Farnborough, GU14 7SR

FOXBOROUGH CONSULTING ★
30 Camp Road, Farnborough, GU14 6EW
Tel: 01252 510333
Resident Partners/Directors: ICAEW Members
S R Edwards, A J Parsons

GRAHAM BEST & CO ◈
189 Lynchford Road, Farnborough, GU14 6HD
Tel: 01252 378100
Principal: ICAEW Member
G R Best

HAINES WATTS CONSULTING
30 Camp Road, Farnborough, GU14 6EW
Tel: 01252 510333
Resident Partners/Directors: ICAEW Members
S R Edwards, A J Parsons, B J Potter

HOWARD LEE, FELLOWS & CO ◈
11-14 First Floor, Rushmoor Business Centre, 19 Kingsmead, Farnborough GU14 7SR
Tel: 01252 370269
Fax: 01252 370271
Email: hpl@howardleefellows.co.uk
Website: http://www.howardleefellows.co.uk
Training Contracts Available.
Resident Partners/Directors: ICAEW Members
R K Fellows, H P Lee, J Q Reyersbach
Registered by the ICAEW to carry out company audit work

SPECIALISATIONS – AUDIT & ASSURANCE
Audit — Private Company
Pension Scheme Auditors

SPECIALISATIONS – BUSINESS & GENERAL ADVICE
Management Accounting Consultancy

SPECIALISATIONS – SECTOR
Charities
Clubs/Associations
Construction
Doctors
Estate Agents
Property Development

SPECIALISATIONS – TAXATION
UK Subsidiaries of Overseas Multinationals

Languages Spoken:
German

HW
30 Camp Road, Farnborough, GU14 6EW
Tel: 01252 510333
Resident Partners/Directors: ICAEW Members
S R Edwards, R G McFarlane, A J Parsons, B J Potter

HW CONTROLS & ASSURANCE LLP ★
30 Camp Road, Farnborough, GU14 6EW
Tel: 01252 510333
Resident Partners/Directors: ICAEW Members
A J Parsons, B J Potter

JOHN SIMPKINS & CO
12 Stake Lane, Farnborough, GU14 8NP
Tel: 01252 521772
Principal: ICAEW Member
J Simpkins

MENZIES LLP ◈
Blackwater Valley, 50-58 Victoria Road, Farnborough, GU14 7PG

MISS DENISE THOMAS
10 Fleming Close, Farnborough, GU14 8BT

T.J. PINTON & CO
15 Hazel Avenue, Cove, Farnborough, GU14 0HA

TTCA LTD
269 Farnborough Road, Farnborough, GU14 7LX

FARNHAM

AIMS
Bourne House, 10 Sandrock Hill Road, Wrecclesham, Farnham GU10 4NS

ANTHONY D'ARCY FCA
Bourne House, 10 Sandrock Hill Road, Wrecclesham, Farnham GU10 4NS

AVN PICKTREE LTD ◈
Picktree House, Monks Walk, Farnham, GU9 8HT
Tel: 01252 710333
Fax: 01252 717477
Website: http://www.avnpicktree.com

AWM ACCOUNTANCY & TAXATION LTD
Old Chambers, 93-94 West Street, Farnham, GU9 7EB

BICKNELL SANDERS
Alresford House, 60 West Street, Farnham, GU9 7EH
Tel: 01252 726485
Email: partners@bicknellsanders.co.uk
Website: http://www.bicknellsanders.co.uk
Resident Partners/Directors: ICAEW Members
B S M Lloyd, S R Youl
Resident Partners (Non-ICAEW Members):
N R Bicknell

BLACKWOOD FUTCHER & CO
9 St Georges Yard, Castle Streeet, Farnham, GU9 7LW

E A MATHIESON ASSOCIATES LTD
97 Broomleaf Road, Farnham, GU9 8DH

FOCUS ONLINE ACCOUNTING SERVICES
Suite 3, The Oast House, 5 Mead Lane, Farnham GU9 7DY

FOCUS SYSTEMS DEVELOPMENT LTD
24 Mayfield, Rowledge, Farnham, GU10 4DZ

FRISBY WISHART
2 Lavender Lane, Rowledge, Farnham, GU10 4AY

FRISBY WISHART LTD
2 Lavender Lane, Rowledge, Farnham, GU10 4AY

GRANT THORNTON UK LLP
Suite A, Gostrey House, Union Road, Farnham GU9 7PT
Tel: 01252 734345
Resident Partners/Directors: ICAEW Members
P E Shepherd

I D MACLUCAS & CO
104b Malthouse Yard, West Street, Farnham, GU9 7EN

JEREMY BARNES & CO
Outmoor, Hale House Lane, Churt, Farnham GU10 2NG

JJ ACCOUNTANCY LTD
41 Alma Way, Farnham, GU9 0QN

MAXWELL & CO
10 St Georges Yard, Farnham, GU9 7LW

MAXWELL & CO LTD
10 St Georges Yard, Farnham, GU9 7LW

MILNE ELDRIDGE & CO ◈
The Little House, 88A West Street, Farnham, GU9 7EP
Tel: 01252 723823
Principal: ICAEW Member
R J Smith
Registered by the ICAEW to carry out company audit work
Regulated by the ICAEW for a range of investment business activities

SPECIALISATIONS – AUDIT & ASSURANCE
Audit

SPECIALISATIONS – BUSINESS & GENERAL ADVICE
Book-keeping
Company Formation
Company Secretarial Service
Data Processing Services
Management Advice to Business

SPECIALISATIONS – FINANCIAL REPORTING
Accounts Preparation
Limited Company Accounts
Partnership/Sole Trader Accounts

SPECIALISATIONS – INVESTMENT BUSINESS
Financial Planning and Advice

SPECIALISATIONS – TAXATION
Payroll Service and Advice
Taxation

MORCHARD BISHOP & CO ◈
4 Dene Walk, Lower Bourne, Farnham, GU10 3PL
Tel: 01252 712684
Website: http://www.morchardbishop.com
Principal: ICAEW Member
C V Barker-Benfield

PARFITT & CO ★
22 High Street, Rowledge, Farnham, GU10 4BS

ROGER D PEARCE
11 Upper Bourne Lane, Farnham, GU10 4RQ

RUTTON B VICCAJEE LTD
Red Lion House, London Road, Bentley, Farnham GU10 5HY
Tel: 01420 525 020
Resident Partners/Directors: ICAEW Members
R B Viccajee

TAYLOR COCKS
Abbey House, Hickleys Court, South Street, Farnham GU9 7QQ
Tel: 0870 770 8111
Website: http://www.theaccountants.co.uk
SPECIALISATIONS – AUDIT & ASSURANCE
Audit
Audit — Private Company
SPECIALISATIONS – BUSINESS & GENERAL ADVICE
Book-keeping
Management Advice to Business
Management Consultancy
SPECIALISATIONS – FINANCIAL REPORTING
Accounts Preparation
Limited Company Accounts
SPECIALISATIONS – SECTOR
Doctors
Solicitors
SPECIALISATIONS – TAXATION
Estate and Inheritance
Investigations
Taxation

VICCAJEE MCCALL
Red Lion House, London Road, Bentley, Farnham GU10 5HY
Tel: 01420 525020

VIVIEN M. HIRST
4 White Rose Lane, Lower Bourne, Farnham, GU10 3NG
Tel: 01252 714071
Principal: ICAEW Member
V M Rieden

WISE & CO ◈
Wey Court West, Union Road, Farnham, GU9 7PT
Tel: 01252 711244
Email: info@wiseandco.co.uk
Website: http://www.wiseandco.co.uk
Date Established: 1972
Resident Partners/Directors: ICAEW Members
K P Birch, M J Dickinson, R A Lock, S G Morgan, S M South, T Turner, R F Wise
Resident Partners (Non-ICAEW Members):
S Woodings
Other Offices: Pinewood Studios, Iver Heath, Bucks SL0 0NH
Registered by the ICAEW to carry out company audit work
SPECIALISATIONS – AUDIT & ASSURANCE
Audit
SPECIALISATIONS – BUSINESS & GENERAL ADVICE
Book-keeping
Company Secretarial Service
SPECIALISATIONS – FINANCIAL REPORTING
Accounts Preparation
SPECIALISATIONS – TAXATION
Payroll Service and Advice
Personal
Taxation

FAVERSHAM

BRIAN KELSEY & CO LTD
7a Court Street, Faversham, ME13 7AN
Tel: 01795 538606
Resident Partners/Directors: ICAEW Members
B Kelsey

J R CARROLL
8 Arthur Kennedy Close, Boughton, Faversham, ME13 9BQ

M G MORAN
Nailbourne Oast South Street, Boughton, Faversham, ME13 9NB

MCKENZIE LINDSAY
5 Dodds Court, Preston Street, Faversham, ME13 8PE
Tel: 01795 534285
Principal: ICAEW Member
G D G Lindsay

SOUTH EAST ACCOUNTANCY SERVICES LTD
34 Wells Way, Faversham, ME13 7QP
Tel: 01795 597719
Resident Partners/Directors: ICAEW Members
K R Joiner

THE WALKER BROWN PARTNERSHIP LLP
16 Hilton Close, Faversham, ME13 8NN

FELIXSTOWE

AIMS - SARA E PEARCY
PO Box 108, The Ferry, Felixstowe, IP11 9WF
Tel: 01394 279423
Principal: ICAEW Member
S E Pearcy

BEATONS LTD ◈
York House, 2-4 York Road, Felixstowe, IP11 7QG
Tel: 01394 279692
Email: info@beatons.co.uk
Website: http://www.beatons.co.uk
Resident Partners/Directors: ICAEW Members
R A Beaton, J Oakley
Resident Partners (Non-ICAEW Members):
N Marshall, S Hammond
Other Offices:3 Elm St Ipswich IP1 1EY
Regulated by the ICAEW for a range of investment business activities

INVESTOR IN PEOPLE

BEATONS AUDIT LLP
2/4 York Road, Felixstowe, IP11 7QG
Tel: 01394 279692
Resident Partners/Directors: ICAEW Members
R A Beaton, J Oakley

ROSEMARY UNTHANK
15 Thornley Road, Felixstowe, IP11 7LA
Tel: 01394 284452
Principal: ICAEW Member
R A Unthank

S R RENVOIZE LTD
St Edmunds House, 1 Arwela Road, Felixstowe, IP11 2DG
Tel: 01394 671870
Website: http://www.srrenvoize.co.uk
Resident Partners/Directors: ICAEW Members
S R Renvoize

SM & CO
1 Cranmer House, Maybush Lane, Felixstowe, IP11 7NA
Tel: 01394 277550
Principal: ICAEW Member
S E Marsh

UNTHANK & CO
4 Coniston Close, Felixstowe, IP11 9SW
Tel: 01394 271938
Principal: ICAEW Member
J A S Unthank

FELTHAM

D BOWEN-DAVIES & CO
67 Elmcroft Close, Feltham, TW14 9HJ

M.J. EVANS
Bennetts Farm, 735 Staines Road, Bedfont, Feltham TW14 8PF

PRICEWATERHOUSE-COOPERS
First Floor, 5 New Square, Bedfont Lakes, Feltham TW14 8HA

FERNDOWN

ASHLEY J. B. MEREDITH
22 Riverside Road, West Moors, Ferndown, BH22 0LQ
Tel: 01202 877220
Principal: ICAEW Member
A J B Meredith

DENNIS PAYNE FCA
9 Kingfisher Close, West Moors, Ferndown, BH22 0DX

MONEYWISE SOLUTIONS LTD
9 Sherwood Avenue, Ferndown, BH22 8JS
Tel: 01202 892832
Resident Partners/Directors: ICAEW Members
A C Field

FERRYHILL

FOURWARD DEVELOPMENTS (UK) LTD
37-38 Market Street, Ferryhill, DL17 8JH

FILEY

BLAIR & CO
20 West Avenue, Filey, YO14 9AU

HUNTER GEE HOLROYD
19-21 Belle Vue Street, Filey, YO14 9HU

FLEET

ELIZABETH ROSE
12 Forest Dean, Fleet, GU51 2UQ

ELIZABETH ROSE FCA ATT
12 Forest Dean, Fleet, GU51 2UQ
Tel: 01252 614820
Resident Partners/Directors: ICAEW Members
E Rose

HAMILTON THOMAS
29 Camus Close, Church Crookham, Fleet, GU52 0UT

HANNAY & CO
Norwood House, 73 Elvetham Road, Fleet, GU51 4HL
Tel: 01252 815622
Principal: ICAEW Member
N Gaul

JCS ASSOCIATES ◈
121 Albert Street, Fleet, GU51 3SR
Tel: 01252 812345
Email: info@jcs-a.co.uk
Website: http://www.jcs-a.co.uk
Principal: ICAEW Member
J L Cleden
SPECIALISATIONS – IT
Computer Consultants

LLH INTERIM MANAGEMENT SERVICES LTD
31 Tweseldown Road, Church Crookham, Fleet, GU52 8DE
Tel: 01252 617681
Resident Partners/Directors: ICAEW Members
L L Hesketh

RENDELL THOMPSON ★
32 Aldershot Road, Fleet, GU51 3NN

FLEETWOOD

HAYTONS LTD
20 Melbourne Avenue, Fleetwood, FY7 8AY

JONES HARRIS ◈
17 St Peters Place, Fleetwood, FY7 6EB
Tel: 01253 874255
Resident Partners/Directors: ICAEW Members
C F Bryning, P Neill, A D Newbold, M W Wigley

FOLKESTONE

BERESFORDS
Castle House, Castle Hill Avenue, Folkestone, CT20 2TQ
Tel: 01303 850992
Email: roy@beresfordsaccountants.com
Website: http://www.beresfordsaccountants.com
Date Established: 1958
Resident Partners/Directors: ICAEW Members
R W Adams
Resident Partners (Non-ICAEW Members):
P J Hindle
Registered by the ICAEW to carry out company audit work
SPECIALISATIONS – BUSINESS & GENERAL ADVICE
Franchising

COMLEY CONNOR PROFESSIONAL SERVICES LTD ◈
Ingles Manor, Castle Hill Avenue, Folkestone, CT20 2RD
Tel: 0845 094 0590

D.B. LYE & CO
34 Cheriton Gardens, Folkestone, CT20 2AX
Tel: 01303 251742
Fax: 01303 258039
Resident Partners/Directors: ICAEW Members
I F Cloke, J F Moate

MANAGEMENT OF PERSONAL INSOLVENCIES LTD
93 Sandgate High Street, Sandgate, CT20 2BY

R.K. DOBSON
37 Walton Gardens, Folkestone, CT19 5PR

RICHARDS & CO
Bank Chamber, Canterbury Road, Lyminge, Folkestone CT18 8HU
Tel: 01303 862022

SPAIN BROTHERS & CO
29 Manor Road, Folkestone, CT20 2SE
Tel: 01303 252207
Fax: 01303 256679
Website: http://www.spainbrothers.co.uk
Training Contracts Available.
Resident Partners/Directors: ICAEW Members
F Cheney, J R Glenister
Other Offices: Dover, Canterbury
Registered by the ICAEW to carry out company audit work
Regulated by the ICAEW for a range of investment business activities

FORDINGBRIDGE

LEDGER & CO
Brackendene, Lower Daggons, Fordingbridge, SP6 3EE

MICHAEL GLEDHILL
New Court Cottage, Whitsbury, Fordingbridge, SP6 3QB
Tel: 01725 518627
Principal: ICAEW Member
M Gledhill

SALTRICK & SALTRICK LTD
5 The Glasshouse Studios, Fryern Court Road, Burgate, Fordingbridge SP6 1QX

THREE LINES MANAGEMENT LTD
Unit 17, Sandleheath Industrial Estate, Fordingbridge, SP6 1PA

V CLEMAS LTD
Vicarage Farm, Daggons Road, Alderholt, Fordingbridge SP6 3DN

FOREST ROW

CHARLES LAMB
3 Blacklands Crescent, Forest Row, RH18 5NN

CHARLES LAMB PROFESSIONAL SERVICES LTD
3 Blacklands Crescent, Forest Row, RH18 5NN

DMC PARTNERSHIP ★
Yew Tree House, Lewes Road, Forest Row, RH18 5AA

FOWEY

BENNETT JONES & CO
20 Lostwithiel Street, Fowey, PL23 1BE
Tel: 01726 832383

FRINTON-ON-SEA

A.R. ALEXANDER FCA
6 The Sparlings, Kirby-le-Soken, Frinton-on-Sea, CO13 0HD

KCL MANAGEMENT SERVICES
Kinchyle, Church Lane, Frinton-on-Sea, CO13 0JS

KCL MANAGEMENT SERVICES LTD
Kinchyle, Church Lane, Great Holland, Frinton-on-Sea CO13 0JS
Tel: 01255 678881
Resident Partners/Directors: ICAEW Members
T E Reynolds

MURPHY BRITT WOOD ★
2nd Floor, Estate House, Connaught Avenue, Frinton-on-sea, C013 9AB

NJJT
95a Connaught Avenue, Frinton-on-Sea, CO13 9PS

NJJT LTD
95a Connaught Avenue, Frinton-on-Sea, CO13 9PS

FRODSHAM

ATKINSON & CO
Orchard End, The Hurst, Kingsley, Frodsham WA6 8AU

DAVID EVANS & CO
PO Box 113, Frodsham, WA6 7WS
Tel: 01928 590552
Principal: ICAEW Member
D E Evans

MARK GREEVE ACCOUNTING LTD
10 Keswick Drive, Frodsham, WA6 7LU

FROME

A.A. LIGGATT
Dark Haven, Witham Friary, Frome, BA11 5HF
Tel: 01749 850722
Principal: ICAEW Member
A A Liggatt

ANDREW S. FISHER
7 St Michaels Close, Buckland Dinham, Frome, BA11 2QD
Tel: 01373 471728
Email: asf@andrewsfisher.co.uk
Website: http://www.andrewsfisher.co.uk

Principal: ICAEW Member
A S Fisher
Registered by the ICAEW to carry out company audit work
See display advertisement near this entry.

ANGELA WEST
Sunnybank, Woodlands End, Mells, Frome BA11 3PE

BERKELEY HALL LTD
Vallis House, 57 Vallis Road, Frome, BA11 3EG

MCKIE & CO
Rudge Hill House, Rudge, Frome, BA11 2QG

MCKIE & CO LTD
Rudge Hill House, Rudge, Frome, BA11 2QG

GAINSBOROUGH

BOOTH PARKES & ASSOCIATES LTD
Southolme, Trinity Street, Gainsborough, DN21 2EQ

R.N. STORE & CO
26 Hickman Street, Gainsborough, DN21 2DZ
Tel: 01427 617458
Principal: ICAEW Member
B Dalby

RIGEL WOLF LTD
4A Gainsborough Waterfront Enterprise Centre, Lea Road, Gainsborough, DN21 1LX
Tel: 01427 619503
Resident Partners/Directors: ICAEW Members
S R Smith

WEEDEN LTD
Orchard House, 15 Elizabeth Close, Scotter, Gainsborough DN21 3TA

WRIGHT VIGAR LTD ◈
Britannia House, Marshalls Yard, Gainsborough, DN21 2NA
Tel: 01427 611296
Website: http://www.wrightvigar.co.uk
Resident Partners/Directors: ICAEW Members
P D Harrison

SPECIALISATIONS – AUDIT & ASSURANCE

Audit — Private Company

SPECIALISATIONS – SECTOR

Charities

GATESHEAD

ALCHEMY BUSINESS SOLUTIONS LTD
Unit 1, 1 Tenth Avenue West, Team Valley Trading Estate, Gateshead, NE11 0HL

BELL ANDERSON LTD ◈
264-266 Durham Road, Gateshead, NE8 4JR

CLARKES
Clarke's, First Floor, 5 Walker Terrace, Gateshead NE8 1EB
Tel: 0845 458 1211
Resident Partners/Directors: ICAEW Members
P M Clarke, P Cronin

DE WIT & CO
Audit House, Oakwellgate West, Gateshead, NE8 2AU

H. KINGS
18 Birchfield Gdns, Harlow Green, Gateshead, NE9 7TJ

INSPIRE COMPLIANCE LTD
20 Kingsway House, Team Valley, Gateshead, NE11 0HW

INSPIRE YOUR BUSINESS LTD
20 Kingsway House, Team Valley, Gateshead, NE11 0HW

LAVERICK WALTON & CO
Unit B8, Marquis Court, Team Valley, Gateshead, NE11 0RU
Tel: 0191 491 1777
Resident Partners/Directors: ICAEW Members
D H Richardson, K M Thomson

M B ANDERSON & CO
Lindum, 264-266 Durham Road, Gateshead, NE8 4JR

PRONTAX LTD
25 Briardene Drive, South Wardley, Gateshead, NE10 8AN

QUBIC ASSOCIATES LTD
1 Staithes, The Watermark, Gateshead, NE11 9SN

RHK ◈
Coburg House, 1 Coburg Street, Gateshead, NE8 1NS
Tel: 0191 478 1513
Website: http://www.rhk.co.uk
Resident Partners/Directors: ICAEW Members
D C Hall, G Miller, D J Thompson
Resident Partners (Non-ICAEW Members):
B C Thomas, P Storey
Registered by the ICAEW to carry out company audit work

RHK CORPORATE FINANCE LLP ◈
Coburg House, 1 Coburg Street, Gateshead, NE8 1NS
Tel: 0191 478 1513
Resident Partners/Directors: ICAEW Members
D C Hall, G Miller, D J Thompson

ROSENTHAL & CO
106 High West Street, Gateshead, NE8 1NA

GATWICK

BDO STOY HAYWARD LLP
2 City Place, Beehive Ring Road, Gatwick, West Sussex RH6 0PA
Tel: 01293 591000
Fax: 01293 591001
Resident Partners/Directors: ICAEW Members
J P Austin, J L Gilbey, G E Hutton, S J Keeble, D E Powell, J A Roberts, P E H Smith, N J Taylor, N J Thomas, B Thornton, G J Waterworth, R P Williams
Resident Partners (Non-ICAEW Members):
J R Everingham, M J Chadwick

PRICEWATERHOUSE-COOPERS
First Point, Buckingham Gate, Gatwick, West Sussex RH6 0PP

PRICEWATERHOUSE-COOPERS LLP
First Point, Buckingham Gate, Gatwick Airport, Gatwick RH6 0PP
Tel: 01293 566600
Resident Partners/Directors: ICAEW Members
M M Cross, J G Harrison, G J Lambert, C J Maidment, M H Preston, I R A Prideaux, R J Shapland, G S L Shiels, J H T Wright

GERRARDS CROSS

A.C. WAIN & CO
3 Highlands Close, Chalfont St Peter, Gerrards Cross, SL9 0DR

BEVERLEY SIMPSON & CO LTD
10 Russett Hill, Gerrards Cross, SL9 8JY

BLACKBORN LTD ◈
131 High Street, Chalfont St Peter, Gerrards Cross, SL9 9QJ
Tel: 01753 208080
Email: steve.bowman@blackborn.co.uk
Website: http://www.blackborn.co.uk
Resident Partners/Directors: ICAEW Members
S L Bowman
Registered by the ICAEW to carry out company audit work

DJB TAX LTD
1 Moreland Drive, Gerrards Cross, SL9 8BB

ELAINE HAWKINS
Merok, 34 Camp Road, Gerrards Cross, SL9 7PD

GEOFFREY ALAN WHALEY
23 Hillfield Road, Chalfont St Peter, Gerrards Cross, SL9 0DU
Tel: 01753 883684
Principal: ICAEW Member
G A Whaley

GODFREY ANDERSON & CO
6 Latchmoor Way, Gerrards Cross, SL9 8LP
Tel: 01753 889290
Email: sg@godfreyanderson.co.uk
Website: http://www.godfreyanderson.co.uk
Date Established: 1982
Principal: ICAEW Member
S Godfrey

SPECIALISATIONS – FINANCIAL REPORTING

Accounts Preparation

SPECIALISATIONS – TAXATION

Payroll Service and Advice
Taxation
Value Added Tax

General Description: Free consultation: Fixes price quote: Quality assured.

HUDSON & CO
Sterling House, 20 Station Road, Gerrards Cross, SL9 8EL

HUGO & CO
Beech House, West Hyde Lane, Chalfont St Peter, Gerrards Cross SL9 0QP
Tel: 01753 882123
Fax: 01753 884116
Email: mail@hugo.uk.com
Principal: ICAEW Member
H F Moses
Registered by the ICAEW to carry out company audit work

JASANI & CO
54 Dukes Wood Drive, Gerrards Cross, SL9 7LR

KEEN PHILLIPS LTD
21-23 Station Road, Gerrards Cross, SL9 8ES

LEONARD BROWN LTD
Thornbury House, 16 Woodlands, Gerrards Cross, SL9 8DD
Tel: 01753 888785
Resident Partners/Directors: ICAEW Members
L Brown, R W Lane

MRS P.J.TAYLOR
3 Ninnings Road, Chalfont St Peter, Gerrards Cross, SL9 0EF

NUNN HAYWARD ◈
Sterling House, 20 Station Road, Gerrards Cross, SL9 8EL
Tel: 01753 888211
Fax: 01753 889669
Email: mail@nunn-hayward.com
Website: http://www.nunn-hayward.com
Resident Partners/Directors: ICAEW Members
S Dodd, M D Duke, J M Hemmings, I M Nunn, D J Palmer
Non-resident Partners (ICAEW Members):
P Hayward

continued

NUNN HAYWARD *cont*
Resident Partners (Non-ICAEW Members):
S P Cook
Non-resident Partners (Non-ICAEW Members):
D Butler
Other Offices: Aylesbury, New Malden
Registered by the ICAEW to carry out company audit work
Individual(s) licensed for insolvency work by another RPB

ORION ACCOUNTANCY LTD
30 Garners Road, Chalfont St Peter, Gerrards Cross, SL9 0EZ
Tel: 01494 873506
Resident Partners/Directors: ICAEW Members
A J Pickard, C M Pickard

P T DAVIES & CO LTD
Daleside House, 58 Dukes Wood Drive, Gerrards Cross, SL9 7LF

PHILLIPS & CO
21-23 Station Road, Gerrards Cross, SL9 8ES

R.J. FENSOME & CO
15 Fulmer Drive, Gerrards Cross, SL9 7HH

ROGER M. SALISBURY
Cedar Cottage, Denham Lane, Chalfont St Peter, Gerrards Cross SL9 0QQ
Tel: 01753 892035
Principal: ICAEW Member
R M Salisbury

ROY K. PHILLIPS
7 Bentinck Close, Gerrards Cross, SL9 8SQ
Tel: 01753 888177
Principal: ICAEW Member
R K Phillips

WHEELER & CO
24 Dukes Wood Avenue, Gerrards Cross, SL9 7JT
Tel: 01753 882357
Principal: ICAEW Member
P J Wheeler

WHEELER & CO
24 Dukes Wood Avenue, Gerrards Cross, SL9 7JT
Tel: 01753 882357

WHEELER & CO CA LTD
24 Dukes Wood Avenue, Gerrards Cross, SL9 7JT
Tel: 01753 882357
Resident Partners/Directors: ICAEW Members
P J Wheeler

GILLINGHAM

AJ SHONE & CO
Ashley House, Unit 3, Brickfields Business Park, Gillingham SP8 4PX

ANDREWS & PALMER LTD
32 The Square, Gillingham, SP8 4AR

FREESTONE & CO
1 The Centre, The High Street, Gillingham, SP8 4AB

A.L.LIM
11 Magdalen Close, Hampstead, Gillingham, ME7 3TA

AGGARWAL & CO
3-5 London Road, Rainham, Gillingham, ME8 7RG

AGGARWAL & CO LTD
3-5 London Road, Rainham, Gillingham, ME8 7RG

AHMEDI & CO
17 Duncan Road, Gillingham, ME7 4LA

DANIELS & CO ◈
No 1 The Courtyard, Campus Way, Gillingham Business Park, Gillingham ME8 0NZ
Tel: 01634 238709

DANIELS & CO LLP ◈
No 1 The Courtyard, Campus Way, Gillingham Business Park, Gillingham ME8 0NZ
Tel: 01634 238709
Resident Partners/Directors: ICAEW Members
W R Daniels

DAVID R. PLATT
54 William Street, Rainham, Gillingham, ME8 8HW

JAD ASSOCIATES LTD
4 Bloors Lane, Rainham, Gillingham, ME8 7EG

JAD AUDIT LTD
4 Bloors Lane, Rainham, Gillingham, ME8 7EG

M.C. ASSOCIATES LTD
80c Asquith Road, Wigmore, Gillingham, ME8 0JB
Tel: 01634 238900
Fax: 01634 363494
Email: peter@mc-associates.org
Resident Partners/Directors: ICAEW Members
P M Enright

S. AKBAR & CO
1st Floor Rear, Hamilton House, 84/86 High Street, Rainham, Gillingham ME8 7JH

SAKER & CO
142 Darland Avenue, Gillingham, ME7 3AS

STEPHEN HILL PARTNERSHIP LTD
139-141 Watling Street, Gillingham, ME7 2YY

STEPHEN HILL PARTNERSHIP (HOLDINGS) LTD
139 Watling Street, Gillingham, ME7 2YY

W M M JED & CO
6 Old Barn Close, Hempstead, Gillingham, ME7 3PJ

GLASTONBURY

C.J. WIXEY
Fossil Cottage, Havyatt, Glastonbury, BA6 8LF

MONAHANS ◈
1 St Johns Square, Glastonbury, BA6 9LJ
Tel: 01458 836810
Resident Partners/Directors: ICAEW Members
S A Fry

NICHOLAS C.E. HAYWARD
5 Higher Actis, Glastonbury, BA6 8DR

PENN & COMPANY LLP
Tordown, 5 Ashwell Lane, Glastonbury, BA6 8BG

V.R. ANDREAE
57a Chilkwell Street, Glastonbury, BA6 8DE
Tel: 01458 832452
Principal: ICAEW Member
V R Andreae

GLOSSOP

CROSSFIELDS LTD
85/87 High Street West, Glossop, SK13 8AZ

CROSSLEY LOMAS ◈
Ryecroft, 25 Manor Park Road, Glossop, SK13 7SQ
Tel: 01457 866921
Fax: 01457 855759
Email: enquiries@crossleylomas.co.uk
Resident Partners/Directors: ICAEW Members
J M Davenport, G N Lomas

JOHN INGHAM
5 Victoria Street, Glossop, SK13 8HT
Tel: 01457 865209
Principal: ICAEW Member
J Ingham

LOMAS & CO ◈
Bridge House, 12 Market Street, Glossop, SK13 8AR
Tel: 01457 860285

LOMAS AND COMPANY ACCOUNTANTS LTD
Bridge House, 12 Market Street, Glossop, SK13 8AR

MARK FINK CHARTERED TAX ADVISER
Grove House, Back Rowarth, Glossop, SK13 6ED
Tel: 01457 868369
Principal: ICAEW Member
M R Fink

GLOUCESTER

ARNOLD & CO
Annandale House, 105 Eastgate Street, Gloucester, GL1 1PY

ASHFORD & CO
186 Reservoir Road, Gloucester, GL4 6SB

AVALON ACCOUNTING
11 Penny Close, Longlevens, Gloucester, GL2 0NP

BARTLETT KERSHAW TROTT
4 Pullman Court, Great Western Road, Gloucester, GL1 3ND

BERKELEY HAMILTON LLP
5 Pullman Court, Great Western Road, Gloucester, GL1 3ND

BISHOP FLEMING
21 Highnam Business Park, Highnam, Gloucester, GL2 8DN
Website: http://www.bishopfleming.co.uk

BURTON SWEET
Exhibition House, 23 Spa Road, Gloucester, GL1 1UY

BURTON SWEET LTD
Exhibition House, 23 Spa Road, Gloucester, GL1 1UY

CAROL DUNLOP
Pinnolds, Upton Lane, Brookthorpe, Gloucester GL4 0UT

DAVID EXELL ASSOCIATES
2nd Floor, 65 London Road, Gloucester, GL1 3HF

DAY & CO
23 Park Road, Gloucester, GL1 1LH

EVANS & CO
51 Brunswick Road, Gloucester, GL1 1JS

GORDON LOWTHIAN
Garden Cottage, 109d Tewkesbury Road, Longford, Gloucester GL2 9BN

GORDON LOWTHIAN & CO LTD
Garden Cottage, 109D Tewkesbury Road, Longford, Gloucester GL2 9BN
Tel: 01452 730227
Resident Partners/Directors: ICAEW Members
G G Lowthian

GRIFFITHS MARSHALL ◈
Beaumont House, 172 Southgate Street, Gloucester, GL1 2EZ
Tel: 01452 520000
Resident Partners/Directors: ICAEW Members
R G Apted, C J Bourne, S J Humphries

GUILFOYLE, SAGE & CO
58 Eastgate Street, Gloucester, GL1 1QN

GUILFOYLE SAGE GLOUCESTER
58 Eastgate Street, Gloucester, GL1 1QN

HAZLEWOODS LLP
Windsor House, Barnett Way, Barnwood, Gloucester GL4 3RT
Tel: 01452 634800
Website: http://www.hazlewoods.co.uk
Resident Partners/Directors: ICAEW Members
P Fussell, H G E Grove, C J Harvie, D G Main, D Williams
Resident Partners (Non-ICAEW Members):
D Main

SPECIALISATIONS – FINANCIAL REPORTING

International Reporting Standards (IFRS)

SPECIALISATIONS – FORENSIC ACCOUNTING

Expert Witnesses in Litigation

SPECIALISATIONS – SECTOR

Estate Agents

J.G.C. ABBOTT
6 Stoney Field, Highnam, Gloucester, GL2 8LY
Tel: 01452 415281
Principal: ICAEW Member
J G C Abbott

J W ARNOLD & CO LTD
Annandale House, 105 Eastgate Street, Gloucester, GL1 1PY
Tel: 01452 305428
Resident Partners/Directors: ICAEW Members
J W Arnold

JENSEN & CO
15 Water Wheel Close, Quedgeley, Gloucester, GL2 4XH

JOHN KERSHAW
38 High View, Hempsted, Gloucester, GL2 5LN
Tel: 01452 503646
Resident Partners/Directors: ICAEW Members
Lord Kershaw

KINGSCOTT DIX
60 Kings Walk, Gloucester, GL1 1LA
Tel: 01452 520251
Fax: 01452 309439
Email: kdg@kingscott-dix.co.uk
Website: http://www.kingscott-dix.co.uk
Date Established: 1921
Resident Partners/Directors: ICAEW Members
S Baily, J Gorse, P H Morgan, P A Reynaert, D J Turk

Registered by the ICAEW to carry out company audit work

Regulated by the ICAEW for a range of investment business activities

LAURENCE MYEARS
6 Beechcroft Road, Longlevens, Gloucester, GL2 9HF
Tel: 01452 505707
Principal: ICAEW Member
L C Myears

LITTLE & CO
45 Park Road, Gloucester, GL1 1LP
Tel: 01452 308966
Fax: 01452 302195
Email: mail@littglos.co.uk
Website: http://www.littglos.co.uk
Resident Partners/Directors: ICAEW Members
S T Dudfield, M Woof

Registered by the ICAEW to carry out company audit work

Regulated by the ICAEW for a range of investment business activities

SPECIALISATIONS – FORENSIC ACCOUNTING

Expert Witnesses in Litigation
Forensic Accounting

SPECIALISATIONS – SECTOR

Doctors
Solicitors

General Description: A general practice, specialising in doctors, solicitors and forensic accounting.

MACDONALD & CO
209 Barnwood Road, Gloucester, GL4 3HS
Tel: 01452 616204
Principal: ICAEW Member
L.R. Macdonald

MJ BUSINESS SERVICES LTD ◈
9 Kenilworth Avenue, Gloucester, GL2 0QJ
Tel: 01452 504106
Resident Partners/Directors: ICAEW Members
M J Ghanti

P AND W ACCOUNTANTS
202 Fieldcourt Gardens, Quedgeley, Gloucester, GL2 4UE

P.S. MOON AND CO
P & M Business Centre, 28 Hempsted Lane, Gloucester, GL2 5JA

PAUL DAVIS
57 Chiltern Road, Quedgeley, Gloucester, GL2 4TU
Tel: 01452 721547
Principal: ICAEW Member
P C Davis

PITT, GODDEN & TAYLOR ◈
Brunel House, George Street, Gloucester, GL1 1BZ
Tel: 01452 308153
Email: mike.godden@pg-t.co.uk
Website: http://www.pittgoddentaylor.co.uk
Resident Partners/Directors: ICAEW Members
M D Godden, E H Price, P T Shiers, P J Taylor

Registered by the ICAEW to carry out company audit work

Regulated by the ICAEW for a range of investment business activities

PRICEWATERHOUSE-COOPERS
Lennox House, Beaufort Buildings, Spa Road, Gloucester GL1 1XD

PRICEWATERHOUSE-COOPERS LLP
Lennox House, 7 Beaufort Buildings, Spa Road, Gloucester GL1 1XD
Tel: 01452 332200

QUINEY & CO ◈
Trinley Cottage, Main Road, Tirley, Gloucester GL19 4EU
Tel: 01452 780706
Principal: ICAEW Member
P L Quiney

RIDGE HOUSE ASSOCIATES LTD
Ridge House, Over Old Road, Hartpury, Gloucester GL19 3DH
Tel: 01452 700716
Resident Partners/Directors: ICAEW Members
G E Jell

ROBERT POWELL
A3 Spinnaker House, Spinnaker Road, Hempsted Lane, Gloucester GL2 5FD

ROGER W. TOVEY
30 Maidenhall, Highnam, Gloucester, GL2 8DL
Tel: 01452 301633
Principal: ICAEW Member
R W Tovey

S.K. BHATT
178 Stroud Road, Gloucester, GL1 5JX
Tel: 01452 386084
Principal: ICAEW Member
S K Bhatt

SLOANE WALKER
33 Rosedale Close, Hardwicke, Gloucester, GL2 4JL
Tel: 07790 087335

STELLA JENSEN
15 Water Wheel Close, Quedgeley, Gloucester, GL2 4XH

GODALMING

A.HARRISON & CO ◈
1 St Johns Court, Farncombe Street, Godalming, GU7 3BA
Tel: 01483 420039
Principal: ICAEW Member
A Harrison

BARNETT SPOONER
The Old Steppe House, Brighton Road, Godalming, GU7 1NS

CAROLINE CHETWOOD
Banacle Field, Church Lane, Brook, Godalming GU8 5UQ

CHAMBERLAINS
3 Burford Lea, Elstead, Godalming, GU8 6HT

AVN CHURCHMILL
Churchmill House, Ockford Road, Godalming, GU7 1QY
Tel: 01483 520100
Resident Partners/Directors: ICAEW Members
D C Speller

CLEAVER & CO
114A High Street, Godalming, GU7 1DW

COAKLEY & CO
West House, Milford Road, Elstead, Godalming GU8 6HF
Tel: 01252 702218
Resident Partners/Directors: ICAEW Members
A B Coakley, D B Coakley

DELIA ORME
Branksome House, Filmer Grove, Godalming, GU7 3AB
Tel: 01483 869991
Principal: ICAEW Member
D J Orme

SPECIALISATIONS – TAXATION

Capital Gains — Limited Companies
Capital Gains — Personal
Employee
Estate and Inheritance
Estate Planning
Executorship
Foreign Nationals in the UK
Partnerships and Sole Traders
Personal
Taxation
Trusteeship
Trusts
UK Nationals Overseas

HUGHES WADDELL
The White House, 2 Meadrow, Godalming, GU7 3HN

INMAN WAVERLEY
36 New Road, Milford, Godalming, GU8 5BE

INTEGER
Highview, Latimer Road, Godalming, GU7 1BW

J.F. JACKMAN
Tilthams Farm, Tilthams Corner Road, Godalming, GU7 3DE

JAMES TERRY
Court Vale, Church Lane, Hambledon, Godalming GU8 4DS

KNIGHT EVANS
11 Church Street, Godalming, GU7 1EQ

KNIGHT EVANS LTD
11 Church Street, Godalming, GU7 1EQ

LAVERTY & CO
Rectory Cottage, Church Road, Hascombe, Godalming GU8 4JD

LOVELAWN LTD
Lawn Cottage, Portsmouth Road, Milford, Godalming GU8 5HZ

LUCAS & CO
1 Mint Street, Godalming, GU7 1HE
Tel: 01483 424950
Principal: ICAEW Member
A D Lucas

MOORE PEARMAN
The Old Barn, The Bridge, Lower Eashing, Godalming GU7 2QF

PATRICK FORD ◈
Leybourne Lodge, Combe Lane, Wormley, Godalming GU8 5TP

R. CLAPSHAW
Norney Grange, Shackleford, Godalming, GU8 6AY

ROFFE SWAYNE ◈
Ashcombe Court, Woolsack Way, Godalming, GU7 1LQ
Tel: 01483 416232
Fax: 01483 426617
Website: http://www.roffeswayne.com
Resident Partners/Directors: ICAEW Members
C R Baxter, R W Edmondson, J R Fisher, J A K Gardner, A Kelly, M S Leigh, S E Ward, L A Warner, E F Way

ROGER NEWNES-SMITH
Woodend, Lower Moushill Lane, Milford, Godalming GU8 5JX
Tel: 01483 423001
Principal: ICAEW Member
R Newnes-Smith

SHIPLEYS LLP
3 Godalming Business Centre, Woolsack Way, Godalming, GU7 1XW
Tel: 01483 423607
Fax: 01483 426079
Email: godalming@shipleys.com
Website: http://www.shipleys.com
Resident Partners/Directors: ICAEW Members
J M A Henman, S W Robinson
Resident Partners (Non-ICAEW Members):
M Luckett, S Foster
Other Offices: London, Saffron Walden
Registered by the ICAEW to carry out company audit work
Regulated by the ICAEW for a range of investment business activities

STUART DICK & CO LTD
2nd Floor, River Court, Mill Lane, Godalming GU7 1EY

STUART KAY
Elmdene, Ridgley Road, Chiddingfold, Godalming GU8 4QN

WAKELIN & DAY
9 Pound Lane, Godalming, GU7 1BX
Tel: 01483 423054
Email: office@wakelinandday.co.uk
Website: http://www.wakelinandday.co.uk
Resident Partners/Directors: ICAEW Members
A Day, T A McClure
Registered by the ICAEW to carry out company audit work
General Description: The practice has been established in Godalming since 1978 and offers accountancy services to all small/medium sized companies and businesses, including business and personal tax, advice and planning.

GODSTONE

DERBY & CO
52 Hickmans Close, Godstone, RH9 8EB

THE DIFFERENT ACCOUNTANT
1 Orme Cottages, Tilburstow Hill Road, Godstone, RH9 8NP

HUNTERS
10 Catlin Gardens, Godstone, RH9 8NT

GOOLE

CHATWORTH & CO (BUSINESS SERVICES) LTD
Cowick Grange, West Cowick, Goole, DN14 9DH

JONATHAN CARTER LTD ◈
50-52 Aire Street, Goole, DN14 5NQ

MARTIN DODSWORTH ASSOCIATES
1 Richmond Drive, Goole, DN14 5LF
Tel: 01405 760646
Principal: ICAEW Member
M Dodsworth

TAYLORED ACCOUNTANCY SERVICES ◈
Northfield, Low Street, Carlton, Goole DN14 9PN
Tel: 07841 379211
Principal: ICAEW Member
K Taylor

TOWNENDS ★
Carlisle Chambers, Carlisle Street, Goole, DN14 5DX
Tel: 01405 763341
Resident Partners/Directors: ICAEW Members
A Carroll, P Sharpe, F C Verney

TOWNENDS ACCOUNTANTS LTD
Carlisle Chambers, 8-14 Carlisle Street, Goole, DN14 5DX
Tel: 01405 763341
Resident Partners/Directors: ICAEW Members
A Carroll, P Sharpe, F C Verney

WALTHAMS ◈
64-66 Aire Street, Goole, DN14 5QE
Tel: 01405 767400
Fax: 01405 766172
Email: jc@jonathancarter.co.uk
Website: http://www.jonathancarter.co.uk
Mobile: 07971 557163
Date Established: 2008
Resident Partners/Directors: ICAEW Members
W J Carter, A Ingleton
Languages Spoken:
French

GOSPORT

B DENNIS WOOD
42 Fort Road, Gosport, PO12 2BU
Tel: 02392 521303

BRENT & CO
18 Gosport Business Centre, Frater Gate, Aerodrome Road, Gosport PO13 0FQ

BRENT KING LTD
18 Gosport Business Centre, Frater Gate, Gosport, PO13 0FQ
Tel: 01329 848713
Resident Partners/Directors: ICAEW Members
E M King

CHRISTOPHER MALONE
8 Netley Court, Hayling Close, Priddy's Hard, Gosport PO12 4LX

MARSHALL ROCHE ◈
1 Portland Buildings, Stoke Road, Gosport, PO12 1JH

MARSHALL ROCHE LTD ◈
1 Portland Buildings, Stoke Road, Gosport, PO12 1JH

RLW ASSOCIATES LTD
57 Brockhurst Road, Gosport, PO12 3AP

SDW ASSOCIATES
57 Brockhurst Road, Gosport, PO12 3AP

WOOD, HICKS & CO
Units 1-2, Warrior Court, 9-11 Mumby Road, Gosport, PO12 1BS

GRANGE-OVER-SANDS

IAN DALZELL LTD ◈
Broughton Lodge Mews, Field Broughton, Grange-over-Sands, LA11 6HL
Tel: 01539 532619
Resident Partners/Directors: ICAEW Members
I R Dalzell

GRANTHAM

AIMS MATTHEW PENNIFOLD LTD
Kobia, Low Road, Barrowby, Grantham NG32 1DJ
Tel: 01476 569832
Resident Partners/Directors: ICAEW Members
M J Pennifold

C W BARNES LTD
South Lodge, Ropsley, Grantham, NG33 4AS
Tel: 01476 585000
Fax: 01476 585279
Email: stephen.peck@cwbarnes.co.uk
Website: http://www.cwbarnes.co.uk
Resident Partners/Directors: ICAEW Members
S C Peck, R G Rose
Non-resident Partners (ICAEW Members):
R G Rose
Other Offices: Tolethorpe Lodge, 49 Pinchbeck Road, Spalding, Lincs. PE11 18F (Tel: 01775 1723030) (Fax: 01775 761449)

CALLOW & HOLMES
Tattershall House, 19 St Catherine's Road, Grantham, NG31 6TT
Tel: 01476 572814
Fax: 01476 572813
Email: info@callowandholmes.co.uk
Resident Partners/Directors: ICAEW Members
M Callow
Resident Partners (Non-ICAEW Members):
A D Holmes, C Breeze
Registered by the ICAEW to carry out company audit work

SPECIALISATIONS – AUDIT & ASSURANCE
Audit

SPECIALISATIONS – FINANCIAL REPORTING
Accounts Preparation
Limited Companies

SPECIALISATIONS – FORENSIC ACCOUNTING

Forensic Accounting

SPECIALISATIONS – TAXATION

Partnerships and Sole Traders

CLAVERING & CO
Crew-yard House, Water Lane, Stainby, Grantham NG33 5QZ

DUNCAN & TOPLIS
3 Castlegate, Grantham, NG31 6SF
Tel: 01476 591200
Fax: 01476 591222
Email: info@grantham.duntop.co.uk
Website: http://www.duntop.co.uk
Resident Partners/Directors: ICAEW Members
J D Andrew, M J Argyle, K H Johnson, P S Townsend
Resident Partners (Non-ICAEW Members):
A C Severn, T P A Moore, A R Buchanan
Other Offices: Boston, Lincoln, Louth, Melton Mowbray, Newark, Skegness, Sleaford, Spalding & Stamford
Registered by the ICAEW to carry out company audit work
Regulated by the ICAEW for a range of investment business activities

GRAY & WHITE ★
20 St Catherines Road, Grantham, NG31 6TT
Tel: 01476 564399
Resident Partners/Directors: ICAEW Members
T B Lamin

GUY WOODLAND LTD
65 Langford Gardens, Grantham, NG31 8DW

KINGSTON & CO ◈
Rush Lane End, Sudthorpe Hill, Fulbeck, Grantham NG32 3LE
Tel: 01400 272700
Email: mail@kingstonco.co.uk
Principal: ICAEW Member
A J Kingston
Regulated by the ICAEW for a range of investment business activities

RUPERT KING & CO
Stanton House, 31 Westgate, Grantham, NG31 6LX
Tel: 01476 591111

RUPERT KING & COMPANY LTD
Stanton House, 31 Westgate, Grantham, NG31 6LX

SMARTIE & CO LTD
Rosewood, Gt. Ponton Road, Boothby Pagnell, Grantham NG33 4DH
Tel: 01476 585422
Resident Partners/Directors: ICAEW Members
P J Allen

STREETS LLP ◈
St Peters Chambers, 2 Bath Street, Grantham, NG31 6EG
Tel: 01476 590838
Email: info@streetsweb.co.uk
Website: http://www.streetsweb.co.uk
Resident Partners/Directors: ICAEW Members
M P Bradshaw, J Day, P Tutin

GRAVESEND

ALPHA ADVICE
Greenacre, Meopham Green, Gravesend, DA13 0PY
Tel: 01474 813143
Fax: 01474 814518
Email: alpha@westmacott.net
Mobile: 07966 461120
Principal: ICAEW Member
S F Westmacott

SPECIALISATIONS – BUSINESS & GENERAL ADVICE

Management Accounting Consultancy
Management Advice to Business
Overseas Countries

SPECIALISATIONS – SECTOR

Banks/Financial Institutions
Engineers
Transport

General Description:
Management, due diligence, strategy.

THE CARLEY PARTNERSHIP
St James's House, 8 Overcliffe, Gravesend, DA11 0HJ
Tel: 01474 569032
Resident Partners/Directors: ICAEW Members
A J Gooch, B J Hensman, B Owen
Resident Partners (Non-ICAEW Members):
C M Ralph

FULLERS
The Glebe, Shipley Hills Road, Meopham, Gravesend DA13 0AD
Tel: 01474 815006
Resident Partners/Directors: ICAEW Members
J Fuller, K Fuller

GOATCHER CHANDLER
10 Overcliffe, Gravesend, DA11 0EF

GOATCHER CHANDLER LTD
10 Overcliffe, Gravesend, DA11 0EF

HARRISON BERNSTEIN LTD
10 Harmer Street, Gravesend, DA12 2AX

HITCHCOCK, FRANK & CO
Highfield House, White Horse Road, Holly Hill, Meopham, Gravesend DA13 0UF

INTERNAL AUDIT SERVICES LTD
Brunel House, Ediva Road, Meopham, Gravesend DA13 0ND
Tel: 01474 813052
Fax: 01474 812498
Email: RGC@internalaudit.co.uk
Website: http://www.internalauditgroup.com
Resident Partners/Directors: ICAEW Members
R G Clark

SPECIALISATIONS – AUDIT & ASSURANCE

Internal Audit

SPECIALISATIONS – BUSINESS & GENERAL ADVICE

Risk Management

SPECIALISATIONS – BUSINESS RECOVERY & INSOLVENCY

Reorganisations and Company Reconstructions

KING & TAYLOR
10-12 Wrotham Road, Gravesend, DA11 0PE
Tel: 01474 569777
Email: info@kingandtaylor.co.uk
Resident Partners/Directors: ICAEW Members
L Chesterton, T S Climpson, K Hayman, R G H Hiscock, P Humphries
Registered by the ICAEW to carry out company audit work
Regulated by the ICAEW for a range of investment business activities

KSA
141 Parrock Street, Gravesend, DA12 1EY

M.J. HARRIS & CO
35 Whitehill Road, Gravesend, DA12 5PE

MALCOLM HORTON & CO
57 Windmill Street, Gravesend, DA12 1BB

MALCOLM HORTON & CO LTD ◈
57 Windmill Street, Gravesend, DA12 1BB
Tel: 01474 328882
Resident Partners/Directors: ICAEW Members
M C Horton

METSONS
2 Willow Wood Road, Culverstone Green, Gravesend, DA13 0QT

METSONS ACCOUNTANTS LTD
13A The Parade, Wrotham Road, Meopham, Gravesend DA13 0JL

VITAG LTD
9 Laurel Avenue, Gravesend, DA12 5QP

GRAYS

BLAND BAKER
21 Lodge Lane, Grays, RM17 5RY

FARRAND & CO
6 Prince Phillip Avenue, Grays, RM16 2BS
Tel: 05602 287426
Principal: ICAEW Member
C E Farrand

GOLDIN & CO
5 Drake House, Drake Road, Chafford Hundred, Grays, RM16 6RX

MOTASHAW'S
110 Ward Avenue, Grays, RM17 5RL
Tel: 01375 391139
Principal: ICAEW Member
M M Motashaw

ROWLAND HALL ★
44-54 Orsett Road, Grays, RM17 5ED

STEPHEN ROSSER
43 Bridge Road, Grays, RM17 6BU

GREAT MISSENDEN

C E HILL & CO (UK) LTD ◈
Fairacre, Chiltern Road, Ballinger, Great Missenden HP16 9LJ
Tel: 01494 837696
Resident Partners/Directors: ICAEW Members
C E Hill

CALLICOTT & CO
46 Fairacres, Prestwood, Great Missenden, HP16 0LE

CRISPIN M. WHITE LTD
Brambles, Perks Lane, Prestwood, Great Missenden HP16 0JE
Tel: 01494 868685
Resident Partners/Directors: ICAEW Members
C M White

DIANA DOVE
115 High Street, Prestwood, Great Missenden, HP16 9EU
Tel: 01494 865277
Principal: ICAEW Member
D M Dove

DR R K ASHTON
Upton Cottage, Nairdwood Lane, Prestwood, Great Missenden HP16 0QH

HAROLD K PORTER & CO
Honor House, Honor End Lane, Prestwood, Great Missenden HP16 9QZ

JOLLY & CO
Aashiana, Broomfield Close, Great Missenden, HP16 9HX
Tel: 01494 864530
Principal: ICAEW Member
B S Jolly

KAUAI
Broombarn Lane, Great Missenden, HP16 9JD

KAUAI LTD
Broombarn Lane, Great Missenden, HP16 9JD

LANE ACCOUNTING LTD
The White House, Hotley Bottom Lane, Prestwood, Great Missenden HP16 9PL

MARGARET EMERY
Tretawn, St Christopher Close, Little Kingshill, Great Missenden HP16 0DU

NOEL & CO
4 Parliament Close, Prestwood, Great Missenden, HP16 9DT

PETER MITCHELL & CO
95 High Street, Great Missenden, HP16 0AL
Tel: 01494 866119
Resident Partners/Directors: ICAEW Members
R W Lane, B A Makinson, P J D Mitchell

R.W.N. BARRETT
The Hollies, 33 Wycombe Rd, Prestwood, Great Missenden HP16 0NZ
Tel: 01494 890448
Principal: ICAEW Member
R W N Barrett

WILLS & CO
Chaparral, Windsor Lane, Little Kingshill, Great Missenden HP16 0DP

GREAT YARMOUTH

BERRY & WARREN
Hewett Road, Gapton Hall Ind Estate, Great Yarmouth, NR31 0NN

BLOOMFIELD & CO
9 Queen Street, Great Yarmouth, NR30 2QP
Tel: 01493 844030

BLOOMFIELD BUSINESS SERVICES LTD
9 Queen Street, Great Yarmouth, NR30 2QP
Tel: 01493 844030
Resident Partners/Directors: ICAEW Members
J C Bloomfield

CROSS & FAIRHEAD
5 Queen Street, Great Yarmouth, NR30 2QP

CROSS & FAIRHEAD BUSINESS CONSULTANTS LTD
5 Queen Street, Great Yarmouth, NR30 2QP

J.O. RUSSELL
38 Leathway, Ormesby St Margaret, Great Yarmouth, NR29 3QA
Tel: 01493 731395
Principal: ICAEW Member
J O Russell

LOVEWELL BLAKE ◈
Sixty Six North Quay, Great Yarmouth, NR30 1HE
Tel: 01493 335100
Fax: 01493 335133
Email: chd@lovewell-blake.co.uk
Website: http://www.lovewell-blake.co.uk
Date Established: 1858
Resident Partners/Directors: ICAEW Members
S De-Lacy Adams, C H Dicker, R Leggett, R Morris
General Description: The practice has 21 partners and our other offices are listed under our Norwich entry.

M. HOOSE & CO ◈
18/19 South Quay, Great Yarmouth, NR30 2RG
Tel: 01493 842637
Email: tim@mhoose.co.uk
Principal: ICAEW Member
T M Thomas
Registered by the ICAEW to carry out company audit work
Regulated by the ICAEW for a range of investment business activities

PKF (UK) LLP
East Coast House, Galahad Road, Beacon Park, Gorleston, Great Yarmouth NR31 7RU
Tel: 01493 382500
Email: info.gtyarmouth@uk.pkf.com
Website: http://www.pkf.co.uk
Resident Partners/Directors: ICAEW Members
N P Hallett, R A Hawkins, M J Muskett

GREENFORD

ASHTONS
79 Ashness Gardens, Greenford, UB6 0RW
Tel: 020 8900 0031
Principal: ICAEW Member
V M Nathwani
General Description: The firm provides a full range of services to small businesses and individuals.

BRAAMS
First Floor, Allied Sainif House, 412 Greenford Road, Greenford UB6 9AH
Tel: 020 8575 9920
Principal: ICAEW Member
S R Voralia

CHAUDHRI & CHAUDHRI
47 Hodder Drive, Perivale, Greenford, UB6 8LL

CRANLEIGH-SWASH & CO
Greenford Business Centre, I C G House, Station Approach, Oldfield Lane North, Greenford UB6 0AL
Tel: 020 8813 2800
Principal: ICAEW Member
P A Cranleigh-Swash

DISTINCTIVE ACCOUNTANCY LTD
First Floor, Allied Sainif House, 412 Greenford Road, Greenford UB6 9AH
Tel: 020 8575 9920
Resident Partners/Directors: ICAEW Members
S R Voralia

K K ASSOCIATES
Flat 5, Perivale Lodge, Perivale Lane, Perivale, Greenford UB6 8TW

LAM & CO
94 Orchard Gate, Greenford, UB6 0QP

MURRAYS
Greenford Business Centre, I C G House, Station Approach, Oldfield Lane North, Greenford UB6 0AL
Tel: 020 8813 2800

NANAVATI & CO ◈
34 Burwell Avenue, Greenford, UB6 0NU

R.S. PATEL & CO
43 Costons Avenue, Greenford, UB6 8RJ

REHNCYSHAHEEN
1276-1278 Greenford Road, Greenford, Middlesex, UB6 0HH
Tel: 020 8864 9065
Fax: 020 8864 9096
Email: rehncyshaheen@yahoo.com
Website: http://www.rehncyshaheen.com
Resident Partners/Directors: ICAEW Members
J S Rehncy
Non-resident Partners (ICAEW Members):
J S Rehney
Resident Partners (Non-ICAEW Members):
A M Shaheen
Registered by the ICAEW to carry out company audit work

SPECIALISATIONS – BUSINESS & GENERAL ADVICE
Book-keeping

SPECIALISATIONS – TAXATION
Payroll Service and Advice

GRIMSBY

A P ROBINSON LLP
107 Cleethorpe Road, Grimsby, DN31 3ER

ACL
88 Woodhall Drive, Waltham, Grimsby, DN37 0UT

B.H. BELK & CO
35 Hainton Avenue, Grimsby, DN32 9AY

BYGOTT & CO
1-3 Dudley Street, Grimsby, Lincolnshire, DN31 2AW

DJM ACCOUNTANCY LTD
32 Highfield Road, North Thoresby, Grimsby, DN36 5RT

DUNCAN ANDERSON & CO
Temple Chambers, 4 Abbey Road, Grimsby, DN32 0HF

F.W. PETER TABOIS
95 Welholme Avenue, Grimsby, DN32 0BP
Tel: 01472 750850
Principal: ICAEW Member
F W P Tabois

FORRESTER BOYD
26 South Saint Mary's Gate, Grimsby, North Lincolnshire, DN31 1LW
Tel: 01472 350601
Email: grimsby@forrester-boyd.co.uk
Website: http://www.forrester-boyd.co.uk
Resident Partners/Directors: ICAEW Members
M A Beckett, N Ellis, D J Everatt, P S Fearn, K S Hopper, P J Roberts, T I Robinson, M R G Smith
Resident Partners (Non-ICAEW Members):
R H Rowell
Other Offices: Louth, Scunthorpe
Registered by the ICAEW to carry out company audit work
Authorised and regulated by the Financial Services Authority for investment business

HEMMING, VINCENT
31 Abbey Road, Grimsby, DN32 0HQ
Tel: 01472 357038
Principal: ICAEW Member
P M J Vincent

HW
117-119 Cleethorpe Road, Grimsby, Lincolnshire, DN31 3ET
Tel: 01472 382844
Resident Partners/Directors: ICAEW Members
M S Cousins, C G Dedman, A S Minifie, M L Stothard, J A Toulson

HW TAYLOR PRATCHETT
117-119 Cleethorpe Road, Grimsby, DN31 3ET

J R GILLINGWATER
15 Pelham Avenue, Grimsby, DN33 3NA

JOHN R. AGNEW
11 Waterloo Drive, Scartho Top, Grimsby, DN33 3SQ

K.R. CHARLTON
17 Butt Lane, Laceby, Grimsby, DN37 7BB

N C TAYLOR LTD
Temple Chambers, 4 Abbey Road, Grimsby, DN32 0HF
Tel: 01472 348011
Resident Partners/Directors: ICAEW Members
N C Taylor

PELHAM
Pelham Business Centre, 16 Dudley Street, Grimsby, DN31 2AB

SMETHURST & BUCKTON
12 Abbey Road, Grimsby, DN32 0HL
Tel: 01472 357125

SMETHURST & BUCKTON LTD
12 Abbey Road, Grimsby, DN32 0HL

T RAWLINSON & CO LTD
127 Cleethorpe Road, Grimsby, DN31 3EW

TAX ASSIST ACCOUNTANTS
Unit 37, Cleethorpes Enterprise Centre, Wilton Road, Jackson Place, Humberston, Grimsby South Humberside DN36 4AS

TAYLOR & CO
Temple Chambers, 4 Abbey Road, Grimsby, DN32 0HF
Tel: 01472 348011

TENON LTD
Europarc Innovation Centre, Innovation Way, Grimsby, DN37 9TT
Tel: 01472 500360

WILSON SHARPE & CO ◈
27 Osborne Street, Grimsby, DN31 1NU
Tel: 01472 348315
Resident Partners/Directors: ICAEW Members
C Sharpe, Stewart Wilson

GUILDFORD

A.J. BENNEWITH & CO ◈
Hitherbury House, 97 Portsmouth Road, Guildford, GU2 4YF
Tel: 01483 539777
Principal: ICAEW Member
A J Bennewith, H Cheesman

AFM
Unit 4, Kernel Court, Walnut Tree Close, Guildford, GU1 4UD

ALAN VAUSE
Wood End, High Cotts Lane, West Clandon, Guildford GU4 7XA
Tel: 01483 222644
Principal: ICAEW Member
A C Vause

ALLIOTTS ◈
Friary Court, 13-21 High Street, Guildford, GU1 3DL
Tel: 01483 533119
Email: guildford@alliotts.com
Website: http://www.alliotts.com
Resident Partners/Directors: ICAEW Members
P J Edwards, R D E Hopes, S J Meredith
Resident Partners (Non-ICAEW Members):
D C Snell
Other Offices: London, Harrow
Overseas Offices: Worldwide through Alliott Group
Registered by the ICAEW to carry out company audit work
Authorised and regulated by the Financial Services Authority for investment business

ALUN CAREW LTD
Cyder House, 11 Pilgrims Way, Guildford, GU4 8AD

ANDREW F. WYE LTD
24 Marlyns Drive, Burpham, Guildford, GU4 7LT

ANSTEE ASSOCIATES
The Old Mission Hall, 53a Woking Road, Guildford, GU1 1QD

ASHDOWN PRICE
4 Beaufort, Parklands, Guildford, GU2 2JX

BAKER TILLY
The Clock House, 140 London Road, Guildford, GU1 1UW
Tel: 01483 307000
Resident Partners/Directors: ICAEW Members
D J Worrow

BAKER TILLY
The Clock House, 140 London Road, Guildford, GU1 1UW
Tel: 01483 307000
Resident Partners/Directors: ICAEW Members
R M Hamlin, C I Hurren, C D Roberts, L F Speller, D C Stewart, D J Worrow

BAKER TILLY
The Clock House, 140 London Road, Guildford, GU1 1UW

BAKER TILLY RESTRUCTURING AND RECOVERY LLP
The Clock House, 140 London Road, Guildford, GU1 1UW
Tel: 01483 307000
Resident Partners/Directors: ICAEW Members
M B Rodgers, M R M Wild

BAKER TILLY REVAS LTD
The Clock House, 140 London Road, Guildford, GU1 1UW

BAKER TILLY TAX AND ADVISORY SERVICES LLP
The Clock House, 140 London Road, Guildford, GU1 1UW
Tel: 01483 307000
Resident Partners/Directors: ICAEW Members
L J Ballard, J R Burnie, R M Hamlin, M J A Holland, K C Holliday, C I Hurren, C D Roberts, M B Rodgers, L F Speller, D C Stewart, M R M Wild, D J Worrow
Resident Partners (Non-ICAEW Members):
M D Collins, M G Down, G P Heynes

BESSLER HENDRIE
Albury Mill, Mill Lane, Chilworth, Guildford GU4 8RU
Tel: 01483 240240
Fax: 01483 240241
Email: bh@besslerhendrie.co.uk
Resident Partners/Directors: ICAEW Members
P A Bessler, N I Bolt, C D Chamberlain, J M Hendrie, P R Nicholls
Registered by the ICAEW to carry out company audit work
Regulated by the ICAEW for a range of investment business activities

BREWERS
Bourne House, Queen Street, Gomshall, Guildford GU5 9LY

BRISTOW BURRELL ◈
4 Riverview, Walnut Tree Close, Guildford, GU1 4UX
Tel: 01483 573287
Fax: 01483 459304
Email: office@bristowburrell.co.uk
Date Established: 1972
Training Contracts Available.

continued

BRISTOW BURRELL *cont*
Resident Partners/Directors: ICAEW Members
G W Hetherington, W B D Sleap, R Spicer
Registered by the ICAEW to carry out company audit work
See display advertisement near this entry.

CALDWELL PENN
1 Bramley Business Centre, Station Road, Bramley, Guildford GU5 0AZ

CAREW & CO
Cyder House, 11 Pilgrims Way, Guildford, GU4 8AD

CMB PARTNERSHIP ◈
Chapel House, 1 Chapel Street, Guildford, GU1 3UH
Tel: 01483 455508
Resident Partners/Directors: ICAEW Members
R M Brown, C P Campbell, P Martin

CREACTION LTD
27 Meads Road, Guildford, GU1 2NB

DAYMAR LTD
15 Partridge Way, Merrow Park, Guildford, GU4 7DW
Tel: 01483 457901
Resident Partners/Directors: ICAEW Members
D J Pugh

DJB AUDIT LTD
3000 Cathedral Hill, Guildford, GU2 7YB

ELLIS BANKS
Sophy Cottage, Ripley Road, East Clandon, Guildford GU4 7SG

FJA ◈
1 Shalford Road, Guildford, GU1 3XL
Tel: 01483 564216
Principal: ICAEW Member
F Anayi

GEOFFREY COLLINS & CO
Parallel House, 32 London Road, Guildford, GU1 2AB
Tel: 0845 330 9916

HANDLEY ROBERTS ★
4 Quarry Court, Lime Quarry Mews, Guildford, GU1 2RD
Tel: 01483 456677

HEATHER & CO LTD ◈
Longlac, White House Lane, Jacobs Well, Guildford GU4 7PT
Tel: 01483 568082
Resident Partners/Directors: ICAEW Members
S J Heather

HELEN LEE
55 Wodeland Avenue, Guildford, GU2 4LA
Tel: 01483 822655
Principal: ICAEW Member
H M Lee

I.A. ANDERSON & CO
1 Three Pears Road, Merrow, Guildford, GU1 2XU
Tel: 01483 534427
Principal: ICAEW Member
I A Anderson

J.P. SURREY
Mulberry House, 8 Horseshoe Lane West, Guildford, GU1 2SX

JAMES RICHARDSON
The Clock House, 140 London Road, Guildford, GU1 1UW

JANE H. GILLBE
Annfield House, 5 Maori Road, Guildford, GU1 2EG

JOHN N. ALLEN
15 Ellis Avenue, Onslow Village, Guildford, GU2 7SR

KEITH JONES
Pendower, Laustan Close, Merrow, Guildford GU1 2TS

KEITH MCDONALD
27 Meads Road, Guildford, GU1 2NB

KIMBERS
25 Cardwells Keep, Guildford, GU2 9PD
Tel: 01483 560603
Principal: ICAEW Member
M D Kimber

LANCE HAVELL
77 Cumberland Avenue, Guildford, GU2 9RH

LINDA J. SHARPIN ◈
Mayfield House, 2 Ganghill, Guildford, GU1 1XE
Tel: 01483 839561
Principal: ICAEW Member
L J Sharpin

LYNETTE BARLING
4 Wych Elm Rise, Guildford, GU1 3TH

M. DINE
Stoke Lodge, Aldersey Road, Guildford, GU1 2ES

MCPHERSONS
60 Chertsey Street, Guildford, GU1 4HL

MCPHERSONS ACCOUNTANCY LTD
60 Chertsey Street, Guildford, GU1 4HL

MBI
Second Floor, Tunsgate Square, 98-110 High Street, Guildford GU1 3HE

MBI COAKLEY LTD
Second Floor, Tunsgate Square, 98-110 High Street, Guildford GU1 3HE
Tel: 0845 310 2776
Resident Partners/Directors: ICAEW Members
D B Coakley
Individual(s) licensed for insolvency work by the ICAEW
Individual(s) licensed for insolvency work by another RPB

MOORE STEPHENS LLP ◈
Priory House, Pilgrims Court, Sydenham Road, Guildford GU1 3RX

MORLEY TIPPETT
White Park Barn, Loseley Park, Guildford, GU3 1HS
Tel: 01483 450518
Email: jonathan.tippett@morleytippett.co.uk
Website: http://www.morleytippett.co.uk
Principal: ICAEW Member
J C M Tippett

SPECIALISATIONS – SECTOR

Agriculture

SPECIALISATIONS – TAXATION

Personal
Trusts

NEXIA SMITH & WILLIAMSON AUDIT LTD
1 Bishops Wharf, Walnut Tree Close, Guildford, GU1 4RA

NIHONBO LTD
Stonelands, Thorncombe Street, Bramley, Guildford GU5 0LU
Tel: 01428 681574
Resident Partners/Directors: ICAEW Members
J P A Snelling

PERERA LYNCH
Hornhatch Farm, Rices Corner, New Road, Shalford, Guildford GU4 8HS
Tel: 01483 574143
Principal: ICAEW Member
R J C Lynch

PKF (UK) LLP
Pannell House, Park Street, Guildford, GU1 4HN
Tel: 01483 564646
Email: info.guildford@uk.pkf.com
Website: http://www.pkf.co.uk
Resident Partners/Directors: ICAEW Members
M Bridge, S C Collins, R J Faulkner, J C Giles, J W M Hills, V A Martin-Long, R R Whitlock
Resident Partners (Non-ICAEW Members):
P Jun Tai, C Latos, W Jeffries, P Potter

POWELL & CO
Manor Cottage, Shamley Green, Guildford, GU5 0UD
Tel: 01483 892394
Principal: ICAEW Member
S A W Powell

RANDALL GREENE
Parallel House, 32/34 London Road, Guildford, GU1 2AB
Tel: 01483 230440
Fax: 01483 230441
Email: mail@randallgreene.com
Principal: ICAEW Member
C R Greene

SPECIALISATIONS – FINANCIAL REPORTING

Limited Companies

SPECIALISATIONS – INVESTMENT BUSINESS

Planning

SPECIALISATIONS – TAXATION

Estate and Inheritance
Estate Planning
Executorship
Personal
Taxation
Trusteeship
Trusts

General Description: Niche private client firm for tax, trust, accounting services.

RICHARD FLOYD & CO
29 Roseacre Gardens, Chilworth, Guildford, GU4 8RQ

S. DUNNING FCA
8 Dunlin Rise, Merrow, Guildford, GU4 7DX
Tel: 01483 827694
Principal: ICAEW Member
S Dunning

S P 2 CONSULTING LTD ◈
Long Spinney, Burrows Lane, Gomshall, Guildford GU5 9QE
Tel: 01483 203167
Resident Partners/Directors: ICAEW Members
S E Parker

SMITH & WILLIAMSON LTD
1 Bishops Wharf, Walnut Tree Close, Guildford, GU1 4RA
Tel: 01483 407100
Fax: 01483 301232
Email: firstname.lastname@smith.williamson.co.uk
Website: http://www.smith.williamson.co.uk
Resident Partners/Directors: ICAEW Members
S R J Briggs
Resident Partners (Non-ICAEW Members):
M I Keane, R W L Horton
General Description: Smith & Williamson is an independent professional and financial services group employing over 1400 people. We are leading providers of investment management, financial advisory and accountancy services to

private clients, professional practices and mid-sized companies. Nexia Smith & Williamson Audit (Bristol) LLP provides audit services to complement the specialist financial advisory services provided by Smith & Williamson.

STONHAM.CO
1 Farnham Road, Guildford, GU2 4RG

VENTURE ALLIANCE CORPORATE FINANCE LTD ◈
18 Chinthurst Park, Shalford, Guildford, GU4 8JH
Tel: 01483 300098
Resident Partners/Directors: ICAEW Members
P G Catherall, Z Mursaleen, S C Radford

W.A. HODGETTS
Berachah, 1a Laustan Close, Merrow, Guildford GU1 2TS

WHITTINGTONS ◈
1 High Street, Guildford, GU2 4HP
Tel: 01483 456363
Email: peter@blackcataccounts.com
Principal: ICAEW Member
P D Raper

WILKINS KENNEDY ◈
Mount Manor House, 16 The Mount, Guildford, GU2 4HS
Tel: 01483 306318
Website: http://www.wilkinskennedy.com
Resident Partners/Directors: ICAEW Members
K R Young
Other Offices: Amersham, Ashford, Egham, Hertford, London, Orpington, Reading, Romsey, Southend, Winchester
Overseas Offices: Stanley, Falkland Islands
Registered by the ICAEW to carry out company audit work

SPECIALISATIONS – BUSINESS & GENERAL ADVICE

Acquisitions and Mergers
Disposal of Businesses
Outsourcing - Financial Services

SPECIALISATIONS – BUSINESS RECOVERY & INSOLVENCY

Bankruptcies
Corporate Recovery
Liquidations
Reorganisations and Company Reconstructions

SPECIALISATIONS – FORENSIC ACCOUNTING

Expert Witnesses in Litigation

SPECIALISATIONS – SECTOR

Charities
Construction
Property
Solicitors

GUISBOROUGH

DRAYCOTT & KIRK ◈
Cleveland House, 92 Westgate, Guisborough, TS14 6AP
Tel: 01287 634281
Resident Partners/Directors: ICAEW Members
R M Draycott, R D Kirk

LEGG & CO
1 Westerdale Court, Guisborough, TS14 6FB

MICHAEL GALE & CO
1a Chaloner Street, Guisborough, TS14 6QD

MICHAEL GALE & CO LTD
1 Chaloner Street, Guisborough, TS14 6QD

S V BYE ◈
New Garth House, Upper Garth Gardens, Guisborough, TS14 6HA
Tel: 01287 612 000
Resident Partners/Directors: ICAEW Members
M A Beeforth, E F Gosney, E Hamilton, D C Robinson

HAILSHAM

A.B. GRIFFITHS & CO LTD
93 Ersham Road, Hailsham, BN27 3LH

DAVISON CBS
Rushwyck House, Old Road, Herstmonceux, Hailsham BN27 1PU

HANDLEY ROBERTS ★
1 The Courtyard, Chalvington, Hailsham, BN27 3TD
Tel: 01323 811111
Resident Partners/Directors: ICAEW Members
W J Handley

JAMES POLLARD
The Old Farm, Trolliloes, Cowbeech, Hailsham BN27 4QR

MANAGEMENT CONSULTANCY SERVICES LTD ◈
Carters Corner Farm, Cowbeech Hill, Cowbeech, Hailsham BN27 4JA

PLUMMER PARSONS
5 North Street, Hailsham, BN27 1DQ

PLUMMER PARSONS ACCOUNTANTS LTD ◈
5 North Street, Hailsham, BN27 1DQ

WATSON ASSOCIATES ★
30-34 North Street, Hailsham, BN27 1DW

HALESOWEN

ASHCROFTS
34 Hartsbourne Drive, Halesowen, B62 8ST

BOWKER, STEVENS & CO
Suite No. 2, Centre Court, Vine Lane, Halesowen B63 3EB
Tel: 0121 585 6866
Principal: ICAEW Member
K F Cooke

BURNLEY & EVANS
7 Centre Court, Vine Lane, Halesowen, B63 3EB

D TURBERFIELD
35b Beecher Street, Halesowen, B63 2DP

DAVID CUTTER & CO
2 Lyttleton Court, Birmingham Street, Halesowen, B63 3HN

E R GROVE & CO LTD
Grove House, Unit 1, Coombswood Court, Steelpark Road, Halesowen, B62 8BF

HARRISON JONES & CO
Excelsior House, Mucklow Hill, Halesowen, B62 8EP
Tel: 0121 585 5228
Principal: ICAEW Member
P Harrison

HENN & WESTWOOD
Rumbow House, Rumbow, Halesowen, B63 3HU
Tel: 01902 870700
Resident Partners/Directors: ICAEW Members
R W Aldridge, E Lockey

HSP NICKLIN
Church Court, Stourbridge Road, Halesowen, B63 3TT
Tel: 0121 550 9916
Resident Partners/Directors: ICAEW Members
C R Cook, I A Davies, H J Owen

SPECIALISATIONS – SECTOR

Doctors

KENNETH JONES & CO LTD
4 Summer Hill, Halesowen, B63 3BU
Tel: 0121 550 1111
Resident Partners/Directors: ICAEW Members
K E Jones

KINGETT'S
Carolyn House, 5 Dudley Road, Halesowen, B63 3LS

NICKLIN ACCOUNTANCY SERVICES LTD
Church Court, Stourbridge Road, Halesowen, B63 3TT

NICKLIN LLP
Church Court, Stourbridge Road, Halesowen, B63 3TT
Tel: 0121 550 9916
Fax: 0121 550 9390
Email: info@nicklins.co.uk
Website: http://www.nicklins.co.uk
Training Contracts Available.
Resident Partners/Directors: ICAEW Members
C R Cook, H J Owen
Registered by the ICAEW to carry out company audit work
Regulated by the ICAEW for a range of investment business activities

INVESTOR IN PEOPLE

SPECIALISATIONS – AUDIT & ASSURANCE

Assurance Services

SPECIALISATIONS – FINANCIAL REPORTING

Foreign Subsidiary Companies

SPECIALISATIONS – INVESTMENT BUSINESS

Financial Planning and Advice

SPECIALISATIONS – TAXATION

Taxation

STEPHEN W. JONES ◈
King Edward House, 82 Stourbridge Road, Halesowen, B63 3UP
Tel: 0121 550 0065
Principal: ICAEW Member
S W Jones

STEVEN GURMIN
122 Hamilton Avenue, Halesowen, B62 8SJ

HALESWORTH

LOVEWELL BLAKE ◈
The Wherry, Quay Street, Halesworth, IP19 8ET
Tel: 01986 873163
Fax: 01986 874523
Email: bcb@lovewell-blake.co.uk
Website: http://www.lovewell-blake.co.uk
Resident Partners (Non-ICAEW Members):
B C Bale

continued

LOVEWELL BLAKE *cont*
General Description: The practice has 21 partners and our other offices are listed under our Norwich entry.

PHILIP GORROD
High Hill House, 30 London Road, Halesworth, IP19 8LR
Tel: 01986 875354
Principal: ICAEW Member
P J Gorrod

HALIFAX

A.S. ROBINSON
17 Ingham Close, Bradshaw, Halifax, HX2 9PQ
Tel: 01422 245889
Principal: ICAEW Member
A S Robinson

B M HOWARTH ◈
West House, King Cross Road, Halifax, HX1 1EB
Tel: 01422 352517
Email: halifax@bm-howarth.co.uk
Resident Partners/Directors: ICAEW Members
C Bell, C R Moorby

B M HOWARTH LTD
West House, Kings Cross Road, Halifax, HX1 1EB

BAIRSTOW & ATKINSON ◈
Carlton House, Bull Close Lane, Halifax, HX1 2EG
Tel: 01422 366388
Resident Partners/Directors: ICAEW Members
G R Andrews, A Bamforth, B Craven, P Dyson
Registered by the ICAEW to carry out company audit work
Regulated by the ICAEW for a range of investment business activities

BEGBIES TRAYNOR LTD
36 Clare Road, Halifax, HX1 2HX
Tel: 01422 348448
Resident Partners (Non-ICAEW Members):
P Sargent
SPECIALISATIONS – BUSINESS RECOVERY & INSOLVENCY
Bankruptcies
Corporate Recovery
Liquidations

BOSTOCKS, BOYCE WELCH
The Counting House, Tower Buildings, Wade House Road, Shelf, Halifax HX3 7PB
Tel: 01274 673642
Resident Partners/Directors: ICAEW Members
A K Biggin

BOSTOCKS, BOYCE WELCH
Empire House, 15 Mulcture Hall Road, Halifax, HX1 1SP
Tel: 01422 359412
Resident Partners/Directors: ICAEW Members
D B Tempest

CROWTHERS LTD
20 Upper Washer Lane, King Cross, Halifax, HX2 7DR

THE DORAN CONSULTANCY
1-2 Hill End House, Norwood Green, Halifax, HX3 8QE
Tel: 01274 600403
Principal: ICAEW Member
J Doran

GEOFFREY ELLIS & CO
Pyenot House, Knowle Top Road, Lightcliffe, Halifax HX3 8SW

HANDLEY & CO
Fern Dene, Savile Rd, Halifax, HX1 2BA
Tel: 01422 366652
Principal: ICAEW Member
J Handley

LAMBERT ROPER & HORSFIELD LTD
The Old Woolcombers Mill, 12-14 Union Street South, Halifax, HX1 2LE
Tel: 01422 360788
Email: mail@lrh.co.uk
Website: http://www.lrh.co.uk
Training Contracts Available.
Resident Partners/Directors: ICAEW Members
N I Frost, K F Lyons, D A Roper, D Thornton
Other Offices: Horbury, Wakefield
Registered by the ICAEW to carry out company audit work
Regulated by the ICAEW for a range of investment business activities
General Description: Specialists in business development and corporate finance. Our one-stop shop approach encompasses wealth management. Members of the UK 200 Group and The Corporate Finance Network.

LEYBOURNE & CO
25 Crossley Hill, Halifax, HX3 0PL

LINDLEY ADAMS
28 Prescott Street, Halifax, HX1 2JL

LINDLEY ADAMS LTD
28 Prescott Street, Halifax, HX1 2JL

LOUISE HIGSON ACA
Dean House Farm, Dean House Lane, Stainland, Halifax HX4 9LG

MARGARET PEARSON
2 Mayfield, Hipperholme, Halifax, HX3 8JY

MATTHEWS, BROOKE, TAYLOR & CO
West House, Kings Cross Road, Halifax, HX1 1EB
Tel: 01422 352517

MURGATROYD & CO
12 Popples Drive, Halifax, HX2 9SQ

P. HALEY & CO ◈
Poverty Hall, Lower Ellistones, Greetland, Halifax HX4 8NG
Tel: 01422 376690
Principal: ICAEW Member
P Haley

PETER CROWTHER & CO ◈
50 Broomfield Avenue, Halifax, HX3 0JF

PPI ACCOUNTING LTD
Horley Green House, Horley Green Road, Claremount, Halifax HX3 6AS

RICHARD DUPUY
159 King Cross Road, Halifax, HX1 3LN
Tel: 01422 342315
Principal: ICAEW Member
R Dupuy

RILEY & CO
52 St Johns Lane, Halifax, HX1 2BW
Tel: 01422 341019
Email: mail@rileyandco.co.uk
Website: http://www.rileyandco.co.uk
Registered by the ICAEW to carry out company audit work
Regulated by the ICAEW for a range of investment business activities
SPECIALISATIONS – BUSINESS & GENERAL ADVICE
Book-keeping
SPECIALISATIONS – SECTOR
Charities
Solicitors
SPECIALISATIONS – TAXATION
Investigations
General Description: Expert guidance with a personal touch to small and medium sized businesses and individuals.

RILEY & CO LTD
52 St Johns Lane, Halifax, HX1 2BW

SIGMA
68 Godfrey Road, Halifax, HX3 0ST

SPENSER, WILSON & CO ◈
Equitable House, 55 Pellon Lane, Halifax, HX1 5SP
Tel: 01422 331001
Fax: 01422 365070
Email: enquiries@spenserwilson.co.uk
Website: http://www.spenserwilson.co.uk
Date Established: 1919
Resident Partners/Directors: ICAEW Members
R Hemblys, P Seton, E A Short, J C Yewdall
Registered by the ICAEW to carry out company audit work
Regulated by the ICAEW for a range of investment business activities

STARKEY SAUNDERS
4 Clare Road, Halifax, HX1 2HX

SUTCLIFFE & RILEY ★
3 Central Street, Halifax, HX1 1HU

TOREVELL DENT (BRADFORD) LLP ★
1-3 St Annes Place, Halifax, HX1 5RB

HALSTEAD

HOWLETTS
Aleys Barn, Swan Chase, Swan Street, Sible Hedingham, Halstead CO9 3RB

M W BRAY
Byndes Farm, Pebmarsh, Halstead, CO9 2LZ
Tel: 01787 269009
Principal: ICAEW Member
M W Bray

MOULSHAM AUDITS LTD
Falcon House, 3 King Street, Castle Hedingham, Halstead CO9 3ER

PAUL SUCKLING & CO
Mousetraps, Hall Green, Little Yeldham, Halstead CO9 4LF

QUANTIC ACCOUNTANCY LTD ◈
Mount Nebo, Brickwall Farm, Sible Hedingham, Halstead CO9 3RH
Tel: 01787 460300
Resident Partners/Directors: ICAEW Members
G B Halfhide

RICHARD EDWARDS & CO ★
The Maltings, Rosemary Lane, Halstead, CO9 1HZ

HAMPTON

AKCA CONSULTING ◈
124 Buckingham Road, Hampton, TW12 3JA

AKCA CONSULTING LTD
124 Buckingham Road, Hampton, TW12 3JR
Tel: 020 8487 0483
Resident Partners/Directors: ICAEW Members
A P B Karandawala
SPECIALISATIONS – BUSINESS & GENERAL ADVICE
Management Advice to Business
Management Consultancy

HAMPTON MANAGEMENT RESOURCES LTD
37 Linden Road, Hampton, TW12 2JG

JRG AUBER LTD
2 Castle Business Village, Station Road, Hampton, TW12 2BX

KING & CO
The Dell, Old Farm Road, Hampton, TW12 3RJ
Tel: 020 8979 8139
Principal: ICAEW Member
M C A King

LEE GALLANT
4 Johnsons Drive, Hampton, TW12 2EQ

NIGEL PRICE
Elmestree House, 12 Hawley Close, Hampton, TW12 3XX
Tel: 020 8941 1870
Principal: ICAEW Member
D N Price

PB ASSOCIATES
2 Castle Business Village, Station Road, Hampton, TW12 2BX
Tel: 020 8892 3100
Resident Partners/Directors: ICAEW Members
R J Clement, G P Rees, A Sharif

PENNINGTONS
5 Bushy Park Mews, 53 High Street, Hampton Hill, Hampton TW12 1NH

PETER EDNEY & CO
95 Station Road, Hampton, TW12 2BD
Tel: 020 8979 0287
Principal: ICAEW Member
P W Edney

SRN SONICO
60 Wensleydale Road, Hampton, TW12 2LX

STEPHEN BAUGHAN
3 Ormond Drive, Hampton, TW12 2TP

SUBHASH S KAMATH
267 Uxbridge Road, Hampton Hill, Hampton, TW12 1AR

HARLESTON

HELEN SIDA
Bramble Cottage, Middle Road, Denton, Harleston IP20 0AJ

HELEN SIDA LTD
Bramble Cottage, Middle Road, Denton, Harleston IP20 0AL

TRINITY ACCOUNTING SERVICES LTD
1a Mayflower Way, Harleston, IP20 9EB

HARLOW

GIESS WALLIS CRISP
10/12 Mulberry Green, Harlow, CM17 0ET
Tel: 01279 427431
Fax: 01279 641337
Email: post@gwc-accountants.co.uk
Website: http://www.gwc-accountants.co.uk
Date Established: 1974
Resident Partners/Directors: ICAEW Members
G Armitage, T Crisp, D J Giess, A B Taffs, M Wallis
Registered by the ICAEW to carry out company audit work
Regulated by the ICAEW for a range of investment business activities
SPECIALISATIONS – AUDIT & ASSURANCE
Audit
SPECIALISATIONS – BUSINESS & GENERAL ADVICE
Acquisitions and Mergers
Book-keeping
Company Formation
Management Consultancy
SPECIALISATIONS – FINANCIAL REPORTING
Accounts Preparation
Partnership/Sole Trader Accounts
SPECIALISATIONS – FORENSIC ACCOUNTING
Expert Witnesses in Litigation
SPECIALISATIONS – IT
Computerised Accounting Systems
SPECIALISATIONS – TAXATION
Estate Planning
Payroll Service and Advice
Taxation

M G WHITE & CO ◈
48 Brook Lane Field, Harlow, CM18 7AU
Tel: 07967 828213
Principal: ICAEW Member
M G White

N.K. SUTARIA & CO
Unison, Epping Road, Roydon, Harlow CM19 5HN

PARRY & CO
Unit 1, Temple House Estate, 6 West Road, Harlow CM20 2DU
Tel: 01279 641885
Email: phil@parryandco.com
Resident Partners/Directors: ICAEW Members
C L Crewe, P J Parry
Registered by the ICAEW to carry out company audit work
SPECIALISATIONS – FINANCIAL REPORTING
Limited Company Accounts
Partnership/Sole Trader Accounts
SPECIALISATIONS – TAXATION
Self Assessment Advice
Taxation

PAUL J COOPER
Crumps Cottage, Harlow Common, Harlow, CM17 9NE

PHILLIPS & CO
52 The Chase, Harlow, CM17 9JA
Tel: 01279 410033
Principal: ICAEW Member
M J Phillips

RICHARD BROWN & CO
1 High Street, Roydon, Harlow, CM19 5HJ

HARPENDEN

ANDREW WIGGETT
1st Floor, 15 Station Road, Harpenden, AL5 4SQ
Tel: 01582 712836
Fax: 01582 461169
Email: linda.wiggetts@btclick.com
Principal: ICAEW Member
A J Wiggett
Registered by the ICAEW to carry out company audit work
Regulated by the ICAEW for a range of investment business activities

CONNOR SPENCER & CO
The Leys, Suite 1, 2c Leyton Road, Harpenden AL5 2TL

DIANA GODDEN
65 Alzey Gardens, Harpenden, AL5 5SY

HARDING & CO
11 Kingcroft Road, Harpenden, AL5 1EH

HICKS AND CO ◈
Vaughan Chambers, Vaughan Road, Harpenden, AL5 4EE
Tel: 01582 766677
Fax: 01582 769977
Email: admin@hicks.co.uk
Website: http://www.hicks.co.uk
Date Established: 1980
Resident Partners/Directors: ICAEW Members
M F Corrie, P Dean
Resident Partners (Non-ICAEW Members):
P Sadler
Registered by the ICAEW to carry out company audit work
Authorised and regulated by the Financial Services Authority for investment business

HYMAN CAPITAL SERVICES LTD
33 West Common Way, Harpenden, AL5 2LH

LIBERTY BISHOP C.A LTD
Clayton House, 3 Vaughan Road, Harpenden, AL5 4EF

MAIDMENT JUDD
Charter House, Marlborough Park, Southdown Road, Harpenden AL5 1NL

MJ BROOKS CONSULTANCY LTD
9 Waterside, Station Road, Harpenden, AL5 4US
Tel: 01582 463777
Resident Partners/Directors: ICAEW Members
M J Brooks

NAUGHTEN & CO
2 Carlton Bank, Station Road, Harpenden, AL5 4SU

OUSTON, SIDDERS & CO
9 Aplins Close, Harpenden, AL5 2PZ

PAK YEE & CO
6 The Cleave, Harpenden, AL5 5SJ

R M BATCHELOR ACA
70 Chesterton Avenue, Harpenden, AL5 5SU
Tel: 07721 477795
Principal: ICAEW Member
R M Batchelor

RJN ASSOCIATES LTD
28 Penny Croft, Harpenden, AL5 2PB
Tel: 01582 766770
Resident Partners/Directors: ICAEW Members
R J Andrews

SALLY FERGUSON & CO
66 Luton Road, Harpenden, AL5 2UR
Tel: 01582 622010
Principal: ICAEW Member
S R Ferguson

T AND C SERVICES LTD
76 Townsend Lane, Harpenden, AL5 2RQ
Tel: 01582 622232
Resident Partners/Directors: ICAEW Members
K B Last

THORNTONS
2 Tuffnells Way, Harpenden, AL5 3HH
Tel: 01582 468771
Principal: ICAEW Member
J R Thornton

VICKY PLATT
8 Moreton Avenue, Harpenden, AL5 2ET
Tel: 01582 469988
Principal: ICAEW Member
Vicky C Platt

WHITBY RANDALL & CO
2 Victoria Road, Harpenden, AL5 4EA

WILLIAM SADDLETON
94 Cowper Road, Harpenden, AL5 5NH

HARROGATE

BFE BRAYS
6 Cambridge Crescent, Harrogate, HG1 1PE

BFE BRAYS LTD
6 Cambridge Crescent, Harrogate, HG1 1PE
Tel: 01423 505955
Resident Partners/Directors: ICAEW Members
J M Farndale

THE BURTWISTLE PARTNERSHIP ◈
24 High Street, Pateley Bridge, Harrogate, HG3 5JU
Tel: 01423 711748

THE BURTWISTLE PARTNERSHIP ◈
22 Victoria Avenue, Harrogate, HG1 5PR
Tel: 01423 525641
Resident Partners/Directors: ICAEW Members
D Brown

BUSHELLS ◈
6 Victoria Avenue, Harrogate, HG1 1ED
Tel: 01423 566588
Principal: ICAEW Member
P W Bushell
Registered by the ICAEW to carry out company audit work

C.M.F. PIDGEON ◈
Sandaway, Daleside Park, Darley, Harrogate HG3 2PX
Tel: 01423 780565
Principal: ICAEW Member
C M F Pidgeon

COOK TROTTER LTD
3 Sceptre House, Hornbeam Square North, Hornbeam Park, Harrogate HG2 8PB

DAVID REEVE
Harvern, Colber Lane, Bishop Thornton, Harrogate HG3 3JR
Tel: 01423 771239
Principal: ICAEW Member
D M Reeve

DSC ◈
4 Princes Square, Harrogate, HG1 1LX
Tel: 01423 560547
Resident Partners/Directors: ICAEW Members
J O Campbell, S G Pease

EURA AUDIT UK
Cliff Sidwell Floor, Lishman Chambers, 12 Princes Square, Harrogate HG1 1LY

EURA AUDIT UK
12 Princes Square, Harrogate, HG1 1LY

FISHER WILKINSON
44 Cheltenham Mount, Harrogate, HG1 1DL
Tel: 01423 522451
Resident Partners/Directors: ICAEW Members
D J Fisher, A K Wilkinson

HALL ACCOUNTANCY SERVICES LTD
Sunnycroft, Glasshouses, Pateley Bridge, Harrogate HG3 5QY

HATTERSLEY CLARK
Hammerain House, Hookstone Avenue, Harrogate, HG2 8ER
Tel: 01423 876346
Resident Partners/Directors: ICAEW Members
J C H Clark

HOLEYS
Stuart House, 15/17 North Park Road, Harrogate, HG1 5PD
Tel: 01423 566086
Email: enquiries@holeys.co.uk
Website: http://www.holeys.co.uk
Resident Partners/Directors: ICAEW Members
P C P Durrant, B G Robinson, P Stephenson, T B Yates
Registered by the ICAEW to carry out company audit work

SPECIALISATIONS – AUDIT & ASSURANCE

Audit — Private Company

SPECIALISATIONS – IT

E-commerce

HOWARD MATTHEWS PARTNERSHIP ◈
Queensgate House, 23 North Park Road, Harrogate, HG1 5PD
Tel: 01423 524322
Email: mail@howardmatthews.co.uk
Website: http://www.howardmatthews.co.uk
Resident Partners/Directors: ICAEW Members
A G Crowther, H J Matthews, P D Whetstone

HPH
21 Victoria Avenue, Harrogate, HG1 5RD
Tel: 01423 520623
Resident Partners/Directors: ICAEW Members
A C Rodaway

J.H. WOOD-MITCHELL
3rd Floor, 22 Devonshire Place, Harrogate, HG1 4AA
Tel: 01423 566357
Principal: ICAEW Member
J H Wood-Mitchell

K.H. WRIGLEY & CO
2 Garden Court, Hollins Hall, Lund Lane, Hampsthwaite, Harrogate HG3 2GN

LITHGOW PERKINS LLP
Crown Chambers, Princes Street, Harrogate, HG1 1NJ

MANCHULA LTD
7 Fulwith Close, Harrogate, HG2 8HP

MARK RUMBOLD
20 Stanhope Drive, Harrogate, HG2 7RE

MICHAEL J.R. HEATLEY
4 Gentian Glade, Harrogate, HG3 2NT
Tel: 01423 509629
Principal: ICAEW Member
M J R Heatley

MITCHELLS GROUP LTD
5 Hornbeam Square South, Hornbeam Business Park, Harrogate, HG2 8NB

MITCHELLS (UK) LTD
5 Hornbeam Square South, Hornbeam Business Park, Harrogate, HG2 8NB

OPUS SERVICES LTD
The Laurels, 2 St Leonards Road, Harrogate, HG2 8NX

PATHFINDER STRATEGIC PARTNERS LLP ◈
The Royd, 40 Duchy Road, Harrogate, HG1 2ER

ROBSONS
1a Sykes Grove, Harrogate, HG1 2DB
Tel: 01423 566605
Principal: ICAEW Member
K M Robson

ROUND HALL LTD
14-15 Regent Parade, Harrogate, HG1 5AW

RSM BENTLEY JENNISON ◈
The Hamlet, Hornbeam Park, Harrogate, HG2 8RE
Tel: 01423 859459
Fax: 01423 859460
Email: frank.shackleton@rsmbentleyjennison.com
Website: http://www.rsmbentleyjennison.com
Resident Partners/Directors: ICAEW Members
F M Shackleton
Registered by the ICAEW to carry out company audit work
Authorised and regulated by the Financial Services Authority for investment business

RUTHVEN & CO
Parkside House, 17 East Parade, Harrogate, HG1 5LF

SAFFERY CHAMPNESS ◈
Sovereign House, 6 Windsor Court, Clarence Drive, Harrogate HG1 2PE
Tel: 01423 568012
Fax: 01423 501 798
Website: http://www.saffery.com
Training Contracts Available.
Resident Partners/Directors: ICAEW Members
C J H Adams, A R Robinson
Resident Partners (Non-ICAEW Members):
M A J Holden
Other Offices: Bournemouth, Bristol, Edinburgh, Geneva, Guernsey, High Wycombe, Inverness, London, Manchester, Peterborough
Registered by the ICAEW to carry out company audit work
Regulated by the ICAEW for a range of investment business activities

INVESTOR IN PEOPLE

General Description: See London office entry.

TENON LTD
The Exchange, Station Parade, Harrogate, HG1 1TS
Tel: 01423 503217

THOMPSONS
19 East Parade, Harrogate, HG1 5LF

TLP
3 Greengate, Cardale Park, Harrogate, HG3 1GY

YPO
The Granary, Haggs Farm Business Park, Haggs Road, Harrogate HG3 1EQ
Tel: 01423 878801
Fax: 01423 878809
Email: info@ypoc.org.uk
Mobile: 07768 792771
Date Established: 2001
Resident Partners/Directors: ICAEW Members
W R Gilbert, K A Weston
Registered by the ICAEW to carry out company audit work
Regulated by the ICAEW for a range of investment business activities

HARROW

A J SHAH & CO
Suite E, Fifth Floor, Queens House, Kymberley Road, Harrow, HA1 1US

A J SHAH & CO
8 Pinner View, Harrow, HA1 4QA
Tel: 020 8427 2594
Principal: ICAEW Member
A J Shah

A.M. SHAH & SONS
211 Signal House, 16 Lyon Road, Harrow, HA1 2AQ

A-SPIRE BUSINESS PARTNERS LTD
32 Byron Hill Road, Harrow, HA2 0HY

ABBOTS ★
Printing House, 66 Lower Road, Harrow, HA2 0DH

ADAMS MOORHOUSE
4 Churchill Court, 58 Station Road, North Harrow, Harrow HA2 7ST

AHMED & CO
Ferrari House, 2nd Floor, 102 College Road, Harrow HA1 1ES

ALAN COOPER SAUNDERS ANGEL ◈
Kenton House, 666 Kenton Road, Harrow, HA3 9QN
Tel: 020 8204 9166
Fax: 020 8206 1980
Resident Partners/Directors: ICAEW Members
A A Cooper, M Schuz, R V Stocker
Resident Partners (Non-ICAEW Members):
L C Markoulias, A Michael
Registered by the ICAEW to carry out company audit work
Regulated by the ICAEW for a range of investment business activities

ALAN SECKER & CO ◈
Ground Floor, 4 Churchill Court, 58 Station Road, North Harrow, Harrow HA2 7SA

ALAN SOLOMONS & CO
2 Gayton Road, Harrow, HA1 2XU

ALLIOTTS ◈
Congress House, 14 Lyon Road, Harrow, HA1 2EN
Tel: 020 8861 1771
Email: harrow@alliotts.com
Website: http://www.alliotts.com
Resident Partners/Directors: ICAEW Members
R S Curtis, I Davies, I Gibbon, P C Guinn
Resident Partners (Non-ICAEW Members):
J Withey
Other Offices: London, Guildford
Overseas Offices: Worldwide through Alliott Group
Registered by the ICAEW to carry out company audit work
Authorised and regulated by the Financial Services Authority for investment business

SPECIALISATIONS – BUSINESS & GENERAL ADVICE
Acquisitions and Mergers
Management Advice to Business
Takeovers

SPECIALISATIONS – FINANCIAL REPORTING
Limited Companies
Partnership/Sole Trader Accounts

SPECIALISATIONS – TAXATION
Employee
Executorship
National Insurance Advice

ANDREW KAYE & CO LTD
62 Hesta Buildings, 58-62 High Street, Harrow-on-the-Hill, Harrow HA1 3LL

ANWAR CHAUDHARY & CO
9 Littleton Road, Harrow, HA1 3SY
Tel: 020 8423 6209
Fax: 020 8423 3035
Principal: ICAEW Member
A U H Chaudhary
Registered by the ICAEW to carry out company audit work
Regulated by the ICAEW for a range of investment business activities

ASAD A. RUSHD & CO
74 Walton Road, Harrow, HA1 4UU
Tel: 020 8427 1385
Principal: ICAEW Member
A A Rushd

ASHLEY NATHOO & CO LTD
213b Station Road, Harrow, HA1 2TP

ASHMAR & CO
Marlborough House, 159 High Street, Wealdstone, Harrow HA3 5DX
Tel: 020 8930 8030

ATKINS & PARTNERS
3rd Floor, Brent House, 214 Kenton Road, Harrow, HA3 8BT
Tel: 020 8909 2008
Fax: 020 8909 2011
Email: atkinsitf@aol.com
Principal: ICAEW Member
A M Thanawala
Registered by the ICAEW to carry out company audit work
Regulated by the ICAEW for a range of investment business activities

AZR LTD
2 Gayton Road, Harrow, HA1 2XU
Tel: 020 8901 7520
Fax: 020 8901 4001
Email: zraniwala@azrltd.com
Resident Partners/Directors: ICAEW Members
A Raniwala, Z F H Raniwala
Registered by the ICAEW to carry out company audit work
Regulated by the ICAEW for a range of investment business activities

SPECIALISATIONS – AUDIT & ASSURANCE
Audit
Audit — Private Company

SPECIALISATIONS – BUSINESS & GENERAL ADVICE
Book-keeping
Company Formation
Company Secretarial Service
Management Accounting Consultancy

SPECIALISATIONS – FINANCIAL REPORTING
Accounts Preparation
Audit Exemption Report
Limited Company Accounts
Limited Liability Partnership
Partnership/Sole Trader Accounts

SPECIALISATIONS – TAXATION
Payroll Service and Advice
Taxation
Value Added Tax

B.B. MEHTA & CO
28 Lindsay Drive, Kenton, Harrow, HA3 0TD
Tel: 020 8206 1003
Principal: ICAEW Member
B B Mehta

B J MISTRY & CO
Flat 7, Hanover Court, 112-116 Bessborough Road, Harrow HA1 3DU

BAJAJ & COMPANY. ◈
111 Imperial Drive, North Harrow, Harrow, HA2 7HW
Tel: 020 8866 5558
Principal: ICAEW Member
P K Bajaj

BANCE
11 Bulmer Gardens, Harrow, HA3 0PA

BANCE
276 Preston Road, Harrow, HA3 0QA

BANCE CONSULTANTS LTD
Bance Consultants Limited, 11 Bulmer Gardens, Harrow, HA3 0PA

BANNER & ASSOCIATES LTD
29 Byron Road, Harrow, HA1 1JR

BARBER & CO
2 Jardine House, The Harrovian Bus' Village, Bessborough Road, Harrow HA1 3EX

BENDEL & CO
5 Whitegate Gardens, Harrow Weald, Harrow, HA3 6BW

BHAGANI & CO
Station House, 11 Masons Avenue, Harrow, HA3 5AH

BHATT & CO
20 College Close, Harrow Weald, Harrow, HA3 7BZ
Tel: 020 8420 6145
Principal: ICAEW Member
S L Bhatt

BIPIN VYAS & CO ◈
34 Butler Road, Harrow, HA1 4DR
Tel: 020 8864 3791
Principal: ICAEW Member
B C Vyas

BOLTON SMITH & CO LTD ★
158 High Street, Wealdstone, Harrow, HA3 7AX

CAMERON & ASSOCIATES LTD
35-37 Lowlands Road, Harrow, HA1 3AW

CARRINGTONS ★
Carrington House, 170 Greenford Road, Harrow, HA1 3QX
Tel: 020 8426 5200
Resident Partners/Directors: ICAEW Members
R N Morjaria

CHAPMAN ASSOCIATES
31 Northwick Circle, Harrow, HA3 0EE

CHAPMAN ASSOCIATES (CA) LTD
31 Northwick Circle, Harrow, HA3 0EE

CHARLES L. WYBURN & CO ◈
23 Bellfield Avenue, Harrow, HA3 6ST
Tel: 020 8428 6279
Principal: ICAEW Member
C L Wyburn
Registered by the ICAEW to carry out company audit work
Regulated by the ICAEW for a range of investment business activities

CHARLES RIPPIN & TURNER ◈
Middlesex House, 130 College Road, Harrow, HA1 1BQ
Tel: 020 8420 0540
Email: info@charlesrippin.co.uk
Resident Partners/Directors: ICAEW Members
V Acharya, D Clough
Regulated by the ICAEW for a range of investment business activities

SPECIALISATIONS – SECTOR
Doctors

CHARTERHOUSE (ACCOUNTANTS) LLP
88-98 College Road, Harrow, HA1 1RA
Tel: 020 8863 4566
Fax: 020 8861 2460
Email: info@charter-house.net
Website: http://www.charter-house.net
Resident Partners/Directors: ICAEW Members
M Ackenson, E C Bischoff, J M Edmond, H A Harris, P Ramsey, M J Siddiqui
Resident Partners (Non-ICAEW Members):
D White

CHOTAI & CO
3 Ambassador House, Wolseley Road, Harrow, HA3 5RT
Tel: 020 8861 6000
Principal: ICAEW Member
M M Chotai

COLLINS & CO
2nd Floor, 116 College Road, Harrow, HA1 1BQ
Tel: 020 8427 1888
Principal: ICAEW Member
M N Collins

COMPLETE AUDIT AND ACCOUNTING SOLUTIONS LTD
118-120 Kenton Road, Harrow, HA3 8AL

COOPER GIBSON
32 Parkfield Gardens, Harrow, HA2 6JR
Tel: 020 8427 3603
Principal: ICAEW Member
M R Gibson

CRANENBURGH LTD
88 College Road, Harrow, HA1 1BQ
Tel: 020 8863 8660
Resident Partners/Directors: ICAEW Members
P J Cranenburgh

D.J. COLSON
35 Pebworth Road, Harrow, HA1 3UD

D.M. SHAH
3 Alicia Avenue, Kenton, Harrow, HA3 8HW
Tel: 020 8907 7812
Principal: ICAEW Member
D M Shah

D.S A-WALIA & CO
5 Amery Road, Harrow, HA1 3UH

DATTANI ◈
Scottish Provident House, 76-80 College Road, Harrow, HA1 1BQ
Tel: 020 8427 4004
Principal: ICAEW Member
N Dattani

DAVE & CO
11 Ormesby Way, Kenton, Harrow, HA3 9SE

DAVID MORGAN & CO
52 High Street, Harrow, HA1 3LL

DAVIS & CO ◈
22A Herga Court, Sudbury Hill, Harrow, HA1 3RS
Tel: 020 8764 8320
Principal: ICAEW Member
D P Patel

DUA & CO ◈
Letchford House, Headstone Lane, Harrow, HA3 6PE

DVS TAX LTD
13 Hillbury Avenue, Kenton, Harrow, HA3 8EP

ESKAYS & CO
34 Bellfield Avenue, Harrow, HA3 6SX

F.S. DALAL & CO
4/6 Peterborough Road, 1st Floor, Harrow, HA1 2BQ

FETHERSTONES
276 Preston Road, Harrow, HA3 0QA

FETHERSTONES LTD
276 Preston Road, Harrow, HA3 0QA

FOFARIA & SHAH ★
425 Kenton Road, Kenton, Harrow, HA3 0XY
Tel: 020 8204 1877
Resident Partners/Directors: ICAEW Members
K N Fofaria

FOSTER LEWIS STONE ★
302-308 Preston Road, Harrow, HA3 0QP

GB & CO
Brent House, 214 Kenton Road, Harrow, HA3 8BT
Tel: 020 8909 1614
Principal: ICAEW Member
G Beshahwred

GEE AGGAR & CO
15 Sudbury Court Road, Harrow, HA1 3SD

GEORGE & CO
246 High Road, Harrow Weald, Harrow, HA3 7BB

GP & CO
105 Streatfield Road, Kenton, Harrow, HA3 9BL

HAMMONDS CONSULTANTS LTD
21 The Broadwalk, Pinner Road, Harrow, HA2 6ED

HILL WOOLDRIDGE & CO
Hill Wooldridge & Co Limited, 107 Hindes Road, Harrow, HA1 1RU
Tel: 020 8427 1944
Fax: 020 8863 2081
Email: info@hillwooldridge.co.uk
Website: http://www.hillwooldridge.co.uk
Date Established: 1928
Training Contracts Available.

SPECIALISATIONS – AUDIT & ASSURANCE
Audit

SPECIALISATIONS – BUSINESS & GENERAL ADVICE
Book-keeping
Company Secretarial Service

SPECIALISATIONS – FINANCIAL REPORTING
Accounts Preparation

SPECIALISATIONS – TAXATION
Taxation

Languages Spoken:
Italian
See display advertisement near this entry.

HILL WOOLDRIDGE & CO LTD ◈
107 Hindes Road, Harrow, HA1 1RU
Tel: 020 8427 1944
Resident Partners/Directors: ICAEW Members
G D Allen, I B Park, L Perdoni, J E Soughton

HOWARD N. KENTON
2 Gayton Road, Harrow, HA1 2XU

J W GROGAN
95 Headstone Lane, Harrow, HA2 6JL

JAMEN JONES
77 Manor Way, Harrow, HA2 6BZ

JOHN CUMMING ROSS LTD
Kirkland House, 11-15 Peterborough Road, Harrow, HA1 2AX
Tel: 020 8864 6689
Resident Partners/Directors: ICAEW Members
B B Patel

JSP ACCOUNTANTS
10 College Road, Harrow, HA1 1BE
Tel: 020 8427 0086

JSP ACCOUNTANTS LTD
First Floor, 10 College Road, Harrow, HA1 1BE

JSW ASSOCIATES
Talbot House, 204-226 Imperial Drive, Harrow, HA2 7HH

JSW ASSOCIATES LTD
Talbot House, 204-226 Imperial Drive, Harrow, HA2 7HH

K.D. MISTRY & CO
70 Station Road, North Harrow, Harrow, HA2 7SJ

K.N. SHAH & CO
232a Northolt Road, Harrow, HA2 8DU
Tel: 020 8423 4484
Principal: ICAEW Member
K N Shah

KANAK JUTHANI
6 Brent House, 214 Kenton Road, Harrow, HA3 8BT

LAKE & CO
25a Kenton Park Parade, Kenton Road,Kenton, Harrow, HA3 8DN
Tel: 020 8907 4475
Principal: ICAEW Member
S Lakhani

LAWRENCE & CO ◈
132/134 College Road, Harrow, HA1 1BQ
Tel: 020 8424 9777
Resident Partners/Directors: ICAEW Members
J P Chatwani, R N Popat

LAWRENCE GRANT KIBEL LTD ◈
Hygeia House, 66 College Road, Harrow, HA1 1BE
Tel: 020 8861 7555
Resident Partners/Directors: ICAEW Members
S D Kibel

LAWRENCE JOHNS
202 Northolt Road, Harrow, HA2 0EX

LAWRENCE WONG & CO
2 Parkfield Gardens, North Harrow, Harrow, HA2 6JR
Tel: 020 8427 8717
Principal: ICAEW Member
L C T Wong

LEFTLEY ROWE & CO ◈
The Heights, 59-65 Lowlands Road, Harrow, HA1 3AW
Tel: 020 8515 9797
Email: kevin@leftley-rowe.co.uk
Website: http://www.leftley-rowe.co.uk
Training Contracts Available.
Resident Partners/Directors: ICAEW Members
H Alibhai, J R Dutton, J W Rowe, K J Wright
Registered by the ICAEW to carry out company audit work

SPECIALISATIONS – AUDIT & ASSURANCE

Audit — Private Company

SPECIALISATIONS – BUSINESS & GENERAL ADVICE

Book-keeping
Company Formation
Management Accounting
Consultancy

SPECIALISATIONS – SECTOR

Charities
Dentists/Opticians

SPECIALISATIONS – TAXATION

Payroll Service and Advice
UK Subsidiaries of Overseas Multinationals

See display advertisement near this entry.

LESLEY ANN COOPER
160 Whitmore Road, Harrow, HA1 4AQ
Tel: 0208 8641024
Principal: ICAEW Member
L A Cooper

LINK ◈
1 Admiral House, Cardinal Way, Harrow, HA3 5TE
Tel: 020 8515 2680
Website: http://www.linkca.co.uk
Principal: ICAEW Member
J Kotecha

SPECIALISATIONS – IT

Computer Consultants

SPECIALISATIONS – SECTOR

Hotels/Public Houses
Solicitors

SPECIALISATIONS – TAXATION

Investigations
Self Assessment Advice

M.C. PATEL & CO ★
Hillingdon House, 386/388 Kenton Road, Kenton, Harrow HA3 9DP
Tel: 020 8907 8847
Resident Partners/Directors: ICAEW Members
I N Patel, M C Patel

M J GOLZ & CO
Odeon House, 146 College Road, Harrow, HA1 1BH

M. PATTNI & CO ◈
21 Kingshill Drive, Kenton, Harrow, HA3 8TD
Tel: 020 8907 1807
Principal: ICAEW Member
M M Pattni

MACILVIN MOORE REVERES LLP
7 St John's Road, Harrow, HA1 2EY

MCT PARTNERSHIP
1 Warner House, Harrovian Business Village, Bessborough Road, Harrow HA1 3EX
Tel: 020 8423 6060
Fax: 020 8423 6868
Email: profit@mctpartners.com
Resident Partners/Directors: ICAEW Members
K G Patel, R M Robinson, M C Thakkar
Resident Partners (Non-ICAEW Members):
S Ruparellia

MANIK & CO
7 Manning Gardens, Kenton, Harrow, HA3 0PF
Tel: 020 8907 8677
Principal: ICAEW Member
M T Manikkavasagan

MAPLEWOODS PARTNERSHIP ★
74 The Drive, North Harrow, Harrow, HA2 7EJ

MERALIS
First Floor, Scottish Provident House, 76-80 College Road, Harrow HA1 1BQ

MICHAEL H. SCOTT & CO
107 Kenton Road, Kenton, Harrow, HA3 0AN

N.M. SHAH & CO ◈
The Pavilion, 56 Rosslyn Crescent, Harrow, HA1 2SZ

N.P. SHAH & CO
Unit A2 Livingstone Court, 55 Peel Road, Wealdstone, Harrow HA3 7QT
Tel: 020 8427 5252
Principal: ICAEW Member
N P Shah

N.R. PATEL & CO
19 Hill Crescent, Harrow, HA1 2PW

NAGLE JAMES ASSOCIATES LTD
51/53 Station Road, Harrow, HA1 2TY

NAGLE JAMES FINANCIAL PLANNING LTD
51/53 Station Road, Harrow, HA1 2TY

NAGLE JAY LTD
100 College Road, Harrow, HA1 1BQ

NCR ACCOUNTANTS LTD
Miller House, Rosslyn Crescent, Harrow, HA1 2RZ

NEIL SCOTT & CO
107 Kenton Road, Kenton, Harrow, HA3 0AN

NEWMAN & PARTNERS ◈
Lynwood House, 373/375 Station Road, Harrow, HA1 2AW
Tel: 020 8357 2727
Fax: 020 8357 2027
Email: accounts@newmanandpartners.co.uk
Website: http://www.newmanandpartners.com
Resident Partners/Directors: ICAEW Members
D M Finn, A R Gangola, A Koshal, R Nyman, H V Patel, L R Perez, P Radia

continued

NEWMAN & PARTNERS *cont*
Non-resident Partners (Non-ICAEW Members):
P Stafford
Other Offices: Southend
Registered by the ICAEW to carry out company audit work
Authorised and regulated by the Financial Services Authority for investment business

P.H. ROSS AND CO
18 Woodcock Dell Avenue, Kenton, Harrow, HA3 0NS

P LEIWY & CO LTD
74 Salisbury Road, Harrow, HA1 1NZ
Tel: 020 8357 0423
Resident Partners/Directors: ICAEW Members
P Leiwy

P R PATEL & CO
2 Admiral House, Cardinal Way, Harrow, HA3 5UT
Tel: 020 8427 5550
Principal: ICAEW Member
P R Patel

PARESH SHAH ◈
128 Malvern Gardens, Harrow, HA3 9PG
Tel: 020 8204 1531
Principal: ICAEW Member
P L Shah

PAUL CATHERALL
Holm Oak, Mount Park Avenue, Harrow on the Hill, Harrow HA1 3JN

PEER ROBERTS LTD
The Pavilion, 56 Rosslyn Crescent, Harrow, HA1 2SZ
Tel: 020 8863 2234
Resident Partners/Directors: ICAEW Members
D D Shah

PEERS ROBERTS
The Pavilion, 56 Rosslyn Crescent, Harrow, HA1 2SZ

AIMS - PHILIP WILSON
90 Pinner Park Avenue, Harrow, HA2 6JU
Tel: 020 8428 8982
Principal: ICAEW Member
P A D Wilson

PRICE MANN & CO ◈
447 Kenton Road, Harrow, HA3 0XY
Tel: 020 8204 2228
Resident Partners/Directors: ICAEW Members
B T G Hindocha, V T Hindocha

R H ACCOUNTANCY SERVICES LTD
22 Beresford Road, Harrow, HA1 4QZ

R.H. PARRY FCA CTA
59 Woodcock Dell Avenue, Kenton, Harrow, HA3 0NU
Tel: 020 8904 0800
Principal: ICAEW Member
R H Parry

RE10 & EQUALIP
Suite 215, Signal House, Lyon Road, Harrow HA1 2AQ

RICHARD SHEPPARD & CO
8 Blackwell Close, Harrow Weald, Harrow, HA3 6JY

RICHMAN & CO
293 Kenton Lane, Harrow, HA3 8RR
Tel: 020 8907 3481
Principal: ICAEW Member
M Richman

RNS BUSINESS SOLUTIONS LTD
276 Preston Road, Harrow, HA3 0QA
Tel: 020 8385 2000
Website: http://www.r-n-s.com
Resident Partners/Directors: ICAEW Members
R N Sangani

RYLAND CONSULTING
5 Yeading Avenue, Rayners Lane, Harrow, HA2 9RL

S. EBRAHIM
5 Porlock Avenue, Harrow, HA2 0AP
Tel: 020 8248 0943
Principal: ICAEW Member
S Ebrahim

S. HUSAIN & CO
83 Corbins Lane, South Harrow, Harrow, HA2 8EN

SAMJIS
4 Fulwood Court, Kenton Rd, Harrow, HA3 8AA

SAYMUR ACCOUNTANTS ◈
1st Floor, 27 Peterborough Road, Harrow, HA1 2AU

SAYMUR ACCOUNTANTS LTD
1st Floor, 27 Peterborough Road, Harrow, HA1 2AU

SCION CONSULTING
Suite 608, State House, 176 Station Road, Harrow HA1 2AE

SHERIDAN CLARKE
Bridge House, 25-27 The Bridge, Harrow, HA3 5AB
Tel: 020 8861 4244
Principal: ICAEW Member
A T Clarke

SHERIDAN CLARKE LTD ◈
Bridge House, 25-27 The Bridge, Wealdstone, Harrow HA3 5AB
Tel: 020 8861 4244
Resident Partners/Directors: ICAEW Members
A T Clarke

SPROULL & CO
31-33 College Road, Harrow, HA1 1EJ

ST-PARTNERSHIP ◈
Mandeville House, 45-47 Tudor Road, Harrow, HA3 5PQ
Tel: 020 8863 3337
Resident Partners/Directors: ICAEW Members
V N Shah, N J Thakker

STEPHEN DANIEL & CO
138 Pinner Road, Harrow, HA1 4JE
Tel: 020 8426 0991
Email: partners@stephendaniel.co.uk
Resident Partners/Directors: ICAEW Members
B S Freedman, M J Kraus

STERLING
505 Pinner Road, Harrow, HA2 6EH
Tel: 020 8515 2929
Fax: 020 8515 2939
Email: bharat@sterlingca.com
Website: http://www.sterlingca.com
Resident Partners/Directors: ICAEW Members
D K Doshi, J J Ved
Resident Partners (Non-ICAEW Members):
P Jariwala, B Vanza
Registered by the ICAEW to carry out company audit work
Regulated by the ICAEW for a range of investment business activities
See display advertisement near this entry.

VIPIN RAJA & CO
2nd Floor, 100 College Road, Harrow, HA1 1BQ
Tel: 020 8427 2446
Principal: ICAEW Member
V M Raja

ZAKARIYA & CO
17 Perwell Avenue, Harrow, HA2 9LR

HARTFIELD

CAROLINE A. VICKERY FCA
Wealden Farm, Parrock Lane, Upper Hartfield, Hartfield TN7 4AT
Tel: 01342 825145
Email: cavickery@barristernet.co.uk
Principal: ICAEW Member
C A Vickery
Registered by the ICAEW to carry out company audit work

R H JACKSON AND CO
1 Wroth Tyes Cottage, Upper Hartfield, Hartfield, TN7 4DY

HARTLEPOOL

ADR BUSINESS SERVICES LTD
21 Hylton Road, West Park, Hartlepool, TS26 0AG

ALISTAIR D. ROSS
21 Hylton Road, West Park, Hartlepool, TS26 0AG

CENSIS
Exchange Building, 66 Church Street, Hartlepool, TS24 7DN
Tel: 01429 869148
Resident Partners/Directors: ICAEW Members
S M Close, K T E Harrison

EDWARD EGGLESTONE & CO
3-5 Scarborough Street, Hartlepool, TS24 7DA
Tel: 01429 234656
Fax: 01429 866828
Email: ed@edegg.com
Date Established: 1984
Resident Partners/Directors: ICAEW Members
E Egglestone
Regulated by the ICAEW for a range of investment business activities

FLANNAGANS
Frederick house, Dean Group Business Park, Brenda Road, Hartlepool TS25 2BS

HORWATH CLARK WHITEHILL (NORTH EAST) LLP ◈
Oakland House, 40 Victoria Road, Hartlepool, TS26 8DD
Tel: 01429 234414
Resident Partners/Directors: ICAEW Members
S A M M Adams, D R Boyd, C Davey, P Harrison, H O'Driscoll, P N Olsen

KING, HOPE & CO
18 Scarborough Street, Hartlepool, TS24 7DA
Tel: 01429 273492
Resident Partners/Directors: ICAEW Members
S W Gardner
See display advertisement near this entry.

MD ACCOUNTANTS LTD
Frederick House, Dean Group Business Park, Brenda Road, Hartlepool TS25 2BS

VANTIS GROUP LTD ◈
17/25 Scarborough Street, Hartlepool, TS24 7DA
Tel: 01429 272 109
Website: http://www.vantisplc.com/hartlepool
Resident Partners/Directors: ICAEW Members
D S Burns
General Description: ICAEW Registered.

WM FORTUNE & SON
Collingwood House, Church Square, Hartlepool, TS24 7EN
Tel: 01429 274408
Fax: 01429 276851
Email: fortunes@globalnet.co.uk
Date Established: 1897
Principal: ICAEW Member
T A Atkinson
Registered by the ICAEW to carry out company audit work
Regulated by the ICAEW for a range of investment business activities

SPECIALISATIONS – AUDIT & ASSURANCE
Audit

SPECIALISATIONS – FINANCIAL REPORTING
Accounts Preparation

HARWICH

BOND PARTNERS LLP
Haven House, Albemarle Street, Harwich, CO12 3HL

BROOKS STENNING
St Marys House, Clacton Road, Little Oakley, Harwich CO12 5JL

DOWSONS
195 Main Road, Harwich, CO12 3PH
Tel: 01255 502003
Principal: ICAEW Member
P Goswell

HASLEMERE

A & N
2 Kings Road, Haslemere, GU27 2QA

BRENDA CANNON
Well Lane House, Well Lane, Haslemere, GU27 2LB

CHRISTINE JOHNSON & CO LTD
Westwood, Midhurst Road, Kingsley Green, Haslemere GU27 3LL
Tel: 01428 658188
Resident Partners/Directors: ICAEW Members
C E Johnson

HARRIS CARR LTD
Cheriton, Farnham Lane, Haslemere, GU27 1HD
Tel: 01428 654653
Resident Partners/Directors: ICAEW Members
O R Smyth

KNOX CROPPER
24 Petworth Road, Haslemere, GU27 2HR
Tel: 01428 652788
Fax: 01428 661272
Email: haslemere@knoxcropper.com
Resident Partners/Directors: ICAEW Members
B E Marshall
Registered by the ICAEW to carry out company audit work
Regulated by the ICAEW for a range of investment business activities

SPECIALISATIONS – BUSINESS & GENERAL ADVICE
Company Formation

SPECIALISATIONS – SECTOR
Solicitors

SPECIALISATIONS – TAXATION
Estate and Inheritance
Partnerships and Sole Traders
Trusts

MICHAEL K ROSSOR
5 Courts Mount Road, Haslemere, GU27 2PR

R W BOWDEN-SMITH
6 Roedeer Copse, Haslemere, GU27 1RF
Tel: 01428 656993
Principal: ICAEW Member
R W Bowden-Smith

TULIP TREE ACCOUNTING AND CONSULTANCY ★
Tulip House, 7 Williamson Close, Grayswood, Haslemere GU27 2DA

HASSOCKS

BOND PARTNERS LLP
Old Coach House, Stanford Avenue, Hassocks, BN6 8JL

JOHN LEA & CO LTD
Naldretts Tower House, Mill Lane, Hurstpierpoint, Hassocks BN6 9HL

JOHN RITCHIE
Downsview, 1 Brambles, Hassocks, BN6 8EQ

P.A. FIELD & CO
Hare Knap, Lewes Road, Ditchling, Hassocks BN6 8TY
Tel: 01273 842227
Principal: ICAEW Member
P M A Field

PRW FINANCIAL SERVICES LTD
10 The Minnels, Hassocks, BN6 8QW

ROBERT PINNOCK
25 Hurst Road, Hassocks, BN6 9NJ

SUSSEX ACCOUNTANCY SERVICES LTD
5 Bankside, Hassocks, BN6 8EL

SYKES, DALBY & TRUELOVE
63 High Street, Hurstpierpoint, Hassocks, BN6 9RE

HASTINGS

AIMS - ANTHONY MACKENZIE FCA
77 St Helens Park Road, Hastings, TN34 2JW

AJS & ASSOCIATES ★
Fairlynck, 43 Battery Hill, Fairlight, Hastings TN35 4AP

ASHDOWN HURREY LLP ◈
20 Havelock Road, Hastings, TN34 1BP
Tel: 01424 720222

BATCHELOR & CO ◈
14 Wellington Square, Hastings, TN34 1PB
Tel: 01424 203045
Principal: ICAEW Member
M K Batchelor

DEEKS EVANS ◈
36 Cambridge Road, Hastings, TN34 1DU
Tel: 01424 423422
Fax: 01424 426397
Email: emhastings@deeksevans.co.uk
Website: http://www.deeksevans.com
Resident Partners/Directors: ICAEW Members
D J A Deeks, S R Toulson
Other Offices: Tunbridge Wells
Registered by the ICAEW to carry out company audit work
Regulated by the ICAEW for a range of investment business activities
SPECIALISATIONS – AUDIT & ASSURANCE
Audit
SPECIALISATIONS – FINANCIAL REPORTING
Accounts Preparation
SPECIALISATIONS – IT
Computer Systems and Consultancy
SPECIALISATIONS – TAXATION
Taxation

MCPHERSON & PARTNERS
2 Cambridge Gardens, Hastings, TN34 1EH

MCPHERSON & PARTNERS (HASTINGS) LLP
2 Cambridge Gardens, Hastings, TN34 1EH

MANNINGTONS
7-9 Wellington Square, Hastings, TN34 1PD

P.A. JANKS & CO
2 The Coppice, Priory Park, Hastings, TN34 1YR

SILK & CO ◈
23 Havelock Road, Hastings, TN34 1BP
Tel: 01424 722844
Principal: ICAEW Member
A P Silk

WILLIAMS & CO
4 Cambridge Gardens, Hastings, TN34 1EH

HATFIELD

AKK CONSULTANTS LTD
45 Mymms Drive, Brookmans Park, Hatfield, AL9 7AE

AMI ASSOCIATES LTD
2nd Floor, Titan Court, 3 Bishop Square, Hatfield, AL10 9NA

BDO STOY HAYWARD LLP
Prospect Place, 85 Great North Road, Hatfield, AL9 5BS
Tel: 01707 255888
Fax: 01707 255890
Resident Partners/Directors: ICAEW Members
J L Barker, G M Brooks, G B Ives, R N Kelly, J H Mann, K M Storan
Resident Partners (Non-ICAEW Members):
G S Kinlan, A L Jarrold

CAMPBELL PARK ◈
54 Woods Avenue, Hatfield, AL10 8LY
Tel: 0845 638 3708
Principal: ICAEW Member
E C Park

DAYALJEE & CO
1 Fawn Court, The Ryde, Hatfield, AL9 5DJ
Tel: 01707 268741
Fax: 01707 270148
Principal: ICAEW Member
S D D Chauhan
Registered by the ICAEW to carry out company audit work

HASSELL & CO
Erry Lodge, 3 Wilkins Green Lane, Hatfield, AL10 9RT

HASSELL FORENSIC ACCOUNTING LTD
Erry Lodge, 3 Wilkins Green Lane, Hatfield, AL10 9RT
Tel: 01707 273588
Resident Partners/Directors: ICAEW Members
S R Hassell
SPECIALISATIONS – FORENSIC ACCOUNTING
Forensic Accounting

HBB AUDIT LTD
Bridge House, 25 Fiddle Bridge Lane, Hatfield, AL10 0SP
Tel: 01707 897000
Resident Partners/Directors: ICAEW Members
A B Lovett, I G Pratt, P A R Skipper

IAN PRATT LTD
Bridge house, 25 Fiddle Bridge Lane, Hatfield, AL10 0SP
Tel: 01707 897000
Resident Partners/Directors: ICAEW Members
I G Pratt, P A R Skipper

KABAN & CO
Marquis House, 68 Great North Road, Hatfield, AL9 5ER
Tel: 01707 257815

KEELINGS
Broad House, 1 The Broadway, Old Hatfield, Hatfield AL9 5BG

KEELINGS LTD
Broad House, 1 The Broadway, Hatfield, AL9 5BG
Tel: 01707 258844
Fax: 01707 258811
Email: enquiries@keelings.co.uk
Website: http://www.keelings.co.uk
Resident Partners/Directors: ICAEW Members
J Faulkner, E Pritchard, C T Wright
Registered by the ICAEW to carry out company audit work
SPECIALISATIONS – SECTOR
Doctors
Registered Social Landlords
General Description: Keelings is a well-established practice with a modern outlook at the smaller end of the medium-sized firms. We offer clients a complete financial service with the emphasis very much on individual requirements.

LOVETTS
Bridge House, 25 Fiddle Bridge Lane, Hatfield, AL10 0SP
Tel: 01707 897000
Website: http://www.lovettsaccts.co.uk

N.J. HEATON
Hadleigh, Moffats Lane, Brookmans Park, Hatfield AL9 7RU

NEWMAN MORRIS
York House, 14 Salisbury Square, Hatfield, AL9 5AD

NEWMAN MORRIS LTD
York House, 14 Salisbury Square, Hatfield, AL9 5AD

PERCEPTURE LTD ◈
Marquis House, 68 Great North Road, Hatfield, AL9 5ER
Tel: 01707 257815
Resident Partners/Directors: ICAEW Members
T Kaban
Registered by the ICAEW to carry out company audit work
Regulated by the ICAEW for a range of investment business activities
General Description: Small firm, extensive services.

RAY ADAMS
York House, 14 Salisbury Square, Hatfield, AL9 5AD

HAVANT

J CASEY & CO
55 Southbrook Road, Havant, PO9 1RL

MORRIS CROCKER ◈
Station House, 50 North Street, Havant, PO9 1QU
Tel: 02392 484356
Resident Partners/Directors: ICAEW Members
V A Fenner, K M Gilbert, R W Hayes, R M L Perry

MORRIS CROCKER LTD
Station House, North Street, Havant, PO9 1QU

ROTHMAN PANTALL & CO
24 Park Road South, Havant, PO9 1HB
Tel: 02392 482683
Resident Partners/Directors: ICAEW Members
J L Shaw
Resident Partners (Non-ICAEW Members):
R Hutchinson

WARD & CO
International House, 12a Homewell, Havant, PO9 1EE

HAVERHILL

DILLOWAYS LTD
Weavers, 6 Hamlet Road, Haverhill, CB9 8EE

DPR ACCOUNTANCY LTD ◈
72 Arrendene Road, Haverhill, CB9 9JT
Tel: 01440 702339
Resident Partners/Directors: ICAEW Members
S J Lawes, S M Lawes

DPR ACCOUNTANCY LTD ◈
72 Arrendene Road, Haverhill, CB9 9JT
Tel: 01440 702339
Registered by the ICAEW to carry out company audit work

PETER MAYSTON
Jacobs Farm, Wiggens Green, Helions Bumpstead, Haverhill CB9 7AD

HAWES

O'REILLY
Kiln Hill, Market Place, Hawes, DL8 3RA
Tel: 01969 667428
Email: hawes@o-reilly.co.uk
Non-resident Partners (ICAEW Members):
A Little

HAYES

THE CORPORATE PRACTICE LTD
65 Delamere Road, Hayes, UB4 0NN
Tel: 020 8606 6750
Resident Partners/Directors: ICAEW Members
D Arora

F.A. MAGEE & CO ◈
Wimborne House, 4-6 Pump Lane, Hayes, UB3 3NB
Tel: 020 8573 3939
Resident Partners/Directors: ICAEW Members
A Davies, W S Davies
Registered by the ICAEW to carry out company audit work

J S GULATI & CO
1286 Uxbridge Road, Hayes, UB4 8JG

J S GULATI & CO LTD ◈
4 Peter James Business Centre, Pump Lane, Hayes, UB3 3NT
Tel: 020 8573 5329
Resident Partners/Directors: ICAEW Members
J Singh

KINGSTON SMITH LLP
800 Uxbridge Road, Hayes, UB4 0RS
Tel: 020 8848 5500
Fax: 020 8848 5501
Email: ks@kingstonsmith.co.uk
Website: http://www.kingstonsmith.co.uk
Resident Partners/Directors: ICAEW Members
M B Penfold, J P Seymour
Registered by the ICAEW to carry out company audit work
Regulated by the ICAEW for a range of investment business activities

S.W.FRANKSON & CO
Bridge House, 119-123 Station Road, Hayes, UB3 4BX

TAPARIA & CO
Taparia House, 1096 Uxbridge Road, Hayes, UB4 8QH

HAYLE

PETER SANDERS
68 Hayle Terrace, Hayle, TR27 4BT
Tel: 01736 755755
Principal: ICAEW Member
P H Sanders

PRYOR, BEGENT, FRY & CO
13/15 Commercial Road, Hayle, TR27 4DE
Tel: 01736 753357
Website: http://www.pryerbegentfryco.me.uk
Resident Partners/Directors: ICAEW Members
E T Pascoe
Registered by the ICAEW to carry out company audit work
Regulated by the ICAEW for a range of investment business activities

HAYLING ISLAND

C.J. DRISCOLL
The Old Surgery, 19 Mengham Lane, Hayling Island, PO11 9JT
Tel: 02392 465024
Resident Partners/Directors: ICAEW Members
C N Clarke, C J Driscoll

JGM ACCOUNTING SERVICES
71 Church Road, Hayling Island, PO11 0NR

HAYWARDS HEATH

A.N. LAMB
14 The Droveway, Lucastes Lane, Haywards Heath, RH16 1LL

ANDREW HITCHCOCK
9 Chaucer Court, Winnals Park, Paddockhall Road, Haywards Heath RH16 1EU
Tel: 01444 448900
Principal: ICAEW Member
A P Hitchcock

B.E.M.CARTER
Russetts, Coach and Horses Lane, Dane Hill, Haywards Heath RH17 7JF

BRANSBY & CO
5 Bedales, Lewes Road, Haywards Heath, RH17 7TE

BRIAN COOK ASSOCIATES
Marine House, 151 Western Road, Haywards Heath, RH16 3LH
Tel: 01444 473783
Resident Partners/Directors: ICAEW Members
B T Cook

C.A. BROWN
24 Woodlands Road, Haywards Heath, RH16 3JU
Tel: 01444 453451
Principal: ICAEW Member
C A Brown

CARTER NICHOLLS
Victoria House, Stanbridge Industrial Park, Staplefield Lane, Staplefield, Haywards Heath RH17 6AS

CARTER NICHOLLS LTD
Victoria House, Stanbridge Industrial Park, Staplefield Lane, Staplefield, Haywards Heath RH17 6AS

COULTHARDS MACKENZIE
14 More House Farm, Business Centre, Wivelsfield, Haywards Heath RH17 7RE

DAVID LANGRIDGE
77A High Street, Lindfield, Haywards Heath, RH16 2HN
Tel: 01444 483820
Principal: ICAEW Member
D H Langridge

GILLARDS ◈
4 Heath Square, Boltro Road, Haywards Heath, RH16 1BL
Tel: 01444 414491
Principal: ICAEW Member
D J Gillard

GUY BERKELEY - AIMS ACCOUNTANTS FOR BUSINESS
11 Manor Drive, Cuckfield, Haywards Heath, RH17 5BT
Tel: 01444 410041
Principal: ICAEW Member
R G Berkeley

HARDING & HARDING LLP ◈
Little Keysford, Treemans Road, Horsted Keynes, Haywards Heath RH17 7EA

HEM MAHADEO & CO
47 Hazelgrove Road, Haywards Heath, RH16 3PH

J R I MITCHELL FCA
44 Lucastes Road, Haywards Heath, RH16 1JP

MICHAEL TARRANT
The Priory, Haywards Heath, RH16 3LB

PELICAN CONSULTANCY LTD
6 Cockhaise Cottages, Monteswood Lane, Lindfield, Haywards Heath RH16 2QP
Tel: 01444 487766
Resident Partners/Directors: ICAEW Members
V F N Blackburn

PRB MARTIN POLLINS LLP
Kingfisher House, Hurstwood Grange, Hurstwood Lane, Haywards Heath RH17 7QX
Tel: 01444 458252
Resident Partners/Directors: ICAEW Members
K M Lo, S C Power, C D Whitley-Jones
Resident Partners (Non-ICAEW Members):
J R Forgham

continued

PRB MARTIN POLLINS LLP
cont

SPECIALISATIONS – AUDIT & ASSURANCE

Audit — Private Company

See display advertisement near this entry.

PRISM GROUP LTD
The Old Sawmill, Copyhold Lane, Lindfield, Haywards Heath RH16 1XT

RICHARD PLACE DOBSON LLP
Brackenhurst, Little London, Selsfield Road, Ardingly, Haywards Heath RH17 6TJ

RICHES CONSULTING
Old Jarretts Farmhouse, Brantridge Lane, Balcombe, Haywards Heath, RH17 6JR

HEANOR

A. R. GORING ◈
91a Hassock Lane North, Shipley, Heanor, DE75 7JB
Tel: 01773 719525
Principal: ICAEW Member
A R Goring

P J HAMSON & CO LTD
1B Geofrey Street, Heanor, DE75 7GB

HEATHFIELD

ASH TREE ACCOUNTING LTD ◈
1 Ash Tree Close, Heathfield, TN21 8BF

BROWN RUSSELL
71a and 71c High Street, Heathfield, TN21 8HU

BROWN RUSSELL LTD
71a and 71c High Street, Heathfield, TN21 8HU

HOWARD & CO
Bridge House, High Street, Horam, Heathfield TN21 0EY
Tel: 01435 813166
Principal: ICAEW Member
D H Robinson

THE KINGS MILL PARTNERSHIP
Ashdown House, High Street, Cross in Hand, Heathfield TN21 0SR
Tel: 01435 865353
Resident Partners/Directors: ICAEW Members
P Haining

MANNINGTONS
8 High Street, Heathfield, TN21 8LS

RICHARD PLACE & CO
3 Silveroaks Farm, Waldron, Heathfield, TN21 0RS
Tel: 01435 813810
Resident Partners/Directors: ICAEW Members
C C James

HEBBURN

JOHN WELSH
147 Victoria Road West, Hebburn, NE31 1UT

MACKENZIE & CO
34 Hazelmoor, Hebburn Village, Hebburn, NE31 1DH

HEBDEN BRIDGE

CRESSWELL CRABTREE & SONS
Barclays Bank Chambers, Market Street, Hebden Bridge, HX7 6AA
Tel: 01422 842431
Resident Partners/Directors: ICAEW Members
G Beever, J Dakin, T A Marshall, G Roper, P S Vine

HELSTON

A.P. BANKS
Saffron Meadow, Manaccan, Helston, TR12 6EN

AP BANKS & CO
Saffron Meadow, Manaccan, Helston, TR12 6EN

ATKINS FERRIE
1 Water-Ma-Trout, Helston, TR13 0LW

BRIAN W. HOWARD
Argel Vean, Parknoweth, Churchtown Cury, Helston TR12 7BW
Tel: 01326 240813
Principal: ICAEW Member
B W Howard

BRIANTS ◈
Tilney, Newtown St Martin, Helston, TR12 6DP
Tel: 01326 231054

HARMAN & CO
Glenesk House, Newtown in St Martin, Helston, TR12 6DP

KITCHEN & BROWN ◈
Alpha House, 40 Coinagehall Street, Helston, TR13 8EQ
Tel: 01326 572524
Email: info@kitchenandbrown.co.uk
Resident Partners/Directors: ICAEW Members
B J Drew, D Goodman

Registered by the ICAEW to carry out company audit work

Regulated by the ICAEW for a range of investment business activities

MACLEOD & TONKIN ★
North End, Porthleven, Helston, TR13 9JP

MACLEOD & TONKIN ★
54 Coinagehall Street, Helston, TR13 8EL
Tel: 01326 572422
Resident Partners/Directors: ICAEW Members
J C Coulson

PAUL & MAUNDRELL ◈
13 Church Street, Helston, TR13 8TD
Tel: 01326 572728

PRYOR, BEGENT, FRY & CO
97 Meneage Street, Helston, TR13 8RE
Tel: 01326 562276
Resident Partners/Directors: ICAEW Members
S M Coates, A J Fry

PURNELLS ◈
Trewoon, Poldhu Cove, Mullion, Helston TR12 7JB
Tel: 01326 240680
Fax: 01326 241519
Email: ray@purnells.co.uk
Website: http://www.purnells.co.uk
Resident Partners/Directors: ICAEW Members
R H Purnell
Other Offices: Newport, South Wales
Individual(s) licensed for insolvency work by another RPB

INVESTOR IN PEOPLE

SPECIALISATIONS – BUSINESS RECOVERY & INSOLVENCY

Bankruptcies
Corporate Recovery
Liquidations
Reorganisations and Company Reconstructions

T M WEBSTER & CO
6 Lanheverne Parc, St Keverne, Helston, TR12 6LX

THOMAS & CO
Coolibah House, Polhorman Lane, Mullion, Helston TR12 7JD

HEMEL HEMPSTEAD

ALAN CROPPER & CO
4 The Cloisters, Barnacres Road, Hemel Hempstead, HP3 8UJ

BRADING & CO
5 Kilncroft, Hemel Hempstead, HP3 8HH

C.P. O'DONNELL & CO
Homeland, Hempstead Road, Bovingdon, Hemel Hempstead HP3 0HF
Tel: 01442 269527
Principal: ICAEW Member
C.P. O'Donnell

CLADD BECK LTD
56a London Road, Apsley, Hemel Hempstead, HP3 9SB
Tel: 01442 253482
Resident Partners/Directors: ICAEW Members
S M Beck

CRANLEIGH-SWASH & CO
83 High Street, Hemel Hempstead, HP1 3AH
Tel: 01442 214666

CURTIS & CO
14 Crossfell Road, Hemel Hempstead, HP3 8RF
Tel: 01442 506376
Principal: ICAEW Member
P J Curtis

DAVID LINDON & CO
Avaland House, 110 London Road, Apsley, Hemel Hempstead HP3 9SD
Tel: 01442 251553
Resident Partners/Directors: ICAEW Members
J M L Hankinson, D R Tossell

DEREK GREENE & CO
33 Minoan Drive, Apsley, Hemel Hempstead, HP3 9WA
Tel: 01442 231454
Principal: ICAEW Member
D L Greene

E.S.E.SOLOMON
Le Chalet, Long Lane, Bovingdon, Hemel Hempstead HP3 0NE

G. YOUNG & CO
49 Deaconsfield Road, Hemel Hempstead, HP3 9HZ
Tel: 01442 242696
Principal: ICAEW Member
G Young

GARY J. HARDING ◈
24 Brickfield Avenue, Leverstock Green, Hemel Hempstead, HP3 8NP
Tel: 01442 262659
Email: gary@garyjharding.co.uk
Principal: ICAEW Member
G J Harding

GRANT THORNTON UK LLP
Bryanston Court, Selden Hill, Hemel Hempstead, HP2 4TN
Tel: 01442 260200
Resident Partners/Directors: ICAEW Members
M J Biles, P S Burton, J Newton, C E Shanbury
Resident Partners (Non-ICAEW Members):
A Merchant

HILLIER HOPKINS LLP ◈
Charter Court, Midland Road, Hemel Hempstead, HP2 5GE
Tel: 01442 269341
Email: info@hhllp.co.uk
Website: http://www.hillierhopkins.co.uk
Resident Partners/Directors: ICAEW Members
I N Abrey, R W Badger, M J Culshaw, G D Franklin, J L Franks, C J Howe, M A Kent, C Leach, M C Minett, D W Nye
Resident Partners (Non-ICAEW Members):
B Sherwood
Other Offices: Aylesbury, Watford, London
Registered by the ICAEW to carry out company audit work
Authorised and regulated by the Financial Services Authority for investment business

INVESTOR IN PEOPLE

General Description: Chartered accountants and tax advisers.

J.D. MURPHY
28 Wrensfield, Hemel Hempstead, HP1 1RN

JACQUELINE NUNN FCA
271 St Albans Road, Hemel Hempstead, HP2 4RP

JAMES DINSDALE FCA
206a Lawn Lane, Hemel Hempstead, HP13 9JF

KELVIN ARCHER
Cob Suite, Old Swan House, 29 High Street, Hemel Hempstead, HP1 3AA
Tel: 01442 235525
Principal: ICAEW Member
K Archer

KIRTON & CO
3 Primrose Close, Hemel Hempstead, HP1 2DL
Tel: 01442 241414
Principal: ICAEW Member
S E Kirton

KNOX CROPPER
153-155 London Road, Hemel Hempstead, HP3 9SQ

LACKMAKER & CO
10 Bradden Lane, Gaddesden Row, Hemel Hempstead, HP2 6HZ

MARION KING
13 Pinecroft, Hemel Hempstead, HP3 8AW

MJ FINN & CO
44 Crescent Road, Hemel Hempstead, HP2 4AH
Tel: 01442 397589
Principal: ICAEW Member
M J Finn

MORGAN ROSE ◈
37 Marlowes, Hemel Hempstead, HP1 1LD

PETER GREGORY & ASSOCIATES
1 Mark Road, Hemel Hempstead, HP2 7BN

PINKHAM BLAIR ◈
87A High Street, The Old Town, Hemel Hempstead, HP1 3AH
Tel: 01442 220150
Resident Partners/Directors: ICAEW Members
D A Blair, D J Pinkham
Registered by the ICAEW to carry out company audit work
Regulated by the ICAEW for a range of investment business activities

TAX AND FIGURES LLP
Hamilton House, 111 Marlowes, Hemel Hempstead, HP1 1BB
Tel: 01442 450480
Email: robert@taxandfigures.com
Principal: ICAEW Member
R Insalaco

V.R. PATEL
7 Greenway, Hemel Hempstead, HP2 4QG

VERULAM BUSINESS SERVICES
Willow Cottage, 19 Pancake Lane, Leverstock Green, Hemel Hempstead HP2 4NB

WEST & CO
Old Hempstead House, 10 Queensway, Hemel Hempstead, HP1 1LR

HENFIELD

MALCOLM REID & CO
Caudle Street, High Street, Henfield, BN5 9DQ
Tel: 01273 492204
Principal: ICAEW Member
M Reid

HENLEY-IN-ARDEN

CULLINGWORTH & CO ◈
96 High Street, Henley-In-Arden, Warwickshire, B95 5BY
Tel: 01564 795755
Principal: ICAEW Member
R Cullingworth

R K THOMAS
Glebe Farm, Aston Cantlow, Henley-In-Arden, B95 6JL

HENLEY-ON-THAMES

ADAMS LEE CLARK ◈
Adam House, 71 Bell Street, Henley-on-thames, RG9 2BD
Tel: 01491 578177
Email: enquiries@adamsleeclark.co.uk
Website: http://www.adamsleeclark.co.uk
Resident Partners/Directors: ICAEW Members
K M Halliwell, R Thirkettle

APPLE TREE ACCOUNTANCY & TAXATION SERVICES LTD
Stoke Row, Henley-On-Thames, RG9 5QR

ARAWN JOHNSON
Great Wood Cottage, Skirmett, Henley-On-Thames, RG9 6TD
Tel: 01491 526104
Principal: ICAEW Member
A A Johnson

BRUTON CHARLES ▽ ◈
The Coach House, Greys Green Business Centre, Rotherfield Greys, Henley-On-Thames RG9 4QG
Tel: 01491 629829
Website: http://www.brutoncharles.co.uk
Resident Partners/Directors: ICAEW Members
J C R Lawrence-Archer, K A Roberts
Resident Partners (Non-ICAEW Members):
M G Lynskey
Registered by the ICAEW to carry out company audit work
Regulated by the ICAEW for a range of investment business activities

DAVID CAIRNS
North Lea House, 66 Northfield End, Henley-on-thames, RG9 2JN

DUNCAN W. COOPER
Tuckers Cottage, Maidensgrove Common, Henley-on-thames, RG9 6EX

E. JONES & ASSOCIATES
10a Hart Street, Henley-On-Thames, RG9 2AU
Tel: 01491 411063
Principal: ICAEW Member
E Jones

HENLEY ACCOUNTING SERVICES
Cedar Court, 9/11 Fairmile, Henley-On-Thames, RG9 2JR

HMT ASSURANCE
5 Fairmile, Henley-On-Thames, RG9 2JR

HMT ASSURANCE LLP
5 Fairmile, Henley-On-Thames, RG9 2JR

HURST MORRISON THOMSON
5 Fairmile, Henley-On-Thames, RG9 2JR

HURST MORRISON THOMSON
5 Fairmile, Henley-On-Thames, RG9 2JR

HURST MORRISON THOMSON LLP
5 Fairmile, Henley-On-Thames, RG9 2JR

HURST MORRISON THOMSON LLP
The Hub, 14 Station Road, Henley-On-Thames, RG9 1AY

JAMES COWPER
North Lea House, 66 Northfield End, Henley-On-Thames, RG9 2BE

JOHN HALSALL
Cherwell, Remenham Lane, Remenham, Henley-on-thames RG9 3DB

JOHN R CHAMBERLAIN
Westcott, 16 Western Road, Henley-on-thames, RG9 1JL

KENCH
10 Station Road, Henley-On-Thames, RG9 1AY

KENCH & CO LTD ◈
10 Station Road, Henley-On-Thames, RG9 1AY
Tel: 01491 578207
Website: http://www.kench.co.uk
Resident Partners/Directors: ICAEW Members
R L Evans, E A Kench
Resident Partners (Non-ICAEW Members):
L J Manson

KNOX & EAMES ★
The Business Centre, Greys Green Farm, Rotherfield Greys, Henley-on-thames RG9 4QG

LEANDER
17 Harpsden Road, Henley-On-Thames, RG9 1EE

M.G. WORTLEY & CO
Bramble Lodge, Colstrope Lane, Hambleden, Henley-on-thames RG9 6SL

MYFD
Chiltern House, 45 Station Road, Henley-On-Thames, RG9 1AT

MYFD LTD
Chiltern House, 45 Station Road, Henley-On-Thames, RG9 1AT

P J BEEDHAM LTD
Graffix House, Newton Business Park, Henley-On-Thames, RG9 1HG
Tel: 01491 578881
Email: mail@pjbeedham.co.uk
Website: http://www.pjbeedham.co.uk

P.J. FIELD
Monkey Lodge, Skirmett Road, Hambleden, Henley-on-thames RG9 6SX

PAUL DIXON & ASSOCIATES
Byeways, Mill Road, Lower Shiplake, Henley-on-thames RG9 3LW
Tel: 0118 940 1917
Email: paulfdixon@aol.com
Principal: ICAEW Member
P F Dixon
Registered by the ICAEW to carry out company audit work

RUSKELLS LTD
The Coach House, Hambleden, Henley-On-Thames, RG9 6RJ

SHEPHERD & CO
Old London House, High Street, Stoke Row, Henley-On-Thames RG9 5QL

SNOWDON ROBERTSON & CO
The Old Pheasant, Parmoor, Hambleden, Henley-on-thames RG9 6NH
Tel: 01491 413775
Principal: ICAEW Member
A W S Robertson

SOLUTIONS 4 BUSINESS LLP
5 Fairmile, Henley-On-Thames, RG9 2JR

VILLARS HAYWARD
Boston House, 2A Boston Road, Henley-on-thames, RG9 1DY
Tel: 01491 411077
Fax: 01491 410199
Email: mail@villars-hayward.co.uk
Website: http://www.villars-hayward.co.uk
Resident Partners/Directors: ICAEW Members
J Hayward, N M Smith
Registered by the ICAEW to carry out company audit work
Regulated by the ICAEW for a range of investment business activities

HENLOW

SUSAN WATSON ACCOUNTANCY SERVICES
28 Oak Drive, Henlow, SG16 6BX

HEREFORD

ALAN C. PRENDERGAST
Leicester House, Castle Street, Hay On Wye, Hereford HR3 5DF
Tel: 01497 821279
Principal: ICAEW Member
A C Prendergast

BAKER TILLY
Elgar House, Holmer Road, Hereford, HR4 9SF
Tel: 01432 352222
Resident Partners (Non-ICAEW Members):
M A Bevan, A J Davies, R G Mason

BAKER TILLY
Elgar House, Holmer Road, Hereford, HR4 9SF

BAKER TILLY TAX AND ADVISORY SERVICES LLP
Elgar House, Holmer Road, Hereford, HR4 9SF
Tel: 01432 352222
Resident Partners/Directors: ICAEW Members
M R Garner, C N Willetts
Resident Partners (Non-ICAEW Members):
M A Bevan, A J Davies, M Horwood, R G Mason

BONELLE & CO LTD
1 Wyecliffe Terrace, Bath Street, Hereford, HR1 2HG

CHRIS DUCKETT ◈
Thorn Office Centre, Straight Mile Road, Rotherwas, Hereford HR2 6JT

CROWN & CO ACCOUNTANTS LTD
Coed Lank Farm, Broad Oak, Hereford, HR2 8QY

D.A. SCOTT
1 Merryhill Park, Belmont, Hereford, HR2 9SS
Tel: 01432 271828
Principal: ICAEW Member
D A Scott

DIANA DUGGAN & CO
27 East Street, Hereford, HR1 2LU
Tel: 01432 273845
Principal: ICAEW Member
D M Duggan
Registered by the ICAEW to carry out company audit work

HAWKINS PRIDAY ★
Charlton House, St Nicholas Street, Hereford, HR4 0BG
Tel: 01432 274432
Email: enquiries@hawkinspriday.co.uk
Resident Partners/Directors: ICAEW Members
K C McLellan
Resident Partners (Non-ICAEW Members):
K P Alexander

THE HUTCHINSON PARTNERSHIP
The Bull Pen, Amberley Court, Sutton St Nicholas, Hereford HR1 3BX

THE HUTCHINSON PARTNERSHIP LTD
The Bull Pen, Amberley Court, Sutton St Nicholas, Hereford HR1 3BX

INGRAM & TERRY LTD
Sullivan House, 72-80 Widemarsh Street, Hereford, HR4 9HG

J.A. COUND & CO
Caple Mead, How Caple, Hereford, HR1 4TA
Tel: 01989 740333
Principal: ICAEW Member
J A Vanston

KENDALL WADLEY LLP ◈
21 St Owen Street, Hereford, HR1 2JB
Tel: 01432 356462
Website: http://www.kwca.co.uk
Resident Partners/Directors: ICAEW Members
L B Jones
Registered by the ICAEW to carry out company audit work

KING, MORTER, PROUD & CO
Broadlands, Hay-on-Wye, Hereford, HR3 5AP

KNIPE WHITING HEATH LTD
Turpins, St Weonards, Hereford, HR2 8QG

MAINWARING DEAN ASSOCIATES
Millfield House, Eaton Bishop, Hereford, HR2 9QS
Tel: 01981 250800
Principal: ICAEW Member
R E K Mainwaring

MARTIN, NYE & CO ★
Great Trelandon Farm, Longtown, Hereford, HR2 0LU

MUNDY & CO
15 Williams Mead, Bartestree, Hereford, HR1 4BT

R J FRANCIS & CO
Franklin House, Commercial Road, Hereford, HR1 2AZ

RACHEL E. SCOTT & CO
The Old Vicarage, Wellington, Hereford, HR4 8AU

RICHARD HUGHES & CO LTD
95 St Peters Close, Moreton-on-Lugg, Hereford, HR4 8DN

THORNE & CO (ROSS-ON-WYE) LTD
The Courtyard, High Town, Hay-on-Wye, Hereford HR3 5AE

THORNE WIDGERY
33 Bridge Street, Hereford, HR4 9DQ

THORNE WIDGERY ACCOUNTANCY LTD
33 Bridge Street, Hereford, HR4 9JQ

W J JAMES & CO LTD ◈
Manchester House, 3a Castle Street, Hay-on-Wye, Hereford HR3 5DF
Tel: 01497 822150
Registered by the ICAEW to carry out company audit work

YOUNG & CO ◈
Bewell House, Bewell Street, Hereford, HR4 0BA
Tel: 01432 263282
Resident Partners/Directors: ICAEW Members
G M John, L J Rogers
Resident Partners (Non-ICAEW Members):
I S Griffiths, S Moody
Other Offices: Saundersfoot, Pembrokeshire
Registered by the ICAEW to carry out company audit work
Regulated by the ICAEW for a range of investment business activities

HERNE BAY

ALAN RATFORD & CO
20 School Lane, Herne, Herne Bay, CT6 7AL

H & E JOHNSON
Sandall House, 230 High Street, Herne Bay, CT6 5AX

HILARY ADAMS LTD
158 High Street, Herne Bay, CT6 5NP
Tel: 01227 740036
Email: hilary@hilaryadams.co.uk
Website: http://www.hilaryadams.co.uk
Resident Partners/Directors: ICAEW Members
H J Adams
Other Offices:30 The Square, Birchington, Unit 5 Anthony's Way, Rochester

MCCABE FORD WILLIAMS ◈
41-43 William Street, Herne Bay, CT6 5NT
Tel: 01227 373271
Email: hernebay@mfw.co.uk
Website: http://www.mfw.co.uk
Resident Partners/Directors: ICAEW Members
D J Cork, M P Whittaker
Registered by the ICAEW to carry out company audit work
Individual(s) licensed for insolvency work by the ICAEW

MICHAEL CURD & CO LTD ◈
149-151 Mortimer Street, Herne Bay, CT6 5HA
Tel: 01227 366265
Resident Partners/Directors: ICAEW Members
D Warren

MUMFORD & CO LTD
Sandall House, 230 High Street, Herne Bay, CT6 5AX

HERTFORD

COOK & PARTNERS LTD
Manufactory House, Bell Lane, Hertford, SG14 1BP
Tel: 01992 554444
Fax: 01992 552678
Email: info@cookpartners.co.uk
Website: http://www.cookpartners.co.uk
Resident Partners/Directors: ICAEW Members
M G Cook, M Jones, D Wye
Registered by the ICAEW to carry out company audit work
Regulated by the ICAEW for a range of investment business activities

DAVID SUCKLING & CO
6 Hartham Lane, Hertford, SG14 1QN
Tel: 01992 552435
Principal: ICAEW Member
David Suckling

GARY J. CANSICK & CO
Janelle House, Hartham Lane, Hertford, SG14 1QN
Tel: 01992 584692
Fax: 01992 551161
Principal: ICAEW Member
G J Cansick
Registered by the ICAEW to carry out company audit work
SPECIALISATIONS – AUDIT & ASSURANCE
Audit
SPECIALISATIONS – BUSINESS & GENERAL ADVICE
Company Formation
Management Accounting Consultancy
SPECIALISATIONS – FINANCIAL REPORTING
Limited Company Accounts
Partnership/Sole Trader Accounts
SPECIALISATIONS – TAXATION
Partnerships and Sole Traders
Personal

J.B. DALE ◈
41a Chambers Street, Hertford, SG14 1PL
Tel: 01992 550836

J.K. RESEARCH LTD
6-8 The Wash, Hertford, SG14 1PX

J LOCKS LTD
18 Willowmead, Hertford, SG14 2AT
Tel: 01992 584111
Resident Partners/Directors: ICAEW Members
J G M Locks

J V WILSON & CO
41a Chambers Street, Hertford, SG14 1PL

JULIAN ELLIS
15A Bull Plain, Hertford, SG14 1DX
Tel: 01992 550424
Email: info@julianellis.co.uk
Website: http://www.julianellis.co.uk
Principal: ICAEW Member
J Ellis

JULIE HANSON
The Heights, High Molewood, Hertford, SG14 2PL

MALCOLM G. FRY
12 Oak Grove, Hertford, SG13 8AT

MALONEY & CO
33 Newland Gardens, Hertford, SG13 7WN
Tel: 07786 863083
Resident Partners/Directors: ICAEW Members
C G Maloney

MEYER WILLIAMS ★
Queen Alexandra House, 2 Bluecoats Avenue, Hertford, SG14 1PB
Tel: 01992 550721
Fax: 01992 558866
Website: http://www.meyerwilliams.co.uk
Resident Partners/Directors: ICAEW Members
N R Jones, J L Meyer
Resident Partners (Non-ICAEW Members):
S Everett
Registered by the ICAEW to carry out company audit work
Regulated by the ICAEW for a range of investment business activities

NEIL SIMPSON & CO
12 Church Road, Bengeo, Hertford, SG14 3DP
Tel: 01992 505788
Principal: ICAEW Member
N F Simpson

PHILIP T. CHAVE & CO ◈
Belfry House, Bell Lane, Hertford, SG14 1BP
Tel: 01992 500111
Fax: 01992 582886
Email: ptc@ptchavefca.freeserve.co.uk
Date Established: 1974
Principal: ICAEW Member
P T Chave
Registered by the ICAEW to carry out company audit work
SPECIALISATIONS – FINANCIAL REPORTING
Limited Company Accounts
Partnership/Sole Trader Accounts
SPECIALISATIONS – IT
Computer Systems and Consultancy
SPECIALISATIONS – TAXATION
Payroll Service and Advice
Taxation
See display advertisement near this entry.

ROGER CELIA
23 Lodge Close, Hertford, SG14 3DH
Tel: 01992 589538
Principal: ICAEW Member
R Celia

THOMAS DAVID
Orchard House, 5 The Orchard, Hertford, SG14 3HQ
Tel: 01992 536483
Resident Partners/Directors: ICAEW Members
T J Mines

THOMAS DAVID
6-7 Castle Gate, Castle Street, Hertford, SG14 1HD

WILKINS KENNEDY ◈
Cecil House, 52 St Andrew Street, Hertford, SG14 1JA
Tel: 01992 550847
Website: http://www.wilkinskennedy.com
Training Contracts Available.
Resident Partners/Directors: ICAEW Members
T B L Feller, I A Jefferson, A L Nayler, R Shastri
Other Offices: London, Amersham, Ashford, Egham, Orpington, Southend, Guildford, Reading, Romsey, Winchester
Overseas Offices: Stanley, Falkland Islands
Registered by the ICAEW to carry out company audit work
Regulated by the ICAEW for a range of investment business activities
SPECIALISATIONS – BUSINESS & GENERAL ADVICE
Acquisitions and Mergers
Disposal of Businesses
Outsourcing - Financial Services
SPECIALISATIONS – FORENSIC ACCOUNTING
Expert Witnesses in Litigation
Forensic Accounting
SPECIALISATIONS – SECTOR

continued

WILKINS KENNEDY *cont*
Agriculture
Charities
Construction
Entertainers
Insurance Brokers
Property
Solicitors

WORTONS
23 Bull Plain, Hertford, SG14 1DX

HESSLE

BOND PARTNERS LLP
Hesslewood Hall, Business Centre, Ferriby Road, Hessle HU13 0LH

CLIVE WILSON & CO
385 Boothferry Road, Hessle, HU13 0JJ
Tel: 01482 640334
Principal: ICAEW Member
C S Wilson

HARRIS, LACEY AND SWAIN ◈
8 Waterside Business Park, Livingstone Road, Hessle, HU13 0EN
Tel: 01482 646440
Resident Partners/Directors: ICAEW Members
R D Lacey, F C Swain

STEPHEN R. ALLEN & CO
Appletree Court, 2A Vicarage Lane, Hessle, HU13 9LQ
Tel: 01482 645051
Principal: ICAEW Member
S R Allen

HEXHAM

ARMSTRONG WATSON ◈
Milburn House, Hexham Business Park, Burn Lane, Hexham NE46 3RU
Tel: 01434 375550
Fax: 01434 603984
Resident Partners/Directors: ICAEW Members
A C Robinson
Resident Partners (Non-ICAEW Members):
A Bullock
General Description:
Accountants & financial advisers. 35 partners. Ranked 26th in a survey of UK Accountancy profession. Specialises in: corporate finance; corporate accounts; business services; payroll services; computer solutions; financial advice & wealth management; insolvency & corporate recovery.

BLUEFACE CONSULTING
Mill Farm, Allendale, Hexham, NE47 9EQ

BLUEFACE CONSULTING LTD
Mill Farm, Allendale, Hexham, NE47 9EQ

G PROUDLOCK & CO
8 Gilesgate, Hexham, NE46 3NJ

MCCOWIE & CO ★
Hexham Auction Mart Premises, Tyne Green, Hexham, NE46 3SG

PATRICIA J. ARNOLD & CO ◈
Black House, Dipton Mill Road, Hexham, NE46 1RZ
Tel: 01434 606624
Email: patricia@pjarnold.co.uk
Principal: ICAEW Member
P J R Arnold

PAUL S AXCELL ◈
Kiln Cottage, Fourstones, Hexham, NE47 5DH
Tel: 01434 674757
Principal: ICAEW Member
P S Axcell

ROWLANDS
5-7 Eastgate, Hexham, NE46 1BH

STOKOE RODGER
St Matthews House, Haugh Lane, Hexham, NE46 3PU
Tel: 01434 604031
Fax: 01434 600690
Email: enquiries@stokoerodger.co.uk
Website: http://www.stokoerodger.co.uk
Resident Partners/Directors: ICAEW Members
M M Bradley, S G Charlton, I R Christer
Non-resident Partners (ICAEW Members):
D E Stokoe
Non-resident Partners (Non-ICAEW Members):
P Killen
Registered by the ICAEW to carry out company audit work
Regulated by the ICAEW for a range of investment business activities

WILLIS SCOTT GROUP ★
Mallan House, Bridge End, Hexham, NE46 4DQ

HIGH PEAK

A. ALLEN & SON
45 Union Road, New Mills, High Peak, SK22 3EL
Tel: 01663 744845
Email: mail@aallenandson.co.uk
Principal: ICAEW Member
D C Cooper

DAY & CO
1 Hunters Green Close, Chinley, High Peak, SK23 6DF

IAN J. SENIOR
18 Market Place, Chapel-en-le-Frith, High Peak, SK23 0EN

SOVEREIGN PAYROLL SERVICES
42 Market Street, Whaley Bridge, High Peak, SK23 7LP

WESTON & CO
10 Chendre Close, Hayfield, High Peak, SK22 2PH
Tel: 01663 744677
Principal: ICAEW Member
R C Weston

HIGH WYCOMBE

A.J. DILWORTH
Annapurna House, Stag Lane, Great Kingshill, High Wycombe HP15 6EW

ABIX ACCOUNTING
20 Meare Estate, Wooburn Green, High Wycombe, HP10 0DX
Tel: 01628 530775
Principal: ICAEW Member
E J Pecover

AIMS
35 New Road, Great Kingshill, High Wycombe, HP15 6DR

AIMS - NIGEL ROCK COOPER ACA
15 Juniper Court, Juniper Lane, Flackwell Heath, High Wycombe HP10 9HG

B. DUNTON & CO
Millstone, Off Barleyfields, Wooburn Moor, High Wycombe HP10 0NH

BEATTIE & CO
The Old Studio, High Street, West Wycombe, High Wycombe HP14 3AB

BETTRIDGE & CO ◈
2nd Floor, 27 High Street, High Wycombe, HP11 2AE
Tel: 01494 524020
Principal: ICAEW Member
M G Bettridge

BRIDGEN, WATKINS & WAINWRIGHT
10 Dashwood Avenue, High Wycombe, HP12 3DN

C.J. LEGGATE & ASSOCIATES
Analyst House, 15 New Road, High Wycombe, HP12 4LH

CANNON MOORCROFT LTD
3 Manor Courtyard, Hughenden Avenue, High Wycombe, HP13 5RE
Tel: 01494 450123
Email: canmoor@cannonmoorcroft.co.uk
Website: http://www.cannonmoorcroft.co.uk
Resident Partners/Directors: ICAEW Members
M S Ashcroft, P H Cannon, J L Moorcroft
Resident Partners (Non-ICAEW Members):
K D I Simmen, S E Lewis
Registered by the ICAEW to carry out company audit work
Regulated by the ICAEW for a range of investment business activities

CENTRE FOR EDUCATION & FINANCE MANAGEMENT LTD
Red Lion House, 9-10 High Street, High Wycombe, HP11 2AZ

CHRISTINE DICKSON
Red Lion House, 9-10 High Street, High Wycombe, HP11 2AZ

CHRISTOPHER J. MAWHOOD & CO ◈
75 Brands Hill Avenue, High Wycombe, HP13 5PY
Tel: 01494 529719
Principal: ICAEW Member
C J Mawhood

CHRISTOPHER JEWELL
Torvista, Heathfield Road, Sands, High Wycombe HP12 4DG

EHJ SERVICES LTD
Acorn Cottage, Rays Lane, Penn, High Wycombe HP10 8LH

FEILDING & CO
Highfields, 11 Marlow Road, High Wycombe, HP11 1TA
Tel: 01494 459765
Principal: ICAEW Member
P R Feilding

FISH PARTNERSHIP LLP ◈
The Mill House, Boundary Road, Loudwater, High Wycombe HP10 9QN
Tel: 01628 527956
Resident Partners/Directors: ICAEW Members
M J Sheehy
Resident Partners (Non-ICAEW Members):
P C Laird
Registered by the ICAEW to carry out company audit work

INVESTOR IN PEOPLE

GRANT THORNTON UK LLP
Bradenham Manor, Bradenham, High Wycombe, HP14 4HF

H R C LEWIS & CO
54 Amersham Hill Drive, High Wycombe, HP13 6QY

H W ◈
Sterling House, 5 Buckingham Place, Bellfield Rd West, High Wycombe HP13 5HQ
Tel: 01494 452921
Resident Partners/Directors: ICAEW Members
C M Fletcher, V A Fox, A E Golding, G A Heywood

J D ASSOCIATES
7 Whitfield Road, Hughenden Valley, High Wycombe, HP14 4NZ
Tel: 01494 564413

J.H.P DEVEREUX
J.H.P. Devereux, 7 Whitfield Road, Hughenden Valley, High Wycombe HP14 4NZ
Tel: 01494 564413
Principal: ICAEW Member
J H P Devereux

JAY & CO
12 Cherry Tree Close, Hughenden Valley, High Wycombe, HP14 4LP

JMBT LTD
The Old Studio, High Street, West Wycombe, High Wycombe HP14 3AB

KINGON & CO
Green Pastures, Bullocks Farm Lane, Wheeler End, High Wycombe HP14 3NQ
Tel: 01494 882889
Resident Partners/Directors: ICAEW Members
N B Kingon, W M Kingon

MACINTYRE HUDSON CORPORATE FINANCE LTD ◈
31 Castle Street, High Wycombe, HP13 6RU
Tel: 01494 441226
Website: http://www.macintyrehudson.co.uk
Resident Partners/Directors: ICAEW Members
A C Cook
Authorised and regulated by the Financial Services Authority for investment business

MACINTYRE HUDSON LLP ◈
31 Castle Street, High Wycombe, HP13 6RU
Tel: 01494 441226
Website: http://www.macintyrehudson.co.uk
Resident Partners/Directors: ICAEW Members
P J Byrne, A C Cook, B K Silva
Resident Partners (Non-ICAEW Members):
P G King
Regulated by the ICAEW for a range of investment business activities

ML & JP RUTT
7 Shepherds Fold, Holmer Green, High Wycombe, HP15 6XZ

ML AND JP RUTT
7 Shepherds Fold, Holmer Green, High Wycombe, HP15 6XZ
Tel: 01494 714414
Fax: 01494 717336
Email: mike@ruttaccounting.co.uk
Mobile: 07831 493359
Date Established: 1979
Principal: ICAEW Member
M L Rutt

MURRAY ACCOUNTING SERVICES LTD
Blackberry Cottage, Church Road, Tylers Green, Penn, High Wycombe HP10 8LP

P.A. COOK AND CO
Crown House, London Road, Loudwater, High Wycombe HP10 9TJ
Tel: 01494 533581
Principal: ICAEW Member
P A Cook

P A COOK & CO (OXFORD) LTD
Crown House, London Road, Loudwater, High Wycombe HP10 9TJ
Tel: 01494 533581
Resident Partners/Directors: ICAEW Members
P A Cook

PARSONS & CO
4 Park Lane, Hazlemere, High Wycombe, HP15 7HY

PETER MASON
35 New Road, Great Kingshill, High Wycombe, HP15 6DR

PHILLIP P. EVANS
Crown House, London Road, Loudwater, High Wycombe HP10 9TJ

PITMAN COHEN LLP
1st Floor, Wheelrod House, 23a Brendon Street, High Wycombe HP13 6LJ

ROBERT W. ROBINSON
58 Coppice Farm Road, Penn, High Wycombe, HP10 8AH

SAFFERY CHAMPNESS ◈
Fox House, 26 Temple End, High Wycombe, HP13 5DR
Tel: 01494 464666
Fax: 01494 459618
Website: http://www.saffery.com
Training Contracts Available.
Resident Partners/Directors: ICAEW Members
K T Bartlett, L J Sowden
Other Offices: Bournemouth, Bristol, Edinburgh, Geneva, Guernsey, Harrogate, Inverness, London, Manchester, Peterborough
Registered by the ICAEW to carry out company audit work
Regulated by the ICAEW for a range of investment business activities

INVESTOR IN PEOPLE

General Description: See our London office entry.

SALMON & CO
4 Buckingham Place, Bellfield Road, High Wycombe, HP13 5HQ
Tel: 01494 448857
Principal: ICAEW Member
R C Salmon

SAMANTHA KELLY ACA
10 Ferniefields, High Wycombe, HP12 4SP
Tel: 01494 447890
Principal: ICAEW Member
S Kelly

SAVAGE & CO ◈
Victoria House, Desborough Street, High Wycombe, HP11 2NF
Tel: 01494 601111
Principal: ICAEW Member
P R Savage

SEYMOUR TAYLOR ◈
57 London Road, High Wycombe, HP11 1BS
Tel: 01494 552100
Fax: 01494 461157
Email: enquiries@stca.co.uk
Website: http://www.stca.co.uk
Date Established: 1917
Resident Partners/Directors: ICAEW Members
C J Baker, G J Francis, F W Johnston, S J Turner
Resident Partners (Non-ICAEW Members):
E J A Harrington, M J Marshall

continued

SEYMOUR TAYLOR
cont
Registered by the ICAEW to carry out company audit work
Licensed by another DPB to carry on investment business

SPECIALISATIONS – AUDIT & ASSURANCE
Audit
Pension Scheme Auditors

SPECIALISATIONS – BUSINESS & GENERAL ADVICE
Acquisitions and Mergers
Company Formation
Company Secretarial Service
Disposal of Businesses
Management Advice to Business
Outsourcing - Financial Services

SPECIALISATIONS – FINANCIAL REPORTING
Accounts Preparation
Audit Exemption Report
Foreign Subsidiary Companies
International Reporting Standards (IFRS)
Limited Company Accounts
Partnership/Sole Trader Accounts

SPECIALISATIONS – FORENSIC ACCOUNTING
Expert Witnesses in Litigation

SPECIALISATIONS – INVESTMENT BUSINESS
Financial Planning and Advice

SPECIALISATIONS – SECTOR
Charities
Construction
FSA Members
Retailers
Solicitors

SPECIALISATIONS – TAXATION
Foreign Nationals in the UK
PAYE Advice
Payroll Service and Advice
Taxation
UK Subsidiaries of Overseas Multinationals

THAMES VALLEY ACCOUNTANT
75 Brands Hill Avenue, High Wycombe, HP13 5PY

WESTERNSHARE LTD ◈
28 Riverside Business Centre, High Wycombe, HP11 2LT
Tel: 01494 893439
Resident Partners/Directors:
ICAEW Members
F M S Ashton
See display advertisement near this entry.

HIGHBRIDGE

PAUL VENN MA FCA
3 Market Street, Highbridge, TA9 3BW

HINCKLEY

A J DOWSETT & CO ◈
17 Station Road, Hinckley, LE10 1AW
Tel: 01455 230537
Resident Partners/Directors:
ICAEW Members
A J Dowsett, B A Moore

BREALEY FOSTER & CO
Edwards Centre, The Horsefair, Hinckley, LE10 0AN

CHARLES STRINGER
17 Frith Way, Hinckley, LE10 0JE
Tel: 01455 617890
Fax: 0870 622 1891
Email: chas01@ntlworld.com
Principal: ICAEW Member
C G G Stringer

LESTER & CO
25 Station Road, Hinckley, LE10 1AP
Tel: 01455 637291
Resident Partners/Directors:
ICAEW Members
M A Lester, M P Lester

HINDHEAD

PHILIP MOORE
Torridon, Wood Road, Hindhead, GU26 6PX
Tel: 01428 604364
Principal: ICAEW Member
P G Moore

RICHARD B. PENNINGTON
Firnook, Linkside East, Hindhead, GU26 6NY
Tel: 01428 606322
Principal: ICAEW Member
R B Pennington

SIMPSONS ◈
Hunters, Headley Road, Grayshott, Hindhead GU26 6DL
Tel: 01428 608900
Principal: ICAEW Member
D W Richards

HITCHIN

ALAN HARTLEY
5 West Lane, Pirton, Hitchin, SG5 3RA

ALLAN SMITH ACCOUNTING & TAX LTD
5 The Green, Codicote, Hitchin, SG4 8UR

ASHLEYS
Invision House, Wilbury Way, Hitchin, SG4 0TY

ASHLEYS (HITCHIN) LTD
Invision House, Knowl Piece, Wilbury Way, Hitchin SG4 0TY

BRADSHAW JOHNSON
13 Bancroft, Hitchin, SG5 1JQ
Tel: 01462 454545
Email: mail@bjca.co.uk
Resident Partners/Directors:
ICAEW Members
N Harding, S Pike
Other Offices:30 Cambridge Street, St Neots, Cambs (Tel: 01480 404000)
Registered by another RSB to carry out company audit work
Licensed by another DPB to carry on investment business

BRIDGEN, WATKINS & WAINWRIGHT
Unit 7, Titmore Green, Little Wymondley, Hitchin SG4 7JT

CHANCELLERS ★ ◈
38/39 Bucklersbury, Hitchin, SG5 1BG
Tel: 01462 620100
Email: hitchin@chancellers.co.uk
Website: http://www.chancellers.co.uk
Training Contracts Available.
Resident Partners/Directors:
ICAEW Members
R A Owen, N K Sarna
Registered by the ICAEW to carry out company audit work

CLARK & CO ACCOUNTANTS LTD
Red Ski House, Fairclough Hall, Halls Green, Weston, Hitchin SG4 7DP

COOMBS (BEDFORD) LTD
Coombs, 20 Strathmore Avenue, Hitchin, SG5 1SL

DEREK WILLOWS LTD
12 Saxon Avenue, Stotfold, Hitchin, SG5 4DD
Tel: 01462 642517
Resident Partners/Directors:
ICAEW Members
D F Willows

GEOFFREY HODGE
30 Market Place, Hitchin, SG5 1DY

GODFREY LAWS & CO LTD ◈
69 Knowl Piece, Wilbury Way, Hitchin, SG4 0TY
Tel: 01462 421521
Resident Partners/Directors:
ICAEW Members
H C S Ashmore

HITCHIN PRACTICE LTD
Hemmings, Kings Walden, Hitchin, SG4 8NW
Tel: 01438 871795
Resident Partners/Directors:
ICAEW Members
A J W Brown

HW ASSOCIATES ◈
Portmill House, Portmill Lane, Hitchin, SG5 1DJ
Tel: 01462 420042
Email: info@hw-associates.co.uk
Website: http://www.hw-associates.co.uk
Resident Partners/Directors:
ICAEW Members
M Hjertzen, F Reid

J.M. CHAPMAN
22 St Albans Road, Codicote, Hitchin, SG4 8UT

JONES, HUNT & CO
Ickleford Manor, Turnpike Lane, Ickleford, Hitchin SG5 3XE

JOSOLYNE ROGERS
107 Bancroft, Hitchin, SG5 1NB

MILLINGTON HORE
9 Arlesey Road, Ickleford, Hitchin, SG5 3UN

PHILIP M DOE
24 The Ridgeway, Codicote, Hitchin, SG4 8YP

R.E. SMITHSON
14 Lister Avenue, Hitchin, SG4 9ES

R.W. WOMWELL ◈
Suite 11, Woodside House, 18 Walsworth Road, Hitchin SG4 9SP
Tel: 01462 441034
Principal: ICAEW Member
R W Womwell
Registered by the ICAEW to carry out company audit work
Regulated by the ICAEW for a range of investment business activities

THE RED SKY PARTNERSHIP LTD
Red Sky House, Fairclough Hall, Halls Green, Weston, Hitchin SG4 7DP

S.C. M. ACCOUNTANCY SERVICES LTD
28 Witter Avenue, Ickleford, Hitchin, SG5 3UF

S. MCCOMBIE & CO
First Floor, 99 Bancroft, Hitchin, SG5 1NQ

SKEELES & ZANINI ◈
1a Bearton Green, Hitchin, SG5 1UN
Tel: 01462 433284
Principal: ICAEW Member
J W Skeeles

HOCKLEY

ANSER CONSULTING LTD ◈
Suite 3, Warren House, 10 - 20 Main Road, Hockley SS5 4QS

ANSERS!
Suite 3, Warren House, Main Road, Hockley SS5 4QS

JOHN S CULWICK
9 Uplands Road, Hockley, SS5 4DL

HEDGES CHANDLER
36 The Westerings, Hockley, SS5 4NY

MICHAEL ADAMSON & CO
224 Ferry Road, Hullbridge, Hockley, SS5 6ND

HODDESDON

AT ACCOUNTING
171 Lampits, Hoddesdon, EN11 8EF

G.H. ATTENBOROUGH & CO LTD ◈
1 Tower House, Tower Centre, Hoddesdon, EN11 8UR
Tel: 01992 468536
Resident Partners/Directors:
ICAEW Members
Howard Connor
Registered by the ICAEW to carry out company audit work
Regulated by the ICAEW for a range of investment business activities

GILLANI & CO
Conduit House, Conduit Lane, Hoddesdon, EN11 8EP

HBAS LTD
Amwell House, 19 Amwell Street, Hoddesdon, EN11 8TS

ROBERTS & CO (ACCOUNTANTS) LTD
2 Tower House, Hoddesdon, EN11 8UR
Tel: 01992 467788
Resident Partners/Directors:
ICAEW Members
D G Roberts, J A Roberts

ROBERTS & CO (ACCOUNTANTS) LTD
2 Tower House, Hoddesdon, EN11 8TJ
Tel: 01992 467788

HOLMFIRTH

A M ROGERS
Yorkshire House, 7 South Lane, Holmfirth, HD9 1HN

ALEXA-RAE LTD
Victoria Court, 91 Huddersfield Road, Holmfirth, HD9 3JA

H P WADSWORTH ◈
8A Hey Cliff Road, Holmfirth, HD9 1XD

HPW
9 Hey Cliff Road, Holmfirth, HD9 1XD

JOHN C WALKER
11 Allergill Park, Upperthong, Holmfirth, HD9 3XH
Tel: 01484 687946
Principal: ICAEW Member
J C Walker

MICHAEL BELL & CO ◈
4 Greenfield Road, Holmfirth, HD9 2JT

HOLSWORTHY

CRICK & CO
8 Chapel Street, Holsworthy, EX22 6AY

SIMPKINS EDWARDS
12 The Square, Holsworthy, EX22 6DL
Tel: 01409 253620
Email: holsworthy@simpkinsedwards.co.uk
Website: http://www.simpkinsedwards.co.uk
Resident Partners/Directors:
ICAEW Members
J C House
Registered by the ICAEW to carry out company audit work
Regulated by the ICAEW for a range of investment business activities

THOMAS WESTCOTT ★
London House, Fore Street, Holsworthy, EX22 6EB
Tel: 01409 253297
Resident Partners/Directors:
ICAEW Members
M Ohlsen, V Parnell

HOLT

LARKING GOWEN ◈
43 Bull Street, Holt, NR25 6HP
Tel: 01263 712017
Non-resident Partners (ICAEW Members):
P J Moy
Resident Partners (Non-ICAEW Members):
C S Scargill

SORRELL
Glaven Farm Barn, Thornage Road, Letheringsett, Holt NR25 7JE

SORRELL LTD
Glaven Farm Barn, Thornage Road, Letheringsett, Holt NR25 7JE

TREVOR C. DAVIES
Brent Cottage, Hilltop, Cley-next-the-Sea, Holt NR25 7SD
Tel: 01263 740060
Principal: ICAEW Member
T C Davies

HONITON

ASSETWISE LTD
3 Hatcher Close, Honiton, EX14 2YG
Tel: 01404 44827
Resident Partners/Directors:
ICAEW Members
D A Jones

CHURCHILL & CO
Wessex House, 66 High Street, Honiton, EX14 1PD

NINELIVES LTD
3 Hatcher Close, Honiton, EX14 2YG
Tel: 01404 44827
Resident Partners/Directors:
ICAEW Members
D A Jones

NORTHAMS
21/23 New Street, Honiton, EX14 1HA

SIMPKINS EDWARDS
The Royal British Legion Club, 51 Dowell Street, Honiton, EX14 8NB
Tel: 01392 211233

THOMAS WESTCOTT ★
Queens House, New Street, Honiton, EX14 1BJ
Tel: 01404 540054
Resident Partners/Directors:
ICAEW Members
G J Sindle

TOSH & CO
105B High Str, Honiton, EX14 1PE
Tel: 01404 46556
Principal: ICAEW Member
P M Tosh

WAUGH & CO
Springs, Millhayes, Stockland, Honiton EX14 9DB
Tel: 01404 881528
Principal: ICAEW Member
E P G Waugh

HOOK

CRANLEYS ◈
31 Goose Green, Hook, RG27 9QY

JANE MOORE
3 John Morgan Close, Hook, RG27 9RP

K.R. BURGIN
1 Dairy Walk, Hartley Wintney, Hook, RG27 8XX
Tel: 01252 845123
Principal: ICAEW Member
K R Burgin

N.L. HUNT
18 Garden Close, Hook, RG27 9QZ

PETER GODDARD & CO
125 High Street, Odiham, Hook, RG29 1LA

ROBERT CULVER LTD
Field House, Brackley Avenue, Hartley Wintney, Hook RG27 8QU

S CHARLES MESHER & CO ◈
4 Newnham Park, Hook, RG27 9QL

SHEPHERD ACCOUNTANCY LTD
27 Nursery Close, Hook, RG27 9QX

SLH ACCOUNTING
5 Northwick, Eversley, Hook, RG27 0SD
Tel: 07515 963779
Principal: ICAEW Member
S L Harvey

STEPHEN R THOMAS
Hawthorn House, Tunnel Lane, North Warnborough, Hook RG29 1JT
Tel: 01256 703254
Principal: ICAEW Member
S R Thomas

TWISSELL NEILSON & CO
Belgravia House, High Street, Hartley Wintney, Hook RG27 8NS
Tel: 01252 843883
Email: twiss@ukonline.co.uk
Principal: ICAEW Member
M J Twissell

WILLAN & WILLAN
The Old Post Office, High Street, Hartley Wintney, Hook RG27 8NZ

HOPE VALLEY

A BRIGHTMORE & CO ◈
Fairholme Bungalow, Hathersage Road, Bamford, Hope Valley S33 0EB
Tel: 01433 651758

ARP BRIGHTMORE LTD ◈
Fairholme Bungalow, Hathersage Road, Bamford, Hope Valley S33 0EB
Tel: 01433 651758
Resident Partners/Directors:
ICAEW Members
A R P Brightmore

DAVID WATSON
Knoll Farm, Aston Lane, Hope, Hope Valley S33 6RA
Tel: 01433 621509
Email: david.watson4@breathe.com
Principal: ICAEW Member
D I Watson

GILLIAN NOWELL
Eccles House Telebusiness Centre, Eccles Lane, Hope Valley, S33 6RW
Tel: 01433 621221
Principal: ICAEW Member
G Nowell

HORLEY

CHARLES & COMPANY ACCOUNTANCY LTD
1st Floor, 16 Massetts Road, Horley, RH6 7DE

CLB GATWICK LLP ◈
Imperial Buildings, Victoria Road, Horley, RH6 7PZ
Tel: 01293 776411
Resident Partners/Directors: ICAEW Members
F S K Durrani, M R Neve, J C Pannett

FURSDON CONSULTING
The Old Stables, Grange Manor, Shipley Bridge Lane, Shipley Bridge, Horley RH6 9TL

FURSDON CONSULTING LTD
The Old Stables, Grange Manor, Shipley Bridge Lane, Shipley Bridge, Horley RH6 9TL

REEVES+NEYLAN LLP
Dartel House, 39-41 High Street, Horley, RH6 7BN
Tel: 01293 776152
Registered by the ICAEW to carry out company audit work
Regulated by the ICAEW for a range of investment business activities

HORNCASTLE

DEXTER & SHARPE ★
Rollestone House, Bridge Street, Horncastle, LN9 5HZ

HORNCHURCH

ABIDIN & CO
65 Butts Green Road, Hornchurch, RM11 2JS

ALMOND & CO
Suite 2, Interwood House, Stafford House, Hornchurch RM11 2ER
Tel: 01708 446100
Principal: ICAEW Member
G J Almond

B. KOTEN & CO (ACCOUNTANTS) ★ ◈
16 Whitethorn Gardens, Hornchurch, RM11 2AL
Tel: 01708 441699
Resident Partners/Directors: ICAEW Members
B Koten

CHAKKO HARRIS
Interwood House, Stafford Avenue, Hornchurch, RM11 2ER
Tel: 01708 471511
Email: info@chakkoharris.com
Website: http://www.chakkoharris.com
Principal: ICAEW Member
I M Gorsuch
Registered by the ICAEW to carry out company audit work

G.W. JAY
Dhe'n Chy, 21 Spingate Close, Hornchurch, RM12 6SW
Tel: 01708 449089
Principal: ICAEW Member
G W Jay

JAN WATKINSON & CO
8 Mallinson Close, Hornchurch, RM12 5HA

KASE ACCOUNTANCY SERVICES LTD
Excel House, 1 Hornminster Glen, Hornchurch, RM11 3XL

ROBERTSON MILROY & CO ◈
Coopers House, 65 Wingletye Lane, Hornchurch, RM11 3AT
Tel: 01708 475220
Principal: ICAEW Member
M P Robertson

ROBERTSON MILROY LTD ◈
Coopers House, 65 Wingletye Road, Hornchurch, RM11 3AT
Tel: 01708 475220
Website: http://www.robertsonmilroy.com
Resident Partners/Directors: ICAEW Members
M P Robertson

SPECIALISATIONS – FORENSIC ACCOUNTING

Forensic Accounting

S.E. BIBBY & CO
1 Wych Elm Close, Hornchurch, RM11 3AJ
Tel: 01708 452909
Principal: ICAEW Member
S E Bibby

SHROFF ACCOUNTANCY SERVICES
Excel House, 1 Hornminster Glen, Hornchurch, RM11 3XL

SYNERGY BUSINESS SOLUTIONS UK LTD
1 Fordyce Close, Hornchurch, RM11 3LE

VANTIS BUSINESS RECOVERY SERVICES
43-45 Butts Green Road, Hornchurch, RM11 2JX
Tel: 01708 458 211
Website: http://www.vantisplc.com/businessrecovery
Principal: ICAEW Member
J S French
Individual(s) licensed for insolvency work by another RPB

SPECIALISATIONS – BUSINESS RECOVERY & INSOLVENCY

Bankruptcies
Corporate Recovery
Liquidations

WOODS & CO
1 Fordyce Close, Hornchurch, RM11 3LE

HORNSEA

SOWERBY FRS
66 Newbegin, Hornsea, HU18 1AD

HORSHAM

ABACUSHOUSE.COM LLP
Abacus House, Wickhurst Lane, Broadbridge Heath, Horsham RH12 3LY

ABC 123 LTD ◈
Sanford House, Medwin Walk, Horsham, RH12 1AG

AIMS - DAVID SMITH
Church Street House, Church Street, Rudgwick, Horsham RH12 3EH
Tel: 01403 823666
Principal: ICAEW Member
D P A Smith

ALLAN WILLMOTT
Bramley, Farthings Hill, Horsham, RH12 1TS

BALDWIN SCOFIELD & CO ◈
3 New House Farm Business Centre, Old Crawley Road, Horsham, RH12 4RU
Tel: 01293 851715
Resident Partners/Directors: ICAEW Members
N M Baldwin

CHRISTOPHER J HOLMES
27 Cootes Avenue, Horsham, RH12 2AD
Tel: 01403 260862
Principal: ICAEW Member
C J Holmes

D A CLARK & CO LTD ◈
4 Peel House, Barttelot Road, Horsham, RH12 1DE
Tel: 01403 218390
Email: david@daclark.co.uk
Website: http://www.daclark.co.uk
Date Established: 1986
Resident Partners/Directors: ICAEW Members
D A Clark
Registered by the ICAEW to carry out company audit work

DAVID LANGLEY
Walden Close, Cowfold Road, West Grinstead, Horsham RH13 8LY
Tel: 01403 865648
Principal: ICAEW Member
D J Langley

SPECIALISATIONS – TAXATION

Self Assessment Advice
Taxation

GOODRICH MORRISON & CO
10 Durfold Road, Horsham, RH12 5HZ

HARTLEY FOWLER LLP ◈
44 Springfield Road, Horsham, RH12 2PD
Tel: 01403 254322
Fax: 01403 266498
Email: info.hsm@hartleyfowler.com
Website: http://www.hartleyfowler.com
Training Contracts Available.
Resident Partners/Directors: ICAEW Members
P R Collins, I R Gilchrist
Registered by the ICAEW to carry out company audit work
Regulated by the ICAEW for a range of investment business activities

HOLDING & CO
49 London Road, Horsham, RH12 1AN

INDIGO TAX & ACCOUNTANCY LTD
The Barn, Brighton Road, Lower Beeding, Horsham, RH13 6PT
Tel: 01403 892683
Resident Partners/Directors: ICAEW Members
T A Noon

MB ACCOUNTANCY LTD
Peacehaven, Coltstaple Lane, Newfoundout, Horsham RH13 9BB
Tel: 01403 733974
Resident Partners/Directors: ICAEW Members
M A Bushnell

MORRIS PALMER LTD ◈
Barttelot Court, Barttelot Road, Horsham, RH12 1DQ
Tel: 01403 750444
Resident Partners/Directors: ICAEW Members
M A C Carter

N.R. WARD
36 Brushwood Road, Horsham, RH12 4PE
Tel: 01403 269144
Principal: ICAEW Member
N R Ward

PARR & CO
The Old Farm Shop, Homelands Farm, Bines Road, Partridge Green, Horsham RH13 8EQ

PETER GRIFFITHS & CO ◈
1a Comptons Lane, Horsham, RH13 5NJ

R.J. DUNSCOMBE
68 Hillmead, Horsham, RH12 2PX
Tel: 01403 251163
Principal: ICAEW Member
R J Dunscombe

RICHARD J. WILKINS
45 Lambs Farm Road, Horsham, RH12 4DB

RICHARD PLACE PALMER
52a Carfax, Horsham, RH12 1EQ

RITCHIE PHILLIPS
The Old Granary, Field Place Estate, Byfleets Lane, Broadbridge Heath, Horsham RH12 3PB
Tel: 0870 881 2870
Principal: ICAEW Member
S D Ritchie

ROUTLEDGE TAYLOR
Abacus House, Wickhurst Lane, Broadbridge Heath, Horsham RH12 3LY

SPOFFORTHS LLP ◈
1 Horsham Gates, North Street, Horsham, RH13 5PJ
Tel: 01403 253282
Resident Partners/Directors: ICAEW Members
E J Case, S G Ediss, K A Johnson, P R Lansberry, R C P P Spofforth
Resident Partners (Non-ICAEW Members):
B Elkins, S P Maggs

STONER COTTINGHAM
42 London Rd, Horsham, RH12 1AY
Tel: 01403 263904
Fax: 01403 211844
Email: admin@stonercottingham.co.uk
Website: http://www.stonercottingham.co.uk
Resident Partners/Directors: ICAEW Members
S R Cottingham, D J Stoner
Registered by the ICAEW to carry out company audit work
Regulated by the ICAEW for a range of investment business activities
See display advertisement near this entry.

UMESH PATEL & CO
1 Kings Court, Harwood Road, Horsham, RH13 5UR
Tel: 01403 217810
Principal: ICAEW Member
U D Patel

WILKINS KENNEDY
6 Kings Court, Harwood Road, Horsham, RH13 5UR

HOUGHTON LE SPRING

ALUN DUNNING
25 Front Street, Hetton-le-Hole, Houghton Le Spring, DH5 9PF

M.G ARCHBOLD
63 Castlefields, Bournmoor, Houghton Le Spring, DH4 6HJ

PAUL PURDHAM
26 Millers Hill, Houghton Le Spring, DH4 7AJ

PULLAN BARNES ◈
Stephenson House, Richard Street, Hetton-le-Hole, Houghton Le Spring, Tyne and Wear DH5 9HW
Tel: 0191 517 0116
Resident Partners/Directors: ICAEW Members
Y Bari, M Barnes, K Pullan
Other Offices:49 Front St. Framwellgate Moor, Durham City DH1 5BL
(Tel: 0191 384 7206)

ROBERT MILLER & CO
Kings Hall, Imperial Buildings, Houghton Le Spring, DH4 4DJ

ROBERT MILLER & COMPANY (HOUGHTON) LTD
Kings Hall, Imperial Buildings, Houghton Le Spring, DH4 4DJ

HOUNSLOW

A.K. SHARMA & CO
413 Great West Road, Hounslow, TW5 0BY

A.R.N. GUPTA & CO
501 Great West Road, Hounslow, TW5 0BS

AMRIT GADHOK
201 Brabazon Road, Heston, Hounslow, TW5 9LW

ATOM CONSULTING LTD
Premier House, 50-52 Cross Lances Road, Hounslow, TW3 2AA

CARRINGTONS LTD ◈
6 Maple Grove Business Centre, Lawrence Road, Hounslow, TW4 6DR
Tel: 020 8577 1717
Resident Partners/Directors: ICAEW Members
A K Bhamm

CHARLES STUART LLP ◈
36 Bath Road, Hounslow, TW3 3EF
Tel: 020 8577 1000
Email: value@csuk.com
Website: http://www.csuk.com
Resident Partners/Directors: ICAEW Members
R N G Johnson, A L Magagnin, L J Penny
Other Offices: Datchet
Registered by the ICAEW to carry out company audit work
Regulated by the ICAEW for a range of investment business activities

SPECIALISATIONS – SECTOR

Property

SPECIALISATIONS – TAXATION

Investigations
UK Subsidiaries of Overseas Multinationals

General Description: Small & medium business specialists. Chartered tax advisers.

EESH AGGARWAL
100 Hibernia Road, Hounslow, TW3 3RN

GANDHI & CO
113 Kingsley Road, Hounslow, TW3 4AJ
Tel: 020 8570 4499
Principal: ICAEW Member
J B Gandhi

HICKS & CO ★ ◈
53 Lampton Road, Hounslow, TW3 1LY
Tel: 020 8572 0931
Resident Partners/Directors: ICAEW Members
P M Cobden

LEVER BROS & CO ◈
104 Cromwell Road, Hounslow, TW3 3QJ
Tel: 020 8569 5569
Resident Partners/Directors: ICAEW Members
G J Marrett
Resident Partners (Non-ICAEW Members):
S A Raja

R.K. SETHI & CO
140 Springwell Road, Hounslow, TW5 9BP

SANSON LTD
Universal Buildings, Green Lane, Nr Heathrow Airport, Hounslow TW4 6DF

SIVA YOGAN & CO
Hounslow Business Park, Unit 6, Hounslow, TW3 3UD
Tel: 020 8572 2112
Resident Partners/Directors: ICAEW Members
N Ariaratnam

HOVE

ACUMENSA ★
Cornelius House, 178-180 Church Road, Hove, BN3 2DJ

AGUTTER, HELEN ACA
48 Albany Villas, Hove, BN3 2RW

ATKINSONS ◈
Palmeira Avenue Mansions, 19 Church Road, Hove, BN3 2FA
Tel: 01273 771122
Fax: 01273 771166
Email: info@atkinsonsca.co.uk
Website: http://www.atkinsonsca.co.uk
Principal: ICAEW Member
R B Atkinson
Other Offices: New Malden, Surrey
(Tel: 020 8949 2202)
Registered by the ICAEW to carry out company audit work

SPECIALISATIONS – AUDIT & ASSURANCE
Audit — Private Company

SPECIALISATIONS – BUSINESS & GENERAL ADVICE
Book-keeping

SPECIALISATIONS – FORENSIC ACCOUNTING
Forensic Accounting

SPECIALISATIONS – IT
Information Technology

SPECIALISATIONS – TAXATION
Back Duty
Estate Planning
Offshore Companies
Self Assessment Advice
Trusts
Value Added Tax

General Description: Firm established in 1962. Dealing mainly with small and medium sized businesses. Cost effective for small limited company audits.
Languages Spoken:
French, German, Spanish

BRISTOW STILL
39 Sackville Road, Hove, BN3 3WD
Tel: 01273 326409
Resident Partners/Directors: ICAEW Members
I Cleaver, D R Still

CHAMPNESS & SARGANT
8 The Green, Hove, BN3 6TH

CHANTREY VELLACOTT DFK LLP
1st Floor, 16-17 Boundary Road, Hove, BN3 4AN
Tel: 01273 421200
Fax: 01273 417330
Email: info@cvdfk.com
Website: http://www.cvdfk.com
Resident Partners/Directors: ICAEW Members
D J Oprey
Resident Partners (Non-ICAEW Members):
K W Touhey
Other Offices: Colchester, Croydon, Leicester, London, Northampton, Reading, Stevenage, Watford
Registered by the ICAEW to carry out company audit work
Regulated by the ICAEW for a range of investment business activities
Individual(s) licensed for insolvency work by the ICAEW

INVESTOR IN PEOPLE

CLARK BROWNSCOMBE ◈
8 The Drive, Hove, BN3 3JT
Tel: 01273 739277
Resident Partners/Directors: ICAEW Members
N W H Ericsson, P J Thacker

DERRICK J. NUNN
54 Shirley Street, Hove, BN3 3WG
Tel: 01273 748680
Principal: ICAEW Member
D J Nunn

EAST PARTNERSHIP LTD
Mill House, 103 Holmes Avenue, Hove, BN3 7LE
Tel: 01273 279082
Resident Partners/Directors: ICAEW Members
D J Elder

FREDK A.J. COULDERY
81 Hove Park Road, Hove, BN3 6LN
Tel: 01273 555750
Principal: ICAEW Member
F A J Couldery

GARY REVEL-CHION
1 Coleman Avenue, Hove, BN3 5ND
Tel: 01273 207450
Principal: ICAEW Member
G Revel-Chion

GGS CONSULTING LTD
197-201 Church Road, Hove, BN3 2AH

HUMPHREY & CO
Curtis House, Third Avenue, Hove, BN3 2PD

HWCA (BRIGHTON) LTD
201 Dyke Road, Hove, BN3 1TL
Tel: 01273 739533
Resident Partners/Directors: ICAEW Members
G C Fairclough, C A Hunt

I.N. MOKHTAR & CO
7 Chartfield, Hove, BN3 7RD
Tel: 01273 561195
Fax: 01273 882889
Principal: ICAEW Member
I N Mokhtar
General Description: General and management accounting services on contract basis. Also services as CPAs for preparation of US tax returns and UK/US tax advice for individuals and companies.

J.SRINIVASAN CROUCH & CO
40A Rutland Gardens, Hove, BN3 5PB

JOHN & CO
60 Lansdowne Place, Hove, BN3 1FG
Tel: 01273 730248
Principal: ICAEW Member
D P Grammer

JONATHAN ECCLES
Flat 2, 54-55 Ventnor Villas, Hove, BN3 3DB

JULIAN WILLS
12A Courtenay Gate, Courtenay Terrace, Kingsway, Hove BN3 2WJ

K P TANNER LTD ◈
3-4 Westbourne Gardens, Hove, BN3 5PL
Tel: 01273 729307
Resident Partners/Directors: ICAEW Members
K P Tanner

M.J. COMENS
Suite 1, 1 Boundary Road, Hove, BN3 4EH
Tel: 01273 416663
Principal: ICAEW Member
M J Comens

MICHAEL T. PARKER
2 St Aubyns Mansions, Kings Esplanade, Hove, BN3 2WQ

MOKHTAR EDWARDS & CO
7 Chartfield, Hove, BN3 7RD
Tel: 01273 561195
Principal: ICAEW Member
I N Mokhtar

OUTSOURCE BUSINESS LTD ◈
5A Wilbury Grove, Hove, BN3 3JQ
Tel: 01273 728908
Resident Partners/Directors: ICAEW Members
J C C Young

PARKERS BUSINESS SERVICES LTD ◈
Cornelius House, 178-180 Church Road, Hove, BN3 2DJ
Tel: 01273 722505
Resident Partners/Directors: ICAEW Members
C J Arbenz, D I Jemmett, S G Monk, E C Raynor

PARKERS BUSINESS SERVICES LTD ◈
Cornelius House, 178-180 Church Road, Hove, BN3 2DJ
Fax: 01273 204773
Email: info@parkerpartnership.co.uk
Website: http://www.parkerpartnership.com

Registered by the ICAEW to carry out company audit work

Regulated by the ICAEW for a range of investment business activities

SPECIALISATIONS – TAXATION

UK Subsidiaries of Overseas Multinationals

R.C.A. ANDREWS
7 Hill Drive, Hove, BN3 6QN

SPIRO WILLIAMS & CO
9 Albert Mews, Third Avenue, Hove, BN3 2PP

SPW (UK) LLP
Cornelius House, 178-180 Church Road, Hove, BN3 2DJ

SUSAN E. AINLEY
39 Fourth Avenue, Hove, BN3 2PN

T TIFFIN NASH & CO
33 Lawrence Road, Hove, BN3 5QA

TIDMARSH & CO
Wallace House, 45 Portland Road, Hove, BN3 5DQ

UHY HACKER YOUNG
168 Church Road, Hove, BN3 2DL

UHY HACKER YOUNG
168 Church Road, Hove, BN3 2DL
Tel: 01273 726445
Resident Partners/Directors: ICAEW Members
G Davies, G J Epstein, D A Guest, R B Simmons, S Thantrey

UHY HACKER YOUNG (S E) LTD
168 Church Road, Hove, BN3 2DL
Tel: 01273 726445
Resident Partners/Directors: ICAEW Members
G J Epstein, D A Guest, R B Simmons, S Thantrey

VICTOR BOORMAN & CO ★
Europa House, Goldstone Villas, Hove, BN3 3RQ
Tel: 01273 321956
Fax: 01273 329246
Email: info@boormans.com
Website: http://www.boormans.com
Resident Partners/Directors: ICAEW Members
S R A Holmes, K B Jordan
Resident Partners (Non-ICAEW Members):
R S Browning

Registered by the ICAEW to carry out company audit work

Regulated by the ICAEW for a range of investment business activities

WILSON SANDFORD & CO ◈
85 Church Road, Hove, BN3 2BB
Tel: 01273 821441

WILSON SANDFORD LTD ◈
85 Church Road, Hove, BN3 2BB
Tel: 01273 821441
Date Established: 1982
Resident Partners/Directors: ICAEW Members
J H Mainwood, A C Sandford, R F S Wilson
Non-resident Partners (ICAEW Members):
A C Sandford
Resident Partners (Non-ICAEW Members):
S Smith, M Jester

Registered by the ICAEW to carry out company audit work

Regulated by the ICAEW for a range of investment business activities

SPECIALISATIONS – AUDIT & ASSURANCE

Audit

SPECIALISATIONS – BUSINESS & GENERAL ADVICE

Acquisitions and Mergers
Company Formation

SPECIALISATIONS – FINANCIAL REPORTING

Accounts Preparation

SPECIALISATIONS – TAXATION

Payroll Service and Advice
Taxation

General Description: 4 Resident Directors and 20 staff. Clients throughout Sussex and London. Members of UK 200 group. http://www.wilsonsanford.co.uk.
See display advertisement near this entry.

HUDDERSFIELD

A.J. MINDHAM & CO
1 Westleigh Hall, Wakefield Road, Denby Dale, Huddersfield HD8 8QJ

AIMS - DAVID DYSON
11 Brecon Avenue, Lindley, Huddersfield, HD3 3QF

APPLETON DALE LTD
Orchard House, 347c Wakefield Road, Denby Dale, Huddersfield HD8 8RT
Tel: 01484 865516
Resident Partners/Directors: ICAEW Members
A Cliffe, P J Cliffe, D R Taylor

ARMITAGE & CO
1 New Street, Slaithwaite, Huddersfield, HD7 5AB

ATRAXA CONSULTING LTD
Brooke's Mill, Armitage Bridge, Huddersfield, HD4 7NR

BAMFORTH & CO
4 Follingworth Lane, Slaithwaite, Huddersfield, HD7 5XD

BUSINESS ADVANTAGE LTD
4 Follingworth Lane, Slaithwaite, Huddersfield, HD7 5XD

CHRISTOPHER R. CLARKE
26 Elm Court, Highburton, Huddersfield, HD8 0TB
Tel: 01484 604467
Principal: ICAEW Member
C R Clarke

CONNELLY & CO
Permanent House, 1 Dundas Street, Huddersfield, HD1 2EX

CONNELLY & CO LTD
Permanent House, 1 Dundas Street, Huddersfield, HD1 2EX

D & A HILL
18 T8/9 Brookes Mill, Armitage Bridge, Huddersfield, HD4 7NR
Tel: 01484 302090
Email: andyhill@dahill.co.uk
Resident Partners/Directors: ICAEW Members
A Hill

GIBSON BOOTH
New Court, Abbey Road North, Shepley, Huddersfield HD8 8BJ
Tel: 01484 600234
Fax: 01484 607871
Email: info@gibson-booth.co.uk
Resident Partners/Directors: ICAEW Members
S Lindley, A R J Russell, R Umbers
Resident Partners (Non-ICAEW Members):
R Hesketh, P I Ballesta

Registered by the ICAEW to carry out company audit work

Regulated by the ICAEW for a range of investment business activities

H P WADSWORTH
Springfield Hall, 2 Thornhill Road, Huddersfield, HD3 3AU

IAN R. NORTH ◈
16 Thorpes Avenue, Denby Dale, Huddersfield, HD8 8SP
Tel: 01484 865239
Principal: ICAEW Member
I R North

KUBINSKI ◈
Eldon House, 201 Penistone Road, Kirkburton, Huddersfield HD8 0PE
Tel: 01484 604454
Resident Partners/Directors: ICAEW Members
A K Kubinski, J A Kubinski

LISTER, GILLEARD & CO
Standard House, George Street, Huddersfield, HD1 2JF

MAZARS CORPORATE FINANCE LTD ◈
Norwich Union House, 26 High Street, Huddersfield, HD1 2LN

MICHAEL WATERSON
Fenay Cottage, Fenay Lane, Fenay Bridge, Huddersfield HD8 0LJ
Tel: 01484 429387
Principal: ICAEW Member
M Waterson

MILNSBRIDGE ACCOUNTANCY
62 Market Street, Milnsbridge, Huddersfield, HD3 4HT

PAUL BOOTHROYD
1 Potters Walk, Golcar, Huddersfield, HD7 4HH

RACHEL DUNHILL
31 Crown Street, Scissett, Huddersfield, HD8 9JN

REVELL WARD
7th Floor, 30 Market Street, Huddersfield, HD1 2NE

REVELL WARD LLP ◈
7th Floor, 30 Market Street, Huddersfield, HD1 2NE

RICHARD AIREY LTD
2 Church Lane, Clayton West, Huddersfield, HD8 9LY
Tel: 01484 860880
Resident Partners/Directors: ICAEW Members
R A Airey

S P CROWTHER & CO LTD
Woodland View House, 675 Leeds Road, Huddersfield, HD2 1YY

SHEARDS
Vernon House, 40 New North Road, Huddersfield, HD1 5LS
Tel: 01484 541155
Fax: 01484 427712
Email: advice@sheards.co.uk
Website: http://www.sheards.co.uk
Date Established: 1903
Resident Partners/Directors: ICAEW Members
C Atkinson, R J Lay, K Winterburn

Registered by the ICAEW to carry out company audit work

INVESTOR IN PEOPLE

General Description: We provide a professional and personal service to small to medium sized enterprises and individuals.

SHEARDS CONSULTING LTD
Vernon House, 40 New North Road, Huddersfield, HD1 5LS

SIMPSON WOOD
Bank Chambers, Market Street, Huddersfield, HD1 2EW
Tel: 01484 534431
Resident Partners/Directors: ICAEW Members
G D T Cliffe, M Fielding, D J McAllister

STEAD ROBINSON LTD
Whitby Court, Abbey Road, Shepley, Huddersfield HD8 8ER

SUSAN C. STOTT
34 Tom Lane, Crosland Moor, Huddersfield, HD4 5PS
Tel: 01484 652494
Principal: ICAEW Member
S C Stott

TENON AUDIT LTD
100 Wakefield Road, Lepton, Huddersfield, HD8 0DL

TOREVELL DENT (BRADFORD) LLP ★
Prospect House, Prospect Street, Huddersfield, HD1 2NU

WALKER & SUTCLIFFE
12 Greenhead Road, Huddersfield, HD1 4EN

WALTER DAWSON & SON
Revenue Chambers, St Peters Street, Huddersfield, HD1 1DL
Tel: 01484 424678
Resident Partners/Directors: ICAEW Members
A Mitchell

WHEAWILL & SUDWORTH ◈
P.O. Box B30, 35 Westgate, Huddersfield, HD1 1PA
Tel: 01484 423691
Fax: 01484 518803
Email: david.butterworth@wheawills.co.uk
Date Established: 1876
Training Contracts Available.
Resident Partners/Directors: ICAEW Members
C E Barratt, M S Bland, D M Butterworth, A Hayer, A J Lee, D Sinclair
Registered by the ICAEW to carry out company audit work
Regulated by the ICAEW for a range of investment business activities

SPECIALISATIONS – FORENSIC ACCOUNTING
Forensic Accounting

SPECIALISATIONS – SECTOR
Doctors
Solicitors

General Description: Personal and corporate tax planning, outsourcing, corporate finance, forensic and litigation support, assurance services.

WILKINSON & CO
68 Thorpe Lane, Almondbury, Huddersfield, HD5 8UF
Tel: 01484 349468
Principal: ICAEW Member
A H Wilkinson
Individual(s) licensed for insolvency work by the ICAEW

SPECIALISATIONS – BUSINESS RECOVERY & INSOLVENCY
Bankruptcies
Liquidations

HULL

A. MACDONALD & CO
21 Parliament Street, Hull, HU1 2BL
Tel: 01482 324664
Email: enquiries@a-macdonald.co.uk
Principal: ICAEW Member
S Scargill
Registered by the ICAEW to carry out company audit work
Regulated by the ICAEW for a range of investment business activities

ANDREW COOPER & CO
650 Anlaby Road, Hull, HU3 6UU
Tel: 01482 509950

ATKINSONS
60 Commercial Road, Hull, HU1 2SG
Tel: 01482 226791
Website: http://www.atkinsonco.com
Registered by the ICAEW to carry out company audit work
General Description: Accountants & financial advisers. 35 partners. Ranked 26th in a survey of UK Accountancy profession. Specialises in: corporate finance; corporate accounts; business services; payroll services; computer solutions; financial advice & wealth management; insolvency & corporate recovery.

BAKER TILLY
Wilberforce Court, Alfred Gelder Street, Hull, HU1 1YH
Tel: 01482 327406
Resident Partners/Directors: ICAEW Members
J W Barker, Y M Buck, R D King, M J Standish
Resident Partners (Non-ICAEW Members):
A M Capes

BAKER TILLY
Wilberforce Court, Alfred Gelder Street, Hull, HU1 1YH

BAKER TILLY RESTRUCTURING AND RECOVERY LLP
Wilberforce Court, Alfred Gelder Street, Hull, HU1 1YH
Tel: 01482 327406
Resident Partners/Directors: ICAEW Members
A D Pillmoor

BAKER TILLY TAX AND ADVISORY SERVICES LLP
Wilberforce Court, Alfred Gelder Street, Hull, HU1 1YH
Tel: 01482 327406
Resident Partners/Directors: ICAEW Members
J W Barker, Y M Buck, J L Hall, J C Kaiser, R D King, A Mould, A D Pillmoor, M J Standish
Resident Partners (Non-ICAEW Members):
A M Capes

BEGBIES TRAYNOR
The Stables, The Maltings, Silvester Street, Hull HU1 3HA
Tel: 01482 483060

CAMERON, FERRIBY & CO
Wykeland House, 47 Queen Street, Hull, HU1 1UU
Tel: 01482 214422
Fax: 01482 212995
Email: info@cameronferriby.co.uk
Website: http://www.cameronferriby.co.uk
Principal: ICAEW Member
R A Cameron
Registered by the ICAEW to carry out company audit work
Regulated by the ICAEW for a range of investment business activities
See display advertisement near this entry.

CHEETHAM ALLEN ◈
17 Wright St, Hull, HU2 8HU
Tel: 01482 223630
Resident Partners/Directors: ICAEW Members
J B Cheetham

CRUMPTON & CO LTD
682 Anlaby Road, Hull, HU3 6UZ
Tel: 01482 568378
Resident Partners/Directors: ICAEW Members
N D Crumpton

D. BERRIDGE
31 Westella Way, Kirk Ella, Hull, HU10 7LN
Tel: 01482 650747
Principal: ICAEW Member
D Berridge

D.I. BROCKLESBY & CO
91 Westella Rd, Kirk Ella, Hull, HU10 7QR

DAVID TURNER & CO
Studio 701, 17 Princess Street, Hull, HU2 8BJ

DODGSON & CO ◈
The Meredith Group, 23-33 Reform Street, Hull, HU2 8EF
Tel: 01482 222301
Fax: 01482 323762
Email: david@dodgsonandco.co.uk
Principal: ICAEW Member
D H Dodgson

DUTTON MOORE
6 Silver Street, Hull, HU1 1JA

DUTTON MOORE
451 Holderness Road, Hull, HU8 8JT

ERNST & YOUNG LLP
PO Box 3, Lowgate House, Lowgate, Hull HU1 1JJ
Tel: 01482 590300

GARTON GRAHAM & CO
56 Grammar School Yard, Hull, HU1 2NB
Tel: 01482 213555
Resident Partners/Directors: ICAEW Members
P M Garton, D W Graham

GLEW,DUNN & CO
83 Spring Bank, Hull, HU3 1AG

GRAYBROWNE LTD ◈
The Counting House, Nelson Street, Hull, HU1 1XE
Tel: 01482 225564
Fax: 01482 213301
Email: gb@graybrowne.co.uk
Resident Partners/Directors: ICAEW Members
N V Browne, A L Gray

GRAYS
1 Parliament Street, Hull, HU1 2AS
Tel: 01482 223687
Fax: 01482 585210
Resident Partners/Directors: ICAEW Members
M W Marsden
Registered by the ICAEW to carry out company audit work
Regulated by the ICAEW for a range of investment business activities

HOLDSTOCK NICHOLLS TRAIN & CO ★
593 Anlaby Road, Hull, HU3 6ST
Tel: 01482 504114
Resident Partners/Directors: ICAEW Members
C S Wright

HW
The Deep Business Centre, Tower Street, Hull, HU1 4BG
Tel: 01482 382844

JACKSONS
Enterprise Centre, Samman House, 4 Bowlalley Lane, Hull HU1 1XR

KEITH USHER
10 Riplingham Road, Kirk Ella, Hull, HU10 7TP
Tel: 01482 658152
Principal: ICAEW Member
K Usher

LEGGOTT J.E.
Wayside Cottage, Great Hatfield, Hull, HU11 4UR

MAJORS
8 King Street, Market Square, Hull, HU1 2JJ

MIKE J R TWIDDLE & CO LTD
5 Iona Close, Langsett Road, Sutton, Hull HU8 9XU

MWS BUSINESS MANAGEMENT LTD ◈
6 Earls Court, Priory Park East, Hull, HU4 7DY
Tel: 01482 605444
Resident Partners/Directors: ICAEW Members
M W Sadofsky

NEWSHAM & CO ◈
11 Allanhall Way, Kirk Ella, Hull, HU10 7QU
Tel: 01482 650297
Website: http://www.newshamandco.com
Resident Partners/Directors: ICAEW Members
H Newsham

NORRIE GIBSON & CO
Grosvenor House, 102 Beverley Road, Hull, HU3 1YA

NORRIE GIBSON & CO LTD
Grosvenor House, 102 Beverley Road, Hull, HU3 1YA

PGS ACCOUNTANCY LTD
54 Ridgestone Avenue, Bilton, Kingston-Upon-Hull, Hull, HU11 4AJ

PHILLIP COOPER & CO
9 Dock Street, Hull, HU1 3DL
Tel: 01482 216958

PHILLIP COOPER & CO LTD
9 Dock Street, Hull, HU1 3DL
Tel: 01482 216958
Resident Partners/Directors: ICAEW Members
P Cooper

PRICEWATERHOUSE-COOPERS
Queen Victoria House, P O Box 88, Guildhall Road, Hull HU1 1HH

PRICEWATERHOUSE-COOPERS LLP
2 Humber Quays, Wellington Street West, Hull, HU1 2BN
Tel: 01482 224111
Resident Partners/Directors: ICAEW Members
T P B Charge

RIMINGTONS ◈
14 Hill Brow, Kirk Ella, Hull, HU10 7PP
Tel: 01482 650255
Principal: ICAEW Member
C L Rimington

SADOFSKYS ◈
Princes House, Wright Street, Hull, HU2 8HX
Tel: 01482 228488
Fax: 01482 228489
Email: consult@sadofskys.co.uk
Website: http://www.sadofskys.co.uk
Resident Partners/Directors: ICAEW Members
A Brocklehurst, S D Grassby, C Knaggs, A M Steele
Resident Partners (Non-ICAEW Members):
A Drant

SEARBY & CO ◈
Compass House, 17-19 Empringham Street, Hull, HU9 1RP
Tel: 01482 225392
Resident Partners/Directors: ICAEW Members
D N Searby, G D Searby

SIGMA SOLUTIONS
Regents Court, Princess Street, Hull, HU2 8BA

SMAILES GOLDIE ◈
Regents Court, Princess Street, Hull, HU2 8BA

STREETS NORTHERN LLP ◈
Halifax House, 30 George Street, Hull, HU1 3AJ
Tel: 01482 225399
Email: info@streetsweb.co.uk
Website: http://www.streetsweb.co.uk
Resident Partners/Directors: ICAEW Members
A R Manderfield

TENON LTD
Lowgate House, Hull, HU1 1EL
Tel: 01482 333777

TRY LUNN & CO
Roland House, Princes Dock Street, Hull, HU1 2LD

WWW ATKINSONCOCOM LTD ◈
60 Commercial Road, Hull, HU1 2SG
Tel: 01482 226791
Resident Partners/Directors: ICAEW Members
S A Atkinson, B R Macdonald

HUNGERFORD

B.J. SCOTT
High Barn, Hunters Meadow, Great Shefford, Hungerford RG17 7EQ
Tel: 01488 648672
Principal: ICAEW Member
B J Scott

BRADING CRYER
107 High Street, Hungerford, RG17 0NB
Tel: 01488 682546
Principal: ICAEW Member
D W Cryer

FINANCIAL DIRECTION
The Annexe, Garden House, Shefford Woodlands, Hungerford RG17 7AR

LJ SMITH ACCOUNTANTS LTD
Orwell House, 50 High Street, Hungerford, RG17 0NE

NASH & CO
Highclose Farm, Bath Road, Hungerford, RG17 0SP

PBA ACCOUNTANTS ★
130 High Street, Hungerford, RG17 0DL

HUNSTANTON

KATHRYN GIGG ◈
The Office, 20 Kings Lynn Road, Hunstanton, PE36 5HP
Tel: 01485 534800
Principal: ICAEW Member
K H Gigg

HUNTINGDON

ADRIAN H.A. ACTON
3 Townsend Close, Wyton, Huntingdon, PE28 2AR
Tel: 01480 464268
Principal: ICAEW Member
A H A Acton

BENTEN & YEANDLE ★
108 High Street, Ramsey, Huntingdon, PE26 1BS
Tel: 01487 812441
Resident Partners/Directors: ICAEW Members
E J Edwards

BULLEY DAVEY ★ ◈
Welbeck House, Spitfire Close, Ermine Business Park, Huntingdon PE29 6XY
Tel: 01480 454456
Resident Partners (Non-ICAEW Members):
J C Fisher, N J Barks

D.R. PANDYA
Porch House, Little Raveley, Huntingdon, PE28 2NQ

DAVID JEFFREYS
First Floor, 4 Princes Street, Huntingdon, PE29 3PA

DAVID JEFFREYS LTD ◈
First Floor, 4 Princes Street, Huntingdon, PE29 3PA

DUTTELLIS PRODUCTIONS LTD ◈
44 Bluegate, Godmanchester, Huntingdon, PE29 2EZ
Tel: 01480 413615
Resident Partners/Directors: ICAEW Members
M R Ellis

HUNTINGDON

E JOHNSTON & CO
17 Crowhill, Godmanchester, Huntingdon, PE29 2LP
Tel: 01480 411684
Principal: ICAEW Member
Mrs Elaine Johnston

ENSORS ◈
Warwick House, Ermine Business Park, Spitfire Close, Huntingdon PE29 6XY
Tel: 01480 417800
Resident Partners/Directors: ICAEW Members
R P Williams

HHG BUSINESS SERVICES LTD
Hill House, Shelton Road, Upper Dean, Huntingdon PE28 0NQ

IAIN D. MUSPRATT
Backwater House, 50 Common Lane, Hemingford Abbots, Huntingdon PE28 9AW

J.A. FINCH
30 Sweetings Road, Godmanchester, Huntingdon, PE29 2JS

J.A. MITCHLEY
17 Frogs Hall, Bluntisham, Huntingdon, PE28 3XD
Tel: 01487 841662
Principal: ICAEW Member
J A Mitchley

JOANNA WILLIAMS ◈
Manor Farm, Church Road, Glatton, Huntingdon PE28 5RR
Tel: 01487 830264

K.C. ALLEN
49B Post Street, Godmanchester, Huntingdon, PE29 2AQ

KINNAIRD HILL ◈
Montagu House, 81 High Street, Huntingdon, PE29 3NY
Tel: 01480 453112
Fax: 01480 431 200
Email: enquiries@kinnairdhill.co.uk
Website: http://www.kinnairdhill.co.uk
Resident Partners/Directors: ICAEW Members
A J Hurford, T P Johnson

M.P. DAY ACCOUNTING SERVICES
19 Orchard Lane, Brampton, Huntingdon, PE28 4TF

WHITING & PARTNERS ◈
Eagle House, Great Whyte, Ramsey, Huntingdon PE26 1HB
Tel: 01487 813751
Resident Partners/Directors: ICAEW Members
B J Carroll, J J Harrison

WILLIAMS ACCOUNTANCY SERVICES LTD ◈
Manor Farm, Church Road, Glatton, Huntingdon PE28 5RR

THE YOUNG CO ◈
Ground Floor, 2B Vantage Park, Washingley Road, Huntingdon PE29 6SR
Tel: 01480 435525
Email: ray@theyoungcompany.co.uk
Principal: ICAEW Member
R A Young
Registered by the ICAEW to carry out company audit work
Regulated by the ICAEW for a range of investment business activities

HYDE

GRAHAM H. WOOD & CO
225 Market Street, Hyde, SK14 1HF
Tel: 0161 368 9331
Fax: 0161 367 8346
Email: email@grahamwood.co.uk
Resident Partners/Directors: ICAEW Members
S J Booth
Resident Partners (Non-ICAEW Members):
B A Berry
Registered by the ICAEW to carry out company audit work
Regulated by the ICAEW for a range of investment business activities

SPECIALISATIONS – AUDIT & ASSURANCE
Audit

SPECIALISATIONS – BUSINESS & GENERAL ADVICE
Company Formation

SPECIALISATIONS – FINANCIAL REPORTING
Accounts Preparation
Limited Company Accounts
Partnership/Sole Trader Accounts

SPECIALISATIONS – TAXATION
Payroll Service and Advice
Taxation

PARKER GRADWELL & CO
17 Chapel Street, Hyde, SK14 1LF
Tel: 0161 368 6427
Resident Partners/Directors: ICAEW Members
C A Gorst, S W Johnson
See display advertisement near this entry.

PJH & CO
39A Mottram Moor, Mottram, Hyde, SK14 6LA

HYTHE

ANDRE PETER
First Floor, The Old Auction Rooms, Marine Walk Street, Hythe CT21 5NW
Tel: 07721 511578
Principal: ICAEW Member
A C Peter

DAVID LEE
26 Old London Road, Hythe, CT21 4DQ

HARRIS COOMBS & CO ★
16 Lower Corniche, Hythe, CT21 5TP
Tel: 01303 230704

HENRY REEVES & SON ★ ◈
127 High Street, Hythe, CT21 5JJ
Tel: 01622 756849
Resident Partners/Directors: ICAEW Members
J W Whiting

NORTH & CO (ACCOUNTS & TAX) LTD
Suite 3, The Old Stables, Hillhurst Farm, Westenhanger, Hythe CT21 4HU
Tel: 01303 265188
Resident Partners/Directors: ICAEW Members
B E North

ILFORD

A.K.SAHA & CO
40 Highcliffe Gardens, Ilford, IG4 5HR
Tel: 020 8924 8265
Principal: ICAEW Member
A K Saha

A.K. VALERA
343 High Road, Ilford, IG1 1TE

ABACUS & CO
416 Green Lane, Ilford, IG3 9JX

ACCOUNTING FOR YOU
4 Morrab Gardens, Ilford, IG3 9HL

AHMED ASLAM & CO ★ ◈
130 Cranbrook Road, Ilford, IG1 4LZ

AHMED-CLIFFORDS
153 Beehive Lane, Ilford, IG4 5DX

AHMED-CLIFFORDS LTD
153 Beehive Lane, Ilford, IG4 5DX

ALLAN STEINBERG & CO
25A York Road, Ilford, IG1 3AD

AYTONS
32 Bathurst Road, Ilford, IG1 4LA

C.J. PATEL & CO
112 Hamilton Avenue, Ilford, IG6 1AB
Tel: 020 8518 0302
Principal: ICAEW Member
C J Patel

CARL ASSOCIATES ★
186 Wanstead Park Road, Ilford, IG1 3TR

CHANDLER & GEORGES
14 Bentley Drive, Ilford, IG2 6QD
Tel: 020 8761 2213

CURTIS & CO
Bank Chambers, 1-3 Woodford Avenue, Gants Hill, Ilford IG2 6UF

DARVIN & CO
62 Redbridge Lane East, Redbridge, Ilford, IG4 5EZ

DAVIS GRANT LLP
Treviot House, 186-192 High Road, Ilford, IG1 1LR
Tel: 020 8477 0000
Fax: 020 8477 0001
Email: info@davisgrant.co.uk
Website: http://www.davisgrant.co.uk
Resident Partners/Directors: ICAEW Members
B G Chernoff, N M Driver
Resident Partners (Non-ICAEW Members):
J Gandesha
Registered by another RSB to carry out company audit work
Licensed by another DPB to carry on investment business

DEIGHAN PERKINS
6th Floor, Newbury House, 890-900 Eastern Avenue, Ilford IG2 7HH
Tel: 020 8590 2454
Fax: 020 8599 2874
Email: dp@deighanperkins.com
Website: http://www.deighanperkins.com
Training Contracts Available.
Resident Partners/Directors: ICAEW Members
A W Deighan, K M Perkins
Registered by the ICAEW to carry out company audit work

F.AHMED
232 Perth Road, Ilford, IG2 6DY

FREDERICKS LTD ◈
5th Floor, Newbury House, 890-900 Eastern Avenue, Newbury Park, Ilford IG2 7HH
Tel: 020 8554 6262
Fax: 020 8590 3848
Website: http://www.fredericksaccountants.co.uk
Resident Partners/Directors: ICAEW Members
S G Duker
Registered by the ICAEW to carry out company audit work
Regulated by the ICAEW for a range of investment business activities

SPECIALISATIONS – AUDIT & ASSURANCE
Audit
Audit — Private Company

SPECIALISATIONS – BUSINESS & GENERAL ADVICE
Book-keeping
Company Formation
Company Secretarial Service

SPECIALISATIONS – FINANCIAL REPORTING
Accounts Preparation
Audit Exemption Report
Limited Companies
Limited Company Accounts
Partnership/Sole Trader Accounts

SPECIALISATIONS – TAXATION
Capital Gains — Limited Companies
Capital Gains — Personal
Partnerships and Sole Traders
PAYE Advice
Payroll Service and Advice
Personal
Self Assessment Advice
Small Traders
Taxation
Value Added Tax

G.C. DAS & CO
57 Icknield Drive, Gants Hill, Ilford, IG2 6SE
Tel: 020 8491 9083
Principal: ICAEW Member
G C Das

IAN B. STEINBERG ◈
40 Woodford Avenue, Gants Hill, Ilford, IG2 6XQ
Tel: 020 8550 0434
Principal: ICAEW Member
I B Steinberg

INGER & CO
7 Redbridge Lane East, Redbridge, Ilford, IG4 5ET

KENNARD SAMUELS
Lear House, 259 Cranbrook Road, Ilford, IG1 4TG

KILSI & CO
27 Montreal Road, Ilford, IG1 4SH

LEIBOVITCH & CO
249 Cranbrook Road, Ilford, IG1 4TG

MEHTA AND CO ◈
221 Cranbrook Road, Ilford, IG1 4TD
Tel: 020 8554 6511
Principal: ICAEW Member
R H L Mehta

MOHINDRA & CO ◈
Finance Place, 9 Widecombe Gardens, Ilford, IG4 5LR
Tel: 020 8220 0910
Email: service@mohco.com
Principal: ICAEW Member
M Mohindra
Authorised and regulated by the Financial Services Authority for investment business

N SEERUNGUM & CO
25 Vicarage Lane, Ilford, IG1 4AG

NAZIM & CO
Suite 1a, Cranbrook House, 61 Cranbrook Road, Ilford IG1 4PG

PETER C. EVERITT
36 Donington Avenue, Barkingside, Ilford, IG6 1DP

PETER H. HUBBARD
Wycliffe House, 245 Cranbrook Road, Ilford, IG1 4TD

PRESTONS ◈
364-368 Cranbrook Road, Gants Hill, Ilford, IG2 6HY
Tel: 020 8518 5566
Resident Partners/Directors: ICAEW Members
A Mehta, A H Patel

PRESTONS & JACKSONS PARTNERSHIP LLP ◈
364-368 Cranbrook Road, Ilford, IG2 6HY
Tel: 020 8518 5566
Resident Partners/Directors: ICAEW Members
A Mehta, A H Patel

R.G. RUPAL LTD
30 Fernhall Drive, Ilford, IG4 5BW
Tel: 020 8551 0057
Resident Partners/Directors: ICAEW Members
R G Rupal

RE ELLIOTT & CO
25 Westrow Gardens, Seven Kings, Ilford, IG3 9NE

ROBERT M. PRESTON
47 Peaketon Avenue, Redbridge, Ilford, IG4 5PG

ROBINSON STERLING
277 Ilford Lane, Ilford, IG1 2SD

S KAINTH & CO
34 Belvedere Avenue, Clayhall, Ilford, IG5 0UE

SALMAN ROSS
141 Woodlands Road, Ilford, IG1 1JR

THAKER & CO
31 Southwood Gardens, Gants Hill, Ilford, IG2 6YF
Tel: 020 8551 7851
Principal: ICAEW Member
B J Thaker

TISH LEIBOVITCH ★
249 Cranbrook Road, Ilford, IG1 4TG

VALERA
343 High Road, Ilford, IG1 1TE
Tel: 020 8478 6857

VISION CONSULTING ◈
426 Cranbrook Road, Ilford, IG2 6HW
Tel: 020 8554 2135
Email: office@vision-consulting.net
Principal: ICAEW Member
G Alahi
Registered by the ICAEW to carry out company audit work

WONG & CO
70 Airthrie Road, Goodmayes, Ilford, IG3 9QU

YADAV & CO
87 Lansdowne Road, Seven Kings, Ilford, IG3 8NG

ZHM CONSULTANTS
64 Kimberley Avenue, Ilford, IG2 7AS

ILFRACOMBE

KINO & CO
Swale Dale, Castle Hill, Ilfracombe, EX34 9HX

THOMAS WESTCOTT ★
96 High Street, Ilfracombe, EX34 9NH
Tel: 01271 863662
Resident Partners/Directors: ICAEW Members
S A Cresswell

ILKESTON

BEATTIE MOULDS ◈
20 Burns Street, Ilkeston, DE7 8AA

GORINGS
The Laurels, St Mary Street, Ilkeston, DE7 8BQ
Tel: 0115 932 4254
Email: davidb@gorilk.co.uk
Resident Partners/Directors: ICAEW Members
D H Bigland, D A Grace

SPECIALISATIONS – TAXATION
Estate Planning

GREGORY PRIESTLEY & STEWART
16 Queen Street, Ilkeston, DE7 5GT

MABE ALLEN LLP ◈
29 St Mary Street, Ilkeston, DE7 8AB
Tel: 0115 932 3995
Resident Partners/Directors: ICAEW Members
B Sutton

MCINTOSH (ILKESTON) LTD
20 Burns Street, Ilkeston, DE7 8AA

ROBERT LEE
18 The Village, West Hallam, Ilkeston, DE7 6GR
Tel: 0115 944 4745
Principal: ICAEW Member
C R Lee

SMITH COOPER ◈
The Old Police Station,
Wharncliffe Road, Ilkeston,
DE7 5GF
Tel: 0115 932 0237

ILKLEY

ADAMS & CO (ILKLEY) LTD
Moors House, 11 South
Hawksworth Street, Ilkley,
LS29 9DX
Tel: 01943 817045
Resident Partners/Directors: ICAEW Members
J B Adams

CAROLINE WOOD A.C.A.
Low Field House, Bleach Mill
Lane, Menston, Ilkley
LS29 6AW

CHADWICKS
16a Menston Old Lane, Burley in
Wharfedale, Ilkley, LS29 7QQ
Tel: 01943 862870

CHADWICKS ACCOUNTANTS LTD
16a Menston Old Lane, Burley in
Wharfedale, Ilkley, LS29 7QQ
Tel: 01943 862870
Resident Partners/Directors: ICAEW Members
B Chadwick

CLOUGH, TOMBLIN & CO
Nat.Westminster Bank Chmbrs,
The Grove, Ilkley, LS29 9LS
Tel: 01943 607967
Resident Partners/Directors: ICAEW Members
D A Crowther, D N Riley, J
Spenceley

CONNECT FINANCIAL MANAGEMENT LTD
29 Beverley Rise, Ilkley,
LS29 9DB

D M FLATHER
15 Goodwood, Owler Park Road,
Ilkley, LS29 0BY

DAVID PULLAN & CO
24a Brook Street, Ilkley,
LS29 8DE
Tel: 01943 609988
Principal: ICAEW Member
D J S Pullan

K.P. BONNEY & CO LLP
50 Cleasby Road, Menston,
Ilkley, LS29 6JA
Tel: 01943 870933
Resident Partners/Directors: ICAEW Members
K P Bonney

KEITH BRIDGFORD & CO
17 The Grove, Ilkley, LS29 9LW
Tel: 01943 601872
Principal: ICAEW Member
J M Bridgford
Registered by the ICAEW to carry out company audit work
Regulated by the ICAEW for a range of investment business activities

KIRSTY BARKER
47 Sun Lane, Burley in
Wharfedale, Ilkley, LS29 7LG

LINDA LITTLE
12 Beverley Rise, Ilkley,
LS29 9DB
Tel: 01943 601748
Principal: ICAEW Member
L M Little

PETER DURBIN & COMPANY LTD
Holiday House, Valley Road,
Ilkley, LS29 8PA

PHIL MCPHAIL
6 North Parade, Burley in
Wharfedale, Ilkley, LS29 7JR

PMC LTD
6 North Parade, Burley in
Wharfedale, Ilkley, LS29 7JR

R.J. WEBB & CO
26 Ben Rhydding Road, Ilkley,
LS29 8RL
Tel: 01943 600902
Principal: ICAEW Member
R J Webb

TERRY J GREAVES
8 Hodgson Fold, Addingham,
Ilkley, LS29 0HA

WINTERSGILL ASSOCIATES
10-12 The Grove, Ilkley,
LS29 9EG

WINTERSGILL ASSOCIATES LTD ◈
Suite 1, 10-12 The Grove, Ilkley,
LS29 9EG

ILMINSTER

MITCHAMS
1 Cornhill, Ilminster, TA19 0AD

R.G. MAJOR
The Burrows, Windmill Hill,
Ashill, Ilminster TA19 9NT
Tel: 01823 480754
Principal: ICAEW Member
R G Major

ROBERT STONE & CO
The Old Post Office, Barrington,
Ilminster, TA19 0JB

INGATESTONE

COLIN M.W. TODD
36 Tor Bryan, Ingatestone,
CM4 9JZ

JOHN L BIRD
Furze Hall, Ingatestone,
CM4 0PB

LEE STEVENS
Tyelands, Parsonage Lane,
Margaretting, Ingatestone
CM4 9JL
Tel: 01277 354419
Principal: ICAEW Member
L S Stevens

NEVILLE R. BULL
32 Well Lane, Stock,
Ingatestone, CM4 9LZ
Tel: 01277 840063
Principal: ICAEW Member
N R Bull

TAYLOR, VINEY & MARLOW
46-54 High Street, Ingatestone,
CM4 9DW
Tel: 01277 355235
Fax: 01277 353021
Email: info@tvmaccounts.co.uk
Website: http://www.tvmaccounts.co.uk
Resident Partners/Directors: ICAEW Members
S McCallum, A J Smith, D J
Stevens
Resident Partners (Non-ICAEW Members):
S McCallum, S Pinion
Other Offices: Leigh-on-Sea
Registered by the ICAEW to carry out company audit work
Regulated by the ICAEW for a range of investment business activities

SPECIALISATIONS – AUDIT & ASSURANCE

Audit
Audit — Private Company
Pension Scheme Auditors

SPECIALISATIONS – BUSINESS & GENERAL ADVICE

Book-keeping
Company Formation
Company Secretarial Service
Management Advice to Business

SPECIALISATIONS – FINANCIAL REPORTING

Accounts Preparation
Audit Exemption Report
Financial Reporting
Limited Companies
Limited Company Accounts
Limited Liability Partnership
Partnership/Sole Trader Accounts

SPECIALISATIONS – TAXATION

Capital Gains — Limited Companies
Capital Gains — Personal
Partnerships and Sole Traders
PAYE Advice
Payroll Service and Advice
Personal
Self Assessment Advice
Small Traders
Taxation
Value Added Tax

IPSWICH

AIMS ACCOUNTANTS FOR BUSINESS
107 Humber Doucy Lane,
Ipswich, IP4 3NU
Tel: 01473 714164
Principal: ICAEW Member
A P Lloyd

ARCD ASSOCIATES LTD
42 Wright Lane, Kesgrave,
Ipswich, IP5 2FA

BALLAMS ★
Crane Court, 302 London Road,
Ipswich, IP2 0AJ
Tel: 01473 216994
Website: http://www.ballams.co.uk
Resident Partners/Directors: ICAEW Members
S L Fayers, S C Marriage
Resident Partners (Non-ICAEW Members):
M J Mortimer, M K Howes

BEATONS LTD
3 Elm Street, Ipswich, IP1 1EY

BEATONS AUDIT LLP
3 Elm Street, Ipswich, IP1 1EY

C.M.G. ASSOCIATES
5th Floor, Chalfont Square, Old
Foundry Road, Ipswich IP4 2AJ
Tel: 01473 254400
Resident Partners/Directors: ICAEW Members
P R Clements, S Foster, H A
Goldstein

DAVID VERNEY PARTNERSHIP LTD ◈
Felaw Maltings, 44 Felaw Street,
Ipswich, IP2 8SJ
Tel: 01473 407311
Email: david@davidverney.co.uk
Resident Partners/Directors: ICAEW Members
D J Verney

DUNOAK LTD
Oak House, 2 Woodward Close,
Ipswich, IP2 0EA

E.S. BALL
14 Vere Gardens, The Grove,
Henley Road, Ipswich IP1 4NZ

ENSORS ◈
Cardinal House, 46 St Nicholas
Street, Ipswich, IP1 1TT
Tel: 01473 220022
Fax: 01473 220033
Email: mail@ensors.co.uk
Website: http://www.ensors.co.uk
Resident Partners/Directors: ICAEW Members
J A Card, D S P Clifford, S M
Law, R D Leggett, J O
Matthews, H S Rumsey, S M
Runnacles, D P Scrivener
Other Offices: Bury St
Edmunds, Cambridge,
Saxmundham, Huntingdon
Registered by the ICAEW to carry out company audit work
Regulated by the ICAEW for a range of investment business activities
Individual(s) licensed for insolvency work by the ICAEW

SPECIALISATIONS – AUDIT & ASSURANCE

Audit

SPECIALISATIONS – BUSINESS & GENERAL ADVICE

Book-keeping
Management Advice to Business

SPECIALISATIONS – BUSINESS RECOVERY & INSOLVENCY

Corporate Recovery

SPECIALISATIONS – FINANCIAL REPORTING

Accounts Preparation

SPECIALISATIONS – INVESTMENT BUSINESS

Financial Planning and Advice

SPECIALISATIONS – TAXATION

Estate Planning
Payroll Service and Advice

FRANKLINS
Bury Road, Hitcham, Ipswich, IP7 7PP
Tel: 01449 741333
Resident Partners/Directors: ICAEW Members
D J Franklin

G. HILDER
The Alde Suite, 8 Wherry Lane, Ipswich, IP4 1LG

GRANT THORNTON UK LLP
Crown House, Crown Street, Ipswich, IP1 3HS
Tel: 01473 221491
Resident Partners/Directors: ICAEW Members
J R Brown, R J Chaplin, P J Hall
Non-resident Partners (ICAEW Members):
I S Carr
Non-resident Partners (Non-ICAEW Members):
G J Markham

HANCOCK M.E.
2 Burls Yard, Crown Street, Needham Market, Ipswich IP6 8AJ
Tel: 01449 722549
Principal: ICAEW Member
M E Hancock

HARRY MOORE
2 Limekiln Close, Claydon, Ipswich, IP6 0AW
Tel: 01473 830991
Principal: ICAEW Member
H C Moore

IAN MCKECHNIE AND COMPANY LTD ◈
21 Birchwood Drive, Rushmere St Andrew, Ipswich, IP5 1EB

ISLES, STORER & EMSDEN ★
129 High Street, Needham Market, Ipswich, IP6 8DH

IZOD BASSETT
105 High Street, Needham Market, Ipswich, IP6 8DQ

LARKING GOWEN ◈
16a Falcon Street, Ipswich, IP1 1SL
Tel: 01473 259984
Resident Partners/Directors: ICAEW Members
R Girling
Resident Partners (Non-ICAEW Members):
D G King

LARKING GOWEN IPSWICH LTD
Unit 41, Claydon Business Park, Great Blakenham, Ipswich IP6 0NL

MCTEAR WILLIAMS & WOOD ★ ◈
19 Silent Street, Ipswich, IP1 1TF
Tel: 01473 218191
Non-resident Partners (Non-ICAEW Members):
D Wood

NIGEL ALLISON LTD
Mistyleigh, Swilland, Ipswich, IP6 9LX
Tel: 01473 735787
Resident Partners/Directors: ICAEW Members
N D Allison

PKF (UK) LLP
16 The Havens, Ransomes Europark, Ipswich, IP3 9SJ
Tel: 01473 320700
Email: info.ipswich@uk.pkf.com
Website: http://www.pkf.co.uk
Resident Partners/Directors: ICAEW Members
D P Eagles, K Ferguson, P J Harrup, T W Ingram, M Martin, G J Randall
Resident Partners (Non-ICAEW Members):
D S Merrygold

R.J. KETTLEWELL & CO
43 Ann Beaumont Way, Hadleigh, Ipswich, IP7 6SB
Tel: 01473 827206
Principal: ICAEW Member
R J Kettlewell

RICHARD SPARKES
Garden Cottage, Barking, Ipswich, IP6 8HJ

ROSEMARY J. STEINSON ◈
Glenesk, Holbrook, Ipswich, IP9 2PZ
Tel: 01473 327631
Principal: ICAEW Member
R J Steinson

SARAH ABBOTT AND CO
4 Lancaster Road, Ipswich, IP4 2NY

SARAH ABBOTT AND CO LTD
4 Lancaster Road, Ipswich, IP4 2NY
Tel: 01473 255047
Resident Partners/Directors: ICAEW Members
S E Abbott

SCRUTTON BLAND
Accountants | Business Partners | Financial Advisers | Insurance Brokers

SCRUTTON BLAND
Sanderson House, Museum Street, Ipswich, IP1 1HE
Tel: 01473 259201
Fax: 01473 231643
Email: mail@scruttonbland.co.uk
Website: http://www.scruttonbland.co.uk
Resident Partners/Directors: ICAEW Members
S V Gull, J B McElhinney, J C Pickering
Resident Partners (Non-ICAEW Members):
N H Hutchinson, S S Gravener, J J Fayers, N L Banks

Registered by the ICAEW to carry out company audit work

Regulated by the ICAEW for a range of investment business activities

General Description: We have 12 partners and 2 offices in the area and can provide a full range of services to our clients. We are pleased to be members of Nexia International.

DEBEN ACCOUNTING SERVICES
270 Colchester Road, Ipswich, IP4 4QX

TIMOTHY N. HORNE
Bay Villa, 40 Church Road, Otley, Ipswich IP6 9NP

WALTER WRIGHT ◈
89 High Street, Hadleigh, Ipswich, IP7 5EA
Tel: 01473 822143
Email: info@walterwright.co.uk
Website: http://www.walterwright.co.uk
Resident Partners/Directors: ICAEW Members
K N Brown, P R Garrard, D Simcox
Resident Partners (Non-ICAEW Members):
M J Hill

Registered by the ICAEW to carry out company audit work

Regulated by the ICAEW for a range of investment business activities

INVESTOR IN PEOPLE

ISLES OF SCILLY

CRANE & JOHNSTON LTD
Bank Chambers, The Bank, St Mary's, Isles of Scilly TR21 0HY

GIBSONS
Belmont, Church Road, St Mary's, Isles of Scilly TR21 0NA

PETER CRANE & CO LTD
Bank Chambers, The Bank, St Mary's, Isles of Scilly TR21 0HY

ISLEWORTH

ACCOUNTANCY MANAGEMENT SERVICES LTD
South Street House, 51 South Street, Isleworth, TW7 7AA
Tel: 020 8847 2222
Resident Partners/Directors: ICAEW Members
P D Alexander

CHOWDHARY & CO
46 Syon Lane, Osterley, Isleworth, TW7 5NQ

G.J.BURGESS & CO
175 Jersey Road, Osterley, Isleworth, TW7 4QJ

KENNETH D. ELLIOTT
22 Oaklands Avenue, Isleworth, TW7 5PX
Tel: 020 8568 0746
Principal: ICAEW Member
K D Elliott

MARTIN DAWE
16 St Christophers Close, Isleworth, TW7 4NP

MITTEL & CO
16 Worton Gardens, Isleworth, TW7 4BB

R SADLIER
22 Heather Close, Isleworth, TW7 7PR

SB & CO ◈
55 Syon Park Gardens, Isleworth, TW7 5NE

IVER

A.R. HAMILTON
Roebuck House, 16 Somerset Way, Iver, SL0 9AF
Tel: 01753 653380
Principal: ICAEW Member
A R Hamilton

IVAN SOPHER & CO
Room 75, Admin Buliding, Pinewood Studios, Pinewood Road, Iver SL0 0NH

KEEN, DICEY, GROVER
Bathurst House, 50 Bathurst Walk, Iver, SL0 9BH
Tel: 01753 652098
Fax: 01753 630221
Email: kdg@kdg.co.uk
Resident Partners/Directors: ICAEW Members
G J G Davies, A G Roberts
Registered by the ICAEW to carry out company audit work
Regulated by the ICAEW for a range of investment business activities

NYMAN LIBSON PAUL ◈
Pinewood Studios, Room 107, Pinewood Road, Iver, SL0 0NH
Tel: 01753 656428

TEATHER & CO
Tile Oak, Old Slade Lane, Richings Park, Iver SL0 9DR
Tel: 01753 655544

TEATHER & CO LTD
Tile Oak, Old Slade Lane, Richings Park, Iver SL0 9DR
Tel: 01753 655544
Resident Partners/Directors: ICAEW Members
K M Teather

WILL PAINE FCA ◈
3 Honeysuckle Close, Iver, SL0 0LZ

IVYBRIDGE

AIMS - HILARY DINSDALE
Pathways, Highland Street, Ivybridge, PL21 9AG

ANGUS HANDASYDE DICK
Lower Shearlangstone, Modbury, Ivybridge, PL21 0TQ

D.E. BOULTER
New Mills Cottage, Ermington, Ivybridge, PL21 0LH
Tel: 01548 830184
Principal: ICAEW Member
D E Boulter

RICHARD J. SMITH & CO ★
53 Fore Street, Ivybridge, PL21 9AE
Tel: 01752 690101
Fax: 01752 690808
Email: info@richardjsmith.com
Resident Partners/Directors: ICAEW Members
G R Frampton
Individual(s) licensed for insolvency work by the ICAEW

SPECIALISATIONS – BUSINESS RECOVERY & INSOLVENCY
Bankruptcies
Corporate Recovery
Liquidations

SPECIALISATIONS – FORENSIC ACCOUNTING
Expert Witnesses in Litigation
Forensic Accounting

General Description: Insolvency and forensic accounting specialists.

JARROW

UHY TORGERSENS LTD ◈
7 Grange Road West, Jarrow, NE32 3JA
Tel: 0191 428 0001
Resident Partners/Directors: ICAEW Members
D M Johnson, P N Newbold, S J Torgersen

UHY TORGERSENS INCORPORATING BRIAN GREEN & CO ◈
7 Grange Road West, Jarrow, NE32 3JA
Tel: 0191 428 0001
Email: enquiries@briangreen.co.uk
Website: http://www.uhy-torgersens.com

KEIGHLEY

BAKER FOX LTD
Owl Cotes Barn, Mire Close Lane, Cowling, Keighley BD22 0LE
Tel: 01535 630202
Resident Partners/Directors: ICAEW Members
A Hitch

BAKER TILLY
Holly House, Spring Gardens Lane, Keighley, BD20 6LE

BAKER TILLY TAX AND ADVISORY SERVICES LLP
Holly House, Spring Gardens Lane, Keighley, BD20 6LE
Tel: 01535 607361
Resident Partners/Directors: ICAEW Members
C P Cotton

BAKER TILLY UK AUDIT LLP
Holly House, Spring Gardens Lane, Keighley, BD20 6LE
Tel: 01535 607361
Resident Partners/Directors: ICAEW Members
C P Cotton

BURTON & CO
Sovereign House, Bradford Road, Riddlesden, Keighley BD20 5EW

CLOUGH & COMPANY LLP
15/17 Devonshire Street, Keighley, BD21 2BH
Tel: 01535 662511
Email: cloughs@clough.co.uk
Resident Partners/Directors: ICAEW Members
N C Westman
Resident Partners (Non-ICAEW Members):
S N Wilson

EDDISONS
16-18 Devonshire Street, Keighley, BD21 2DG

JOHN D PORRITT
16 Gledhow Drive, Oxenhope, Keighley, BD22 9SA

LINDLEY ADAMS LTD
82 Keighley Road, Cowling, Keighley, BD22 0BA

MW DENTON
29 Devonshire Street, Keighley, BD21 2BH
Tel: 01535 690190

MW DENTON LTD
29 Devonshire Street, Keighley, BD21 2BH
Tel: 01535 690190
Resident Partners/Directors: ICAEW Members
M W Denton

THE NORTON PARTNERSHIP ★
The Croft, Park Road, Cross Hills, Keighley BD20 8BG

S.R. JONES
Middle Lane Ends Farm, Lane Ends Lane, Cowling, Keighley BD22 0LD

SUNDERLAND DRIVER
Orchard House, Aire Valley Business Centre, Keighley, BD21 3DU
Tel: 01535 665327
Email: robert@sundriver.co.uk
Principal: ICAEW Member
R Greenwood

WALKERS ◈
16/18 Devonshire Street, Keighley, BD21 2DG
Tel: 01535 600900
Resident Partners/Directors: ICAEW Members
A Day, N L Hudson, M W Procter, A F Simpson, R F Walker
Registered by the ICAEW to carry out company audit work
Regulated by the ICAEW for a range of investment business activities

WRAY ACCOUNTANTS LTD
PO Box 413, Keighley, BD22 9WX
Tel: 01535 645900
Resident Partners/Directors: ICAEW Members
P F Wray

KENDAL

3CA LTD ◈
Kent Cottage, Bridge Lane, Kendal, LA9 7DD
Tel: 01539 721002
Resident Partners/Directors: ICAEW Members
Stuart Jones

AIMS - JEFFS & CO
1 Beacon Buildings, Yard 23, Stramongate, Kendal, LA9 4BH

ALAN REED (ACT) LTD
4 Kent View, Kendal, LA9 4DZ
Tel: 01539 723840
Resident Partners/Directors: ICAEW Members
A R Reed

ARMSTRONG WATSON ◈
48 Stramongate, Kendal, LA9 4BD
Tel: 01539 942030
Fax: 01539 735282
Email: clientservice@armstrongwatson.co.uk
Website: http://www.armstrongwatson.co.uk
Resident Partners/Directors: ICAEW Members
R A Rankin, D J Threlkeld
General Description: Accountants & financial advisers. 35 partners. Ranked 26th in a survey of UK Accountancy profession. Specialises in: corporate finance; corporate accounts; business services; payroll services; computer solutions; financial planning & wealth management; insolvency & corporate recovery.

GOSTLING LTD
29a Lowther Street, Kendal, LA9 4DH
Tel: 01539 728270

HANLEY & CO
25 Main Street, Staveley, Kendal, LA8 9LU
Tel: 01539 821869
Resident Partners/Directors: ICAEW Members
M A Booth, J G Gilbertson

INGALLS
Libra House, Murley Moss Bus Village, Oxenholme Road, Kendal LA9 7RL
Tel: 01539 721548
Resident Partners/Directors: ICAEW Members
D Fell, A M Thompson

JACKSON & GRAHAM ◈
Lynn Garth, Gillinggate, Kendal, LA9 4JB
Tel: 01539 720526

LAMONT PRIDMORE
136 Highgate, Kendal, LA9 4HW

LOWE & WHITWELL
134 Highgate, Kendal, LA9 4HL

MOORE & SMALLEY LLP
Kendal House, Murley Moss Business Village, Oxenholme Road, Kendal LA9 7RL

NEIL WEBSTER & CO LTD
14 Finkle Street, Kendal, LA9 4AB

STABLES THOMPSON & BRISCOE
Lowther House, Lowther Street, Kendal, LA9 4DX

STABLES THOMPSON & BRISCOE LTD
Lowther House, Lowther Street, Kendal, LA9 4DX
Tel: 01539 720465
Fax: 01539 740209
Website: http://www.stb-accountants.co.uk
Date Established: 1930
Resident Partners/Directors: ICAEW Members
D Briscoe, K Cook
Registered by the ICAEW to carry out company audit work

TENON LTD
Station House, Station Road, Kendal, LA9 6RY
Tel: 01539 725032

TENON AUDIT LTD ◈
Station House, Station Road, Kendal, LA9 6RY
Tel: 01539 725032

KENILWORTH

BERNARD ROGERS & CO
Bank Gallery, High Street, Kenilworth, CV8 1LY
Tel: 01926 851516
Principal: ICAEW Member
B A Rogers

BRADLEY CAVE
18 Jordan Close, Kenilworth, CV8 2AE
Tel: 01926 864332
Principal: ICAEW Member
M W Todd

CRANER & CO
33 Glasshouse Lane, Kenilworth, CV8 2AH
Tel: 01926 511878
Principal: ICAEW Member
J E Craner

D H SALMON
25 Mayfield Drive, Kenilworth, CV8 2SW

FLEMONS & CO ◈
70 Priory Road, Kenilworth, CV8 1LQ
Tel: 01926 512763
Email: flemons@flemons.uk.com
Website: http://www.flemons.uk.com
Resident Partners/Directors: ICAEW Members
A M Flemons, G B Flemons

FOLKES WORTON & WOOD
56-58A Warwick Road, Kenilworth, CV8 1HH

JOHN L DAVIES
24 Thirlestane Close, Kenilworth, CV8 2PW

LANE & CO
4 Saville Grove, Kenilworth, CV8 2PR

M.F. FRENCH
Coleridge, 92 Leamington Road, Kenilworth, CV8 2AA

N.P. HOTEN
25 Rouncil Lane, Kenilworth, CV8 1FN

PEARL & CO
57a Warwick Road, Kenilworth, CV8 1HN

SIMMS HANSON ★
51 Windy Arbour, Kenilworth, CV8 2BB
Tel: 01926 852376
Resident Partners/Directors: ICAEW Members
R H Simms

KENLEY

A.R. CONSULTING LTD
57 Abbots Lane, Kenley, CR8 5JG
Tel: 0700 593 1123
Resident Partners/Directors: ICAEW Members
R Selvarajah

AR CONSULTING
57 Abbots Lane, Kenley, CR8 5JG

KESWICK

CHRIS LANGHAM CONSULTING
Prospect House, Portinscale, Keswick, CA12 5RD
Tel: 01768 774601
Resident Partners/Directors: ICAEW Members
C R D Langham

KESWICK ACCOUNTANTS LTD
Bracken Hue, Millbeck, Keswick, CA12 4PS

LAMONT PRIDMORE
8 Stanger Street, Keswick, CA12 5JU

SAINT & CO ▽ ◈
Barclays Bank Chambers, Market Square, Keswick, CA12 5BE
Tel: 01768 773239
Email: keswick@saint.co.uk
Website: http://www.saint.co.uk
Resident Partners/Directors: ICAEW Members
W G P Moore
Registered by the ICAEW to carry out company audit work
Authorised and regulated by the Financial Services Authority for investment business

KETTERING

AIMS ACCOUNTANTS FOR BUSINESS
3 Grindleford Close, Desborough, Kettering, NN14 2FG

AIMS - ROSEMARY JOHNSON
3 Grindleford Close, Desborough, Kettering, NN14 2FG

ATL ACCOUNTANTS
3 Tynan Close, Kettering, NN15 5YA

BEWERS TURNER & CO
Portland House, Station Road, Kettering, NN15 7HH

BEWERS TURNER & CO
Portland House, 1 Station Road, Kettering, NN15 7HH

BEWERS TURNER & CO LTD
Portland House, Station Road, Kettering, NN15 7HH

CARYL CHAMBERS LTD
Kamara, 6a Church Street, Burton Latimer, Kettering NN15 5LU

CFW
1 Sterling Court, Loddington, Kettering, NN14 1RZ

DAVID LEVERETT
Crugybar, 66 St Marys Road, Kettering, NN15 7BW

DESERET ACCOUNTANTS LTD
4 Thorpe Court, Thorpe Waterville, Kettering, NN14 3ED

GRANT THORNTON UK LLP
Grant Thornton House, Kettering Parkway, Kettering Venture Park, Kettering NN15 6XR
Tel: 01536 310000
Resident Partners/Directors: ICAEW Members
T Baldry, T J Blades, K A Gale, A.G. O'Rourke, A M Slack
Non-resident Partners (ICAEW Members):
R Wheatley, J Corbishley
Resident Partners (Non-ICAEW Members):
G J Markham

H.W. LASKEY AND CO LTD
26-28 Headlands, Kettering, NN15 7HP

HARVEY SPRIGGS ◈
Dovecote House, 11 Malvern Close, Kettering, NN16 9JP
Tel: 01536 522209
Principal: ICAEW Member
H J W Spriggs

HAWES STRICKLAND
Federation House, 36-38 Rockingham Road, Kettering, NN16 8JS
Tel: 01536 514844
Resident Partners/Directors: ICAEW Members
T J Hawes, T B Strickland

HMJT
Federation House, 36/38 Rockingham Road, Kettering, NN16 8JS

J. BEATTIE & CO
23 Bowling Green Road, Kettering, NN15 7QW
Tel: 01536 515387
Principal: ICAEW Member
J Beattie

JOHN S. WARD & CO ★
1 London Road, Kettering, NN16 0EF

JOHN SOWERBY
9 Dyson Drive, Kettering, NN16 9HR

JON ESSAM & CO LTD
Cottingham Way, Thrapston, Kettering, NN14 4PL

KATHY W. WEBSTER
23 St Marys Road, Kettering, NN15 7BP

MEADOWS ◈
1 Kings Court, Kettering Parkway, Kettering, NN15 6WJ
Tel: 01536 512217
Fax: 01536 410585
Email: duncan.childs@meadows-co.co.uk
Website: http://www.meadows-co.co.uk
Resident Partners/Directors: ICAEW Members
D P Childs, D H Kelland, D O H Parker, N Rowland
Resident Partners (Non-ICAEW Members):
D T Lally
Registered by the ICAEW to carry out company audit work
SPECIALISATIONS – FINANCIAL REPORTING
Accounts Preparation

MOORE STEPHENS ◈
Sovereign House, 7 Station Road, Kettering, NN15 7HH

PHILIP HECTOR & CO ◈
Unit 6, Grange Road Business Estate, Geddington, Kettering NN14 1AL
Tel: 01536 460066
Principal: ICAEW Member
J P Hector

PINPOINT ACCOUNTANCY SOLUTIONS
12 Cornfield Way, Burton Latimer, Kettering, NN15 5YH

RMH
Kingswood, School Lane, Denford, Kettering NN14 4PZ

SMITH, HODGE & BAXTER ★ ◈
Thorpe House, 93 Headlands, Kettering, NN15 6BL
Tel: 01536 514871
Email: info@smith-hodge.co.uk
Website: http://www.smith-hodge.co.uk
Resident Partners/Directors: ICAEW Members
A P Armer, D G Bale, I J Chown, J G Hatcher
Resident Partners (Non-ICAEW Members):
K A Weston
Registered by the ICAEW to carry out company audit work
Regulated by the ICAEW for a range of investment business activities

WILDMAN & CO
Goss Court, 36a High Street, Thrapston, Kettering NN14 4JH
Tel: 01832 733021
Principal: ICAEW Member
M R Wildman

WK ACCOUNTANTS
5 Welland Court, Desborough, Kettering, NN14 2PQ

KIDDERMINSTER

BILLINGHAM & CO LTD
4 Masons Yard, Mill Street, Kidderminster, DY11 6UY

CHARLES A. SHERREY F.C.A.
Falcons Rest, Fairfield Lane, Wolverley, Kidderminster DY11 5QJ

G.H.HERBERT & CO ◈
227 Marlpool Lane, Kidderminster, DY11 5DL
Tel: 01562 751111
Principal: ICAEW Member
G H Herbert
SPECIALISATIONS – FINANCIAL REPORTING
Limited Companies
SPECIALISATIONS – TAXATION
Payroll Service and Advice
Self Assessment Advice
General Description: A local practice serving individuals and small businesses.

HORWATH CLARK WHITEHILL LLP
Foley House, 123 Stourport Road, Kidderminster, DY11 7BW
Tel: 01562 60101
Resident Partners/Directors: ICAEW Members
K D Bartlett, R D Darlaston, H C Drew, J F Hancox, R I J Wherton

JENNIFER PAUL
8 Southall Drive, Hartlebury, Kidderminster, DY11 7LD

LAMBERT & CO
The Malt House, Mortimer Hill, Cleobury Mortimer, Kidderminster DY14 8QQ
Tel: 01299 271200
Principal: ICAEW Member
R J Lambert
SPECIALISATIONS – SECTOR
Doctors

LAUD GRICE & CO ◈
Scotland House, 12 Comberton Hill, Kidderminster, DY10 1QG

M J RILEY & CO
22 Church Street, Kidderminster, DY10 2AW
Tel: 01562 822196
Principal: ICAEW Member
M J Riley

MND TRAINING & CONSULTANCY
2 Hillgrove Gardens, Kidderminster, DY10 3AN

PINNER DARLINGTON
25 Church Street, Kidderminster, DY10 2AW
Tel: 01562 822138
Resident Partners/Directors: ICAEW Members
K Minett

PRICE PEARSON LTD ◈
6 Church Street, Kidderminster, DY10 2AD
Tel: 01562 744444
Email: info@pricepearson.com
Website: http://www.pricepearson.co.uk
Training Contracts Available.
Resident Partners/Directors: ICAEW Members
C Cooper, S Garrington
Registered by the ICAEW to carry out company audit work
Regulated by the ICAEW for a range of investment business activities
SPECIALISATIONS – AUDIT & ASSURANCE
Audit — Private Company
SPECIALISATIONS – BUSINESS & GENERAL ADVICE
Acquisitions and Mergers
Disposal of Businesses
SPECIALISATIONS – TAXATION
Back Duty

R.A.B. VINER & CO
C/o Digital Copier Systems Ltd, Systems House, 42 Broad Street, Kidderminster DY10 2LY

ROY LOTE
Exchequer House, 117 Lea Street, Kidderminster, DY10 1SN

ROY LOTE FCA
Exchequer House, 117 Lea Street, Kidderminster, DY10 1SN
Tel: 01562 754605

TELLING R.C.
Warecott, Old Worcester Road, Hartlebury, Kidderminster DY11 7XL

WORTON LLP
Beauchamp House, 402-403 Stourport Road, Kidderminster, DY11 7BG

WORTON ROCK
Beauchamp House, 402/403 Stourport Road, Kidderminster, DY11 7BG

KIDLINGTON

CHAPMAN ROBINSON & MOORE LTD
30 Bankside Court, Stationfields, Kidlington, OX5 1JE

HW
Sterling House, 19-23 High Street, Kidlington, OX5 2DH
Tel: 01865 378282
Resident Partners/Directors: ICAEW Members
S H Garrett, R H Style, D A Teckoe

LUCAS ACCOUNTANCY LTD ◈
The Dell, 4 Ingleby Paddocks, Enslow, Kidlington OX5 3ET
Tel: 01869 351678
Resident Partners/Directors: ICAEW Members
K J Lucas

R J RICE
144 Cromwell Way, Kidlington, OX5 2LJ
Tel: 01865 372075
Principal: ICAEW Member
R J Rice

KING'S LYNN

AIMS ACCOUNTANTS FOR BUSINESS
Keeper's Cottage, 21 Rougham End, Weasenham All Saints, King's Lynn PE32 2SN

AIMS - MICHAEL MANSFIELD
Keeper's Cottage, 21 Rougham End, Weasenham All Saints, King's Lynn PE32 2SN

ANGLIAN ACCOUNTANCY SERVICES LTD
36-38 King Street, King's Lynn, PE30 1ES

AVN ARENA LTD
42 Chapel Street, King's Lynn, PE30 1EF
Tel: 01553 773125
Fax: 01553 691057
Email: enquiries@avnarena.com
Website: http://www.avnarena.com
Resident Partners/Directors: ICAEW Members
N C Tunnard
Registered by the ICAEW to carry out company audit work
Regulated by the ICAEW for a range of investment business activities

BURRELLS ACCOUNTANCY LTD
Jubilee House, Jubilee Court, Dersingham, King's Lynn PE31 6HH

THE CHAMBER OF EXPERTS ◈
48 The Street, Sporle, King's Lynn, PE32 2DR
Tel: 01760 725880
Principal: ICAEW Member
T Vogel

D.R. CARTER
Park Farm, Mileham, King's Lynn, PE32 2RD

FD MANAGEMENT SERVICES LTD
New Inn Cottage, Dereham Road, Litcham, King's Lynn PE32 2NT

G K HEWKIN
The Croft, Water End Lane, Beeston, King's Lynn PE32 2NL

G K HEWKIN & CO LTD
The Croft, Water End Lane, Beeston, King's Lynn PE32 2NL

HAYHOW & CO
19 King St, King's Lynn, PE30 1HB
Tel: 01553 764711
Fax: 01553 767152
Email: admin@hayhow.com
Website: http://www.hayhow.com
Resident Partners/Directors: ICAEW Members
R S Peck
Resident Partners (Non-ICAEW Members):
J D Gladman
Registered by the ICAEW to carry out company audit work
Regulated by the ICAEW for a range of investment business activities

JOHN STENT
7 Mason Gardens, West Winch, King's Lynn, PE33 0RU
Tel: 01553 840008
Principal: ICAEW Member
J H Stent

JONES & WATSHAM
42 Hall Orchards, Middleton, King's Lynn, PE32 1RY
Tel: 01553 841090
Principal: ICAEW Member
R H Ballinger

KIRBY AND HASLAM ◈
11 King Street, King's Lynn, PE30 1ET
Tel: 01553 761316
Resident Partners/Directors: ICAEW Members
N G Kirby

KIRBY AND HASLAM LTD ◈
11 King Street, King's Lynn, PE30 1ET
Tel: 01553 761316
Email: neil.kirby@kirbyandhaslam.com
Website: http://www.kirbyandhaslam.com
Resident Partners (Non-ICAEW Members):
A F Haslam
Registered by the ICAEW to carry out company audit work
Regulated by the ICAEW for a range of investment business activities

MAPUS-SMITH & LEMMON LLP
48 King Street, King's Lynn, PE30 1HE
Tel: 01553 774761
Website: http://www.mapus.co.uk
Resident Partners/Directors: ICAEW Members
S T Boote, J W Hall, M J Jay
Registered by the ICAEW to carry out company audit work
Regulated by the ICAEW for a range of investment business activities

MELVYN GREENHALGH
34 Cedar Grove, North Runcton, King's Lynn, PE33 0QZ

ROBERT POLA
The Dormers, Low Road, Congham, King's Lynn PE32 1AE

STEPHENSON SMART ★
22-26 King Street, King's Lynn, PE30 1HJ
Tel: 01553 774104
Fax: 01553 692602
Email: contact-us@stephenson-smart.com
DX: 57805 KING'S LYNN
Website: http://www.stephenson-smart.com
Training Contracts Available.
Resident Partners/Directors: ICAEW Members
M J Andrews, A C Dodds, P Lofting
Non-resident Partners (ICAEW Members):
N R Ward
Resident Partners (Non-ICAEW Members):
K T Turner
Other Offices: Fakenham
Registered by the ICAEW to carry out company audit work
Regulated by the ICAEW for a range of investment business activities

SPECIALISATIONS – AUDIT & ASSURANCE
Audit — Private Company

SPECIALISATIONS – BUSINESS & GENERAL ADVICE
Book-keeping

SPECIALISATIONS – FINANCIAL REPORTING
Accounts Preparation
Limited Company Accounts
Partnership/Sole Trader Accounts

SPECIALISATIONS – TAXATION
Investigations
Payroll Service and Advice

THAIN WILDBUR
36-38 King Street, King's Lynn, PE30 1ES

WHITING & PARTNERS ◈
Berol House, Oldmedow Road, King's Lynn, PE30 4JJ
Tel: 01553 774745
Resident Partners/Directors: ICAEW Members
J D Cater

KINGS LANGLEY

FOWLER & TREMBLING
2 Forge Close, Chipperfield, Kings Langley, WD4 9DL
Tel: 01923 269550
Resident Partners/Directors: ICAEW Members
R C Fowler

GARY JOBSEY & CO
3 Barnsway, Love Lane, Kings Langley, WD4 9PW

GOWERS LTD ◈
The Old School House, Bridge Road, Hunton Bridge, Kings Langley WD4 8SZ
Tel: 01923 264060
Resident Partners/Directors: ICAEW Members
M L S Bach, I A Carter, A E J Gower, D M Green, M J Woodbridge

M W KERR
116 Chipperfield Road, Kings Langley, WD4 9JD
Tel: 01923 261475
Principal: ICAEW Member
M W Kerr

MICHAEL MORTON & CO
Strathmore, The Nap, Kings Langley, WD4 8ES

MORLEYS ◈
Nabobs, Kings Lane, Chipperfield, Kings Langley WD4 9EP

PINKERTONS
116 Chipperfield Road, Kings Langley, WD4 9JD

ROY FARRANT - AIMS ACCOUNTANTS ◈
14 Le Corte Close, Kings Langley, WD4 9PS
Tel: 01923 606 135
Principal: ICAEW Member
R D Farrant

STEPHEN KING
South Cot, Wayside, Chipperfield, Kings Langley WD4 9JJ

KINGSBRIDGE

ABREHART LILLEY
75a Fore Street, Kingsbridge, TQ7 1AB

ABREHART LILLEY LTD
75a Fore Street, Kingsbridge, TQ7 1AB

MALCOLM FRANKE & CO LTD
Campania, Links Road, South Milton, Kingsbridge TQ7 3JR
Tel: 01548 562320
Resident Partners/Directors: ICAEW Members
M D Franke

MICHAEL LOCKE & CO LTD
89 Fore Street, Kingsbridge, TQ7 1AB

TIM PATTERSON
Wits End, Promenade, Kingsbridge, TQ7 1JF

KINGSTON UPON THAMES

C.M. MITCHELL
111 Wolsey Drive, Kingston Upon Thames, KT2 5DR
Tel: 020 8546 7682
Principal: ICAEW Member
C M Mitchell

COLLARDS ★
2 High Street, Kingston Upon Thames, KT1 1EY

DAVID HOWARD ◈
1 Park Road, Hampton Wick, Kingston Upon Thames, KT1 4AS
Tel: 020 8977 3439
Fax: 020 8943 2820
Email: accountant@davidhoward.co.uk
Website: http://www.davidhoward.co.uk
Resident Partners/Directors: ICAEW Members
S A Bishop, N King
Resident Partners (Non-ICAEW Members):
P Lane
Other Offices:47 Queens Road, Weybridge, Surrey (Tel: 01932 855644)
Registered by the ICAEW to carry out company audit work
SPECIALISATIONS – BUSINESS & GENERAL ADVICE
Book-keeping
Book-keeping Systems
Company Secretarial Service
Management Advice to Business
SPECIALISATIONS – FINANCIAL REPORTING
Accounts Preparation
Limited Companies
SPECIALISATIONS – IT
Computerised Accounting Systems
SPECIALISATIONS – SECTOR
Charities
Construction
Property
Property Development
SPECIALISATIONS – TAXATION
Payroll Service and Advice
Self Assessment Advice
Small Traders
Taxation

GARNERS
Bermuda House, 45 High Street, Hampton Wick, Kingston Upon Thames KT1 4EH

GARNERS LTD ◈
Bermuda House, 45 High Street, Hampton Wick, Kingston Upon Thames KT1 4EH
Tel: 020 8943 2191
Fax: 020 8977 9347
Email: info@garners.co.uk
Website: http://www.garners.co.uk
Date Established: 1954
Resident Partners/Directors: ICAEW Members
S W Francis, J C Temlett
Registered by the ICAEW to carry out company audit work
Regulated by the ICAEW for a range of investment business activities
SPECIALISATIONS – AUDIT & ASSURANCE
Audit
SPECIALISATIONS – BUSINESS & GENERAL ADVICE
Company Secretarial Service
SPECIALISATIONS – FINANCIAL REPORTING
Accounts Preparation
SPECIALISATIONS – TAXATION
Payroll Service and Advice
Taxation
Languages Spoken:
Cantonese
See display advertisement near this entry.

GRENVILLE BARKER & CO LTD
15 Lingfield Avenue, Kingston Upon Thames, KT1 2TL

HAINES WATTS
76 Cambridge Road, Kingston Upon Thames, KT1 3NA
Tel: 020 8549 5137
Fax: 020 8546 3022
Training Contracts Available.
Resident Partners/Directors: ICAEW Members
A M Bodkin, D G Demetriou, H L Rieupeyroux
Non-resident Partners (ICAEW Members):
G M Laughton, P Simmons
Resident Partners (Non-ICAEW Members):
A J Wordingham, C G Collins
Non-resident Partners (Non-ICAEW Members):
M Davidson

HEENANS
KBC Kingston Exchange, 12-50 Kingsgate Road, Kingston Upon Thames, KT2 5AA

J TANNA & CO ◈
180 London Road, Kingston Upon Thames, KT2 6QW
Tel: 020 8546 6873

JAMES WORLEY & SONS
9 Bridle Close, Surbiton Road, Kingston Upon Thames, KT1 2JW

K.S. GORING & CO
35 Coombe Road, Kingston Upon Thames, KT2 7BA
Tel: 020 8546 4343
Principal: ICAEW Member
K S Goring

M.O. SAMPSON & CO ★
42 Kew Court, Richmond Road, Kingston Upon Thames, KT2 5BF
Tel: 020 8549 5922
Resident Partners/Directors: ICAEW Members
M O Sampson

MARKS BLOOM
60/62 Old London Road, Kingston Upon Thames, KT2 6QZ
Tel: 020 8549 9951
Email: audit@marksbloom.co.uk
Website: http://www.marksbloom.co.uk
Resident Partners/Directors: ICAEW Members
D R Evans, P Weinberg, A J Whelan
Registered by the ICAEW to carry out company audit work
Individual(s) licensed for insolvency work by the ICAEW

MENZIES LLP ◈
3rd Floor Kings House, 12-42 Wood Street, Kingston Upon Thames, KT1 1TG

ORBITAL INSURANCE SERVICES LTD
180 London Road, Kingston Upon Thames, KT2 6QW
Tel: 020 8546 6873
Resident Partners/Directors: ICAEW Members
V M Shah

OSBORNES ACCOUNTANTS LTD
20 Market Place, Kingston Upon Thames, KT1 1JP
Tel: 0208 974 8811
Resident Partners/Directors: ICAEW Members
P J Osborne

PETER DA COSTA & CO
56 Richmond Park Road, Kingston Upon Thames, KT2 6AJ
Tel: 020 8547 3111
Principal: ICAEW Member
P M W Da Costa

RICHARD FLOYD & CO
9 Bridle Close, Surbiton Road, Kingston Upon Thames, KT1 2JW
Tel: 020 8547 1888

WHEELER, HEGARTY & CO
Forest Lodge, Kingston Hill, Kingston Upon Thames, KT2 7JZ
Tel: 020 8546 3700
Principal: ICAEW Member
B P Hegarty

WILLIAM THOMPSON ACCOUNTING SERVICES
19 Tangmere Grove, Kingston Upon Thames, KT2 5GT

KINGSWINFORD

A.S. BROOKES & CO ◈
19 Claydon Road, Wall Heath, Kingswinford, DY6 0HR
Tel: 01384 293624
Principal: ICAEW Member
A S Brookes

ALTUS BUSINESS CONSULTING
193 Mount Pleasant, Kingswinford, DY6 9SP

D TURBERFIELD
Portway House, Stream Road, Kingswinford, DY6 9NT

DAWN CANN ACCOUNTING SERVICE
26 Dawley Road, Wall Heath, Kingswinford, DY6 9BH

FRENCH LUDLAM & CO LTD
661 High Street, Kingswinford, DY6 8AL

PRINCEP PARDOE ◈
794 High Street, Kingswinford, DY6 8BQ
Tel: 01384 401050
Principal: ICAEW Member
K A Biggs

V.J. CURRIE ◈
45 Lynwood Avenue, Wall Heath, Kingswinford, DY6 9AL
Tel: 01384 292477
Principal: ICAEW Member
V J Currie

WILKES TRANTER & CO LTD ◈
Brook House, Moss Grove, Kingswinford, DY6 9HS
Tel: 01384 295500
Resident Partners/Directors: ICAEW Members
S E W Tranter

KINGTON

DAVIES EDWARDS & CO ★
Albion House, 2 Bridge Street, Kington, HR5 3DL

JAMES HOLYOAK & PARKER LTD
32 Duke Street, Kington, HR5 3BW

POWELL & CO
53 High Street, Kington, HR5 3BJ

KIRKBY STEPHEN

JOHN ANDREW
Green Tree Barn, Faraday Road, Kirkby Stephen, CA17 4QL
Tel: 01768 371600
Principal: ICAEW Member
J Andrew

O'REILLY
2 Olde Bank House, Market St, Kirkby Stephen, CA17 4QS
Tel: 017683 71328
Resident Partners (Non-ICAEW Members):
G Ritzema

KNARESBOROUGH

BUTLER & CO
1 Manor Park, Arkendale, Knaresborough, HG5 0QH

EURA AUDIT UK
Grimstow House, 8 York Place, Knaresborough, HG5 0AA

G A BRIGGS FCA
Manor Farm, Farnham, Knaresborough, HG5 9JE

HAYWOOD & CO
Conyngham Hall, Knaresborough, HG5 9AY

LESLIE COULDWELL & CO
Barclays Bank Chambers, 37 High Street, Knaresborough, HG5 0HB
Tel: 01423 867431
Principal: ICAEW Member
L S Couldwell

M.W.B. EDWARDS
Gracegarth, Wetherby Road, Knaresborough, HG5 8LQ
Tel: 01423 865057
Principal: ICAEW Member
M W B Edwards

PETER E. DOYLE
8 Tentergate Gardens, Knaresborough, HG5 9BL
Tel: 01423 864339
Principal: ICAEW Member
P E Doyle

PETER WALKER
6 Aspin Lane, Knaresborough, HG5 8ED

KNEBWORTH

HUTOKSHI MADON
1 Bellamy Close, Knebworth, SG3 6EH

JAMES & CO
The Old Vineyard, 52 Stevenage Road, Knebworth, SG3 6NN

KEITH BLAXILL LTD
12 Stevenage Road, Knebworth, SG3 6AW

LOUISE COOKE
36 Stevenage Road, Knebworth, SG3 6NN

MRS T. STORAN
Highlands, 72 Stevenage Road, Knebworth, SG3 6NN

TRACY STORAN
Highlands, 72 Stevenage Road, Knebworth, SG3 6NN

KNUTSFORD

ANDREA DOBSON & CO
10 Freshfields, Knutsford, WA16 0NR

ARCHERS
7 Gaskell Avenue, Knutsford, WA16 0DA

AXEL
3 Minshull Street, Knutsford, WA16 6HG

DAVID EDGE
2 Sandlebridge Lane, Knutsford, WA16 7SD

F.P. DELAUNAY
49 Beggarmans Lane, Knutsford, WA16 9BA
Tel: 01565 651706
Principal: ICAEW Member
F P Delaunay

GREEN CORPORATES LTD
Brandon House, King Street, Knutsford, WA16 6DX

HADFIELD & CO ◈
17 King Street, Knutsford, WA16 6DW
Tel: 01565 652002
Resident Partners/Directors: ICAEW Members
P J Hadfield, P R Hadfield

JENNIFER TODD
Fairgreen Cottage, Clamhunger Lane, Mere, Knutsford WA16 6QG
Tel: 01565 832895
Principal: ICAEW Member
J Todd

LONGDALE RESTRUCTURING LLP Ⓜ
Langdale, Legh Road, Knutsford, WA16 8NT

MELLOR & CO
1st Floor, 31 Sandiway, Knutsford, WA16 8BU

TIM R ANDERSON
56 Glebelands Road, Knutsford, WA16 9DZ

LANCASTER

ARMSTRONG WATSON ◈
1c King Street, Bentham, Lancaster, LA2 7HG
Tel: 01524 61368

CLB COOPERS ★
Fleet House, New Road, Lancaster, LA1 1EZ
Tel: 01524 541200
Fax: 01524 541201
Email: lancaster@clbcoopers.co.uk
Website: http://www.clbcoopers.co.uk
Training Contracts Available.
Resident Partners/Directors: ICAEW Members
M G Garrett, P A Whiteway
Resident Partners (Non-ICAEW Members):
D Chadwick
Registered by the ICAEW to carry out company audit work
Regulated by the ICAEW for a range of investment business activities
General Description: CLB Coopers - Delivering solutions through excellence.

COLMAN, WHITTAKER & ROSCOW ◈
The Close, Queen Square, Lancaster, LA1 1RS

DODD & CO
No 8 Willow Mill, Fell View, Caton, Lancaster LA2 9RA
Tel: 01524 849588

J A FELL & CO ★
White Cross, South Road, Lancaster, LA1 4XQ
Tel: 01524 844266
Resident Partners/Directors: ICAEW Members
J A Fell

LANGDALE ◈
Enterprise House, 56-58 Main Street, High Bentham, Lancaster LA2 7HY
Tel: 01524 263000
Fax: 01524 263111
Email: professionals@langdalesaccountants.co.uk
Principal: ICAEW Member
G W Langdale

SPECIALISATIONS – BUSINESS & GENERAL ADVICE
Management Accounting Consultancy
Management Advice to Business

SPECIALISATIONS – IT
Computerised Accounting Systems

SPECIALISATIONS – TAXATION
Payroll Service and Advice
Taxation

Languages Spoken:
Spanish

MEWITH HEAD ACCOUNTING LTD
The Farmhouse, Mewith Head, High Bentham, Lancaster LA2 7AP

MOORE & SMALLEY LLP
Priory Close, St Mary's Gate, Lancaster, LA1 1XB
Tel: 01524 62801
Resident Partners/Directors: ICAEW Members
D A Bennett, D G Evans, J Tombs

PAUL CLEGG & CO
Riverside Offices, Second Floor, 26 St Georges Quay, Lancaster LA1 1RD

PD ACCOUNTANCY SERVICES
9 Coolidge Avenue, Lancaster, LA1 5ER

PKF (UK) LLP
The Gatehouse, White Cross, South Road, Lancaster LA1 4XQ
Tel: 01524 383954
Email: info.lancaster@uk.pkf.com
Website: http://www.pkf.co.uk
Non-resident Partners (ICAEW Members):
J Newell

SCOTT & WILKINSON
Dalton House, 9 Dalton Square, Lancaster, LA1 1WD
Tel: 01524 67111
Fax: 01524 62906
Website: http://www.scott-wilkinson.com
Resident Partners/Directors: ICAEW Members
R J Gaskell, N J Martin, P Wilkinson
Resident Partners (Non-ICAEW Members):
T M Preece
Registered by the ICAEW to carry out company audit work
Regulated by the ICAEW for a range of investment business activities

SHAWS ATS LTD
Mingulay, Farleton, Lancaster, LA2 9LF

TAYLOR, ROBERTSON & WILLETT LTD
95 King Street, Lancaster, LA1 1RH

TOWERS & GORNALL ★
Main Street, Bentham, Lancaster, LA2 7HQ

LANCING

TILL & CLOAKE ◈
70 South Street, Lancing, BN15 8AJ
Tel: 01903 854686
Principal: ICAEW Member
R S Cloake

LANGPORT

BUTTERWORTH JONES ◈
Sansom House, Bow Street, Langport, TA10 9PR
Tel: 01458 250208
Fax: 01458 252425
Email: langport@butterworthjones.co.uk
Resident Partners/Directors: ICAEW Members
R M Jones
Registered by the ICAEW to carry out company audit work
Regulated by the ICAEW for a range of investment business activities

IAN BOAGE & CO
Rookery Barn, Yew Tree Farm, Low Ham, Langport TA10 9DW
Tel: 01458 253402
Principal: ICAEW Member
I N Boage

PINKHAM & CO
Morningside, North Street, Langport, TA10 9RH

LAUNCESTON

ANDREW LAW
1a Madford Lane, Launceston, PL15 9EB

ANDREW LAW ACCOUNTANTS LTD
1A Madford Lane, Launceston, PL15 9EB

BLACKLER & CO ★
The Barn Office, Tredivett Mill, Little Comfort, Launceston PL15 9NA

HODGSONS ◈
12 Southgate Street, Launceston, PL15 9DP
Tel: 01566 772177
Fax: 01566 772257
Email: office@hodgsons.uk.com
Website: http://www.hodgsons.uk.com
Resident Partners/Directors: ICAEW Members
P J D Hodgson, P J M Stevenson
Resident Partners (Non-ICAEW Members):
P C Sanderson
Other Offices: Falmouth
Registered by the ICAEW to carry out company audit work
Regulated by the ICAEW for a range of investment business activities

NEVILL HOVEY & CO LTD ◈
Southgate Close, Launceston, PL15 9DU
Tel: 01566 772109
Resident Partners/Directors: ICAEW Members
T J Smith, H M Williams

PJM ACCOUNTANCY
Trevean, Yeolmbridge, Launceston, PL15 8NJ
Tel: 01566 773615
Principal: ICAEW Member
P J McAughey

POTTER BAKER ◈
20 Western Road, Launceston, PL15 7BA
Tel: 01566 772157
Fax: 01566 775507
Email: info@potterbaker.co.uk
Website: http://www.potterbaker.co.uk
Resident Partners/Directors: ICAEW Members
A D Baker, M J Wevill
Resident Partners (Non-ICAEW Members):
C K Hill
Other Offices: Tavistock
Registered by the ICAEW to carry out company audit work
Authorised and regulated by the Financial Services Authority for investment business

RICHARD F. HOPPER
Chinthurst, 30 St Stephens Hill, Launceston, PL15 8HN
Tel: 01566 778841
Principal: ICAEW Member
R F Hopper

SALLY REED LTD ◈
27F Pennygillam Way, Launceston, PL15 7ED
Tel: 01566 777189
Email: sally@sallyreed.co.uk
Website: http://www.sallyreed.co.uk
Resident Partners/Directors: ICAEW Members
S A Reed

T D CHAPMAN & CO
33 Westgate Street, Launceston, PL15 7AD

LEAMINGTON SPA

AGK LTD ◈
18 Victoria Terrace, Leamington Spa, CV31 3AB
Tel: 01926 451933

ANDREW ROLLS
3 Pound Lane, Leamington Spa, CV32 7RT

ANTHONY BREAKWELL
67 Willes Road, Leamington Spa, CV31 1BW

MCA BRESLINS
Beauchamp House, 1 Kenilworth Road, Leamington Spa, CV32 5TG

DAFFERNS LLP
Warwick House, 32 Clarendon Street, Leamington Spa, CV32 4PG

THE GRAHAM FULFORD PARTNERSHIP
Fulford House, Newbold Terrace, Leamington Spa, CV32 4EA

HARRISON BEALE & OWEN
Highdown House, 11 Highdown Road, Sydenham, Leamington Spa CV31 1XT

HARRISON BEALE & OWEN LTD ◈
Highdown House, 11 Highdown Road, Leamington Spa, CV31 1XT

HARRISON BEALE & OWEN MANAGEMENT SERVICES
Highdown House, 11 Highdown Road, Sydenham, Leamington Spa CV31 1XT

INFOCUS BUSINESS SERVICES LTD
1 Althorpe Street, Leamington Spa, CV31 1NQ

J.W.G. BLACKWELL
6 Hallfields, Radford Semele, Leamington Spa, CV31 1TS

JANE SMITH
8 Kingland Drive, Leamington Spa, CV32 6BL

MCA BRESLINS LEAMINGTON LTD
Beauchamp House, 1 Kenilworth Road, Leamington Spa, CV31 1BB

MICHAEL FAIRBOTHAM - AIMS
11 Simpkins Close, Weston Under Wetherley, Leamington Spa, CV33 9GE

MOFFAT GILBERT
5 Clarendon Place, Leamington Spa, CV32 5QL
Tel: 01926 334373
Fax: 01926 881464
Email: moffat@btinternet.com
Date Established: 1973
Training Contracts Available.
Resident Partners/Directors: ICAEW Members
G R F Gilbert, S Moffat
Registered by the ICAEW to carry out company audit work

OLLIS & CO
2 Hamilton Terrace, Holly Walk, Leamington Spa, CV32 4LY

THE OLLIS PARTNERSHIP LTD
2 Hamilton Terrace, Holly Walk, Leamington Spa, CV32 4LY
Tel: 01926 335381
Email: enquiries@ollisandco.com
Resident Partners/Directors: ICAEW Members
J A Davies, D L Page, W R Preston, I Randle, R M Smith
Resident Partners (Non-ICAEW Members):
S D J Megeney
Registered by the ICAEW to carry out company audit work

PINK GERBIL LTD
Mansfield Barn, Fosse Way, Harbury, Leamington Spa CV33 9SR

R W GOLDER
28 Beaufort Avenue, New Cubbington, Leamington Spa, CV32 7TA

TGFP LTD
Fulford House, Newbold Terrace, Leamington Spa, CV32 4EA

LEATHERHEAD

ACCOUNTANCY & TAX ADVISERS LTD
Fetcham Park House, Lower Road, Fetcham, Leatherhead KT22 9HD
Tel: 01372 450048
Resident Partners/Directors: ICAEW Members
R W Jones

AIMS - ELIZABETH BINGHAM
The Thatched House, The Downs, Leatherhead, KT22 8LH

BOLTON & CO ACCOUNTANTS LTD
Squirrels Wood, Reigate Road, Leatherhead, KT22 8QY
Tel: 01372 273 669
Resident Partners/Directors: ICAEW Members
T D Bolton

BOOKHAM ACCOUNTING AND TAX SERVICES
Fownhope, Childs Hall Road, Bookham, Leatherhead KT23 3QG
Tel: 01372 451463
Principal: ICAEW Member
M J Pearce

BOURNE & CO
19 High Street, Bookham, Leatherhead, KT23 4AA
Tel: 01372 454602
Principal: ICAEW Member
A C A Bourne

CHESSMAN LTD
Wrenfield, The Chase, Oxshott, Leatherhead KT22 0HR

CHRISTOPHER B. FRY & CO
Claire House, Bridge Street, Leatherhead, KT22 8BZ

COVA & CO
Pedlars March, 4 Meadway, Oxshott, Leatherhead KT22 0LZ

CRILLY & CO
Wyvern House, 1 Church Road, Bookham, Leatherhead KT23 3PD

D.M. HAMILTON
58 Church Street, Leatherhead, KT22 8DW

G. O'BRIEN
Ullenwood, Manor Close, East Horsley, Leatherhead KT24 6SA

GEORGE DOUGHERTY
Chestnuts, Lower Farm Road, Effingham, Leatherhead KT24 5JJ

H.C.SAMUEL & CO
Glen View, Epsom Road, West Horsley, Leatherhead KT24 6AL
Tel: 01483 282507
Principal: ICAEW Member
J D Hattersley

IAN RANKIN & CO
4 Blades Close, Leatherhead, KT22 7JY
Tel: 01372 276390
Principal: ICAEW Member
I T Rankin

J. BERGER
Courtlands Cottage, 62 Copsem Lane, Oxshott, Leatherhead KT22 0NT

J.C. WIGLEY FCA
68 Hilley Field Lane, Fetcham, Leatherhead, KT22 9UU

JA LOVELESS FCA
The Lilacs, 25 Church Road, Leatherhead, KT22 8AT

KATE HAYNES LTD
129 Woodlands Road, Little Bookham, Leatherhead, KT23 4HN

MAXINE HIGGINS
Pentire, Orchard Close, East Horsley, Leatherhead KT24 5EZ

MENZIES LLP ◈
Ashcombe House, 5 The Crescent, Leatherhead, KT22 8DY

R.C. BUTLER
83 Strathcona Avenue, Bookham, Leatherhead, KT23 4HS

R.L.B. MARSHALL
51 Clare Crescent, Leatherhead, KT22 7RA

ROBERTS REDMAN
27 St Johns Avenue, Leatherhead, KT22 7HT

ROCHMAN GOODMANS ◈
29 Barrett Road, Fetcham, Leatherhead, KT22 9HL
Tel: 01372 451521
Fax: 01372 451774
Email: paul@rochgood.co.uk
Principal: ICAEW Member
P H Rochman
SPECIALISATIONS – SECTOR

Artists/Graphic Designers
Journalists/Writers/Copywriters
Media

S J BALMONT
11 Lodge Road, Fetcham, Leatherhead, KT22 9QY

TAKE ACCOUNT LTD
Winterfold, Norrels Drive, East Horsley, Leatherhead KT24 5DR

VIRIDIS CONSULTING LTD
9 Kenyons, West Horsley, Leatherhead, KT24 6HX

W.B. HENDERSON
Pachesham Gates, Oxshott Road, Leatherhead, KT22 0ER

WALDMAN & CO
Clevelands, Steels Lane, Oxshott, Leatherhead KT22 0RF
Tel: 01372 849880
Principal: ICAEW Member
N D Waldman

LEDBURY

CROWTHERS ACCOUNTANTS LTD
10 The Southend, Ledbury, HR8 2EY
Tel: 01531 631500
Resident Partners/Directors: ICAEW Members
R F Beard

DAVIES & CO
136 Bridge Street, Ledbury, HR8 2AS

EDWARD WATKINS & CO
Glenmoir, New Street, Ledbury, HR8 2DX
Tel: 01531 631100
Principal: ICAEW Member
E W Watkins

JONATHAN ANDREW
1A The Homend, Ledbury, HR8 1BN
Tel: 01531 635760
Email: jonathanandrew@btconnect.com
Principal: ICAEW Member
J G Andrew

LUCY R. HILL
1 Victoria Row, Wellington Heath, Ledbury, HR8 1LX
Tel: 01531 632707
Principal: ICAEW Member
L R Hill

R.C. DOBSON & CO
Bredon View, Hollybush, Ledbury, HR8 1ET
Tel: 01531 650308
Principal: ICAEW Member
R C Dobson

R.M. WILLGOOSE
Chestnut End, Leddington, Ledbury, HR8 2LG
Tel: 01531 635579
Fax: 01531 634025
Email: richard.willgoose@fireflyuk.net
Date Established: 1987
Principal: ICAEW Member
R M Willgoose
Registered by the ICAEW to carry out company audit work

SUSAN BARNWELL
The Former Vicarage, Much Marcle, Ledbury, HR8 2NL
Tel: 01531 660730
Principal: ICAEW Member
S M Barnwell

LEE-ON-THE-SOLENT

COCHRANE & CO ACCOUNTANTS LTD
38 Kings Road, Lee-On-the-Solent, PO13 9NU

D B RAYNER & CO
96a High Street, Lee-On-the-Solent, PO13 9DA

K W BARRON LTD
27 Grove Road, Lee-On-the-Solent, PO13 9JA

TANIA WILKIE & CO LTD
52 Portsmouth Road, Lee-On-the-Solent, PO13 9AG
Tel: 02392 556960
Resident Partners/Directors: ICAEW Members
T Wilkie

LEEDS

A & R ACCOUNTANCY LTD
Tarn House, 77 High Street, Yeadon, Leeds LS19 7SP

A & R ACCOUNTANCY LTD
23 Lyndhurst Road, Scholes, Leeds, LS15 4BP

A.M. QUEST & CO
311 Roundhay Road, Leeds, LS8 4HT

A.M. SHERMAN & CO
96 Lidgett Lane, Leeds, LS8 1HR

ANDON FRERES
Cavendish House, St Andrew's Court, Burley Street, Leeds LS3 1JY
Tel: 0113 244 5540
Principal: ICAEW Member
A Jones

ANDREW SHEARER
Town House, 16-18 Town Street, Horsforth, Leeds LS18 4RJ
Tel: 0113 258 2700
Principal: ICAEW Member
A C Shearer

ANNE KIERNAN
Drumlahan House, Milner Lane, Thorner, Leeds LS14 3AG

ARGENTICA LTD
356 Broadway, Horsforth, Leeds, LS18 4RE

ARMSTRONG WATSON ◈
Central House, 47 St Pauls Street, Leeds, LS1 2TE
Tel: 0113 384 3840
Fax: 0113 384 3841
Email: clientservice@armstrongwatson.co.uk
Website: http://www.armstrongwatson.co.uk
Resident Partners/Directors: ICAEW Members
C P Barrett, W J Booth, N J Emmott, S R Palmer, D Samson
Resident Partners (Non-ICAEW Members):
R Whitehead, M Kienlen
General Description:
Accountants & financial advisers. 35 partners. Ranked 26th in a survey of UK Accountancy profession. Specialises in: corporate accounts; business services; corporate finance; financial planning & wealth management; payroll services; computer solutions; insolvency & corporate recovery.

BAKER TILLY
2 Whitehall Quay, Leeds, LS1 4HG
Tel: 0113 285 5000
Resident Partners/Directors: ICAEW Members
D J Bagley, H M Morrison, M V Pownall
Resident Partners (Non-ICAEW Members):
A Baker, D J Darroch

BAKER TILLY
2 Whitehall Quay, Leeds, LS1 4HG
Tel: 0113 285 5000
Resident Partners/Directors: ICAEW Members
P Byrne, A C R Elston, M A Jackson, R H King, S Mullins

BAKER TILLY
2 Whitehall Quay, Leeds, LS1 4HG

BAKER TILLY RESTRUCTURING AND RECOVERY LLP
2 Whitehall Quay, Leeds, LS1 4HG
Tel: 0113 285 5000
Resident Partners/Directors: ICAEW Members
A D Allen, D J Glossop, R G Maclaverty, P E Pierce, M N Ranson

BAKER TILLY TAX AND ADVISORY SERVICES LLP
2 Whitehall Quay, Leeds, LS1 4HG
Tel: 0113 285 5000
Resident Partners/Directors: ICAEW Members
A D Allen, D J Bagley, P Byrne, A C R Elston, D J Glossop, A E Greenwood, D A Heaton, M A Jackson, R H King, R G Maclaverty, H M Morrison, S Mullins, K P O'Connor, T F X Parr, P E Pierce, M V Pownall, M N Ranson
Resident Partners (Non-ICAEW Members):
A Baker, D J Darroch

BARRETT J.
6 Primley Park Road, Leeds, LS17 7HS

BARTFIELDS BUSINESS SERVICES LLP ◈
Burley House, 12 Clarendon Road, Leeds, LS2 9NF
Tel: 0113 244 9051
Email: info@bartfield.co.uk
Website: http://www.bartfield.co.uk
Resident Partners/Directors: ICAEW Members
G M A Bell, M Cawley, R S Davidson, P F Goddard, D P Miller
Non-resident Partners (ICAEW Members):
M Gibson
Resident Partners (Non-ICAEW Members):
M Lowell
Other Offices: Rothwell
SPECIALISATIONS – FORENSIC ACCOUNTING

Forensic Accounting

continued

BARTFIELDS BUSINESS SERVICES LLP *cont*

SPECIALISATIONS – IT

Computerised Accounting Systems

SPECIALISATIONS – TAXATION

Investigations
Taxation

General Description: Representatives covering the UK and worldwide, specialists in tax planning, forensic accounting and IT consultancy.

BARTFIELDS BUSINESS SERVICES LLP
1st Floor, 57a Commercial Street, Rothwell, Leeds LS26 0QD

BARTFIELDS (UK) LTD
57a Commercial Street, Rothwell, Leeds, LS26 0QD

BARTFIELDS (UK) LTD ◈
Burley House, 12 Clarendon Road, Leeds, LS2 9NF
Tel: 0113 244 9051
Email: info@bartfield.co.uk
Website: http://www.bartfield.co.uk
Non-resident Partners (ICAEW Members):
M Gibson
Resident Partners (Non-ICAEW Members):
M Lowell
Other Offices: Rothwell

SPECIALISATIONS – FORENSIC ACCOUNTING

Forensic Accounting

SPECIALISATIONS – IT

Computerised Accounting Systems

SPECIALISATIONS – TAXATION

Investigations
Taxation

General Description: Representatives covering the UK and worldwide. Specialists in tax planning, forensic accounting and IT consultancy.

BATY CASSON LONG ◈
Shears Yard, 21 Wharf Street, The Calls, Leeds LS2 7EQ
Tel: 0113 242 5848
Principal: ICAEW Member
J A Baty

BCL ACCOUNTANTS LTD
30-38 Dock Street, Leeds, LS10 1JF

BDO STOY HAYWARD LLP
1 Bridgewater Place, Water Lane, Leeds, LS11 5RU
Tel: 0113 244 3839
Fax: 0113 204 1200
Resident Partners/Directors: ICAEW Members
I Beaumont, T P Clarke, M J Copley, W Holmes, M E Hunt, N G Wharton, J P Whitworth
Resident Partners (Non-ICAEW Members):
S P Bevan, T Jones, F G Newton, T S Underwood, A Mahon

BEGBIES TRAYNOR
Glendevon House, Hawthorn Park, Coal Road, Leeds LS14 1PQ
Tel: 0113 237 5560
Website: http://www.begbies-traynor.com
Resident Partners/Directors: ICAEW Members
J N R Pitts

SPECIALISATIONS – BUSINESS RECOVERY & INSOLVENCY

Bankruptcies
Corporate Recovery
Liquidations
Reorganisations and Company Reconstructions

BEGBIES TRAYNOR
9th Floor, Bond Court, Leeds, LS1 2JZ
Tel: 0113 244 0044
Fax: 0113 244 5820
Website: http://www.begbies-traynor.com
Resident Partners/Directors: ICAEW Members
R A H Maxwell, R N I Pughe, M E G Saville
Resident Partners (Non-ICAEW Members):
R Sadler
Individual(s) licensed for insolvency work by another RPB

SPECIALISATIONS – BUSINESS RECOVERY & INSOLVENCY

Bankruptcies
Corporate Recovery
Liquidations
Reorganisations and Company Reconstructions

SPECIALISATIONS – FORENSIC ACCOUNTING

Expert Witnesses in Litigation
Forensic Accounting

BENSON WALKER & CO
1 Bachelor Lane, Horsforth, Leeds, LS18 5NA

BENTLEY JENNISON ◈
2 Wellington Place, Leeds, LS1 4AP

BIRDSALL & BENNETT LLP
Tranquillity House, 1 Tranquility, Crossgates, Leeds LS15 8QU

BOTROS & CO
4 Northwest Business Park, Servia Hill, Leeds, LS6 2QH
Tel: 0113 244 4379
Principal: ICAEW Member
S E Botros

BRADY & CO
19 Wentworth Crescent, Alwoodley, Leeds, LS17 7TW

BRIAN ZIFF LTD
3 Lakeland Crescent, Leeds, LS17 7PS

BRIGHT SPARK ACCOUNTANTS
3 Fieldhead Drive, Guiseley, Leeds, LS20 8DX
Tel: 01943 877115
Website: http://www.brightsparkaccountants.co.uk
Principal: ICAEW Member
K J Spark

BROWN BUTLER ◈
Apsley House, 78 Wellington Street, Leeds, LS1 2JT

BTG MCINNES CORPORATE FINANCE
9th Floor, Bond Court, Leeds, LS1 2JZ

BUCKLE BARTON ◈
Sanderson House, Station Road, Horsforth, Leeds LS18 5NT

BURROW & CROWE
8-9 Feast Field, Town Street, Horsforth, Leeds LS18 4TJ

BWC BUSINESS SOLUTIONS
8 Park Place, Leeds, LS1 2RU

BWC BUSINESS SOLUTIONS LTD
8 Park Place, Leeds, LS1 2RU

CEILIC LTD
5 Miles Garth, Bardsey, Leeds, LS17 9BW
Tel: 01937 574495
Resident Partners/Directors: ICAEW Members
A W A Bates

CERTAX ACCOUNTING (LEEDS & WETHERBY)
41 Belvedere Court, Alwoodley, Leeds, LS17 8NF

CHAMBERLAIN & CO
24-26 Aire Street, Leeds, LS1 4HT

CHILD & CO
20 Kirkgate, Sherburn In Elmet, Leeds, LS25 6BL
Tel: 01977 683438
Resident Partners/Directors: ICAEW Members
A E Child, R Child, J S Dawson, J P Monaghan

CLEMMENCE & CO ◈
Linton, Rawdon Hall Drive, Rawdon, Leeds LS19 6HD
Tel: 0113 250 1555
Principal: ICAEW Member
J W Clemmence

D & J RANDLES LTD
4 The Crescent, Adel, Leeds, LS16 6AA

D.J. WILLIAMS
18 Hillway, Tranmere Park, Guiseley, Leeds LS20 8HB

DAVID B. CAVILL
49 West End Grove, Horsforth, Leeds, LS18 5JJ

DELOITTE & TOUCHE LLP ◈
1 City Square, Leeds, LS1 2AL
Tel: 0113 243 9021
Website: http://www.deloitte.co.uk
Resident Partners/Directors: ICAEW Members
D P T Belward, I Brown, R Brown, D F Butters, R W H Esler, D Griffiths, M A Jenkins, D M Johnson, M G Kilburn, S P Manning, M J Oldham, C D Powell, I G Sargeant, R D Seldon, G Taylor, T Teji, P M Thompson, P J Thomson, R J Williams, S C Williams

DEREK OWRAM
Meadow Bank, 2 Hall Rise, Bramhope, Leeds LS16 9JG
Tel: 0113 284 3301
Principal: ICAEW Member
D Owram

DUNCAN BARR ASSOCIATES LTD ◈
Canalside Buildings, Graingers Way, Roundhouse Business Park, Leeds LS12 1AH
Tel: 0113 244 9811
Resident Partners/Directors: ICAEW Members
D C A Barr

EAVES AND CO
12 York Place, Leeds, LS1 2DS
Tel: 0113 203 1502

EJK ASSOCIATES LTD
2 Church Court, Morley, Leeds, LS27 9TN
Tel: 0113 253 5232
Resident Partners/Directors: ICAEW Members
E J Kirkwood

ELSPETH CONSULTING
50 Denton Avenue, Leeds, LS8 1LE

ENDLESS LLP
3 Whitehall Quay, Leeds, LS1 4BF

ERNST & YOUNG LLP
1 Bridgewater Place, Water Lane, Leeds, LS11 5QR
Tel: 0113 298 2200
Resident Partners/Directors: ICAEW Members
E M Barber, T D G Dewar, T A Ducker, P B Hilling, I R Hobson, N A Holyoake, C J Kelly, S W Watson, T J A West

FARRAR SMITH
Suite 5, Gledhow Mount Mansion, Roxholme Grove, Leeds LS7 4JJ

FORD CAMPBELL FREEDMAN LLP ◈
34 Park Cross Street, Leeds, LS1 2QH
Tel: 0113 245 7222

Resident Partners/Directors: ICAEW Members
J R Butcher, A S Campbell, A J Ford, K M Frisby

FOSTERS
Unit 3, Friends School, Low Green, Rawdon, Leeds LS19 6HB

FRANK W. DOBBY & CO
55 Fountain St, Morley, Leeds, LS27 0AA

G.L. BARKER & CO LLP ★
45-49 Austhorpe Road, Crossgates, Leeds, LS15 8BA

GARBUTT & ELLIOTT LTD ◈
2 Stable Court, Elmete Lane, Beechwoods, Leeds LS8 2LQ
Tel: 0113 273 9600
Fax: 0113 273 9601
Email: info@garbutt-elliott.co.uk
Website: http://www.garbutt-elliott.co.uk
Training Contracts Available.
Resident Partners/Directors: ICAEW Members
R G Feltham, R J Green
Resident Partners (Non-ICAEW Members):
N Shaw
Other Offices: York

GEOFFREY MARTIN & CO ★ ◈
St James's House, 28 Park Place, Leeds, LS1 2SP
Tel: 0113 244 5141
Resident Partners/Directors: ICAEW Members
J H Twizell
Individual(s) licensed for insolvency work by the ICAEW
Individual(s) licensed for insolvency work by another RPB
SPECIALISATIONS – BUSINESS RECOVERY & INSOLVENCY
Bankruptcies
Corporate Recovery
Liquidations
Reorganisations and Company Reconstructions
General Description: Leading independent corporate recovery and insolvency practice.

GEORGE ALLEN & CO
6 Lakeside View, Rawdon, Leeds, LS19 6RN

GLEEK CADMAN ROSS ◈
96 Marsh Lane, Leeds, LS9 8SR
Tel: 0113 235 0066
Resident Partners/Directors: ICAEW Members
C Cadman, D J Gleek, M L Ross

GLEEK CADMAN ROSS LLP
96 Marsh Lane, Leeds, LS9 8SR

GRANT THORNTON UK LLP
1 Whitehall Riverside, Whitehall Road, Leeds, LS1 4BN
Tel: 0113 209 5514
Resident Partners/Directors: ICAEW Members
G M Barber, M A Chatten, C M S J Clements, A R Dean, S M Ellis, K Hinds, T J W Lincoln, I R Marwood, M E Miller, A D Moore, G A Nunns, B A Senior, P W Spinks, A J Walton, J S Wilkinson, A Wood
Resident Partners (Non-ICAEW Members):
M L Burke, J P McLean, J C Riley, S Howard, W M Oxley, N K Sengupta

GRANTS
11 Park Place, Leeds, LS1 2RX

HAYTON ACCOUNTANCY
22 The Boyle, Barwick in Elmet, Leeds, LS15 4JN

HAYTON ACCOUNTANCY LTD
22 The Boyle, Barwick in Elmet, Leeds, LS15 4JN
Tel: 0113 393 5123
Resident Partners/Directors: ICAEW Members
J P Hayton

HENTON & CO
St Andrews House, St Andrews Street, Leeds, LS3 1LF

HENTON & CO LLP ◈
St Andrews House, St Andrews Street, Leeds, LS3 1LF
Tel: 0113 246 7900
Resident Partners/Directors: ICAEW Members
A Ahmad, N Ahmed, S Gray

HIBBERT & CO ◈
480a Roundhay Road, Leeds, LS8 2HU
Tel: 0113 235 0700
Principal: ICAEW Member
T N Hibbert

HOLLINGS CROWE STORR & CO ◈
46/48 Otley Road, Guiseley, Leeds, LS20 8AH
Tel: 01943 874185

HOPE AGAR LTD
24a Marsh Street, Rothwell, Leeds, LS26 0BB
Tel: 0113 205 9335
Resident Partners/Directors: ICAEW Members
K T Rhodes

HOWARD MATTHEWS PARTNERSHIP
Lidgett House, Lidgett Lane, Garforth, Leeds LS25 1LL

HOWARTH CORPORATE FINANCE LTD
64 Wellington Street, Leeds, LS1 2EE

HSA ABBEY BERGER
2 Woodside Mews, Clayton Wood Close, Leeds, LS16 6QE
Tel: 0113 230 5510
Email: info@hsatheaccountants.co.uk
Website: http://www.hsatheaccountants.co.uk
Resident Partners/Directors: ICAEW Members
M W F Ringrose

HUQUE CHAUDHRY ASSOCIATES LTD
Roundhay Chambers, 199 Roundhay Road, Leeds, LS8 5AN

HW (LEEDS) LLP
Sterling House, 1 Sheepscar Court, Northside Business Park, Meanwood Road, Leeds LS7 2BB
Tel: 0113 398 1100
Resident Partners/Directors: ICAEW Members
P L Bancroft, P P Caine, A S Minifie, A M Sacks, M A Stanyard, J F Sutton

HWSEG LTD
27 Harrogate Road, Chapel Allerton, Leeds, LS7 3PD
Tel: 0113 239 2200
Resident Partners/Directors: ICAEW Members
R V Apps

I.H. BUTLER & CO
25 Gainsborough Drive, Adel, Leeds, LS16 7PF
Tel: 0113 230 1528
Principal: ICAEW Member
I H Butler

IAN MILNER
2 Langthorne Court, Morley, Leeds, LS27 9DR

IAN PICKUP & CO
123 New Road Side, Horsforth, Leeds, LS18 4QD
Tel: 01132 583343
Principal: ICAEW Member
I C Pickup
Registered by the ICAEW to carry out company audit work
SPECIALISATIONS – SECTOR
Charities

INDENDENT FORENSIC ACCOUNTING LTD
24 North Park Avenue, Roundhay, Leeds, LS8 1DN

INTEGRA CORPORATE FINANCE LTD
1 Whitehall, Whitehall Road, Leeds, LS1 4HR

J.C. FOSTER
77B Broadgate Lane, Horsforth, Leeds, LS18 5DU

J MAYS
10 Kirkdale Crescent, Leeds, LS12 6AS

J.R. HUNTER
12 Church Meadow, Sherburn in Elmet, Leeds, LS25 6NX

J.S. CULLEN & CO
Barclays Bank Chambers, High Street, Yeadon, Leeds LS19 7PP

JACKIE SHEMILT
2 Billing Drive, Leeds, LS19 6QR
Tel: 0113 250 6219
Principal: ICAEW Member
J R Shemilt

JACOBS & CO
Credcoll House, 96 Marsh Lane, Leeds, LS9 8SR

JOHN BUNSTER
24 Hillway, Tranmere Park, Guiseley, Leeds LS20 8HB

JOHN H FOX & CO
14 North Park Grove, Roundhay, Leeds, LS8 1JJ

JOHN M NIXON & CO ◈
39 Wynford Avenue, West Park, Leeds, LS16 6JN
Tel: 0113 261 9100
Principal: ICAEW Member
J M Nixon

JOHN V. BLAKEBOROUGH
5 Adel Park Croft, Leeds, LS16 8HT

JOSEPHS
Devonshire House, Suite 7, Devonshire Avenue, Leeds LS8 1AY

JP CONSULTING
62 Ash Hill Drive, Shadwell, Leeds, LS17 8JR

KATHARINE WIDDOWSON
406 Otley Road, Leeds, LS16 8AD

KATIA BARBER ASSOCIATES ◈
West View, Wood Lane, Bardsey, Leeds LS17 9AW
Tel: 01937 574544
Principal: ICAEW Member
K Barber

KB ACCOUNTANCY
Croft House Farm, Biggin Lane, Little Fenton, Leeds LS24 6HQ

KELLY ASSOCIATES ★
4 Club Lane, Rodley, Leeds, LS13 1JG
Tel: 0113 256 6546
Resident Partners/Directors: ICAEW Members
S Kelly
Resident Partners (Non-ICAEW Members):
J Kelly

KELLY WILLIAMS
135/137 Queen Street, Morley, Leeds, LS27 8HE
Tel: 01132 520553
Principal: ICAEW Member
P Kelly

KIRK NEWSHOLME LTD ◈
Richmond House, 16 Blenheim Terrace, Leeds, LS2 9HN
Tel: 0113 389 6200
Resident Partners/Directors: ICAEW Members
G Kirk, N A Rayland, M D Templeton, J L Wright

KPMG LLP
1 The Embankment, Neville Street, Leeds, LS1 4DW
Tel: 0113 231 3000
Resident Partners/Directors: ICAEW Members
P G Abram, M A Atherton, J Campbell, J L Ellacott, M G Firmin, R K Gabbertas, C R Hearld, A M Legg, K M McKay, R I Moffatt, D Morritt, D L Mycock, K T Orr, A J Stone, A J Walker, S R Walker
Resident Partners (Non-ICAEW Members):
M D Avery, D C Callinan, A Dhallai, R D Fleming, I Hasdell, M Linter, W R Middleton, M G Till, I Warman

LEE & CO ◈
Crown House, Armley Road, Leeds, LS12 2EJ
Tel: 0113 247 0047
Resident Partners/Directors: ICAEW Members
P Lee, A M McClean
Registered by the ICAEW to carry out company audit work
Regulated by the ICAEW for a range of investment business activities
Individual(s) licensed for insolvency work by the ICAEW

LEON, SCHILLER
100 High Ash Drive, Leeds, LS17 8RE

M. PROUDLOCK & CO LTD
Titan House, Station Road, Horforth, Leeds LS18 5PA
Tel: 0113 239 0099
Resident Partners/Directors: ICAEW Members
S G Carley

MALCOLM JONES & CO LLP
West Hill House, Allerton Hill, Chapel Allerton, Leeds LS7 3QB

MALL & CO
4 Queen Street, Leeds, LS1 2TW
Tel: 0113 297 8888
Resident Partners/Directors: ICAEW Members
L M Cheung, M R Geale, L J Howe
SPECIALISATIONS – FORENSIC ACCOUNTING
Expert Witnesses in Litigation
Forensic Accounting

MAZARS CORPORATE FINANCE LTD
Mazars House, Gelderd Road, Gildersome, Leeds LS27 7JN

MAZARS LLP ◈
Mazars House, Gelderd Road, Gildersome, Leeds LS27 7JN
Tel: 0113 204 9797
Resident Partners/Directors: ICAEW Members
S Davies, O G Hoffman, J C Holroyd, A G Smith, D Smithson, I G Wrightson
Resident Partners (Non-ICAEW Members):
P Charlton, R Garrod, R D Adamson, A I Archibald
Registered by the ICAEW to carry out company audit work
Authorised and regulated by the Financial Services Authority for investment business

MGE CONSULTING LTD
12 West Park Avenue, Leeds, LS8 2HG

MICHAEL DACK & CO ◈
75 Great George Street, Leeds, LS1 3BR
Tel: 0113 243 3559
Principal: ICAEW Member
M J Dack

MICHAEL J SAFFER & CO
Northern House, 87 Town Street, Horsforth, Leeds LS18 5BP
Tel: 0113 258 6660
Principal: ICAEW Member
M J Saffer

MITCHELLS
St Michaels Mews, 18-22 St Michaels Road, Leeds, LS6 3AW

MITCHELLS GROUP
St Michaels Mews, 18 St Michaels Road, Leeds, LS6 3AW

MITCHELLS GROUP LTD
St Michaels Mews, 18 St Michaels Road, Leeds, LS6 3AW

MITCHELLS (UK) LTD
St Michaels Mews, 18-22 St Michaels Road, Leeds, LS6 3AW

MJB CONSULTANTS & CORPORATE FINANCE LTD
3 Mavis Avenue, Cookridge, Leeds, LS16 7LJ

MJB CONSULTANTS & CORPORATE FINANCE LTD
Tarn House, 77 High Street, Yeadon, Leeds LS19 7SP

MONTPELIER PROFESSIONAL (LEEDS) LTD
Sanderson House, Station Road, Horsforth, Leeds LS18 5NT

MORTON SMITHIES
The Studio, Lower Lodge, Weetwood Lane, Leeds LS16 5PH

MORTON SMITHIES CONSULTANCY LTD
The Studio, Lower Lodge, Weetwood Lane, Leeds LS16 5PH

NIGEL WYATT & COMPANY LTD ◈
125 Main Street, Garforth, Leeds, LS25 1AF

NOVIS & CO
1 Victoria Court, Bank Square, Morley, Leeds LS27 9SE
Tel: 0113 252 5911
Email: info@novis.co.uk
Website: http://www.novis.co.uk

NOVIS HOWARTH LTD
1 Victoria Court, Bank Square, Morley, Leeds LS27 9SE

OLIVER & CO ◈
259 Otley Road, West Park, Leeds, LS16 5LQ
Tel: 0113 224 9999
Principal: ICAEW Member
S J Oliver
Registered by the ICAEW to carry out company audit work
Regulated by the ICAEW for a range of investment business activities

THE P&A PARTNERSHIP ★
1 Whitehall, Leeds, LS1 4HR

P AND CO LLP
Unit 2A, Provident House, Vicar Lane, Leeds LS2 7NL

PARK PLACE CORPORATE FINANCE
19 Park Place, Leeds, LS1 2SJ

PARK PLACE CORPORATE FINANCE LLP
19 Park Place, Leeds, LS1 2SJ
Tel: 0113 242 8000
Resident Partners/Directors: ICAEW Members
D R Hardless, J E Stones

PAUL RABY
3 Victoria Drive, Morley, Leeds, LS27 8QT
Tel: 0113 253 3183
Principal: ICAEW Member
P Raby

PC & CO
44 Lower Town Street, Bramley, Leeds, LS13 2BW
Tel: 0113 236 2560

PEARSON JONES PLC
Clayton Wood Close, West Park Ring Road, Leeds, LS16 6QE

PETER HIRST & CO
The Coach House, Outwood Lane, Horsforth, Leeds LS18 4HR

PHILIP ODDY
Albion House, 24 Roundhay Road, Leeds, LS7 1BT

PITAYANUKUL & CO LTD
Unit 2a, Provident House, Vicar Lane, Leeds LS2 7NL

PKF (UK) LLP
Pannell House, 6 Queen Street, Leeds, LS1 2TW
Tel: 0113 228 0000
Email: info.leeds@uk.pkf.com
Website: http://www.pkf.co.uk
Resident Partners/Directors: ICAEW Members
P M Clarke, L M Cooper, C W A Escott, M Ferris, S P Jessop, J M Lister, R F McNaughton, O T Morton, I C Schofield
Resident Partners (Non-ICAEW Members):
W Duncan

PRICEWATERHOUSE-COOPERS
Benson House, 33 Wellington Street, Leeds, LS1 4JP

PRICEWATERHOUSE-COOPERS LLP
Benson House, 33 Wellington Street, Leeds, LS1 4JP
Tel: 0113 289 4000
Resident Partners/Directors: ICAEW Members
S J Bradburn, D Bryant, R L Casson, D I Coe, S J Denison, I H Elliott, S A Ellis, I D Green, M A Hannam, I A Hill, M A Hodgson, E Klempka, I M Looker, R Marsh, R T McMillan, I J Morrison, P Nixon, G M Singer, A M Stephenson, N M Ward, G L Ward-Thompson, J P Zigmond

R. JACKSON
18 Plane Tree Croft, Leeds, LS17 8UQ

R.R. BUNDEY
171 Wigton Lane, Leeds, LS17 8SH
Tel: 0113 269 1928
Principal: ICAEW Member
R R Bundey

RAWLINSONS
Suite 23, 10 Butts Court, Leeds, LS1 5JS

REHMAN MICHAEL & CO
277 Roundhay Road, Leeds, LS8 4HS

RICHARD APPS
3 Strickland Avenue, Shadwell, Leeds, LS17 8JX

RICHARD SMEDLEY PRIVATE CLIENTS ◈
Oakford House, 291 Low Lane, Horsforth, Leeds LS18 5NU
Tel: 0113 258 2221
Registered by the ICAEW to carry out company audit work
Regulated by the ICAEW for a range of investment business activities

ROTHWELL & CO
S & R Rothwell Ltd, 4 Hall Close, Bramhope, Leeds LS16 9JQ

RSM BENTLEY JENNISON ◈
6th Floor, 2 Wellington Place, Leeds, LS1 4AP
Tel: 0113 244 5451
Fax: 0113 242 6308
Email: neil.sevitt@rsmbentleyjennison.com
Website: http://www.rsmbentleyjennison.com
Resident Partners/Directors: ICAEW Members
R S Bright, A J Dunwell, I J Fraser, I P Hart, M A Jenner, A A Marshall, N P Sevitt, N A Wainman
Registered by the ICAEW to carry out company audit work
Authorised and regulated by the Financial Services Authority for investment business

RUSSELL SMITH
69 Round Foundry, Media Centre, Foundry Street, Leeds LS11 5QP

RUSSELL SMITH TAX & ACCOUNTANCY SERVICES LTD
69 Foundry Street, Leeds, LS11 5QP

S & R ROTHWELL LTD
4 Hall Close, Bramhope, Leeds, LS16 9JQ
Tel: 0113 284 3979
Resident Partners/Directors: ICAEW Members
R E Rothwell, S C Rothwell

S.J. GAUNT
42 Wike Ridge Avenue, Alwoodley, Leeds, LS17 9NL

SAGARS LLP ◈
Elizabeth House, Queen Street, Leeds, LS1 2TW
Tel: 0113 297 6789
Fax: 0113 297 6790
Email: advice@sagars.co.uk
Website: http://www.sagars.co.uk
Training Contracts Available.
Resident Partners/Directors: ICAEW Members
J Beevers, C W Jones, P D Mitchell, K Naylor, C D M Smetham
Resident Partners (Non-ICAEW Members):
F W Beadle
Registered by the ICAEW to carry out company audit work
Regulated by the ICAEW for a range of investment business activities

INVESTOR IN PEOPLE

Languages Spoken:
Spanish, French, Greek

SIMON CROSS
34 Church Avenue, Swillington, Leeds, LS26 8QH

SJ MORRELL
The Triangle, Grafton Villas, Crossgates, Leeds LS15 8SH

SOCHALL SMITH LTD
3 Park Square, Leeds, LS1 2NE
Tel: 0113 243 4765
Resident Partners/Directors: ICAEW Members
A S Charles, D J G Paylor

SOUTH SOLUTIONS LTD
10 Lyndhurst Close, Scholes, Leeds, LS15 4AQ

STERLING CORPORATE FINANCE
12 York Place, Leeds, LS1 2DS

STERLING CORPORATE FINANCE LLP ◈
12 York Place, Leeds, LS1 2DS

SW ACCOUNTANTS LTD
51 Eaton Hill, Cookridge, Leeds, LS16 6SE

T.R.H. MCOWAT
8 Armley Grange Drive, Leeds, LS12 3QH
Tel: 0113 263 8989
Principal: ICAEW Member
T R H McOwat

TASKER ACCOUNTING SERVICES LTD
74 Hawthorn Drive, Yeadon, Leeds, LS19 7XB
Tel: 0113 239 1611
Resident Partners/Directors: ICAEW Members
C J Tasker

TAX CENTRES UK LTD
Roundhay Chambers, 199 Roundhay Road, Leeds, LS8 5AN

TEMPORAL LENNON & COMPANY LTD
96a Town Street, Armley, Leeds, LS12 3HN

THOMAS COOMBS & SON
Century House, 29 Clarendon Road, Leeds, LS2 9PG
Tel: 0113 244 9512
Resident Partners/Directors: ICAEW Members
S M Adam, C Darwin, G Jenkinson, J C Murtland
Registered by the ICAEW to carry out company audit work
Regulated by the ICAEW for a range of investment business activities

TOM HARRISON INSOLVENCY SERVICES
Concourse House, 432 Dewsbury Road, Leeds, LS11 7DF
Tel: 0113 272 6071
Principal: ICAEW Member
T C E Harrison

TREVELYAN & COMPANY LTD
Charles House, 20/22 Elland Road, Churwell Hill, Leeds LS27 7SS

VOLANS, LEACH & SCHOFIELD ★ ◈
10 Blenheim Terrace, Woodhouse Lane, Leeds, LS2 9HX
Tel: 0113 245 7031
Resident Partners/Directors: ICAEW Members
C S K Smart

WALTER DAWSON & SON
9 Kerry Street, Horsforth, Leeds, LS18 4AW
Tel: 0113 258 4728

WHITESIDES ◈
6 & 7 Feast Field, Horsforth, Leeds, LS18 4TJ
Tel: 0113 258 2437
Email: office@whitesidesca.com
Website: http://www.whitesidesca.com

SPECIALISATIONS – AUDIT & ASSURANCE

Audit

SPECIALISATIONS – BUSINESS & GENERAL ADVICE

Book-keeping
Book-keeping Systems
Company Formation
Management Accounting Consultancy
Management Consultancy

SPECIALISATIONS – FINANCIAL REPORTING

Accounts Preparation
Limited Companies
Partnership/Sole Trader Accounts

SPECIALISATIONS – IT

Computerised Accounting Systems

SPECIALISATIONS – SECTOR

Architects/Surveyors
Barristers
Construction
Corporate
Dentists/Opticians
Doctors
Engineers
Estate Agents
Manufacturing
Property
Solicitors

SPECIALISATIONS – TAXATION

Capital Gains — Limited Companies
Capital Gains — Personal
Partnerships and Sole Traders
Payroll Service and Advice
Self Assessment Advice
Taxation

General Description: Not all accountants are the same. We aim to provide a proactive business consultancy approach to owner-managed businesses, together with a personal and professional service on accounting and taxation matters.

WHS ACCOUNTANTS LTD
Elmville House, 305 Roundhay Road, Leeds, LS8 4HT
Tel: 0113 249 1101
Resident Partners/Directors: ICAEW Members
C J Hill, G Sheard

WILSON & CO
Joseph's Well, Hanover Walk, Park Lane, Leeds LS3 1AB

WINBURN GLASS NORFOLK ◈
Convention House, St Mary's Street, Leeds, LS9 7DP
Tel: 0113 248 7211
Resident Partners/Directors: ICAEW Members
C Glass, R Stubley, M J Tindall, M Winburn

WINE & CO
20-22 Bridge End, Leeds, LS1 4DJ

YORKSHIRE AUDIT BUREAU
Roundhay Chambers, 199 Roundhay Road, Leeds, LS8 5AN

YORKSHIRE AUDIT BUREAU LTD
Roundhay Chambers, 199 Roundhay Road, Leeds, LS8 5AN

LEEK

AFFORD BOND (STAFFORDSHIRE) LLP
Ford House, Market Street, Leek, ST13 6JA

ANDERSON & SHEPHERD
Shepson House, 29 Stockwell Street, Leek, ST13 6DH
Tel: 01538 388450
Resident Partners/Directors: ICAEW Members
M E Anderson, P A Shepherd
Registered by the ICAEW to carry out company audit work

FEARNS MARRIOTT
Ford House, Market Street, Leek, ST13 6JA
Tel: 01538 399231
Fax: 01538 372398
Email: fearnsmarriott@fenetre.co.uk
Resident Partners/Directors: ICAEW Members
P Grindey, P Marriott
Registered by the ICAEW to carry out company audit work
Regulated by the ICAEW for a range of investment business activities

HOWSONS
50 Broad Street, Leek, ST13 5NS

J.M. KERR & CO
26 Spencer Avenue, Leek, ST13 5PA

PAUL BEASLEY
Dampier House, Dampier Street, Leek, ST13 5PF
Tel: 01538 387821
Principal: ICAEW Member
P J Beasley

THOMPSON WRIGHT ◈
11 Cawdry Buildings, Fountain Street, Leek, ST13 6JP
Tel: 01538 372972

LEICESTER

A. BROADWELL
15 Dalby Avenue, Bushby, Leicester, LE7 9RE
Tel: 0116 241 6422
Principal: ICAEW Member
A Broadwell

A MENDES & CO LTD
55A London Road, Leicester, LE2 0PE
Tel: 0116 254 3143
Fax: 0116 285 4453
Email: anton1750@hotmail.com
Resident Partners/Directors: ICAEW Members
A F R Mendes

ACCOUNTABILITY GB LTD
Portland House, 21 Narborough Road, Cosby, Leicester LE9 1TA

ACTONS
178 Westcotes Drive, Leicester, LE3 0SP

AGK LTD
246 Narborough Road, Leicester, LE3 2FU
Tel: 0116 287 324
Resident Partners/Directors: ICAEW Members
A G Kagdadia

AGK LTD ◈
246 Narborough Road, Leicester, LE3 2AP
Tel: 0116 282 7324

AIMS ACCOUNTANTS FOR BUSINESS - KATHRYN DAVIES
28 Laureston Drive, Leicester, LE2 2AQ

AIMS ACCOUNTANTS FOR BUSINESS - KATHRYN DAVIES
PO Box 6419, Earl Shilton, Leicester, LE9 7ZJ
Tel: 0116 212 4868
Resident Partners/Directors: ICAEW Members
K A Davies

AIMS - ANDREW TILBROOK
47 Scraptoft Lane, Leicester, LE5 2FD
Tel: 0116 221 3072
Principal: ICAEW Member
A C Tilbrook

ALACRITY ACCOUNTANCY
21 High View Close, Hamilton, Leicester, LE4 9LJ

ALACRITY ACCOUNTANCY LTD
21 High View Close, Hamilton, Leicester, LE4 9LJ
Tel: 0116 276 0707
Resident Partners/Directors: ICAEW Members
V Kotecha

ANDREW C.M. SIME
6 Bostock Close, Elmesthorpe, Leicester, LE9 7SR

ANGELA BOWNESS
44 Stoughton Drive, Leicester, LE5 6AN

ASHGATES ★
Christopher House, 94b London Road, Leicester, LE2 0QS

BENNETT JOLLY
4 Hollies Way, Thurnby, Leicester, LE7 9RJ
Tel: 0116 241 3121
Principal: ICAEW Member
T A Jolly

BERRY & PARTNERS
West Walk House, 99 Princess Road East, Leicester, LE1 7LF

BLUE SKIES ACCOUNTANCY LTD
17 Millbrook Drive, Broughton Astley, Leicester, LE9 6UX

BPC CHANDARANA & CO ◈
Prebend House, 72 London Road, Leicester, LE2 0QR

BPC CHANDARANA & CO LTD ◈
Prebend House, 72 London Road, Leicester, LE2 0QR
Tel: 0116 254 9892
Resident Partners/Directors: ICAEW Members
B P Chandarana, R Chandarana

BROOKS & CO
9A Leicester Road, Blaby, Leicester, LE8 4GR

BURTON WALLIS LTD
63 Fosse Way, Syston, Leicester, LE7 1NF
Tel: 0116 260 9715
Resident Partners/Directors: ICAEW Members
R F Boot

C M WEST & CO
Meadow View, Elm Tree Road, Cosby, Leicester LE9 1SR

CB ASSOCIATES LTD
39 Castle Street, Leicester, LE1 5WN

CBA INSOLVENCY PRACTITIONERS
39 Castle Street, Leicester, LE1 5WN

CHAMBERLAIN CLARK
7a The Drive, Countesthorpe, Leicester, LE8 5PB

CHANTREY VELLACOTT DFK LLP
Artisan House, 6 Princess Road West, Leicester, LE1 6TP
Tel: 0116 247 1393
Fax: 0116 254 2814
Email: info@cvdfk.com
Website: http://www.cvdfk.com
Non-resident Partners (ICAEW Members):
E S Harris
Other Offices: Croydon, London, Northampton, Reading, Watford, Brighton & Hove, Colchester, Stevenage
Registered by the ICAEW to carry out company audit work
Regulated by the ICAEW for a range of investment business activities

INVESTOR IN PEOPLE

CHEYETTE & CO
167 London Road, Leicester, LE2 1EG

CLEAR & LANE
340 Melton Road, Leicester, LE4 7SL

CONLEY WARD ★
1168/1170 Melton Road, Syston, Leicester, LE7 2HB
Tel: 0116 269 8484
Resident Partners/Directors: ICAEW Members
P Conley

COOKES
4 Powys Avenue, Oadby, Leicester, LE2 2DP
Tel: 0116 270 4524
Resident Partners/Directors: ICAEW Members
A R Cooke, E Cooke

COOPER PARRY LLP ◈
1 Colton Square, Leicester, LE1 1QH
Tel: 0116 262 9922
Fax: 0116 262 8219
Email: advice@cooperparry.com
Website: http://www.cooperparry.com
Resident Partners/Directors: ICAEW Members
K J Harris, H L Walker
Other Offices: Nottingham and Derby

D.P. ROOZE
122 Glenfield Frith Drive, Glenfield, Leicester, LE3 8PS
Tel: 0116 287 9635
Fax: 0116 287 9635
Principal: ICAEW Member
D P Rooze

DAVID HARRIS ◈
Lyn House, 39 The Parade, Oadby, Leicester LE2 5BB
Tel: 0116 271 3130
Principal: ICAEW Member
D F Harris

DAVID T. LANGMAN
7 De Montfort Mews, Leicester, LE1 7FW
Tel: 0116 254 9897
Fax: 0116 254 9190
Email: david@dtlangmanfca.fsnet.co.uk
Date Established: 1977
Principal: ICAEW Member
D T Langman
Regulated by the ICAEW for a range of investment business activities

DEMONTFORT SOLUTIONS LTD ◈
32 De Montfort Street, Leicester, LE1 7GD
Tel: 0116 254 4316
Resident Partners/Directors: ICAEW Members
A Kataria

EDWARD O KIRWAN
3 Pine Tree Garden, Oadby, Leicester, LE2 5UT

ERIC M. COBLEY
204A Uppingham Road, Leicester, LE5 0QG

F.W. TYLER
9 Colby Drive, Thurmaston, Leicester, LE4 8LD

FINDLAY JAMES
143 Loughborough Road, Leicester, LE4 5LR

G.D. PRICE & CO ◈
25 Mill Lane, Newbold Verdon, Leicester, LE9 9PT
Tel: 01455 828484
Principal: ICAEW Member
G D Price

GHUMRA & CO LTD
24 Vulcan House, Vulcan Road, Leicester, LE5 3EF
Tel: 0116 262 5161
Resident Partners/Directors: ICAEW Members
Y O Ghumra

THE GILLAIN PARTNERSHIP
The Gillain Partnership LLP, 135 Spencefield Lane, Evington, Leicester LE5 6GG

THE GILLAIN PARTNERSHIP LLP
135 Spencefield Lane, Evington, Leicester, LE5 6GG

GRAHAM BARNES
19A The Nook, Anstey, Leicester, LE7 7AZ

GRANT THORNTON UK LLP
8 West Walk, Leicester, LE1 7NH
Tel: 0116 247 1234
Resident Partners/Directors: ICAEW Members
J Bowler, C J N Frostwick, I R Johnson
Resident Partners (Non-ICAEW Members):
M Abdulhusein

GUTTERIDGE SCANLAN
5 High View Close, Hamilton Office Park, Hamilton, Leicester LE4 9LJ
Tel: 0116 276 8788
Principal: ICAEW Member
W A Scanlan

H. K. POPAT & CO
Kabason House, 30 Greenbank Drive, Oadby, Leicester LE2 5RP

HAYLES & PARTNERS LTD ◈
39 Castle Street, Leicester, LE1 5WN
Tel: 0116 233 8500
Resident Partners/Directors: ICAEW Members
G L Banks, S P Davies, D M Langham, P J Morris
Resident Partners (Non-ICAEW Members):
P W Angus
Registered by the ICAEW to carry out company audit work
Regulated by the ICAEW for a range of investment business activities
See display advertisement near this entry.

HILARY HARPER ACCOUNTANCY SERVICES LTD
The Pines, Cranhill Farm, Harborough Road, Billesdon, Leicester LE7 9EL

HKP KABASON LTD
Kabason House, 30 Greenbank Drive, Oadby, Leicester LE2 5RP

HLB VANTIS AUDIT PLC
Stoughton House, Harborough Road, Oadby, Leicester LE2 4LP
Tel: 0116 272 8200
Website: http://www.hlbvantisaudit.com
Training Contracts Available.
Registered by the ICAEW to carry out company audit work
Regulated by the ICAEW for a range of investment business activities

SPECIALISATIONS – AUDIT & ASSURANCE
Audit
Audit — Private Company
Audit — Public Company

SPECIALISATIONS – FINANCIAL REPORTING
Audit Exemption Report

HSP
Whiteacres, Cambridge Road, Whetstone, Leicester LE8 6ZG

HSP TAX LTD
Whiteacres, Cambridge Road, Whetstone, Leicester LE8 6ZG

HWCA LTD ◈
Hamilton Office Park, 31 High View Close, Leicester, LE4 9LJ
Tel: 0116 276 2761
Resident Partners/Directors: ICAEW Members
S K Khullar

I A OSMAN & COMPANY LTD
Riverside House, Riverside Court, Wharf Way, Glen Parva, Leicester LE2 9TF

IRELAND & LONGHILL
10 Station Street, Kibworth Beauchamp, Leicester, LE8 0LN
Tel: 0116 279 3704
Resident Partners/Directors: ICAEW Members
J W Ireland, S A Longhill

J.A. MARVIN
8 Highmeres Road, Leicester, LE4 9LZ
Tel: 01162 761940
Principal: ICAEW Member
J A Marvin

J. DAVISON & CO
The Firs, Cold Newton, Leicester, LE7 9DA

J L GLASS LTD
47 High Street, Kibworth, Leicester, LE8 0HS
Tel: 07909 691821
Email: jenny@jennyglass.co.uk
Mobile: 07909 691821
Resident Partners/Directors: ICAEW Members
J L Glass

J.L. GLASS LTD
47 High Street, Kibworth, Leicester, LE8 0HS

J.M. MACKENZIE
119 Coverside Road, Great Glen, Leicester, LE8 9EB
Tel: 0116 259 2604
Principal: ICAEW Member
J.M. Mackenzie

JOHN BIRD
38 Northgate Street, Leicester, LE3 5BY
Tel: 0116 222 1824
Principal: ICAEW Member
J W Bird

JOHN MILLWARD
2 Kite Close, Broughton Astley, Leicester, LE9 6RY

JOHNSON MURKETT & HURST
38 Millstone Lane, Leicester, LE1 5JN
Tel: 0116 262 7408
Website: http://www.jmhaccounts.co.uk
Registered by the ICAEW to carry out company audit work
Regulated by the ICAEW for a range of investment business activities

K.G. SOLANKI & CO
Hamilton House, 315 St Saviours Road, Leicester, LE5 4HG

KEMP TAYLOR LLP ◈
The Oval, 14 West Walk, Leicester, LE1 7NA
Tel: 0116 2575 480
Email: info@kemptaylor.com
Website: http://www.kemptaylor.com
Resident Partners/Directors: ICAEW Members
P N Foxon, G W Newbury, A K Taylor
Registered by the ICAEW to carry out company audit work
Regulated by the ICAEW for a range of investment business activities

SPECIALISATIONS – BUSINESS & GENERAL ADVICE
Acquisitions and Mergers

SPECIALISATIONS – SECTOR
Architects/Surveyors
Artists/Graphic Designers
Charities
Construction
Property Development

General Description: See www.kemptaylor.com.
Languages Spoken:
French

KENNETH LAW SOWMAN & CO
3 Leicester Road, Oadby, Leicester, LE2 5BD
Tel: 0116 271 0871
Principal: ICAEW Member
C S Sowman

KING FREEMAN ◈
1st Floor, Kimberley House, Vaughan Way, Leicester LE1 4SG
Tel: 0116 253 6115
Resident Partners/Directors: ICAEW Members
T J Freeman, G D King, J W Sibley

KINGSMEAD ACCOUNTING LTD
3 North Street, Oadby, Leicester, LE2 5AH

KPMG LLP
1 Waterloo Way, Leicester, LE1 6LP
Tel: 0116 256 6000
Resident Partners/Directors: ICAEW Members
I J Borley, M J D Lane, I S Smith

LAKHANI & CO
25 Station Road, Desford, Leicester, LE9 9FN
Tel: 01455 824809
Principal: ICAEW Member
A G Lakhani

LANCHESTER HOUSE ASSOCIATES LLP
Lanchester House, Main Street, Great Glen, Leicester LE8 9GH

LEADER D.M.
34 Elizabeth Drive, Oadby, Leicester, LE2 4RD

LONERGAN & CO
107A London Road, Leicester, LE2 0PF

M CUBED ◈
186 London Road, Leicester, LE2 1ND
Tel: 07725 562020
Resident Partners/Directors: ICAEW Members
A N Mamujee, K N A Mamujee

MACINTYRE HUDSON LLP ◈
Lyndale House, Ervington Court, Harcourt Way, Meridian Business Park, Leicester LE19 1WL
Tel: 0116 289 4289
Website: http://www.macintyrehudson.co.uk
Resident Partners/Directors: ICAEW Members
I C Betteridge, M H Faulknall, R A Nelson

Regulated by the ICAEW for a range of investment business activities

MALCOLM VEALL & CO LTD
87B Queens Raod, Clarendon Park, Leicester, LE2 1TT

MARK J REES ◈
Granville Hall, Granville Road, Leicester, LE1 7RU
Tel: 0116 254 9018
Email: scc@markjrees.co.uk
Website: http://www.markjrees.co.uk
Resident Partners/Directors:
ICAEW Members
S C Collier, M R Harrison, P Hollinshead, R King, A Rhodes, D P Vice

MAYFIELD & CO ◈
2nd Floor, 27 The Crescent, King Street, Leicester LE1 6RX

MAYFIELD & CO (ACCOUNTANTS) LTD
2nd Floor, 27 The Crescent, King Street, Leicester LE1 6RX

MICHAEL CHARLTON
19 Lodge Road, Fleckney, Leicester, LE8 8BX

MICHAEL HOLLIS
Woodland House, 24 Meadowbrook Road, Kibworth Beauchamp, Leicester LE8 0HU

MICHAEL JONES
St Bernards, 28 The Ridgeway, Rothley, Leicester LE7 7LE
Tel: 0116 230 2060
Principal: ICAEW Member
M Jones

MODI & CO LTD
27 High View Close, Hamilton Office Park, Leicester, LE4 9LJ
Tel: 0116 246 3790
Resident Partners/Directors:
ICAEW Members
B V Modi

MONCUR CHARLES & CO LTD
6 Bostock Close, Elmesthorpe, Leicester, LE9 7SR

N R PEPLOW
Chesterfield House, 45 Main Street, Great Glen, Leicester LE8 9GH

NEWBY CASTLEMAN ◈
West Walk Building, 110 Regent Road, Leicester, LE1 7LT
Tel: 0116 254 9262
Fax: 0116 247 0021
Email: sdc@newbyc.co.uk
Website: http://www.newbycastleman.co.uk
Resident Partners/Directors:
ICAEW Members
P D Brown, C J Castleman, M D Castleman, S D Castleman
Other Offices: Loughborough, Melton Mowbray, Nottingham, Oakham

Registered by the ICAEW to carry out company audit work

Regulated by the ICAEW for a range of investment business activities

See display advertisement near this entry.

OLD MILL ASSOCIATES (BA) LTD
53 Old Mill Road, Broughton Astley, Leicester, LE9 6PQ
Tel: 01455 285587
Resident Partners/Directors:
ICAEW Members
P R Newbold

P CLARKE FCA
48 Dorothy Avenue, Glen Parva, Leicester, LE2 9JD

P.J. COLLEDGE
16 Conaglen Road, Aylestone, Leicester, LE2 8LD
Tel: 0116 283 3663
Principal: ICAEW Member
P J Colledge

PETER J COONEY
42 London Road, Oadby, Leicester, LE2 5DH
Tel: 0116 271 7722
Principal: ICAEW Member
P J Cooney

PKF (UK) LLP
Pannell House, 159 Charles Street, Leicester, LE1 1LD
Tel: 0116 250 4400
Email: info.leicester@uk.pkf.com
Website: http://www.pkf.co.uk
Resident Partners/Directors:
ICAEW Members
N Bathia, S King, E H Saunders, A D R Tiplady
Resident Partners (Non-ICAEW Members):
E T Kerr

POWER THOMPSON ★ ◈
199 Clarendon Park Road, Leicester, LE2 3AN
Tel: 0116 270 9228
Fax: 0116 270 2237
Email: christhompson@powerthompson.co.uk
Website: http://www.powerthompson.co.uk
Training Contracts Available.
Resident Partners/Directors:
ICAEW Members
C J Thompson
Resident Partners (Non-ICAEW Members):
J E Power

Registered by the ICAEW to carry out company audit work

Regulated by the ICAEW for a range of investment business activities

POWRIE APPLEBY LLP
Queen Anne House, 4, 6 & 8 New Street, Leicester, LE1 5NR
Tel: 0116 248 7500
Fax: 0116 248 7510
Email: enquiries@powrieappleby.com
Website: http://www.powrieappleby.com
Date Established: 1999
Resident Partners/Directors:
ICAEW Members
D Powrie, C P Walker
Resident Partners (Non-ICAEW Members):
N A Smith

SPECIALISATIONS – TAXATION

Capital Gains — Limited Companies
Capital Gains — Personal
Employee
Estate and Inheritance
Estate Planning
Foreign Nationals in the UK
Offshore Companies
Partnerships and Sole Traders
Personal
Taxation
Trusts
UK Companies Overseas
UK Nationals Overseas

R.W. PAIN AND CO
41 Welford Road, Leicester, LE2 7AE

ROBERTSON & CO
169 Spencefield Lane, Leicester, LE5 6GG
Tel: 0116 241 8762
Principal: ICAEW Member
J D Robertson

THE ROWLEYS PARTNERSHIP LTD ◈
6 Dominus Way, Meridian Business Park, Leicester, LE19 1RP
Tel: 0116 282 7000
Email: post@rowleys.biz
Website: http://www.rowleys.biz
Date Established: 1922
Resident Partners/Directors:
ICAEW Members
M O Hook, A H Jarvis, R J Radford, P T Swann-Jones
Resident Partners (Non-ICAEW Members):
C E Shevas
Registered by the ICAEW to carry out company audit work

S B JONES & CO ◈
67 Abbots Road North, Humberstone, Leicester, LE5 1DD

S P K SHAH & CO LTD ◈
216 Melton Road, Leicester, LE4 7PG
Tel: 0116 261 0450
Resident Partners/Directors:
ICAEW Members
P K Shah, S K Shah

S.R. WARBURTON
34 Cherry Tree Avenue, Kirby Muxloe, Leicester, LE9 2HN
Tel: 0116 238 7612
Principal: ICAEW Member
S R Warburton

SHARMAN FIELDING
59 Hinckley Road, Leicester, LE3 0TB

SHARMAN FIELDING
9 University Road, Leicester, LE1 7RA

SHIRE ★
4 Long Street, Stoney Stanton, Leicester, LE9 4DQ

SMITH COOPER ◈
47 New Walk, Leicester, LE1 6TE
Tel: 0116 266 8966

SMITH PARTNERSHIP
5 Sedgefield Drive, Thurnby, Leicester, LE7 9PT

SOMERBYS ◈
30 Nelson Street, Leicester, LE1 7BA
Tel: 0116 279 5700
Email: advice@somerbys.co.uk
Website: http://www.somerbys.co.uk
Registered by the ICAEW to carry out company audit work
Regulated by the ICAEW for a range of investment business activities

SOMERBYS LTD
30 Nelson Street, Leicester, LE1 7BA

STONEYGATE CONSULTING LTD
16 Morland Avenue, Stoneygate, Leicester, LE2 2PE

STURGESS HUTCHINSON
10 Station Road, Earl Shilton, Leicester, LE9 7GA

STURGESS HUTCHINSON LTD
10 Station Road, Earl Shilton, Leicester, LE9 7GA

SUE MOORE
Orchard House, Main Street, Countesthorpe, Leicester LE8 5QX
Tel: 0116 277 2664
Principal: ICAEW Member
S E Moore

SWEETING & CO
22 Willowbrook Close, Broughton Astley, Leicester, LE9 6HF
Tel: 01455 283118
Principal: ICAEW Member
R C A Sweeting

TANNA & CO
2nd Floor, 89 London Road, Leicester, LE2 0PF
Tel: 0116 255 7227

TANNA & CO LTD
2nd Floor, 89 London Road, Leicester, LE2 0PF
Tel: 0116 2557227
Resident Partners/Directors: ICAEW Members
S A Tanna

TENON LTD
1 Bede Island Road, Bede Island Business Park, Leicester, LE2 7EA
Tel: 0116 222 1101

TENON AUDIT LTD
1 Bede Island Road, Bede Island Business Park, Leicester, LE2 7EA
Tel: 0116 222 1101

TESSA FOWLER LTD
2 Woods Close, Oadby, Leicester, LE2 4FJ
Tel: 0116 271 3521
Resident Partners/Directors: ICAEW Members
T D Fowler

THAKRAR & CO
48 Dean Road, Leicester, LE4 6GN

THOMAS MAY & CO
Allen House, Newarke Street, Leicester, LE1 5SG
Tel: 0116 233 5959
Fax: 0116 233 5958
Email: leicester@thomasmay.co.uk
Website: http://www.thomasmay.co.uk
Resident Partners/Directors: ICAEW Members
K Bathia, J A Calow, B S Carruthers, Mrs S D Major, S E Marshall, D M Radford, S A Scott
Registered by the ICAEW to carry out company audit work
Regulated by the ICAEW for a range of investment business activities

TONY J SMART
29 Lancaster Way, Glen Parva, Leicester, LE2 9UA
Tel: 0116 278 3462
Principal: ICAEW Member
T J Smart

TORR WATERFIELD LTD ◈
Park House, 37 Clarence Street, Leicester, LE1 3RW
Tel: 0116 2423400
Website: http://www.torrwaterfield.co.uk
Resident Partners/Directors: ICAEW Members
N R Ford, T Simpson
Resident Partners (Non-ICAEW Members):
M A Torr, M C Waterfield, M J Green
Registered by another RSB to carry out company audit work

TREVOR JF DAY
13 Heythrop Close, Oadby, Leicester, LE2 4SL
Tel: 0116 271 9188
Principal: ICAEW Member
T J F Day

TREVOR WRIGHT
2 Wayside Drive, Oadby, Leicester, LE2 4NU
Tel: 0116 271 7646
Principal: ICAEW Member
T Wright

VANTIS BUSINESS RECOVERY SERVICES
Stoughton House, Harborough Road, Leicester, LE2 4LP
Tel: 0116 272 8200
Website: http://www.vantisplc.com/businessrecovery
Individual(s) licensed for insolvency work by another RPB

SPECIALISATIONS – BUSINESS RECOVERY & INSOLVENCY
Bankruptcies
Corporate Recovery
Liquidations

VANTIS FINANCIAL MANAGEMENT LTD
Stoughton House, Harborough Road, Leicester, LE2 4LP
Tel: 0116 2728200
Website: http://www.vantisplc.com/financialmanagement
Authorised and regulated by the Financial Services Authority for investment business

SPECIALISATIONS – INVESTMENT BUSINESS
Financial Planning and Advice
Pensions Advice
Planning
General Description: CEDR accredited.

VANTIS GROUP LTD
Stoughton House, Harborough Road, Oadby, Leicester LE2 4LP
Tel: 0116 272 8200
Website: http://www.vantisplc.com/leicester
General Description: ICAEW Registered.

ACCOUNTANCY
INSOLVENCY
CORPORATE FINANCE
TAX ADVISORY

WM PROSERV ◈
The Old Mill, 9 Soar Lane, Leicester, LE3 5DE
Tel: 0116 242 5100
Fax: 0116 242 5200
Email: info@wmproserv.co.uk
DX: 711931 LEICESTER 5
Website: http://www.wmproserv.co.uk
Registered by the ICAEW to carry out company audit work
Regulated by the ICAEW for a range of investment business activities
Individual(s) licensed for insolvency work by the ICAEW

SPECIALISATIONS – FORENSIC ACCOUNTING
Forensic Accounting

WM PROSERV LLP
The Old Mill, 9 Soar Lane, Leicester, LE3 5DE

WOODGATES
Century House, 100 London Road, Leicester, LE2 0QS

YP FINANCE LTD
51 Vulcan Road, Leicester, LE5 3ED

LEIGH

BIRCHALL & CO
87 Chestnut Drive, Leigh, WN7 3JX
Tel: 01942 601175
Principal: ICAEW Member
S R Birchall

HAYWARD COOPER & CO
57 Lord Street, Leigh, WN7 1BY

JACKSON STEPHEN LLP ◈
Broseley House, 116 Bradshawgate, Leigh, WN7 4NT

SHADDICK SMITH LLP ◈
Bank Chambers, 7 Market Street, Leigh, WN7 1ED

TOPPING PARTNERSHIP
40 Church Street, Leigh, WN7 1BB
Tel: 01942 671245
Resident Partners/Directors: ICAEW Members
P J Bentham

LEIGH-ON-SEA

A BAWS
70 Elm Road, Leigh-on-sea, SS9 1SJ

A.L. HOWARD
Highlands, 15 Vernon Road, Leigh-on-sea, SS9 2NG

AJB ACCOUNTING SERVICES LTD
2 Ruskin Lodge, 20 Victor Drive, Leigh-on-sea, SS9 1PP

ALAN KITSON & COMPANY LTD
65 Kingswood Chase, Leigh-on-Sea, SS9 3BB
Tel: 01702 474882
Resident Partners/Directors: ICAEW Members
A P Kitson

ALAN RUSH & CO ◈
1349/1353 London Road, Leigh-on-sea, SS9 2AB
Tel: 01702 472345
Principal: ICAEW Member
R N Raichura

ATHERTON BAILEY LLP
De Vine House, 1299-1301 London Road, Leigh-on-Sea, SS9 2AD

BARRONS
Monometer House, Rectory Grove, Leigh-on-Sea, SS9 2HN

BUCKLEY WATSON
57a The Broadway, Leigh-on-sea, SS9 1PE

BUTLER & SPELLER ★
1436 London Road, Leigh-on-Sea, SS9 2UL
Tel: 01702 482391
Resident Partners/Directors: ICAEW Members
J S Speller

CKS ◈
1 Church Hill, Leigh-on-Sea, SS9 2DE
Tel: 01702 710898

CKS ACCOUNTANCY LTD
1 Church Hill, Leigh-on-Sea, SS9 2DE
Tel: 01702 710898
Principal: ICAEW Member
A J Clarke

CLOUDERS ★
Charter House, 103-105 Leigh Road, Leigh-on-Sea, SS9 1JL
Tel: 01702 470033
Resident Partners/Directors: ICAEW Members
C E Binnie

DE VINES ACCOUNTANTS LTD ◈
DeVine House, 1299-1301 London Road, Leigh-on-Sea, SS9 2AD
Tel: 01702 480008
Resident Partners/Directors: ICAEW Members
R M D Collini, C R Purdy

GARETH A. DAVIES SERVICES LTD
Spec House, 83 Elm Road, Leigh-on-Sea, SS9 1SP

GARETH DAVIES
Spec House, 83 Elm Road, Leigh-on-Sea, SS9 1SP

GARY SHORT & CO
64 Warren Road, Leigh-on-sea, SS9 3TS

GRAHAM LONG
107 The Broadway, Leigh-on-sea, SS9 1PG

THE HUDSON PARTNERSHIP LTD
361 Rayleigh Road, Eastwood, Leigh-on-Sea, SS9 5PS
Tel: 01702 520042
Registered by the ICAEW to carry out company audit work

ISW ACCOUNTANCY
6 Alan Close, Leigh-on-Sea, SS9 5RX

K.I.M. BUSINESS SERVICES LTD
111 Tankerville Drive, Leigh-on-Sea, SS9 3DB

KENNETH R. DANIELS & CO
Turnpike House, 1208-1210 London Road, Leigh-on-Sea, SS9 2UA

NASEBY DAVIES LTD
Spec House, 83 Elm Road, Leigh-on-sea, SS9 1SP

NEVILL, STORMONT & CO
1155 A London Road, Leigh-on-Sea, SS9 3JE

PLATT RUSHTON LLP
1759 London Road, Leigh-on-Sea, SS9 2RZ

RICHARD SPARROW
25 Glen Road, Leigh-on-Sea, SS9 1EU

RODNEY M. DOSSETT
55 Grand Parade, Leigh-on-sea, SS9 1DT
Tel: 01702 715522
Principal: ICAEW Member
R M Dossett

S.J. EARL
22 The Fairway, Leigh-on-sea, SS9 4QL

SEGRAVE & PARTNERS
Turnpike House, 1208/1210 London Road, Leigh-on-sea, SS9 2UA
Tel: 01702 477444
Resident Partners/Directors: ICAEW Members
A R R Bowman, J P Francis, J N Smith

STEMA SERVICES LTD
198 Station Road, Leigh-on-Sea, SS9 3BS

TAYLOR, VINEY & MARLOW
1422-4 London Road, Leigh-on-sea, SS9 2UL

WALLER & BYFORD ◈
Clements House, 1279 London Road, Leigh-on-sea, SS9 2AD

WALSH & CO ★
977 London Road, Leigh-on-Sea, SS9 3LB
Tel: 01702 476800
Email: info@walshifp.co.uk
Website: http://www.walshifp.co.uk
Mobile: 07788 672257
Resident Partners/Directors: ICAEW Members
G M Walsh
Authorised and regulated by the Financial Services Authority for investment business

SPECIALISATIONS – INVESTMENT BUSINESS
Financial Planning and Advice
Planning

SPECIALISATIONS – TAXATION
Estate and Inheritance
Estate Planning
Taxation
UK Nationals Overseas

General Description: We offer independent financial planning to clients and are members of the Institute of Financial Planning.

WALSHTAX
977 London Road, Leigh-on-Sea, SS9 3LB

WALSHTAX LTD
977 London Road, Leigh-on-Sea, SS9 3LB
Tel: 01702 476800
Email: gary@walshtax.co.uk
Resident Partners/Directors: ICAEW Members
G M Walsh

LEIGHTON BUZZARD

A.D. BETLEY
27 Redwood Glade, Leighton Buzzard, LU7 3JT

ACCOUNTANCY AND TAX SOLUTIONS LTD
Unit 2, Hockliffe Business Park, Watling Street, Hockliffe, Leighton Buzzard LU7 9NB

ASHBY'S ◈
Morton House, 9 Beacon Court, Pitstone Green Business Park, Pitstone, Leighton Buzzard, LU7 9GY

B W WILSON
4 Saturn Close, Leighton Buzzard, LU7 3UU

BREEN & CO
12 Church Square, Leighton Buzzard, LU7 1AE

BRIAN CARTER & CO
River House, 6 Firs Path, Leighton Buzzard, LU7 3JG

BRINE & CO
PO Box 6210, Leighton Buzzard, LU7 0ZN
Tel: 01296 688109
Principal: ICAEW Member
J Brine

C.B. HOARE
The Old Farmhouse, 10 The Green, Cheddington, Leighton Buzzard LU7 0RJ

THE COOK PARTNERSHIP LTD
6 Windmill Close, Ivinghoe, Leighton Buzzard, LU7 9EW

ECL HOWARD WATSON SMITH
E C L House, Lake Street, Leighton Buzzard, LU7 1RT

ECL HOWARD WATSON SMITH LLP
E C L House, Lake Street, Leighton Buzzard, LU7 1RT

GLOVER AND CO
Unit 2, Hockliffe Business Park, Watling Street, Hockliffe, Leighton Buzzard LU7 9NB

GRAHAM HUNT & CO
Unit 15, Hockliffe Business Park, Watling Street, Hockliffe, Leighton Buzzard LU7 9NB

HILLS & BURGESS
20 Bridge Street, Leighton Buzzard, LU7 1AL
Tel: 01525 372361
Fax: 01525 851560
Email: info@hillsburgess.co.uk
Resident Partners/Directors: ICAEW Members
P R Dodson, J Roberts
Registered by the ICAEW to carry out company audit work

HOPKINS & HOPKINS
York House, 81 North Street, Leighton Buzzard, LU7 1EL
Tel: 01525 373786

HOPKINS & HOPKINS LTD
York House, 81 North Street, Leighton Buzzard, LU7 1EL
Tel: 01525 373786
Resident Partners/Directors: ICAEW Members
M P Hopkins

IAN N. EDWARDS
141 Grasmere Way, Leighton Buzzard, LU7 2QH
Tel: 01525 378186
Principal: ICAEW Member
I N Edwards

SPECIALISATIONS – FINANCIAL REPORTING
Accounts Preparation
Partnership/Sole Trader Accounts

SPECIALISATIONS – SECTOR
Traders — General

continued

IAN N. EDWARDS *cont*

SPECIALISATIONS – TAXATION

Employee
Partnerships and Sole Traders
Personal
Small Traders
Taxation

J.R. WILLIAMS & CO
38 Wellcroft, Ivinghoe, Leighton Buzzard, LU7 9EF
Tel: 01296 661541
Principal: ICAEW Member
J R Williams

PEARCE AITCHISON
1 Church Square, Leighton Buzzard, LU7 1AE
Tel: 01525 373767
Principal: ICAEW Member
C F Pearce

PKW ASSOCIATES
Second Floor, 1 Church Square, Leighton Buzzard, LU7 1AE

R.A. & D.A. THOMPSON
30 High Street, Leighton Buzzard, LU7 1EA

SMETHERS & CO
41 Albion Road, Pitstone, Leighton Buzzard, LU7 9AY

LEOMINSTER

ARMSTRONG ROGERS & CO
18 Etnam Street, Leominster, HR6 8AQ

COCKETT & CO LTD
2e Rainbow Street, Leominster, HR6 8DQ
Tel: 01568 616664
Resident Partners/Directors: ICAEW Members
L D Cockett

DAVIES EDWARDS & CO ★
West Lodge, Rainbow Street, Leominster, HR6 8DQ

E MARY GROVE
Beechwood, Stoke Prior, Leominster, HR6 0LN
Tel: 01568 797984
Principal: ICAEW Member
E M Grove

LETCHWORTH GARDEN CITY

COLTON & CO
2 Blackmore, Letchworth Garden City, SG6 2SX

UHY GEORGE HAY ◈
The Wynd, Letchworth Garden City, SG6 3EN
Tel: 01462 679477
Email: letchworth@georgehay.co.uk
Website: http://www.georgehay.co.uk
Resident Partners/Directors: ICAEW Members
R C Dilley
Resident Partners (Non-ICAEW Members):
K W Middleton
Registered by the ICAEW to carry out company audit work
Regulated by the ICAEW for a range of investment business activities

JULIE DINGWALL
93 Willian Way, Letchworth Garden City, SG6 2HY
Tel: 01462 685779
Principal: ICAEW Member
J P Dingwall

KEENS SHAY KEENS LETCHWORTH
5 Gernon Walk, Letchworth Garden City, SG6 3HW
Tel: 01462 683831
Principal: ICAEW Member
B J Nicholl
Registered by the ICAEW to carry out company audit work

SAMUEL S. DICKER
32 Chatterton, Letchworth Garden City, SG6 2JY
Tel: 01462 686346
Principal: ICAEW Member
S S Dicker

T.G. DEAKIN
36 Berkeley, Letchworth Garden City, SG6 2HA
Tel: 07742518612
Principal: ICAEW Member
T G Deakin

WKH ◈
PO Box 501, The Nexus Building, Broadway, Letchworth Garden City SG6 9BL
Tel: 01462 687333
Website: http://www.wkhca.co.uk
Training Contracts Available.
Resident Partners/Directors: ICAEW Members
S F Guyton, C D Maylin, J P Sheehan, N D Willimer, P M Woodhall
Resident Partners (Non-ICAEW Members):
P E Marsden
Registered by the ICAEW to carry out company audit work
Regulated by the ICAEW for a range of investment business activities

INVESTOR IN PEOPLE

WRAY & CO
36 Berkeley, Letchworth Garden City, SG6 2HA
Tel: 01462 672733
Principal: ICAEW Member
Mrs S Deakin Wray

LEWES

AKM CONSULTING
PO Box 84, South Chailey, Lewes, BN8 4XB

ASPEN WAITE LTD
Suite G/4, Waterside Centre, North Street, Lewes BN7 2PE

ASPEN WAITE EDENS
Suite G4, Waterside Business Centre, Lewes, BN7 2PE

AXTONS
The Mews, St Nicholas Lane, Lewes, BN7 2JZ

B. WAINWRIGHT & CO
1st Floor, Harveys Depot, Daveys Lane, Lewes BN7 2BQ
Tel: 01273 488481
Principal: ICAEW Member
B F Wainwright

BROOKES SIVYER LTD
The Old Chapel, High Street, East Hoathly, Lewes BN8 6DR

CHARLES R. DEAN BSC ACA
Limbers Mead, Old Barn Lane, South Chailey, Lewes BN8 4AS
Tel: 01273 401955
Principal: ICAEW Member
C R Dean

CLARK BROWNSCOMBE ◈
33 Cliffe High Street, Lewes, BN7 2AN
Tel: 01273 476311
Resident Partners/Directors: ICAEW Members
V M R Anderson, D R Scrivins

GILLARD WATSON
7 The Pagets, Newick, Lewes, BN8 4PW
Tel: 01825 722280
Principal: ICAEW Member
T Watson

KEYMER HASLAM & CO
1 West St, Lewes, BN7 2NZ

KNILL JAMES
One Bell Lane, Lewes, BN7 1JU
Tel: 01273 480480
Fax: 01273 476941
Email: kevin@knilljames.co.uk
Website: http://www.knilljames.co.uk
Date Established: 1887
Resident Partners/Directors: ICAEW Members
S M Foster, J C Ketley, K S Powell, N Rawson
Registered by the ICAEW to carry out company audit work
Regulated by the ICAEW for a range of investment business activities

SPECIALISATIONS – AUDIT & ASSURANCE

Audit

SPECIALISATIONS – BUSINESS & GENERAL ADVICE

Management Advice to Business

SPECIALISATIONS – FINANCIAL REPORTING

Financial Reporting

SPECIALISATIONS – TAXATION

Taxation

PAUL E GILES
Thane House, 22 King Henry's Road, Lewes, BN7 1BU
Tel: 01273 472730
Principal: ICAEW Member
P E Giles

PAUL SENTANCE
Woodlea, 20 High Hurst Close, Newick, Lewes BN8 4NJ

LEYBURN

THE BARKER PARTNERSHIP
Penthwaite, St Matthew's Terrace, Leyburn, DL8 5EL

O'REILLY
Thornborough Hall, Leyburn, DL8 5AB

LEYLAND

BROWN & LONSDALE
Springfield House, 41-45 Chapel Brow, Leyland, PR25 3NH

JOHN L DALTON & CO LTD
47 St Pauls Close, Farington Moss, Leyland, PR26 6RT

N TOWERS & CO LTD
63 Spring Meadow, Clayton-le-Woods, Leyland, PR25 5UR
Tel: 01772 431672
Resident Partners/Directors: ICAEW Members
N C Towers

PILKINGTONS ◈
135 Towngate, Leyland, PR25 2LH

LICHFIELD

AIMS - ANDREW TYZZER
3 Foden Close, Shenstone, Lichfield, WS14 0LE

AUSTEN PRINCE LTD
59 St Johns Hill, Shenstone, Lichfield, WS14 0JD
Tel: 01543 481131
Resident Partners/Directors: ICAEW Members
D A Prince

BLOOMER HEAVEN
Causeway House, 18 Dam Street, Lichfield, WS13 6AA

BLOOMER HEAVEN LTD
Causeway House, 18 Dam Street, Lichfield, WS13 6AA

CHAPMAN HIGGS
58 Birchwood Road, Lichfield, WS14 9UW
Tel: 01543 262972
Principal: ICAEW Member
P A Higgs

CHURCHILLS ◈
1st Floor, Shenstone Station, Station Road, Shenstone, Lichfield WS14 0NW
Tel: 01543 481611
Email: ian@churchillfca.co.uk
Resident Partners/Directors: ICAEW Members
I S Brown, M Tomlinson
Registered by the ICAEW to carry out company audit work

DAINS LLP
St Johns Court, Wiltell Road, Lichfield, WS14 9DS
Tel: 0845 555 8844
Fax: 01543 415465
Email: lichfield@dains.com
Website: http://www.dains.com
Date Established: 1926
Resident Partners/Directors: ICAEW Members
H M P Reynolds, M F P Smith
Non-resident Partners (ICAEW Members):
P D Bradshaw, N D Smith, A R Massey, S G Wright, A P Morris
Resident Partners (Non-ICAEW Members):
M Castree, N Hawksley
Non-resident Partners (Non-ICAEW Members):
A McQuillan, R C McNeilly, S C Bursell
Other Offices: Coleshill, Burton, Rugeley, Swadlincote, Birmingham
Registered by the ICAEW to carry out company audit work
Regulated by the ICAEW for a range of investment business activities
Individual(s) licensed for insolvency work by the ICAEW
Individual(s) licensed for insolvency work by another RPB

DAVID EVANS & CO
Stowegate House, 37 Lombard Street, Lichfield, WS13 6DP

GROUCOTT MOOR LTD
Lombard House, Cross Keys, Lichfield, WS13 6DN

HOWARD WILLIS & CO
69 St Johns Hill, Shenstone, Lichfield, WS14 0JE
Tel: 01543 483348

HOWARD WILLIS & CO LTD
69 St Johns Hill, Shenstone, Lichfield, WS14 0JE
Tel: 01543 483348
Resident Partners/Directors: ICAEW Members
J H Willis

JONATHAN LOESCHER & CO LTD
Cherry Trees, 17 Flats Lane, Weeford, Lichfield WS14 9QQ

L J GOODWIN & CO LTD
6 Parkside Court, Greenhough Road, Lichfield, WS13 7AU

LINDLEY & CO ★
17 Millbrook Drive, Shenstone, Lichfield, WS14 0JL

LITTING ASSOCIATES LTD
74 Abbotsford Road, Lichfield, WS14 9XL

MNW
62 Church Street, Whittington, Lichfield, WS14 9JX

PRITCHARD ACCOUNTANCY SERVICES LTD
46 Millbrook Drive, Shenstone, Lichfield, WS14 0JL

RICHARD NEWTON
Hademore Farmhouse, Fisherwick, Lichfield, WS14 9JL

SHERWOOD HALL ASSOCIATES LTD
1st Floor, Langton House, Bird Street, Lichfield WS13 6PY

STERLING FINANCIAL ACCOUNTANCY SERVICES LTD ◈
27 Lincoln Croft, Shenstone, Lichfield, WS14 0ND
Tel: 01543 483500

TOMKINSON TEAL ◈
Hanover Court, 5 Queen Street, Lichfield, WS13 6QD
Tel: 01543 255612
Email: enquiries@tomkinsonteal.co.uk
Website: http://www.tomkinsonteal.co.uk
Resident Partners/Directors: ICAEW Members
K J Teal, D W Tomkinson
Registered by the ICAEW to carry out company audit work
Regulated by the ICAEW for a range of investment business activities

UNDERWOOD KINSON
35 Market Street, Lichfield, WS13 6LA
Tel: 01543 414454
Email: mike@lichfieldbusiness.co.uk
Principal: ICAEW Member
M J Kinson
Registered by the ICAEW to carry out company audit work

LIGHTWATER

IVAN F KEW & CO
130 Ambleside Road, Lightwater, GU18 5UN
Tel: 01276 450030
Principal: ICAEW Member
I F Kew

LINCOLN

ANTHONY & CO
Anthony House, 8 Vicarage Lane, Scothern, Lincoln LN2 2UB

ANTHONY & CO (LINCOLN) LTD ◈
Anthony House, 8 Vicarage Lane, Scothern, Lincoln LN2 2UB
Tel: 01673 861487
Resident Partners/Directors: ICAEW Members
J M Anthony

CAMAMILE ASSOCIATES LTD
15 Newland, Lincoln, LN1 1XG

CHRISTINE PEACOCK & CO
The Old Station House, Sleaford Road, Dunston, Lincoln LN4 2HA

CHRISTINE PEACOCK & CO LTD
The Old Station House, Sleaford Road, Dunston, Lincoln LN4 2HA

CLIVE KETTLEY
80 Nettleham Road, Lincoln, LN2 1RR

DAVID A. DODDS & CO
Boundary Farm, South Scarle Lane, Swinderby, Lincoln LN6 9JA

DAVID J HACKETT
100 Newland, Lincoln, LN1 1YA
Tel: 01522 521343
Principal: ICAEW Member
D J Hackett

DUNCAN & TOPLIS
4 Henley Way, Doddington Road, Lincoln, LN6 3QR
Tel: 01522 507000
Fax: 01522 507022
Email: info@lincoln.duntop.co.uk
Website: http://www.duntop.co.uk
Resident Partners/Directors: ICAEW Members
D A Brain, S N Syddall
General Description: Other offices please see Grantham.

FARRARS ◈
Acorn House, 4 Mill Fields, Bassingham, Lincoln LN5 9NP
Tel: 01522 789131
Resident Partners/Directors: ICAEW Members
C Farrar

FRANK KIRKHAM
Greetwell Place, 2 Limekiln Way, Lincoln, LN2 4US
Tel: 01522 544004
Resident Partners/Directors: ICAEW Members
F D Kirkham

GRAHAM WINSTANLEY
North Barn, Torgate Farm, Torgate Lane, Bassingham, Lincoln LN5 9JG
Tel: 0845 090 0081
Principal: ICAEW Member
G Winstanley

GRAHAM WINSTANLEY LTD
Manor Farm, Moor Lane, Aubourn, Lincoln LN5 9DX
Tel: 0845 090 0081
Resident Partners/Directors: ICAEW Members
G Winstanley

HARRY JEFFERY & CO LTD
St Lawrence, 28 Station Road, Bardney, Lincoln LN3 5UD
Tel: 01526 397448
Resident Partners/Directors: ICAEW Members
H E Jeffery

IAN W. SMITH
6 The Hawthorns, Nettleham, Lincoln, LN2 2GD

JOHN HORTON LTD
15 Malham Drive, Lincoln, LN6 0XD
Tel: 01522 500260
Resident Partners/Directors: ICAEW Members
J P Horton

JULIA DAVEY
60 Fen Road, Timberland, Lincoln, LN4 3SD

MCGREGORS CORPORATE
Unit 8, Checkpoint Court, Sadler, Lincoln LN6 3PW

MCGREGORS CORPORATE (LINCOLN) LTD
Unit 8, Checkpoint Court, Sadler Road, Lincoln LN6 3PW

MUMBY HEPPENSTALL ◈
Wellingore Hall, Wellingore, Lincoln, LN5 0HX
Tel: 01522 811694
Resident Partners/Directors: ICAEW Members
C Heppenstall, J A D Mumby

N P SHARPE LTD
84 Nettleham Road, Lincoln, LN2 1RR

NICHOLSONS ◈
Newland House, The Point, Weaver Road, Lincoln LN6 3QN
Tel: 0845 276 6555
Fax: 0845 276 6559
Email: info@nicholsonsca.co.uk
Website: http://www.nicholsonsca.co.uk
Resident Partners/Directors: ICAEW Members
N D Douglas, R Grayson, R J Hallsworth, S M Kerby, E L Murray
Registered by the ICAEW to carry out company audit work
Authorised and regulated by the Financial Services Authority for investment business

SPECIALISATIONS – AUDIT & ASSURANCE
Audit

SPECIALISATIONS – BUSINESS & GENERAL ADVICE
Management Advice to Business

SPECIALISATIONS – FINANCIAL REPORTING
Accounts Preparation

SPECIALISATIONS – INVESTMENT BUSINESS
Financial Planning and Advice

General Description: Leading firm of Lincolnshire chartered accountants and pro-active business advisers.
See display advertisement near this entry.

PAUL REDMOND
32 Curle Avenue, Lincoln, LN2 4AN
Tel: 01522 526676
Principal: ICAEW Member
P Redmond

PAUL SHARMAN LTD
Kimberley, 5 Middle Street, Dunston, Lincoln LN4 2EW

PGN ALLPORT
Friars Orchard, Nocton Road, Potterhanworth, Lincoln LN4 2DN

PKF (UK) LLP
St Hughs, 23 Newport, Lincoln, LN1 3DN
Tel: 01522 531441
Email: info.lincoln@uk.pkf.com
Website: http://www.pkf.co.uk
Resident Partners/Directors: ICAEW Members
A M Kerry, J A Kirkham

R.P. ELLIS
The Priory, 414 Newark Road, Lincoln, LN6 8RX

RICHARD ATKINSON & CO(ACCOUNTANTS) LTD
21a Newland, Lincoln, LN1 1XP
Tel: 01522 520001

ROBERT M SPENCER FCA
Heritage House, 6 Wragby Road, Sudbrooke, Lincoln LN2 2QU

RUSSELL PAYNE & CO LTD
157/159 Burton Road, Lincoln, LN1 3LW

SANDERS & CO
The Old Rectory, Long Lane, South Hykeham, Lincoln LN6 9NX

SAUL FAIRHOLM ◈
12 Tentercroft Street, Lincoln, LN5 7DB
Tel: 01522 537575
Email: enquiries@saulfairholm.co.uk
Website: http://www.saulfairholm.co.uk
Resident Partners/Directors: ICAEW Members
S L Tointon, R M Welsh, R M White
Other Offices:24 Exchange Street, Retford, DN22 6DT (Tel: 01777 861170)
Registered by the ICAEW to carry out company audit work
Regulated by the ICAEW for a range of investment business activities

STREETS FINANCIAL CONSULTING PLC
Tower House, Lucy Tower Street, Lincoln, LN1 1XW

STREETS LLP ◈
Tower House, Lucy Tower Street, Lincoln, LN1 1XW
Tel: 01522 551200
Email: info@streetsweb.co.uk
Website: http://www.streetsweb.co.uk
Resident Partners/Directors: ICAEW Members
R Godley, L J Lord, S W Sargent, P Tutin, R J Ward

STREETS TAX LLP
Tower House, Lucy Tower Street, Lincoln, LN1 1XW

STREETS WHITMARSH STERLAND
Tower House, Lucy Tower Street, Lincoln, LN1 1XW

STREETS WHITMARSH STERLAND LLP
Tower House, Lucy Tower Street, Lincoln, LN1 1XW

THORNALLEY & CO
143 Burton Road, Lincoln, LN1 3LN
Tel: 01522 511011

THORNALLEY & CO LTD
143 Burton Road, Lincoln, LN1 3LN
Tel: 01522 511011
Resident Partners/Directors: ICAEW Members
H R Lovett

WRIGHT VIGAR LTD ◈
15 Newland, Lincoln, LN1 1XG
Tel: 01522 531341
Website: http://www.wrightvigar.co.uk
Resident Partners/Directors: ICAEW Members
C J Shelbourne, R L J Vigar
Other Offices: Gainsborough, Sleaford, Retford, London
Registered by the ICAEW to carry out company audit work
Regulated by the ICAEW for a range of investment business activities

SPECIALISATIONS – AUDIT & ASSURANCE
Audit — Private Company

SPECIALISATIONS – SECTOR
Charities

LINGFIELD

C.B. EDWARDS & CO
Little Rushford, Lingfield, RH7 6DA

EDITH JESSUP
Nobles Green, Mill Lane, Dormansland, Lingfield RH7 6NL

KEMSLEY & CO
Carewell Lodge, Racecourse Road, Dormansland, Lingfield RH7 6PP

ROGER LUGG & CO
23 High Street, Lingfield, RH7 6AA

STUART S.E. GREEN
The Glenn, 19 Lingfield Common Road, Lingfield, RH7 6BU

LIPHOOK

ANNE ALDERMAN
13 Mill Vale Meadows, Milland, Liphook, GU30 7LZ
Tel: 01428 741397
Principal: ICAEW Member
A Alderman

AVN PICKTREE ◈
Weyside, Passfield Road, Passfield, Liphook GU30 7RU

CAROLINE PRITCHARD
16 Huron Drive, Liphook, GU30 7TZ

I.G. CHAMBERS
Compass House, 15 West Meade, Milland, Liphook GU30 7NB

INDIGO TAX & ACCOUNTANCY LTD
24 Erles Road, Liphook, GU30 7BW

M.J.HOSMER ◈
Unit 2b, 24 Longmoor Road, Liphook, GU30 7NY
Tel: 01428 727250
Principal: ICAEW Member
M J Hosmer

THE MAK PRACTICE
Chiltlee Manor, Haslemere Road, Liphook, GU30 7AZ

TRAVISS & CO
Newtown House, Newtown Road, Liphook, GU30 7DX

WESTON & CO
1 Arundel Close, Lynchborough Road, Passfield, Liphook GU30 7RW
Tel: 01428 751850
Principal: ICAEW Member
D J Weston

LISKEARD

BATTERBEE THOMPSON & CO LTD
Upper Woolston, Liskeard, PL14 3ND

DEACON JEWELL LTD
7 West Street, Liskeard, PL14 6BW
Tel: 01579 343401
Resident Partners/Directors: ICAEW Members
G A Deacon, M J Jewell

ENGLAND & CO
18 Trevecca Terrace, Liskeard, PL14 6RH
Tel: 01579 347349
Website: http://www.englandac.co.uk
Principal: ICAEW Member
T M T England

PARKER-JONES & CO
21 West Street, Liskeard, PL14 6BW

PARKER-JONES & CO LTD
21 West Street, Liskeard, PL14 6BW

WARD RANDALL LTD
The Parade, Liskeard, PL14 6AF

LISS

ASHBY & CO
North Bank, 14 Bishearne Gardens, Liss, GU33 7SB

CHRISTOPHER BROWN ◈
Bracken Wood, Rake Hanger, Hill Brow, Liss GU33 7NP

HAND IN HAND BUSINESS SOLUTIONS LTD
1 & 2 Hillbrow House, Linden Drive, Liss, GU33 7RJ

HOWARD SMITH & CO LTD
1 & 2 Hillbrow House, Linden Drive, Liss, GU33 7RJ

MRS RUTH BAMFORD ACA
1 Elm Terrace, Hawkley Road, Liss, GU33 6JH

LITTLEHAMPTON

BOTTING & CO ★
28 High Street, Littlehampton, BN17 5EE
Tel: 01903 713508
Resident Partners/Directors: ICAEW Members
S D Wilkinson

FINCH LYNTON LTD
2/4 Ash Lane, Rustington, Littlehampton, BN16 3BZ

INDIGO TAX & ACCOUNTANCY LTD
41 Meadowside, Angmering, Littlehampton, BN16 4BW

J P MARTELL & CO LTD
22 Bushby Avenue, Rustington, Littlehampton, BN16 2BY

JUSTICE & CO
15 Darlington Close, Bramley Green, Angmering, Littlehampton BN16 4GS
Tel: 01903 783335
Principal: ICAEW Member
C R Justice

LUCRAFT, HODGSON & DAWES
2/4 Ash Lane, Rustington, Littlehampton, BN16 3BZ

M.K. ASHBROOK
59-61 Sea Lane, Rustington, Littlehampton, BN16 2RQ
Tel: 01903 778880
Principal: ICAEW Member
M K Ashbrook

MOORE STEPHENS (SOUTH) LLP
55 Sea Lane, Rustington, Littlehampton, BN16 2RQ

LIVERPOOL

A.L. GORST & CO ◈
13 Allerton Road, Liverpool, L18 1LG
Tel: 0151 734 0606
Principal: ICAEW Member
P Sands

ADAMS & CO ACCOUNTANTS LTD
Unit 2, Freeport Industrial Park, Seaforth, Liverpool L21 1JD
Tel: 0151 282 0271
Resident Partners/Directors: ICAEW Members
D R Potts

ADDITIONS ACCOUNTANTS LTD
Queen Insurance Building, 7 Queen Avenue, Dale Street, Liverpool L2 4TZ
Tel: 0151 236 4554
Fax: 0151 236 3554
Email: info@additionsgroup.com
Website: http://www.additionsgroup.com
Resident Partners/Directors: ICAEW Members
M C Jones
Registered by the ICAEW to carry out company audit work

AIMS ACCOUNTANTS FOR BUSINESS
3 Ambassador Drive, Halewood, Liverpool, L26 6LT
Tel: 0151 487 6643

ALAN RUMPH & CO
Jubilee House, Altcar Road, Formby, Liverpool L37 8DL
Tel: 01704 879482
Principal: ICAEW Member
A Rumph

ALAN S JOHNSON
42 Crosby Road North, Waterloo, Liverpool, L22 4QQ

ALEXANDER MYERSON & CO ◈
Alexander House, 61 Rodney Street, Liverpool, L1 9ER
Tel: 0151 709 9999
Email: info@myersons.com
Website: http://www.myersons.com
Resident Partners/Directors: ICAEW Members
R G Myerson, I Swerdlow
Resident Partners (Non-ICAEW Members):
M B Cohen, A Cahill
Regulated by the ICAEW for a range of investment business activities

AMANDA FAIRCLOUGH ASSOCIATES
Holy Spirit Community Hall, East Prescot Road, Liverpool, L14 2EH
Tel: 0151 228 9677
Principal: ICAEW Member
A A C Fairclough

BAILEY PAGE & ROPER ◈
Suite 416-419, The Cotton Exchange, Old Hall Street, Liverpool L3 9LQ

BAKER TILLY
Number One Old Hall Street, Liverpool, L3 9SX
Tel: 0151 600 2600
Resident Partners/Directors: ICAEW Members
E R Aitken, A H Baker

BAKER TILLY
1 Old Hall Street, Liverpool, L3 9SX

BAKER TILLY TAX AND ADVISORY SERVICES LLP
1 Old Hall Street, Liverpool, L3 9SX
Tel: 0151 600 2600
Resident Partners/Directors: ICAEW Members
E R Aitken, A H Baker, A J Lloyd

BATTEN HUGHES & CO LTD
173 College Road, Crosby, Liverpool, L23 3AT

BCG
303 The Corn Exchange, Fenwick Street, Liverpool, L2 7QH

BCG GROUP LTD
3rd Floor, The Cotton Exchange, Fenwick Street, Liverpool L2 7QL

BEGBIES TRAYNOR LTD
1 Old Hall Street, Liverpool, L3 9HF
Tel: 0151 227 4010
Resident Partners (Non-ICAEW Members):
D Moore
SPECIALISATIONS – BUSINESS RECOVERY & INSOLVENCY
Bankruptcies
Corporate Recovery
Liquidations

BOND PARTNERS LLP
5th Floor, The Corn Exchange, Fenwick Street, Liverpool L2 7QS

BRESNAN WALSH ◈
3 Temple Square, Liverpool, L2 5BA
Tel: 0151 236 1494
Fax: 0151 258 1516
Email: mail@bresnanwalsh.co.uk
Website: http://www.bresnanwalsh.co.uk
Principal: ICAEW Member
P H Taaffe
Registered by the ICAEW to carry out company audit work

CATHY HOOD
137 Barlows Lane, Liverpool, L9 9HZ

CHADWICK LLP
Tower Building, Water Street, Liverpool, L3 1PQ
Tel: 0151 236 6262
Fax: 0151 236 6004
Email: liverpool@chadwickllp.co.uk
Website: http://www.chadwickllp.co.uk
Training Contracts Available.
Resident Partners/Directors: ICAEW Members
R J F Burrows
Non-resident Partners (ICAEW Members):
P Dawes, K Simmons, M Hodges
Resident Partners (Non-ICAEW Members):
D Nicholls
Other Offices: Manchester
SPECIALISATIONS – AUDIT & ASSURANCE
Audit
SPECIALISATIONS – BUSINESS & GENERAL ADVICE
Acquisitions and Mergers
Management Accounting
Consultancy
SPECIALISATIONS – FINANCIAL REPORTING
International Reporting Standards (IFRS)
SPECIALISATIONS – SECTOR
Higher Education/Research Establishments
SPECIALISATIONS – TAXATION
Payroll Service and Advice
Taxation
General Description: We are a North West independent business advisory and accountancy practice with 6 partners and 2 directors. Our work includes corporate finance, tax solutions, general advisory (audit, AIM flotation's and forensic), management accounting and payroll. We also act for a wide range of industry sectors.
See display advertisement near this entry.

COBHAM MURPHY LTD
116 Duke Street, Liverpool, L1 5JW

COBHAMS LTD
73 Liverpool Road, Crosby, Liverpool, L23 5SE

COLIN WOLSTENHOLME
1 Brockholme Road, Liverpool, L18 4QG

THE COMPANY SPECIALISTS (ACCOUNTING SERVICES) LTD
53 Rodney Street, Liverpool, L1 9ER

D.L. CONNOR
11 Michael's Close, Formby, Liverpool, L37 3HU

DE CONSULTANCY LTD ◈
11 North Road, Liverpool, L19 0LP
Tel: 0151 427 9440
Resident Partners/Directors: ICAEW Members
D Ewing

DELOITTE & TOUCHE LLP ◈
Horton House, Exchange Flags, Liverpool, L2 3PG
Tel: 0151 236 0941
Website: http://www.deloitte.co.uk
Resident Partners/Directors: ICAEW Members
S J Beech

DUNCAN SHEARD GLASS ◈
Castle Chambers, 43 Castle St, Liverpool, L2 9TL
Tel: 0151 243 1200
Fax: 0151 236 1430
Email: merseyside@dsg.uk.com
Website: http://www.dsg.uk.com
Resident Partners/Directors: ICAEW Members
J M Ellis, P Hyland, A D Moss, W Pattison, L Staniforth
Non-resident Partners (ICAEW Members):
I A Douglas, C J Wheatley
Other Offices: Flintshire, Southport
Registered by the ICAEW to carry out company audit work
Regulated by the ICAEW for a range of investment business activities

EDWARD ROBINSON & CO
Suite 26, Century Buildings, Brunswick Business Park, Tower Street, Liverpool L3 4BJ
Tel: 01517 088565
Fax: 0151 702 5606
Email: info@ercacc.co.uk
Resident Partners/Directors: ICAEW Members
R W J Brown, D A Pattinson, E Robinson, M R Wrigglesworth
Resident Partners (Non-ICAEW Members):
P Kemp
Other Offices: Suite 51, Chester Enterprise Centre, Hoole Bridge, Chester, CH2 3NE (Tel: 01244 315553)
Registered by the ICAEW to carry out company audit work

EILEEN M. QUINN
Chelford, Glendyke Road, Liverpool, L18 6JR

ERIC T. OWEN F.C.A
25 Lynton Green, Woolton, Liverpool, L25 6JB
Tel: 0151 421 0797
Principal: ICAEW Member
E T Owen

ERNST & YOUNG LLP
20 Chapel Street, Liverpool, L3 9AG
Tel: 0151 210 4200
Resident Partners/Directors: ICAEW Members
C Fairhurst, B Flynn

FLETCHER & CO
25 York Close, Freshfield, Liverpool, L37 7HZ

GASKING, LACE & CO ◈
30 Crosby Road North, Waterloo, Liverpool, L22 4QF
Tel: 0151 928 1019
Resident Partners/Directors: ICAEW Members
C P Antrobus

GLF CARTER RICHARDS
4th Floor, Federation House, Hope Street, Liverpool L1 9BW

GLYN PIKE
10 Mark Road, Hightown, Liverpool, L38 0BH

GRANT THORNTON UK LLP
1st Floor, Royal Liver Building, Pier Head, Liverpool L3 1PS
Tel: 0151 224 7200
Resident Partners/Directors: ICAEW Members
M G Cox, M C Dawson, K M Engel, J N Hutton, N J Sturmey
Resident Partners (Non-ICAEW Members):
C J Williams

GUILD, APPLETON & CO ★
19 Old Hall Street, Liverpool, L3 9JQ

H. LYON & CO
9 Wokingham Grove, Liverpool, L36 5YX

HADLEY & CO
65 Penrhyn Avenue, Litherland, Liverpool, L21 6ND

HAMILTON-BURKE DUFAU LTD
Gladstone House, 2 Church Road, Wavertree, Liverpool L15 9EG
Tel: 0151 733 0864
Fax: 0151 735 0370
Email: info@hbdltd.com
Resident Partners/Directors: ICAEW Members
I D Hamilton-Burke
Registered by the ICAEW to carry out company audit work
Regulated by the ICAEW for a range of investment business activities
General Description: A member of Alliott Group, a worldwide network of independent firms.

HASSARD-JONES LTD
9 Northmead Road, Allerton, Liverpool, L19 5NN

HERIOT HUGHES
42 Crosby Road North, Liverpool, L22 4QQ

HUGHES & CO
Bank Buildings, 173 College Road, Crosby, Liverpool L23 3AT

HURST (LIVERPOOL) LLP
Orleans House, Edmund Street, Liverpool, L2 9NG
Tel: 0151 237 5900
Website: http://www.hurst.co.uk
Resident Partners/Directors: ICAEW Members
H M G Hurst
Resident Partners (Non-ICAEW Members):
C Jackson
SPECIALISATIONS – AUDIT & ASSURANCE
Pension Scheme Auditors

SPECIALISATIONS – FORENSIC ACCOUNTING

Forensic Accounting

SPECIALISATIONS – TAXATION

UK Companies Overseas
UK Subsidiaries of Overseas Multinationals

HW ◈

Pacific Chambers, 11-13 Victoria Street, Liverpool, Lancashire L2 5QQ
Tel: 0151 227 3463
Resident Partners/Directors: ICAEW Members
G C Fairclough, F J Murphy, L R Silverman

J.F. GUYERS

1 Hornby Chase, Old Hall Gardens, Liverpool, L31 5PP
Tel: 0151 531 8925
Principal: ICAEW Member
J F Guyers

J.M. TAGGART

64 Eshe Road North, Blundellsands, Liverpool, L23 8UF

JBS ACCOUNTANTS LLP

102 Cotton Exchange Building, Old Hall Street, Liverpool, L3 9LQ

JOHN HARRILD & CO

501A Prescot Road, Old Swan, Liverpool, L13 3BU

JOHN KERR ◈

369-375 Eaton Road, West Derby, Liverpool, L12 2AH
Tel: 0151 228 8977
Email: advice@jkca.co.uk
Website: http://www.jkca.co.uk
Resident Partners/Directors: ICAEW Members
J Casimo, D S Glover, J F E Kerr

Registered by the ICAEW to carry out company audit work

Authorised and regulated by the Financial Services Authority for investment business

JONATHAN CHAYTOR

The Old Vicarage, Lord Sefton Way, Great Altcar, Liverpool L37 5AA

KEMP & CO ◈

Room 2-02, The Cotton Exchange Building, Old Hall Street, Liverpool L3 9LQ
Tel: 0151 236 1523
Email: kempandcompany@btconnect.com
Resident Partners/Directors: ICAEW Members
M A Todd

KING NAGUS BAKERMAN

KNB House, 7 Rodney Street, Liverpool, L1 9HZ

KINGHAM & CO

Kingham Chambers, 5 Nelson Street, Liverpool, L1 5DW

KPMG LLP

8 Princes Parade, Liverpool, L3 1QH
Tel: 0151 473 5100
Resident Partners/Directors: ICAEW Members
J O'Brien

LANGTONS

The Plaza, 100 Old Hall Street, Liverpool, L3 9QJ

LONSDALE & MARSH

Orleans House, Edmund Street, Liverpool, L3 9NG
Tel: 0151 236 8211
Email: info@lonsdales.co.uk
Resident Partners/Directors: ICAEW Members
O J Grills, E F McElroy, N J O'Donovan, J R M Simcox, A C Thompson
Other Offices:4 Derby Street West, Ormskirk, L39 3NH (Tel: 01695 573688)

Registered by the ICAEW to carry out company audit work

Regulated by the ICAEW for a range of investment business activities

LUMINARY FINANCE LLP

Horton House, Exchange Flags, Liverpool, L2 3YL

M.H. SMITH

3 Ambassador Drive, Halewood, Liverpool, L26 6LT
Tel: 0151 487 6643
Principal: ICAEW Member
M H Smith

MACFARLANE + CO

2nd Floor, Cunard Building, Water Street, Liverpool L3 1DS
Tel: 0151 236 6161
Email: all@macca.co.uk
Resident Partners/Directors: ICAEW Members
K J L Green, A T R Macfarlane, A P Morris, T Pritchard
Resident Partners (Non-ICAEW Members):
P C Kurthausen, J S Elliott

MALTHOUSE & CO

America House, Rumford Court, Rumford Place, Liverpool L3 9DD

MALTHOUSE & COMPANY LTD

America House, Rumford Court, Rumford Place, Liverpool L3 9DD

MANOR LAWSON ◈

292 Aigburth Road, Liverpool, L17 9PW
Tel: 0151 728 8435
Principal: ICAEW Member
M A Greaves

MATTHEWS SUTTON & CO LTD ◈

48-52 Penny Lane, Mossley Hill, Liverpool, L18 1DG
Tel: 0151 734 4789
Resident Partners/Directors: ICAEW Members
S M Matthews, P M Sutton

MELVILLE MORRIS

Musker Buildings, 1 Stanley Street, Liverpool, L1 6AA

MICHELLE BAGGALEY

17 Walsingham Road, Childwall, Liverpool, L16 3NR

MITCHELL CHARLESWORTH ◈

5 Temple Square, Temple Street, Liverpool, L2 5RH
Tel: 0151 255 2300
Resident Partners/Directors: ICAEW Members
D J Antonia, P L Griffiths, A J Lavelle, C H Plummer, P N Wainwright

MOORE STEPHENS

110-114 Duke Street, Liverpool, L1 5AG
Tel: 0151 703 1080
Resident Partners/Directors: ICAEW Members
J Glasby, S R Jones, B McGain, K J Miller

MUSKER & GARRETT

Edward House, North Mersey Business Centre, Woodward Road, Knowsley Industrial Park, Liverpool L33 7UY

MUSKER & GARRETT LTD

Edward House, North Mersey Business Centre, Woodward Road, Knowsley Industrial Park, Liverpool L33 7UY

NEIL WRIGHT & CO

166 Linacre Road, Litherland, Liverpool, L21 8JU
Tel: 0151 933 1964
Principal: ICAEW Member
N J Wright

NORMAN YOU

72 Rodney Street, Liverpool, L1 9AF

OSCAR IP & CO

14 Meldon Close, Liverpool, L12 0RS

PARKIN S. BOOTH & CO ★

44 Old Hall Street, Liverpool, L3 9EB
Tel: 0151 236 4331
Fax: 0151 255 0108
Email: lp@parkinsbooth.co.uk
Resident Partners/Directors: ICAEW Members
P J Fleming
Resident Partners (Non-ICAEW Members):
I C Brown, J C Moran, J R Booth, R M Rutherford
Other Offices: Chester, Llandudno, Warrington
Individual(s) licensed for insolvency work by the ICAEW

SPECIALISATIONS – BUSINESS RECOVERY & INSOLVENCY

Bankruptcies
Corporate Recovery
Liquidations

General Description: The firm which was founded over 80 years ago deals solely with insolvency matters including liquidations, administrations, receiverships, bankruptcies and voluntary arrangements.

PHILLIP J BIRD LTD ◈

55 Queens Road, Formby, Liverpool, L37 2HG
Tel: 07989 767852
Resident Partners/Directors: ICAEW Members
P J Bird

PKF (UK) LLP

5 Temple Square, Temple Street, Liverpool, L2 5RH
Tel: 0151 237 4500
Email: info.liverpool@uk.pkf.com
Website: http://www.pkf.co.uk
Resident Partners/Directors: ICAEW Members
M Fairhurst, J H H Mounsey, J D Newell, B G Ricketts
Resident Partners (Non-ICAEW Members):
J Jackson, P McGrath

PRICEWATERHOUSE-COOPERS

8 Princes Parade, St Nicholas Place, Liverpool, L3 1QJ

PRICEWATERHOUSE-COOPERS LLP

8 Princes Parade, St Nicholas Place, Liverpool, L3 1QJ
Tel: 0151 227 4242

ROBERT PARRY

377 Woolton Road, Woolton, Liverpool, L25 4SX

RUSSELL & CO

50 Bridge Road, Litherland, Liverpool, L21 6PH

S.J. BURNS & CO

Jubilee House, Suite 9A, Altcar Road, Formby, Liverpool L37 8DL
Tel: 01704 833095
Principal: ICAEW Member
S J Burns

S.S. MCDERMOTT

15 Childwall Crescent, Childwall, Liverpool, L16 7PG
Tel: 0151 722 9221
Principal: ICAEW Member
S S McDermott

S. SAMUELS & CO

503 Smithdown Road, Liverpool, L15 5AE

SANDRA HUGHES

14 College Avenue, Freshfield, Liverpool, L37 3JL

SHAHABUDDIN & CO LTD
Lombard Chambers, Ormond Street, Liverpool, L3 9NA
Tel: 0151 236 3627
Resident Partners/Directors: ICAEW Members
K Shahabuddin, K F Shahabuddin, K I Shahabuddin

THE SHARMAN PARTNERSHIP
4 Coronation Road, Crosby, Liverpool, L23 3BJ

SLOAN & CO ◈
Granite Buildings, 6 Stanley Street, Liverpool, L1 6AF
Tel: 0151 227 1769
Resident Partners/Directors: ICAEW Members
R B Alvis, S W Kayne

STANSFIELD & CO ◈
Suite 303, Queens Dock Business Centre, Norfolk Street, Liverpool L1 0BG
Tel: 0151 709 9124
Principal: ICAEW Member
A Stansfield

STEPHEN FOSTER & CO
1 Eastdale Road, Liverpool, L15 4HN

THE STEVE STUART PARTNERSHIP LLP
Ground Floor, 24 Queen Avenue, Queen Insurance Building, Dale Street, Liverpool L2 4TZ

STUART BURTON & CO
18 Crosby Road North, Waterloo, Liverpool, L22 4QF
Tel: 0151 928 6463
Principal: ICAEW Member
B S Burton

STUART GORDON
Suite 3 Capital House, Speke Hall Road, Hunts Cross, Liverpool L24 9GB

STUBBS PARKIN TAYLOR & CO LTD
Marion House, 23-25 Elbow Lane, Formby, Liverpool L37 4AB

THOMAS ASSOCIATES ◈
5 Union Court, Liverpool, L2 4SJ
Tel: 0151 236 9466
Principal: ICAEW Member
M A Thomas

VANGUARD CORPORATE FINANCE ◈
The Liverpool SciencePark, 131 Mount Pleasant, Liverpool, L3 5TF
Tel: 0151 705 3520
Resident Partners/Directors: ICAEW Members
B F McCann

VERINDER & ASSOCIATES ◈
1-3 Crosby Road South, Liverpool, L22 1RG
Tel: 0151 949 0065
Principal: ICAEW Member
A L Verinder

W R FELL & CO
11 Lingdales, Formby, Liverpool, L37 7HA

WHITNALLS ★
1st Floor, Cotton House, Old Hall Street, Liverpool L3 9TX

WHITNALLS ★
44A Liverpool Road, Lydiate, Liverpool, L31 2LZ

WILSON HENRY LLP ◈
145 Edge Lane, Edge Hill, Liverpool, L7 2PF
Tel: 0151 264 8888
Resident Partners/Directors: ICAEW Members
P A Alcock, H S Henry, D J Kirby
See display advertisement near this entry.

LIVERSEDGE

HELLIWELL HANDSCOMB
15 Littlethorpe Hill, Hartshead, Liversedge, WF15 8AZ
Tel: 01274 877087
Resident Partners/Directors: ICAEW Members
G D Handscomb, L Handscomb

LONGFIELD

A J BURTON LTD
16 Lapwings, Longfield, DA3 7NH
Tel: 01474 704181
Resident Partners/Directors: ICAEW Members
A J Burton

DIANE J. BRYANT
Eversley, Gorse Way, Hartley, Longfield DA3 8AF

FOX & CO
15 Merton Avenue, Hartley, Longfield, DA3 7EB

PORTLOCK & CO
Ash House, Ash Road, New Ash Green, Longfield DA3 8JD
Tel: 01474 879399
Fax: 01474 879399
Email: portlocks@btconnect.com
Website: http://www.portlocks.co.uk
Principal: ICAEW Member
D I Macleod

Registered by the ICAEW to carry out company audit work

Regulated by the ICAEW for a range of investment business activities

WEST REYNOLDS ★ ◈
Black Barn, Gay Dawn Farm, Valley Road, Fawkham, Longfield DA3 8LX

LOOE

METHERELL GARD
Old Memorial Hall, Morval, Looe, PL13 1PN
Tel: 01503 240940
Resident Partners/Directors: ICAEW Members
J B Kitson, K E Mordan

LOSTWITHIEL

AC GREENHAM LTD
Bryally House, Duke Street, Lostwithiel, PL22 0AG

LOUGHBOROUGH

A.J. CARTE
215 Nanpantan Road, Loughborough, LE11 3YD

ACCOUNTS4BUSINESS
20 Moscow Lane, Shepshed, Loughborough, LE12 9EX

ALEXANDER WHITING & CO LTD
Shelthorpe Lodge, 6 Chestnuts Close, Sutton Bonington, Loughborough LE12 5RJ

BROCKHURST DAVIES LTD ◈
11 The Office Village, North Road, Loughborough, LE11 1QJ
Tel: 01509 239492
Resident Partners/Directors: ICAEW Members
A J Bentley, N H Brockhurst, J E Davies

COUND & CO LLP
27 Granby Street, Loughborough, LE11 3DU
Tel: 01509 214163
Resident Partners/Directors: ICAEW Members
D R Gradon, J R King

DAVID J BARNETT ◈
The Point, Granite Way, Mountsorrel, Loughborough, LE12 7TZ
Tel: 01509 222412
Principal: ICAEW Member
D J Barnett

DOYLE & CO
Wymeswold Hall, East Road, Wymeswold, Loughborough LE12 6ST

E HODGKINSON & CO
Brooklyn House, Brook Street, Shepshed, Loughborough LE12 9RG

ELWELL WATCHORN & SAXTON LLP
109 Swan Street, Sileby, Loughborough, LE12 7NN

FARRARS
8 Hillcrest Drive, Loughborough, LE11 2GX

GODKIN & CO LTD ◈
105 Derby Road, Loughborough, LE11 5AE
Tel: 01509 214496
Resident Partners/Directors: ICAEW Members
P R Blakemore

J.A. HEARD & CO
36 The Green, Long Whatton, Loughborough, LE12 5DB

JOHN CARTER
20 Eyebrook Close, Loughborough, LE11 4PS

JOHN F. MOULD & CO
19/20 Baxter Gate, Loughborough, LE11 1TG

K RIMMER SERVICES LTD
15 Condon Road, Barrow Upon Soar, Loughborough, LE12 8NQ
Tel: 01509 414689
Resident Partners/Directors: ICAEW Members
K Rimmer

KEITH RIMMER
15 Condon Road, Barrow upon Soar, Loughborough, LE12 8NQ
Tel: 01509 414689

LEWIS ACCOUNTING LTD
26 Brookfields Way, East Leake, Loughborough, LE12 6HD

MARSH & MOSS LTD ◈
The Gables, Bishop Meadow Road, Loughborough, LE11 5RQ
Tel: 01509 212668

NEWBY CASTLEMAN ◈
Eltham House, 6 Forest Road, Loughborough, LE11 3NP
Tel: 01509 263500
Fax: 01509 234811
Email: dmh@newbyc.co.uk
Resident Partners/Directors: ICAEW Members
D M Hastings
Other Offices: Leicester, Melton Mowbray, Oakham, Nottingham
Registered by the ICAEW to carry out company audit work
Regulated by the ICAEW for a range of investment business activities
See display advertisement near this entry.

NIGEL RICKS & CO
Rose Villa, 42 Glebe Street, Loughborough, LE11 1JR

ROBERT WHOWELL & PARTNERS
78 Loughborough Road, Quorn, Loughborough, LE12 8DX
Tel: 01509 622830
Resident Partners/Directors: ICAEW Members
I C F S Agar, J W Mills, B Peake, J R Whowell, R H Whowell

TURNER & SMITH ★ ◈
Westgate House, Royland Road, Loughborough, LE11 2EH
Tel: 01509 212890
Website: http://www.turnerandsmith.co.uk
Resident Partners/Directors: ICAEW Members
R J Lester, R Neal
Resident Partners (Non-ICAEW Members):
R A Graham
Registered by the ICAEW to carry out company audit work
Regulated by the ICAEW for a range of investment business activities

SPECIALISATIONS – SECTOR

Agriculture
Property Development
Property Investment
Solicitors
Travel Industry

LOUGHTON

ASHTON HART DAVID LEE ★
Sterling House, Langston Road, Loughton, IG10 3FA

B.W. HOLMAN & CO
First Floor Suite, Enterprise House, 10 Church Hill, Loughton IG10 1LA

COOPER PAUL ◈
Abacus House, 14-18 Forest Road, Loughton, IG10 1DX

F. HEANEY
22 Hillcrest Road, Loughton, IG10 4QQ

G.J. FENNELL
41 River Way, Loughton, IG10 3LJ
Tel: 020 8524 0119
Principal: ICAEW Member
G J Fennell

HASLERS ◈
Old Station Road, Loughton, IG10 4PL
Tel: 020 8418 3333
Fax: 020 8418 3334
Email: advice@haslers.com
Website: http://www.haslers.com
Training Contracts Available.
Resident Partners/Directors: ICAEW Members
M J Anderson, S Baskin, D J Berkley, S J Blake, L A Busby, M P Gould, R A J Hooper, L A Jacobs, P D Kurup, C Munro, G C Reed, L E Shafier, S M Simmons, C A Wiseman
Resident Partners (Non-ICAEW Members):
J O'Shea, M Watts, D Dougal
Other Offices:1 Poultry, London EC2R 8JR (Tel: 020 7643 2239), 137 High Street, Quarry Bank, West Midlands,DY5 2AF (Tel: 01384 238141)
Registered by the ICAEW to carry out company audit work
Regulated by the ICAEW for a range of investment business activities
Individual(s) licensed for insolvency work by the ICAEW

INVESTOR IN PEOPLE

SPECIALISATIONS – AUDIT & ASSURANCE

Audit

SPECIALISATIONS – BUSINESS & GENERAL ADVICE

Acquisitions and Mergers
Company Formation
Company Secretarial Service
Disposal of Businesses
Divorce/Matrimonial
Management Advice to Business
Takeovers

SPECIALISATIONS – BUSINESS RECOVERY & INSOLVENCY

Bankruptcies
Corporate Recovery
Liquidations
Reorganisations and Company Reconstructions

SPECIALISATIONS – FORENSIC ACCOUNTING

Expert Witnesses in Litigation
Forensic Accounting

SPECIALISATIONS – SECTOR

Charities
Church
Clothing/Textiles
Clubs/Associations
Corporate
Dentists/Opticians
Doctors
FSA Members
Hotels/Public Houses
Insurance Brokers
Nursing Homes/Clinics
Property
Schools
Solicitors

continued

HASLERS *cont*

SPECIALISATIONS – TAXATION

Estate and Inheritance
Investigations
Taxation
Value Added Tax

General Description: With some 120 staff and 17 partners we are one of the largest independent firms in NE London. We aim to provide a high quality service with a personal touch. In addition to tax and corporate compliance work, we are particularly known for our expertise in tax planning, insolvency, corporate finance, financial services and forensic accounting & dispute resolution.

HLB VANTIS AUDIT PLC
Crown House, 151 High Road, Loughton, IG10 4LG
Tel: 0208 502 0411
Website: http://www.hlbvantisaudit.com
Training Contracts Available.
Resident Partners/Directors: ICAEW Members
J A Rickler
Registered by the ICAEW to carry out company audit work
Regulated by the ICAEW for a range of investment business activities

SPECIALISATIONS – AUDIT & ASSURANCE

Audit
Audit — Private Company
Audit — Public Company

SPECIALISATIONS – FINANCIAL REPORTING

Audit Exemption Report

JEFFREYS LIVEMORE
112 The Lindens, Loughton, IG10 3HU

LORD ASSOCIATES LTD ◈
Caxton House, Old Station Road, Loughton, IG10 4PE

MARSHALL FRIEDNER & CO
9 Tycehurst Hill, Loughton, IG10 1BX

MORGAN CORPORATE FINANCE LTD
Crown House, 151 High Road, Loughton, IG10 4LG

P.J. HEWITT & CO
Crown House, High Road, Loughton, IG10 4LG

S & J PARTNERSHIP
1st Floor, 110 High Road, Loughton, IG10 4HJ

STURMANS
The Seedbed Centre, Langston Road, Loughton, IG10 3TQ

THORNTONRONES
1st Floor, 167 High Road, Loughton, IG10 4LF

THORNTONRONES LTD
1st Floor, 167 High Road, Loughton, IG10 4LF
Tel: 020 8418 9333
Fax: 020 8418 9444
Email: info@thorntonrones.co.uk
Website: http://www.thorntonrones.co.uk
Resident Partners/Directors: ICAEW Members
R J Rones
Individual(s) licensed for insolvency work by the ICAEW

SPECIALISATIONS – BUSINESS RECOVERY & INSOLVENCY

Bankruptcies
Corporate Recovery
Liquidations

TOTAL ACCOUNTING SOLUTIONS LTD
68 Habgood Road, Loughton, IG10 1HE

VANTIS GROUP LTD ◈
3rd Floor, Crown House, 151 High Road, Loughton IG10 4LG
Tel: 0208 502 0411
Website: http://www.vantisplc.com/loughton
Resident Partners/Directors: ICAEW Members
J A Rickler
General Description: ICAEW Registered.

LOUTH

DUNCAN & TOPLIS
15 Chequergate, Louth, LN11 0LJ
Tel: 01507 604841
Fax: 01507 600963
Email: info@louth.duntop.co.uk
Website: http://www.duntop.co.uk
Resident Partners/Directors: ICAEW Members
N P Cudmore
General Description: Other offices please see Grantham.

FORRESTER BOYD
Waynflete House, 139 Eastgate, Louth, LN11 9QQ
Tel: 01507 606111
Resident Partners/Directors: ICAEW Members
S A Czornyj, C P Hunt, A G Nesbitt

FRANKLIN
Orchard Cottage, Manby Middlegate, Grimoldby, Louth LN11 8HE
Tel: 01507 328010

N 4 TAX LTD
The Old Vicarage, Scamblesby, Louth, LN11 9XL
Tel: 01507 343737
Resident Partners/Directors: ICAEW Members
N J Duncumb

N J DUNCUMB
The Old Vicarage, Scamblesby, Louth, LN11 9XL

LOWESTOFT

A P BEMMENT & CO LTD
101 Bridge Road, Oulton Broad, Lowestoft, NR32 3LN

BARNARD SAMPSON
30 Gordon Road, Lowestoft, NR32 1NP
Tel: 01502 565201
Fax: 01502 562321
Email: mikebarnard@barnardsampson.co.uk
Resident Partners/Directors: ICAEW Members
M J Barnard
Registered by the ICAEW to carry out company audit work
Authorised and regulated by the Financial Services Authority for investment business

CUNNINGHAMS
61 Alexandra Road, Lowestoft, NR32 1PL
Tel: 01502 562326
Resident Partners/Directors: ICAEW Members
M A Smith

HARTLEY & CO
Surrey Chambers, 9 Surrey Street, Lowestoft, NR32 1LJ

J.C. MARJORAM & CO
486 London Road South, Lowestoft, NR33 0LB
Tel: 01502 516592
Principal: ICAEW Member
J C Marjoram

LOVEWELL BLAKE ◈
89 Bridge Road, Oulton Broad, Lowestoft, NR32 3LN
Tel: 01502 563921
Fax: 01502 584630
Email: cra@lovewell-blake.co.uk
Website: http://www.lovewell-blake.co.uk
Resident Partners/Directors: ICAEW Members
C R Ashe, P Briddon
Resident Partners (Non-ICAEW Members):
M D Haylett, A J Turner
Individual(s) licensed for insolvency work by the ICAEW
General Description: The practice has 21 partners and our other offices are listed under our Norwich entry.

MOBBS, WHITE & CO
17 Surrey Street, Lowestoft, NR32 1LW
Tel: 01502 565857
Principal: ICAEW Member
D J White

PETER M. GRINSTED
Caloundra, Lyncroft Road, Pakefield, Lowestoft NR33 7AT
Tel: 01502 508596
Principal: ICAEW Member
P M Grinsted

RICHARD SULLIVAN LTD
Romany Rise, Broadview Road, Lowestoft, NR32 3PL

THE TAX SURGERY LTD
Surrey Chambers, Surrey Street, Lowestoft, NR32 1LJ

LUDLOW

BDWM ◈
Stone House Farm, Bitterley, Ludlow, SY8 3HQ

COX AMBREY LTD ◈
Manor Barn, Orleton, Ludlow, SY8 4HR

DRE & CO ◈
Unit 5, The Business Quarter, Eco Park Road, Ludlow SY8 1FD
Tel: 01584 875715

DYKE RUSCOE & HAYES LTD
53 Mill Street, Ludlow, SY8 1BB

JOHN COX FCA
The Rickyard, Orleton, Ludlow, SY8 4HR

SYKES & CO ★
14 Corve Street, Ludlow, SY8 1DA
Tel: 01584 874707
Fax: 01584 874706
Email: post@sykesandco.co.uk
Resident Partners/Directors: ICAEW Members
C M Henry
Resident Partners (Non-ICAEW Members):
D C F Hill
Other Offices: Bishops Castle, SY9 5AE
(Tel: 01588 638426)
Registered by the ICAEW to carry out company audit work
Regulated by the ICAEW for a range of investment business activities

WHITTINGHAM RIDDELL LLP ◈
4 The Business Quarter, Eco Park Road, Ludlow, SY8 1FD
Tel: 01584 872952
Email: wr@whittinghamriddell.co.uk
Other Offices: Shrewsbury, Newtown, Welshpool

LUTON

A1 ACCOUNTING SERVICE ◈
Bramingham Business Park, Enterprise Way, Luton, LU3 4BF
Tel: 01587 883301

AJC ACCOUNTANCY SERVICES
D26 Basepoint Business Centre, 110 Butterfield, Luton, LU2 8DL

BARNETT, HILL & CO
1 Hazelbury Crescent, Luton, LU1 1DS
Tel: 01582 731353
Principal: ICAEW Member
G J Taylor

CARSON & CO
Unit 3, Dukes Court, Wellington Street, Luton LU1 5AF

DAVID MOULDING
The Atrium, Park Street West, Luton, LU1 3BE

E GEORGAS & CO
40 Kilmarnock Drive, Bushmead, Luton, LU2 7YP
Tel: 01582 416809
Fax: 01582 486440
Date Established: 1984
Principal: ICAEW Member
E Georgas
Registered by the ICAEW to carry out company audit work

ERNST & YOUNG LLP
400 Capability Green, Luton, LU1 3LU
Tel: 01582 643000
Resident Partners/Directors: ICAEW Members
P D Bateson, A S Clewer, R W King, D A Murray, V C Thakrar

FKCA LTD
Prospero House, 46/48 Rothesay Road, Luton, LU1 1QZ

FOXLEY KINGHAM
46/48 Rothesay Road, Luton, LU1 1QZ

HOLMES PEAT THORPE
Unit F21, Basepoint Business & Innovation Centre, 110 Butterfield, Great Marlings, Luton LU2 8DL

HPT (LUTON) LTD
Unit F21, Basepoint Business & Innovation Centre, 110 Butterfield, Great Marlings, Luton LU2 8DL

I. HUSSAIN & CO
11 George Street West, Luton, LU1 2BJ

J FORSYTH
19 Cutenhoe Road, Luton, LU1 3NB

KEENS SHAY KEENS LTD ◈
Christchurch House, Upper George Street, Luton, LU1 2RS
Tel: 01582 651000
Email: luton@ksk.co.uk
Website: http://www.ksk.co.uk
Training Contracts Available.
Resident Partners/Directors: ICAEW Members
P Howkins, G Saunders, J J Tyrrell, J S Vincent
Registered by the ICAEW to carry out company audit work
Regulated by the ICAEW for a range of investment business activities

KURBAN ABJI
46 Westbourne Road, Luton, LU4 8JD

LEWIS & LEWIS
209 High Town Road, Luton, LU2 0BZ
Tel: 01582 726379
Principal: ICAEW Member
M J Catlin

MAKAN & MAKAN ◈
Dukes Court, 91 Wellington Street, Luton, LU1 5AF
Tel: 01582 720206
Principal: ICAEW Member
D Makan

MARTIN & CO
71 Ashcroft Road, Stopsley, Luton, LU2 9AX

MAZARS CORPORATE FINANCE LTD ◈
The Atrium, Park Street West, Luton, LU1 3BE

MAZARS LLP ◈
The Atrium, Park Street West, Luton, LU1 3BE
Tel: 01582 700700
Resident Partners/Directors: ICAEW Members
R M Benson, J M Berry, L A Brook, J G Chastney, M D Pickard, C A Scarr, A L Williamson
Registered by the ICAEW to carry out company audit work
Authorised and regulated by the Financial Services Authority for investment business

MILLER & CO
86 Princess Street, Luton, LU1 5AT
Tel: 01582 400199
Email: admin@miller-luton.co.uk
Resident Partners/Directors: ICAEW Members
R Cox, P Stevenson
Registered by the ICAEW to carry out company audit work
Regulated by the ICAEW for a range of investment business activities
SPECIALISATIONS – AUDIT & ASSURANCE
Audit
SPECIALISATIONS – BUSINESS & GENERAL ADVICE
Company Formation
Company Secretarial Service
SPECIALISATIONS – FINANCIAL REPORTING
Accounts Preparation
SPECIALISATIONS – TAXATION
Payroll Service and Advice
Taxation

MURRAYOUNG LTD
15 Home Farm, Luton Hoo Estate, Luton, LU1 3TD

NEILS LTD
3 Dukes Court, Wellington Street, Luton, LU1 5AF

NOTTS LTD ◈
38 Rothesay Road, Luton, LU1 1QZ
Tel: 01582 458777
Resident Partners/Directors: ICAEW Members
C G Nott
Registered by the ICAEW to carry out company audit work
Regulated by the ICAEW for a range of investment business activities

PETER GEORGE FCA
Redshanks, West Street, Lilley, Luton LU2 8LH

RCI
Third Floor, 2-12 Victoria Street, Luton, LU1 2UA

RCI AUDIT AND ASSURANCE SERVICES LTD
2-12 Victoria Street, Luton, LU1 2UA

RCI (LONDON) LTD
Third Floor, 2-12 Victoria Street, Luton, LU1 2UA

RCI (LUTON) LTD
Third Floor, 2-12 Victoria Street, Luton, LU1 2UA

SPIRO NEIL
3 Dukes Court, Wellington Street, Luton, LU1 5AF

STOTEN GILLAM LTD ◈
Bramingham Business Park, Enterprise Way, Luton, LU3 4BU
Tel: 01582 594000

THOMAS COX & CO
4 Home farm, Luton Hoo Estate, Luton, LU1 3TD

WHYATT & CO
3 Pinford Dell, Wigmore Park, Luton, LU2 9SD
Tel: 01582 614762
Principal: ICAEW Member
C R J Whyatt

LUTTERWORTH

A.C. CAMPLEJOHN
The Old Rectory, Main Street, Frolesworth, Lutterworth LE17 5EE

AIMS - ROBERT LAMIN
Church Farm, Church Lane, Shearsby, Lutterworth LE17 6PG

CROWFOOT AND CO
Lonsdale, High Street, Lutterworth, LE17 4AD

DOLFINBLUE LTD
6 Marlborough Place, Lutterworth, LE17 4DE

JAMES P CUNNINGTON ◈
Highcroft Cottage, 33 Berridges Lane, Husbands Bosworth, Lutterworth LE17 6LE
Tel: 01858 880090
Principal: ICAEW Member
J P Cunnington

RUPERT H ALLIBONE FCA
Hunters View, Stemborough Lane, Leire, Lutterworth LE17 5EX

SIMPSON & CO
21 High Street, Lutterworth, LE17 4AT

SIMPSON & CO (ACCOUNTANTS) LTD
21 High Street, Lutterworth, LE17 4AT

STEPHEN WILLCOX
Frogwell House, Cotesbach, Lutterworth, LE17 4HZ

LYDNEY

CLARK WILLETTS & CO
5a Newerne Street, Lydney, GL15 5RA

JEREMY WILLIAMS & CO
Newerne Street Chambers, 45 Newerne Street, Lydney, GL15 5RA
Tel: 01594 843635
Principal: ICAEW Member
J R E Williams

MAKINSON & CO
1 Hill Street, Lydney, GL15 5HB
Tel: 01594 842188
Resident Partners/Directors: ICAEW Members
K Watkins

NEWSHAM TAX
1 New Mills, Forest Road, Lydney, GL15 4ET

WILDIN & CO
Kings Buildings, Hill Street, Lydney, GL15 5HE

WILDIN & CO (ACCOUNTANTS AND FINANCIAL ADVISERS) LTD
Kings Buildings, Lydney, GL15 5HE

LYME REGIS

LENTELLS LTD
St Georges House, Uplyme Business Park, Uplyme Road, Lyme Regis DT7 3LS
Tel: 01297 443182
Registered by the ICAEW to carry out company audit work
Regulated by the ICAEW for a range of investment business activities

SMALL BUSINESS CENTRE
14 Somer Fields, Lyme Regis, DT7 3EL

WHITEHEAD & CO
Penfold, Cannington Lane, Uplyme, Lyme Regis DT7 3SW

LYMINGTON

BRIDGEMAN
Dell House, Lower Buckland Road, Lymington, SO41 9DS

C.B. HESLOP & CO
111 Milford Road, Lymington, SO41 8DN

D.N.W. SHORES
Hillrise, Hare Lane, Hordle, Lymington SO41 0GE

GRIFFITHS & CO
97a High Street, Lymington, SO41 9AP

HOPE JONES
Lymington House, 73 High St, Lymington, SO41 9ZA

JOHN GRAVES FCA
Heatherlea House, East End, Lymington, SO41 5ST
Tel: 01590 626448
Principal: ICAEW Member
J M Graves

MARIE-ANNE ROSE
Bay Tree Cottage, Crabbswood Lane, Sway, Lymington SO41 6EQ

MARTIN GEE
17 Angel Courtyard, High Street, Lymington, SO41 9AP

MASSEY & MASSEY ★
Linden House, No 1 The Square, Pennington, Lymington SO41 8GN

RODNEY H. DE MELLO
The Orangery, 12a Lawn Road, Milford-on-Sea, Lymington SO41 0QZ
Tel: 01590 644558
Principal: ICAEW Member
R H De Mello

S.G. HIGH & CO
Little Normandy, Normandy Lane, Lymington, SO41 8AE

THE TAX & ACCOUNTANCY PRACTICE LTD ◈
1 The Old School, The Square, Pennington, Lymington SO41 8GN
Tel: 01590 677799
Resident Partners/Directors:
ICAEW Members
C Lewis

WESTLAKE CLARK
7 Lynwood Court, Priestlands Place, Lymington, SO41 9GA
Tel: 01590 672674
Email: lym@westlakeclark.com
Resident Partners/Directors:
ICAEW Members
J M Watson
Registered by the ICAEW to carry out company audit work
Regulated by the ICAEW for a range of investment business activities

LYMM

AIMS - JESSE OLDFIELD ◈
Broomedge Post Office, 286 Higher Lane, Lymm, WA13 0RW

ERIC SYKES
62 Higher Lane, Lymm, WA13 0BG

JUSTIN C SMITH
4 Hollygrove Court, 42 Booths Hill Road, Lymm, WA13 0DP

LYNDHURST

GODFREY WHITEHEAD
The Okefield, Beaulieu Road, Lyndhurst, SO43 7DA
Tel: 02380 282676
Principal: ICAEW Member
G Whitehead

LYNTON

DAVISONS LTD
42-43 Lee Road, Lynton, EX35 6BS

LYTHAM ST ANNES

ASHWORTH TREASURE
17-19 Park Street, Lytham St Annes, FY8 5LU

ASHWORTH TREASURE LTD
17-19 Park Street, Lytham St Annes, FY8 5LU

ASHWORTH TREASURE (BOC) LTD
17-19 Park Street, Lytham St Annes, FY8 5LU

FREEMAN RICH
284 Clifton Drive South, Lytham St Annes, FY8 1LH
Tel: 01253 712231
Resident Partners/Directors:
ICAEW Members
J R Duckworth, W J Turley
Individual(s) licensed for insolvency work by another RPB

J. DAVIES
9 Dunes House, 1 Fairhaven Road, Lytham St Annes, FY8 1NN
Tel: 01253 789299
Principal: ICAEW Member
J Davies

JACQUELINE BROCKLEHURST
21 Poulton Avenue, Lytham St Annes, FY8 3JR

JAMES C. BRYAN
Rockcliffe, Woodville Court, 6 Woodville Terrace, Lytham St Annes, FY8 5QB

JPH LTD
3a Clifton Square, Lytham, Lytham St Annes, FY8 5JP

LAKIN & CO ◈
The Neuk, 46 Caryl Road, Lytham St Annes, FY8 2QB

LATHAM LEES COSTA ▽
12 Park St, Lytham, Lytham St Annes, FY8 5LU

M.J. WARD & CO
6 Chislehurst Place, West Park, Lytham St Annes, FY8 4RU
Tel: 01772 254877
Principal: ICAEW Member
M J Ward

MARTIN EDWARD GUNSON ◈
Bank House, 9 Dicconson Terrace, Lytham, Lytham St Annes FY8 5JY
Tel: 01253 739611
Principal: ICAEW Member
M E Gunson

P.S. WALLACE & CO
284 Clifton Drive South, St Annes, Lytham St Annes, FY8 1LH
Tel: 01253 782792
Principal: ICAEW Member
P S Wallace
Individual(s) licensed for insolvency work by another RPB

RACHEL BATTERSBY BSC (HONS) ACA CTA
11 Newbury Road, Lytham St Annes, FY8 1DG

RD BATHO & CO
12A West Beach, Lytham St Annes, FY8 5QH

ROBIN UPTON INSOLVENCY
284 Clifton Drive South, St Annes, Lytham St Annes, FY8 1LH
Tel: 01253 788077
Principal: ICAEW Member
R A Upton
Individual(s) licensed for insolvency work by another RPB

TRC ACCOUNTANCY LTD
26 Coopers Row, Lytham St Annes, FY8 4UD

W & H
327 Clifton Drive South, Lytham St Annes, FY8 1HN

WHITEHEAD & HOWARTH
327 Clifton Drive South, Lytham St Annes, FY8 1HN

WHITTLES LLP ◈
1 Richmond Road, Lytham St Annes, FY8 1PE

MABLETHORPE

AIMS - MARIA HYDE
2 Masons Close, Sandilands, Mablethorpe, LN12 2SE
Tel: 01507 442727
Principal: ICAEW Member
M A Hyde

PHILIP ROSS & CO
2a Knowle Street, Mablethorpe, LN12 2BG
Tel: 01507 472727
Principal: ICAEW Member
C P H Ross

MACCLESFIELD

AIMS - CHRIS TARBARD
5 Huxley Close, Macclesfield, SK10 3DG

ALAN CLARKE FCA
Heawood House, Congleton Road, Nether, Alderley, Macclesfield SK10 4TN
Tel: 01625 585026
Principal: ICAEW Member
A Clarke

BATESONS
2 Statham Court, Statham Street, Macclesfield, SK11 6XN

BENNETT BROOKS & CO LTD.
2 Maple Court, Davenport Street, Macclesfield, SK10 1JE

BLOWER & CO
26 Legh Road, Prestbury, Macclesfield, SK10 4HX

BOWN, LLOYD & CO
13 Cambridge Road, Macclesfield, SK11 8JL

C PIMBLOTT & CO
341/343 Park Lane, Macclesfield, SK11 8JR

CORPORATE AUDIT SOLUTIONS
Georges Court, Chestergate, Macclesfield, SK11 6DP

DRABBLE & CO
Eddisbury House Farm, Back Eddisbury Road, Macclesfield, SK11 0AD

DRABBLE & CO
1 Wellington Road, Bollington, Macclesfield, SK10 5JR

GUTHRIE ACCOUNTANCY SERVICES LTD
Georgia House, Chatham Street, Macclesfield, SK11 6ED
Tel: 01625 424066
Resident Partners/Directors: ICAEW Members
G R Guthrie

HARTS LLP ◈
Chester House, 68 Chestergate, Macclesfield, SK11 6DY
Tel: 01625 669669
Resident Partners/Directors: ICAEW Members
A Naylor, D A J Taylor

HEYWOOD SHEPHERD
1 Park Street, Macclesfield, SK11 6SR
Tel: 01625 427459
Resident Partners/Directors: ICAEW Members
N A Kennington, C Sloan, D Southall

J.D. HEWITSON FCA
2 Withinlee Cottages, Tudor Drive, Prestbury, Macclesfield SK10 4UU
Tel: 01625 824956
Principal: ICAEW Member
J D Hewitson

J.R. ATKINS & CO
3 Beech Lane, Macclesfield, SK10 2DR
Tel: 01625 422972
Principal: ICAEW Member
A J Heard

JOHN NICOL & CO
161 Park Lane, Macclesfield, SK11 6UB
Tel: 01625 511182
Principal: ICAEW Member
J Nicol

JOSOLYNE & CO
Silk House, Park Green, Macclesfield, SK11 7QW
Tel: 01625 442800
Fax: 01625 511327
Email: mail@josolyne.co.uk
Website: http://www.josolyne.co.uk
Date Established: 1892
Resident Partners/Directors: ICAEW Members
A J Earnshaw, K McAulay, N M Pace
Registered by the ICAEW to carry out company audit work
Regulated by the ICAEW for a range of investment business activities

SPECIALISATIONS – SECTOR

Doctors

KIME, O'BRIEN
1 Church Mews, Churchill Way, Macclesfield, SK11 6AY

LENNARD DAKIN
88 Great King Street, Macclesfield, SK11 6PW
Tel: 01625 420344
Principal: ICAEW Member
M J Lennard

MCELLIN KELLY
Abacus House, 35 Cumberland Street, Macclesfield, SK10 1DD

R. SUTTON & CO
25 Park Street, Macclesfield, SK11 6SS
Tel: 01625 425074
Principal: ICAEW Member
W D Williams

TAXASSIST ACCOUNTANTS
12 Hibel Road, Macclesfield, SK10 2AB

THOMPSON WRIGHT ◈
9 Prestbury Road, Macclesfield, SK10 1AU
Tel: 01625 422707

WHITE & CO
30 Grimshaw Lane, Bollington, Macclesfield, SK10 5NB

WHITE & COMPANY (UK) LTD ◈
30 Grimshaw Lane, Bollington, Macclesfield, SK10 5NB

MAIDENHEAD

ACCOUNTING PROFESSIONALS LTD
18 West Mead, Maidenhead, SL6 7HQ
Tel: 01628 633713
Resident Partners/Directors: ICAEW Members
M K Malhotra

AMANDA BELL MA (CANTAB) FCA
18 Purssell Close, Maidenhead, SL6 3XU

ARMSTRONG BELL
18 Purssell Close, Maidenhead, SL6 3XU

ATKINSON HUNTER & CO
Weir Bank, Monkey Island Lane, Bray, Maidenhead SL6 2EA

C.C.EVANS
25 Clarefield Drive, Pinkneys Green, Maidenhead, SL6 5DW
Tel: 01628 627934
Principal: ICAEW Member
C C Evans

CAMWELL CONSULTING ★
Broadway House, 21 Broadway, Maidenhead, SL6 1NJ

CAMWELLS ★
21 Broadway, Maidenhead, SL6 1NJ

CHRISTOPHER G GLOVER
2 New Road, Cookham, Maidenhead, SL6 9HD

D J MACAULAY
Morcroft, Ellington Road, Taplow, Maidenhead SL6 0BA
Tel: 01628 777974

D J MACAULAY ACCOUNTANCY LTD
Morcroft, Ellington Road, Taplow, Maidenhead SL6 0BA
Tel: 01628 777974
Resident Partners/Directors: ICAEW Members
D J Macaulay

DIANE WILDING & ASSOCIATES LTD
64 Harrow Lane, Maidenhead, SL6 7PA
Tel: 01628 771312
Resident Partners/Directors: ICAEW Members
D J Wilding

DONALD REID & CO ◈
Prince Albert House, 20 King Street, Maidenhead, SL6 1DT
Tel: 01628 760000
Website: http://www.donaldreid.co.uk
Resident Partners/Directors: ICAEW Members
D R Gordon-Smith, D C W Reid
Registered by the ICAEW to carry out company audit work

EASTMOND & CO
4 Cordwallis Street, Maidenhead, SL6 7BE

EASTMOND & CO LTD
4 Cordwallis Street, Maidenhead, SL6 7BE

FINTECH
Ballards, Jobs Lane, Cookham, Maidenhead SL6 9TX
Tel: 01628 488000

HALE & CO ◈
14 Craufurd Rise, Maidenhead, SL6 7LX
Tel: 01628 626333
Fax: 01628 770340
Website: http://www.haleandco.co.uk
Training Contracts Available.
Resident Partners/Directors: ICAEW Members
D Cole, J A Daniell, S M Egan, C J Krol
Registered by the ICAEW to carry out company audit work
Authorised and regulated by the Financial Services Authority for investment business

SPECIALISATIONS – AUDIT & ASSURANCE

Assurance Services
Audit

SPECIALISATIONS – BUSINESS & GENERAL ADVICE

Book-keeping
Company Formation
Company Secretarial Service
Management Accounting Consultancy

SPECIALISATIONS – FINANCIAL REPORTING

Accounts Preparation

SPECIALISATIONS – INVESTMENT BUSINESS

Financial Planning and Advice

SPECIALISATIONS – IT

Computer Systems and Consultancy

SPECIALISATIONS – SECTOR

Property
Solicitors

SPECIALISATIONS – TAXATION

Estate Planning
Payroll Service and Advice
Taxation

HANNAWAYS LLP
Trios House, Reform Road, Maidenhead, SL6 8BY

Harper Broom
CHARTERED ACCOUNTANTS

HARPER BROOM ◈
Aston House, York Road, Maidenhead, SL6 1SF
Tel: 01628 785000
Fax: 01628 781178
Email: mail@harperbroom.com
Website: http://www.harperbroom.com
Date Established: 1895
Training Contracts Available.
Resident Partners/Directors:
ICAEW Members
J A Broom, F Masterman-Smith

HIGGINS DAY
19 York Rd, Maidenhead, SL6 1SQ
Tel: 01628 778733
Fax: 01628 770793
Email: admin@higginsday.co.uk
Principal: ICAEW Member
S N Higgins
Registered by the ICAEW to carry out company audit work

SPECIALISATIONS – AUDIT & ASSURANCE

Audit

SPECIALISATIONS – BUSINESS & GENERAL ADVICE

Book-keeping

continued

HIGGINS DAY *cont*

SPECIALISATIONS – FINANCIAL REPORTING

Accounts Preparation
Limited Company Accounts
Partnership/Sole Trader Accounts

SPECIALISATIONS – TAXATION

Payroll Service and Advice
Taxation

IAN PEACOCK
11 Manor Lane, Maidenhead, SL6 2QN
Tel: 01628 580380
Principal: ICAEW Member
I G Peacock

IAN S ANDERSON
Chartam House, 16a College Avenue, Maidenhead, SL6 6AX

J.JOBSON & CO
15 Birdwood Road, Maidenhead, SL6 5AP

KHOSHABA & CO
15 Harefield Road, Maidenhead, SL6 5EA
Tel: 01628 777136
Principal: ICAEW Member
R K Khoshaba

KNIGHT & CO ◈
11 Castle Hill, Maidenhead, SL6 4AA
Tel: 01628 631056
Email: geoffk@knightandcompany.co.uk
Website: http://www.knightandcompany.co.uk
Principal: ICAEW Member
G W Knight

Registered by the ICAEW to carry out company audit work

Regulated by the ICAEW for a range of investment business activities

LEADBETTER STAFF & CO ★
2nd Floor, Park House, Park Street, Maidenhead SL6 1SL

OPPENHEIMS
PO Box 3578, Maidenhead, SL6 3WH

OPPENHEIMS ACCOUNTANCY LTD
PO Box 2385, Maidenhead, SL6 7WQ

OWEN ACCOUNTANCY
April Cottage, Poundfield Lane, Cookham, Maidenhead SL6 9RY
Tel: 01628 532365
Principal: ICAEW Member
M A Owen

PETER UPTON LTD ◈
The Counting House, 7 Bridge Street, Maidenhead, SL6 8PA
Tel: 01628 781636
Resident Partners/Directors: ICAEW Members
J H P Upton

SANDRA BROWN & CO
Sunnyside, Holyport Street, Holyport, Maidenhead SL6 2JR
Tel: 01628 770880
Principal: ICAEW Member
S K Brown

SIAN TINDAL
The Brew House, School Lane, Cookham, Maidenhead SL6 9QN

STILES & CO ★
2 Lake End Court, Taplow Road, Taplow, Maidenhead SL6 0JQ

T.E.T.GOWER
12 Birdwood Road, Maidenhead, SL6 5AP

THAKRAR COOMBS & CO ★
The Dairy House, Moneyrow Green, Holyport, Maidenhead SL6 2ND

VICTORIA PARK
85 St Marks Crescent, Maidenhead, SL6 5DQ

W.J. MOUNT
15 Loosen Drive, Maidenhead, SL6 3UR

MAIDSTONE

ACCSYS ◈
PO Box 1218, Detling, Maidstone, ME14 9JS

ACCSYS BUSINESS ADVISERS LTD ◈
PO Box 1218, Detling, Maidstone, ME14 3HX
Tel: 01622 630080
Website: http://www.accsysltd.co.uk
Resident Partners/Directors: ICAEW Members
W H A Wood

ATHERTON BAILEY LLP
Kent House, Romney Place, Maidstone, ME15 6LH

AUSTEN & CO
57 Upper Fant Road, Maidstone, ME16 8BU
Tel: 01622 750504
Principal: ICAEW Member
M Cascioli

BAKER TOMLINSON
PO Box 1077, 13 Victoria Street, Maidstone, ME14 9AQ

BERRY & CO ◈
7 Clarendon Place, King Street, Maidstone, ME14 1BQ
Tel: 01622 755427
Email: info@berryandcompany.co.uk
Date Established: 1931
Resident Partners/Directors: ICAEW Members
A D Cornish, D R May
Other Offices:24 Ashford Road, Tenterden, Kent

Registered by the ICAEW to carry out company audit work

Regulated by the ICAEW for a range of investment business activities

BURNS WARING & PARTNERS LTD ◈
Denning House, 1 London Road, Maidstone, ME16 8HS

CHARCROFT BAKER
5 West Court, Enterprise Road, Maidstone, ME15 6JD

DAY, SMITH & HUNTER ◈
Globe House, Eclipse Park, Sittingbourne Road, Maidstone ME14 3EN
Tel: 01622 690666
Email: info@dsh.co.uk
Website: http://www.dsh.co.uk
Resident Partners/Directors: ICAEW Members
B A Aitken, N Caldwell, R Coates, S Ellmers, S J Farrant, J G Moore, M Startup, P Wilson
Resident Partners (Non-ICAEW Members):
R E Churchill
Other Offices: Rickmansworth, Hertfordshire

Registered by the ICAEW to carry out company audit work

Regulated by the ICAEW for a range of investment business activities

DCA ASSOCIATES
Suite 18, Kent House, Romney Place, Maidstone ME15 6LH

DCA ASSOCIATES LTD
Suite 18, Kent House, Romney Place, Maidstone ME15 6LH

DENDY NEVILLE LTD ◈
3-4 Bower Terrace, Maidstone, ME16 8RY
Tel: 01622 686441
Email: enquiries@dendyneville.co.uk
Website: http://www.dendyneville.co.uk
Training Contracts Available.
Resident Partners/Directors: ICAEW Members
D M Hill, D Williams
Resident Partners (Non-ICAEW Members):
D K Muggridge, A M Perkins

Registered by the ICAEW to carry out company audit work

Regulated by the ICAEW for a range of investment business activities

DIAMOND ACCOUNTING SERVICES
43 Tarragon Road, Maidstone, ME16 0UR

FINDLAY JAMES
Cornwallis House, Pudding Lane, Maidstone, ME14 1NH

FOURWOOD SERVICES LTD
18 Cedar Drive, Barming, Maidstone, ME16 9HD

GARDINER & CO
White House, Ulcombe Hill, Ulcombe, Maidstone ME17 1DJ

GEORGE & CO
Thornhill House, 26 Fisher Street, Maidstone, ME14 2SU
Tel: 01622 693125
Principal: ICAEW Member
G H Charilaou

HADDON HALL
8 Petlands, Boughton Monchelsea, Maidstone, ME17 4SL

HORWATH CLARK WHITEHILL LLP ◈
10 Palace Avenue, Maidstone, ME15 6NF
Tel: 01622 767676
Email: kent@horwath.co.uk
Website: http://www.horwathcw.co.uk
Training Contracts Available.
Resident Partners/Directors: ICAEW Members
C M Gandon, D A J May, K A Newman, G J P E Struyven, M J Subert, I Weekes
Registered by the ICAEW to carry out company audit work
See display advertisement near this entry.

HWCA LTD ◈
4-5 Kings Row, Armstrong Road, Maidstone, ME15 6AQ
Tel: 01622 692255
Resident Partners/Directors: ICAEW Members
A D Brand, F C James, P J Sutton

JAMES MAGEE
34 Bower Mount Road, Maidstone, ME16 8AU

JON MITCHELL
183 Ashford Road, Maidstone, ME14 4NE

LARKINGS LTD
Cornwallis House, Pudding Lane, Maidstone, ME14 1NH

LEVICKS
West Hill, 61 London Road, Maidstone, ME16 8TX
Tel: 01622 759121
Resident Partners/Directors: ICAEW Members
J Griggs, K Luxford, J Williamson
See display advertisement near this entry.

LOGIKA LTD
12 Romney Place, Maidstone, ME15 6LE

MCCABE FORD WILLIAMS ◈
Market House, 17 Hart Street, Maidstone, ME16 8RA

MARIANNE DADD ACA
3 Catchment Cottages, Hampstead Lane, Yalding, Maidstone ME18 6HL
Tel: 07966 687522
Principal: ICAEW Member
M Dadd

MICHAEL D. NICHOLS
28 Boughton Lane, Loose, Maidstone, ME15 9QN
Tel: 01622 745629
Fax: 01622 747230
Email: accounts.nichols@virgin.net
Website: http://www.michaeldnichols.co.uk
Principal: ICAEW Member
M D Nichols

SPECIALISATIONS – BUSINESS & GENERAL ADVICE
Administration
Book-keeping
Company Formation

SPECIALISATIONS – FINANCIAL REPORTING
Limited Company Accounts
Partnership/Sole Trader Accounts

SPECIALISATIONS – TAXATION
Partnerships and Sole Traders
Payroll Service and Advice
Self Assessment Advice
Taxation
Value Added Tax

MUSKET LANE ENTERPRISES LTD ◈
Autumn Cottage, Musket Lane, Hollingbourne, Maidstone ME17 1UY
Tel: 01622 880580
Resident Partners/Directors: ICAEW Members
P J Lee

NASH HARVEY LLP
The Granary, Hermitage Court, Hermitage Lane, Maidstone ME16 9NT

NOMIZON ASSOCIATES ◈
The Old Rectory, Sutton Road, Langley, Maidstone ME17 3LY
Tel: 01622 861911
Principal: ICAEW Member
J E Toppin

OSBORNE FORBES LTD
90-92 King Street, Maidstone, ME14 1BH

THE PRINT PARTNER
4 Denning Close, Maidstone, ME16 0WT

ROGER VICKERY
Little Boyton, Boyton Court Road, Sutton Valence, Maidstone ME17 3EG
Tel: 01622 842500
Principal: ICAEW Member
R J Vickery

SARAH C READ LTD
31-33 Albion Place, Maidstone, ME14 5DZ

SMITH & WILLIAMSON LTD
First Floor, 89 King Street, Maidstone, ME14 1BG
Email: firstname.lastname@smith.williamson.co.uk
Website: http://www.smith.williamson.co.uk
Resident Partners/Directors: ICAEW Members
S J Tancock
General Description: Smith & Williamson is an independent professional and financial services group employing over 1400 people. We are leading providers of investment management, financial advisory and accountancy services to private clients, professional practices and mid-sized companies. Nexia Smith & Williamson Audit (Bristol) LLP provides audit services to complement the specialist financial advisory services provided by Smith & Williamson.

STANLEY HOLMES LTD
Barham Court, Teston, Maidstone, ME18 5BZ

STEPHEN HILL MID KENT LTD
31 - 33 Albion Place, Maidstone, ME14 5DZ

STONES ACCOUNTANCY LTD
196 Loose Road, Maidstone, ME15 7UF

T.L. BURTON ◈
Accountants Place, Heath Road, Linton, Maidstone ME17 4NU
Tel: 01622 747800
Principal: ICAEW Member
T L Burton

TRANSFER PRICING ASSOCIATES LTD
Kent House, Romney Place, Maidstone, ME15 6LH

WIGGINS & CO ◈
The Old Stables, East Lenham Farm, Ashford Road, Lenham, Maidstone ME17 2DP
Tel: 01622 858877
Principal: ICAEW Member
L M Wiggins

WORMALD ACCOUNTANTS LTD
Equitable House, 3 Ashford Road, Maidstone, ME14 5BJ

MALDON

BARRIE HARDING & CO
Hollyoak House, Mead Pastures, Woodham Walter, Maldon CM9 6PY
Tel: 01245 226468
Principal: ICAEW Member
B D Harding
Individual(s) licensed for insolvency work by the ICAEW
SPECIALISATIONS – BUSINESS & GENERAL ADVICE
Debt Counselling
SPECIALISATIONS – BUSINESS RECOVERY & INSOLVENCY
Liquidations

I D CHILD ACA
68 Cherry Garden Road, Maldon, CM9 6ET

J.R. WILLIAMS & CO
1 Beeches Road, Heybridge, Maldon, CM9 4SL
Tel: 01621 855577
Principal: ICAEW Member
J R Williams

JONATHAN P B HARRIS FCA
The Paddock, Ulting Lane, Ulting, Maldon CM9 6QY
Tel: 01245 380328
Principal: ICAEW Member
J P B Harris

LAMBERT CHAPMAN LLP ◈
The Customs House, 112b High Street, Maldon, CM9 5ET
Tel: 01621 852191
Resident Partners/Directors: ICAEW Members
J M Smith-Daye
SPECIALISATIONS – BUSINESS & GENERAL ADVICE
Management Advice to Business
SPECIALISATIONS – FINANCIAL REPORTING
Accounts Preparation
SPECIALISATIONS – SECTOR
Agriculture
SPECIALISATIONS – TAXATION
Taxation

M.W. AMOR
4 The Colliers, Heybridge Basin, Maldon, CM9 4SE
Tel: 01621 857080
Principal: ICAEW Member
M W Amor

MAYNARD HEADY
2nd Floor, 40/42 High Street, Maldon, CM9 5PN
Tel: 01621 851592
Resident Partners/Directors: ICAEW Members
D M Curtis, P B Dixon, G Tidbury, C H Wilson

MICHAEL J. VENTHAM
Unit 22A, West Station Yard, Spital Road, Maldon CM9 6TS

MJV & CO LTD
Unit 22A, West Station Yard, Spital Road, Maldon CM9 6TS

TOWNSEND & CO ACCOUNTANTS LTD
Office 3, Kings Head Centre, 38 High Street, Maldon CM9 5PN

VERNON WRIGHT & CO
40-42 High Street, Maldon, CM9 5PN

VERNON WRIGHT & CO LTD
40-42 High Street, Maldon, CM9 5PN

MALMESBURY

BLES & CO
Lower Moor Farm, Charlton, Malmesbury, SN16 9DY
Tel: 01666 826699
Principal: ICAEW Member
R M Garforth-Bles

CARRICK
10 Oxford Street, Malmesbury, SN16 9AZ

DUNCAN JOYCE & ASSOCIATES
36-38 Cross Hayes, Malmesbury, SN16 3BG
Tel: 01666 824466
Principal: ICAEW Member
D N Joyce

GREYWALLS
Silver Street, Minety, Malmesbury, SN16 9QU

GREYWALLS ACCOUNTANTS LTD
Greywalls, Silver Street, Minety, Malmesbury SN16 9QU

JENNIFER COLE
The Rookery, Burton Hill, Malmesbury, SN16 0EL
Tel: 01666 829363
Principal: ICAEW Member
J D Cole

MOORE STEPHENS ★
The Old Bank, 10 High Street, Malmesbury, SN16 9AU

MORGWN ATKINS LTD
17 St Marys Street, Malmesbury, SN16 0BJ

PETER I.W. MARSDEN LTD
Moor Farm, Ashton Road, Minety, Malmesbury SN16 9QP

PICKERING
10 Oxford Street, Malmesbury, SN16 9AZ

MALTON

ASHBY, BERRY & CO
19 Wheelgate, Malton, YO17 7HT

HARDCASTLE FRANCE ◈
30 Yorkersgate, Malton, YO17 7AW
Tel: 01653 692107
Fax: 01653 697549
Email: accountants@hardcastlefrance.co.uk
Resident Partners/Directors: ICAEW Members
C G Payne, I D Walker
Registered by the ICAEW to carry out company audit work
Regulated by the ICAEW for a range of investment business activities

J W SMITH & CO LTD
17a Yorkersgate, Malton, YO17 7AA

JW SMITH (MALTON) LTD ◈
17a Yorkersgate, Malton, YO17 7AA

STEPHEN DOUGLAS
Cornwell House, Amotherby, Malton, YO17 6TL
Tel: 01653 691227
Principal: ICAEW Member
S Douglas

TOWNSEND HARRISON LTD
13 Yorkersgate, Malton, YO17 7AA

MALVERN

AIMS - JOHN MACE
54 King Edwards Road, Malvern, WR14 4AJ

ALLAN BROWN & CO
18/22 Church Street, Great Malvern, Malvern, WR14 2AY

ALLAN BROWN ACCOUNTANCY & TAXATION SERVICES LTD
18/22 Church Street, Malvern, WR14 2AY

CROWTHER BEARD LLP
215 Worcester Road, Malvern Link, Malvern, WR14 1SP

FORRESTER & CO
33 Graham Road, Malvern, WR14 2HU
Tel: 01684 561703
Principal: ICAEW Member
N Forrester

FORRESTER & COMPANY (MALVERN) LTD
33 Graham Road, Malvern, WR14 2HU

FORWIL SERVICES
16 The Crescent, Colwall, Malvern, WR13 6QN
Tel: 01684 540595

GALLIERS & CO ◈
Wizzard's Knoll, 33 Cockshot Road, Malvern, WR14 2TT
Tel: 01684 565050
Principal: ICAEW Member
C S Galliers

IAIN A SELKIRK
P O Box 96, Flat 14, Malvern House, Abbey Road, Malvern WR14 3HG

J R PALMER
16 The Crescent, Colwall, Malvern, WR13 6QN

KENDALL WADLEY LLP ◈
Granta Lodge, 71 Graham Road, Malvern, WR14 2JS
Tel: 01684 892666
Website: http://www.kwca.co.uk
Resident Partners/Directors: ICAEW Members
M A Ashworth, C W Brickell, E D Needham
Registered by the ICAEW to carry out company audit work

MAGNES ACCOUNTANTS
52 Fruitlands, Malvern, WR14 4XA

P. BRADFORD
Abbey Cottage, Kings Road, Malvern, WR14 4HL

PATRICIA BERNARD
1 Chapel Close, Leigh Sinton, Malvern, WR13 5BP
Tel: 01886 833468
Principal: ICAEW Member
P J Bernard

PAUL CLIXBY ◈
27 Hornyold Road, Malvern, WR14 1QQ
Tel: 01684 565100
Principal: ICAEW Member
P A Clixby

MANCHESTER

A. PHILLIPS & CO
Wilsons Park, Monsall Road, Newton Heath, Manchester M40 8WN

A2E VENTURE CATALYST LTD ◈
57 Princess Street, Manchester, M2 4EQ
Tel: 0161 923 6000
Resident Partners/Directors: ICAEW Members
S A Amiri
SPECIALISATIONS – BUSINESS & GENERAL ADVICE
Acquisitions and Mergers
Management Consultancy

ACCUMA INSOLVENCY PRACTITIONERS LTD
City Tower, Piccadilly Plaza, Manchester, M1 4BT

ADDING VALUE ACCOUNTANCY
10 Rochford Avenue, Whitefield, Manchester, M45 7PS

ADLERS
349 Bury Old Road, Prestwich, Manchester, M25 1PY

AFORTIS LTD
2 Pennyblack Court, Barton Road, Worsley, Manchester M28 2PD

AKC
42 Charles Street, Manchester, M1 7DB

AKC LTD
42 Charles Street, Manchester, M1 7DB

ALAN BARR & CO
146/148 Bury Old Road, Whitefield, Manchester, M45 6AT
Tel: 0161 796 2250
Principal: ICAEW Member
A M Barr

ALEXANDER & CO ◈
17 St Ann's Square, Manchester, M2 7PW
Tel: 0161 832 4841
Fax: 0161 835 2539
Email: partners@alexander.co.uk
Website: http://www.alexander.co.uk
Resident Partners/Directors: ICAEW Members
F Atkinson, A H Berg, J I Evans, S Jolley, G S Kramrisch, S Topperman, S Verber

Registered by the ICAEW to carry out company audit work

Regulated by the ICAEW for a range of investment business activities

SPECIALISATIONS – AUDIT & ASSURANCE

Assurance Services

SPECIALISATIONS – BUSINESS & GENERAL ADVICE

Acquisitions and Mergers

SPECIALISATIONS – FORENSIC ACCOUNTING

Forensic Accounting

SPECIALISATIONS – TAXATION

Investigations

ALEXANDER BURSK ★ ◈
Parkgates, Bury New Road, Prestwich, Manchester M25 0JW
Tel: 0161 773 7737
Resident Partners/Directors: ICAEW Members
B Fine, B M Shafar

ALLAN PYE
12th Floor, Bank House, Charlotte Street, Manchester M1 4ET
Tel: 0161 228 7727
Principal: ICAEW Member
A Pye

ALVI & CO
15 Manley Road, Manchester, M16 8PN

AMIRI ASSOCIATES ◈
57 Princess Street, Manchester, M2 4EQ

ANDREW POLLOCK
The Triangle, 3rd Floor MLS, Exchange Square, Manchester M4 3TR

ANGEL ACCOUNTANCY SERVICES
3 Stobart Avenue, Prestwich, Manchester, M25 0AJ

ASHRAF AHMED & CO
112 Dickenson Road, Rusholme, Manchester, M14 5HJ

BAKER TILLY
Brazennose House, Lincoln Square, Manchester, M2 5BL
Tel: 0161 834 5777
Resident Partners/Directors: ICAEW Members
G Houghton, D A Thorpe, G E Wightwick

BAKER TILLY
Brazennose House, Lincoln Square, Manchester, M2 5BL
Tel: 0161 834 5777
Resident Partners/Directors: ICAEW Members
G P Bond, D C Buxton, M J Gregg, E B Simon, D A Thorpe, G E Wightwick

BAKER TILLY
Brazennose House, Lincoln Square, Manchester, M2 5BL

BAKER TILLY RESTRUCTURING AND RECOVERY LLP
Brazennose House, Lincoln Square, Manchester, M2 5BL
Tel: 0161 834 5777
Resident Partners/Directors: ICAEW Members
M A Blakemore, L J Cooper

BAKER TILLY REVAS LTD
Brazennose House, Lincoln Square, Manchester, M2 5BL

BAKER TILLY TAX AND ADVISORY SERVICES LLP
Brazennose House, Lincoln Square, Manchester, M2 5BL
Tel: 0161 834 5777
Resident Partners/Directors: ICAEW Members
C P Abrahams, M A Blakemore, G P Bond, D C Buxton, L J Cooper, M J Gregg, G Houghton, W J Oates, E B Simon, D A Thorpe, G E Wightwick
Resident Partners (Non-ICAEW Members):
C Smyth, D Robbins

BALLARD CAMPBELL & PARTNERS LTD
81 King Street, Manchester, M2 4ST

BALLARD CAMPBELL CORPORATE FINANCE
81 King Street, Manchester, M2 4ST

BDO STOY HAYWARD LLP
Commercial Buildings, 11-15 Cross Street, Manchester, M2 1WE
Tel: 0161 817 7500
Fax: 0161 817 7683
Resident Partners/Directors: ICAEW Members
M F Dawson, A J Denton, A M Dumbleton, M Dunham, C Heatlie, G D Lane, A D Marsden, D J Power, J T Rye, E P Solomons, P C Storer, P Terry, B Wilkinson
Resident Partners (Non-ICAEW Members):
J K Adam, C G Sparkes, J A Jones, E H Dwan, A P Lines

BEEVER AND STRUTHERS ◈
St George's House, 215-219 Chester Road, Manchester, M15 4JE
Tel: 0161 832 4901
Fax: 0161 835 3668
Email: b.s@beeverstruthers.co.uk
Website: http://www.beeverstruthers.co.uk
Training Contracts Available.
Resident Partners/Directors: ICAEW Members
J M Adams, S Boyes, M Hallows, D N Hunter, J R Jones, C M Kennedy, T V Maher, A J McLaren, C Monk, C Porritt, P J Roberts, I E Round, P Shaw, A J Speakman, J P Walmsley, P R Wilson
Non-resident Partners (ICAEW Members):
N W Stevens
Other Offices: Alperton House, Bridgewater Road, Wembley HA0 1EH, Email: info@bandslondon.com
(Tel: 020 8902 0809)
(Fax: 020 8902 2722), 17 Stamford New Road, Altrincham, Cheshire WA14 1BN
(Tel: 0161 832 4901)
(Fax: 0161 928 8384)

Registered by the ICAEW to carry out company audit work

Regulated by the ICAEW for a range of investment business activities

SPECIALISATIONS – AUDIT & ASSURANCE

Assurance Services
Audit
Audit — Private Company
Audit — Public Company
Internal Audit
Pension Scheme Auditors

SPECIALISATIONS – BUSINESS & GENERAL ADVICE

Acquisitions and Mergers
Company Secretarial Service
Disposal of Businesses
Divorce/Matrimonial
Management Accounting Consultancy
Management Consultancy
Outsourcing - Financial Services
Risk Management

SPECIALISATIONS – FINANCIAL REPORTING

Accounts Preparation
Audit Exemption Report
Financial Reporting
Limited Company Accounts
Limited Liability Partnership
Partnership/Sole Trader Accounts

SPECIALISATIONS – FORENSIC ACCOUNTING

Expert Witnesses in Litigation
Forensic Accounting

SPECIALISATIONS – INVESTMENT BUSINESS

Pensions Advice
Planning

SPECIALISATIONS – SECTOR

Barristers
Charities
Corporate
Dentists/Opticians
Doctors
FSA Members
Manufacturing
Nursing Homes/Clinics
Property
Registered Social Landlords
Schools
Solicitors
Trade Assoc/Unions/Friendly Societies

SPECIALISATIONS – TAXATION

Capital Gains — Limited Companies
Capital Gains — Personal
Employee
Estate and Inheritance
Estate Planning
Executorship
Foreign Nationals in the UK
Investigations
National Insurance Advice
Partnerships and Sole Traders
PAYE Advice
Payroll Service and Advice
Personal
Self Assessment Advice
Small Traders

continued

BEEVER AND STRUTHERS *cont*

Taxation
Trusteeship
Trusts
Value Added Tax

BEGBIES TRAYNOR LTD
340 Deansgate, Manchester, M3 4LY
Tel: 0161 8371700
Website: http://www.begbies-traynor.com
Resident Partners/Directors: ICAEW Members
S L Conn, G N Lee, J A Reynard, P Stanley, R W Traynor, G J Woodward
Resident Partners (Non-ICAEW Members):
S Conn, J Wright, G Lee, A Dick

SPECIALISATIONS – BUSINESS RECOVERY & INSOLVENCY

Bankruptcies
Corporate Recovery
Liquidations
Reorganisations and Company Reconstructions

SPECIALISATIONS – FORENSIC ACCOUNTING

Expert Witnesses in Litigation
Forensic Accounting

BELFIELD & CO
15 Medlock Road, Failsworth, Manchester, M35 9UA
Tel: 0161 474 7479
Principal: ICAEW Member
R J Belfield

BOLTON CONSULTING LTD
16 Lee Fold, Tyldesley, Manchester, M29 7FQ

BRIGHT PARTNERSHIP
Queen's Chambers, 5 John Dalton Street, Manchester, M2 6FT

BRODY LEE KERSHAW & CO
10 Charlotte Street, Manchester, M1 4EX

BTG MCINNES CORPORATE FINANCE
340 Deansgate, Manchester, M3 4LY

BTG MCINNES CORPORATE FINANCE LLP
340 Deansgate, Manchester, M3 4LY

BUKHARI & CO
389 Wilbraham Road, Chorlton Cum Hardy, Manchester, M21 0UT

C.K. CHUI & CO
1st Floor, 2 Waterloo Street, Manchester, M1 6HX

C K WONG & CO
Citibase, 40 Princess Street, Manchester, M1 6DE

CADISHEAD ACCOUNTANCY SERVICES LTD ◈
Britannic House, 657 Liverpool Road, Irlam, Manchester M44 5XD
Tel: 0161 775 2884
Resident Partners/Directors: ICAEW Members
C A Wilkinson

CARMICHAEL & CO
Ford Campbell Business Centre, New Bailey Street, Manchester, M3 5ER

CASSONS ◈
Rational House, 64 Bridge Street, Manchester, M3 3BN
Tel: 0845 337 9409
Fax: 0845 337 9408
Email: welcome@cassons.co.uk
Website: http://www.cassons.co.uk
Resident Partners/Directors: ICAEW Members
C A Hayman, N C Stockton
Resident Partners (Non-ICAEW Members):
T Reynolds
Other Offices: Haslingden, Lancashire
Registered by the ICAEW to carry out company audit work
Authorised and regulated by the Financial Services Authority for investment business

SPECIALISATIONS – BUSINESS & GENERAL ADVICE

Investment Appraisal

SPECIALISATIONS – FORENSIC ACCOUNTING

Expert Witnesses in Litigation
Forensic Accounting

SPECIALISATIONS – INVESTMENT BUSINESS

Pensions Advice

SPECIALISATIONS – SECTOR

Barristers
Dentists/Opticians
Doctors
Entertainers
Solicitors

SPECIALISATIONS – TAXATION

Estate Planning

CB PARTNERSHIP ★
119 Bury Old Road, Whitefield, Manchester, M45 7AY

CHADWICK
The Lexicon, 10-12 Mount Street, Manchester, M2 5NT

CHADWICK CORPORATE FINANCE
The Lexicon, 10-12 Mount Street, Manchester, M2 5NT
Tel: 0161 832 6088
Resident Partners/Directors: ICAEW Members
K P Simmons

CHADWICK LLP
The Lexicon, 10-12 Mount Street, Manchester, M2 5NT
Tel: 0161 832 6088
Fax: 0161 834 9053
Email: manchester@chadwickllp.co.uk
Website: http://www.chadwickllp.co.uk
Training Contracts Available.
Resident Partners/Directors: ICAEW Members
P L Dawes, D M Garvey, K P Simmons
Non-resident Partners (ICAEW Members):
R Burrows
Non-resident Partners (Non-ICAEW Members):
D Nicholls
Other Offices: Liverpool

SPECIALISATIONS – AUDIT & ASSURANCE

Audit

SPECIALISATIONS – BUSINESS & GENERAL ADVICE

Acquisitions and Mergers
Management Accounting Consultancy

SPECIALISATIONS – FINANCIAL REPORTING

International Reporting Standards (IFRS)

SPECIALISATIONS – SECTOR

Higher Education/Research Establishments

SPECIALISATIONS – TAXATION

Payroll Service and Advice
Taxation

General Description: We are a North West independent business advisory and accountancy practice with 6 partners and 2 directors. Our work includes corporate finance, tax solutions, general advisory (audit, AIM flotation's and forensic), management accounting and payroll. We also act for a wide range of industry sectors.

CHADWICK & COMPANY (MANCHESTER) LTD
Capital House, 272 Manchester Road, Droylsden, Manchester M43 6PW

CHADWICK TAX SOLUTIONS
The Lexicon, 10-12 Mount Street, Manchester, M2 5NT

CHAMPION
1 Worsley Court, High Street, Worsley, Manchester M28 3NJ

CHAMPION
1 Worsley Court, High Street, Worsley, Manchester M28 3NJ

CHAMPION ACCOUNTANTS LLP
1 Worsley Court, High Street, Worsley, Manchester M28 3NJ
Tel: 0161 703 2500
Fax: 0161 703 8212
Email: info@champion-accountants.co.uk
Website: http://www.champion-accountants.co.uk
Resident Partners/Directors: ICAEW Members
G Cosgrove, A J Flanagan, A M Hopwood, D L Thorn, M Turner, D A T Wood
Non-resident Partners (Non-ICAEW Members):
R Thompson, G Hyde
Other Offices: Southport, Chester, Preston, Blackpool

CHAMPION BUSINESS SOLUTIONS LTD
1 Worsley Court, High Street, Worsley, Manchester M28 3NJ
Tel: 0161 703 2500
Fax: 0161 703 8212
Email: info@champion-accountants.co.uk
Website: http://www.champion-accountants.co.uk
Other Offices: Chester, Preston, Blackpool, Southport

CHAMPION CONSULTING LTD
1 Worsley Court, High Street, Worsley, Manchester M28 3NJ

CHAPMAN & CO
39 Ferndene Road, Whitefield, Manchester, M45 6RB
Tel: 0161 798 9838
Principal: ICAEW Member
M S Chapman

CHCA LTD
456 Chester Road, Old Trafford, Manchester, M16 9HD

CHISTIAN DOUGLASS
2 Jordan Street, Knott Mill, Manchester, M15 4PY
Tel: 0161 236 6163

CHITTENDEN HORLEY
456 Chester Road, Old Trafford, Manchester, M16 9HD

CHITTENDEN HORLEY LTD
456 Chester Road, Old Trafford, Manchester, M16 9HD

CHRISTIAN DOUGLASS LLP
2 Jordan Street, Knott Mill, Manchester, M15 4PY
Tel: 0161 236 6163
Email: info@christiandouglass.com
Website: http://www.christiandouglass.com
Resident Partners/Directors: ICAEW Members
G Storey, N Warburton
Registered by the ICAEW to carry out company audit work

Regulated by the ICAEW for a range of investment business activities

CLARKE BELL LTD
Parsonage Chambers, 3 The Parsonage, Manchester, M3 2HW
Tel: 0161 907 4044
Resident Partners/Directors: ICAEW Members
J P Bell

CLB COOPERS ★ ◈
Century House, 11 St Peters Square, Manchester, M2 3DN
Tel: 0161 245 1000
Fax: 0161 245 1001
Email: manchester@clbcoopers.co.uk
Website: http://www.clbcoopers.co.uk
Training Contracts Available.
Resident Partners/Directors: ICAEW Members
D R Clift, R Schofield, M Sykes, D J Travis
Resident Partners (Non-ICAEW Members):
M T Getliffe, D E Hill, A J White, S J Lindsay

Registered by the ICAEW to carry out company audit work

Regulated by the ICAEW for a range of investment business activities
Individual(s) licensed for insolvency work by the ICAEW

SPECIALISATIONS – BUSINESS RECOVERY & INSOLVENCY

Corporate Recovery
Liquidations

SPECIALISATIONS – TAXATION

Investigations

General Description: CLB Coopers - Delivering solutions through excellence.

CLEARWATER CORPORATE FINANCE LLP
Sovereign House, 12-18 Queen Street, Manchester, M2 5HS

COLE ASSOCIATES CORPORATE FINANCE
4th Floor, 81 King Street, Manchester, M2 4ST
Tel: 0161 832 9945
Principal: ICAEW Member
J B Cole

COLIN WILKINSON ◈
Britannic House, 657 Liverpool Road, Irlam, Manchester M44 5XD
Tel: 0161 775 2884
Principal: ICAEW Member
C A Wilkinson

COMMUNITY ACCOUNTANCY SERVICE LTD
The Grange, Pilgrim Drive, Beswick, Manchester M11 3TQ
Tel: 0161 230 1429
Resident Partners/Directors: ICAEW Members
E L Anderson

COOMBES CORPORATE FINANCE LLP
Adamson House, Towers Business Park, Wilmslow Road, Manchester M20 2YY

COWGILL HOLLOWAY LLP
4th Floor, 49 Peter Street, Manchester, M2 3NG
Tel: 0161 827 1200
Fax: 0161 827 1201
Date Established: 2006
Resident Partners/Directors: ICAEW Members
M M Parmar, P W Stringer
Non-resident Partners (ICAEW Members):
P Stansfield, S Stead, A Ball, P Cowgill, J Marshall, M Murphy
Resident Partners (Non-ICAEW Members):
I Johnson
Non-resident Partners (Non-ICAEW Members):
S Galhagar

Registered by the ICAEW to carry out company audit work

Regulated by the ICAEW for a range of investment business activities

CRAWLEY & CO
47 Newton Street, Manchester, M1 1FT
Tel: 0161 228 7269
Principal: ICAEW Member
J Crawley

DAGGETT AND CO ◈
516 Wilmslow Road, Withington, Manchester, M20 4BS
Tel: 01614 487171
Principal: ICAEW Member
T M Daggett

Registered by the ICAEW to carry out company audit work

Regulated by the ICAEW for a range of investment business activities

DAVID ELLIOTT ASSOCIATES
Manchester Business Park, 3000 Aviator Way, Manchester, M22 5TG

DAVID M. OTHICK
12 Parr Fold Avenue, Worsley, Manchester, M28 7HD

DBF ASSOCIATES
Sahaj Anand Business Centre, 10 Park Place, Manchester, M4 4EY

DE LA WYCHE TRAVIS & CO
Crown House, Trafford Park Road, Trafford Park, Manchester M17 1HG

DELOITTE & TOUCHE LLP ◈
PO Box 500, 2 Hardman Street, Manchester, M60 2AT
Tel: 0161 832 3555
Website: http://www.deloitte.co.uk
Resident Partners/Directors: ICAEW Members
A W Beardsworth, C R Bell, J E Birkett, J A Clark, S D Cuerden, W K Dawson, T Edge, M Einollahi, A J Farnworth, A D Fendall, S J Fraser, D S Hughes, D C R Jones, P J Loftus, P N C Lupton, D O'Leary, D R Sanders, M J Smith, M Stephenson, P R Trickett, A J Westbrook, B J White, A P Wilde

DTE ◈
1 North Parade, Manchester, M3 2NH

DTE CORPORATE RECOVERY AND INSOLVENCY SERVICES LTD
1 North Parade, Parsonage Gardens, Manchester, M3 2NH

EASTWOODS
Coral House, 42 Charles Street, Manchester, M1 7DB

ELIZABETH WHITELEY ACCOUNTANCY LTD
2 The Meade, Chorlton, Manchester, M21 8FA
Tel: 0161 881 2721
Resident Partners/Directors: ICAEW Members
E Whiteley

ELLIOTT BUSINESS ADVISORY SERVICES LTD
Manchester Business Park, 3000 Aviator Way, Manchester, M22 5TG

ERNST & YOUNG LLP
100 Barbirolli Square, Manchester, M2 3EY
Tel: 0161 333 3000
Resident Partners/Directors: ICAEW Members
S Allport, D Brewin, J P Gregory, N D Handler, K R Hills, T A Jack, M F Jones, M D Leary, D W Leather, E J McGrath, E O'Donnell, T S Oldfield, M J Portnoy, M A Senior, S A Smith, M J Wildig, T M Wood

EVERETTS
86 Bury Old Road, Cheetham Village, Manchester, M8 5BW
Tel: 0161 795 0047
Principal: ICAEW Member
S J Kay

F. MAZLOOMIAN & CO
73/75 Princess Street, Manchester, M2 4EG
Tel: 0161 237 9900
Principal: ICAEW Member
F Mazloomian

FINLAY ROBERTSON
Suite 5B, Brook House, 77 Fountain Street, Manchester M2 2EE

FORENSIC ACCOUNTING SOLUTIONS
6th Floor, 49 King Street, Manchester, M2 7AY

FREEDMAN, FRANKL & TAYLOR ◈
Reedham House, 31 King Street West, Manchester, M3 2PJ
Tel: 0161 834 2574
Email: mail@fft.co.uk
Website: http://www.fft.co.uk
Resident Partners/Directors: ICAEW Members
A S R Cohen, R I Frankl, I Sluckis, P J Stoker, K Taylor, T H Whitehurst

G.A.HARRIS & CO
Unit C & D, Jubilee Park, Hanson Close, Middleton, Manchester M24 2UH

G.A.HARRIS & CO
6 St Mary's Road, Prestwich, Manchester, M25 1AP

GARBUTT & ELLIOTT LTD
Peter House, Oxford Street, Manchester, M1 5AN
Tel: 0161 602 3250

GEORGE & CO
Gorsi House, Hamer Street, Off Cross Lane, Radcliffe, Manchester M26 2RS

GODFREY HOLLAND
Venture House, 341 Palatine Road, Northenden, Manchester M22 4FY
Tel: 0161 998 8668

GODFREY HOLLAND LTD
Venture House, 341 Palatine Road, Northenden, Manchester M22 4FY
Tel: 0161 998 8668
Resident Partners/Directors: ICAEW Members
A N Vause

GOODMANS ◈
138 Bury Old Road, Whitefield, Manchester, M45 6AT
Tel: 0161 28 05666
Principal: ICAEW Member
R A Goodman

GORDON LEVY LTD
23 New Mount Street, Manchester, M4 4DE

GORTONS ◈
Stanmore House, 64-68 Blackburn Street, Radcliffe, Manchester M26 2JS
Tel: 0161 723 6420
Resident Partners/Directors: ICAEW Members
A J Gorton, D J Gorton

GRAHAM I. RYDER
120 Ashton Road, Denton, Manchester, M34 3JE

GRANT THORNTON UK LLP
4 Hardman Square, Spinningfields, Manchester, M3 3EB
Tel: 0161 953 6900
Resident Partners/Directors: ICAEW Members
S R Baker, D L Barnes, N E Farr, E J G Healey, J M Kearns, J C Loebl, S L Longworth, P S Prior, L Ross, A A Sharifi, J M Shinnick, G D Williams, T J L Wilson
Resident Partners (Non-ICAEW Members):
A Sofield, K L Campbell, G P Summers, G J Whittaker, P S Wilde, I Falconer, A Westhead

GUEST & CO
91 Princess Street, Manchester, M1 4HT
Tel: 0161 228 2071
Principal: ICAEW Member
J A Guest

HAFFNER, HOFF & CO ★
3rd Floor, Manchester House, 86 Princess St, Manchester M1 6NP
Tel: 0161 236 4107
Fax: 0161 236 8503
Email: haffhoff@haffhoff.co.uk
Date Established: 1947
Resident Partners/Directors: ICAEW Members
A L Haffner
Resident Partners (Non-ICAEW Members):
M Hoff, D Schwarz
Registered by the ICAEW to carry out company audit work
Regulated by the ICAEW for a range of investment business activities

SPECIALISATIONS – FINANCIAL REPORTING
Accounts Preparation
Limited Company Accounts

SPECIALISATIONS – SECTOR
Barristers
Charities
Property
Property Investment

Languages Spoken:
Hebrew, Yiddish

HAINES WATTS CORPORATE FINANCE (NW) ★
1st Floor, Northern Assurance Buildings, Albert Square, 9-21 Princess Street, Manchester M2 4DN
Tel: 0161 832 6413
Resident Partners/Directors: ICAEW Members
G C Fairclough, D M Fort, A M W Godfrey, S T Moriarty, A N Sumner, J L Whittick

HALL LIDDY
12 St John Street, Manchester, M3 4DY
Tel: 0161 832 7571
Resident Partners/Directors: ICAEW Members
D J Hall, D P Liddy, A J Pow

SPECIALISATIONS – SECTOR
Doctors

HALLIDAYS LTD
Portland Buildings, 127-129 Portland Street, Manchester, M1 4PZ

HARRIS ◈
75 Mosley Street, Manchester, M2 3HR

HAS LTD
Prince Albert House, 2b Mather Avenue, Prestwich, Manchester M25 0LA

HAYES & CO
6 Eckersley Precinct, Alma Street, Atherton, Manchester M46 0DR
Tel: 01942 888001
Email: admin@hayesandco.co.uk
Resident Partners/Directors: ICAEW Members
A J Wardle

Horwath Clark Whitehill

HORWATH CLARK WHITEHILL LLP
Arkwright House, Parsonage Gardens, Manchester, M3 2HP
Tel: 0161 214 7500
Website: http://www.horwathcw.com/hwclarkwhitehill/ouroffices/manchester.cfm
Training Contracts Available.
Resident Partners/Directors: ICAEW Members
M J H Jayson, S C Livingston, D V Szulist, J Wolf
Registered by the ICAEW to carry out company audit work
Authorised and regulated by the Financial Services Authority for investment business

SPECIALISATIONS – AUDIT & ASSURANCE
Audit

SPECIALISATIONS – FINANCIAL REPORTING
Accounts Preparation

SPECIALISATIONS – INVESTMENT BUSINESS
Financial Planning and Advice

SPECIALISATIONS – TAXATION
Taxation

HSA ASSOCIATES ★
89 Chorley Road, Swinton, Manchester, M27 4AA

HURST CORPORATE FINANCE ◈
Centurion House, 129 Deansgate, Manchester, M3 3WR
Tel: 0161 4772474

HWCA LTD ◈
Northern Assurance Buildings, Albert Square, 9-21 Princess Street, Manchester M2 4DN
Tel: 0161 832 6413
Resident Partners/Directors: ICAEW Members
F J Cresswell, D M Fort, J E Pomfret

IMPACT BUSINESS MANAGEMENT LTD
Bankfield Road, Tyldesley, Manchester, M29 8QH

INFINITY ASSET MANAGEMENT LLP
26th Floor, City Tower, Piccadilly Plaza, Manchester M1 4BD

ISLAM & AHMED LTD
68 Seymour Grove, Old Trafford, Manchester, M16 0LN

J MORRIS & CO
17 St Anns Square, Manchester, M2 7PW

J ROEBUCK & CO LTD
148 Droylsden Road, Audenshaw, Manchester, M34 5SJ

JA
9 Hudswell Close, Whitefield, Manchester, M45 7UD

JACK ROSS ◈
Barnfield House, The Approach, Manchester, M3 7BX

JEFFREY A HUDDART ◈
164 Walkden Road, Worsley, Manchester, M28 7DP
Tel: 0161 703 8353
Principal: ICAEW Member
J A Huddart
Registered by the ICAEW to carry out company audit work
Regulated by the ICAEW for a range of investment business activities

JOHN A. PORTER & CO ★
74 Dickenson Road, Manchester, M14 5HF

JON CHILD & CO
107 Oldham Street, Manchester, M4 1LW

JONES, LANG & PARTNERS
105-107 Chorley Road, Swinton, Manchester, M27 4AA

JT FINANCIAL SERVICES
163 Lily Hill Street, Whitefield, Manchester, M45 7SP

KAY JOHNSON GEE ◈
Griffin Court, 201 Chapel Street, Manchester, M3 5EQ
Tel: 0161 832 6221
Fax: 0161 834 8479
Email: info@kayjohnsongee.com
Website: http://www.kayjohnsongee.com
Date Established: 1947
Resident Partners/Directors: ICAEW Members
J E Avery-Gee, J L V Beressi, R Blaskey
Resident Partners (Non-ICAEW Members):
R E Ward
Registered by the ICAEW to carry out company audit work
Regulated by the ICAEW for a range of investment business activities
Individual(s) licensed for insolvency work by the ICAEW

KPMG LLP
St James' Square, Manchester, M2 6DS
Tel: 0161 246 4000
Resident Partners/Directors: ICAEW Members
D J Bills, J M Boyers, S Burdass, J J Costello, D J Costley-Wood, M C G Edge, W A Enevoldson, R V Evans, C R Fry, D P Gascoigne, I M Goalen, B Green, C D Hewson, S P Heywood, J M Holt, J Hughes, J P F Hurst, R A Little, C Mayo, G Odlin, N J Plumb, R C Powell, N Quayle, T M E Rees
Resident Partners (Non-ICAEW Members):
A R Cawley, S Musa, M A O'Flaherty, R J Philpott, L E Stone, M Walker

KROLL TALBOT HUGHES
The Observatory, Chapel Walks, Manchester, M2 1HL

LEON & HERMAN & CO ◈
7 Christie Way, Christie Fields, Manchester, M21 7QY
Tel: 0161 249 5040
Fax: 0161 448 9287
Email: alanc@leonherman.co.uk
Website: http://www.leonherman.co.uk

Resident Partners/Directors: ICAEW Members
A J Cohen
Resident Partners (Non-ICAEW Members):
D Swann
Registered by the ICAEW to carry out company audit work
Regulated by the ICAEW for a range of investment business activities

LEWIS ALEXANDER & CONNAUGHTON
Second Floor, Boulton House, 17-21 Chorlton Street, Manchester M1 3HY

LEWIS HASSELL
235 Bury New Road, Whitefield, Manchester, M45 8QP

LIZ CLARK
32 Sandhurst Avenue, West Didsbury, Manchester, M20 1ED
Tel: 0161 286 9052
Principal: ICAEW Member
E Clark

LLOYD MARVIN LTD
4 Penarth Road, Northenden, Manchester, M22 4AR

LLOYD PIGGOTT
Wellington House, 1st Floor, 39-41 Piccadilly, Manchester M1 1LQ

LLOYD PIGGOTT LTD
Wellington House, 1st Floor, 39-41 Piccadilly, Manchester M1 1LQ

LLOYD PIGGOTT (POYNTON) LTD
Wellington House, 39a Piccadilly, Manchester, M1 1LQ

LOPIAN, GROSS, BARNETT & CO ◈
6th Floor, Cardinal House, 20 St Marys Parsonage, Manchester M3 2LG
Tel: 0161 832 8721
Fax: 0161 835 3085
Email: alex.kahan@lopiangb.co.uk
Website: http://www.lopiangb.co.uk
Date Established: 1951
Resident Partners/Directors: ICAEW Members
E Epstein, S Kahan, D Z Lopian, S A Lopian, J H Selig, B P White
Registered by the ICAEW to carry out company audit work
Regulated by the ICAEW for a range of investment business activities
General Description: We are a general practice providing an all-round and comprehensive accountancy service for growing enterprises. The practice has built a reputation for developing proactive solutions to clients' problems across the full spectrum of professional accountancy services with a recognised strength in the property sector, service industries and trusts and tax planning, including non-residents and non-domicile aspects.

M. EPSTEIN & CO
250 Middleton Road, Crumpsall, Manchester, M8 4WA

M. SEITLER & CO
18 Ravensway, Prestwich, Manchester, M25 0EU

MCR ★
11 St James's Square, Manchester, M2 6WH

MALCOLM ROUSSAK & CO
52 Bury Old Road, Whitefield, Manchester, M45 6TL
Tel: 0161 773 4588
Fax: 0161 773 9939
Email: roussakm@aol.com
Principal: ICAEW Member
M Roussak

MANAGEMENT OF PERSONAL INSOLVENCIES LTD
Ford Campbell Business Centre, New Bailey Street, Manchester, M3 5ER

MARIOS ARISTOU KRITICOS & CO
16 Adamson Gardens, Manchester, M20 2TQ

MAZARS CORPORATE FINANCE LTD ◈
Merchant Exchange, Whitworth Street West, Manchester, M1 5WG

MAZARS LLP ◈
Merchant Exchange, Whitworth Street West, Manchester, M1 5WG
Tel: 0161 209 5050
Resident Partners/Directors: ICAEW Members
T A Askham, T W Hudson, S Rai
Registered by the ICAEW to carry out company audit work
Authorised and regulated by the Financial Services Authority for investment business
Individual(s) licensed for insolvency work by the ICAEW

MICHAEL BROOKES & CO ◈
Hampton House, Oldham Road, Middleton, Manchester M24 1GT
Tel: 0161 655 2000
Fax: 0161 653 5358
Principal: ICAEW Member
M Brookes

MICHAEL J. LEAHY
47 Vicars Road, Chorlton-Cum-Hardy, Manchester, M21 9JB
Tel: 0161 881 5692
Principal: ICAEW Member
M J Leahy

MITCHELL CHARLESWORTH ◈
Brazennose House West, Brazennose Street, Manchester, M2 5FE
Tel: 0161 817 6100
Resident Partners/Directors: ICAEW Members
P N Booth, A Buckley, D Frangleton, G M Weisgard

MOFFATT & CO
396 Wilmslow Road, Withington, Manchester, M20 3BN
Tel: 0161 434 8416
Resident Partners/Directors: ICAEW Members
M J Leahy, P F Mundy, J C Saxon, C Warren

MOKHTASSI
169 Kingsway, Manchester, M19 2ND

MONTPELIER AUDIT LTD
Montpelier House, 62-66 Deansgate, Manchester, M3 2EN

MONTPELIER PROFESSIONAL (MANCHESTER) LTD
Montpelier House, 62-66 Deansgate, Manchester, M3 2EN

MOORE STEPHENS
6th Floor, Blackfriars House, The Parsonage, Manchester M3 2JA
Tel: 0161 832 4281
Resident Partners/Directors: ICAEW Members
P D R Holden, P G D Holden

MUNAVER RASUL
265 Talbot Road, Stretford, Manchester, M32 0YW

NABARRO POOLE
31 Church Road, Northenden, Manchester, M22 4NN

NAIRNE, SON & GREEN ◈
477 Chester Road, Manchester, M16 9HF
Tel: 0161 872 1701
Fax: 0161 876 4752
Email: jmedge@nairnes.co.uk
Resident Partners/Directors: ICAEW Members
J M Edge, C Roberts
Registered by the ICAEW to carry out company audit work
Regulated by the ICAEW for a range of investment business activities

NICOLA JONES
30 Tamar Close, Whitefield, Manchester, M45 8SJ
Tel: 0161 272 1132
Principal: ICAEW Member
N Jones

NJB FINANCIAL CONSULTANTS LTD
2 The Straits, Astley, Tyldesley, Manchester M29 7RR

NORTHLINE BUSINESS CONSULTANTS LTD ◈
2nd Floor, Clarendon Centre, 38 Clarendon Road, Monton, Eccles, Manchester M30 9ES

P & CO
48 Faulkner Street, Manchester, M1 4FH

P AND CO LLP
48 Faulkner Street, Manchester, M1 4FH

PERCY WESTHEAD & CO
Greg's Buildings, 1 Booth Street, Manchester, M2 4AD

PETER M. HOLIDAY ◈
Western House, 44 Western Road, Urmston, Manchester M41 6LF
Tel: 0161 747 9366
Principal: ICAEW Member
P M Holiday

PHILIP MARTIN LTD ◈
Crown House, 4 High Street, Tyldesley, Manchester M29 8AL
Tel: 01942 887872
Resident Partners/Directors: ICAEW Members
P J Martin

PHILIP POTTER
20 Egerton Road, Monton, Eccles, Manchester M30 9LR

PKF (UK) LLP
Sovereign House, Queen Street, Manchester, M2 5HR
Tel: 0161 832 5481
Email: info.manchester@uk.pkf.com
Website: http://www.pkf.co.uk
Resident Partners/Directors: ICAEW Members
D G Bancroft, I A Bingham, C M Brook, F J Cooke, T J Entwistle, T A Frost, M D Gibson, J F Grogan, J D Hiley, I C Marsden, I E Mills, H F Sharpe, R D Smith
Resident Partners (Non-ICAEW Members):
K Bailey

POWELL & POWELL LTD ◈
13-15 Edge Lane, Stretford, Manchester, M32 8HN

PRICEWATERHOUSE-COOPERS
Abacus Court, 6 Minshull Street, Manchester, M1 3ED

PRICEWATERHOUSE-COOPERS
101 Barbirolli Square, Lower Mosley Street, Manchester, M2 3PW

PRICEWATERHOUSE-COOPERS LLP
Abacus Court, 6 Minshull Street, Manchester, M1 3ED
Tel: 0161 236 9191

PRICEWATERHOUSE-COOPERS LLP
101 Barbirolli Square, Lower Mosley Street, Manchester, M2 3PW
Tel: 0161 245 2000
Resident Partners/Directors: ICAEW Members
C M Adshead, S W Beet, N W E Boden, M C Bolton, R Bunter, D J Burn, B L Clark, J S Cowling, C S Gillespie, N J P Gower, M A Heath, S A Herbert, A J Lever, D W McKeith, P A Meades, C O'Hare, J P Rayner, N J Richens, D A Roper, P B Smith, S N Warriner, M J Wilde

PROUD GOULBOURN
608 Liverpool Road, Irlam, Manchester, M44 5AA
Tel: 0161 777 6116
Principal: ICAEW Member
K A Rogers
Registered by the ICAEW to carry out company audit work

QAYYUM & CO ◈
Portland House, 431 Chester Road, Manchester, M16 9HA
Tel: 0161 877 9222
Principal: ICAEW Member
A Qayyum
Registered by the ICAEW to carry out company audit work
Regulated by the ICAEW for a range of investment business activities

R.A. MOORE
421 Middleton Rd, Middleton, Manchester, M24 4QZ

R & M
Repeat House, Bright Road, Manchester, M30 0WG

R FOSTER & CO (ACCOUNTANTS) LTD
Orchid House, 243 Elliott Street, Tyldesley, Manchester M29 8DG

RAY (ACCOUNTANTS) LTD
78 Dickenson Road, Rusholme, Manchester, M14 5HF

RICHARDSON & CO
Summerville, 65 Daisy Bank Rd, Victoria Pk, Manchester M14 5QL
Tel: 0161 256 2481
Principal: ICAEW Member
E K Richardson

RIDGETOWN LLP
82 King Street, Manchester, M2 4WQ

RILEY MOSS LTD
1st Floor, 9 Stocks Street, Manchester, M8 8GW

ROBBINS PARTNERSHIP
176 Monton Road, Monton, Eccles, Manchester M30 9GA
Tel: 0161 789 3508
Resident Partners/Directors: ICAEW Members
A Ioannou, D C Robbins

ROHANS AUDITORS LTD
Adamson House, Towers Business Park, Didsbury, Manchester M20 2YY

ROSENBERG & CO
28A Bury New Road, Prestwich, Manchester, M25 0LD
Tel: 0161 773 5557
Principal: ICAEW Member
H Rosenberg
Registered by the ICAEW to carry out company audit work

ROSH FD LTD ◈
Charlotte House, 10 Charlotte Street, Manchester, M1 4EX

ROYCE PEELING GREEN
The Copper Room, Deva Centre, Trinity Way, Manchester M3 7BG

ROYCE PEELING GREEN LTD
The Copper Room, Deva Centre, Trinity Way, Manchester M3 7BG
Tel: 0161 608 0000
Fax: 0161 608 0001
Email: info@rpg.co.uk
Website: http://www.rpg.co.uk
Training Contracts Available.
Resident Partners/Directors: ICAEW Members
J S Brownson, P J Buckley, A Burnett, S Murrills, I Paramor, C Poston, P Randall, J J Redmond, C Slater
Resident Partners (Non-ICAEW Members):
P R Owen, J Jones
Other Offices:15 Buckingham Gate, London SW1E 6LB (Tel: 020 7963 9032), The Roe, St Asaph, Denbighshire, LL17 0HY
Registered by the ICAEW to carry out company audit work
Regulated by the ICAEW for a range of investment business activities
Individual(s) licensed for insolvency work by the ICAEW
Individual(s) licensed for insolvency work by another RPB

RPG
The Copper Room, Deva Centre, Trinity Way, Manchester M3 7BG

RSM BENTLEY JENNISON ◈
26 Pall Mall, Manchester, M2 1JR
Tel: 0161 819 3030
Principal: ICAEW Member
R G Evans, P R Langhorn, G Lovell, C Hine
Registered by the ICAEW to carry out company audit work

RWF RUBINSTEIN
171 Bury New Road, Whitefield, Manchester, M45 6AB

S. CROWTHER & CO
91 Glebelands Road, Prestwich, Manchester, M25 1WF

S. DAVIES & CO
148 Bury New Road, Whitefield, Manchester, M45 6AD
Tel: 0161 280 8820
Principal: ICAEW Member
S Davies

SADDIQUE & CO
78 Dickenson Road, Rusholme, Manchester, M14 5HF
Tel: 0161 257 2100

SADIQ, METCALFE & CO
94 Dickenson Road, Manchester, M14 5HJ

SAFFERY CHAMPNESS ◈
City Tower, Piccadilly Plaza, Manchester, M1 4BT
Tel: 0161 200 8383
Fax: 0161 200 8384
Website: http://www.saffery.com
Training Contracts Available.
Resident Partners/Directors: ICAEW Members
M J Harrison, S R Kite
Other Offices: Bournemouth, Bristol, Edinburgh, Geneva, Guernsey, Harrogate, High Wycombe, Inverness, London, Peterborough
Registered by the ICAEW to carry out company audit work
Regulated by the ICAEW for a range of investment business activities

INVESTOR IN PEOPLE

General Description: See London office entry.

SCB (ACCOUNTANTS) LTD
31 Sackville Street, Manchester, M1 3LZ

SHACTER COHEN BOR
29-31 Sackville Street, Manchester, M1 3LZ

SHAIK & CO LTD
1145 Oldham Road, Newton Heath, Manchester, M40 2FU
Tel: 0161 683 5591
Fax: 0161 683 0300
Email: shaikcoltd@yahoo.co.uk
Date Established: 1989
Resident Partners/Directors: ICAEW Members
A A Shaik
Registered by the ICAEW to carry out company audit work

SHANE O'NEILL ESQ. BA ACA
26 Montreal Street, Levenshulme, Manchester, M19 3BY

SHAW AUSTIN ◈
47 Manchester Road, Denton, Manchester, M34 2AF
Tel: 0161 336 3639

SIMPSON BURGESS NASH LTD
Ground Floor, Maclaren House, Lancastrian Office Centre, Talbot Road, Old Trafford, Manchester M32 0FP

SLADE & COOPER
6 Mount Street, Manchester, M2 5NS
Tel: 0161 831 0100
SPECIALISATIONS – SECTOR

Charities

SLADE & COOPER LTD
6 Mount Street, Manchester, M2 5NS
Tel: 0161 831 0100
Website: http://www.sladecooper.co.uk
Resident Partners/Directors: ICAEW Members
P M Cowham
Resident Partners (Non-ICAEW Members):
S Cooper, J Gore-Langton
SPECIALISATIONS – SECTOR

Charities

STANLEY L. FELDMAN
7 Pinfold Court, Pinfold Lane, Whitefield, Manchester M45 7NZ
Tel: 0161 766 4362
Principal: ICAEW Member
S L Feldman

SUMM.IT
74 Gartside Street, Spinningfields, Manchester, M3 3EL

SUMMIT ACCOUNTING SOLUTIONS LLP
74 Gartside Street, Spinningfields, Manchester, M3 3EL

TAXASSIST ACCOUNTANTS MANCHESTER ◈
Unit 1 City Point, 156 Chapel Street, Manchester, M3 6BF
Tel: 0161 834 6660
Email: peterrushton@taxassist.co.uk
Principal: ICAEW Member
P S Rushton

TENON LTD
Arkwright House, Parsonage Gardens, Manchester, M3 2LF
Tel: 0161 834 3313
Resident Partners/Directors: ICAEW Members
C Ratten

TENON LTD
York House, 20 York Street, Manchester, M2 3BB
Tel: 0161 200 6080

TESCIUBA LTD ◈
Sunlight House, Quay Street, Manchester, M3 3JZ
Tel: 0161 834 9221
Resident Partners/Directors: ICAEW Members
A J Tesciuba

TF & PARTNERS LTD
New Maxdov House, 130 Bury New Road, Prestwich, Manchester M25 0AA

TFD DUNHAMS ◈
11 Warwick Road, Old Trafford, Manchester, M16 0QQ

TMG CORPORATE FINANCE
16 Oxford Court, Manchester, M2 3WQ

TOMLINSONS ★
St John's Court, 72 Gartside Street, Manchester, M3 3EL

TONY FREEMAN & CO
New Maxdov House, 130 Bury New Road, Prestwich, Manchester M25 0AA

UHY HACKER YOUNG
St James Buildings, 79 Oxford Street, Manchester, M1 6HT

UHY HACKER YOUNG MANCHESTER LLP ◈
St James Buildings, 79 Oxford Street, Manchester, M1 6HT
Tel: 0161 236 6936
Fax: 0161 228 0117
Email: manchester@uhy-uk.com
Website: http://www.uhy-uk.com
Training Contracts Available.
Resident Partners/Directors: ICAEW Members
N C Gawthorpe, S J Lawson, C S Maudsley, D Symonds, M D Wasinski
Resident Partners (Non-ICAEW Members):
E Stanton, B J Leyland, M Robertson, G Clarke, N A Hancock, R S Holt
Registered by the ICAEW to carry out company audit work
Regulated by the ICAEW for a range of investment business activities

SPECIALISATIONS – AUDIT & ASSURANCE
Audit

SPECIALISATIONS – BUSINESS & GENERAL ADVICE
Acquisitions and Mergers
Book-keeping
Company Secretarial Service
Management Accounting
Consultancy

SPECIALISATIONS – FINANCIAL REPORTING
Accounts Preparation
Limited Company Accounts

SPECIALISATIONS – INVESTMENT BUSINESS
Planning

SPECIALISATIONS – SECTOR
Construction
Corporate
FSA Members
Property Development
Property Investment
Solicitors
Travel Industry

SPECIALISATIONS – TAXATION
Personal
Taxation
Value Added Tax

General Description: The practice was established in the 1920's and its growth has been based upon a personal and professional service to clients of all sizes.

UHY HACKER YOUNG TURNAROUND AND RECOVERY
St James Buildings, 79 Oxford Street, Manchester, M1 6HT

USHERS LTD
76 Manchester Road, Denton, Manchester, M34 3PS
Tel: 0161 336 2222
Resident Partners/Directors: ICAEW Members
D T Lever, A C Walton

VORA & CO
30 Pasture Field Road, Peel Hall, Manchester, M22 5JU

WALTER RIDGWAY & SON LTD
69 Flixton Road, Urmston, Manchester, M41 5AN
Tel: 0161 748 5624
Email: admin@walter-ridgway.co.uk
Resident Partners/Directors: ICAEW Members
D Pick

WARBURTON AND CO LTD
806 Hyde Road, Gorton, Manchester, M18 7JD
Tel: 0161 223 6007
Resident Partners/Directors: ICAEW Members
I G Warburton

WILDS
Lancaster House, 70-76 Blackburn Street, Radcliffe, Manchester M26 2JW

WILDS LTD
Lancaster House, 70-76 Blackburn Street, Radcliffe, Manchester M26 2JW

WILLIAMS & CO ◈
New Maxdov House, 130 Bury New Road, Prestwich, Manchester M25 0AA
Tel: 0161 773 2006
Principal: ICAEW Member
R I Williams

WOOD BROOKS & CO
2 Jordan Street, Knott Mill, Manchester, M15 4PY
Tel: 0161 236 6163

MANSFIELD

ADKIN SINCLAIR
Sterling House, 32 St John Street, Mansfield, NG18 1QJ

ADKIN SINCLAIR LLP
Sterling House, 32 St John Street, Mansfield, NG18 1QJ

APC
7 St John Street, Mansfield, NG18 1QH

APC ACCOUNTANTS LTD
7 St John Street, Mansfield, NG18 1QH

BARNETT & TURNER ◈
Cromwell House, 68 West Gate, Mansfield, NG18 1RR
Tel: 01623 659659
Resident Partners/Directors: ICAEW Members
Y Lovett, D Wilson

BEELEY HAWLEY & CO LTD ◈
44 Nottingham Road, Mansfield, NG18 1BL
Tel: 01623 645705
Resident Partners/Directors: ICAEW Members
G M Beeley, P M Beeley, R M Callingham

FINDLAY JAMES
Rees House, Nursery Street, Mansfield, NG18 2AG

GREGORY PRIESTLEY & STEWART ★ ◈
Rees House, 26 Nursery Street, Mansfield, NG18 2AG
Tel: 01623 420194

K.J.EATON & CO (ACCOUNTANTS) LTD
Edwinstowe House, High Street, Edwinstowe, Mansfield NG21 9PR
Tel: 01623 827976
Resident Partners/Directors: ICAEW Members
P D Eaton

M.G. QUELCH & CO ◈
5 Brewers Way, Mansfield, NG18 3GL
Tel: 01623 420745
Principal: ICAEW Member
M G Quelch
Registered by the ICAEW to carry out company audit work
General Description: Accounts, Audit and Tax for owner-managed businesses.
Languages Spoken:
French

MCGREGORS (MANSFIELD) LTD
90 Nottingham Road, Mansfield, NG18 1BP

NICHOLAS & WALTERS
54/56 Victoria Street, Shirebrook, Mansfield, NG20 8AQ

SEALS KING & CO LTD ◈
17 Brunts Street, Mansfield, NG18 1AX

SLANEY & CO
26 St John Street, Mansfield, NG18 1QJ

STOPFORD ASSOCIATES
Synergy House, 3 Acorn Business Park, Commercial Gate, Mansfield NG18 1EX

STOPFORD ASSOCIATES LTD
Synergy House, 3 Acorn Business Park, Commercial Gate, Mansfield NG18 1EX

STUART BRANDRETH
41 Chestnut Drive, Berry Hill, Mansfield, NG18 4PW
Tel: 01623 659086
Principal: ICAEW Member
S Brandreth

SUNAXIS LTD
Hillingdon, High Oakham Hill, Mansfield, NG18 5AH

WALL AND PARTNERS ◈
3 & 5 Commercial Gate, Mansfield, NG18 1EJ
Tel: 01623 623248
Resident Partners/Directors: ICAEW Members
R Field, M Longden, S N Robinson
Resident Partners (Non-ICAEW Members):
J Adams

MARAZION

GOODHEADS
Oceans End, Rose Hill, Marazion, TR17 0HB
Tel: 01736 710530
Principal: ICAEW Member
C Goodhead

MARCH

WHITING & PARTNERS ◈
The Old School House, Dartford Road, March, PE15 8AE
Tel: 01354 652304
Resident Partners/Directors: ICAEW Members
A Band, N A E Handley, M N Haydon

MARGATE

DAVID T FORSYTH
13 Barn Crescent, Margate, CT9 5HF

G.R. WEBB
107 Canterbury Road, Margate, CT9 5AX

J MICHAEL & CO LTD
274 Northdown Road, Cliftonville, Margate, CT9 2PT

LAKIN CLARK
1 Union Crescent, Margate, CT9 1NR
Tel: 01843 221449
Resident Partners/Directors: ICAEW Members
N J Cripps, A J Foale, C J Jarrett

PERCY GORE & CO
39 Hawley Square, Margate, CT9 1NZ
Tel: 01843 220567
Fax: 01843 228540
Email: advice@percygore.co.uk
Resident Partners/Directors: ICAEW Members
A R J Leal, H N Mockett, G C Simpson, N G F Wreford
Registered by the ICAEW to carry out company audit work
Regulated by the ICAEW for a range of investment business activities

SPURLING CANNON LTD
165-167 Northdown Road, Cliftonville, Margate, CT9 2PA

MARKET DRAYTON

BARRINGTONS LTD ◈
18 Queen Street, Market Drayton, TF9 1PX
Tel: 01630 652813
Email: mdadmin@barraccount.co.uk
Website: http://www.barringtons-online.co.uk
Resident Partners/Directors: ICAEW Members
A G Wilshaw
Registered by the ICAEW to carry out company audit work

SPECIALISATIONS – BUSINESS RECOVERY & INSOLVENCY

Bankruptcies
Corporate Recovery
Liquidations

SPECIALISATIONS – SECTOR

Agriculture

General Description: Licensed insolvency practitioner.

CLIFFORD & CO ◈
11 Manor Farm Drive, Hinstock, Market Drayton, TF9 2SN

HAINSWORTH KERRY PRACTICE
Old Links Rectory, Links Green, Hinstock, Market Drayton TF9 2NH
Tel: 01952 550180
Principal: ICAEW Member
K J Hainsworth

HOWSONS ◈
Poynton House, Shropshire Street, Market Drayton, TF9 3DD
Tel: 01630 652751
Non-resident Partners (ICAEW Members):
M N Davies
Other Offices: Stoke, Leek, Uttoxeter, Newport, Burslem, Alsager

STUBBS PARKIN & SOUTH
28 Cheshire Street, Market Drayton, TF9 1PF
Tel: 01630 653555
Fax: 01630 655806
Email: mail@spsdrayton.com
Resident Partners/Directors: ICAEW Members
N D G Shanks
Non-resident Partners (ICAEW Members):
J M A Birtles, D J Kelsall
Resident Partners (Non-ICAEW Members):
R M Dodington
Other Offices: Wem, Whitchurch
Registered by the ICAEW to carry out company audit work

SPECIALISATIONS – SECTOR

Agriculture
Insurance Brokers
Solicitors

MARKET HARBOROUGH

BERRY ACCOUNTANTS
Bowden House, 36 Northampton Road, Market Harborough, LE16 9HE
Tel: 01858 467474
Fax: 01858 464111
Email: accountants@berry.uk.com
Website: http://www.berry.uk.com
Resident Partners/Directors: ICAEW Members
A C Neal, M A Woods
Resident Partners (Non-ICAEW Members):
R Walden
Registered by the ICAEW to carry out company audit work
Regulated by the ICAEW for a range of investment business activities

BERRY KEARSLEY STOCKWELL LTD
12 The Square, Market Harborough, LE16 7PA

CUTHBERTSON HEWITT LTD
5 Hill Gardens, Market Harborough, LE16 9EB
Tel: 01858 433512
Resident Partners/Directors: ICAEW Members
C Cuthbertson

E T PEIRSON & SONS
21 The Point, Rockingham Road, Market Harborough, LE16 7NU
Tel: 01858 464400
Resident Partners/Directors: ICAEW Members
A A Bentley, S E Faire
See display advertisement near this entry.

GOWARDS
102 Burnmill Road, Market Harborough, LE16 7JG
Tel: 07941 760980
Principal: ICAEW Member
S P Davies

JANET ROBERTS ◈
112 St Marys Road, Market Harborough, LE16 7DX
Tel: 01858 461567
Principal: ICAEW Member
J M Roberts

M. INGRAM
7 Spring Terrace, Medbourne, Market Harborough, LE16 8ES

MAYFIELD & CO
1st Floor, Fountain Court, High Street, Market Harborough LE16 7AF

MAYFIELD & CO (ACCOUNTANTS) LTD
1st Floor, Fountain Court, High Street, Market Harborough LE16 7AF

PARTRIDGE & CO
The Old Malt House, The Green, Clipston, Market Harborough LE16 9RS

MARKET RASEN

ANN K ROBINSON
13b Market Place, Caistor, Market Rasen, LN7 6TW

DAVID BOTTOMLEY
The Old Rectory, Owmby Cliff Road, Owmby-by-Spital, Market Rasen LN8 2HL
Tel: 01673 878063
Principal: ICAEW Member
D R Bottomley

KAY V. STRAWSON & CO LTD
Red Cottage, Moor Road, Walesby, Market Rasen LN8 3UR

R.G.D. MAUNSELL & CO
Pear Tree Cottage, 27 Rasen Road, Tealby, Market Rasen LN8 3XL
Tel: 01673 838883
Principal: ICAEW Member
R G D Maunsell

RM CROWDER LTD
Rest Haven, North Kelsey Road, Caistor, Market Rasen LN7 6SF
Tel: 01472 859261
Resident Partners/Directors: ICAEW Members
R M Crowder

MARKFIELD

C.A. COX
18 Chambers Close, Markfield, LE67 9NB

MARLBOROUGH

BEW & CO LTD
130 High Street, Marlborough, SN8 1LZ
Tel: 01672 514582
Resident Partners/Directors: ICAEW Members
B K Froud, A P King

COLIN G. HORWOOD
Glebelands, Mildenhall, Marlborough, SN8 2LR

COLLINGBOURNE CONSULTANTS
Glebe View House, Collingbourne Kingston, Marlborough, SN8 3SE

DAVID OWEN & CO ◈
126 High St, Marlborough, SN8 1LZ
Tel: 01672 512163
Email: marlborough@davidowen.co.uk
Website: http://www.dowen.com
Resident Partners/Directors: ICAEW Members
N J Gamage
Resident Partners (Non-ICAEW Members):
T A Roberts
Other Offices:17 Market Place, Devizies
Registered by the ICAEW to carry out company audit work
Regulated by the ICAEW for a range of investment business activities

DUNCAN KING
2 Macneice Drive, Barton Park, Marlborough, SN8 1TR

JOHN F. WILLIAMS & CO LTD
Elizabethan House, 8 George Lane, Marlborough, SN8 4BT
Tel: 01672 513230
Resident Partners/Directors: ICAEW Members
J F Williams

LAUNCESTON LTD
2 Barley Fields, Dark Lane, East Grafton, Marlborough SN8 3DR
Tel: 01672 811118
Resident Partners/Directors: ICAEW Members
T M Riordan

ROGER JOHN & CO
1 Farrar Drive, Marlborough, SN8 1TP

MARLOW

COLIN LEWIN & CO
Mercury House, 19-21 Chapel Street, Marlow, SL7 3HN
Tel: 01628 890504
Principal: ICAEW Member
C Lewin

COLSTON BUSH
43 High Street, Marlow, SL7 1BA
Tel: 01628 475477
Email: advice@colstonbush.co.uk
Resident Partners/Directors: ICAEW Members
I S Petty, D Postlethwaite, M H P Spittle
Registered by the ICAEW to carry out company audit work
Regulated by the ICAEW for a range of investment business activities

D.K. RAY & CO
20 Victoria Road, Marlow, SL7 1DW

E&R CONSULTING LTD
5 Highfield Park, Marlow, SL7 2DE

FINANCIAL PROGRESSION LTD
5 Taylors Close, Marlow, SL7 1PR
Tel: 01628 473667
Email: adrian@financialprogression.co.uk
Mobile: 07841 725666
Resident Partners/Directors: ICAEW Members
A L T Jenkins

IAN HINCKLEY
3 Balfour Place, Marlow, SL7 3TB

PETER MANLEY
2 Marlow House, Institute Road, Marlow, SL7 1BB
Tel: 01628 472132
Principal: ICAEW Member
P Manley

RICHARD WALSH
Jonquils, Marlow Common, Marlow, SL7 2JQ

RICHARDSON JONES
Mercury House, 19/21 Chapel Street, Marlow, SL7 3HN
Tel: 01628 475455

RICHARDSON JONES LTD
Mercury House, 19/21 Chapel Street, Marlow, SL7 3HN
Tel: 01628 475455
Fax: 01628 476348
Email: mail@rjca.co.uk
Website: http://www.rjca.co.uk
Resident Partners/Directors: ICAEW Members
C D Jones, D C Porter, G A Thrush
Registered by the ICAEW to carry out company audit work

VANTIS BUSINESS RECOVERY SERVICES
81 Station Road, Marlow, SL7 1NS
Tel: 01628 478 100
Website: http://www.vantisplc.com/businessrecovery
Individual(s) licensed for insolvency work by another RPB

SPECIALISATIONS – BUSINESS RECOVERY & INSOLVENCY

Bankruptcies
Corporate Recovery
Liquidations

MARTOCK

DEREK J READ & CO
107 North Street, Martock, TA12 6EJ

DEREK J READ & CO
107 North Street, Martock, TA12 6EJ

DEREK J READ LTD
107 North Street, Martock, TA12 6EJ

MARYPORT

GIBBONS & CO
Netherall Chambers, 2 Curzon Street, Maryport, CA15 6LL

MATLOCK

ANNE GRIFFITHS
Lant Lodge Farm, Tansley, Matlock, DE4 5FW
Tel: 01246 590993
Principal: ICAEW Member
A T Griffiths

SPECIALISATIONS – TAXATION

Capital Gains — Personal
Partnerships and Sole Traders
Self Assessment Advice

CHAMBERS COPE & PARTNERS LTD
121 Smedley Street, Matlock, DE4 3JG

DAVID FEARN
Darley Forest Grange, Flash Lane, Darley Moor, Matlock DE4 5LJ
Tel: 01629 734667
Principal: ICAEW Member
J D Fearn

IAN L. CAMERON
100 Northwood Lane, Darley Dale, Matlock, DE4 2HR

JOHN STONE
Hillcrest, Main Street, Elton, Matlock DE4 2BU

LIBCUS LTD ◈
Speedwell Mill, Old Coach Road, Tansley, Matlock DE4 5FY
Tel: 01629 761680
Resident Partners/Directors: ICAEW Members
N E Riley

SPECIALISATIONS – BUSINESS & GENERAL ADVICE

Acquisitions and Mergers
Book-keeping
Company Formation
Divorce/Matrimonial
Feasibility Studies
Management Advice to Business
Management Consultancy

General Description: Business advisors, company doctors and specialists in business turnaround.

MILLS & BLACK
Derwent House, 141-143 Dale Road, Matlock, DE4 3LU
Tel: 01629 583271
Resident Partners/Directors: ICAEW Members
R S Hardy, I M Hayes, S Nicholson

R.M. JOHNSON
36 Wolds Rise, Matlock, DE4 3HJ

RAINSFORD & CO
Low Leas House, Lea, Matlock, DE4 5JR
Tel: 01629 534538
Principal: ICAEW Member
V M Rainsford

MELKSHAM

DAVID SCOTT
440 Carnation Lane, Bowerhill, Melksham, SN12 6RD
Tel: 01225 702916
Principal: ICAEW Member
D V Scott

O'HARA WOOD
5 King Street, Melksham, SN12 6HB

PETER BARCLAY LTD
1st Floor, 11 Church Street, Melksham, SN12 6LS

MELTON CONSTABLE

JANE B. CLAYTON
Growle Abbey, High Road, Briston, Melton Constable NR24 2JH

MELTON MOWBRAY

AJB CONSULTANCY
Ashby Pastures Farm, Great Dalby Road, Ashby Folville, Melton Mowbray LE14 2TU

C J LAWMAN FCA
44 Hall Orchard Lane, Frisby on the Wreake, Melton Mowbray, LE14 2NH

CLAYTON & BREWILL ◈
County Chambers, Kings Road, Melton Mowbray, LE13 1QF

COATES FRANKLIN LTD ◈
Accountancy House, Station Road, Upper Broughton, Melton Mowbray LE14 3BQ
Tel: 08704 873873
Resident Partners/Directors: ICAEW Members
S R Coates

COBLEY & CO ◈
26 Beechwood Avenue, Melton Mowbray, LE13 1RT

COULTER & CO
1st Floor, 4 Sherrard Street, Melton Mowbray, LE13 1XJ

DEBLAW LTD
44 Hall Orchard Lane, Frisby-On-The-Wreake, Melton Mowbray, LE14 2NH

DELTA TAX SERVICES
6 Fair Field, Waltham on the Wolds, Melton Mowbray, LE14 4AX

DUNCAN & TOPLIS
26 Park Road, Melton Mowbray, LE13 1TT
Tel: 01664 561001
Fax: 01664 410719
Email: info@melton.duntop.co.uk
Website: http://www.duntop.co.uk
Resident Partners/Directors: ICAEW Members
J E Green
Registered by the ICAEW to carry out company audit work
Regulated by the ICAEW for a range of investment business activities
General Description: Other offices please see Grantham.

J.H. TREASE & CO
Parkdene, Wilton Road, Melton Mowbray, LE13 0UJ
Tel: 01664 563993

JOHN K SHEPHERD FCA
33 Beechwood Avenue, Melton Mowbray, LE13 1RT

NEWBY CASTLEMAN ◈
22 Park Road, Melton Mowbray, LE13 1TT
Tel: 01664 563084
Fax: 01664 410013
Email: rlw@newbyc.co.uk
Resident Partners/Directors: ICAEW Members
R L Woolley
Other Offices: Leicester, Oakham, Loughborough, Nottingham
Registered by the ICAEW to carry out company audit work
Regulated by the ICAEW for a range of investment business activities
See display advertisement near this entry.

NICHOLAS D MORGAN
5 Walnut Paddocks, Harby, Melton Mowbray, LE14 4BD
Tel: 01949 860727
Principal: ICAEW Member
N D Morgan

OAKS FINANCIAL LTD
Race Course Farm, Mary Lane, Bescaby, Melton Mowbray, Leicestershire LE14 4AU

OAKWOOD ACCOUNTANCY LTD ◈
26 Beechwood Avenue, Melton Mowbray, LE13 1RT

PAYNE WALKER LTD
Suite 2, 10 High Street, Melton Mowbray, LE13 0TR
Tel: 01664 562987
Resident Partners/Directors: ICAEW Members
P Stephenson

RACHEL ROBERTS
27 Ankle Hill, Melton Mowbray, LE13 0QJ
Tel: 01664 565647
Principal: ICAEW Member
R J S Roberts

SIMON N. COWMAN
Mayfield, 8 Brooksby Road, Hoby, Melton Mowbray LE14 3EA

TENON LTD
Suite 4, 10 High Street, Melton Mowbray, LE13 0TR
Tel: 01664 562060

TIMOTHY S COCKCROFT
Vale Cottage, 16 Watsons Lane, Harby, Melton Mowbray LE14 4DD

W.H. ROBERTS & CO
The Old Rectory, Church Lane, Hoby, Melton Mowbray LE14 3DR
Tel: 01664 434557
Principal: ICAEW Member
W H Roberts

W. OSBORNE & CO
Harwood House, Park Road, Melton Mowbray, LE13 1TX
Tel: 01664 564581
Resident Partners/Directors: ICAEW Members
M W Osborne, W Osborne

MEXBOROUGH

LEESING MARRISON LEE & CO
46 Main Street, Mexborough, S64 9DU

LEESING MARRISON LEE LTD
46 Main Street, Mexborough, S64 9DU

TIPTAFT, SMITH & CO
Montagu Chambers, Montagu Square, Mexborough, S64 9AJ

MIDDLESBROUGH

CHIPCHASE MANNERS ◈
384 Linthorpe Road, Middlesbrough, TS5 6HA

CHUHAN & SINGH PARTNERSHIP LTD
81 Borough Road, Middlesbrough, TS1 3AA
Tel: 01642 244090

COUSINS & CO
The Vanguard Suite, Broadcasting House, Newport Road, Middlesbrough TS1 5JA

FRANK BROWN & WALFORD
314 Linthorpe Road, Middlesbrough, TS1 3QX
Tel: 01642 225421
Principal: ICAEW Member
A Walker

GILCHRIST TASH ◈
Cleveland Buildings, Queen's Square, Middlesbrough, TS2 1PA
Tel: 01642 248387
Resident Partners/Directors: ICAEW Members
C T McBride, P M Millar, F M Parkin, D L Steel

GILCHRIST TASH ◈
27 College Square, Stokesley, Middlesbrough, TS9 5DN
Tel: 01642 713233

HLB VANTIS AUDIT PLC
New Exchange Buildings, Queens Square, Middlesbrough, TS2 1AA
Tel: 01642 221331
Website: http://www.hlbvantisaudit.com
Training Contracts Available.
Registered by the ICAEW to carry out company audit work
Regulated by the ICAEW for a range of investment business activities
SPECIALISATIONS – AUDIT & ASSURANCE
Audit
Audit — Private Company
Audit — Public Company
SPECIALISATIONS – FINANCIAL REPORTING
Audit Exemption Report

IRVINE & CO
10 Dikes Lane, Great Ayton, Middlesbrough, TS9 6HJ
Tel: 01642 722446
Principal: ICAEW Member
G P J Irvine

KEITH ROBINSON & CO ◈
10 Woodlands Road, Middlesbrough, TS1 3BE
Tel: 01642 225325
Resident Partners/Directors: ICAEW Members
K Robinson, T Truran

KEITH ROBSON
117 Roman Road, Middlesbrough, TS5 5QB

LAWSON & CO
FPCI Group Building, Ellerbeck Way, Stokesley Ind Park, Stokesley, Middlesbrough TS9 5JZ

LEONARD BYE
80 Borough Road, Middlesbrough, TS1 2JN
Tel: 01642 246006
Fax: 01642 211160
Email: david@byes.com
Website: http://www.byes.com
Resident Partners/Directors: ICAEW Members
D R Arkley

M. WASLEY CHAPMAN & CO
95/97 Acklam Road, Middlesbrough, TS5 5HR

N.I. COULTHARD
145 Albert Road, Middlesbrough, TS1 2PP

NEIL WALTON LTD
Bank Foot Farm, Ingleby Greenhow, Great Ayton, Middlesbrough TS9 6LP
Tel: 01642 724455
Resident Partners/Directors: ICAEW Members
N Walton

P.M. COOK & CO
273 Linthorpe Road, Middlesbrough, TS1 3QS

PAUL TRANTER & CO
31 High Street, Stokesley, North Yorkshire, TS9 5AD
Tel: 01642 710603
Principal: ICAEW Member
P A Tranter

R J STANTON & CO
Mill Hill, Chop Gate, Stokesley, Middlesbrough TS9 7HY

SOCHALL SMITH LTD
Queens Court Business Centre, Newport Road, Middlesbrough, TS1 5EH

SWALLOW & CO ◈
Commercial House, 10 Bridge Road, Stokesley, Middlesbrough TS9 5AA
Tel: 01642 711407
Resident Partners/Directors: ICAEW Members
D A Swallow

TAYLORS
51 High Street, Stokesley, Middlesbrough, TS9 5AD

TENON LTD
Cleveland Business Centre, 1 Watson Street, Middlesbrough, TS1 2RQ
Tel: 01642 227534

VANTIS GROUP LTD ◈
New Exchange Buildings, Queens Square, Middlesbrough, TS2 1AA
Tel: 01642 221 331
Website: http://www.vantisplc.com/middlesbrough
Resident Partners/Directors: ICAEW Members
G A Fotheringham
General Description: ICAEW Registered.

MIDDLEWICH

ANDREW NAYLOR & CO
51 Glastonbury Drive, Middlewich, CW10 9HR

AP SMITH ATKINS AND CO ◈
18 Tewkesbury Close, Middlewich, CW10 9HT
Tel: 01606 841735
Principal: ICAEW Member
A Hickson

J.A. DAWSON
Old Post Office Chambers, St Michaels Way, Middlewich, CW10 9QN

MIDDLEWICH TAXSHOP
64 Lewin Street, Middlewich, CW10 9AS

P K HARDY LTD
12 Shropshire Close, Middlewich, CW10 9ES
Tel: 01606 737815
Resident Partners/Directors: ICAEW Members
P K Hardy

TAYLOR & CO
64 Lewin Street, Middlewich, CW10 9AS

MIDHURST

BAYLY & CO ◈
Peachey House, Bepton Road, Midhurst, GU29 9LU
Tel: 01730 816360
Resident Partners/Directors: ICAEW Members
B M Bayly

GOODALE MARDLE LTD
Flat 3, Grange House, Grange Road, Midhurst GU29 9LS

ROBERT G W DONEY LTD
Sunnyfield, Church Road, West Lavington, Midhurst GU29 0EH
Tel: 01730 814180
Resident Partners/Directors: ICAEW Members
R G W Doney

MILLOM

ARMSTRONG WATSON ◈
34 Lapstone Rd, Millom, LA18 4BU
Tel: 01229 412420

SAINT & CO ▽ ◈
31 Lapstone Road, Millom, LA18 4BT
Tel: 01229 772203
Email: millom@saint.co.uk
Website: http://www.saint.co.uk
Registered by the ICAEW to carry out company audit work
Authorised and regulated by the Financial Services Authority for investment business

MILTON KEYNES

ABISERVE
1 Scotch Firs, Wavendon Gate, Milton Keynes, MK7 7RR

ALAN TAYLOR
28 Aldrich Drive, Willen, Milton Keynes, MK15 9LU

B.J. PATEL
76 Buckingham Road, Bletchley, Milton Keynes, MK3 5HL

BAKER TILLY
5th Floor, Exchange House, 446 Midsummer Boulevard, Milton Keynes MK9 2EA
Tel: 01908 687800
Resident Partners/Directors: ICAEW Members
J Y Farmbrough

BAKER TILLY
5th Floor, Exchange House, 446 Midsummer Boulevard, Milton Keynes MK9 2EA
Tel: 01908 687800
Resident Partners/Directors: ICAEW Members
J Y Farmbrough, A D Lawes, T S Luddington, J D A Read, T J Saunders

BAKER TILLY
5th Floor, Exchange House, 446 Midsummer Boulevard, Milton Keynes MK9 2EA

BAKER TILLY RESTRUCTURING AND RECOVERY LLP
Exchange House, 446 Midsummer Boulevard, Milton Keynes, MK9 2EA
Tel: 01908 687800
Resident Partners/Directors: ICAEW Members
G P Bushby, J Y Farmbrough

BAKER TILLY TAX AND ADVISORY SERVICES LLP
5th Floor, Exchange House, 446 Midsummer Boulevard, Milton Keynes MK9 2EA
Tel: 01908 687800
Resident Partners/Directors: ICAEW Members
G P Bushby, J Y Farmbrough, A D Lawes, T S Luddington, J D A Read, T J Saunders
Resident Partners (Non-ICAEW Members):
J M Hooper

BARRY HAMPSON
63 Passmore, Tinkers Bridge, Milton Keynes, MK6 3DY
Tel: 01908 664182
Principal: ICAEW Member
B E Hampson

BEGBIES TRAYNOR
Calverton House, Tilers Road, Kiln Farm, Milton Keynes MK11 3LL
Tel: 01908 261300
Resident Partners/Directors: ICAEW Members
P M Davis
Resident Partners (Non-ICAEW Members):
T Dolder
SPECIALISATIONS – BUSINESS RECOVERY & INSOLVENCY
Bankruptcies
Corporate Recovery
Liquidations

BISHOPS
2 Water End Barns, Water End, Eversholt, Milton Keynes MK17 9EA
Tel: 01525 288162

BISHOPS ACCOUNTANCY PRACTICE LTD
2 Water End Barns, Water End, Eversholt, Milton Keynes MK17 9EA

BJ ◈
Cedar House, Breckland, Linford Wood, Milton Keynes MK14 6EX
Tel: 01908 577450
Fax: 01908 606842
Email: john.bennett@rsmbentleyjennison.com
Website: http://www.rsmbentleyjennison.com
Resident Partners/Directors: ICAEW Members
J Bennett, M J Phillips
Registered by the ICAEW to carry out company audit work

BOURNER BULLOCK
Chancery House, 199 Silbury Boulevard, Milton Keynes, MK9 1JL
Tel: 01908 237306
Fax: 01908 237304
Email: bb@bournerbullock.co.uk
Website: http://www.bournerbullock.co.uk
Resident Partners/Directors: ICAEW Members
H J Dell, A R Nicholson
Other Offices: London

SPECIALISATIONS – AUDIT & ASSURANCE
Assurance Services
Audit
Audit — Private Company

SPECIALISATIONS – BUSINESS & GENERAL ADVICE
Book-keeping Systems
Company Secretarial Service
Europe
Management Advice to Business
Management Consultancy

SPECIALISATIONS – FINANCIAL REPORTING
Accounts Preparation
Financial Reporting
Foreign Subsidiary Companies
Partnership/Sole Trader Accounts

SPECIALISATIONS – FORENSIC ACCOUNTING
Expert Witnesses in Litigation

SPECIALISATIONS – SECTOR
Charities
Media
New Media
Property Development
Property Investment
Solicitors

SPECIALISATIONS – TAXATION
Taxation
Value Added Tax

CAMFIELD CHAPMAN LOWE
9 High Street, Woburn Sands, Milton Keynes, MK17 8RF
Tel: 01908 583800
Fax: 01908 584500
Email: post@camfieldchapmanlowe.co.uk
Website: http://www.camfieldchapman.lowe.co.uk
Registered by the ICAEW to carry out company audit work
Regulated by the ICAEW for a range of investment business activities

CAMFIELD CHAPMAN LOWE LTD
9 High Street, Woburn Sands, Milton Keynes, MK17 8RF

CARRINGTON MAY ◈
31 Walker Avenue, Wolverton Mill East, Milton Keynes, MK12 5TW

CHANCERY (UK) LLP ◈
Chancery Pavilion, Boycott Avenue, Oldbrook, Milton Keynes MK6 2TA
Tel: 01908 699600
Fax: 01908 699699
Email: accounts@chancerypartnership.com
Website: http://www.chancerypartnership.com
Mobile: 07736 769738
Date Established: 1997
Training Contracts Available.
Resident Partners/Directors: ICAEW Members
S James, E S Roberts
Resident Partners (Non-ICAEW Members):
P Nichols, K A Nichols
Registered by the ICAEW to carry out company audit work
Authorised and regulated by the Financial Services Authority for investment business

SPECIALISATIONS – AUDIT & ASSURANCE
Audit

SPECIALISATIONS – BUSINESS & GENERAL ADVICE
Acquisitions and Mergers
Book-keeping
Company Formation
Investment Appraisal
Management Accounting
Consultancy

SPECIALISATIONS – FINANCIAL REPORTING
Accounts Preparation
Financial Reporting
International Reporting Standards (IFRS)
Limited Companies
Limited Liability Partnership
Partnership/Sole Trader Accounts

SPECIALISATIONS – FORENSIC ACCOUNTING
Forensic Accounting

SPECIALISATIONS – INVESTMENT BUSINESS
Financial Planning and Advice

SPECIALISATIONS – TAXATION
Capital Gains — Limited Companies
Capital Gains — Personal
Estate and Inheritance
Partnerships and Sole Traders
PAYE Advice
Trusts
Value Added Tax

General Description:
Specialists in tax mitigation.
Languages Spoken:
German, French

CHARTNERS LTD
3 Turpyn Court, Woughton on the Green, Milton Keynes, MK6 3BW

CHRIS REID LTD
Brick House, 150A Station Road, Woburn Sands, Milton Keynes MK17 8SG
Tel: 0845 505 0700
Resident Partners/Directors: ICAEW Members
C Reid

CLIFFORD TOWERS
9 High Street, Stony Stratford, Milton Keynes, MK11 1AA

D.J. RANSON
17 Willets Rise, Shenley Church End, Milton Keynes, MK5 6JW

DAVID PETERS
Beechfield, 7 Goodman Gardens, Woughton on the Green, Milton Keynes MK6 3EP

DELOITTE & TOUCHE LLP ◈
Ashton House, Silbury Boulevard, Milton Keynes, MK9 2HG
Tel: 01908 666665
Website: http://www.deloitte.co.uk

FCA SOLUTIONS
44 Kelling Way, Broughton, Milton Keynes, MK10 9NW

FCA SOLUTIONS LTD
44 Kelling Way, Broughton, Milton Keynes, MK10 9NW

FISHER MORRIS GARRAD
80A High Street, Stony Stratford, Milton Keynes, MK11 1AH

FORTY-TWO CONSULTING LLP
Silverstone House, Newport Road, Woolstone, Milton Keynes MK15 0AA
Tel: 01908 251111
Resident Partners/Directors: ICAEW Members
N G Jones

G P FINANCIAL MANAGEMENT LTD
8-9 The Old Yard, Lodge Farm Business Centre, Wolverton Road, Castlethorpe, Milton Keynes MK19 7ES

GALLAGHERS
33a High Street, Stony Stratford, Milton Keynes, MK11 1AA
Tel: 01908 305270
Principal: ICAEW Member
J J Gallagher

GPFM
8-9 The Old Yard, Lodge Farm Business Centre, Wolverton Road, Castlethorpe, Milton Keynes MK19 7ES

GRANT THORNTON UK LLP
Grant Thornton House, 202 Silbury Boulevard, Milton Keynes, MK9 1LW
Tel: 01908 660666
Resident Partners/Directors: ICAEW Members
P J Barrett, P V Burrows, M J Burt, P J Crooks, M A Gomersall, S J Jones, P E Simpson, M L Turner

GRASSO PARKER GREEN LLP
GPG House, Walker Avenue, Wolverton Mill, Milton Keynes MK12 5TW

HAYSOM SILVERTON & PARTNERS
Norfolk House Centre, 82 Saxon Gate West, Milton Keynes, MK9 2DL

HAYSOM SILVERTON & PARTNERS
Norfolk House Centre, 82 Saxon Gate West, Milton Keynes, MK9 2DL

HAYSOM SILVERTON & PARTNERS LTD
Norfolk House Centre, 82 Saxon Gate West, Milton Keynes, MK9 2DL

HWS ◈
1st Floor St Giles Hse, 15-21 Victoria Road, Bletchley, Milton Keynes MK2 2NG
Tel: 01908 376424
Email: info@hwsmk.co.uk
Website: http://www.hwsmk.co.uk
Resident Partners/Directors: ICAEW Members
A G Freeman, M P Maguire
Registered by the ICAEW to carry out company audit work

Regulated by the ICAEW for a range of investment business activities

JAQUEST & CO

29 Little Meadow, Loughton, Milton Keynes, MK5 8EH
Tel: 01908 240988
Fax: 01908 240988
Email: gordonjaquest@msn.com
Principal: ICAEW Member
G N Jaquest

Registered by the ICAEW to carry out company audit work

Regulated by the ICAEW for a range of investment business activities

SPECIALISATIONS – AUDIT & ASSURANCE

Audit

SPECIALISATIONS – FINANCIAL REPORTING

Accounts Preparation
Limited Companies

SPECIALISATIONS – TAXATION

Foreign Nationals in the UK
Partnerships and Sole Traders

General Description: The firm provides a wide range of accounting, audit, taxation and consultancy services to individuals, partnerships and limited companies of all sizes, using the latest information technology.

JENNER & CO

245 Queensway, Bletchley, Milton Keynes, MK2 2EH

JEREMY HOPKINSON & CO

12 Heath Road, Great Brickhill, Milton Keynes, MK17 9AL
Tel: 01525 261674
Principal: ICAEW Member
J S F Hopkinson

KEENS SHAY KEENS MILTON KEYNES ◈

Sovereign Court, 230 Upper Fifth Street, Milton Keynes, MK9 2HR
Tel: 01908 674484
Fax: 01908 690371
Email: ksk@keens.co.uk
Website: http://www.keens.co.uk
Training Contracts Available.
Resident Partners/Directors: ICAEW Members
P A Davis, M Rayner
Resident Partners (Non-ICAEW Members):
P R Whiteley
Overseas Offices: Keens Shay Keens - Grange County, 23332 Mill Creek Drive, Laguna Hills, CA 92653. California Website: http://www.keenshay.com (Tel: 00 949 460 4595)

Registered by the ICAEW to carry out company audit work

Regulated by the ICAEW for a range of investment business activities

SPECIALISATIONS – AUDIT & ASSURANCE

Audit

SPECIALISATIONS – BUSINESS & GENERAL ADVICE

Book-keeping
Company Formation
Company Secretarial Service
Management Advice to Business

SPECIALISATIONS – FINANCIAL REPORTING

Accounts Preparation
Financial Reporting
Foreign Subsidiary Companies
Limited Liability Partnership

SPECIALISATIONS – FORENSIC ACCOUNTING

Forensic Accounting

SPECIALISATIONS – INVESTMENT BUSINESS

Financial Planning and Advice

SPECIALISATIONS – IT

Computerised Accounting Systems

SPECIALISATIONS – SECTOR

Charities
Corporate
Dentists/Opticians
Doctors
Estate Agents
Manufacturing
Property
Rubber and Plastics Industry
Schools
Solicitors

SPECIALISATIONS – TAXATION

Estate and Inheritance
Estate Planning
Partnerships and Sole Traders
Payroll Service and Advice
Personal
Taxation
UK Subsidiaries of Overseas Multinationals

General Description: General practitioners specialising in advice on setting up new companies & branches, for UK and overseas companies, together with comprehensive advice to owner-managed and growing businesses.

KPMG LLP

Altius House, 1 North Fourth Street, Milton Keynes, MK9 1NE
Tel: 01908 844800
Resident Partners/Directors: ICAEW Members
S J S Muncey, P Selvey, S J Wardell, R A Watson

MACINTYRE HUDSON CORPORATE FINANCE LTD ◈

Moorgate House, 201 Silbury Boulevard, Milton Keynes, MK9 1LZ
Tel: 01908 662255
Website: http://www.macintyrehudson.co.uk
Resident Partners/Directors: ICAEW Members
R T Persaud, L Whitehead

Authorised and regulated by the Financial Services Authority for investment business

MACINTYRE HUDSON LLP ◈

Moorgate House, 201 Silbury Boulevard, Milton Keynes, MK9 1LZ
Tel: 01908 662255
Fax: 01908 678247
Website: http://www.macintyrehudson.co.uk
Resident Partners/Directors: ICAEW Members
M Hayes, R B Panter, R T Persaud, L Whitehead
Resident Partners (Non-ICAEW Members):
S A Vitiello, M Green-Marguest, A Kariya, A Snowdon, L Waghorn, P G King, N C May, E Olson, R Salter
Other Offices: Bedford, Chelmsford, High Wycombe, Leicester, London City, Northampton, Peterborough, North London, Milton Keynes

SPECIALISATIONS – AUDIT & ASSURANCE

Audit

SPECIALISATIONS – BUSINESS & GENERAL ADVICE

Book-keeping
Management Advice to Business

SPECIALISATIONS – FINANCIAL REPORTING

Accounts Preparation

SPECIALISATIONS – TAXATION

Taxation
Value Added Tax

General Description: Chartered accountants and business advisors working with entrepreneurial businesses, groups and multinationals. We provide a range of services and specialist advice, including audit and assurance, tax planning and compliance, payroll and VAT, strategic consultancy services, outsourcing, corporate finance and professional training.

MANCINI LTD

10 Shallowford Grove, Furzton, Milton Keynes, MK4 1ND

MAZARS CORPORATE FINANCE LTD ◈

Sovereign Court, Witan Gate, Milton Keynes, MK9 2HP
Tel: 01908 664466

MAZARS LLP ◈

Sovereign Court, Witan Gate, Milton Keynes, MK9 2HP
Tel: 01908 664466
Resident Partners/Directors: ICAEW Members
S R Brown, S Eames, G J Hall, C A Jackson, K M Moss, L R Pentelow, S M Tubb, P A Verity
Resident Partners (Non-ICAEW Members):
M J Standish, C Goodwin, G H Lewis

Registered by the ICAEW to carry out company audit work

Authorised and regulated by the Financial Services Authority for investment business

MERCER & HOLE ◈

Silbury Court, 420 Silbury Boulevard, Milton Keynes, MK9 2AF
Tel: 01908 605552
Website: http://www.mercerhole.co.uk
Resident Partners/Directors: ICAEW Members
P J Godfrey-Evans, M G Joy, P A Maberly, H J Wilkinson

MERCER & HOLE TRUSTEES LTD

Silbury Court, 420 Silbury Boulevard, Milton Keynes, MK9 2AF
Tel: 01908 605552
Resident Partners/Directors: ICAEW Members
H J Wilkinson

NA JUDD LTD ◈

MK Business Centre, Foxhunter Drive, Linford Wood, Milton Keynes MK14 6GE
Tel: 01908 698760
Resident Partners/Directors: ICAEW Members
N A Judd

NA JUDD CORPORATE FINANCE ◈

MK Business Centre, Foxhunter Drive, Linford Wood, Milton Keynes MK14 6GE
Tel: 01908 698760

PARTH ◈

Navin House, 2 Mavoncliff Drive, Tattenhoe, Milton Keynes MK4 3DP
Tel: 01908 536578

PARTH LTD

Navin House, 2 Mavoncliff Drive, Tattenhoe, Milton Keynes MK4 3DP

PRICEWATERHOUSE-COOPERS

Central Business Exchange, Midsummer Boulevard, Milton Keynes, MK9 2DF

PRICEWATERHOUSE-COOPERS LLP
Exchange House, Central Business Exchange, Midsummer Boulevard, Milton Keynes MK9 2DF
Tel: 01908 353000
Resident Partners/Directors: ICAEW Members
J A Bradshaw, A P W Groves, R W Wilson

R F LANDER
Spinney Corner, Green Lane, Aspley Guise, Milton Keynes MK17 8EN

R.J. CLADD
33 Great Linch, Middleton, Milton Keynes, MK10 9BF
Tel: 01908 606882
Email: roger@rjcladdfca.co.uk
Date Established: 1989
Principal: ICAEW Member
R J Cladd
Regulated by the ICAEW for a range of investment business activities
SPECIALISATIONS – FINANCIAL REPORTING
Accounts Preparation
SPECIALISATIONS – TAXATION
Partnerships and Sole Traders
Self Assessment Advice
Small Traders

REID & CO CORPORATE SERVICES LTD
Witan Court, 305 Upper Fourth Street, Central, Milton Keynes MK9 1EH

RICHARD HORSLEY & CO LTD
Acorn House, 395d Midsummer Boulevard, Milton Keynes, MK9 3HP
Tel: 01908 231711
Resident Partners/Directors: ICAEW Members
R G C Horsley

S.R. LYNN & CO
11 Warren Yard, Wolverton Mill, Milton Keynes, MK12 5NW

SACKMAN & CO LTD ◈
Unit L32, MK Two Business Centre, Barton Road, Water Eaton, Milton Keynes MK2 3HU

SUMIT (UK) LTD
10A Quilter Meadow, Old Farm Park, Milton Keynes, MK7 8QD

THOMAS, WOOD & CO
84a High Street, Stony Stratford, Milton Keynes, MK11 1AH
Tel: 01908 262462

THOMPSON BALCH LTD
Sovereign House, 15 Towcester Road, Old Stratford, Milton Keynes MK19 6AN

THOMPSONS MK LTD
1 Hathaway Court, Crownhill, Milton Keynes, MK8 0LG

WADOCK LTD
84a High Street, Stony Stratford, Milton Keynes, MK11 1AH
Tel: 01908 262462
Resident Partners/Directors: ICAEW Members
A D Wood

WALKER, GREEN & CO
30-32 The Concourse, Brunel Centre, Bletchley, Milton Keynes, MK2 2HE
Tel: 01908 370022
Principal: ICAEW Member
C H Walker

WALKER SUTCLIFFE & COOPER
4 The Square, Aspley Guise, Milton Keynes, MK17 8DF

WEBB ACCOUNTANCY SERVICES LTD
19 Diamond Court, Opal Drive, Fox Milne, Milton Keynes MK15 0DU

MINEHEAD

AIMS - ANDREW FAY
30 West Street, Dunster, Minehead, TA24 6SN
Tel: 01643 821224
Principal: ICAEW Member
A P A Fay

AMHERST & SHAPLAND
4 Irnham Rd, Minehead, TA24 5DG

AMHERST & SHAPLAND LTD
4 Irnham Road, Minehead, TA24 5DG

G.DOBSON
Middle Croft House, Bossington Lane, Porlock, Minehead TA24 8HD

JAMES ACCOUNTING LTD
6 Blenheim Mews, Minehead, TA24 5QZ
Tel: 01643 706237
Resident Partners/Directors: ICAEW Members
N C James

MIRFIELD

BARNES BUSINESS SERVICES LTD ◈
30 Blake Hall Road, Mirfield, WF14 9NS
Tel: 01924 492692
Resident Partners/Directors: ICAEW Members
J C R Barnes

CHRIS MAKIN MEDIATOR
Well Cottage, 39 Water Royd Lane, Mirfield, WF14 9SF
Tel: 01924 495888
Fax: 01924 484421
Email: chris@chrismakin.co.uk
DX: 29648 MIRFIELD
Website: http://www.chrismakin.co.uk
Mobile: 07887 660072
Principal: ICAEW Member
N C Makin
SPECIALISATIONS – FORENSIC ACCOUNTING
Expert Witnesses in Litigation

DAVID CRAMP
120A Huddersfield Road, Mirfield, WF14 8AB

ELAINE WHITING
Great Gable, 225 Kitson Hill Rd, Mirfield, WF14 9DS

JESSOP & BARNES BUSINESS ADVISER LTD
32 Coppin Hall Lane, Mirfield, WF14 0EJ

TAX ASSIST ACCOUNTANTS ◈
192D Huddersfield Road, Mirfield, WF14 8AU

MITCHAM

AKRAM SIDDIQI & CO
58 Almond Way, Mitcham, CR4 1LN

BLYTHE & CO
354 London Road, Mitcham, CR4 3ND

K.P. ROSE
155 Sherwood Park Road, Mitcham, CR4 1NJ
Tel: 020 8764 0064
Principal: ICAEW Member
K P Rose

N.J. BROWN
36 Kingsleigh Place, Mitcham, CR4 4NU

MITCHELDEAN

MILLHALL CONSULTANTS LTD
Carlson Suite, Vantage Point Business Village, Mitcheldean, GL17 0DD

MORDEN

BUCKLEYS
Marshall House, 124 Middleton Road, Morden, SM4 6RW
Tel: 020 8687 4119
Fax: 020 8687 4170
Email: jan@avnchurchmill.co.uk
Mobile: 07774 947557
Principal: ICAEW Member
M Moore
Other Offices: Churchmill House, Ockford Road, Godalming, Surrey GU7 1QY
General Description: The firm provides a complete range of accountancy, taxation and other financial services. An individual and quality service is provided.

CHURCHMILL HOUSE LTD
Marshall House, 124 Middleton Road, Morden, SM4 6RW

JOHN GALE ASSOCIATES
415 Hillcross Avenue, Morden, SM4 4BZ
Tel: 020 8542 7869
Principal: ICAEW Member
J R Gale

MERKLER, SHARP & CO
Crown Lodge, Crown Road, Morden, SM4 5BY

OSSMAN CONSULTING LTD
319 Hillcross Avenue, Morden, SM4 4BX

VBP & CO
19 Morden Court Parade, London Road, Morden, SM4 5HJ

MORECAMBE

COATES & CO ◈
2 Fairhope Avenue, Bare, Morecambe, LA4 6JZ
Tel: 01524 831353
Fax: 01524 411664
Email: tony@tcoates.co.uk
Website: http://www.coatesca.co.uk
Mobile: 07850 269106
Date Established: 1993
Principal: ICAEW Member
A Coates
SPECIALISATIONS – BUSINESS & GENERAL ADVICE
Book-keeping
SPECIALISATIONS – FINANCIAL REPORTING
Accounts Preparation
Limited Company Accounts
Partnership/Sole Trader Accounts
SPECIALISATIONS – TAXATION
PAYE Advice
Payroll Service and Advice
Self Assessment Advice
Taxation
General Description: Small business specialists. Free initial consultation.

COLMAN, WHITTAKER & ROSCOW
118 Thornton Road, Morecambe, LA4 5PL

EURA AUDIT UK ★
370 Heysham Road, Heysham, Morecambe, LA3 2BJ

EURA AUDIT UK
370 Heysham Road, Heysham, Morecambe, LA3 2BJ

GEORGE WHITTAKER FCA
28 Northumberland Street, Morecambe, LA4 4AY

GOSTLING LTD
18 Skipton Street, Morecambe, LA4 4AR

MANGO
28 Northumberland Street, Morecambe, LA4 4AY

MANGO BUSINESS MANAGEMENT
28 Northumberland Street, Morecambe, LA4 4AY

WATERS & ATKINSON
The Old Court House, Clark Street, Morecambe, LA4 5HR

MORETON-IN-MARSH

BARRY S. DARE
Mill Dene, Blockley, Moreton-in-marsh, GL56 9HU

BRUCE SUTHERLAND & CO ★
Moreton House, Moreton-in-marsh, GL56 0LH

BRUCE SUTHERLAND & CO
Moreton House, Moreton-in-marsh, GL56 0LH

HELEN CALDER
Black Cat Cottage, Broadwell Road, Oddington, Moreton-in-marsh GL56 0UX

TAYABALI-TOMLIN LTD ◈
Kenton House, Oxford Street, Moreton-In-Marsh, GL56 0LA
Tel: 01608 650450
Fax: 01608 651815
Email: enquiries@tayabalitomlin.com
Website: http://www.tayabalitomlin.com
Resident Partners/Directors: ICAEW Members
A N Damery, A F Noorani

SPECIALISATIONS – BUSINESS & GENERAL ADVICE

Book-keeping
Company Formation
Company Secretarial Service

SPECIALISATIONS – FINANCIAL REPORTING

Accounts Preparation
Limited Companies
Limited Company Accounts
Partnership/Sole Trader Accounts

SPECIALISATIONS – TAXATION

Partnerships and Sole Traders
Payroll Service and Advice
Personal
Taxation

MORPETH

GREAVES GRINDLE
20 Queen St, Amble, Morpeth, NE65 0BZ

MCCOWIE & CO ★
12 Manchester Street, Morpeth, NE61 1BH

MOUAT ACCOUNTANCY LTD
Newton Red House, Mitford, Morpeth, NE61 3QW

NICKALLS & CO LTD
4 Bridge Street, Amble, Morpeth, NE65 0DR

PETER HEATHERINGTON ◈
Dene House, Hartburn, Morpeth, NE61 4JB
Tel: 01670 772690
Principal: ICAEW Member
P Heatherington

QUANTIS LTD
13 Newgate Street, Morpeth, NE61 1AL

RICHARD THOMPSON ◈
Borough Hall, Wellway, Morpeth, NE61 1BN
Tel: 01670 514433
Principal: ICAEW Member
R Thompson

RYECROFT GLENTON ◈
Barclays Bank Chambers, Rothbury, Morpeth, NE65 7SS
Tel: 01669 620 360
Fax: 01669 622854
Email: advice@ryecroft-glenton.co.uk
Website: http://www.ryecroft-glenton.co.uk
Non-resident Partners (ICAEW Members):
A A E Glenton, J P Charlton

RYECROFT GLENTON ◈
55 Newgate Street, Morpeth, NE61 1AY
Tel: 01670 512102
Fax: 01670 510385
Email: advice@ryecroft-glenton.co.uk
Website: http://www.ryecroft-glenton.co.uk
Resident Partners/Directors: ICAEW Members
G Cawthorn
Non-resident Partners (ICAEW Members):
J G White
Registered by the ICAEW to carry out company audit work
Regulated by the ICAEW for a range of investment business activities

THE STUDIO PRACTICE LTD
Holly House, 2 Hardy Close, Swarland, Morpeth NE65 9PG
Tel: 01670 283236
Resident Partners/Directors: ICAEW Members
S Shell

TAIT WALKER
10 Manchester Street, Morpeth, NE61 1BH

MUCH WENLOCK

AIMS - GRAHAME HURST
The Hermitage, Longville In The Dale, Much Wenlock, TF13 6DS
Tel: 01694 771622
Principal: ICAEW Member
D G Hurst

PRIORY CHECKPOINT LTD
6 Bull Ring, Much Wenlock, TF13 6HS

NANTWICH

A. PRINCEP
22 Hornby Drive, Nantwich, CW5 6JP

AFFORD ASTBURY BOND LLP ◈
31 Wellington Road, Nantwich, CW5 7ED

AFFORD BOND
31 Wellington Road, Nantwich, CW5 7ED

COOPER TAYLOR ◈
The Dowery, 22 Barker Street, Nantwich, CW5 5TE
Tel: 01270 623821
Email: office@coopertaylor.co.uk
Principal: ICAEW Member
P C Taylor
Regulated by the ICAEW for a range of investment business activities

HOWARD WORTH ★
Bank Chambers, 3 Churchyardside, Nantwich, CW5 5DE

LAYFIELD & CO LTD ◈
The Lodge, Whitehouse Lane, Nantwich, CW5 6HQ

LYON GRIFFITHS LTD
63-67 Welsh Row, Nantwich, CW5 5EW
Tel: 01270 624445
Fax: 01270 623916
Email: info@lyongriffiths.co.uk
Website: http://www.lyongriffiths.co.uk
Resident Partners/Directors: ICAEW Members
R Morris, A Weaver
Resident Partners (Non-ICAEW Members):
J A T Stokes
Registered by the ICAEW to carry out company audit work
Authorised and regulated by the Financial Services Authority for investment business

NELSON

AINSWORTHS
Charter House, Stansfield Street, Nelson, BB9 9XY
Tel: 01282 695111

AINSWORTHS LTD
Charter House, Stansfield Street, Nelson, BB9 9XY
Tel: 01282 695111
Resident Partners/Directors: ICAEW Members
P F Carney, I M W Dugmore, J Storey

EMMETT & CO (NELSON) LTD
11 Market Square, Nelson, BB9 7LP
Tel: 01282 616299
Resident Partners/Directors: ICAEW Members
C Emmett

TENON LTD
Suite 5, Bridgewater House, Surrey Road, Nelson BB9 7TZ
Tel: 01282 617800

TURNER & CO
Suite 211, Lomeshaye Business Village, Turner Road, Nelson BB9 7DR

NESTON

B.A. CAWSEY FCA
Heronmead, Neston Road, Ness, Neston CH64 4AP

BENJAMIN MORRIS & CO
Brook House, 18a Brook Street, Neston, CH64 9XL

DRIFFIELD & CO
11 Grenfell Close, Parkgate, Neston, CH64 6TU
Tel: 01513 368189
Principal: ICAEW Member
A E Driffield

SPECIALISATIONS – FINANCIAL REPORTING

Accounts Preparation
Limited Company Accounts
Partnership/Sole Trader Accounts

SPECIALISATIONS – TAXATION

Taxation

DUNCAN BOXWELL & COMPANY LTD ◈
Montrose House, Clayhill Industrial Park, Neston, CH64 3RU
Tel: 0151 336 7375
Resident Partners/Directors: ICAEW Members
D H Boxwell, C J Taylor

GUY PAYNE & CO ◈
Hale Buildings, 5 Parkgate Road, Neston, CH64 9XF
Tel: 0151 353 0067
Principal: ICAEW Member
G S J Payne

JOHNSON & CO
14 Parkgate Road, Neston, CH64 9XE
Tel: 0151 353 0389
Principal: ICAEW Member
J W Ferguson

M A RAJA & CO
20 Bowring Drive, Parkgate, Neston, CH64 6ST

MELVYN F. GODDARD & CO
1 Peerswood Court, Little Neston, Neston, CH64 0US

PHILLIP BATES & CO LTD
1-3 Chester Road, Neston, CH64 9PA

RON WELSH & CO
Mannamead, Church Lane, Neston, CH64 9US

RON WELSH (NORTH WEST) LTD
Mannamead, Church Lane, Neston, CH64 9US

NEW MALDEN

ALFRED NEILL & CO
34 Hollington Crescent, New Malden, KT3 6RR

ATKINSONS ◈
86 Burlington Road, New Malden, KT3 4NT
Tel: 020 8949 2202
Date Established: 1962
Non-resident Partners (ICAEW Members):
A Atkinson
Other Offices:19 Church Road, Hove, BN3 2FA
Registered by the ICAEW to carry out company audit work

SPECIALISATIONS – AUDIT & ASSURANCE
Audit — Private Company

SPECIALISATIONS – BUSINESS & GENERAL ADVICE
Book-keeping

SPECIALISATIONS – FORENSIC ACCOUNTING
Forensic Accounting

SPECIALISATIONS – IT
Computerised Accounting Systems
Information Technology

SPECIALISATIONS – TAXATION
Back Duty
Estate Planning
Offshore Companies
Self Assessment Advice
Trusts
Value Added Tax

BARBARA GABRIEL
156 Clarence Avenue, New Malden, KT3 3DY

GOODIN REID & CO
7 Woodside Road, New Malden, KT3 3AH

HOWARD MARKS & CO
21 Bodley Road, New Malden, KT3 5QD
Tel: 020 8942 6505
Fax: 020 8942 6505
Email: howmar999@aol.com
Date Established: 1985
Principal: ICAEW Member
H J Marks

M.ALAM
144 Motspur Park, New Malden, KT3 6PF

NAGARIA & CO ◈
21 Alverstone Road, New Malden, KT3 4BA
Tel: 020 8949 6666
Principal: ICAEW Member
R S Shah

NASIR MAHMUD ◈
Falcon House, 257 Burlington Road, New Malden, KT3 4NE
Tel: 020 8949 7770
Fax: 020 8942 4455
Principal: ICAEW Member
N Mahmud
Registered by the ICAEW to carry out company audit work
Regulated by the ICAEW for a range of investment business activities

SPECIALISATIONS – AUDIT & ASSURANCE
Audit

SPECIALISATIONS – FINANCIAL REPORTING
Accounts Preparation

SPECIALISATIONS – TAXATION
Taxation

General Description: Small businesses including Limited Company audits and general accountancy work.
Languages Spoken:
Urdu, Bengali, Punjabi

NUNN HAYWARD
66-70 Coombe Road, New Malden, KT3 4QW
Tel: 020 8336 2166
Resident Partners/Directors: ICAEW Members
P S Hayward

PLG CONSULTING LTD
78 Tennyson Avenue, Motspur Park, New Malden, KT3 6LZ

PRACSERVE LTD
Falcon House, 257 Burlington Road, New Malden, KT3 4NE

S BAILEY & CO LTD
53 Malden Hill, New Malden, KT3 4DS

SHEETEN AMIN
8 Langley Grove, New Malden, KT3 3AL

SLOANE WINCKLESS & CO
Britannia Chambers, 181-185 High Street, New Malden, KT3 4BH
Tel: 020 8949 6921
Fax: 020 8336 1068
Email: sw&co@auditing.demon.co.uk
Date Established: 1977
See display advertisement near this entry.

SLOANE WINCKLESS & CO LTD
Britannia Chambers, 181-185 High Street, New Malden, KT3 4BH
Tel: 020 8949 6921
Fax: 020 8336 1068
Email: sw&co@auditing.demon.co.uk
Website: http://www.sloanewinckless.co.uk
Date Established: 1977
Resident Partners/Directors: ICAEW Members
Neil A R Winckless
Registered by the ICAEW to carry out company audit work
Regulated by the ICAEW for a range of investment business activities

NEW MILTON

DAVID J HOUSE LTD
21 Barton Court Avenue, Barton on Sea, New Milton, BH25 7EP
Tel: 01425 627560
Resident Partners/Directors: ICAEW Members
D J House

FIONA E DAVIES
3 Barton Common Lane, New Milton, BH25 5PS

HOPE JONES
Dunlop House, 23a Spencer Road, New Milton, BH25 6BZ
Tel: 01425 612696
Resident Partners/Directors: ICAEW Members
A B Maugham
See display advertisement near this entry.

P J GREENACRE & CO LTD
The Old Bakery, Tiptoe Road, Wootton, New Milton BH25 5SJ

PRINCECROFT WILLIS LLP
The George Business Centre, Christchurch Road, New Milton, BH25 6QJ

PW BUSINESS SOLUTIONS ★
The Coach House, George Business Centre, Christchurch Road, New Milton BH25 6QJ

TERENCE L SMITH & CO
38A Station Road, New Milton, BH25 6JX
Tel: 01425 621032
Email: ENQCA@davidshores.co.uk
Website: http://www.davidshores.co.uk
Registered by the ICAEW to carry out company audit work

WESTLAKE CLARK
Nat West Bank Chambers, 55 Station Road, New Milton, BH25 6JA
Tel: 01425 620611
Email: nm@westlakeclark.com
Resident Partners/Directors: ICAEW Members
P D Clegg, F J Legris, Z K Redmill
Registered by the ICAEW to carry out company audit work
Regulated by the ICAEW for a range of investment business activities
Languages Spoken:
French

NEW ROMNEY

STEPHEN HILL MID KENT ◈
44 High Street, New Romney, TN28 8BZ
Tel: 01797 366203
Email: enquiries@stephenhillmidkent.co.uk
Website: http://www.stephenhillmidkent.co.uk
Resident Partners/Directors: ICAEW Members
T N B Lister

STEPHEN HILL MID KENT LTD
44 High Street, New Romney, TN28 8BZ

TERRY BEAK & CO ◈
5 Hamilton Close, Littlestone, New Romney, TN28 8NU
Tel: 01797 364854
Principal: ICAEW Member
T J Beak

NEWARK

ACCOUNTANCY (EAST NOTTS) LTD ◈
Spinners, Old Great North Road, Sutton-on-Trent, Newark NG23 6QL
Tel: 01636 821741
Resident Partners/Directors: ICAEW Members
G I Ladds

AIMS ACCOUNTANTS FOR BUSINESS
30 Church Street, Long Bennington, Newark, NG23 5EN

AIMS - NICK TOTHAM
30 Church Street, Long Bennington, Newark, NG23 5EN

BARKER MAULE & CO
27/33 Castle Gate, Newark, NG24 1BA
Tel: 01636 704154
Resident Partners/Directors: ICAEW Members
T P Geraghty, H A Rashid
Resident Partners (Non-ICAEW Members):
R W Spencer

BRIAN DRAKE & CO
The Counting House, Forest Road, New Ollerton, Newark NG22 9QS

DAVID BEAUMONT LTD
58 Valley Prospect, Newark, NG24 4QW
Tel: 01636 679078
Resident Partners/Directors: ICAEW Members
D Beaumont

DAVID PATTINSON
233 London Road, Balderton, Newark, NG24 3HA
Tel: 01636 706543
Principal: ICAEW Member
D Pattinson

DUNCAN & TOPLIS
14 London Road, Newark, NG24 1TW
Tel: 01636 640321
Fax: 01636 640050
Email: info@newark.duntop.co.uk
Website: http://www.duntop.co.uk
Resident Partners/Directors: ICAEW Members
M H Chatterton, I Phillips
Resident Partners (Non-ICAEW Members):
S Shaw
Registered by the ICAEW to carry out company audit work
Regulated by the ICAEW for a range of investment business activities
General Description: Other offices please see Grantham.

HARRISON FARROW
Newnham House, 3 Kings Road, Newark, NG24 1EW
Tel: 01636 674373
Resident Partners/Directors: ICAEW Members
B K Farrow, A J Harrison

HOBSONS
International House, Brunel Drive, Newark, NG24 2EG
Tel: 01636 702100

IAN MASON
17 Glebe Park, Balderton, Newark, NG24 3GN
Tel: 01636 651764
Principal: ICAEW Member
I Mason

J.A.GEORGE
The Old School House, 108 Low St, Collingham, Newark NG23 7NL
Tel: 01636 892358
Email: jagschool@aol.com
Principal: ICAEW Member
J A George

MALCOLM ELLISON
25A Lombard Street, Newark, NG24 1XG
Tel: 01636 708630
Principal: ICAEW Member
M Ellison

OAKES & CO
P.O. Box 7541, 19 Autumncroft Road, Beacon Fields, Newark NG24 2LW
Tel: 01636 640414
Resident Partners/Directors: ICAEW Members
R J Oakes

PM&G LTD
Mainwood Farm, Kneesall, Newark, NG22 0AH
Tel: 01636 636343
Resident Partners/Directors: ICAEW Members
P Gladwin, P Mitchell

ROD GEORGE
The Red House, 18 High Street, Collingham, Newark NG23 7LA

ROLAND ELLMER
33 Balderton Gate, Newark, NG24 1UE

STEPHENSON NUTTALL & CO
Ossington Chambers, 6-8 Castle Gate, Newark, NG24 1AX
Tel: 01636 705624
Email: info@stephensonnuttall.com
Resident Partners/Directors: ICAEW Members
A P Haigh, T F Hudson, Sir Peter Parker

NEWBURY

A-COUNT-A-BILITY
33 Westgate Road, Newbury, RG14 6AU

A-COUNT-A-BILITY LTD ◈
33 Westgate Road, Newbury, RG14 6AU
Tel: 01635 826124
Website: http://www.a-count-a-bility.co.uk
Resident Partners/Directors: ICAEW Members
C A Billington

BEECROFT & ASSOCIATES
The Laurels, Wickham Heath, Newbury, RG20 8PG

BHARATI PATEL
27b Priory Road, Newbury, RG14 7QS

DAVID GOLBY
High Street Cottage, Compton, Newbury, RG20 6NL
Tel: 01635 578215
Principal: ICAEW Member
D C Golby
See display advertisement near this entry.

EJ BUSINESS CONSULTANTS LTD
2b Northbrook Court, Park Street, Newbury, RG14 1EA

EJBC AFFORDABLE ACCOUNTING SOLUTIONS
2b Northbrook Court, Park Street, Newbury, RG14 1EA

ELEANOR A RICE
13 Buckingham Road, Newbury, RG14 6DH

ELIZABETH M ANFIELD
6 Tudor Road, Newbury, RG14 7PU
Tel: 01635 42210
Principal: ICAEW Member
E M Anfield

F.F. LEACH & CO
5a The Broadway, Newbury, RG14 1AS
Tel: 01635 33181
Resident Partners/Directors: ICAEW Members
W Sandford

FRANCIS RANDELL LTD
36 Westgate Road, Newbury, RG14 6AU

GRIFFINS ◈
Griffins Court, 24-32 London Road, Newbury, RG14 1JX
Tel: 01635 265265
Fax: 01635 265260
Email: team@griffins.co.uk
Website: http://www.griffins.co.uk
Training Contracts Available.
Resident Partners/Directors: ICAEW Members
T G Boothby, C P Duggan, B A Elliott, J Piercy, N S Pomroy, K H Weeks
Resident Partners (Non-ICAEW Members):
S Pallett, C Rumble, R Honeywill
Registered by the ICAEW to carry out company audit work
Regulated by the ICAEW for a range of investment business activities

INVESTOR IN PEOPLE

Languages Spoken:
French

HYNES & COMPANY (NEWBURY) LTD
Anstell House, Donnington Square, Newbury, RG14 1PP
Tel: 07785 392930
Resident Partners/Directors: ICAEW Members
G T Hynes

JAMES COWPER ◈
Phoenix House, 50 Bartholomew Street, Newbury, RG14 5QA
Tel: 01635 35255
Resident Partners/Directors: ICAEW Members
R C Holland, A Rann, M Riggall, P W Treadgold

K E TUBBY
Showell, New Road, Greenham, Newbury RG14 7RY
Tel: 01635 48114
Fax: 01635 48116
Email: kevintubby@aol.com
Principal: ICAEW Member
K E Tubby

MAUGHANS LTD
Norfolk House, 75 Bartholomew Street, Newbury, RG14 5DU
Tel: 01635 33760
Fax: 01635 44804
Email: nickm@maughans.freeserve.co.uk
Resident Partners/Directors: ICAEW Members
N J Maughan
Registered by the ICAEW to carry out company audit work

SPECIALISATIONS – AUDIT & ASSURANCE
Audit — Private Company

SPECIALISATIONS – FINANCIAL REPORTING
Accounts Preparation
Limited Company Accounts
Partnership/Sole Trader Accounts

SPECIALISATIONS – TAXATION
Taxation

General Description: A general practice firm offering professional and efficient auditing, accountancy and taxation services to individuals, sole traders, partnerships and limited companies.

MK SHERIDAN & CO
Oakways, Tubbs Lane, Highclere, Newbury RG20 9PQ

PAUL M BOWERS
3 Herewood Close, Newbury, RG14 1PY
Tel: 01635 46701
Email: paulmbowers@btinternet.com
Principal: ICAEW Member
P M Bowers
Regulated by the ICAEW for a range of investment business activities

SPECIALISATIONS – TAXATION
Capital Gains — Personal
Estate and Inheritance
Partnerships and Sole Traders
Personal
Self Assessment Advice
Trusts

RICHARD & SUE GARNER ◈
7 Kingsland House, 135 Andover Road, Newbury, RG14 6JL
Tel: 01635 552822
Resident Partners/Directors: ICAEW Members
R W Garner, S Garner

ROSS BROOKE LTD ◈
21-22 Park Way, Newbury, RG14 1EE
Tel: 01635 555666
Email: admin@ross-brooke.co.uk
Website: http://www.ross-brooke.co.uk
Resident Partners/Directors: ICAEW Members
M R W Brooke, P S Brown
Resident Partners (Non-ICAEW Members):
C J Davies
Other Offices:23 Wood Street, Old Town, Swindon, Wilts SN1 4AN
Registered by the ICAEW to carry out company audit work
Regulated by the ICAEW for a range of investment business activities

SHERIDAN STRATEGIC SERVICES LTD ◈
Oakways, Tubbs Lane, Highclere, Newbury RG20 9PQ

SILBURY BUSINESS ADVISERS LTD
Norfolk House, 75 Bartholomew Street, Newbury, RG14 5DU
Tel: 01635 37299

SME ACCOUNTING SERVICES LTD
24 Speen Lane, Speen, Newbury, RG14 1RN

SUM IT ACCOUNTS LTD
29 Greenlands Road, Newbury, RG14 7JS

TILEY & CO
Parkway Cottage, Andover Road, Highclere, Newbury RG20 9QU
Tel: 01635 254987
Email: theoffice@tileyandco.com
Resident Partners/Directors: ICAEW Members
A Tiley, M S Tiley
Registered by the ICAEW to carry out company audit work
Regulated by the ICAEW for a range of investment business activities

TITCHENERS LTD
16 The Broadway, Newbury, RG14 1AU

NEWCASTLE-UNDER-LYME

A.A. BALL
4 Lidgate Walk, Westbury Park, Clayton, Newcastle-Under-Lyme ST5 4LT

B N JACKSON NORTON ★
Alstoon Emery House, 33 Marsh Parade, Newcastle-Under-Lyme, ST5 1BT

BARRINGTONS LTD ◈
570-572 Etruria Road, Newcastle, ST5 0SU
Tel: 01782 713700
Email: ncadmin@barraccount.co.uk
Website: http://www.barringtons-online.com
Mobile: 07831 817905
Resident Partners/Directors: ICAEW Members
A M Bridge, N B Cooper, P B Wood
Resident Partners (Non-ICAEW Members):
C D Woodward
Registered by the ICAEW to carry out company audit work
Individual(s) licensed for insolvency work by the ICAEW

SPECIALISATIONS – BUSINESS RECOVERY & INSOLVENCY
Bankruptcies
Corporate Recovery
Liquidations

SPECIALISATIONS – FORENSIC ACCOUNTING
Expert Witnesses in Litigation

SPECIALISATIONS – TAXATION
Customs Duty
Value Added Tax

COLCLOUGH, HARRALL & CO
50 King Street, Newcastle, ST5 1HX
Tel: 01782 611828
Principal: ICAEW Member
J C Harrall

DEAN STATHAM ◈
29 King Street, Newcastle-Under-Lyme, ST5 1ER

DEAN STATHAM LLP ◈
29 King Street, Newcastle-Under-Lyme, ST5 1ER
Tel: 01782 614618
Email: newcastle@dsonline.co.uk
Resident Partners/Directors: ICAEW Members
D W Beardmore, R W Bladen, P A Dann
Registered by the ICAEW to carry out company audit work
Individual(s) licensed for insolvency work by another RPB

FINDLAY JAMES
38 Hassell Street, Newcastle-Under-Lyme, ST5 1BB

HARDINGS ◈
6 Marsh Parade, Newcastle, ST5 1DU
Tel: 01782 617868
Email: info@hardingsaccountants.co.uk
Resident Partners/Directors: ICAEW Members
B S Baggaley, E M Fox, T R McNeal

J.K. HUTCHINSON
8 Hillview Crescent, Baldwins Gate, Newcastle-Under-Lyme, ST5 5DE

JACKSONS
98 Lancaster Road, Newcastle-Under-Lyme, ST5 1DS

JANET M. WHITE ACA
43 Sparch Hollow, Newcastle-Under-Lyme, ST5 9PE
Tel: 01782 624871
Principal: ICAEW Member
J M White

JOHN D. OWEN
34-38 King Street, Newcastle-Under-Lyme, ST5 1HX
Tel: 01782 617306
Principal: ICAEW Member
J D Owen

KB ACCOUNTANCY SERVICES LTD
153/155 High Street, Wolstanton, Newcastle-Under-Lyme, ST5 0EJ
Tel: 01782 637473
Resident Partners/Directors: ICAEW Members
K Burgess

RICHARD F HAWKINS LTD
Linport, 59 Oaklands Avenue, Porthill, Newcastle-Under-Lyme ST5 0DR

SLATERS
Lymore Villa, 162a London Road, Chesterton, Newcastle-Under-Lyme ST5 7JB

THOMPSON WRIGHT ◈
Ebenezer House, Ryecroft, Newcastle, ST5 2BE
Tel: 01782 613141
Email: tw@twca.co.uk
Website: http://www.twca.co.uk
Resident Partners/Directors: ICAEW Members
K Evans, R L Thompson, D H Tooth, D Wright

NEWCASTLE UPON TYNE

A.D. MICHELSON
33 North Avenue, Gosforth, Newcastle Upon Tyne, NE3 4DQ

ADRIAN J. WRIGHT
38 Eastern Way, Darras Hall, Ponteland, Newcastle Upon Tyne NE20 9PF
Tel: 01661 821881
Principal: ICAEW Member
A J Wright

ALAN WILKIE
19 Edlingham Close, South Gosforth, Newcastle Upon Tyne, NE3 1RH
Tel: 0191 284 9433
Principal: ICAEW Member
A D Wilkie

ASKEY & CO
25 Whitebridge Parkway, Gosforth, Newcastle Upon Tyne, NE3 5LU
Tel: 0191 285 7978
Email: stephen@saskey.wanadoo.co.uk
Principal: ICAEW Member
J S Askey

B R & S SUTTON LTD
1a Fernville Avenue, Sunniside, Whickham, Newcastle Upon Tyne NE16 5PE

BAKER TILLY
1 St James Gate, Newcastle Upon Tyne, NE1 4AD
Tel: 0191 255 7000
Resident Partners (Non-ICAEW Members):
A S Toner

BAKER TILLY
1 St James Gate, Newcastle Upon Tyne, NE1 4AD
Tel: 0191 255 7000
Resident Partners/Directors: ICAEW Members
G Elliott, C Lauder, C Leece
Resident Partners (Non-ICAEW Members):
S L Railton

BAKER TILLY
1 St James Gate, Newcastle Upon Tyne, NE1 4AD

BAKER TILLY TAX AND ADVISORY SERVICES LLP
1 St James Gate, Newcastle Upon Tyne, NE1 4AD
Tel: 0191 255 7000
Resident Partners/Directors: ICAEW Members
G Elliott, C Lauder, C Leece, A M Suggett
Resident Partners (Non-ICAEW Members):
G Hare, J S Meakin, S L Railton, A S Toner

BEGBIES TRAYNOR (CENTRAL) LLP
Ground Floor, 2 Collingwood Street, Newcastle Upon Tyne, NE1 1JF

BLAND & WOOD
Planet Place, Killingworth, Newcastle Upon Tyne, NE12 6RD

BLOCKS
Roseworth, Roseworth Crescent, Gosforth, Newcastle Upon Tyne NE3 1NR
Tel: 0191 213 5569
Principal: ICAEW Member
P R Block

BRENNAN NEIL & LEONARD ◈
32 Brenkley Way, Blezard Business Park, Seaton Burn, Newcastle Upon Tyne NE13 6DS
Tel: 0191 236 8007
Resident Partners/Directors: ICAEW Members
M E Brennan, J Hall, J D Leonard, T W R Neil
Registered by the ICAEW to carry out company audit work

BREWSTER & BROWN ★
129 New Bridge Street, Newcastle Upon Tyne, NE1 2SW

BROWNS
42 Greenhaugh, West Moor, Newcastle Upon Tyne, NE12 7WA

BTG MCINNES CORPORATE FINANCE
2 Collingwood Street, Newcastle Upon Tyne, NE1 1JF

BUSINESS CONSULTANCY SERVICES
1st Floor, 2c St Mary's Green, Front Street, Whickham, Newcastle Upon Tyne NE16 4DN
Tel: 0191 488 3231
Fax: 0191 488 3236
Email: b_cs@btconnect.com
Principal: ICAEW Member
S Waller

SPECIALISATIONS – FINANCIAL REPORTING

Accounts Preparation
Limited Companies

Partnership/Sole Trader Accounts

SPECIALISATIONS – TAXATION

Partnerships and Sole Traders
Personal
Self Assessment Advice
Small Traders
Taxation
See display advertisement near this entry.

CHARLTON WILLIAMSON
77 Osborne Road, Jesmond, Newcastle Upon Tyne, NE2 2AN
Tel: 0191 281 8877

THE CHARLTON WILLIAMSON PARTNERSHIP LLP
77 Osborne Road, Jesmond, Newcastle Upon Tyne, NE2 2AN
Tel: 0191 2818877
Resident Partners/Directors: ICAEW Members
D Charlton

CLEMENTS & CO
2 Eslington Terrace, Jesmond, Newcastle Upon Tyne, NE2 4RJ
Tel: 0191 281 6006
Fax: 0191 281 0660
Email: clementsandco@aol.com
Principal: ICAEW Member
I R Clements

COLIN STEEN
19 Polwarth Drive, Brunton Park, Newcastle Upon Tyne, NE3 5NH

CTC
13 Portland Terrace, Jesmond, Newcastle Upon Tyne, NE2 1SN
Tel: 0191 281 2271
Resident Partners/Directors: ICAEW Members
P Clark, P Cole, A B Twaddle
Resident Partners (Non-ICAEW Members):
L Stabler

DAVID L. KILNER
7 Eldon Square, Newcastle Upon Tyne, NE1 7JG
Tel: 0191 222 1757
Fax: 0191 222 1758
Email: dlk@davidkilner.co.uk
Principal: ICAEW Member
D L Kilner

DELOITTE & TOUCHE LLP ◈
Gainsborough House, 34-40 Grey Street, Newcastle Upon Tyne, NE1 6AE
Tel: 0191 261 4111
Website: http://www.deloitte.co.uk
Resident Partners/Directors: ICAEW Members
J W Charlton, S J Cottee, P E Feechan, D P Wilkinson, P T Williamson

DOUGLAS SHAW LTD
7 Brenkley Way, Blezard Business Park, Seaton Burn, Newcastle Upon Tyne NE13 6DS

ERNST & YOUNG LLP
Citygate, St James' Boulevard, Newcastle Upon Tyne, NE1 4JD
Tel: 0191 247 2500
Resident Partners/Directors: ICAEW Members
M A B Hatton, D A O'Hanlon, A Spence, P G Willey

FITZPATRICKROYLE
105 Moorside North, Fenham, Newcastle Upon Tyne, NE4 9DY

FREEMAN RICH
Milburn House, Dean Street, Newcastle Upon Tyne, NE1 1LE
Tel: 0191 261 1839
Individual(s) licensed for insolvency work by another RPB

FUTERS ACCOUNTANCY & FINANCE
1 Westwood Avenue, Newcastle Upon Tyne, NE6 5QT

G.T. GRANT & CO
79 High Street, Gosforth, Newcastle Upon Tyne, NE3 4AA

GARBUTT & ELLIOTT LTD
Cuthbert House, All Saints Business Centre, Newcastle Upon Tyne, NE1 2ET

GLEN C RODGER LTD
Cragside House, Heaton Road, Newcastle Upon Tyne, NE6 1SE
Tel: 0191 276 1311
Website: http://www.glencrodger.co.uk
Resident Partners/Directors: ICAEW Members
R A Purvis, E Watson

GOSFORTH ACCOUNTANCY SERVICES LTD
8 Moor Court, Westfield, Gosforth, Newcastle Upon Tyne NE3 4YD

GRANT THORNTON UK LLP
Earl Grey House, 75-85 Grey Street, Newcastle Upon Tyne, NE1 6EF
Tel: 0191 261 2631
Non-resident Partners (ICAEW Members):
J P F McLean

GW ROBINSONS LLP
1 Croft Stairs, City Road, Newcastle Upon Tyne, NE1 2HG

HENDERSONS
Sterling House, Brunswick Industrial Estate, Newcastle Upon Tyne, NE13 7BA
Tel: 0191 217 0052
Fax: 0191 217 0053
Website: http://www.hendersonsca.co.uk
Principal: ICAEW Member
S Faid
Registered by the ICAEW to carry out company audit work

HIGHVIEW MANAGEMENT SERVICES LTD
9 Wolsingham Road, Gosforth, Newcastle Upon Tyne, NE3 4RP

HW ◈
Floor 11, Cale Cross House, 156 Pilgrim Street, Newcastle Upon Tyne, NORTHUMBERLAND NE1 6SU
Tel: 0845 6733 337
Resident Partners/Directors: ICAEW Members
D M Burn, S Richardson

I. THOMPSON & CO
The Arcade, Belsay, Newcastle Upon Tyne, NE20 0DY
Tel: 01661 881659
Principal: ICAEW Member
I Thompson

INSIGHT NE ★ ◈
46 Grosvenor Place, Jesmond, Newcastle Upon Tyne, NE2 2RE
Tel: 0191 281 1969
Resident Partners/Directors: ICAEW Members
J Griffiths

J.H. FOSTER & CO
Unit D Benfield Business Park, Benfield Road, Newcastle Upon Tyne, NE6 4NQ

JOSEPH MILLER & CO
Floor A, Milburn House, Dean Street, Newcastle Upon Tyne NE1 1LE

KINNAIR & CO ◈
Aston House, Redburn Road, Newcastle Upon Tyne, NE5 1NB
Tel: 0191 286 7777
Resident Partners/Directors: ICAEW Members
M L C Mak, G Murray

KINSEY JONES ◈
4 Lansdowne Terrace, Gosforth, Newcastle Upon Tyne, NE3 1HN

KPMG LLP
Quayside House, 110 Quayside, Newcastle Upon Tyne, NE1 3DX
Tel: 0191 401 3700
Resident Partners/Directors: ICAEW Members
R J Bottomley, D J Elliott, M R Thompson

L&J ACCOUNTING SERVICES LTD
22 The Grove, Benton, Newcastle Upon Tyne, NE12 9PE

LEARCHILD LTD ◈
4 Lansdowne Terrace, Gosforth, Newcastle Upon Tyne, NE3 1HN
Tel: 0191 284 4411
Resident Partners/Directors: ICAEW Members
D S Kinsey

LEATHERS LLP
17th Floor, Cale Cross House, Pilgrim Street, Newcastle Upon Tyne NE1 6SU

M.M. WALLACE
8 Moor Court, Westfield, Gosforth, Newcastle Upon Tyne NE3 4YD

MCCOWIE & CO ★
52-54 Leazes Park Rd, Newcastle Upon Tyne, NE1 4PG

MANOR CLOSE LTD
114-116 High Street, Gosforth, Newcastle Upon Tyne, NE3 1HB

N.A. ALLEN
2 Dewhurst Terrace, Sunniside, Newcastle Upon Tyne, NE16 5LP

P.S. WALLACE & CO
Floor D, Milburn House, Dean Street, Newcastle Upon Tyne NE1 1LE
Tel: 0191 260 2251
Individual(s) licensed for insolvency work by another RPB

P SIBBALD
19 Denewood, Forest Hall, Newcastle Upon Tyne, NE12 7FA

P SIBBALD (ACCOUNTANCY) LTD
19 Denewood, Forest Hall, Newcastle Upon Tyne, NE12 7FA

P.W.A. BROWN
Church Cottage, 1 East Close, Matfen, Newcastle Upon Tyne NE20 0TF

PARRY CONSULTING
20 Holly Avenue, Jesmond, Newcastle Upon Tyne, NE2 2PY

PINDER & RATKI
7 Lansdowne Terrace, Gosforth, Newcastle Upon Tyne, NE3 1HN

PLANET BUSINESS SERVICES LTD
Planet Place, Newcastle Upon Tyne, NE12 6RD

PM JOHNSON ◈
Tarag, 48 Rectory Road, Gosforth, Newcastle Upon Tyne NE3 1XP

PRICEWATERHOUSE-COOPERS
89 Sandyford Road, Newcastle Upon Tyne, NE1 8HW

PRICEWATERHOUSE-COOPERS LLP
89 Sandyford Road, Newcastle Upon Tyne, NE1 8HW
Tel: 0191 232 8493
Resident Partners/Directors: ICAEW Members
P J Coward, J A McIntosh, T H R Porter, G J Redman, N M Webster

PROFIT ABILITY NORTH EAST LTD ◈
National Westminster Bank Chambers, 2 Darras Road, Ponteland, Newcastle Upon Tyne NE20 9HA

QUENTIN CAISLEY ◈
32 Clockburnsyde Close, Whickham, Newcastle Upon Tyne, NE16 5UT
Tel: 0191 496 0884
Principal: ICAEW Member
Q Caisley

R L CHARLES LTD
Fernwood House, Fernwood Road, Jesmond, Newcastle Upon Tyne NE2 1TJ

R L CONSTABLE LTD
Robson Laidler, Fernwood House, Fernwood Road, Jesmond, Newcastle Upon Tyne NE2 1TJ

R L MORAN LTD
Fernwood House, Fernwood Road, Jesmond, Newcastle Upon Tyne NE2 1TJ
Tel: 0191 2818191
Resident Partners/Directors: ICAEW Members
M T Moran

RAMSHAW & CO LTD
2nd Floor, Yarm House, Roseworth Crescent, Gosforth, Newcastle Upon Tyne NE3 1NR
Tel: 0191 285 6644
Resident Partners/Directors: ICAEW Members
D S Ramshaw

RIBCHESTERS
Sutherland House, 5-7 The Friars, Newcastle Upon Tyne, NE1 5XE

RICHARD CLEREY & CO
18 Brenkley Way, Blezard Business Park, Seaton Burn, Newcastle Upon Tyne NE13 6DS

RICHARDS & CO
Owners Business Centre, High Street, Newburn, Newcastle Upon Tyne NE15 8LN
Tel: 0191 229 0231
Principal: ICAEW Member
B Richards

RL MCNEIL LTD
Robson Laidler, Fernwood House, Fernwood Road, Jesmond, Newcastle Upon Tyne NE2 1TJ

RL WISEMAN LTD
Robson Laidler, Fernwood House, Fernwood Road, Jesmond, Newcastle Upon Tyne NE2 1TJ

RMT ACCOUNTANTS AND BUSINES ADVISORS ◈
Gosforth Park Avenue, Newcastle Upon Tyne, NE12 8EG
Tel: 0191 256 9500
Resident Partners/Directors: ICAEW Members
M H Gilbert, A A Josephs, J M Pott, S D Slater

ROBERT J. CROWE & CO
93 Jesmond Park West, High Heaton, Newcastle Upon Tyne, NE7 7BY

ROBIN UPTON INSOLVENCY
Milburn House, Dean Street, Newcastle Upon Tyne, NE1 1LE
Tel: 01912 602253
Individual(s) licensed for insolvency work by another RPB

ROBSON LAIDLER LLP
Fernwood House, Fernwood Road, Jesmond, Newcastle Upon Tyne NE2 1TJ

RUSSELL & CO
National Westminster Bank Chambers, 2 Darras Road, Ponteland, Newcastle Upon Tyne NE20 9HA

RYECROFT GLENTON ◈
32 Portland Terrace, Jesmond, Newcastle Upon Tyne, NE2 1QP
Tel: 0191 281 1292
Fax: 0191 212 0075
Email: advice@ryecroft-glenton.co.uk
Website: http://www.ryecroft-glenton.co.uk
Training Contracts Available.
Resident Partners/Directors: ICAEW Members
D R Anderson, D Armstrong, M H Brown, C C Charlton, J P Charlton, A A E Glenton, D J Graham, T J Mallon, G Maughan, D Milligan, C N Pearson, S W Rainbow, C R Robson, I M Smith, J G White, A E Woolhead, N R Wyrley-Birch
Non-resident Partners (ICAEW Members):
G Cawthorn
Registered by the ICAEW to carry out company audit work
Regulated by the ICAEW for a range of investment business activities

S.K. DUGGAL
13 Pelham Court, Newcastle Upon Tyne, NE3 2YL

STEPHENSON COATES ◈
Asama Court, West 2, Newcastle Business Park, Newcastle Upon Tyne NE4 7YD
Tel: 0191 256 7766
Fax: 0191 256 7676
Email: administrator@stephensoncoates.co.uk
Website: http://www.stephensoncoates.co.uk
Resident Partners/Directors: ICAEW Members
A W Coates, J H Oswald
Resident Partners (Non-ICAEW Members):
P W Docherty
Other Offices:8 Bell Villas, Ponteland, Newcastle upon Tyne NE20 9BE
(Tel: 01661 823693)
(Fax: 01661 823678)
Registered by the ICAEW to carry out company audit work
Regulated by the ICAEW for a range of investment business activities

SPECIALISATIONS – FORENSIC ACCOUNTING
Forensic Accounting

SPECIALISATIONS – SECTOR
Solicitors

STEPHENSON COATES
8 Bell Villas, Ponteland, Newcastle Upon Tyne, NE20 9BE

STOKOE RODGER
24 Lansdowne Terrace, Gosforth, Newcastle Upon Tyne, NE3 1HP
Tel: 0191 284 6291
Fax: 0191 284 6993
Email: p.killen@stokoerodger.co.uk
Website: http://www.stokerodger.co.uk
Resident Partners/Directors: ICAEW Members
D E Stokoe
Non-resident Partners (ICAEW Members):
S G Charlton, M M Bradley, I R Christer
Resident Partners (Non-ICAEW Members):
P Killen
Registered by the ICAEW to carry out company audit work

SYRON & CO
7 Bell Villas, Ponteland, Newcastle Upon Tyne, NE20 9BD
Tel: 01661 825783
Principal: ICAEW Member
D V Syron

TAIT WALKER ◈
Bulman House, Regent Centre, Gosforth, Newcastle Upon Tyne NE3 3LS
Tel: 0191 285 0321
Website: http://www.taitwalker.co.uk
Training Contracts Available.
Resident Partners/Directors: ICAEW Members
D Arthur, M R C Brunton, A Crawley, G S Goldie, A J Moorby, G Moore, S C Plaskitt, M A Smith
Resident Partners (Non-ICAEW Members):
A D Kelly
Other Offices:10 Manchester Street, Morpeth, Northumberland NE61 1BH
(Tel: 01670 513106)
(Fax: 01670 504064), Crutes House, Fudan Way, Teesdale Park, Stockton on Tees, TS17 6EN
(Tel: 01642 676888)
(Fax: 01642 605866)
Registered by the ICAEW to carry out company audit work
Authorised and regulated by the Financial Services Authority for investment business
Individual(s) licensed for insolvency work by the ICAEW

INVESTOR IN PEOPLE

SPECIALISATIONS – AUDIT & ASSURANCE
Audit

SPECIALISATIONS – BUSINESS & GENERAL ADVICE
Acquisitions and Mergers
Disposal of Businesses
Outsourcing - Financial Services
Takeovers

SPECIALISATIONS – BUSINESS RECOVERY & INSOLVENCY
Bankruptcies
Corporate Recovery
Liquidations

SPECIALISATIONS – FINANCIAL REPORTING
Accounts Preparation
Limited Company Accounts

SPECIALISATIONS – FORENSIC ACCOUNTING
Forensic Accounting

SPECIALISATIONS – INVESTMENT BUSINESS
Financial Planning and Advice
Pensions Advice

SPECIALISATIONS – TAXATION
Payroll Service and Advice
Taxation

TETLOW & SMITH ★
3 Eldon Square, Newcastle Upon Tyne, NE1 7JG

TIM MORGAN ◈
7 Fowberry Crescent, Fenham, Newcastle Upon Tyne, NE4 9XH

TYNESIDE ACCOUNTANCY
25 Lanesborough Court, Gosforth, Newcastle Upon Tyne, NE3 3BZ

UHY TORGERSENS ◈
Churchill House, 12 Mosley Street, Newcastle Upon Tyne, NE1 1DE
Tel: 0191 230 0000

UNW LLP ◈
Citygate, St James Boulevard, Newcastle Upon Tyne, NE1 4JE
Tel: 0191 243 6000
Resident Partners/Directors: ICAEW Members
N Bearpark, S Lant, D C Stonehouse, A J G Wilson, C E Young

VED DHAUN & CO
20 Lansdowne Terrace, Gosforth, Newcastle Upon Tyne, NE3 1HP

WILLEY & CO ★
Bainbridge House, 379 Stamfordham Road, Westerhope, Newcastle Upon Tyne NE5 2LH
Tel: 0191 286 9797
Fax: 0191 271 4319
Email: mail@willey-accountants.co.uk
Resident Partners/Directors: ICAEW Members
P J Willey
Resident Partners (Non-ICAEW Members):
J Lyall
Registered by the ICAEW to carry out company audit work
Regulated by the ICAEW for a range of investment business activities

WILLIS SCOTT GROUP ★
Bassett Herron, 391 Benton Road, Four Lane Ends, Newcastle Upon Tyne NE7 7EE

NEWENT

AIMS ACCOUNTANTS FOR BUSINESS ◈
Bramley Place, Orchard Road, 45 The Scarr, Newent GL18 1DQ
Tel: 01531 828 063

BRAMLEY PLACE LTD ◈
Bramley Place, Orchard Road, 45 The Scarr, Newent GL18 1DQ

NEWHAVEN

C. WRIGHT
39 Court Farm Road, Newhaven, BN9 9DH

INTELLIGENT BLUE LTD
66 Haven Way, Newhaven, BN9 9TD
Tel: 01273 510932
Fax: 01273 510940
Email: simon@flory.co.uk
Website: http://www.intelligentbluelimited.com
Mobile: 07808 003178
Resident Partners/Directors: ICAEW Members
S J Flory

SPECIALISATIONS – BUSINESS & GENERAL ADVICE
Administration
Book-keeping
Book-keeping Systems
Disposal of Businesses

SPECIALISATIONS – FINANCIAL REPORTING
Accounts Preparation
Limited Companies
Limited Company Accounts
Limited Liability Partnership
Partnership/Sole Trader Accounts

SPECIALISATIONS – SECTOR
Construction
Hotels/Public Houses
Leisure Industry
Property
Property Development
Traders — General

SPECIALISATIONS – TAXATION
Payroll Service and Advice
Self Assessment Advice
Small Traders
Taxation

General Description: Chartered certified accountants. Specialists in small & medium-sized businesses.

KEVIN ALDERTON & TEAM
14 South Way, Newhaven, BN9 9LL
Tel: 01273 611239

KEVIN ALDERTON & TEAM LTD
14 South Way, Newhaven, BN9 9LL

MARCHANT & CO
2 Court Farm Road, Newhaven, BN9 9DH

SUSSEX AUDIT LTD
66 Haven Way, Newhaven, BN9 9TD
Tel: 01273 510932
Fax: 01273 510940
Resident Partners/Directors: ICAEW Members
S J Flory

NEWMARKET

A.R. WASLIN
17 Rochfort Avenue, Newmarket, CB8 0DL
Tel: 01638 601718
Principal: ICAEW Member
A R Waslin

ASR ADVISORY
30 Westley Crossing, Six Mile Bottom, Newmarket, CB8 0UB

B.Z. ALEXANDER
The Old Post Cottage, Denston, Newmarket, CB8 8PW
Tel: 01440 820675
Principal: ICAEW Member
S V H Bransby-Zachary

BERNARD EDGE & CO
The Old Courts, 147 All Saints Road, Newmarket, CB8 8HH

DEREK BRIAN MURTON
Baden-croft, Falmouth Avenue, Newmarket, CB8 0NB
Tel: 01638 668032
Principal: ICAEW Member
D B Murton

EDWARDS & CO
2 Stud Farm, Burrough Green, Newmarket, CB8 9NH

HARDCASTLE BURTON ◈
90 High Street, Newmarket, CB8 8FE
Tel: 01638 606020
Resident Partners/Directors: ICAEW Members
P J Tostevin

MICHAEL SMY
12 Woodditton Road, Newmarket, CB8 9BQ
Tel: 01638 601198
Principal: ICAEW Member
M D Smy

MOORE & CO
Belvoir House, 1 Rous Road, Newmarket, CB8 8DH
Tel: 01638 664275
Resident Partners/Directors: ICAEW Members
D J Cranness, D W Wright

N ANSON
3 Swan Grove, Exning, Newmarket, CB8 7HX

RAPID RELIEF CONSULTANCY
Cedar Cottage, Burrough Green, Newmarket, CB8 9NE

RAPID RELIEF CONSULTANCY LTD
Cedar Cottage, Burrough Green, Newmarket, CB8 9NE

REBECCA WOODBURN
1 Factory Cottages, Pound Green, Cowlinge, Newmarket CB8 9QQ

RICHARD A. FELL
Albion Lodge, Fordham Road, Newmarket, CB8 7AQ

STACEY & PARTNERS ◈
88 High Street, Newmarket, CB8 8JX
Tel: 01638 564200
Website: http://www.staceys.co.uk
Resident Partners/Directors: ICAEW Members
E J Wager
Registered by the ICAEW to carry out company audit work
Regulated by the ICAEW for a range of investment business activities

STACEY & PARTNERS LTD
88 High Street, Newmarket, CB8 8JX

STREETS WHITMARSH STERLAND LLP
The Railway Station, Green Road, Newmarket, CB8 9WT
Tel: 01638 743825
Email: info@streetsweb.co.uk
Website: http://www.streetsweb.co.uk

WHITMARSH STERLAND
The Railway Station, Green Road, Newmarket, CB8 9WT

WINCH & CO
Yew Tree Cottage, Great Bradley, Newmarket, CB8 9LH

NEWPORT

A.H.CROSS & CO
16 Quay Street, Newport, PO30 5BG

BRIGHT BROWN
Exchange House, St Cross Lane, Newport, PO30 5BZ

BRIGHT BROWN LTD
Exchange House, St Cross Lane, Newport, PO30 5BZ
Tel: 01983 523361
Resident Partners/Directors: ICAEW Members
R Barton, R Fokias, M G Russell, F T Seabourne

HARRISON BLACK
Pyle House, 137 Pyle Street, Newport, PO30 1JW

HARRISON BLACK LTD
Pyle House, 137 Pyle Street, Newport, PO30 1JW

MOORE STEPHENS (SOUTH) LLP
9 St Johns Place, Newport, PO30 1LH

BARRINGTONS LTD ◈
Abbey Court, High Street, Newport, TF10 7BW
Tel: 01952 811745
Fax: 01952 814605
Email: npadmin@barraccount.co.uk
Website: http://www.barringtons-online.com
Registered by the ICAEW to carry out company audit work

SPECIALISATIONS – BUSINESS RECOVERY & INSOLVENCY
Bankruptcies
Corporate Recovery
Liquidations

continued

BARRINGTONS LTD *cont*
SPECIALISATIONS – SECTOR

Agriculture
General Description: Licensed Insolvency Practitioner.

C.R. WALKER
8 Longford Park, Longford, Newport, TF10 8LW

D. BULKELEY-JONES & CO
Millview Cottage, Fernhill Road, Sutton, Newport TF10 8DH
Tel: 01952 820064
Principal: ICAEW Member
D Bulkeley-Jones

HOWSONS ◈
58 High Street, Newport, TF10 7AQ
Tel: 01952 813330
Resident Partners/Directors: ICAEW Members
M N Davies
Other Offices: Stoke on Trent, Leek, Uttoxeter, Market Drayton, Alsager, Burslem

KATES ACCOUNTANCY SERVICES
1 Woodridge Close, Edgmond, Newport, TF10 8JF
Tel: 01952 813123
Email: kate.bowman@devlinfisher.co.uk
Mobile: 07764 892888
Principal: ICAEW Member
K J Bowman

SILVER & CO ◈
9 Salter's Court, Lower Bar, Newport, TF10 7BE

T J SHAW
6 Cherrington Manor Court, Cherrington, Newport, TF10 8PA
Tel: 01952 541035
Principal: ICAEW Member
T J Shaw

WATSON JONES ACCOUNTING LTD
18 Hillside, Lilleshall, Newport, TF10 9HG

NEWPORT PAGNELL

ACCOUNTING AND BUSINESS DEVELOPMENT LTD
Unit 6, Cooksoe Farm, Chicheley, Newport Pagnell MK16 9JP
Tel: 01234 391391
Resident Partners/Directors: ICAEW Members
T A Smith

MARTYN INGLES & CO
50 High Street, Stoke Goldington, Newport Pagnell, MK16 8NR

MICHAEL J EMERY & CO LTD
22 St John Street, Newport Pagnell, MK16 8HJ

NEWQUAY

BYRNE AND CO
Trenhaile Bungalow, St Newlyn East, Newquay, TR8 5JL

KARREK ACCOUNTANTS
9 Hilgrove Road, Newquay, TR7 2QY

KARREK ACCOUNTANTS LTD
9 Hilgrove Road, Newquay, TR7 2QY

NASH & CO
Central House, 4/6 Crantock Street, Newquay, TR7 1JS
Tel: 01637 878663

PETER CRANE & CO
30-32 Trebarwith Crescent, Newquay, TR7 1DX

PETER CRANE & CO LTD
30/32 Trebarwith Crescent, Newquay, TR7 1DX
Tel: 01637 876767
Resident Partners/Directors: ICAEW Members
P A Crane

SOVEREIGN ACCOUNTING SOLUTIONS
Langarth House, Rejerrah, Newquay, TR8 5QB

STEPHEN PEARN & CO ◈
20 Henver Road, Newquay, TR7 3BJ
Tel: 01637 872328
Principal: ICAEW Member
S C Pearn

WHITAKERS ◈
Bryndon House, 5-7 Berry Road, Newquay, TR7 1AD
Tel: 01637 873838
Fax: 01637 850505
Email: mail@wrp.uk.com
Website: http://www.wrp.uk.com
Resident Partners/Directors: ICAEW Members
D P Bennett, F A Cox, J E Cox, N C Powell
Authorised and regulated by the Financial Services Authority for investment business

WINTER RULE ◈
Victoria Parade Buildings, East Street, Newquay, TR7 1BG
Tel: 01637 874234
Website: http://www.winterrule.co.uk
Resident Partners/Directors: ICAEW Members
M S Bentley
Registered by the ICAEW to carry out company audit work

NEWTON ABBOT

A J SHORTRIDGE
Wessex House, Teign Road, Newton Abbot, TQ12 4AA

ADAMS & CO ◈
Pullman House, 7 Battle Road, Heathfield Industrial Estate, Newton Abbot TQ12 6RY

ADDERLEY & CO
Heathcot, Abbotskerswell, Newton Abbot, TQ12 5PW

ANTHONY J. KNAPTON
6 St Johns Close, Bovey Tracey, Newton Abbot, TQ13 9BU
Tel: 01626 832116
Principal: ICAEW Member
A J Knapton

BIBBY'S ◈
19 Old Exeter Street, Chudleigh, Newton Abbot, TQ13 0LD
Tel: 01626 853625

C.H. PEARSON
7 Moore Close, Aller Park, Newton Abbot, TQ12 4TH
Tel: 01626 365524
Principal: ICAEW Member
C H Pearson

CHRIS EDWORTHY
St John House, Trusham, Newton Abbot, TQ13 0NR
Tel: 01626 852735
Principal: ICAEW Member
C J Edworthy

DARNELLS
Quay House, Quay Road, Newton Abbot, TQ12 2BU
Tel: 01626 358500
Fax: 01626 358501
Website: http://www.darnells.co.uk
Resident Partners/Directors: ICAEW Members
S P Murphy, D G Smith
Resident Partners (Non-ICAEW Members):
P A Beard, P A Raisey

DAVID J. EAST
4 St Pauls Road, Newton Abbot, TQ12 2HP
Tel: 01626 362269
Principal: ICAEW Member
D J East

DEVON SQUARE PARTNERS LTD
16 Devon Square, Newton Abbot, TQ12 2HR

FERNLEY NANKIVELL
4 St Paul's Road, Newton Abbot, TQ12 2HP

FRANCIS CLARK ◈
23 Devon Square, Newton Abbot, TQ12 2HU
Tel: 01392 667000
Website: http://www.francisclark.co.uk
Resident Partners/Directors: ICAEW Members
C L Hicks, J M Michelmore
Resident Partners (Non-ICAEW Members):
S J Collins, D A Williams, P A O'Connell
Authorised and regulated by the Financial Services Authority for investment business
General Description: Largest independent firm in the South West, with particular strengths in taxation, VAT, corporate finance, financial planning, forensic accounting, IT and insolvency.

FRANCIS CLARK
Ash House, Canal Way, Kingsteignton, Newton Abbot TQ12 3RZ
Tel: 01626 206296
Resident Partners/Directors: ICAEW Members
R M T Beard

JAMES STEWART & CO
St Marys, Forches Cross, Bovey Road, Newton Abbot TQ12 6PU

JOHN P LISTER
Bay Tree House, 8 Oak Lawn, Newton Abbot, TQ12 1QP
Tel: 01626 361988
Principal: ICAEW Member
J P Lister

LAMEYS ★
One Courtenay Park, Newton Abbot, TQ12 2HD

MICHAEL TRIGG ACCOUNTING LTD ◈
19 Old Exeter Street, Chudleigh, Newton Abbot, TQ13 0LD
Tel: 01626 853625
Resident Partners/Directors: ICAEW Members
M J Trigg
Registered by the ICAEW to carry out company audit work

PEPLOWS ◈
Moorgate House, King Street, Newton Abbot, TQ12 2LG
Tel: 01626 208802
Fax: 01626 208805
Email: enquiries@peplows.co.uk
Website: http://www.peplows.co.uk
Resident Partners/Directors: ICAEW Members
L Lugger, G C Rooke, D A Saxby, M D Young
Other Offices: Exeter, Torquay
Registered by the ICAEW to carry out company audit work
Regulated by the ICAEW for a range of investment business activities

PETER DI GIUSEPPE
Witsend, 10 Poplar Close, Aller Park, Newton Abbot TQ12 4PG
Tel: 01626 351740
Principal: ICAEW Member
P E Di Giuseppe

R.E. STRATFORD & CO
67a Queen St, Newton Abbot, TQ12 2AU
Tel: 01626 354890
Website: http://www.restratford.co.uk
Principal: ICAEW Member
P T S Wyatt

REDMAYNE, PARK & CO ◈
11 Oakford, Kingsteignton, Newton Abbot, TQ12 3EQ
Tel: 01626 363680
Resident Partners/Directors: ICAEW Members
D J Park
Resident Partners (Non-ICAEW Members):
A J Redmayne
Regulated by the ICAEW for a range of investment business activities

REYNOLDS 2000 (TAXATION SERVICES) LTD
Whitstone Farm, Bovey Tracey, Newton Abbot, TQ13 9NA
Tel: 01626 836611
Resident Partners/Directors: ICAEW Members
A L Bunn

RUPP & FRASER
7 St Paul's Road, Newton Abbot, TQ12 2HP

SIMPKINS EDWARDS
C/O Rendells, Rock House, Southcombe Street, Chagford, Newton Abbot TQ13 8AX

VARNEY & CO
46 Mile End Road, Highweek, Newton Abbot, TQ12 1RW

W.N. TOLFREE
6 Ledsgrove, Ipplepen, Newton Abbot, TQ12 5QY

NEWTON AYCLIFFE

DAVID SCOTT & CO
15 Colburn Avenue, Newton Aycliffe, DL5 7HX
Tel: 01325 321833
Principal: ICAEW Member
D T Scott

GEORGE CHARLTON
11 Stoneleigh Court, Woodham Village, Newton Aycliffe, DL5 4TL

MITCHELL GORDON
Room G19, Evans Incubation Bus Centre, Durham Way South, Newton Aycliffe DL5 6XP
Tel: 01325 328825
Resident Partners/Directors: ICAEW Members
M D Gordon, N A Vassilounis

MITCHELL GORDON LTD
Room G19, Evans Incubation Centre, Durham Way South, Newton Aycliffe DL5 6XP
Tel: 01325 328825

NEWTON-LE-WILLOWS

C J BAILEY & CO
145 High Street, Newton-le-willows, WA12 9SQ
Tel: 01925 222003
Fax: 01925 223135
Principal: ICAEW Member
C J Bailey
Registered by the ICAEW to carry out company audit work

MITCHELL & CO
143/147 High Street, Newton-le-willows, WA12 9SQ
Tel: 01925 222003
Principal: ICAEW Member
S E Mitchell

P A HULL & CO
34 Queen Street, Newton-Le-Willows, WA12 9AZ

NORMANTON

ALFRED HAWKINS & CO ★
40-42 Castleford Road, Normanton, WF6 2EE
Tel: 01924 892119
Resident Partners/Directors: ICAEW Members
J C Brearton

PAYLINGS ★
40-42 Castleford Road, Normanton, WF6 2EE

ROLAND HEPWORTH
2 Hall Croft, Normanton, WF6 2DN
Tel: 01924 220351
Principal: ICAEW Member
R Hepworth

NORTH FERRIBY

AITKEN CORPORATE FINANCE LTD
18 High Street, North Ferriby, HU14 3JP
Tel: 01482 640224
Resident Partners/Directors: ICAEW Members
G M Aitken

D.C. MARSHALL & CO
Giles Croft, 1a Ferriby High Road, North Ferriby, HU14 3LD
Tel: 01482 640066
Fax: 01482 640066
Email: david@dcmandco.karoo.co.uk
Principal: ICAEW Member
D C Marshall

G M AITKEN
18 High Street, North Ferriby, HU14 3JP
Tel: 01482 640224
Principal: ICAEW Member
G M Aitken

NORTH SHIELDS

BELL TINDLE WILLIAMSON LLP ◈
The Old Post Office, Saville Street, North Shields, NE30 1AY
Tel: 0191 257 7113
Website: http://www.btw.uk.com
Resident Partners/Directors: ICAEW Members
J Bell, M Tindle, K J Williamson
Other Offices: Coliseum Building, 248 Whitley Road, Whitley Bay, Tyne & Wear NE26 2TE
Registered by the ICAEW to carry out company audit work

BELL TINDLE WILLIAMSON LLP ◈
4 Northumberland Place, North Shields, NE30 1QP
Tel: 0191 257 7113
Email: ns@btw.uk.com
Website: http://www.btw.uk.com
Training Contracts Available.
Resident Partners/Directors: ICAEW Members
J Bell
Registered by the ICAEW to carry out company audit work
Individual(s) licensed for insolvency work by the ICAEW

BLU SKY
17 Northumberland Square, North Shields, NE29 1SA

FITZPATRICKROYLE
16 Stirling Drive, North Shields, NE29 8DJ

HAWDON BELL & CO
4 Northumberland Place, North Shields, NE30 1QP
Tel: 0191 257 7113
Resident Partners/Directors: ICAEW Members
J Bell, M Tindle, K J Williamson
Individual(s) licensed for insolvency work by the ICAEW

READ, MILBURN & CO
71 Howard Street, North Shields, NE30 1AF

ROOTCORZ
21 Washington Terrace, North Shields, NE30 2HG

ROOTCORZ LTD
21 Washington Terrace, North Shields, NE30 2HG

NORTH TAWTON

HERMAN & CO
Clapper Cottage, Bondleigh, North Tawton, EX20 2AU

NORTH WALSHAM

D.J. SWATMAN
24 Wilkinson Way, North Walsham, NR28 9BB

LOVEWELL BLAKE ◈
Brentnall House, Vicarage Street, North Walsham, NR28 9DQ
Tel: 01692 405308
Fax: 01692 404236
Email: mdls@lovewell-blake.co.uk
Website: http://www.lovewell-blake.co.uk
Non-resident Partners (ICAEW Members):
M D L Smith
General Description: The practice has 21 partners and our other offices are listed under our Norwich entry.

SEXTY & CO ★
2A Church Street, North Walsham, NR28 9DA

NORTHALLERTON

AC SAVAGE & CO
275 High Street, Northallerton, DL7 8DW
Tel: 01609 776713
Principal: ICAEW Member
A C Savage

ARMSTRONG WATSON ◈
77 High Street, Northallerton, DL7 8EG
Tel: 01609 702000
Resident Partners/Directors: ICAEW Members
L Parker

EURA AUDIT UK
87 South Parade, Northallerton, DL7 8SJ

HANBY & CO ◈
209 High Street, Northallerton, DL7 8LW
Tel: 01609 771121
Website: http://www.hanbys.co.uk
Resident Partners/Directors: ICAEW Members
P M Brierley, I C Cartwright
Registered by the ICAEW to carry out company audit work
Regulated by the ICAEW for a range of investment business activities

KENNETH EASBY LLP
Oak Mount, Thornfield Business Park, Standard Way, Northallerton DL6 2XQ
Tel: 01609 778789
Resident Partners/Directors: ICAEW Members
K Graham, M Mayman

KING, HOPE & CO ◈
34 Romanby Road, Northallerton, DL7 8NF
Tel: 01609 780909
Resident Partners/Directors: ICAEW Members
S Anderson, P Jackson
Registered by the ICAEW to carry out company audit work

continued

KING, HOPE & CO *cont*

Regulated by the ICAEW for a range of investment business activities

LEONARD BYE

2 Romanby Court, Northallerton, DL7 8PG

R.H. RENWICK

121-123 High Street, Northallerton, DL7 8PQ
Tel: 01609 776200
Principal: ICAEW Member
R H Renwick

NORTHAMPTON

A.J. LEWIS

Pandloss House, 45 Stoke Road, Blisworth, Northampton NN7 3BZ
Tel: 01604 878959
Principal: ICAEW Member
A J Lewis

ABUNDANCE BUSINESS DEVELOPMENT PRACTICES

4 Creative House, Royal Ordnance Depot, Weedon, Northampton NN7 4PS

ACAX ◈

Shilton House, 56 Park Avenue North, Northampton, NN3 2JE
Tel: 01604 510471
Principal: ICAEW Member
K D Hall

AIMS - DAVID TURNER

38 Caxton House, Northampton Science Park, Kings Park Road, Moulton Park, Northampton NN3 6LG

ARCHIE JENNER CONSULTANTS ★

The Old Post Office, 109 Northampton Road, Brixworth, Northampton NN6 9BU
Tel: 01604 881173
Resident Partners/Directors: ICAEW Members
S K Jenner

B J JARVIS & CO LTD

109 Churchill Road, Earls Barton, Northampton, NN6 0RE
Tel: 01604 810489
Resident Partners/Directors: ICAEW Members
B J Jarvis

B.R. BAMFORD

Old School Cottage, 6-7 Moulton Road, Pitsford, Northampton NN6 9AU

BAC AUDITORS

Suite 12, Newton House, Northampton Science Park, Kings Park Road, Moulton Park, Northampton NN3 6LG

BLUE CUBE BUSINESS

10 Cheyne Walk, Northampton, NN1 5PT

BONHAM BAGSHAW

25 Greenfield Avenue, Northampton, NN3 2AA

CHANTREY VELLACOTT DFK LLP

Derngate Mews, Derngate, Northampton, NN1 1UE
Tel: 01604 639257
Fax: 01604 231460
Email: info@cvdfk.com
Website: http://www.cvdfk.com
Resident Partners/Directors: ICAEW Members
E S Harris, J T G Harris, C W Hindle, D Ince
Other Offices: Croydon, Leicester, London, Reading, Watford, Brighton & Hove, Colchester, Stevenage

Registered by the ICAEW to carry out company audit work

Regulated by the ICAEW for a range of investment business activities

INVESTOR IN PEOPLE

CHENEY & CO

310 Wellingborough Road, Northampton, NN1 4EP

CLIFFORD ROBERTS ◈

Pacioli House, 9 Brookfield, Duncan Close, Moulton Park, Northampton NN3 6WL
Tel: 01604 642933
Resident Partners/Directors: ICAEW Members
N Barnes, M V Field, S D Wilch

COTTONS

Regency House, 3 Albion Place, Northampton, NN1 1UD

CUBE PARTNERS LTD

5 Giffard Court, Millbrook Close, Northampton, NN5 5JF

D.J.ROCKALL

14 MacLean Close, Abington, Northampton, NN3 3DJ
Tel: 01604 639483
Principal: ICAEW Member
D J Rockall

D.J. SMITH

23 Welford Road, Kingsthorpe, Northampton, NN2 8AQ
Tel: 01604 711041
Principal: ICAEW Member
D J Smith

DANIEL JEYES

23 Abington Park Crescent, Northampton, NN3 3AD

DNG DOVE NAISH ◈

Eagle House, 28 Billing Road, Northampton, NN1 5AJ
Tel: 01604 657200
Fax: 01604 232251
Email: enquiries@dngca.com
Website: http://www.dngca.com
Resident Partners/Directors: ICAEW Members
V W Griffiths, J R Henderson, A M McGregor, Z B Silins, P J Smith
Resident Partners (Non-ICAEW Members):
D R Wright

ELAINE JONES BOOK-KEEPING

8 Fusilier Way, Weedon, Northampton, NN7 4TH
Tel: 01327 341468
Principal: ICAEW Member
E Jones

ELSBY & CO

Thistle Down Barn, Holcot Lane, Northampton, NN6 0BJ

ELSBY & CO

Thistledown Barn, Holcot Lane, Sywell, Northampton NN6 0BG

ELSBY & CO(NORTHAMPTON) LLP

Thistledown Barn, Holcot Lane, Sywell, Northampton NN6 0BG

ELSBY & CO (SYWELL) LTD

Thistle Down Barn, Holcot Road, Sywell, Northampton NN6 0BJ

ELWELL WATCHORN & SAXTON LLP

14 Queensbridge, Northampton, NN4 7BF

FRAMPTON PITT ★

19 York Road, Northampton, NN1 5QG

GEORGE BROOKE LEWIS

Home Farm, Holdenby, Northampton, NN6 8DJ

GRANT THORNTON UK LLP

Elgin House, Billing Road, Northampton, NN1 5AU
Tel: 01604 623800
Resident Partners/Directors: ICAEW Members
S J Robinson
Non-resident Partners (ICAEW Members):
T J Blades, S J Robinson, K A Gale

HARRIS & CO ◈

2 Pavilion Court, 600 Pavillion Drive, Northampton, NN4 7SL
Tel: 01604 660661
Principal: ICAEW Member
P J Harris

HAWSONS ◈

Jubilee House, 32 Duncan Close, Moulton Park, Northampton NN3 6WL
Tel: 01604 645600
Fax: 01604 670076
Email: email@hawsons.com
Website: http://www.hawsons.co.uk
Resident Partners/Directors: ICAEW Members
D T Cairns, P G Lomas, R Powell

Registered by the ICAEW to carry out company audit work

SPECIALISATIONS – TAXATION

UK Subsidiaries of Overseas Multinationals

General Description: Full service firm.

HW ◈

78 Tenter Road, Moulton Park Industrial Estate, Northampton, NN3 6AX
Tel: 01604 746760
Resident Partners/Directors: ICAEW Members
G J Goss, A S Minifie

J C WOODBURN LTD

37 Brookland Road, Phippsville, Northampton, NN1 4SN
Tel: 01604 710196
Resident Partners/Directors: ICAEW Members
J C Woodburn

J. R. LONG

1 Corbieres Close, New Duston, Northampton, NN5 6QR

J.R. WATSON & CO

Eastgate House, 11 Cheyne Walk, Northampton, NN1 5PT
Tel: 01604 630745
Fax: 01604 234342
Email: sue.leathem@jrwatson.co.uk
Website: http://www.jrwatson.co.uk
Resident Partners/Directors: ICAEW Members
S E Leathem, A Markham, P J Robinson
Resident Partners (Non-ICAEW Members):
R J Vann

Registered by another RSB to carry out company audit work

Regulated by the ICAEW for a range of investment business activities

SPECIALISATIONS – AUDIT & ASSURANCE

Assurance Services
Audit
Pension Scheme Auditors

SPECIALISATIONS – BUSINESS & GENERAL ADVICE

Company Secretarial Service
Management Advice to Business

SPECIALISATIONS – FINANCIAL REPORTING

Accounts Preparation
Audit Exemption Report
Limited Companies
Limited Company Accounts
Limited Liability Partnership
Partnership/Sole Trader Accounts

SPECIALISATIONS – INVESTMENT BUSINESS

Financial Planning and Advice

SPECIALISATIONS – IT

Computer Systems and Consultancy

SPECIALISATIONS – SECTOR

Agriculture
Charities
Clubs/Associations
Construction
Dentists/Opticians
Estate Agents
FSA Members
Paper/Printing/Publishing
Property
Property Investment
Solicitors

SPECIALISATIONS – TAXATION

Capital Gains — Limited Companies
Capital Gains — Personal
Estate and Inheritance
Payroll Service and Advice
Self Assessment Advice
Taxation
Trusts
Value Added Tax

J.W. STEPHENSON
3 Bank Cottages, Teeton, Northampton, NN6 8LL

JENNIFER STURT
16 North Street, Rothersthorpe, Northampton, NN7 3JB

JERVIS & PARTNERS
Cranford House, 20 Harborough Road, Kingsthorpe, Northampton NN2 7AZ
Tel: 01604 714600
Principal: ICAEW Member
R D Jervis

JOHN S.G. CAREW
20 Brunel Drive, Upton Grange, Upton, Northampton NN5 4AF

KAMINI FLETCHER LTD
Russett House, Northampton Road, Chapel Brampton, Northampton NN6 8AE

KEITH LANCHBURY
6 West Street, Moulton, Northampton, NN3 7SB
Tel: 01604 643375
Principal: ICAEW Member
K Lanchbury

KILBY FOX ★
4 Pavilion Court, 600 Pavilion Drive, Northampton, NN4 7SL
Tel: 01604 662670
Resident Partners/Directors: ICAEW Members
C Adkins, C P Beavan

LAKIN ACCOUNTING SERVICES LTD ◈
Manor Lodge, Teeton, Northampton, NN6 8LH
Tel: 01604 505563
Resident Partners/Directors: ICAEW Members
D Lakin

LAURA STURROCK LTD
39 Church Street, Nether Heyford, Northampton, NN7 3LH

LOUISE SHARIF
80 Main Road, Hackleton, Northampton, NN7 2AD

M. & B. J. CONROY ★ ◈
Fishponds House, 700 Wellingborough Road, Billing Park, Northampton NN3 9BQ
Tel: 01604 410232
Resident Partners/Directors: ICAEW Members
M Conroy

MACINTYRE HUDSON LLP ◈
Peterbridge House, The Lakes, Northampton, NN4 7HB
Tel: 01604 624011
Website: http://www.macintyrehudson.co.uk
Resident Partners/Directors: ICAEW Members
M J Brown, M S Herron, S Moore, A J Young
Resident Partners (Non-ICAEW Members):
E Olson, R Salter
Regulated by the ICAEW for a range of investment business activities

MAGGIE HOLLAND
4 Church View, Moulton, Northampton, NN3 7FZ

MALCOLM MILDREN
1 Tanfield Lane, Northampton, NN1 5RN

MARK L. ALDRIDGE & CO
Woodlands Lodge, 2 Penfold Drive, Great Billing, Northampton NN3 9EQ
Tel: 01604 407769
Principal: ICAEW Member
M L Aldridge

SPECIALISATIONS – SECTOR

Agriculture

MAX BAYES LTD
33 Main Road, Hackleton, Northampton, NN7 2AD

MERCER & HOLE ◈
300 Pavilion Drive, Northampton Business Prk, Northampton, NN4 7YE
Tel: 01604 669330
Website: http://www.mercerhole.co.uk
Resident Partners/Directors: ICAEW Members
D Mansell, M A Reed

MOORE STEPHENS ◈
Kings House, 40 Billing Road, Northampton, NN1 5BA

MRS S.M. ROWLEY FCA
223 Fullingdale Road, Northampton, NN3 2QH

NATALIE GREEN & CO
7G Mobbs Miller House, Christchurch Road, Northampton, NN1 5LL
Tel: 01604 601621
Principal: ICAEW Member
N U Green

P.W.HILLYARD
3 Lime Avenue, Northampton, NN3 2HA

PAUL SLATER & CO ★
1 Washington Street, Kings Thorpe, Northampton, NN2 6NN
Tel: 01604 714471
Email: paulslaterandco@aol.com
Resident Partners/Directors: ICAEW Members
P Slater
Resident Partners (Non-ICAEW Members):
T Summerfield

Registered by the ICAEW to carry out company audit work

SPECIALISATIONS – AUDIT & ASSURANCE

Audit

SPECIALISATIONS – FINANCIAL REPORTING

Limited Company Accounts
Partnership/Sole Trader Accounts

SPECIALISATIONS – TAXATION

Payroll Service and Advice
Self Assessment Advice

PEARSENSE LTD
White Cottage, Cold Ashby Road, Guilsborough, Northampton NN6 8QN

PETER MCKAY
73 High Street, Yardley Hastings, Northampton, NN7 1ER
Tel: 01604 696338
Principal: ICAEW Member
P H McKay

PHIPPS HENSON MCALLISTER
22/24 Harborough Road, Kingsthorpe, Northampton, NN2 7AZ
Tel: 01604 718866
Resident Partners/Directors: ICAEW Members
J Austin, P J Phipps, M S Smith, R Whitehouse

PKF (UK) LLP
Beckett House, 14 Billing Road, Northampton, NN1 5AW
Tel: 01604 634843
Email: info.northampton@uk.pkf.com
Website: http://www.pkf.co.uk
Non-resident Partners (Non-ICAEW Members):
E T Kerr

R THOMPSON & CO LTD
305A Wellingborough Road, Northampton, NN1 4EW

ROBINSON CONSULTING
3 Tunnel Hill Mews, Knock Lane, Blisworth, Northampton NN7 3DA

S.G. SCHANSCHIEFF FCA
Rushworth, Church Farm, Church Brampton, Northampton NN6 8BN

S JOHNSON & CO
100 Overstone Road, Sywell, Northampton, NN6 0AW

SAWFORD BULLARD ★
6 Hazelwood Road, Northampton, NN1 1LW
Tel: 01604 635676
Fax: 01604 634266
Email: enquiries@sawford-bullard.co.uk
Website: http://www.sawford-bullard.co.uk
Resident Partners/Directors: ICAEW Members
C P Fletcher

SIMON BOWN ASSOCIATES ◈
Highfield Court, Highfield Park, Creaton, Northampton NN6 8NT
Tel: 01604 505618
Principal: ICAEW Member
S E Bown

THOMPSON & CO
305a Wellingborough Road, Northampton, NN1 4EW

TIM POLLARD LTD
Creeds Farm, Elkington, Northampton, NN6 6NJ

TIWARI & CO
25 Knighton Close, New Duston, Northampton, NN5 6NE
Tel: 01604 521130
Principal: ICAEW Member
S S Tiwari

VICKI JOHNSON
86 Sywell Road, Overstone, Northampton, NN6 0AQ

WARD DAVIS
10 Fusilier Way, Weedon, Northampton, NN7 4TH

WATERSHEDS LTD ◈
2nd Floor, The Old Granary, South Bridge Road, Cotton End, Northampton NN4 8HP
Tel: 01604 660511
Resident Partners/Directors: ICAEW Members
R Buzzoni

WEBB HOUSE
11 Duncan Close, Moulton Park Industrial Estate, Northampton, NN3 6WL

WEBB HOUSE LTD
11 Duncan Close, Moulton Park Industrial Estate, Northampton, NN3 6WL

WS FINANCIAL LTD
48a High Street, Hardingstone, Northampton, NN4 6DA

NORTHOLT

M & N SHETH LTD
84 Carr Road, Northolt, UB5 4RD

M M PATEL & CO
59 Carr Road, Northolt, UB5 4RB

P.T. PATEL & CO
Avad House, Belvue Road, Northolt, UB5 5HY
Tel: 020 8537 7212
Principal: ICAEW Member
P T Patel

NORTHWICH

A.R. UNSWORTH
23 Royal Gardens, Davenham, Northwich, CW9 8HB

AMANDA J MORAN
7 Goosebrook Close, Comberbach, Northwich, CW9 6BX
Tel: 01606 892424
Principal: ICAEW Member
A J Moran

BENNETT BROOKS & CO LTD.
St Georges Court, Winnington Avenue, Northwich, CW8 4EE
Tel: 01606 721300
Resident Partners/Directors: ICAEW Members
N J A White, Y A Wood
Other Offices:33 Allport Lane, Bromborough

SPECIALISATIONS – FORENSIC ACCOUNTING

Expert Witnesses in Litigation
Forensic Accounting

SPECIALISATIONS – SECTOR

Solicitors

BLUEWORM
Winnington Hall, Winnington, Northwich, CW8 4DU

BOARDMAN CONWAY
23A High Street, Weaverham, Northwich, CW8 3HA
Tel: 01606 854508
Resident Partners/Directors: ICAEW Members
S J Conway

BULCOCK & CO ◈
10 The Bull Ring, Northwich, CW9 5BS
Tel: 01606 331631
Fax: 01606 331630
Email: office@bulcock.com
Website: http://www.bulcock.com
Principal: ICAEW Member
M J Bulcock
Registered by the ICAEW to carry out company audit work
Regulated by the ICAEW for a range of investment business activities

BUXTON ACCOUNTING LLP
98 Middlewich Road, Northwich, CW9 7DA

CAMPBELL CROSSLEY & DAVIS
83 London Road, Northwich, CW9 5HQ

DAVID J WATTS
Stoneyford House, Cuddington, Northwich, CW8 2TF
Principal: ICAEW Member
D J Watts

FINDLAY JAMES
The Heysoms, 163 Chester Road, Northwich, CW8 4AQ

GORDON PENNINGTON & CO
1 Hall View Close, Gorstage, Northwich, CW8 2GB
Tel: 01606 851381
Principal: ICAEW Member
G Pennington

H. ROUTLEDGE
3 Sovereign Close, Rudheath, Northwich, CW9 7XN

HOWARD WORTH ★
Drake House, Gadbrook Park, Northwich, CW9 7RA
Tel: 01606 369000
Fax: 01606 369010
Email: northwich@howardworth.co.uk
Website: http://www.howardworth.co.uk
Training Contracts Available.
Resident Partners/Directors: ICAEW Members
K Dickens, M Donnan, R H Rowland, C J Swallow, J H Whalley
Other Offices: Bank Chambers, 3 Churchyardside, Nantwich, Cheshire
(Tel: 01270 626162)
(Fax: 01270 610026)
Registered by the ICAEW to carry out company audit work
Authorised and regulated by the Financial Services Authority for investment business

SPECIALISATIONS – AUDIT & ASSURANCE

Audit

SPECIALISATIONS – FINANCIAL REPORTING

Accounts Preparation

SPECIALISATIONS – INVESTMENT BUSINESS

Financial Planning and Advice

SPECIALISATIONS – TAXATION

Taxation

KAY ◈
59/63 Station Road, Northwich, CW9 5LT
Tel: 01606 814600
Principal: ICAEW Member
L S Burt

MURRAY SMITH
Darland House, 44 Winnington Hill, Northwich, CW8 1AU
Tel: 01606 79411
Fax: 01606 782878
Email: email@murraysmith.com
Website: http://www.murraysmith.com
Licensed by another DPB to carry on investment business

SPECIALISATIONS – SECTOR

Agriculture

MURRAY SMITH LLP
Darland House, 44 Winnigton Hill, Northwich, CW8 1AH

PHILPS WALKER
14 Reedsmere Walk, Comberbach, Northwich, CW9 6BZ
Tel: 01606 892520
Resident Partners/Directors: ICAEW Members
B C L Philps, D G D Walker

NORTHWOOD

A.P. PADAMSEY & CO
7 Merrows Close, Northwood, HA6 2RT

ADRIAN C. MANSBRIDGE & CO ◈
Half Oak House, 28 Watford Road, Northwood, HA6 3NT

BARBARA L. SHEPPARD
23 Brookdene Drive, Northwood, HA6 3NS

CARTNER & CO
47 Sandy Lodge Way, Northwood, HA6 2AR

CHRISTOPHER C. STONE ◈
Flat 3, 27 Dene Road, Northwood, HA6 2BX
Tel: 01923 823501
Principal: ICAEW Member
C C Stone

CHURCHILLS
Lindens House, 16 Copse Wood Way, Northwood, HA6 2UE

DARWINS
54 Batchworth Lane, Northwood, HA6 3HG

DAVID TOOLEY
68 Westbury Road, Northwood, HA6 3BY

DAVID WILSON & CO
7 College Way, Northwood, HA6 2BL
Tel: 01923 821060
Principal: ICAEW Member
D J Wilson

E.G. HUGHES & CO
Glynderi, Batchworth Lane, Northwood, HA6 3HE

F.A. DAWOODKHAN & CO
3 Wildacres, Northwood, HA6 3JD

GIBBORS
19 Ardross Avenue, Northwood, HA6 3DS

GIBBORS ◈
19 Ardross Avenue, Northwood, HA6 3DS

GIBBORS LTD
19 Ardross Avenue, Northwood, HA6 3DS

GITTINS MULDERRIG ◈
6 High Street, Northwood, HA6 1BN
Tel: 01923 822233
Principal: ICAEW Member
B D Mulderrig
See display advertisement near this entry.

GWYNNE-EVANS & CO ◈
49 Sandy Lodge Way, Northwood, HA6 2AR
Tel: 01923 821673
Email: david@gwynne-evans.co.uk

HARDCASTLE BURTON
166 Northwood Way, Northwood, HA6 1RB

INNOVATA BUSINESS SOLUTIONS LTD
26 Rofant Road, Northwood, HA6 3BE

JOHN M. WILLIAMS
9 Wieland Rd, Northwood, HA6 3RD
Tel: 01923 821187
Principal: ICAEW Member
J M Williams

KNS
11 Trinity Close, Northwood, HA6 2AF

KNS LTD
11 Trinity Close, Northwood, HA6 2AF

LACHMAN LIVINGSTONE
136 Pinner Road, Northwood, HA6 1BP

M G BEATTIE & CO LTD
6 Main Avenue, Moor Park, Northwood, HA6 2HJ

MICHAEL HARWOOD
Tinkers Halt, Sandy Lane, Northwood, HA6 3ES

MUNDAY LONG & CO LTD
Alton House, 66 High Street, Northwood, HA6 1BL

NIZAR KANJI & CO
18 The Fairway, Northwood, HA6 3DY

NORTHWOOD MANAGEMENT SERVICES ★
40 Kewferry Road, Northwood, HA6 2PB

PRAKASH RAITHATHA & CO
11 Grove Farm Park, Northwood, HA6 2BQ

R E BISHOP
Little Orchard, 97 Westbury Road, Northwood, HA6 3DA
Tel: 01923 841404
Principal: ICAEW Member
R E Bishop

RAJ RUPANI
1 Eastglade, Eastbury Avenue, Northwood, HA6 3LD

ROBERT CLOW & CO
Hartfield Place, 40-44 High Street, Northwood, HA6 1BN

ROBERT CLOW & CO
Hartfield House, 40-44 High Street, Northwood, HA6 1BN

ROBERT CLOW & CO LTD
40-44 High Street, Northwood, HA6 1BN

ROBERT TOOLEY
38 Farm Way, Northwood, HA6 3EF
Tel: 01923 823557
Principal: ICAEW Member
R G Tooley

RONALD PICARDO
15 Woodridge Way, Northwood, HA6 2BE

ROSENTHAL & CO ◈
9 Davenham Avenue, Northwood, HA6 3HW
Tel: 01923 820333
Email: robert@rcrosenthal.co.uk

Principal: ICAEW Member
R C Rosenthal

SPECIALISATIONS – SECTOR

Doctors

SPECIALISATIONS – TAXATION

Taxation

S. AMIN & CO
10 The Covert, Northwood, HA6 2UD
Tel: 01923 450767
Principal: ICAEW Member
S P Amin

SAGE & CO ◈
38A High Street, Northwood, HA6 1BN

SHAH AND SHIN
42a The Broadway, Joel Street, Northwood, HA6 1PA

SIMMONDS & CO
23 Links Way, Northwood, HA6 2XA

SURY PATEL & CO
18 Batchworth Lane, Northwood, HA6 3AT

TENDLER & CO ◈
7 Frithwood Avenue, Northwood, HA6 3LY

NORWICH

AIMS - JEREMY CLARK ACA
The Moat House, Sallow Lane, Wacton, Norwich NR15 2UL

AIMS - SIMON COX
134 Norwich Road, Stoke Holy Cross, Norwich, NR14 8QJ

ALEATHIA MANN
Springwood Church Lane, Sparham, Norwich, NR9 5PP

ALEATHIA MANN LTD
Springwood, Church Lane, Sparham, Norwich NR9 5PP

ALICIA HOWELL BSC (HONS) ACA
13 Ipswich Grove, Norwich, NR2 2LU
Tel: 01603 620784
Principal: ICAEW Member
A C Howell

ALINE TURNER
Pearle Cottage, Howe, Norwich, NR15 1HD

ARGENTS
15 Palace Street, Norwich, NR3 1RT

BANHAM GRAHAM ◈
Windsor Terrace, 76-80 Thorpe Road, Norwich, NR1 1BA
Tel: 01603 620241
Resident Partners/Directors: ICAEW Members
J A Banham, D H Buck, M M Graham, R H Jarrold, S C Mary, S J Rolfe

BARN OWL ENTERPRISES LTD
Eastgate Cottage, Perrys Lane, Cawston, Norwich NR10 4HJ

BERRY & WARREN
54 Thorpe Road, Norwich, NR1 1RY

BLAKE & CO
Rasdens, The Street, Halvergate, Norwich NR13 3AJ

BOLDERO CHAPLIN
8 Penfold Street, Aylsham, Norwich, NR11 6ET
Tel: 01263 732243
Resident Partners/Directors: ICAEW Members
I G M Boldero

BOND PARTNERS LLP
Aston Barry, Aston House, 58 Thorpe Road, Norwich NR1 1RY

BRADFORD HOUSE ACCOUNTANCY
Bradford House, Yarmouth Road, Stalham, Norwich NR12 9PD
Fax: 01692 580385
Email: info@bradfordhouse.co.uk
Other Offices: Rowan House, 28 Queens Road, Hethersett, Norwich, NR9 3DB
(Tel: 01603 813988)
(Fax: 01603 813989)

BRADFORD HOUSE ACCOUNTANCY
Rowan House, 28 Queens Road, Hethersett, Norwich NR9 3DB

BUSINESS FIGURES LTD
37 Le Strange Close, Norwich, NR2 3PW

CAROL GARDNER
13 High Green, Thorpe Hamlet, Norwich, NR1 4AP

CHRISTOPHER DIX
Eskdale, The Street, Claxton, Norwich NR14 7AS

DAVID J FORD LTD
Little Money Road, Loddon, Norwich, NR14 6JJ

DAVID J FORD FCA
Little Money Road, Loddon, Norwich, NR14 6JJ
Tel: 01508 520500

DAVID POOLE
9 Branksome Road, Norwich, NR4 6SN
Tel: 01603 502964
Principal: ICAEW Member
D E Poole

DAVID SHAWYER & CO LTD
6 Lodge Place, Thunder Lane, Norwich, NR7 0LA
Tel: 01603 431941
Resident Partners/Directors: ICAEW Members
D M Shawyer

GARY MALCOLM & CO LTD
9 Chandlers Court, Eaton, Norwich, NR4 6EY

GOOD FINANCIAL MANAGEMENT ◈
18 Aylesbury Close, New Catton, Norwich, NR3 3LB
Tel: 01603 415397
Principal: ICAEW Member
G J Good

GRANT THORNTON UK LLP
Holland Court, The Close, Norwich, NR1 4DY
Tel: 01603 620481
Resident Partners/Directors: ICAEW Members
M Burrows, P J Harris, R N Proctor, N R Savory
Non-resident Partners (ICAEW Members):
I S Carr

HINES HARVEY WOODS LTD
Queens Head House, The Street, Acle, Norwich NR13 3DX

HORNBEAM ACCOUNTANCY SERVICES LTD ◈
Hornbeam House, Bidwell Road, Rackheath, Norwich NR13 6PT
Tel: 01603 720424
Resident Partners/Directors: ICAEW Members
A R Bloy, P Needham
Registered by the ICAEW to carry out company audit work

HOWARD ROYSE LTD
11 Warren's Way, Tacolneston, Norwich, NR16 1DH

IAN COUZENS LTD
4 Denbigh Road, Norwich, NR2 3AA
Tel: 01603 665768

J.P. WEBSTER
Hales Green Farm, Litchmere Lane, Loddon, Norwich NR14 6QW
Tel: 01508 548080
Principal: ICAEW Member
J P Webster

JAMES F. SEARLE LTD
176 Spixworth Road, Norwich, NR6 7EQ

JANE COURT
Eastgate Cottage, Perrys Lane, Cawston, Norwich NR10 4HJ

JANE WASDEN LTD
77a South Hill Road, Thorpe St Andrew, Norwich, NR7 0LR
Tel: 01603 702474
Resident Partners/Directors: ICAEW Members
J A Wasden

JOHN STENT
14 Townsend Court, Reepham, Norwich, NR10 4LD
Tel: 01603 871092

JOHNSON HOLMES & CO ◈
Towlers Court, 30a Elm Hill, Norwich, NR3 1HG
Tel: 01603 616331
Fax: 01603 664246
Email: johnsonholmesuk@aol.com
Website: http://www.johnsonholmes.co.uk
Resident Partners/Directors: ICAEW Members
G R H Holmes, P A Johnson
Registered by the ICAEW to carry out company audit work
Regulated by the ICAEW for a range of investment business activities
Individual(s) licensed for insolvency work by the ICAEW

JON DODGE & CO LTD
Dencora Court, 2 Meridian Way, Norwich, NR7 0TA

JOSHI & CO
3a Upgate, Poringland, Norwich, NR14 7SH
Tel: 01508 494842
Principal: ICAEW Member
K N V Joshi

JUDY STIRLING
Holly Lodge, 28 Norwich Road, Hethersett, Norwich NR9 3DD
Tel: 01603 811581
Principal: ICAEW Member
J A Stirling

KARL JERMYN
10a Whitlingham Hall, Norwich, NR14 8QH

KEVIN J RHIND
Corner Cottage, Heath Road, Hempstead, Norwich NR12 0SH
Tel: 01692 583010
Principal: ICAEW Member
K J Rhind

KIM MAYFIELD LTD
10 Hillside, Chedgrave, Norwich, NR14 6HZ

KINGDOM POWELL
The Greyhound, Back Street, Reepham, Norwich NR10 4SJ
Tel: 01603 871164
Principal: ICAEW Member
J G Powell

L DAWSON CONSULTING
145 Earlham Road, Norwich, NR2 3RG

LARKING GOWEN ◈
King Street House, 15 Upper King Street, Norwich, NR3 1RB
Tel: 01603 624181
Email: lg@larking-gowen.co.uk
Website: http://www.larking-gowen.co.uk
Resident Partners/Directors: ICAEW Members
M D Balfour, J F H Ellis, I R Fitch, J G Grimmer, D Jefford, B J Pring, J A Richardson, R G Rose, D N Whitehead, J D Woolston
Resident Partners (Non-ICAEW Members):
M R Howard, M D Curtis
Other Offices: Cromer, Dereham, Diss, Fakenham, Holt, Colchester, Ipswich
Registered by the ICAEW to carry out company audit work
Authorised and regulated by the Financial Services Authority for investment business
Individual(s) licensed for insolvency work by the ICAEW
Individual(s) licensed for insolvency work by another RPB

LOUISE MARSDEN LTD
20 Poppyfields, Horsford, Norwich, NR10 3SR

LOVEWELL BLAKE ◈
1a & 1b Cawston Road, Aylsham, Norwich, NR11 6BX
Tel: 01263 732151
Fax: 01263 733200
Email: mdls@lovewell-blake.co.uk
Website: http://www.lovewell-blake.co.uk
Non-resident Partners (ICAEW Members):
M D L Smith
General Description: The practice has 21 partners and our other offices are listed under our Norwich entry.

LOVEWELL BLAKE ◈
102 Prince Of Wales Road, Norwich, NR1 1NY
Tel: 01603 663300
Fax: 01603 692238
Email: pdy@lovewell-blake.co.uk
Website: http://www.lovewell-blake.co.uk
Resident Partners/Directors: ICAEW Members
P J Blythe-Bartram, C A E Fish, R J Gascoyne-Richards, M D L Smith, P D Young
Resident Partners (Non-ICAEW Members):
K B Shorten, S P Scarlett, G M Sillett, S C Watson, P J Bartram, N P Orford
Other Offices: Aylsham, Gt. Yarmouth, Halesworth, Lowestoft, North Walsham, Thetford, Diss
General Description: The practice has 21 partners — see entries for our other offices.

M L CLIFFE
7 Lime Tree Road, Norwich, NR2 2NF

M. R. BARRETT LTD
1 Commonside Cottages, Salle, Norwich, NR10 4EP

M. R. BARRETT F.C.A
1 Commonside, Salle, Norwich, NR10 4EP

M.R. POOLEY
70 Sandy Lane, Norwich, NR1 2NR
Tel: 01603 662277
Principal: ICAEW Member
M R Pooley

MCTEAR WILLIAMS & WOOD ★
90 St Faiths Lane, Norwich, NR1 1NE
Tel: 01603 877540
Resident Partners/Directors: ICAEW Members
A I McTear, C K Williams

MARTIN & ACOCK ◈
2 The Close, Norwich, NR1 4DJ
Tel: 01603 612311
Email: enquiries@martin-acock.com
Website: http://www.martin-acock.com
Resident Partners/Directors: ICAEW Members
C J Dugdale, A J Fish, W P F Hill, M P Jermy, C I H Mawson, M Sargeant
Other Offices: Attleborough, Swaffham, Watton.
Registered by the ICAEW to carry out company audit work
Regulated by the ICAEW for a range of investment business activities

MAYFIELD & CO
10 Hillside, Chedgrave, Norwich, NR14 6HZ

MICHAEL PRITCHARD & CO
Nascot House, Church Lane, Wroxham, Norwich NR12 8SH
Tel: 01603 784647
Principal: ICAEW Member
M A P Pritchard

MICHAEL THOMPSON ACCOUNTANTS LTD
4 Chalk Hill House, 19 Rosary Road, Norwich, NR1 1SZ
Tel: 01603 633355
Resident Partners/Directors: ICAEW Members
R A Goel, M J Thompson

MS SUSAN KEMP ACA
100 Welsford Road, Norwich, NR4 6QH

MURRELLS
Cedar House, 41 Thorpe Road, Norwich, NR1 1ES

N.J. NEWSTEAD
Tumbleweed, Ranworth Road, Blofield Heath, Norwich NR13 4PJ
Tel: 01603 716865
Principal: ICAEW Member
N J Newstead

NIGEL WORDINGHAM LTD
De Vere House, 90 St Faiths Lane, Norwich, NR1 1NE

P & C E SERVICES LTD
1 Cheyney Avenue, Salhouse, Norwich, NR13 6RJ

P.J. SEAL ◈
5 Beechbank Drive, Thorpe End Gardens, Gt Plumstead, Norwich NR13 5BW
Tel: 01603 437677
Principal: ICAEW Member
P J Seal

PACIFIC LTD
1st Floor Woburn House, 84 St Benedicts Street, Norwich, NR2 4AB

PAUL HINDLE
The Old Gamedealers, Dereham Road, Garvestone, Norwich NR9 4QT

PAUL HINDLE LTD
The Old Gamedealers, Dereham Road, Garvestone, Norwich NR9 4QT

PETER SIMON & CO LTD
The Old Maids Head, 110 High Street, Stalham, Norwich NR12 9AU

PKF (UK) LLP
Cedar House, 105 Carrow Road, Norwich, NR1 1HP
Tel: 01603 615914
Email: info.norwich@uk.pkf.com
Website: http://www.pkf.co.uk
Resident Partners/Directors: ICAEW Members
G R Woodford
Resident Partners (Non-ICAEW Members):
A Widdows

PRICE BAILEY LLP ◈
20 Central Avenue, St Andrews Business Park, Thorpe St Andrews, Norwich NR7 0HR
Tel: 01603 709330
Website: http://www.pricebailey.co.uk
Resident Partners (Non-ICAEW Members):
D Moore
Registered by the ICAEW to carry out company audit work
Authorised and regulated by the Financial Services Authority for investment business
Individual(s) licensed for insolvency work by the ICAEW

PRICE BAILEY PRIVATE CLIENT LLP
20 Central Avenue, St Andrews Business Park, Thorpe St Andrews, Norwich NR7 0HR

PRICEWATERHOUSE-COOPERS
The Atrium, St Georges Street, Norwich, NR3 1AG

PRICEWATERHOUSE-COOPERS LLP
The Atrium, St Georges Street, Norwich, NR3 1AG
Tel: 01603 615244
Resident Partners/Directors: ICAEW Members
C Maw, J C Rickett

QUINNEY AND COMPANY LTD
Bank Chambers, Market Place, Reepham, Norwich NR10 4JJ

QUINNEYS
Bank Chambers, Market Place, Reepham, Norwich NR10 4JJ

R.I. CAVELL
155 Reepham Road, Hellesdon, Norwich, NR6 5PW

R SOMERS - ACCOUNTANCY
Woodwell Furlong, Kenninghall, Norwich, NR16 2EP

THE RHP PARTNERSHIP ◈
Lancaster House, 87 Yarmouth Road, Norwich, NR7 0HF
Tel: 01603 703010
Fax: 01603 703015
Email: info@rhp-partnership.co.uk
Website: http://www.rhppartnership.co.uk
Resident Partners/Directors: ICAEW Members
M G Hurst, S M Pring, N A Rudd
Registered by the ICAEW to carry out company audit work
Regulated by the ICAEW for a range of investment business activities

ROGER HOPKINS
18 Princes Street, Norwich, NR3 1AE

ROSTRON & PARTNERS ◈
St Peter's House, Cattle Market Street, Norwich, NR1 3DY
Tel: 01603 619166
Resident Partners/Directors: ICAEW Members
E J Claxton, P J Rostron
Resident Partners (Non-ICAEW Members):
E J Claxton, M M Raper

SEXTY & CO ★
124 Thorpe Road, Norwich, NR1 1RS

SMITHASTON
The Royal, 25 Bank Plain, Norwich, NR2 4SF
Tel: 01603 283630
Principal: ICAEW Member
T Smith

TREVOR DOWSON
Grosvenor House, Prince of Wales Road, Norwich, NR1 1NS

TREVOR M BALL & CO
50 The Cathedral Close, Norwich, NR1 4EG

WALTON DODGE FORENSIC
Dencora Court, 2 Meridian Way, Norwich, NR7 0TA
Tel: 01603 703173
Website: http://www.waltondodgeforensic.co.uk

SPECIALISATIONS – BUSINESS & GENERAL ADVICE
Divorce/Matrimonial

SPECIALISATIONS – FORENSIC ACCOUNTING
Expert Witnesses in Litigation
Forensic Accounting

WALTON DODGE FORENSIC LTD
Dencora Court, 2 Meridian Way, Norwich, NR7 0TA

WILLIAM FISHER
84 St Benedicts Street, Norwich, NR2 4AB

NOTTINGHAM

9INE ACCOUNTING LTD
35a Gordon Road, West Bridgford, Nottingham, NG2 5LL
Tel: 01159 814242
Resident Partners/Directors: ICAEW Members
R Mason

A WEST & CO
550 Valley Road, Basford, Nottingham, NG5 1JJ
Tel: 0115 9427820
Principal: ICAEW Member
A West

ACCOUNTING FOR BUSINESS
26 Quarries Way, Kirkby-in-Ashfield, Nottingham, NG17 8BH

AIMS - GERALDINE SHELLEY FCA
45 Kimberley Road, Nuthall, Nottingham, NG16 1DA

ALAN W. DENHAM
Glen Lea, 25 Manor Close, Edwalton, Nottingham NG12 4BH

ANDREW TURVEY SOLUTIONS LTD
23 Cartwright Way, Beeston, Nottingham, NG9 1RL

ANN GREENWOOD
Wood Farm Cottage, Barton Lane, Thrumpton, Nottingham NG11 0AU

ANTHON MARLOW
3 Cranmer Street, Nottingham, NG3 4GH

B.W. WEST & CO
150 Haydn Road, Sherwood, Nottingham, NG5 2LB
Tel: 0115 962 2393
Principal: ICAEW Member
B W West

BALDWIN COX & CO ◈
15 Foster Avenue, Beeston, Nottingham, NG9 1AE
Tel: 0115 925 1837
Principal: ICAEW Member
M J Cox

BALDWIN COX LTD
15 Foster Avenue, Beeston, Nottingham, NG9 1AE
Tel: 0115 925 1837
Fax: 0115 967 8628
Email: info@baldwincox.co.uk
Website: http://www.baldwincox.co.uk
Resident Partners/Directors: ICAEW Members
A P Crossley
Resident Partners (Non-ICAEW Members):
A E White

BEGBIES TRAYNOR LTD
Regency House, 21 The Ropewalk, Nottingham, NG1 5DU
Tel: 0115 941 9899
Resident Partners (Non-ICAEW Members):
R Saville, P Blair

SPECIALISATIONS – BUSINESS RECOVERY & INSOLVENCY
Bankruptcies
Corporate Recovery
Liquidations

BEXONS ◈
24 Rectory Road, West Bridgford, Nottingham, NG2 6BG
Tel: 0115 982 2272
Principal: ICAEW Member
J P Bexon

BOSTOCKWHITE LTD
Unit 1, Cabourn House, Station Street, Bingham, Nottingham NG13 8AQ

BRIAN A. MORGAN
73 Sheepwalk Lane, Ravenshead, Nottingham, NG15 9FD

BRIAN J. BEATTIE
46 Whitworth Drive, Radcliffe-on-Trent, Nottingham, NG12 2DE
Tel: 0115 910 3035
Principal: ICAEW Member
B J Beattie

BRIAN MEAKIN
Ward Cottage, 83 Main Street, Papplewick, Nottingham NG15 8FE
Tel: 0115 963 6239
Principal: ICAEW Member
B Meakin

BRIELEY GRIMSDELL LTD
12 James Street, Kimberley, Nottingham, NG16 2LP
Tel: 0115 945 8767
Resident Partners/Directors: ICAEW Members
H M Grimsdell

BRIGHT ACCOUNTS & TAX
19-21 Main Street, Keyworth, Nottingham, NG12 5AA

BROOKS MAYFIELD
12 Bridgford Road, West Bridgford, Nottingham, NG2 6AB

C.E. AKEROYD
Sherwood House, 7 Gregory Boulevard, Nottingham, NG7 6LB
Tel: 0115 955 5500
Principal: ICAEW Member
D E G Akeroyd

C.J. LUCKING & CO ◈
34 Cross Street, Long Eaton, Nottingham, NG10 1HD

CARL R. GREGORY & CO
134 Newthorpe Common, Newthorpe, Nottingham, NG16 2EH

CATALYST CORPORATE FINANCE LLP
Castlebridge, Kirtley Drive, Castle Marina, Nottingham NG7 1LD

CJR ACCOUNTANTS LTD
Oxford House, 8 Church Street, Arnold, Nottingham NG5 8FB

CLAYTON & BREWILL
Cawley House, 149-155 Canal Street, Nottingham, NG1 7HR
Tel: 0115 950 3044
Website: http://www.claytonandbrewill.com
Resident Partners/Directors: ICAEW Members
Y J Jackson, N F South, J R Wilson-Mawer

CLAYTON & BREWILL ◈
Wilne House, 10 Salisbury Street, Long Eaton, Nottingham NG10 1BA

CLEARWATER CORPORATE FINANCE LLP
21-23 Castle Gate, Nottingham, NG1 7AQ

COBB BURGIN & CO
129a Middleton Boulevard, Wollaton Park, Nottingham, NG8 1FW
Tel: 0115 928 3900
Resident Partners/Directors: ICAEW Members
N A Burgin, C P Cobb

COLLINS CHAPPLE & CO LTD
Van Gaver House, 48 Bridgford Rd, West Bridgford, Nottingham NG2 6AP

COMPLETE BUSINESS SOLUTIONS (NOTTINGHAM) LTD
5 The Old Stables, Bestwood Country Park, Nottingham, NG5 8ND

COOPER PARRY LLP ◈
14 Park Row, Nottingham, NG1 6GR
Tel: 0115 958 0212
Fax: 0115 958 8800
Email: advice@cooperparry.com
Website: http://www.cooperparry.com
Resident Partners/Directors: ICAEW Members
A J Botham, D A Browne, S R Bryan, T S Courtman, R Jones, E C Rands, C R Shaw, J P Taylor, A H Timms
Other Offices: Derby, Leicester

CURRAN & CO
The Cottage, Donkey Lane, Bradmore, Nottingham NG11 6PG

CURRAN & CO TAX ADVISERS LLP
The Cottage, Donkey Lane, Bradmore, Nottingham NG11 6PG

DAVID PULLEN
24 Katherine Drive, Toton, Beeston, Nottingham NG9 6JB

DAWES & SUTTON
Springfield House, 4 Millicent Road, West Bridgford, Nottingham NG2 7LD
Tel: 0115 981 4809
Fax: 0115 982 7090
Principal: ICAEW Member
L G Sutton

SPECIALISATIONS – SECTOR

Hotels/Public Houses
Leisure Industry

DELOITTE & TOUCHE LLP ◈
1 Woodborough Road, Nottingham, NG1 3FG
Tel: 0115 950 0511
Website: http://www.deloitte.co.uk
Resident Partners/Directors: ICAEW Members
M F Doleman, P L Hipperson

DOUGLAS & CO ◈
21 Trent View Gardens, Radcliffe-on-Trent, Nottingham, NG12 1AY
Tel: 0115 933 3559
Principal: ICAEW Member
J A Douglas

EBS ACCOUNTANTS LTD ◈
Gothic House, Barker Gate, Nottingham, NG1 1JU
Tel: 0115 956 5404
Website: http://www.ebsaccountants.co.uk
Resident Partners/Directors: ICAEW Members
J M Evenden

EDF TAX LLP
Foxhall Business Centre, Foxhall Road, Nottingham, NG7 6LH

ELWELL WATCHORN & SAXTON LLP
Cumberland House, 35 Park Row, Nottingham, NG1 6EE

ERIC G. BOLAM
14 Fox Covert, River View Park, Colwick, Nottingham NG4 2DD

ERNST & YOUNG LLP
City Gate West, Toll House Hill, Nottingham, NG1 5FY
Tel: 0115 954 2090

F B 40 LTD ◈
Haydn House, 309-329 Haydn Road, Nottingham, NG5 1HG
Tel: 0115 960 7111
Resident Partners/Directors: ICAEW Members
S R Adcock, A R Delve, P W Duffin, R A Heason, S R Tysoe, G J Whiting

F.C.R. MOULE & CO
Westminster Buildings, Theatre Square, Nottingham, NG1 6LG
Tel: 0115 941 7517
Principal: ICAEW Member
J K Sheppard

FRANK GORTON ◈
Ashlea House, 56 Loughborough Road, Bunny, Nottingham NG11 6QD
Tel: 0115 921 3318
Principal: ICAEW Member
F Gorton

FRANKLIN UNDERWOOD ★
Lime House, Mere Way, Ruddington Fields Business Park, Nottingham NG11 6JS

FRANKLIN UNDERWOOD CORPORATE PARTNER CONSULTANTS
Limehouse, Mere Way, Ruddington Fields Business Park, Nottingham NG11 6JW

FRASER HAYES PICKARD
7 Nimbus Way, Watnall, Nottingham, NG16 1FP

FRASER PRICE CONSULTING LTD
Suite 1, Enness Building, East Street, Bingham, Nottingham NG13 8DS
Tel: 01949 831213
Resident Partners/Directors: ICAEW Members
N G Fraser

G W LANGFIELD
23 Bostocks Lane, Sandiacre, Nottingham, NG10 5NL

GORINGS ◈
34 Station Road, Sandiacre, Nottingham, NG10 5BG
Tel: 0115 939 5063
Website: http://www.goringsaccountants.co.uk
Resident Partners/Directors: ICAEW Members
M R Allen

GRA ENTERPRISES LTD
15 Perry Road, Sherwood, Nottingham, NG5 3AD
Tel: 0115 969 3000
Fax: 0115 969 2282
Email: gragency@aol.com
Resident Partners/Directors: ICAEW Members
K I Trocki

GRAHAM DAWES
117 Nottingham Road, Kimberley, Nottingham, NG16 2ND

GRANT THORNTON UK LLP
30 Hounds Gate, Nottingham, NG1 7DH
Tel: 0115 948 3483
Resident Partners/Directors: ICAEW Members
R B Thornton
Non-resident Partners (ICAEW Members):
D I H Campbell, M Redfern
Resident Partners (Non-ICAEW Members):
J C Griffin
Non-resident Partners (Non-ICAEW Members):
G Meakin

GREENHALGH BUSINESS SERVICES LTD ◈
2a Peveril Drive, Nottingham, NG7 1DE
Tel: 0115 985 9517
Email: nottingham@greenhalghco.net
Website: http://www.greenhalghco.net
Resident Partners/Directors: ICAEW Members
P A Handley, M Henshaw, C Peacock
Non-resident Partners (Non-ICAEW Members):
N Shaw, G Brockway
Other Offices: Burton Upon Trent, Uttoxeter
Registered by the ICAEW to carry out company audit work

GREGORY PRIESTLEY & STEWART ◈
Lyndhurst, 1 Cranmer Street, Long Eaton, Nottingham NG10 1NJ
Tel: 0115 973 3389
Principal: ICAEW Member
P Stewart

HARRISON & CO
397 Tamworth Road, Long Eaton, Nottingham, NG10 3JP
Tel: 0115 946 8000
Principal: ICAEW Member
J P Harrison

HARWOOD & BALL
46 High Pavement, Nottingham, NG1 1HW

HEATHER BARNES
1 Nottingham Road, Ravenshead, Nottingham, NG15 9HG

HIGSON & CO
White House, Wollaton St, Nottingham, NG1 5GF
Tel: 0115 947 5662
Fax: 0115 947 5746
Email: enquiries@higson-accountants.co.uk
Website: http://www.higson-accountants.co.uk
Date Established: 1936
Training Contracts Available.
Resident Partners/Directors: ICAEW Members
D V Bonnert, H I Ockelford, S C R Skill, G J Strickland, D R Wallwork
Registered by the ICAEW to carry out company audit work
Regulated by the ICAEW for a range of investment business activities
SPECIALISATIONS – AUDIT & ASSURANCE
Audit
SPECIALISATIONS – FINANCIAL REPORTING
Accounts Preparation
SPECIALISATIONS – TAXATION
Taxation

HINDOCHA & CO
V16 Howitt Building, Lenton Boulevard, Nottingham, NG7 2BY
Tel: 0115 970 0744
Fax: 0115 970 0733
Email: service@hindocha-uk.biz
Website: http://www.hindocha-uk.biz
Principal: ICAEW Member
L V Hindocha
Registered by the ICAEW to carry out company audit work
General Description: Well established firm with specialist professionals providing tailor made service package to meet clients' need and aspirations.

HOBSON & CO ACCOUNTANTS LTD
37 Wollaton Road, Beeston, Nottingham, NG9 2NG

HOBSONS
Alexandra House, 43 Alexandra Street, Nottingham, NG5 1AY

HOUGHTON STONE ★
Gothic House, Barker Gate, Nottingham, NG1 1JU

HOWARD USHER
16 Shandwick Close, Arnold, Nottingham, NG5 8AZ

HUW WILLIAMS
217 Musters Road, West Bridgford, Nottingham, NG2 7DT

HUW WILLIAMS LTD
217 Musters Road, West Bridgford, Nottingham, NG2 7DT
Tel: 0115 914 6846
Email: info@huwwilliams.co.uk
Website: http://www.huwwilliams.co.uk
Resident Partners/Directors: ICAEW Members
H R Williams
SPECIALISATIONS – FINANCIAL REPORTING
Limited Company Accounts
Partnership/Sole Trader Accounts
SPECIALISATIONS – TAXATION
Estate and Inheritance
Payroll Service and Advice
Self Assessment Advice
Trusts

ILIFFE POULTER & CO
1A Bonnington Road, Mapperley, Nottingham, NG3 5JR

J.H. TREASE & CO
26 Wilford Lane, West Bridgford, Nottingham, NG2 7QX

J.R. WINFIELD
62 Glendon Drive, Nottingham, NG5 1FP

JOHN H. HADLEY
28 Littlegreen Road, Woodthorpe, Nottingham, NG5 4LN
Tel: 0115 926 3668
Principal: ICAEW Member
J H Hadley

JOHN N.G. HOWITT
2 The Paddock, Attenborough, Beeston, Nottingham, NG9 6AR

JUST AUDIT LTD
Strelley Hall, Nottingham, NG8 6PE
Tel: 01332 883166
Resident Partners/Directors: ICAEW Members
R A Davis

K J EATON & CO ★
32 Main Street, Lambley, Nottingham, NG4 4PN
Tel: 0115 931 2777
Resident Partners/Directors: ICAEW Members
P D Eaton

KEITH TEBBETT
357 Coppice Road, Arnold, Nottingham, NG5 7HH

KEITH WILLIS ASSOCIATES LTD ◈
Gothic House, Barker Gate, Nottingham, NG1 1JU
Tel: 0115 947 6677
Fax: 0115 947 6688
Website: http://www.keithwillis.com
Resident Partners/Directors: ICAEW Members
K A Willis
Registered by another RSB to carry out company audit work
Regulated by the ICAEW for a range of investment business activities
SPECIALISATIONS – AUDIT & ASSURANCE
Audit
SPECIALISATIONS – BUSINESS & GENERAL ADVICE
Management Advice to Business
SPECIALISATIONS – FINANCIAL REPORTING
Accounts Preparation
Limited Company Accounts
Partnership/Sole Trader Accounts
SPECIALISATIONS – IT
Computerised Accounting Systems
General Description: Experienced firm of accountants and consultants offering clients a friendly common sense service at affordable prices.

KENTWELL CORPORATION LTD
86 Musters Road, West Bridgford, Nottingham, NG2 7PS

KILLICKS LTD ◈
35/37 Kingsway, Kirkby-in-Ashfield, Nottingham, NG17 7DR
Tel: 01623 759 511
Resident Partners/Directors: ICAEW Members
M Stafford

KIRK HUGHES MEDLOCK ★
Willson House, 25-31 Derby Road, Nottingham, NG1 5AW

KPMG LLP
St Nicholas House, 31 Park Row, Nottingham, NG1 6FQ
Tel: 0115 935 3535
Resident Partners/Directors: ICAEW Members
M R Beardsley, P D Charles, W R Cox, P G Heath, R J Peberdy, I R Summerton, T M Widdas
Resident Partners (Non-ICAEW Members):
M Patterson

KWAN CHAN ACCOUNTING SERVICES LTD ◈
352a Carlton Hill, Carlton, Nottingham, NG4 1JB

LAMB & CO ★
30 Tranby Gardens, Nottingham, NG8 2AB

LEMANS
29 Arboretum Street, Nottingham, NG1 4JA
Tel: 0115 978 7291
Fax: 0115 942 2523
Email: enquiries@lemans.co.uk
Website: http://www.lemans.co.uk
Resident Partners/Directors: ICAEW Members
T Bailey, D P Groves, D Marshall
Resident Partners (Non-ICAEW Members):
K Mealand, A R Harby
Registered by the ICAEW to carry out company audit work
Regulated by the ICAEW for a range of investment business activities

LING PHIPP ◈
Cliffe Hill House, 22-26 Nottingham Road, Stapleford, Nottingham NG9 8AA
Tel: 0115 949 6838
Resident Partners/Directors: ICAEW Members
P N Horton-Turner, D J Lockwood

LIZ OWEN ACCOUNTING SERVICES
24 Knighton Road, Woodthorpe, Nottingham, NG5 4FL
Tel: 07884 108454
Resident Partners/Directors: ICAEW Members
E J Owen

LONGLEY & CO ◈
81 Melton Road, West Bridgford, Nottingham, NG2 6EN
Tel: 0115 945 5677

LONGLEYS ◈
81 Melton Road, West Bridgford, Nottingham, NG2 6EN
Tel: 0115 945 5677
Principal: ICAEW Member
M R Longley

M. AHMED & CO
83 Park Road, Chilwell, Nottingham, NG9 4DE

M. ASLAM
259 Mansfield Road,
Nottingham, NG1 3FT
Tel: 0115 941 8038
Principal: ICAEW Member
M Aslam

M.R. COWDREY & CO
125 Nottingham Road,
Stapleford, Nottingham,
NG9 8AT

MARSDEN WALKER
164a Derby Road, Stapleford,
Nottingham, NG9 7AY

MARSDEN WALKER LTD
164a Derby Road, Stapleford,
Nottingham, NG9 7AY

MARTIN, NYE & CO ★
Technical & Training Centre,
The Old Rectory, Sawley,
Nottingham NG10 3AB

MAZARS CORPORATE FINANCE LTD ◈
Cartwright House, Tottle Road,
Nottingham, NG2 1RT

MAZARS LLP ◈
Cartwright House, Tottle Road,
Nottingham, NG2 1RT
Tel: 0115 943 5363
Resident Partners/Directors: ICAEW Members
M J Rogers
Resident Partners (Non-ICAEW Members):
P M Lyon
Registered by the ICAEW to carry out company audit work
Authorised and regulated by the Financial Services Authority for investment business

MHA
129 Middleton Boulevard,
Wollaton Park, Nottingham,
NG8 1FW

MINSHALLS
370-374 Nottingham Road,
Newthorpe, Nottingham,
NG16 2ED
Tel: 01773 538930

MINSHALLS LTD ◈
370-374 Nottingham Road,
Newthorpe, Nottingham,
NG16 2ED
Tel: 01773 538930
Resident Partners/Directors: ICAEW Members
M R Minshall

MONCRIEFF & CO
13 Freda Avenue, Gedling,
Nottingham, NG4 4FY

MRS G.E.CASHMORE
The Old Post Office, Edwalton,
Nottingham, NG12 4AB
Tel: 0115 923 2407
Principal: ICAEW Member
G E Cashmore

MSO LTD
57 Woodbank Drive,
Nottingham, NG8 2QW

N R STEVENSON LTD ◈
22 Regent Street, Nottingham,
NG1 5BQ

NEWBY CASTLEMAN ◈
3 Pelham Court, Pelham Rd,
Sherwood Rise, Nottingham
NG5 1AP
Tel: 0115 960 6078
Fax: 0115 960 9879
Email: sgf@newbyc.co.uk
Website: http://www.newbycastleman.co.uk
Resident Partners/Directors: ICAEW Members
S G Foster
Other Offices: Leicester, Loughborough, Melton Mowbray and Oakham
Registered by the ICAEW to carry out company audit work
Regulated by the ICAEW for a range of investment business activities
See display advertisement near this entry.

NEWSUM-SMITH & CO
17 Burleigh Road, West
Bridgford, Nottingham,
NG2 6FP
Tel: 0115 923 1276
Principal: ICAEW Member
A M Newsum-Smith

NOY & PARTNERS ACCOUNTANTS LTD
144 Nottingham Road,
Eastwood, Nottingham,
NG16 3GE

P D EATON & CO
32 Main Street, Lambley,
Nottingham, NG4 4PN
Tel: 0115 931 2777
Principal: ICAEW Member
P D Eaton

P K CONSULTING & ACCOUNTING SERVICES LTD
29 Maidstone Drive, Wollaton,
Nottingham, NG8 2RF
Tel: 0115 916 9874
Resident Partners/Directors: ICAEW Members
P D King

PAGE KIRK
Sherwood House, 7 Gregory
Boulevard, Nottingham,
NG7 6LB

PAGE KIRK LLP ◈
Sherwood House, 7 Gregory
Boulevard, Nottingham,
NG7 6LB
Tel: 0115 955 5500
Fax: 0115 955 5800
Email: enquiries@pagekirk.co.uk
Website: http://www.pagekirk.co.uk
Training Contracts Available.
Resident Partners/Directors: ICAEW Members
I D Barker, R W Bonnello, G S Cree, M P Mellor, P G Staniforth, L A Tooley, J S Wallis
Resident Partners (Non-ICAEW Members):
W J O'Connor
Registered by the ICAEW to carry out company audit work
Authorised and regulated by the Financial Services Authority for investment business

PEARCE & CO
36 Nottingham Road, Lowdham,
Nottingham, NG14 7AP

PETER MARSHALL
20 Highfield Road, Keyworth,
Nottingham, NG12 5JE

PETER R. MOORE
20 Carisbrooke Drive,
Mapperley Park, Nottingham,
NG3 5DS
Tel: 0115 960 9750
Principal: ICAEW Member
P R Moore

PETER S KIRKLAND
30 Sunningdale Drive,
Woodborough, Nottingham,
NG14 6EQ

PHIPP & CO
6 Nottingham Road, Long Eaton,
Nottingham, NG10 1HP
Tel: 0115 972 2313
Resident Partners/Directors: ICAEW Members
G R Hill, M D Saunders

PKF (UK) LLP
Regent House, Clinton Avenue,
Nottingham, NG5 1AZ
Tel: 0115 960 8171
Email: info.nottingham@uk.pkf.com
Website: http://www.pkf.co.uk
Resident Partners/Directors: ICAEW Members
P J Ellis, R L Merchant, P S Thompson, R D Wilson
Resident Partners (Non-ICAEW Members):
L Topliss, F Goodall

QUANTICO
Nottingham Castle Marina,
Marina Road, Nottingham,
NG7 1TN

R.W. JARVIS & CO
26 Wilford Lane, West
Bridgford, Nottingham,
NG2 7QX

RICHARD F WOOD LTD
Oakwood House, 51a Lucknow
Avenue, Mapperley Park,
Nottingham NG3 5AZ

RICHARD J. HILTON
11 Crow Park Drive, Burton Joyce, Nottingham, NG14 5AS
Tel: 0115 931 3201
Principal: ICAEW Member
R J Hilton

RICHARD S BURTON LTD
48c Main Street, Meadow Lane, Burton Joyce, Nottingham NG14 5EX
Tel: 0115 931 3185
Resident Partners/Directors: ICAEW Members
R S Burton

RICHARD WOOD
5a Lucknow Avenue, Morrely Park, Nottingham, NG3 5AZ

ROBERT A. LAWSON
56 Waltham Close, Abbey Park Estate, West Bridgford, Nottingham NG2 6LE

ROBINSON FINANCIAL CONSULTANCY LTD
31 Elmswood Gardens, Sherwood, Nottingham, NG5 4AY

ROGER BURNS
125 Tamworth Road, Long Eaton, Nottingham, NG10 1BH

ROGERS SPENCER
Newstead House, Pelham Road, Nottingham, NG5 1AP
Tel: 0115 960 8412
Fax: 0115 969 1878
Email: advice@rogers-spencer.co.uk
Resident Partners (Non-ICAEW Members):
M Bailey, A Dennis

ROGERS SPENCER LTD
Newstead House, Pelham Road, Nottingham, NG5 1AP
Tel: 0115 960 8412
Resident Partners/Directors: ICAEW Members
S P Allcock

ROY GOLDSBROUGH
10 Quantock Grove, Bingham, Nottingham, NG13 8SE

RSM BENTLEY JENNISON ◈
St Matthew's House, 6 Sherwood Rise, Nottingham, NG7 6JF
Tel: 0115 962 0900
Fax: 0115 962 0965
Email: gary.abbott@rsmbentleyjennison.com
Website: http://www.rsmbentleyjennison.com
Resident Partners/Directors: ICAEW Members
G K Abbott
Registered by the ICAEW to carry out company audit work
Authorised and regulated by the Financial Services Authority for investment business

S. KEITH RHODES BSC FCA
14 Limetree Gardens, Lowdham, Nottingham, NG14 7DJ
Tel: 0115 966 3945
Principal: ICAEW Member
S K Rhodes

SHIRTCLIFFE & CO LTD
668 Woodborough Road, Mapperley, Nottingham, NG3 5FS
Tel: 0115 960 4743
Resident Partners/Directors: ICAEW Members
S J Shirtcliffe

SKYE CORPORATE FINANCE LTD ◈
307 High Road, Chilwell, Beeston, Nottingham NG9 5DL
Tel: 0115 922 0318
Resident Partners/Directors: ICAEW Members
J G Sykes

SMITH COOKSON ◈
4 Yorke Street, Hucknall, Nottingham, NG15 7BT

SMITH COOKSON ACCOUNTANTS LTD
4 Yorke Street, Hucknall, Nottingham, NG15 7BT

SMITH COOPER ◈
Haydn House, 309-329 Haydn Road, Nottingham, NG5 1HG
Tel: 0115 960 7111
Resident Partners/Directors: ICAEW Members
S R Adcock, R A Heason, S R Tysoe, G J Whiting

SMITH EMMERSON
87 Talbot Street, Nottingham, NG1 5GN

SMITH EMMERSON LTD
87 Talbot Street, Nottingham, NG1 5GN

SMITH EMMERSON ACCOUNTANTS LLP
87 Talbot Street, Nottingham, NG1 5GN

SPIRIT ★ ◈
13-15 Regent Street, Nottingham, NG1 5BS
Tel: 0115 941 5193
Resident Partners/Directors: ICAEW Members
J Clifton, P E French

STAFFORD & CO
35/37 Kingsway, Kirkby-in-Ashfield, Nottingham, NG17 7DR
Tel: 01623 759511
Principal: ICAEW Member
M Stafford

STEPHEN T. CLARKE LTD
23 Rolleston Crescent, Watnall, Nottingham, NG16 1JU
Tel: 0115 938 4404
Resident Partners/Directors: ICAEW Members
S T Clarke

SWANDEC LTD ◈
550 Valley Road, Basford, Nottingham, NG5 1JJ
Tel: 0115 942 7820
Resident Partners/Directors: ICAEW Members
A West

T S V DEVADASON
20 Richmond Drive, Mappereley Park, Nottingham, NG3 5EL

T WILFORD PELL & CO
1 Derby Road, Eastwood, Nottingham, NG16 3PA
Tel: 01773 762925
Resident Partners/Directors: ICAEW Members
M A Burnell
Other Offices:17 Newstead Grove, Nottingham NG1 4GZ (Tel: 0115 947 6543)
Registered by the ICAEW to carry out company audit work
Regulated by the ICAEW for a range of investment business activities

T WILFORD PELL & CO
17 Newstead Grove, Nottingham, NG1 4GZ

TCP
10 The Triangle, ng 2 Business Park, Nottingham, NG2 1AE

TCP (GB) LLP
10 The Triangle, ng 2 Business Park, Nottingham, NG2 1AE

TENON LTD
The Poynt Building, 45 Wollaton Street, Nottingham, NG1 5FW
Tel: 0115 9489400

TENON LTD
Griffin House, 32 The Ropewalk, Nottingham, NG1 5DW
Tel: 0115 941 8686

TENON AUDIT LTD
The Poynt Building, 45 Wollaton Street, Nottingham, NG1 5FW
Tel: 0115 948 9400
Resident Partners/Directors: ICAEW Members
A J Hunt

UHY HACKER YOUNG
22 The Ropewalk, Nottingham, NG1 5DT

UHY HACKER YOUNG LLP
110 Nottingham Road, Chilwell, Nottingham, NG9 6DQ

WAKEMAN & CO
Charlton Cottage, Old Forge Lane, Granby, Nottingham NG13 9PS

NUNEATON

BEASLEY & CO
25 Market Place, Nuneaton, CV11 4EG

BOSWORTH BUSINESS MANAGEMENT LTD ◈
37 Northumberland Avenue, Market Bosworth, Nuneaton, CV13 0RJ
Tel: 07050 369499
Resident Partners/Directors: ICAEW Members
H Skeat

FOSTER & CO
144 Malvern Avenue, Nuneaton, CV10 8NB

IVAN J PARRY
2nd Floor, 25 Market Place, Nuneaton, CV11 4EG

M. FRANKLINS ★ ◈
84 Albion Court, Attleborough Road, Nuneaton, CV11 4JJ
Tel: 02476 371888
Resident Partners/Directors: ICAEW Members
M S Franklin

MARLOWE & CO
22 Shawe Avenue, Nuneaton, CV10 0EL
Tel: 02476 736987
Principal: ICAEW Member
M C Kockelbergh

NICOLA FISHER FINANCIAL PLANNING LTD ◈
2 Inchford Close, Nuneaton, CV11 6UF
Tel: 02476 370515
Website: http://www.nicolafisher.co.uk
Resident Partners/Directors: ICAEW Members
N J Fisher

SPECIALISATIONS – TAXATION
Estate and Inheritance
Trusts

PATTINSONS
8 The Courtyard, Goldsmith Way, Eliot Business Park, Nuneaton CV11 7RJ

PATTINSONS ACCOUNTANCY LTD
8 The Courtyard, Goldsmith Way, Eliot Business Park, Nuneaton CV11 7RJ

R.F. SHARROTT & CO ◈
24A Coton Road, Nuneaton, CV11 5TW

R.W.MEREDITH
256 Higham Lane, Nuneaton, CV11 6AR

STEWART, FLETCHER AND BARRETT
Manor Court Chambers, 126 Manor Court Road, Nuneaton, CV11 5HL
Tel: 02476 384171
Fax: 024 7632 5778
Email: enquiries@sfb.uk.com

continued

STEWART, FLETCHER AND BARRETT *cont*
Resident Partners/Directors: ICAEW Members
P Carvell, J Sargent, P R White
Registered by the ICAEW to carry out company audit work

TREVOR BEASLEY & CO LTD
25 Market Place, Nuneaton, CV11 4EG

VALERIE TUNNICLIFF
17 Hebden Way, Nuneaton, CV11 6WL

OAKHAM

AJ CLARK
14 Cricket Lawns, Oakham, LE15 6HT

BRIAN G. NEALE
Was-Thatched, Hambleton, Oakham, LE15 8TH

KEIGHWOOD LTD
12 The Range, Langham, Oakham, LE15 7EB
Tel: 01572 755874
Resident Partners/Directors: ICAEW Members
F K McMorran

NEWBY CASTLEMAN ◈
Suite 3, 40 Melton Road, Oakham, LE15 6AY
Tel: 01572 755573
Fax: 01572 723435
Email: nac@newbyc.co.uk
Other Offices: Leicester, Melton Mowbray, Loughborough, Nottingham
Registered by the ICAEW to carry out company audit work
Regulated by the ICAEW for a range of investment business activities

SOUTHERINGTONS ACCOUNTANTS AND BUSINESS ADVISERS LTD
71 Church Street, Langham, Oakham, LE15 7JE

OKEHAMPTON

AIMS - NIGEL K WAYNE
15a East Street, Okehampton, EX20 1AS

MY BUSINESS CENTRE LTD
Room 1, Bridge House, 25 Fore Street, Okehampton, EX20 1DL
Tel: 01837 55482
Resident Partners/Directors: ICAEW Members
F Rook

ROBERT M HUMPHRY LTD
2 East Street, Okehampton, EX20 1AS
Tel: 01837 54344
Email: admin@rmhumphry.co.uk
Resident Partners/Directors: ICAEW Members
R M Humphry

SIMPKINS EDWARDS
4 Fore Street, Okehampton, EX20 1AD
Tel: 01837 52485
Email: okehampton@simpkinsedwards.co.uk
Website: http://www.simpkinsedwards.co.uk
Resident Partners (Non-ICAEW Members):
R L Bedford
Registered by the ICAEW to carry out company audit work
Regulated by the ICAEW for a range of investment business activities

SIMPKINS EDWARDS
Hatherleigh Market, Hatherleigh, Okehampton, EX20 3HT
Tel: 01837 52485

THOMAS WESTCOTT ★
5 West Street, Okehampton, EX20 1HQ
Tel: 01837 52839

OLD WINDSOR

A.C. BROWN
22 Harwood Gardens, Old Windsor, SL4 2LJ

OLDBURY

BSN ASSOCIATES LTD
3b Swallowfield Courtyard, Wolverhampton Road, Oldbury, B69 2JG

GOMPERTZ, KENDALL & CO ◈
1st Floor, Trigate, 210-222 Hagley Road West, Oldbury B68 0NP
Tel: 0121 434 5577
Principal: ICAEW Member
M W Pearsall

OLDHAM

A J ROBINSON & CO
First Floor Offices, 23 Sam Road, Diggle, Saddleworth, Oldham OL3 5PU

ADRIAN CUNNINGHAM ◈
12 Cornwall Crescent, Diggle,Saddleworth, Oldham, OL3 5PW
Tel: 01457 871098
Principal: ICAEW Member
A T Cunningham

ASHFORD & CO ◈
95A High Street, Lees, Oldham, OL4 4LY
Tel: 0161 652 8780
Resident Partners/Directors: ICAEW Members
D F Ashford

AYZLEWOOD
127 Cottam Street, Oldham, OL1 2NT

AYZLEWOOD ACCOUNTANTS
127 Cottam Street, Oldham, OL1 2NT
Tel: 0161 620 7399
Principal: ICAEW Member
S M Ali

CURTIS & CO
16 Middlefield, Bardsley, Oldham, OL8 2TP

D.R. HARRISON & CO
8 Clydesdale Street, Oldham, OL8 1BT

DAVENPORT HODGKISS ◈
1a Wilton Street, Manchester Road, Hollinwood, Oldham OL9 7NZ
Tel: 0161 624 9314
Email: office@davenporthodgkiss.co.uk
Date Established: 1979
Resident Partners/Directors: ICAEW Members
F L Hodgkiss, D J Walford
Registered by the ICAEW to carry out company audit work

EDWARDS VEEDER
Block E, Brunswick Square, Union Street, Oldham OL1 1DE
Tel: 0161 620 2133

EDWARDS VEEDER (OLDHAM) LLP ◈
Block E, Brunswick Square, Union Street, Oldham OL1 1DE

GATLEY, READ ★ ◈
Prince of Wales House, 18/19 Salmon Fields Business Village, Royton, Oldham OL2 6HT
Tel: 0161 626 5657
Resident Partners/Directors: ICAEW Members
D A Read

GIBSONS ACCOUNTANTS LTD
7 Millbrae Gardens, Shaw, Old Crompton, Oldham OL2 7HQ

GRUNDY, ANDERSON & KERSHAW
123-125 Union Street, Oldham, OL1 1TG
Tel: 0161 624 7827
Fax: 0161 628 7273
Email: info@gakacc.co.uk
Resident Partners/Directors: ICAEW Members
J A Osbaldeston, M S J Royle
Resident Partners (Non-ICAEW Members):
NTO Birtwistle
Registered by the ICAEW to carry out company audit work

HARRISON WALKER
Enterprise House, 2 Pass Street, Oldham, OL9 6HZ
Tel: 0161 628 6212
Principal: ICAEW Member
W N Harrison

J.W. MINTON & CO
103a High Street, Lees, Oldham, OL4 4LY

JOE SALDANHA & CO
164 Rochdale Road, Royton, Oldham, OL2 6QF

JOHN WHONE
2 Sykes Close, Greenfield, Oldham, OL3 7PT
Tel: 01457 870626
Principal: ICAEW Member
J Whone

KATHLEEN M MANNION
221 Chamber Road, Oldham, OL8 4DJ
Tel: 0161 652 5796
Principal: ICAEW Member
K M Mannion

KPPBUSINESS LTD ◈
115 Huddersfield Road, Oldham, OL1 3NY
Tel: 0161 627 0785
Resident Partners/Directors: ICAEW Members
K P Priest

LONGDEN & COOK DENTAL ACCOUNTANCY PRACTICE
113 Union Street, Oldham, OL1 1RU

MEACHER-JONES & COMPANY LTD
141 Union Street, Oldham, OL1 1TE

MJG ACCOUNTS LTD
Hollinwood Business Centre, Albert Street, Oldham, OL8 3QL

MORRIS GREGORY
County End Business Centre, Jackson Street, Springhead, Oldham OL4 4TZ
Tel: 0161 626 3427
Fax: 0161 627 5294
Email: mail@morrisgregory.co.uk
Website: http://www.morrisgregory.co.uk
Resident Partners/Directors: ICAEW Members
A Brooks, J A Ormiston
Registered by the ICAEW to carry out company audit work
Regulated by the ICAEW for a range of investment business activities

S.D. WOOLF & CO
113 Union Street, Oldham, OL1 1RY

SAMUEL SLATER & SONS
11 Queen Street, Oldham, OL1 1RG
Tel: 0161 624 4484
Principal: ICAEW Member
R Butterworth

WRIGLEY PARTINGTON ◈
Sterling House, 501 Middleton Road, Chadderton, Oldham OL9 9LY
Tel: 0161 622 0222
Resident Partners/Directors: ICAEW Members
N C Daniels, A P Dixon, R M Dixon, D N Ducie, D J Huxley, P G Quinn, G R Wilkinson

OLNEY

CLAIRE SAVAGE ◈
37 Olney Road, Emberton, Olney, MK46 5BX
Tel: 01234 241048
Email: hclairesavage@yahoo.com
Principal: ICAEW Member
H C Savage

ONGAR

ANDREW TAFFS
6 Barrons Close, Ongar, CM5 9BJ

CLIFFORD COXE
Greensted Hall, Ongar, CM5 9LD
Tel: 01277 363083
Principal: ICAEW Member
C A M Coxe

DENNIS LEYHANE
46 The Gables, Ongar, CM5 0GA
Tel: 01277 365598
Principal: ICAEW Member
D F Leyhane

R.J. DIXON & CO
6 Woodland Way, Marden Ash, Ongar, CM5 9EP
Tel: 01277 365660
Email: gjwatts@talktalk.net
Principal: ICAEW Member
G J Watts

ORMSKIRK

A. RULE
6 Thornhill, Granville Park West, Aughton, Ormskirk L39 5HD

ADAMS & CO ACCOUNTANTS LTD
Office AO5, Towngate Works, Dark Lane, Mawdesley, Ormskirk L40 2QU
Tel: 01704 822167

ALEXANDER MYERSON & CO ◈
32 Derby Street, Ormskirk, L39 2BY
Tel: 01695 571555
Resident Partners/Directors: ICAEW Members
J K McCormick, P Rothwell
Resident Partners (Non-ICAEW Members):
P Rothwell
Regulated by the ICAEW for a range of investment business activities

CHAYTOR, STEELE & CO
9a Derby Street, Ormskirk, L39 2BJ
Tel: 01695 579606
Email: info@chaytorsteele.co.uk
Resident Partners/Directors: ICAEW Members
P A Atherton, G M Dobson
Registered by the ICAEW to carry out company audit work

COLLINS & CO
73a New Court Way, Ormskirk Business Park, Ormskirk, L39 2YT
Tel: 01695 577557
Principal: ICAEW Member
P J Collins

D.J. QUINE
27 Claremont Drive, Aughton, Ormskirk, L39 4SP

GASKING, LACE & CO ◈
Commercial Chambers, Derby Street, Ormskirk, L39 2BY
Tel: 01695 573877
Resident Partners/Directors: ICAEW Members
J Watson

J.C. BARTON & CO
Martland Buildings, Mart Lane, Burscough, Ormskirk L40 0SD

JVSA ACCOUNTANTS ★ ◈
20 Derby Street, Ormskirk, L39 2BY
Tel: 01695 585333
Email: chris.sales@jvsa.co.uk
Resident Partners/Directors: ICAEW Members
C Sales

L. MORRIS
5 Greystokes, Aughton, Ormskirk, L39 5HE
Tel: 01695 423809
Principal: ICAEW Member
L Morris

M DUNHAM
Carrfields, Carr Lane, Lathom, Ormskirk L40 4BT

M.J. FORSHAW
7 Oak Drive, Burscough, Ormskirk, L40 5BQ

STUDHOLME-BELL LTD
Ash Farm Barn, Blue Stone Lane, Mawdesley, Ormskirk L40 2RQ
Tel: 01704 823684
Resident Partners/Directors: ICAEW Members
A W J Bell

WESLEY & CO
1 Bold Lane, Aughton, Ormskirk, L39 6SG
Tel: 01695 424966
Principal: ICAEW Member
M W Pratt

ORPINGTON

A.J.F.BARRADELL
20 Woodhurst Avenue, Orpington, BR5 1AR

A.R.MOTT
4 Beaumont Road, Orpington, BR5 1JN

BEECHWOOD TAX SERVICES
17 Beechwood Avenue, Orpington, BR6 7EX

BRIAN CLARKE
5 Downsway, Orpington, BR6 9NU
Tel: 01689 861348
Principal: ICAEW Member
B Clarke

CASSIDY & CO
1 Grasmere Avenue, Locksbottom, Orpington, BR6 8HD
Tel: 01689 862935
Principal: ICAEW Member
P G Cassidy

COOLEY & CO
Sampuran House, 3a Chislehurst Road, Orpington, BR6 0DF

COOPER & CO
18 Magdalen Grove, Orpington, BR6 9WE
Tel: 01689 877885
Principal: ICAEW Member
C A Cooper

CULVERHOUSE & CO
7 High Street, Farnborough Village, Orpington, BR6 7BQ

CULVERHOUSE & CO
7 High Street, Farnborough Village, Orpington, BR6 7BQ

CULVERHOUSE & CO LTD
7 High Street, Farnborough, Orpington, BR6 7BQ

DENBY & ASSOCIATES
73a High Street, Orpington, BR6 0JF

GAVIN G. CURTIS
24 Ashley Gardens, Green Street Green, Orpington, BR6 9NH
Tel: 01689 861788
Principal: ICAEW Member
G G Curtis
Registered by the ICAEW to carry out company audit work

GEOFFREY J. GRIGGS
66 Lynwood Grove, Orpington, BR6 0BH
Tel: 01689 837519
Principal: ICAEW Member
G J Griggs

GEORGE EDWARDS
10 Starts Close, Locksbottom, Orpington, BR6 8NU
Tel: 01689 859228
Principal: ICAEW Member
G Edwards

GEORGE RONSON FCA
19 Buckingham Close, Petts Wood, Orpington, BR5 1SA

GRIFFIN SUTTON & PARTNERS
207/215 High Street, Orpington, BR6 0PF

HEWSONS
80 Woodhurst Avenue, Orpington, BR5 1AT
Tel: 01689 838348
Principal: ICAEW Member
N D Hewson
SPECIALISATIONS – SECTOR

Church

J.M. WELLINGTON
13 Lancing Road, Orpington, BR6 0QS
Tel: 01689 813875
Principal: ICAEW Member
J M Wellington

JOHN H. MILLER & CO
The Larches, Sevenoaks Road, Orpington, BR6 7LR

JOHN W ATKINSON FCA
First Floor, Gloucester House, Clarence Court, Rushmore Hill, Orpington BR6 7LZ
Tel: 01689 850110
Principal: ICAEW Member
J W Atkinson

KEITH WITHALL & CO
303 High Street, Orpington, BR6 0NN
Tel: 01689 877174
Principal: ICAEW Member
K B Withall

LATHAM LAMBOURNE
First Floor, Priory Buildings, Church Hill, Orpington, BR6 0HH
Tel: 01689 825563
Resident Partners/Directors: ICAEW Members
J H Lambourne

LE FORTS ◈
Britannia House, Roberts Mews, Orpington, BR6 0JP
Tel: 01689 890900
Principal: ICAEW Member
A R Le Fort

MICHAEL S. REYNOLDS
14 Great Thrift, Orpington, BR5 1NG

PHILIP I. MACORISON
1 Abingdon Way, Orpington, BR6 9WA

R.C SMITH
1 Tower Close, Orpington, BR6 0SP

R.F. CHEESMAN
22 Derwent Drive, Orpington, BR5 1EW

SCORER ACCOUNTING SERVICES ★
33 Waring Drive, Green Street Green, Orpington, BR6 6DN
Tel: 01689 600810
Resident Partners/Directors: ICAEW Members
M F Scorer

STEEL & CO
18 Ladywood Avenue, Petts Wood, Orpington, BR5 1QJ

T.T. HARDEN & CO
35 Meadow Way, Farnborough Park, Orpington, BR6 8LN

V.E. ANDREW (INCORPORATING HOLLAMBY & CO)
47 Oxenden Wood Road, Chelsfield Park, Orpington, BR6 6HP

WILKINS KENNEDY ◈
Greytown House, 221-227 High Street, Orpington, BR6 0NZ
Tel: 01689 827505
Website: http://www.wilkinskennedy.com
Resident Partners/Directors: ICAEW Members
P J Barton, R S Butterfield, S J Harrison, N J Parrett, M A Wilkes
Resident Partners (Non-ICAEW Members):
A Merrett
Other Offices: Amersham, Ashford, Egham, Guildford, Hertford, London, Reading, Romsey, Southend, Winchester
Overseas Offices: Stanley, Falkland Islands
Registered by the ICAEW to carry out company audit work
Regulated by the ICAEW for a range of investment business activities

SPECIALISATIONS – BUSINESS & GENERAL ADVICE
Acquisitions and Mergers
Disposal of Businesses
Outsourcing - Financial Services

SPECIALISATIONS – BUSINESS RECOVERY & INSOLVENCY
Bankruptcies
Corporate Recovery
Liquidations
Reorganisations and Company Reconstructions

SPECIALISATIONS – FORENSIC ACCOUNTING
Expert Witnesses in Litigation
Forensic Accounting

SPECIALISATIONS – SECTOR
Charities
Construction
FSA Members
Insurance Brokers
Property
Solicitors

OSSETT

HALL HAYES & CO
Prospect House, 24 Prospect Road, Ossett, WF5 8AE
Tel: 0845 838 4014
Principal: ICAEW Member
J A Flatters

HOPE AGAR LTD
Ashton House, 19 Prospect Road, Ossett, WF5 8AE
Tel: 01924 261680

JOLLIFFE CORK HARDY
Market Place, Ossett, WF5 8BQ

JOLLIFFE CORK HARDY LLP
Market Place, Ossett, WF5 8BQ
Tel: 01924 271718
Email: john.hardy@jolliffecorkhardy.co.uk
Resident Partners/Directors: ICAEW Members
J P Hardy, A D Hydes, C L Lawton, A R N Perkin

KJA DAWSON BROWN LTD
48 Station Road, Ossett, WF5 8AY

OSWESTRY

COPPINS-HUGHES ◈
The Croft, Pit Lane, Treflach, Oswestry SY10 9HB
Tel: 01691 680950
Principal: ICAEW Member
C H J Hughes

DAVID W. MORGAN
32 Llanforda Rise, Oswestry, SY11 1SY
Tel: 01691 650445
Principal: ICAEW Member
D W Morgan

DRE & CO ◈
7 Lower Brook Street, Oswestry, SY11 2HG
Tel: 01691 654353
Resident Partners/Directors: ICAEW Members
A J Matthews

ELLIOTT & CO
1a Station Buildings, Station Road, Gobowen, Oswestry SY11 3LX
Tel: 01691 680425
Principal: ICAEW Member
A R Elliott

GARNER PUGH & SINCLAIR
3 Belgrave Place, 19 Salop Road, Oswestry, SY11 2NR
Tel: 01691 652044
Email: admin@gpands.co.uk
Resident Partners/Directors: ICAEW Members
D P Evison, M P Evison, J F Hughes

GERAINT HUMPHREYS & CO
5-7 Beatrice Street, Oswestry, SY11 1QE
Tel: 01691 661144
Principal: ICAEW Member
G Humphreys

GITTINS LTD
28 Salop Road, Oswestry, SY11 2NZ
Tel: 01691 654246
Fax: 01691 654830
Website: http://www.tagittins.co.uk
Resident Partners/Directors: ICAEW Members
V E Jones
Other Offices:63 King St, Wrexham (Tel: 01978 264846)
Registered by the ICAEW to carry out company audit work
Regulated by the ICAEW for a range of investment business activities
Languages Spoken:
Welsh

JONES R.A.
Tynycoed, Penybontfawr, Oswestry, SY10 0PB

MARK KENNETT & CO LTD
Market Gate, Salop Road, Oswestry, SY11 2NR
Tel: 01691 650121
Resident Partners/Directors: ICAEW Members
M Kennett

MORRIS COOK ◈
6 Salop Road, Oswestry, SY11 2NU
Tel: 01691 654545
Resident Partners/Directors: ICAEW Members
A C S Clarke

NABARRO POOLE LTD
Unit MO5, Mile Oak Industrial Estate, Maesbury Road, Oswestry SY10 8GA

TMB & CO
Tynycae, Briw, Llangedwyn, Oswestry SY10 9LB
Tel: 01691 791327
Principal: ICAEW Member
T Evans

TURNER PEACHEY ◈
Salop House, Salop Road, Oswestry, SY11 2NS
Tel: 01691 654127
Email: oswestry@turner-peachey.co.uk
Website: http://www.turner-peachey.co.uk
Resident Partners/Directors: ICAEW Members
J Ollier
Other Offices: Bridgnorth, Shrewsbury, Telford, Welshpool
Registered by the ICAEW to carry out company audit work
Regulated by the ICAEW for a range of investment business activities
General Description: A local professional firm offering a wide range of accounting, financial and taxation services.

OTLEY

BFE BRAYS ◈
Building Society Chambers, Wesley Street, Otley, LS21 1AZ
Tel: 01943 462518
Email: otley@bfebrays.co.uk
Website: http://www.bfebrays.co.uk
Resident Partners/Directors: ICAEW Members
L J Bentley, D W Eadon
Other Offices:6 Cambridge Crescent, Harrogate
Registered by the ICAEW to carry out company audit work
Regulated by the ICAEW for a range of investment business activities

BUSINESS FOCUS & SYSTEMS LTD ◈
4 Chevin Mill, Leeds Road, Otley, LS21 1BT
Tel: 01943 855700
Resident Partners/Directors: ICAEW Members
W P Johnston, A M Massarella

HOLLINGS CROWE STORR & CO ◈
14 Beech Hill, Otley, LS21 3AX
Tel: 01943 465010
Email: d.milns@hcsco.co.uk
Website: http://www.hollingscrowestorr.co.uk
Resident Partners/Directors: ICAEW Members
P J Fardell
Non-resident Partners (ICAEW Members):
D H Milns
See display advertisement near this entry.

WALKER BROADBENT ASSOCIATES LTD ◈
Westgate House, 25 Westgate, Otley, LS21 3AT
Tel: 01943 463533
Resident Partners/Directors: ICAEW Members
M V Walker

OTTERY ST. MARY

EASTERBROOK EATON LTD
8 Jesu Street, Ottery St. Mary, EX11 1EU

KIRKNESS & CO
21 Silver Street, Ottery St Mary, EX11 1DB

WEST HILL TAX SERVICES LTD
Cedar Haven, Toadpit Lane, West Hill, Ottery St. Mary EX11 1TR

OXFORD

A C M CROMBIE ◈
20 Sandfield Road, Headington, Oxford, OX3 7RQ

ALCOCK WATSON ASSOCIATES
167 Oxford Road, Cowley, Oxford, OX4 2ES

ANDY WALTON & CO ◈
March Cottage, The Green, Great Milton, Oxford OX44 7NS

ARIES & CO
Unit 10, Boundary Business Park, Garsington, Oxford OX44 9DY
Tel: 01865 361457

ARIES ACCOUNTANTS LTD
Unit 10, Boundary Business Park, Garsington, Oxford OX44 9DY
Tel: 01865 361457
Resident Partners/Directors: ICAEW Members
E Aries

BRONSENS ◈
26 Beaumont Street, Oxford, OX1 2NP
Tel: 01865 552996
Resident Partners/Directors: ICAEW Members
P J Burton, B R Sennett

BUNTING & CO
5 Orchard Close, Wheatley, Oxford, OX33 1US

BUNTING ACCOUNTANTS LTD
5 Orchard Close, Wheatley, Oxford, OX33 1US

CHERYL WATT
3 Haslemere Gardens, Oxford, OX2 8EL
Tel: 01865 553335
Resident Partners/Directors: ICAEW Members
C A Watt

COLIN BURTON FCA
The Old Dairy, 5 North Parade Avenue, Oxford, OX2 6LX

COX HINKINS & CO ★
Charterford House, 75 London Road, Headington, Oxford OX3 9BB
Tel: 01865 742500
Resident Partners/Directors: ICAEW Members
M H Hinkins
Registered by another RSB to carry out company audit work

CRITCHLEYS ◈
Greyfriars Court, Paradise Square, Oxford, OX1 1BE

DAVID COOKE & CO
6 Seacourt Road, Botley, Oxford, OX2 9LD
Tel: 01865 241917
Principal: ICAEW Member
D C S Cooke

GRANT THORNTON UK LLP
1 Westminster Way, Oxford, OX2 0PZ
Tel: 01865 799899
Resident Partners/Directors: ICAEW Members
A R Boby, J E Crookes, K E Fidgeon, W E Hart, T D James, C M Mundy, J L Siemieniuch, S J Vanags

GRASSO PARKER GREEN LLP
New Inn Yard, 108 St Aldates, Oxford, OX1 1BU

HOWARD I. DAY
75 Barton Road, Headington, Oxford, OX3 9JE

HUNTER, MARSHALL & CO LTD
Suite C, 1st Floor, Hinksey Court, West Way, Botley Oxford OX2 9JU

JAMES COWPER ◈
Willow Court, 7 West Way, Botley, Oxford OX2 0JB
Tel: 01865 200500
Resident Partners/Directors: ICAEW Members
S L Bedford, S R Staunton

JOHN HINE & CO ◈
Slade House, Kirtlington, Oxford, OX5 3JA
Tel: 01869 350272
Principal: ICAEW Member
J S Hine

JOHN M HANKS
50 Thames Street, Oxford, OX1 1SU

KING LOOSE & CO
5 South Parade, Summertown, Oxford, OX2 7JL
Tel: 01865 512551
Principal: ICAEW Member
H C Fanthome

LUCY WATSON
80 Warwick Street, Oxford, OX4 1SY

MARK BALE LTD
106 Staunton Road, Headington, Oxford, OX3 7TN
Tel: 01865 744177
Resident Partners/Directors: ICAEW Members
M P B Bale

MAZARS CORPORATE FINANCE LTD
Seacourt Tower, West Way, Oxford, OX2 0JG
Tel: 01865 722744

MAZARS LLP ◈
Seacourt Tower, West Way, Oxford, OX2 0JG
Tel: 01865 722744
Registered by the ICAEW to carry out company audit work
Authorised and regulated by the Financial Services Authority for investment business

MERCER LEWIN
41 Cornmarket Street, Oxford, OX1 3HA

MERCER LEWIN LTD
41 Cornmarket Street, Oxford, OX1 3HA

THE MGROUP PARTNERSHIP ★
Cranbrook House, 287/291 Banbury Road, Oxford, OX2 7JQ
Tel: 01865 552925
Email: team@theMgroup.co.uk
Website: http://www.theMgroup.co.uk
Resident Partners/Directors: ICAEW Members
P M Casterton, G C Lane
Resident Partners (Non-ICAEW Members):
G J McHale, R J Clayton, P D Smith, A D Pridsam
Registered by the ICAEW to carry out company audit work
SPECIALISATIONS – BUSINESS & GENERAL ADVICE
Divorce/Matrimonial
SPECIALISATIONS – TAXATION
UK Companies Overseas

MICHAEL HAMMENT
16 Wentworth Road, Oxford, OX2 7TQ
Tel: 01865 510459

MONICA IRWIN
1 Barn Close, Cumnor Hill, Oxford, OX2 9JP
Tel: 01865 864121
Principal: ICAEW Member
M S Irwin

NJB ◈
122b Woodstock Road, Oxford, OX2 7NF
Tel: 07968 707968
Principal: ICAEW Member
N J Bolam

OUTSOURCING FINANCE LTD
166 Main Road, Long Hanborough, Witney, Oxford OX29 8JY

PAUL WAKEFIELD
Myrtle Cottage, Lower End, Great Milton, Oxford OX44 7NJ

PEARSON BUCHHOLZ
North House, Farmoor Court, Cumnor Road, Farmoor, Oxford OX2 9LU

PEARSON BUCHHOLZ LTD
North House, Farmoor Court, Cumnor Road, Farmoor, Oxford OX2 9LU

PEARSON BUCHHOLZ (TAXATION SERVICES) LTD
North House, Farmoor Court, Cumnor Road, Oxford OX2 9LU

PETER J STEVENSON
8 Harbord Road, Oxford, OX2 8LJ
Tel: 01865 559050
Email: consult@clara.co.uk
Principal: ICAEW Member
P J Stevenson
SPECIALISATIONS – SECTOR

Charities
Church
General Description: Specialist in charity and voluntary sector.

PETER SMITH
Rose Cottage, Brill Road, Horton-Cum-Studley, Oxford OX33 1BN

R.A. HUGHES
76 Oxford Road, Old Marston, Oxford, OX3 0RD
Tel: 01865 240856
Principal: ICAEW Member
R A Hughes

RJ MARSDEN
Park House, 9 Park Town, Oxford, OX2 6SN

ROB MCCULLOCH LTD
18 Barn Close, Cumnor Hill, Oxford, OX2 9JP

S.J. WETHERALL
264 Banbury Road, Oxford, OX2 7DY

SCRUTTONS
2A Bickerton Road, Headington, Oxford, OX3 7LS

SHAW & CO
264 Banbury Road, Oxford, OX2 7DY

SHAW GIBBS LLP
Shaw Gibbs LLP, 264 Banbury Road, Oxford, OX2 7DY
Tel: 01865 292200
Resident Partners/Directors: ICAEW Members
A G Caiger, D P O'Connell, L Watson, I D Wenman, S J Wetherall

T.E.J. TIBBETTS
5 Bow Bank, Longworth, Oxford, OX13 5ER
Tel: 01865 821515
Principal: ICAEW Member
T E J Tibbetts

TAYLOR COCKS ◈
Unit 2, Isis Business Centre, Horspath Road, Oxford OX4 2RD
Tel: 0870 770 8111
Website: http://www.theaccountants.co.uk
SPECIALISATIONS – AUDIT & ASSURANCE
Audit
Audit — Private Company
SPECIALISATIONS – BUSINESS & GENERAL ADVICE
Book-keeping
Management Advice to Business
Management Consultancy
SPECIALISATIONS – FINANCIAL REPORTING
Accounts Preparation
Limited Company Accounts
SPECIALISATIONS – SECTOR

Doctors
Solicitors
SPECIALISATIONS – TAXATION
Estate and Inheritance
Investigations
Taxation

VFDNET ★ ◈
Magdalen Centre, Robert Robinson Avenue, Oxford, OX4 4GA

WELLERS ★
8 King Edward Street, Oxford, OX1 4HS
Tel: 01865 723131
Resident Partners/Directors: ICAEW Members
P J Sharp

WENN TOWNSEND ◈
30 St Giles', Oxford, OX1 3LE
Tel: 01865 559900
Email: partners@wenns.co.uk
Website: http://www.wenntownsend.co.uk
Resident Partners/Directors: ICAEW Members
A K Bahl, L D Benton, G L Cole, J V Gould, A E Haines, K Middleton, L J Palmer, D J Pluck
Other Offices: Abingdon, Cirencester
Registered by the ICAEW to carry out company audit work
See display advertisement near this entry.

OXTED

ANNESLEY TORY & CO
Clock House, Tandridge Lane, Oxted, RH8 9NJ

BARBARA FORREST
17 Orchard Way, Hurst Green, Oxted, RH8 9DJ

DE WARRENNE WALLER AND CO LTD
White Hart House, High Street, Limpsfield, Oxted RH8 0DT
Tel: 01883 730500
Email: info@dwwgroup.com
Resident Partners/Directors: ICAEW Members
J J D Waller
Other Offices:212 Piccadilly, London, W1J 9HF

FISCAL ACTION LTD
4 The Waldrons, Oxted, RH8 9DY

FRITH & CO
Moorgate House, 7b Station Road West, Oxted, RH8 9EE

GARY TOULSON
6 Culver Drive, Oxted, RH8 9HP

LINCROFT & COMPANY LTD
The Old Drapery, 7 Holland Road, Oxted, RH8 9AU

MCKENZIES
14-16 Station Road West, Oxted, RH8 9EP

MICHAEL J.G. TAYLOR
Hunters End, Uvedale Road, Oxted, RH8 0EN
Tel: 01883 715104
Principal: ICAEW Member
M J G Taylor

MOSS JAMES LTD
Titsey Estate Office, Pilgrims Lane, Oxted, RH8 0SE
Tel: 01883 722672
Resident Partners/Directors: ICAEW Members
R J Moss

NESBITS
Robertsfield, Holland Road, Hurst Green, Oxted RH8 9BQ
Tel: 01883 722884
Principal: ICAEW Member
S Nesbit

PROFESSIONAL FINANCIAL CONSULTANTS LTD
14-16 Station Road West, Oxted, RH8 9EP

STEPHEN MATTHEWS
5 Detillens Lane, Oxted, RH8 0DH

TAXSAVERS DIRECT LTD
26 Orchard Way, Oxted, RH8 9DJ

W. HOWARD
102 Bluehouse Lane, Limpsfield, Oxted, RH8 0AJ
Tel: 01883 714622
Principal: ICAEW Member
W Howard

PADSTOW

MATTHEWS COOPER
Virage, 54 Dennis Road,
Padstow, PL28 8DF

PAIGNTON

DAVID J. BEENY & CO
Suite A, Parkside Chambers,
Parkside Road, Paignton
TQ4 6AE
Tel: 01803 524960
Registered by the ICAEW to carry out company audit work

JOHN WAIN & CO
49 Palace Avenue, Paignton,
TQ3 3EN

S G TODD LTD
Little Mount, 9b Southfield
Road, Paignton, TQ3 2SW
Tel: 01803 552082
Resident Partners/Directors:
ICAEW Members
S G Todd

PAR

KIRKHAM PARRY
Stoneybridge House,
Tywardreath, Par, PL24 2TY
Tel: 01726 812888
Principal: ICAEW Member
J P Kirkham Parry

SARAH HARVEY & CO
Swallows Barn, St Sampsons
Close, Tywardreath, Par
PL24 2QZ

PEACEHAVEN

BRADLEY SONI & CO
86 South Coast Rd, Peacehaven,
BN10 8SL
Tel: 01273 582605
Principal: ICAEW Member
P L Soni

JAMES POLLARD
223 South Coast Road,
Peacehaven, BN10 8LB

M.J.N. GOODEY
109 Arundel Road, Peacehaven,
BN10 8HE
Tel: 01273 584287
Principal: ICAEW Member
M J N Goodey

PENRITH

ARMSTRONG WATSON ◈
Birbeck House, Duke Street,
Penrith, CA11 7NA
Tel: 01768 222030
Resident Partners/Directors:
ICAEW Members
M E Hill, S Pinguey

CHRISTIAN DOUGLASS LLP
8 Great Dockray, Penrith,
CA11 7BL
Tel: 01768 899288

DODD & CO
Clint Mill, Cornmarket, Penrith,
CA11 7HW
Tel: 01768 864466
Resident Partners/Directors:
ICAEW Members
J Brown, V Fisher, P F Kendall,
A McViety

GRAHAM DENT & CO
Compton House, 104 Scotland
Road, Penrith, CA11 7NR

MICHAEL WATTS
Raven Gill, Parkhead, Renwick,
Penrith CA10 1JQ
Tel: 01768 898688
Principal: ICAEW Member
C M Watts

MONTPELIER PROFESSIONAL (BORDERS) LTD
Mostyn Hall, Friargate, Penrith,
CA11 7XR

NOBLE
Tarn Villa, Culgaith, Penrith,
CA10 1QL
Tel: 01768 88738

NOBLE ACCOUNTANTS LTD
Tarn Villa, Culgaith, Penrith,
CA10 1QL

O'REILLY
Ullswater House, Duke St,
Penrith, CA11 7LY
Tel: 01768 863651
Fax: 01768 899842
Email: penrith@o-reilly.co.uk
Website: http://www.o-reilly.co.uk
Date Established: 1934
Resident Partners/Directors:
ICAEW Members
G Ritzema
Registered by the ICAEW to carry out company audit work
Authorised and regulated by the Financial Services Authority for investment business

SPECIALISATIONS – SECTOR

Insurance Advice
See display advertisement near this entry.

ROBINSON UDALE LTD
The Old Bank, 41 King Street,
Penrith, CA11 7AY

SAINT & CO ▽ ◈
Poets Walk, Penrith, CA11 7HJ
Tel: 01768 865189
Email: penrith@saint.co.uk
Website: http://www.saint.co.uk
Resident Partners/Directors:
ICAEW Members
R J Kenyon, D A Liddle
Registered by the ICAEW to carry out company audit work
Authorised and regulated by the Financial Services Authority for investment business

STUART OAKE LTD ◈
3 Portland Place, Penrith,
CA11 7QN
Tel: 01768 891078
Resident Partners/Directors:
ICAEW Members
S N Oake

WOOD BROOKS AND CO
8 Great Dockray, Penrith,
CA11 7BL
Tel: 01768 899288
Resident Partners/Directors:
ICAEW Members
P D Brooks, K L Parr
See display advertisement near this entry.

PENRYN

JOHN GIRDLESTONE
Waterside Court, Falmouth
Road, Penryn, TR10 8AW
Tel: 01326 378288
Fax: 01326 378077
Email: john@girdlestone.org.uk
Principal: ICAEW Member
J Girdlestone
Regulated by the ICAEW for a range of investment business activities

PENZANCE

ANTHONY WILLIAMS & CO LTD ◈
14 North Parade, Penzance,
TR18 4SL
Tel: 01736 365151
Resident Partners/Directors:
ICAEW Members
D G Stephens, M J Vickers

CRANE & JOHNSTON LTD
11 Alverton Terrace, Penzance,
TR18 4JH

D.J. REYNOLDS & CO
15 Alverton Street, Penzance,
TR18 2QP
Tel: 01736 332959
Principal: ICAEW Member
D J Reynolds

J.M. TILDESLEY
5 Pednandrea, St Just, Penzance,
TR19 7UA

K.A. COPLAND
Chy-an-Brea, Hea Road,
Heamoor, Penzance TR18 3HB

MICHAEL F. CLIFT-MATTHEWS LTD
21 Clarence Street, Penzance, TR18 2NZ
Tel: 01736 351111
Resident Partners/Directors: ICAEW Members
M F Clift-Matthews

PETER JOHN NORMAN FCA
Bosgarrack, Hellangove Farm, Gulval, Penzance TR20 8XD

STEPHEN HOBSON
3 Sona Merg Close, Heamoor, Penzance, TR18 3QL
Tel: 01736 369674
Principal: ICAEW Member
S M Hobson

WALKER MOYLE
Alverton Manor, Penzance, TR18 4TD
Tel: 01736 362265
Website: http://www.walker-moyle.co.uk
Resident Partners/Directors: ICAEW Members
R M Crookes, C A Moyle, P J Thomas

PERRANPORTH

DAVID PENNINGTON
Cosy Nook, Bolingey, Perranporth, TR6 0AS

DAVID PENNINGTON
Suite Four, The Old Station Business Park, Station Road, Perranporth TR6 0LH

PERSHORE

AIMS - JON SMITH
Mid Thatch, Boon Street, Eckington, Pershore WR10 3BL

ALLCHURCH BAILEY LTD
Alveston House, 11 Broad Street, Pershore, WR10 1BB

CLIFTON-CRICK SHARP & CO ◈
40 High Street, Pershore, WR10 1DP

CROWTHERS
The Courtyard, 19 High Street, Pershore, WR10 1AA
Tel: 01386 552644

CROWTHERS ACCOUNTANTS LTD
The Courtyard, 19 High Street, Pershore, WR10 1AA
Tel: 01386 552644
Resident Partners/Directors: ICAEW Members
J J Crowther, N L Walding

JANET ROBINSON & CO
Victoria Loft, Hill Furze, Bishampton, Pershore WR10 2NB
Tel: 01386 861253
Principal: ICAEW Member
J Robinson

JOHN T. HILL ◈
Sycamore House, Church Street, Birlingham, Pershore WR10 3AQ
Tel: 01386 750147
Email: john@johnthill.fsbusiness.co.uk
Mobile: 07887 520823
Principal: ICAEW Member
J T Hill

MEREDITH THOMAS
Suite No 1, Royal Arcade, Pershore, WR10 1AG
Tel: 01386 553400
Email: info@meredith-thomas.co.uk
Principal: ICAEW Member
C T A Meredith
Regulated by the ICAEW for a range of investment business activities

PAUL JENKINS
39 High Street, Pershore, WR10 1EU
Tel: 01386 552223
Principal: ICAEW Member
T P Jenkins

PETERBOROUGH

A.G. PIRMOHAMED & CO
67 Lincoln Road, Peterborough, PE1 2SD
Tel: 01733 311166
Principal: ICAEW Member
A G Pirmohamed

A N HORNER & CO ◈
Croft House, East Road, Oundle, Peterborough PE8 4BZ
Tel: 01832 273888
Principal: ICAEW Member
A N Horner

BAKER TILLY
Garrick House, 76-80 High Street, Old Fletton, Peterborough PE2 8ST
Tel: 01733 342444
Resident Partners/Directors: ICAEW Members
B J Revell
Resident Partners (Non-ICAEW Members):
J Godfrey, D B Turpin

BAKER TILLY
Garrick House, 76-80 High Street, Old Fletton, Peterborough PE2 8ST

BAKER TILLY TAX AND ADVISORY SERVICES LLP
Garrick House, 76-80 High Street, Old Fletton, Peterborough PE2 8ST
Tel: 01733 342444
Resident Partners/Directors: ICAEW Members
B J Revell
Resident Partners (Non-ICAEW Members):
D B Turpin

BULLEY DAVEY
6 North Street, Oundle, Peterborough, PE8 4AL
Tel: 01832 273150
Website: http://www.bulleydavey.co.uk
Resident Partners/Directors: ICAEW Members
D R Webb
Registered by the ICAEW to carry out company audit work
Regulated by the ICAEW for a range of investment business activities

BULLEY DAVEY ◈
4 Cyrus Way, Cygnet Park, Hampton, Peterborough PE7 8HP
Tel: 01733 569494
Website: http://www.bulleydavey.co.uk
Resident Partners (Non-ICAEW Members):
M Perkins, N J Cheney, I V Brown, A France, J S Higgins, M J Gregson
Registered by the ICAEW to carry out company audit work
Regulated by the ICAEW for a range of investment business activities
Individual(s) licensed for insolvency work by another RPB

BURROWMOOR CONSULTING LTD
200 Broadway, Peterborough, PE1 4DT

BUTLER FANCOURT
Boon Court, Papyrus Road, Werrington, Peterborough PE4 5HQ
Tel: 01733 570877
Resident Partners/Directors: ICAEW Members
C E Butler, M P Fancourt

CHAGANI ◈
37 Kingfishers, Orton Wistow, Peterborough, PE2 6YH
Tel: 01733 391182
Principal: ICAEW Member
A Chagani

ELWELL WATCHORN & SAXTON LLP
2 Axon Commerce Road, Lynch Wood, Peterborough, PE2 6LR

FRASER GORDON LTD
28 Lornas Field, Hampton Hargate, Peterborough, PE7 8AY

GROSS KLEIN
75 Park Road, Peterborough, PE1 2TN

JASANI & CO
214a Lincoln Road, Peterborough, PE1 2NE
Tel: 01223 245551

KEVIN GUINNESS & CO
Sibberton Lodge, Leicester Road, Thornhaugh, Peterborough PE8 6NH

KEVIN M GLADDERS
40 Gildale, Werrington, Peterborough, PE4 6QY
Tel: 01733 579570
Principal: ICAEW Member
K M Gladders

KSA
26 Priestgate, Peterborough, PE1 1WG

M CRIDLAND & ASSOCIATES
Home Farm, Lilford, Oundle, Peterborough PE8 5SG

MACCALLUM & CO
29a Broadway, Peterborough, PE1 1SQ

MACINTYRE HUDSON LLP ◈
8-12 Priestgate, Peterborough, PE1 1JA
Tel: 01733 568491
Website: http://www.macintyrehudson.co.uk
Resident Partners/Directors: ICAEW Members
S Dodds, I G Jacobs, S J Manning
Regulated by the ICAEW for a range of investment business activities

MARK J RUFFLES & CO
4 Baron Court, Werrington, Peterborough, PE4 7ZE
Tel: 01733 574595
Principal: ICAEW Member
M J Ruffles

MOORE STEPHENS ◈
Rutland House, Minerva Business Park, Lynch Wood, Peterborough PE2 6PZ
Tel: 01733 397300
Resident Partners/Directors: ICAEW Members
M E Lumsden, C A Rossiter, R P S Sandbach

MOORE THOMPSON
Bank Chambers, 27a Market Place, Market Deeping, Peterborough PE6 8EA
Tel: 01778 380 850
Fax: 01778 380757
Website: http://www.moorethompson.co.uk
Resident Partners/Directors: ICAEW Members
M Hildred
Non-resident Partners (Non-ICAEW Members):
M Price, A P Heskin, T Martin, M A East, K Maggs, G Reid, M D Longley
Other Offices: Bank House, Broad Street, Spalding, Lincs PE11 1TB, Monica House, St Augustines Road, Wisbech, Cambs, PE13 3AD

P.T. VAUGHAN
31 Temples Court, Helpston, Peterborough, PE6 7EU

PT & AJV BOOKKEEPING SERVICE
31 Temples Court, Helpston, Peterborough, PE6 7EU

R.A. SPIRES & CO
97 Stonald Road, Whittlesey, Peterborough, PE7 1QP

R.M. RAHIM & CO
164 Lincoln Road, Peterborough, PE1 2NW
Tel: 01733 346900
Principal: ICAEW Member
R M Rahim

RAWLINSONS
Ruthlyn House, 90 Lincoln Road, Peterborough, PE1 2SP
Tel: 01733 568321
Fax: 01733 341358
Email: info@rawlinsons.co.uk
Website: http://www.rawlinsons.co.uk
Training Contracts Available.
Resident Partners/Directors: ICAEW Members
C J Collier, A J Cox, C J Crowley, M A Jackson, G H Jones, K N Woodthorpe
Resident Partners (Non-ICAEW Members):
K P Craig
Registered by the ICAEW to carry out company audit work
Authorised and regulated by the Financial Services Authority for investment business

INVESTOR IN PEOPLE

SPECIALISATIONS – FORENSIC ACCOUNTING
Expert Witnesses in Litigation

RCI
First Floor, 254-256 Lincoln Road, Peterborough, PE1 2ND

RCI (LONDON) LTD
341c Lincoln Road, (First Floor), Peterborough, PE1 2PF

RCI (PETERBOROUGH) LTD
254-256 Lincoln Road, Peterborough, PE1 2ND

RNV LTD
21-23 West Street, Oundle, Peterborough, PE8 4EJ

RONA MACCALLUM
127 Atherstone Avenue, Peterborough, PE3 9UJ

SAFFERY CHAMPNESS ◈
Stuart House, City Road, Peterborough, PE1 1QF
Tel: 01733 353300
Fax: 01733 353301
Website: http://www.saffery.com
Training Contracts Available.
Resident Partners/Directors: ICAEW Members
S R Collins
Resident Partners (Non-ICAEW Members):
J M Hill
Other Offices: Bournemouth, Bristol, Edinburgh, Geneva, Guernsey, Harrogate, High Wycombe, Inverness, London, Manchester
Registered by the ICAEW to carry out company audit work
Regulated by the ICAEW for a range of investment business activities

INVESTOR IN PEOPLE

General Description: See London office entry.

ST JAMES ACCOUNTING
53 Manor Way, Deeping St James, Peterborough, PE6 8PS
Tel: 01778 346328

ST JAMES ACCOUNTING LTD
53 Manor Way, Deeping St James, Peterborough, PE6 8PS
Tel: 01778 346328
Resident Partners/Directors: ICAEW Members
T J Cheesman

STEPHENSON SMART & CO ◈
Stephenson House, 15 Church Walk, Peterborough, PE1 2TP
Tel: 01733 343275
Website: http://www.stephensonsmart.com
Resident Partners/Directors: ICAEW Members
P H Evans, P J Lawson, I Walker, G M Wiles
Resident Partners (Non-ICAEW Members):
R J Burborough, K M Hilliard
Registered by the ICAEW to carry out company audit work
Regulated by the ICAEW for a range of investment business activities

STREETS SOUTHERN LLP ◈
87 Park Road, Peterborough, PE1 2TN
Tel: 01733 312191
Email: info@streetsweb.co.uk
Website: http://www.streetsweb.co.uk
Resident Partners/Directors: ICAEW Members
J Day

TAX MANAGEMENT GROUP
Croft House, East Road, Oundle, Peterborough PE8 4BZ
Tel: 01832 273888

VICTORIA HAYNES
4 Temples Court, Helpston, Peterborough, PE6 7EU

VIGAR & CO LLP ◈
14 Swan Court, Forder Way, Hampton, Peterborough PE7 8GX

PETERSFIELD

A.J. STEED
75 Bell Hill, Petersfield, GU32 2EA
Tel: 01730 233580
Principal: ICAEW Member
A J Steed

ADH CONSULTING
28 Tilmore Road, Petersfield, GU32 2HH

ANTROBUS
Antrobus House, 18 College Street, Petersfield, GU31 4AD

ANTROBUS
Chartered Accountants

ANTROBUS ACCOUNTANTS LTD ◈
Antrobus House, 18 College Street, Petersfield, GU31 4AD
Tel: 01730 234500
Email: info@antrobus.biz
Website: http://www.antrobus.biz
Resident Partners/Directors: ICAEW Members
M F Kirby
Registered by the ICAEW to carry out company audit work

BARTER DURGAN & MUIR LTD ◈
35 Lavant Street, Petersfield, GU32 3EL
Tel: 01730 264951
Fax: 01730 267876
Email: admin@barterdm.co.uk
Website: http://www.barterdm.co.uk
Date Established: 1965
Resident Partners/Directors: ICAEW Members
C Elsey

continued

BARTER DURGAN & MUIR LTD *cont*

Registered by the ICAEW to carry out company audit work

Regulated by the ICAEW for a range of investment business activities

SPECIALISATIONS – AUDIT & ASSURANCE

Audit — Private Company

SPECIALISATIONS – BUSINESS & GENERAL ADVICE

Book-keeping
Company Formation
Company Secretarial Service
Data Processing Services
Management Advice to Business

SPECIALISATIONS – FINANCIAL REPORTING

Accounts Preparation
Limited Company Accounts
Partnership/Sole Trader Accounts

SPECIALISATIONS – INVESTMENT BUSINESS

Financial Planning and Advice

SPECIALISATIONS – IT

Computer Systems and Consultancy

SPECIALISATIONS – TAXATION

Payroll Service and Advice
Taxation
Trusteeship

General Description: Please visit our website for full details of our services.

PETWORTH

JGCA LTD
Yew Tree Cottage, Northchapel, Petworth, GU28 9HL
Tel: 01428 707780
Resident Partners/Directors: ICAEW Members
J M Glover

MELANIE SHEPHERD
1 Vine Cottage, Village Green, Northchapel, Petworth GU28 9HU
Tel: 01428 707016
Principal: ICAEW Member
M G Dickens

TAD CONSULTANCY
41 Valentines Lea, Northchapel, Petworth, GU28 9HY

PEWSEY

CHARLTON BAKER
1 Fordbrook House, Fordbrook Business Center, Marlborough Road, Pewsey SN9 5NU

LINDSELL BUSINESS SOLUTIONS LTD
Roanoke, Easton Royal, Pewsey, SN9 5LS
Tel: 01672 811259
Resident Partners/Directors: ICAEW Members
P E Lindsell

MILTON ACCOUNTING
10 Lawn Farm Close, Milton Lilbourne, Pewsey, SN9 5QA

PICKERING

JOHN F. MCGLINCHEY
1st Floor, Champleys Mews, Market Place, Pickering YO18 7AE

JOHNSONS ACCOUNTANTS LTD
2 Hallgarth, Pickering, YO18 7AW

MOORE STEPHENS
50/51 Hungate, Pickering, YO18 7DG

R. DAVID ANDERSON
West Gables, Westgate, Thornton-le-Dale, Pickering YO18 7SG

PINNER

A C TUCKER & CO ◈
Manor Cottage, 18a Waxwell Lane, Pinner, HA5 3EN
Tel: 020 8429 8690

A C TUCKER & CO LTD
Manor Cottage, 18a Waxwell Lane, Pinner, HA5 3EN
Tel: 020 8429 8690
Resident Partners/Directors: ICAEW Members
Alan Tucker

ACCOUNTANCY SOLUTIONS (LEIGH & CO) LTD
3 Shelbourne Close, Pinner, HA5 3AF

AIMS - JUDE BALLARD
28 Deane Croft Road, Pinner, HA5 1SR

AIMS - NEIL CROSSLAND HINCHLIFFE
16 Devonshire Road, Eastcote, Pinner, HA5 1TX
Tel: 020 8866 3070
Principal: ICAEW Member
N. Crossland-Hinchliffe

AINSLEY SOLOMONS LTD
Suite 2, 40 Compton Rise, Pinner, HA5 5HR

AINSLEYS
Suite 2, 40 Compton Rise, Pinner, HA5 5HR
Tel: 020 8868 1660
Principal: ICAEW Member
M F Schiller

ALEXANDER & CO (ACCOUNTANCY) LTD ◈
5 Pembroke Avenue, Pinner, HA5 1JP
Tel: 020 8866 8276
Resident Partners/Directors: ICAEW Members
S L Alexander

ALEXANDER, MOORE & CO
2nd Floor, Monument House, 215 Marsh Road, Pinner HA5 5NE

ALLCHILD ACCOUNTING LTD
4 Howland Court, 20 The Avenue, Hatch End, Pinner HA5 4ET
Tel: 020 8421 6833
Resident Partners/Directors: ICAEW Members
M B Allchild

ANTHONY M. MYERS & CO
28 West End Avenue, Pinner, HA5 1BJ
Tel: 020 8866 5751
Principal: ICAEW Member
A M Myers

ASHLEY KING LTD
Conex House, 148 Field End Road, Eastcote, Pinner HA5 1RT

B. R. SHETH & CO
15 Rosecroft Walk, Pinner, HA5 1LJ
Tel: 020 8930 7340
Principal: ICAEW Member
Bharat Sheth

BANKIM PATEL & CO LTD
42 Anglesmede Crescent, Pinner, HA5 5SP
Tel: 020 8863 1915
Resident Partners/Directors: ICAEW Members
B C Patel

BLACHER ASSOCIATES ★
Monument House, 215 Marsh Road, Pinner, HA5 5NE
Tel: 020 8429 0444
Resident Partners/Directors: ICAEW Members
A K Thakrar

C.H. SISKIN & CO
Mulberry Cottage, Church Lane, Pinner, HA5 3AA

CASTLE RYCE ★
The Clockhouse, 87 Paines Lane, Pinner, HA5 3BY
Tel: 020 8866 4006
Fax: 020 8866 0270
Resident Partners/Directors: ICAEW Members
S C Shah

CHATOO & CO
22 Sherington Ave, Hatch End, Pinner, HA5 4DT
Tel: 020 8428 4484
Principal: ICAEW Member
S A Chatoo

CLIVE GATES
5 Elmcote, 637 Uxbridge Road, Pinner, HA5 3YZ
Tel: 020 8429 7297
Principal: ICAEW Member
C R Gates

COLEMAN & CO
57 West End Lane, Pinner, HA5 1AH
Tel: 020 8866 4860
Principal: ICAEW Member
N J Coleman

COLLETT SMITH, ELLIOTT & CO
The Old Coach House, 179 Moss Lane, Pinner, HA5 3AL
Tel: 020 8868 3482
Resident Partners/Directors: ICAEW Members
P A Elliott, R T Elliott

COPPERSUN
7 Wynlie Gardens, Pinner, HA5 3TN

COPPERSUN LTD
7 Wynlie Gardens, Pinner, HA5 3TN

DATTANI & CO
47 Hill Road, Pinner, HA5 1LB

DEWANIS ◈
Westbury House, 23-25 Bridge Street, Pinner, HA5 3HR
Tel: 020 8429 3636
Website: http://www.dewanis.co.uk
Principal: ICAEW Member
R K Dewani

DOUGLAS COLLIER
42 Central Avenue, Pinner, HA5 5BS
Tel: 020 8931 8881

DOUGLAS COLLIER LTD
42 Central Avenue, Pinner, HA5 5BS
Tel: 020 8931 8881
Resident Partners/Directors: ICAEW Members
D A Collier

SPECIALISATIONS – TAXATION

Self Assessment Advice

HAYDN HUGHES & CO ★ ◈
52 High Street, Pinner, HA5 5PW
Tel: 020 8426 1230

THE HHC PARTNERSHIP ★ ◈
52 High Street, Pinner, HA5 5PW
Tel: 020 8426 1230
Resident Partners/Directors: ICAEW Members
H P Hughes

HUTCHINSON & CO
3 Scot Grove, Pinner, HA5 4RT

I COUNT LTD
26 Boundary Road, Pinner, HA5 1PN
Tel: 020 8429 4956
Resident Partners/Directors: ICAEW Members
R P Bernstein

IAN HOLLAND + CO
The Clock House, 87 Paines Lane, Pinner, HA5 3BZ

J A S BROWN
87 Love Lane, Pinner, HA5 3EY

JOHN A.S. BROWN FCA
87 Love Lane, Pinner, HA5 3EY

LAWRENCE HURST & CO
2nd Floor, Morritt House, 10/12 Love Lane, Pinner, HA5 3EF
Tel: 020 8429 2959
Principal: ICAEW Member
L D Hurst

LEAT THORN & PARTNERS
64 High View, Pinner, HA5 3PB
Tel: 020 8866 1152
Principal: ICAEW Member
A K Jaitly

LEE ASSOCIATES
30 Malpas Drive, Pinner, HA5 1DQ

LEIGH & CO ◈
3 Shelbourne Close, Pinner, HA5 3AF
Tel: 020 8429 3190
Email: michael@leighandco.co.uk
Website: http://www.leighandco.co.uk
Principal: ICAEW Member
M A Leigh

M.G.H. SANDERS
15 Raisins Hill, Pinner, HA5 2BU
Tel: 020 8866 7985
Principal: ICAEW Member
M G H Sanders

MESSRS W EDWARDS & CO
15 Cedar Drive, Pinner, HA5 4BY

NICHOLSON & CO
Monument House, 215 Marsh Road, Pinner, HA5 5NE
Tel: 020 8429 3555
Resident Partners/Directors: ICAEW Members
F B M Lai Cheong, J R Nicholson

OUTSOURCED ACCOUNTANCY SERVICES LTD
22 Westbury Lodge Close, Pinner, HA5 3FG

P. C. DARUWALLA & CO ◈
4 Raisins Hill, Pinner, HA5 2BS
Tel: 020 8866 2089
Fax: 020 8868 2839
Principal: ICAEW Member
P C Daruwalla
Registered by the ICAEW to carry out company audit work
See display advertisement near this entry.

P G ASSOCIATES
19 Anselm Road, Pinner, HA5 4LH

P G (TAXATION CONSULTANTS) LTD
19 Anselm Road, Hatch End, Pinner, HA5 4LH

R P BRAYSHER
2 High Road, Eastcote, Pinner, HA5 2EW

REED RANSTED
Finance House, 522a Uxbridge Road, Pinner, HA5 3PU

RONNIE DAVIDSON ACCOUNTANCY & TAXATION SERVICES
17 Murray Crescent, Pinner, HA5 3QF
Tel: 020 8868 3664
Principal: ICAEW Member
R E Davidson

RUMFORD & CO
Conex House, 148 Field End Road, Eastcote, Pinner HA5 1RT
Tel: 020 8866 1991
Resident Partners/Directors: ICAEW Members
M A M Sharkey, E Vangelatos

S. RAY & CO ◈
52 Royston Park Road, Hatch End, Pinner, HA5 4AF
Tel: 020 8428 0311
Principal: ICAEW Member
S Rai

SARGENT & CO
37 Albury Drive, Pinner, HA5 3RL

SMR ASSOCIATES ◈
25 Woodhall Gate, Pinner, HA5 4TN
Tel: 020 8429 4844
Resident Partners/Directors: ICAEW Members
S M Ruback

SOBELL RHODES ◈
Monument House, 215 Marsh Road, Pinner, HA5 5NE

STANTONS
11 Ferndown Close, Hatch End, Pinner, HA5 3RP

SULTAN BUSINESS MANAGEMENT LTD
Elm Point, East End Way, Pinner, HA5 3BS

T. CASILLAS & CO
27 St Lawrence Drive, Eastcote, Pinner, HA5 2RL

THOMAS NEILSON
108 Catlins Lane, Pinner, HA5 2BX

VICTOR DAVIS & CO
Horning Reach, Royston Park Road, Hatch End, Pinner HA5 4AD

PLYMOUTH

ATKEY GOODMAN ◈
Prudence House, Ashleigh Way, Langage Business Park, Plymouth PL7 5JX
Tel: 01752 334990
Fax: 01752 334991
Email: office@atkey-goodman.co.uk
Website: http://www.atkey-goodman.co.uk
Resident Partners/Directors: ICAEW Members
S D Donovan, S C Morgan
Resident Partners (Non-ICAEW Members):
S G Heath
Registered by the ICAEW to carry out company audit work
Regulated by the ICAEW for a range of investment business activities

BATTERBEE THOMPSON & CO LTD ◈
7 Staddiscombe Road, Staddiscombe, Plymouth, PL9 9NA

BEGBIES TRAYNOR LTD
Princess Court, 23 Princess Street, Plymouth, PL1 2EX
Tel: 01752 252277

BISHOP FLEMING ◈
Cobourg House, Mayflower Street, Plymouth, PL1 1LG
Tel: 01752 262611
Website: http://www.bishopfleming.co.uk
Resident Partners/Directors: ICAEW Members
R G Davey, C P Thomson, P W A Tuckett

BROMHEAD
Harscombe House, 1 Darklake View, Estover, Plymouth PL6 7TL
Tel: 01752 221057
Email: office@bromheadco.co.uk
Website: http://www.bromheadco.co.uk
Resident Partners/Directors: ICAEW Members
L Curtis, J A Groves, P J B Hamon

CAT ACCOUNTING SERVICES
50 Great Woodford Drive, Plympton, Plymouth, PL7 4RL

CONDY MATHIAS ★
6 Houndiscombe Road, Plymouth, PL4 6HH

DAVID PINDER & CO
Woodford Lodge, 70 Larkham Lane, Woodford, Plymouth PL7 4PL

DAVID RICE & CO
117 The Ridgeway, Plymouth, PL7 2AA

DAVID RICE & COMPANY LTD
22 Queen Anne Terrace, North Hill, Plymouth, PL4 8EG
Tel: 01752 669975
Resident Partners/Directors: ICAEW Members
D A Rice, P M Webb
Registered by the ICAEW to carry out company audit work
Regulated by the ICAEW for a range of investment business activities

DAVID RICE & COMPANY LTD
117 Ridgeway, Plymouth, PL7 2AA
Tel: 01752 348834
Registered by the ICAEW to carry out company audit work
Regulated by the ICAEW for a range of investment business activities

ELIZABETH HENWOOD
9 Tor Crescent, Plymouth, PL3 5TW

FINDLAY JAMES
1 Addison Road, North Hill, Plymouth, PL4 8LL

FRANCES A HAYNES
1 Church Hill Road, Hooe, Plymouth, PL9 9SE
Tel: 01752 249712
Principal: ICAEW Member
F A Haynes

FRANCIS CLARK ◈
North Quay House, Sutton Harbour, Plymouth, PL4 0RA
Tel: 01752 301010
Website: http://www.francisclark.co.uk
Resident Partners/Directors: ICAEW Members
I L Burnard, N S Cowen, C D Evans, M A Greaves, P H Lowson
Resident Partners (Non-ICAEW Members):
G P Fox, G D Hutchings
Authorised and regulated by the Financial Services Authority for investment business
General Description: Largest independent firm in the South West, with particular strengths in taxation, VAT, corporate finance, financial planning, forensic accounting, IT and insolvency.

FRANKLINS ACCOUNTANTS LTD
Astor House, 2 Alexandra Road, Mutley Plain, Plymouth PL4 7JR

FRANKLINS ACCOUNTANTS LLP
Astor House, 2 Alexandra Road, Mutley Plain, Plymouth PL4 7JR

FUTURE FIRST
PO Box 132, Plymouth, PL7 1WP

FUTURE FIRST FINANCIAL SOLUTIONS LTD
PO Box 132, Plymouth, PL7 1WP

G J KIRK LIP
6 The Crescent, Plymouth, PL1 3AB

GEOFFREY ROGERS ◈
37 The Millfields, Stonehouse, Plymouth, PL1 3JB

GEOFFREY W. PILLAR & CO
Erme House, Station Road, Plympton, Plymouth PL7 2AU

GRINTER JOHNSON LTD
23 Lockyer Street, Plymouth, PL1 2QZ

H.M. WILLIAMS
Valley House, 53 Valley Road, Plympton, Plymouth PL7 1RF
Tel: 01752 334950
Resident Partners/Directors: ICAEW Members
T J Smith, H M Williams

HAROLD DUCKWORTH & CO
41 Houndiscombe Road, Mutley, Plymouth, PL4 6EX

JONESGILES LTD
Peverell Corner, 246 Peverell Park Road, Plymouth, PL3 4QG

KPMG LLP
Plym House, 3 Longbridge Road, Marsh Mills, Plymouth PL6 8LT
Tel: 01752 632100
Resident Partners/Directors: ICAEW Members
I J Brokenshire

LISA LOWE LTD
The Lodge, 149 Mannamead Road, Plymouth, PL3 5NU
Tel: 01752 768415
Resident Partners/Directors: ICAEW Members
L R Lowe

MARC LAWSON & CO LTD
Unit 7, Brooklands, Budshead Road, Plymouth PL6 5XR

MARK HOLT & CO LTD
Marine Building, Victoria Wharf, Plymouth, PL4 0RF

NEVILLE & CO
10-11 Lynher Buildings, Queen Anne Battery, Plymouth, PL4 0LP
Tel: 01752 672288
Principal: ICAEW Member
R P Neville

NIGEL WEBSTER & CO LTD ◈
129 North Hill, Plymouth, PL4 8JY
Tel: 01752 670066
Resident Partners/Directors: ICAEW Members
A J McSweeny, N B Webster

PARKHURST HILL
Torrington Chambers, 58 North Road East, Plymouth, PL4 6AJ
Tel: 01752 666601
Fax: 01752 666612
Email: ca@parkhurst-hill.co.uk
Website: http://www.parkhurst-hill.co.uk
Resident Partners/Directors: ICAEW Members
K S Clay, L Price, P D Stapleton, D B Tromans, P W Whitby
Registered by the ICAEW to carry out company audit work
Regulated by the ICAEW for a range of investment business activities

SPECIALISATIONS – BUSINESS & GENERAL ADVICE
Europe

SPECIALISATIONS – SECTOR
Charities
Dentists/Opticians
Doctors
Electronics
Estate Agents
Solicitors

SPECIALISATIONS – TAXATION
Estate and Inheritance
Estate Planning

See display advertisement near this entry.

PRICEWATERHOUSE-COOPERS
Princess Court, 23 Princess Street, Plymouth, PL1 2EX

PRICEWATERHOUSE-COOPERS LLP
Princess Court, 23 Princess Street, Plymouth, PL1 2EX
Tel: 01752 267441
Resident Partners/Directors: ICAEW Members
F D Drake

RILEY ◈
51 North Hill, Plymouth, PL4 8HZ
Tel: 01752 203640
Resident Partners/Directors: ICAEW Members

B E Constantine, V P Doyle, D G Powell, J Stacey

SHEPPARDS ACCOUNTANTS LTD
34 Mary Seacole Road, Plymouth, PL1 3JY

SOUND ACCOUNTING
23 Lockyer Road, Mannamead, Plymouth, PL3 4RL

STEPHEN SHAW ACCOUNTANCY SERVICES LTD
9 Blue Haze Close, Plymouth, PL6 7HR

SUSAN HINCHLIFFE & CO LTD ◈
4 Newton Close, Newton Ferrers, Plymouth, PL8 1AL
Tel: 01752 872667
Resident Partners/Directors: ICAEW Members
S J Hinchliffe

TACTICAL TAX PLANNING LTD ◈
53 Inchkeith Road, Plymouth, PL6 6EJ
Tel: 01752 775515
Resident Partners/Directors: ICAEW Members
P Kent

TAXASSIST ACCOUNTANTS ◈
City Business Park, Somerset Place, Plymouth, PL3 4BB
Tel: 01752 551888
Resident Partners/Directors: ICAEW Members
A E Smith

TONY JOPSON & CO
246 Peverell Park Road, Peverell, Plymouth, PL3 4QG

TONY JOPSON & CO LTD
246 Peverell Park Road, Peverell, Plymouth, PL3 4QG
Tel: 01752 775068
Fax: 01752 794876
Email: tony@tonyjopson.co.uk
Website: http://www.tonyjopson.co.uk
Resident Partners/Directors: ICAEW Members
Anthony Jopson
SPECIALISATIONS – BUSINESS RECOVERY & INSOLVENCY
Liquidations

TURNBULL & CO ACCOUNTANTS LTD
Pilgrim House, Oxford Place, Plymouth, PL1 5AJ

POLEGATE

ROWLAND SMITH
46 High Street, Polegate, BN26 6AG

S.J. PICKUP & CO LTD
Long Acre, Milton Street, Polegate, BN26 5RW
Tel: 01323 870425
Resident Partners/Directors: ICAEW Members
L Hughes

PONTEFRACT

D & J RANDLES LTD
Suite 1, 18a Ropergate, Pontefract, WF8 1LP

EMMA J SONIA BSC(HONS) ACA
13 Tarn Hows Walk, Ackworth, Pontefract, WF7 7QS

HBH
15 Ropergate End, Pontefract, WF8 1JT
Tel: 01977 703343
Email: office@h-b-h.co.uk
SPECIALISATIONS – SECTOR
Clubs/Associations

HOLMES BEAUMONT & HOLROYD
15 Ropergate End, Pontefract, WF8 1JT
Tel: 01977 703343
Email: office@h-b-h.co.uk
Resident Partners/Directors: ICAEW Members
K Bramwell, M K Brooke
SPECIALISATIONS – SECTOR
Clubs/Associations

LOFTHOUSE & CO
36 Ropergate, Pontefract, WF8 1LY

RICHARD A. PEPPER
39 Cricketers Close, Ackworth, Pontefract, WF7 7PW
Tel: 01977 615003
Principal: ICAEW Member
R A Pepper

TOWNENDS ★
7-9 Cornmarket, Pontefract, WF8 1AN
Tel: 01977 703357
Resident Partners/Directors: ICAEW Members
T J Maeer, J P Shand, J Williamson

TOWNENDS ACCOUNTANTS LTD
7-9 Cornmarket, Pontefract, WF8 1AN
Tel: 01977 703357
Resident Partners/Directors: ICAEW Members
J P Shand

POOLE

A.G. MINNS
20 Charlotte Close, Poole, BH12 5HR

ACCOUNTING FOR CHARITIES LTD
Arena, Holyrood Close, Poole, BH17 7BA

ADDICUS ◈
1 Winchester Place, North Street, Poole, BH15 1NX

ALLAN BROWNE
34 Frankland Crescent, Parkstone, Poole, BH14 9PX

BALMER & CO ◈
279 Ashley Road, Parkstone, Poole, BH14 9DS

BRETT PITTWOOD
Suite 8, Bourne Gate, 25 Bourne Valley Road, Poole BH12 1DY

BRETT PITTWOOD LTD
Suite 8, Bourne Gate, 25 Bourne Valley Road, Poole BH12 1DY

CGJ PARTNERSHIP ◈
Tower House, Parkstone Road, Poole, BH15 2JH
Tel: 01202 678555
Resident Partners/Directors: ICAEW Members
J S Baker, A R Hill

CLAYTONS
28 Nansen Avenue, Poole, BH15 3DB
Tel: 01202 684371
Principal: ICAEW Member
N E Clayton

D.J. BARNES
6 Cherry Hill Grove, Upton, Poole, BH16 5LP
Tel: 01202 623533
Principal: ICAEW Member
D J D Barnes

D M LINELL & CO
38 Sandbanks Road, Poole, BH14 8BX

EDWARD FRIEL & CO LTD ◈
James House, 40 Lagland Street, Poole, BH15 1QG
Tel: 01202 682355
Resident Partners/Directors: ICAEW Members
E J Friel

H.J. SMITH
9 Western Avenue, Branksome Park, Poole, BH13 7AL

LAWRENCE & CO PROFESSIONAL LTD
52 Parkstone Road, Poole, BH15 2PU
Tel: 01202 679066

MAZARS CORPORATE FINANCE LTD ◈
8 New Fields, 2 Stinsford Road, Nuffield, Poole BH17 0NF
Tel: 01202 680777

MAZARS LLP ◈
8 New Fields, 2 Stinsford Road, Nuffield, Poole BH17 0NF
Tel: 01202 680777
Resident Partners/Directors: ICAEW Members
A J Baxendine, L J Fox, B P Hutchinson, G J Platts, A Simpson
Registered by the ICAEW to carry out company audit work
Authorised and regulated by the Financial Services Authority for investment business

MERVYN BRIGHT
4 Hatherden Avenue, Parkstone, Poole, BH14 0PJ

MICHAEL PEACOCK ACA
62 Charborough Close, Lytchett Matravers, Poole, BH16 6DH

MORRIS LANE & CO ◈
Jonsen House, 43 Commercial Rd, Poole, BH14 0HU
Tel: 01202 715950
Email: mail@morrislane.co.uk
Website: http://www.morrislane.co.uk
Training Contracts Available.
Resident Partners/Directors: ICAEW Members
R P Morris
Resident Partners (Non-ICAEW Members):
C M Tullett
Registered by the ICAEW to carry out company audit work
Regulated by the ICAEW for a range of investment business activities

NORTHPOINT ACCOUNTANTS
Parkstone Bay Marina, Turks Lane, Poole, BH14 8EW

OCEAN (RA) LTD
Suite 6, Bourne Gate, Bourne Valley Road, Poole BH12 1DZ

OCEAN REGISTERED AUDITOR
Suite 6 Bourne Gate, Bourne Valley Road, Poole, BH12 1DZ

PAUL L COLLINS A.C.A
89 Canford Cliffs Road, Poole, BH13 7EW

PAUL W. MAHER & CO
Oakley House, 46 Old Pound Close, Lytchett Matravers, Poole BH16 6BW

PEATS ★
Canford House, Discovery Court, 551-553 Wallisdown Road, Poole BH12 5AG
Tel: 01202 853 226
Fax: 01202 853244
Email: nickpeat@peatsaccountants.co.uk
Resident Partners/Directors: ICAEW Members
N J Peat
Individual(s) licensed for insolvency work by the ICAEW
See display advertisement near this entry.

PETER LUCAS & CO
54 Pilsdon Drive, Canford Heath, Poole, BH17 9HS

PRINCECROFT WILLIS LLP
Towngate House, 2-8 Parkstone Road, Poole, BH15 2PW
Tel: 01202 663600
Fax: 01202 663601
Website: http://www.princecroftwillis.co.uk
Resident Partners/Directors: ICAEW Members
M C C Aitchison, A M Alder, J Belinger, C B Hinwood, S J Hough, M A Johns, W J Law, A J Raymond, J I Robinson, C Rusden, D K Watton
Non-resident Partners (ICAEW Members):
A N Bunston, N J Love, A M Gates
Resident Partners (Non-ICAEW Members):
M Aldridge, J Smith
Other Offices: The George Business Centre, Christchurch Road, New Milton, BH25 6QJ
Registered by the ICAEW to carry out company audit work
Regulated by the ICAEW for a range of investment business activities

PRUE MITCHELL
130 Canford Cliffs Road, Poole, BH13 7ER

PUGSLEY REVILL ★ ◈
2 Kings Crescent, Lower Parkstone, Poole, BH14 9PR

QUAY
Suite 6 Bourne Gate, Bourne Valley Road, Poole, BH12 1DZ

QUAY ACCOUNTING
Suite 6 Bourne Gate, Bourne Valley Road, Poole, BH12 1DZ

QUAY ACCOUNTING LTD
Suite 6, Bourne Gate, Bourne Valley Road, Poole BH12 1DY

R. THOMPSON & CO
6 Worthington Crescent, Poole, BH14 8BW
Tel: 01202 749203
Principal: ICAEW Member
R Thompson

RILEY PARTNERSHIP LTD
25 Hill Street, Poole, BH15 1NR

ROTHMAN PANTALL & CO
52 Parkstone Rd, Poole, BH15 2PU

SUFRAZ & CO
13 Newton Road, Canford Cliffs, Poole, BH13 7EX

T.R. HAMMOND
3 Harbour Hill Road, Poole, BH15 3PX
Tel: 01202 665888
Principal: ICAEW Member
T R Hammond

URBAN ACCOUNTANCY
20 Alverton Avenue, Poole, BH15 2QG
Tel: 01202 747901
Website: http://www.urbanaccountancy.co.uk
Principal: ICAEW Member
H C Urban

W.M.J. POPE
54 Kings Avenue, Parkstone, Poole, BH14 9QJ

WHEATLEY PEARCE LTD
11 Winchester Place, North Street, Poole, BH15 1NX
Tel: 01202 673344
Email: ken@wheatleypearce.co.uk
Resident Partners/Directors: ICAEW Members
G P Bemment, K L Butcher

PORTSMOUTH

CW FELLOWES LTD
Carnac Place, Cams Hall Estate, Fareham, Portsmouth PO1 2QF
Tel: 01329 220554
Resident Partners/Directors: ICAEW Members
P G Blades, D E Dodd

DAVID BAILEY
28 Landport Terrace, Portsmouth, PO1 2RG
Tel: 02392 824242
Email: wendy@davidbailey.co.uk
Website: http://www.davidbailey.co.uk
Date Established: 1976
Resident Partners/Directors: ICAEW Members
W E Hodgson
Registered by the ICAEW to carry out company audit work

SPECIALISATIONS – IT
Computerised Accounting Systems

SPECIALISATIONS – TAXATION
Payroll Service and Advice
Small Traders

DAVIS LOMBARD
22 The Slipway, Marina Keep, Port Solent, Portsmouth PO6 4TR

DAVIS LOMBARD (UK) LTD
22 The Slipway, Port Solent, Portsmouth, PO6 4TR

ENCY ASSOCIATES ★
Printware Court, Cumberland Business Centre, Northumberland Road, Portsmouth PO5 1DS

EVANS, WEIR
155 Havant Road, Drayton, Portsmouth, PO6 2AA

GEOFFREY N. BARNES
12 Fratton Road, Portsmouth, PO1 5BX
Tel: 02392 861456
Fax: 02392 838712
Email: enquiries@geoffreynbarnes.co.uk
Resident Partners/Directors: ICAEW Members
G N Barnes
Resident Partners (Non-ICAEW Members):
M G Wilson

HWCA LTD ◈
Holbrook Court, Cumberland Business Centre, Northumberland Road, Portsmouth PO5 1DS
Tel: 02392 815342
Email: portsmouth@hwca.com
Resident Partners/Directors: ICAEW Members
G R Beer, Z Hogg, M P Middleton

JACKSON & GREEN
173 London Road, North End, Portsmouth, PO2 9AE

JACKSON GREEN CARTER LTD
6 Cumberland Gate, Portsmouth, PO5 1AS
Tel: 02392 756863
Resident Partners/Directors: ICAEW Members
M A C Carter

JONATHAN SANDS ASSOCIATES LTD
12 Fratton Road, Portsmouth, PO1 5BX

KSL
8 Spur Road, Cosham, Portsmouth, PO6 3EB

LEONARD GOLD ◈
24 Landport Terrace, Portsmouth, PO1 2RG
Tel: 02392 829525
Website: http://www.lgold.co.uk
Resident Partners/Directors: ICAEW Members
A Chapman, S B Howarth
Resident Partners (Non-ICAEW Members):
J Watts, N I Khan
Registered by the ICAEW to carry out company audit work
Authorised and regulated by the Financial Services Authority for investment business

MENZIES LLP ◈
Fairfield House, Kingston Crescent, Portsmouth, PO2 8AA

MORLEY AND SCOTT
The Old Treasury, 7 Kings Road, Portsmouth, PO5 4DJ
Tel: 02392 754820
Resident Partners/Directors: ICAEW Members
A K Sainsbury

MORLEY AND SCOTT CORPORATE SERVICES ◈
The Old Treasury, 7 Kings Road, Portsmouth, PO5 4DJ
Tel: 02392 754820
Fax: 02392 730694
Email: ms@morleyandscott.co.uk
Website: http://www.morleyandscott.co.uk
Authorised and regulated by the Financial Services Authority for investment business

MORRIS PALMER (HANTS) LTD
173 London Road, North End, Portsmouth, PO2 9AE

MORRIS PALMER (PORTSMOUTH) LTD
173 London Road, North End, Portsmouth, PO2 9AE

ROTHMAN PANTALL & CO
88 Northern Road, Cosham, Portsmouth, PO6 3ER

ROTHMAN PANTALL & CO ◈
10 Landport Terrace, Portsmouth, PO1 2RG
Tel: 02392 823777
Fax: 02392 824482
Website: http://www.rothman-pantall.co.uk
Resident Partners/Directors: ICAEW Members
T D Stocker

SPECIALISATIONS – AUDIT & ASSURANCE
Audit — Private Company

SPECIALISATIONS – TAXATION
Taxation

THE TAYLOR COCKS PARTNERSHIP LTD ◈
3 Acorn Business Centre, Northharbour Road, Cosham, Portsmouth PO6 3TH
Tel: 0870 770 8111
Website: http://www.theaccountants.co.uk
Resident Partners/Directors: ICAEW Members
S M Cocks, D G Stathopoulos, P N Taylor

SPECIALISATIONS – AUDIT & ASSURANCE
Audit
Audit — Private Company

SPECIALISATIONS – BUSINESS & GENERAL ADVICE
Book-keeping
Management Advice to Business
Management Consultancy

SPECIALISATIONS – FINANCIAL REPORTING
Accounts Preparation
Limited Company Accounts

SPECIALISATIONS – SECTOR
Doctors
Solicitors

SPECIALISATIONS – TAXATION
Estate and Inheritance
Investigations
Taxation

TENON LTD
Technopole, Kingston Crescent, Portsmouth, PO2 8FA
Tel: 02392 658331

TONY COLE & CO
227 London Road, North End, Portsmouth, PO2 9AJ
Tel: 02392 649887
Principal: ICAEW Member
A M Cole

POTTERS BAR

ACCOUNTANCY PLUS PLUS LTD
9 Parkfield View, Potters Bar, EN6 1US
Tel: 01707 651400
Resident Partners/Directors: ICAEW Members
L M Sycamore

B.J. TUTIN & CO
141 Ashwood Road, Potters Bar, EN6 2QD
Tel: 01707 657638
Principal: ICAEW Member
B J Tutin

CAPER GITTINS
28 Mount Grace Road, Potters Bar, EN6 1RD

CAPES GITTINS LTD
28 Mount Grace Road, Potters Bar, EN6 1RD

DKS
30a Station Road, Cuffley, Potters Bar, EN6 4HE

GARLANDS
6 Oakroyd Close, Potters Bar, EN6 2EW

GARLANDS LTD
6 Oakroyd Avenue, Potters Bar, EN6 2EH
Tel: 01707 661740
Resident Partners/Directors: ICAEW Members
R Gadhvi

GEORGE BATES CONSULTANCY
79 Tempest Avenue, Potters Bar, EN6 5LD

GJH ACCOUNTANCY AND TAXATION SERVICES ◈
Five Ways, 57-59 Hatfield Road, Potters Bar, EN6 1HS

GJH ACCOUNTANTS LTD
Fiveways, 57-59 Hatfield Road, Potters Bar, EN6 1HS

GJH ACCOUNTANTS & TAXATION SERVICES ◈
Five Ways, 57-59 Hatfield Road, Potters Bar, EN6 1HS
Tel: 01707 855000
Email: gary@gjhaccountants.co.uk

HOBDAY & CO
35A High Street, Potters Bar, EN6 5AJ
Tel: 01707 649008
Fax: 01707 649041
Resident Partners/Directors: ICAEW Members
H E Hobday, P C Hobday
Registered by the ICAEW to carry out company audit work

LIBRA
30 St Vincents Way, Potters Bar, EN6 2RF

MARK THORNLEY ASSOCIATES
3 Wain Close, Little Heath, Potters Bar, EN6 1NF

MARTYN BRADISH
31 Dugdale Hill Lane, Potters Bar, EN6 2DP
Tel: 01707 850969
Principal: ICAEW Member
M H S Bradish

MICHAEL B TEMPLE
56 Allandale Crescent, Potters Bar, EN6 2JZ

MICHAEL F KEEVIL
Park House, 10 Osborne Road, Potters Bar, EN6 1RZ

NICOLAOU & CO
25 Heath Drive, Potters Bar, EN6 1EN

PETER C. YATES
100 Baker Street, Potters Bar, EN6 2EP
Tel: 01707 643340
Principal: ICAEW Member
P C Yates

ROY JOSEPH & CO ◈
Oakfield House, 22 Church Road, Potters Bar, EN6 1ET
Tel: 01707 852785
Principal: ICAEW Member
R J Medayil

SOUTHAM & CO
23 Penshurst Road, Potters Bar, EN6 5JR

POULTON-LE-FYLDE

THE BECKETT PARTNERSHIP LLP
Beckett House, Sovereign Court, Wyrefields, Poulton Industrial Estate, Poulton-Le-Fylde FY6 8JX

BLEAZARD K
5 Chapel Street, Poulton-le-fylde, FY6 7BQ
Tel: 01253 886775
Principal: ICAEW Member
K Bleazard

J.D. MERCER & CO
9 Chapel Street, Poulton-le-fylde, FY6 7BQ

STAFFORD THURSZ ◈
Cavendish House, Clarke Street, Poulton-Le-Fylde, FY6 8JW
Tel: 01253 899989
Principal: ICAEW Member
R T Stafford

PRENTON

ANDREW R LOVELADY
50 Tollemache Road, Prenton, CH43 8SZ
Tel: 0151 224 1720
Principal: ICAEW Member
A R Lovelady

COOKS
Kingsmead, Upton Rd, Prenton, CH43 7QQ

JAN MCDERMOTT & CO LTD
The Office, Village Road, Prenton, CH43 5SR
Tel: 0845 900 0691
Resident Partners/Directors: ICAEW Members
J S McDermott

K. CLIFFORD COOK
Kingsmead, Upton Road, Prenton, CH43 7QQ

PRESCOT

DAVID W. ADAMS
12 Epping Close, Rainhill, Prescot, L35 0QE
Tel: 0151 289 9724
Principal: ICAEW Member
D W Adams

GKB ◈
13/15 Atherton Street, Prescot, L34 5QN
Tel: 0151 493 9700
Principal: ICAEW Member
G Butterworth

JONATHAN FORD & CO LTD
The Coach House, 31 View Road, Rainhill, Prescot L35 0LF
Tel: 0151 426 4512
Resident Partners/Directors: ICAEW Members
J R Ford

MADDOCKS & GAMBLE LTD
Claren House, 12 Warrington Road, Prescot, L34 5RB

SERGENTS ◈
4 Leyland Street, Prescot, L34 5QP
Tel: 0151 431 2060
Fax: 0151 431 0065
Email: mail@sergents.co.uk
Website: http://www.sergents.co.uk
Training Contracts Available.
Principal: ICAEW Member
A W Sergent
Registered by the ICAEW to carry out company audit work
Regulated by the ICAEW for a range of investment business activities
SPECIALISATIONS – SECTOR
Food Industry
Hotels/Public Houses
Leisure Industry
Schools

TAX RIGHT
35 Montgomery Close, Whiston, Knowsley, Prescot, L35 3RD
Tel: 0151 426 2952
Principal: ICAEW Member
G Wilkinson

PRESTON

A I CHERRY LTD
26 Winckley Square, Preston, PR1 3JJ
Tel: 01772 201015
Resident Partners/Directors: ICAEW Members
A I Cherry

AINSWORTH & CO
19 Sandringham Park Drive, New Longton, Preston, PR4 4ZS

AINSWORTH ACCOUNTANTS LTD
19 Sandringham Park Drive, New Longton, Preston, PR4 4ZS

BARBARA M THOMPSON FCCA ★
Summerdale, Head Dyke Lane, Pilling, Preston PR3 6SJ

BEGBIES TRAYNOR LTD
1 Winckley Court, Chapel Street, Preston, PR1 8BU
Tel: 01772 202000
Website: http://www.begbies-traynor.com
Resident Partners (Non-ICAEW Members):
D Acland, S Williams
SPECIALISATIONS – BUSINESS RECOVERY & INSOLVENCY
Bankruptcies
Corporate Recovery
Liquidations

BIRKINSHAW RAVEN ★ ◈
54a Lightfoot Lane, Fulwood, Preston, PR2 3LR
Tel: 01772 860269
Resident Partners/Directors: ICAEW Members
C S Birkinshaw

BOLLAND ASSOCIATES
8 Camden Place, Preston, PR1 3JL

BOND PARTNERS LLP
Feather House, 1st Floor, 18-20 Berry Lane, Longridge, Preston PR3 3JA

BROOKS & CO
25 Chapel Brow, Leyland, Preston, PR25 3NH

CAMERON VALENTINE LTD ◈
Unit 2, Ferry Road Office Park, Ferry Road, Riversway, Preston PR2 2YH

CAROLE WALKER
47 Brookdale, New Longton, Preston, PR4 4XL

CHAMPION ACCOUNTANTS LLP
4 Nile Close, Nelson Court Business Centre, Riversway, Preston PR2 2XU

CHAMPION STOKES LTD
4 Nile Close, Nelson Court Business Centre, Riversway, Preston PR2 2XU
Tel: 01772 735000
Email: preston@champion-accountants.co.uk
Website: http://www.champion-accountants.co.uk
Resident Partners/Directors: ICAEW Members
G Cosgrove, J Stokes, D A T Wood
Other Offices: Manchester, Southport, Chester, Blackpool

CRYSTAL SECURITIES PRACTICE LTD
Park House, 17 Moor Park Avenue, Preston, PR1 6AS

DAVID R HAZZARD FCA
Dobsons Farm, Sandygate Lane, Broughton, Preston PR3 5LA
Tel: 01772 862161
Principal: ICAEW Member
D R Hazzard

DAVID SORRELL & CO ◈
10a Station Road, Kirkham, Preston, PR4 2AS
Tel: 01772 684618

DAVIES & CRANE
5 Winckley St, Preston, PR1 2AA
Tel: 01772 253656
Email: acs@daviesandcrane.co.uk
Website: http://www.daviesandcrane.co.uk
Resident Partners/Directors: ICAEW Members
R Siddle, J E Stopyra

DOW SCHOFIELD WATTS LLP
Preston Technology Centre, Marsh Lane, Preston, PR1 8UQ

DUNNE & PILKINGTON LTD ◈
135 Towngate, Leyland, Preston, PR25 2LH
Tel: 01772 424255
Resident Partners/Directors: ICAEW Members
C B Pilkington, S Pilkington

ELECTSPACE LTD
Thomas House, Meadowcroft Business Park, Pope Lane, Whitestake, Preston PR4 4AZ

EVOLVEMENT
12 The Vinery, New Longton, Preston, PR4 4YB

FEELEY & CO
11 Glenpark Drive, Hesketh Bank, Preston, PR4 6TA
Tel: 01772 814735
Principal: ICAEW Member
M J E Cookson

FOSTER & CO
80 Lytham Road, Fulwood, Preston, PR2 3AQ

FOSTER & CO LTD
80 Lytham Road, Fulwood, Preston, PR2 3AQ

FRANK BENSON
199 Carr Lane, Tarleton, Preston, PR4 6BY

GARY COTTAM ASSOCIATES LTD
Rural Business Centre, Myerscough College, Myerscough Hall, St Michaels Road, Bilsborrow, Preston PR3 0RY

GPS ACCOUNTING SERVICES
172 Croston Road, Farington Moss, Leyland, Preston, PR26 6PQ
Tel: 01772 468010
Principal: ICAEW Member
G P Snape

HALEYS
Thomas House, Pope Lane, Whitestake, Preston PR4 4AZ

HANLEY & CO LTD
33 Foxwood Drive, Kirkham, Preston, PR4 2DS
Tel: 01772 673377

HAYES & CO
St Andrews House, 3 Tarleton Office Park, Windgate, Tarleton, Preston PR4 6JF

HINDOCHA & CO
19 Harewood Road, Deepdale, Preston, PR1 6XH
Tel: 01772 653313
Principal: ICAEW Member
A D Hindocha

Chartered Accountants

HWCA LTD ◈
120-124 Towngate, Leyland, Preston, PR25 2LQ
Tel: 01772 431233
Website: http://www.hwca.com/preston
Resident Partners/Directors: ICAEW Members
P C Newsham

JAMES TODD & CO
Greenbank House, 141 Adelphi Street, Preston, PR1 7BH
Tel: 01772 251653
Fax: 01772 883595
Email: accountants@jamestodd.co.uk
Website: http://www.jamestodd.co.uk
Resident Partners/Directors: ICAEW Members
R H Brain, J E Standing, J R Stirrup
SPECIALISATIONS – BUSINESS & GENERAL ADVICE
Management Advice to Business
SPECIALISATIONS – TAXATION
Taxation

JOHN V. BARTON
29 Garstang Road, Preston, PR1 1LA
Tel: 01772 257510
Principal: ICAEW Member
J V Barton

JOHN V. BARTON
69a Liverpool Road, Penwortham, Preston, PR1 9XD
Tel: 01772 748098

KPMG LLP
Edward VII Quay, Navigation Way, Ashton-on-Ribble, Preston PR2 2YF
Tel: 01772 722822
Resident Partners/Directors: ICAEW Members
S Hunter, M Newsholme

MCDADE ROBERTS ◈
BTC House, Chapel Hill, Longridge, Preston PR3 1JY
Tel: 01772 786858

MCDADE ROBERTS
65 Church Street, Garstang, Preston, PR3 1YA

MCDADE ROBERTS
316 Blackpool Road, Preston, PR2 3AE
Tel: 01772 717110
Resident Partners/Directors: ICAEW Members
K R Carey, J A Roberts

MICHAEL CROSTON
33 Black Bull Lane, Fulwood, Preston, PR2 3PX
Tel: 01772 719354
Principal: ICAEW Member
M J Croston

MICHAEL J. GORNALL
The Office at Woodcroft, 6 Byerworth Lane North, Garstang, Preston PR3 1QA
Tel: 01995 600029
Resident Partners/Directors: ICAEW Members
M J Gornall

MICHAEL JOHNSON
Hunters Green, Short Lane, Goosnargh, Preston PR3 2JN

MONTPELIER AUDIT LTD
Capital House, 8 Pittman Court, Pittman Way, Fulwood, Preston PR2 9ZG

MONTPELIER PROFESSIONAL (LANCASHIRE) LTD
Charter House, Pittman Way, Fulwood, Preston PR2 9ZD

MOORE & SMALLEY LLP ◈
Richard House, 9 Winckley Square, Preston, PR1 3HP
Tel: 01772 821021
Website: http://www.mooreandsmalley.co.uk
Date Established: 1892
Resident Partners/Directors: ICAEW Members
D A Bennett, M J Briggs, D K Gill, S W Hinnigan, D M Ingram, R A Kenmare, I D Macgregor, T Medcalf, M E Proudfoot, R E Salter, J S Treadwell, D J Walmsley, C A Wilson
Other Offices: Fyde House, Skyways Commerical Campus, Blackpool, Lancashire, FY4 2RP (Tel: 01253 404404), Kendal House, Murley Moss Business Village, Kendal, Cumbria, LA9 7RL
(Tel: 01539 729727), Priory Close, St Mary's Gate, Lancaster, LA1 1XB
(Tel: 01524 62801)

NEIL WALTON ACCOUNTANCY SERVICES
12 The Green, Churchtown, Preston, PR3 0HS

OX SYSTEMS
19 Sandringham Park Drive, New Longton, Preston, PR4 4ZS

P M BROWN & CO
37 Haighton Drive, Fulwood, Preston, PR2 9LU

P M BROWN & COMPANY LTD
37 Haighton Drive, Fulwood, Preston, PR2 9LU

P.S. WALLACE & CO
145 Cromwell Road, Fulwood, Preston, PR2 6YE

R.J. SCURRAH
8 Bonds Lane, Elswick, Preston, PR4 3ZE

R. PICKUP
Keepers Cottage, Sowerby Road, Sowerby, Preston PR3 0TT
Tel: 01995 679257
Principal: ICAEW Member
R Pickup

RAWCLIFFE & CO
13 Poulton Street, Kirkham, Preston, PR4 2AA

RESOURCES
The Hermitage Tower, Elston Lane, Grimsargh, Preston PR2 5LE
Tel: 01772 654371
Resident Partners/Directors: ICAEW Members
J Heaton

RILEY MOSS LTD
Riley House, 183-185 North Road, Preston, PR1 1YQ

ROBERT BAILEY
Slater House, Meadowcroft Business Park, Pope Lane, Whitestake, Preston PR4 4BA

ROBERT BAILEY
102 Woodplumpton Road, Woodplumpton, Preston, PR4 0LJ

ROBINSONS ROSE LTD
3 Nile Close, Nelson Court Business Centre, Riversway, Preston PR2 2XU

ROTHERHAM TAYLOR LTD ◈
21 Navigation Business Village, Navigation Way, Ashton-on-Ribble, Preston PR2 2YP
Tel: 01772 735865

ROWES ACCOUNTANTS
57 Newgate Lane, Whitestake, Preston, PR4 4JU
Tel: 01772 612491
Resident Partners/Directors: ICAEW Members
W E R Oatridge

RUSHTONS
Starkie House, Winckley Square, Preston, PR1 3JJ

SBCA ◈
Park House, 17 Moor Park Avenue, Preston, PR1 6AS
Tel: 01772 204102
Resident Partners/Directors: ICAEW Members
C P Bond

SKM
Pegasus House, 5 Hinckley Court, Mount St, Preston PR1 8BU

SKM ACCOUNTANTS (NORTH WEST) LTD
Pegasus House, 5 Hinckley Court, Mount St, Preston PR1 8BU

TENON LTD
88-96 Market Street West, Preston, PR1 2EU
Tel: 01772 202655

TENON AUDIT LTD ◈
88-96 Market Street West, Preston, PR1 2EU
Tel: 01772 202655

THR ◈
Charter House, Pittman Way, Fulwood, Preston PR2 9ZD

TITUS THORP & AINSWORTH
212 North Road, Preston, PR1 1YP
Tel: 01772 203208
Resident Partners/Directors: ICAEW Members
I M Adams, M Muschamp, B H Taylor

SPECIALISATIONS – TAXATION
Estate Planning
Executorship
Trusts

TLL ACCOUNTANTS LTD
7-9 Station Road, Hesketh Bank, Preston, PR4 6SN
Tel: 01772 812163
Website: http://www.turpinaccountants.com
Resident Partners/Directors: ICAEW Members
D P Lucas
Resident Partners (Non-ICAEW Members):
C M Lees
Other Offices:440 Whalley New Road, Blackburn, Lancashire BB1 9SL
(Tel: 01254 662352)

SPECIALISATIONS – AUDIT & ASSURANCE
Audit

SPECIALISATIONS – BUSINESS & GENERAL ADVICE
Company Formation

SPECIALISATIONS – FINANCIAL REPORTING
Accounts Preparation
Limited Company Accounts

SPECIALISATIONS – SECTOR
Charities
Horticulture

SPECIALISATIONS – TAXATION
Small Traders

TOWERS & GORNALL ★
Abacus House, The Ropewalk, Garstang, Preston PR3 1NS

TURNER AND BROWN
105 Garstang Road, Preston, PR1 1LD
Tel: 01772 825825
Resident Partners/Directors: ICAEW Members
J L Thomas, N A Thomas
Registered by the ICAEW to carry out company audit work

TURNER & TURNER ◈
Bank House, 9 Victoria Road, Fulwood, Preston PR2 8ND
Tel: 01772 716555

TURNER & TURNER (PRESTON) LTD
Bank House, 9 Victoria Road, Fulwood, Preston PR2 8ND

WALLWORK, NELSON & JOHNSON
Chandler House, 7 Ferry Road Office Park, Riversway, Preston PR2 2YH

WHITEHEAD & ALDRICH
5 Ribblesdale Place, Preston, PR1 8BZ
Tel: 01772 259625
Fax: 01772 259628
Email: mail@whiteheadandaldrich.co.uk
Website: http://www.whiteheadandaldrich.co.uk
Training Contracts Available.
Resident Partners/Directors: ICAEW Members
D Greenwood, J D Hughes-Deane, A J Makin, R J D Mullineaux
Registered by the ICAEW to carry out company audit work
Regulated by the ICAEW for a range of investment business activities

SPECIALISATIONS – AUDIT & ASSURANCE
Audit

SPECIALISATIONS – BUSINESS & GENERAL ADVICE
Company Formation

SPECIALISATIONS – FINANCIAL REPORTING
Accounts Preparation
Limited Company Accounts
Partnership/Sole Trader Accounts

SPECIALISATIONS – IT
Computer Systems and Consultancy

continued

WHITEHEAD & ALDRICH
cont
SPECIALISATIONS – TAXATION
Payroll Service and Advice
Taxation

PRINCES RISBOROUGH

LESLEY M. LUNNON
The Pightle, Alscot Lane, Princes Risborough, Princes Risborough HP27 9RU
Tel: 01844 345301
Principal: ICAEW Member
L M Lunnon

MELANIE NAGELE ACA
Christmas Cottage, Chapel Hill, Speen, Princes Risborough HP27 0SP

RAYMOND M A BRETT ◈
Woodside, Westfields, Whiteleaf, Princes Risborough HP27 0LH
Tel: 01844 346099
Principal: ICAEW Member
R M A Brett

S.G. BEALE & CO
3 Redman Court, Bell Street, Princes Risborough, HP27 0AA

WISE & CO
The Old Star, Church Street, Princes Risborough, HP27 9AA
Tel: 01844 274000
Fax: 01844 274444
DX: 54511 PRINCES RISBOROUGH
Principal: ICAEW Member
C J Wise
Registered by the ICAEW to carry out company audit work

YOUDEN & CO
Old Stocks, Crowbrook Road, Monks Risborough, Princes Risborough HP27 9LW
Tel: 01844 342737
Principal: ICAEW Member
J C Youden

PRUDHOE

K.E. BRIGGS
Dukes Hagg Farmhouse, Moor Road, Prudhoe, NE42 5PA

WILLIS SCOTT GROUP ★
17a Front Street, Prudhoe, NE42 5HN

PUDSEY

BROADHEAD PEEL RHODES ◈
27a Lidget Hill, Pudsey, LS28 7LG
Tel: 0113 257 4506
Fax: 0113 257 7086
Email: info@bpr.co.uk
Website: http://www.bpr.co.uk
Resident Partners/Directors: ICAEW Members
P R Brook
Registered by the ICAEW to carry out company audit work
Regulated by the ICAEW for a range of investment business activities

C. UMPLEBY & CO
Westbourne House, 60 Bagley Lane, Farsley, Pudsey LS28 5LY

FULLERTONS
Westbourne House, 60 Bagley Lane, Farsley, Pudsey LS28 5LY
Tel: 0845 226 2703
Principal: ICAEW Member
J R Fullerton

HEATON, LUMB, LISLE ◈
Thorpe House, 61 Richardshaw Lane, Pudsey, LS28 7EL
Tel: 0113 255 3281
Resident Partners/Directors: ICAEW Members
A M Carr, D Lewis

PETER SHAW
1 Radcliffe Gardens, Radcliffe Lane, Pudsey, LS28 8BG

PHIL DODGSON & PARTNERS LTD
49 Chapeltown, Pudsey, LS28 7RZ

THORNHILL ACCOUNTANCY SERVICES
88 Thornhill Street, Calverley, Pudsey, LS28 5PD

PULBOROUGH

AIMS - TREVOR MILLS
High Dyke, Church Lane, Bury, Pulborough RH20 1PB

BLACK & CO
Gorse Cottage, Harborough Hill, West Chiltington, Pulborough RH20 2PW

E.M. MCMANUS
2 Heatherlands, Thakeham Road, Storrington, Pulborough, RH20 3NE
Tel: 01903 741521
Principal: ICAEW Member
E M McManus

INDIGO TAX & ACCOUNTANCY LTD
Flint Cottage, Bignor Park Road, Bury Gate, Pulborough RH20 1EZ

INDIGO TAX & ACCOUNTANCY LTD
20 Steyning Crescent, Storrington, Pulborough, RH20 4QB

INDIGO TAX & ACCOUNTANCY LTD
23 Concorde Close, Storrington, Pulborough, RH20 3JL

JAN MANNING
Lakeland Thatch, Monkmead Lane, West Chiltington, Pulborough RH20 2PG

JOHN A GROU
Finches, Little Hill, West Chiltington, Pulborough RH20 2PU

M W NICHOLSON
17 Curbey Close, West Chiltington, Pulborough, RH20 2HU
Tel: 01798 815366
Principal: ICAEW Member
M W Nicholson

N.C. YOUNGMAN
The Pines, Thakeham Copse, Storrington, Pulborough RH20 3JW

P.H. MICHELL & CO LTD
Providence Cottage, Bracken Lane, Storrington, Pulborough RH20 3HS
Tel: 01903 742253
Resident Partners/Directors: ICAEW Members
P H Michell

SPOFFORTHS ◈
20 Old Mill Square, Storrington, Pulborough, RH20 4NQ
Tel: 01903 743856

TREVOR WATTS
Alcheringa, Silver Wood, West Chiltington, Pulborough RH20 2NG

TREVOR WATTS
P O Box 2162, Pulborough, RH20 2WZ

PURFLEET

GKM ASSOCIATES LTD
8 Caspian Close, Purfleet, RM19 1LH

PURLEY

A H DELAHUNT
Wembury, 4A Green Lane, Purley, CR8 3PG
Tel: 020 8660 2190
Principal: ICAEW Member
A H Delahunt

BASS & CO
123 Riddlesdown Road, Purley, CR8 1DL
Tel: 020 8763 9339
Principal: ICAEW Member
A J Bass

CLIVE BROOKS
50 Smitham Bottom Lane, Purley, CR8 3DB

CLIVE HOWARD DOUST
63 Pampisford Road, Purley, CR8 2NJ

FRANK D REVEL
120 Northwood Avenue, Purley, CR8 2EQ
Tel: 020 8763 2151
Principal: ICAEW Member
F D Revel

K.W. BUNKELL & CO ◈
The Counting House, 1A Furze Hill, Purley, CR8 3LB
Tel: 020 8645 0909
Email: kw.bunkell@virgin.net
Principal: ICAEW Member
K W Bunkell
Registered by the ICAEW to carry out company audit work
Regulated by the ICAEW for a range of investment business activities

LEES
1 Purley Road, Purley, CR8 2HA

LINGHAM & CO
65 Higher Drive, Purley, CR8 2HR

PARAM & CO
18 Foxley Lane, Purley, CR8 3ED
Tel: 020 8660 7747
Principal: ICAEW Member
K Parameswaran

REBELLO & CO ◈
200 Brighton Road, Purley, CR8 4HB
Tel: 020 8668 8119
Fax: 020 8668 8119
Email: rebello@btconnect.com
Date Established: 1975
Principal: ICAEW Member
T P Rebello
Registered by the ICAEW to carry out company audit work
Regulated by the ICAEW for a range of investment business activities
SPECIALISATIONS – AUDIT & ASSURANCE
Audit
SPECIALISATIONS – BUSINESS & GENERAL ADVICE
Book-keeping
Company Formation
SPECIALISATIONS – FINANCIAL REPORTING
Accounts Preparation
SPECIALISATIONS – TAXATION
Payroll Service and Advice
Taxation

RADLETT

BUSINESS ORCHARD
3a Chestnut House, Farm Close, Shenley, Radlett WD7 9AD
Tel: 01923 855525

THE BUSINESS ORCHARD CONSULTANCY LTD
3a Chestnut House, Farm Close, Shenley, Radlett WD7 9AD

CAROL JEFFERIS
3 Upper Station Road, Radlett, WD7 8BY

CHARLES SMITH & CO
Hillside, Gills Hill Lane, Radlett, WD7 8DB

GUNER WOLFSON LTD
9 Beaumont Gate, Shenley Hill, Radlett, WD7 7AR

HEROWN LTD
3 Upper Station Road, Radlett, WD7 8BY
Tel: 01923 859205

INNERVIEW LTD
Station House, 2 Station Road, Radlett, WD7 8JX

K S CARMICHAEL
117 Newberries Avenue, Radlett, WD7 7EN

LEWIS OSBOURNE & CO
5 The Grove, Radlett, WD7 7NF

MALCOLM BIRD
1 Kendals Close, Radlett, WD7 8NQ
Tel: 01923 852465
Principal: ICAEW Member
M K Bird

MASTERS
Knoll Cottage, 15 Gills Hill, Radlett, WD7 8DA
Tel: 01923 859771
Principal: ICAEW Member
R G Masters

NAGLER SIMMONS
5 Beaumont Gate, Shenley Hill, Radlett, WD7 7AR
Tel: 01923 839619
Resident Partners/Directors: ICAEW Members
S M Nagler, P J Simmons

O'CONNOR & CO
22 Kendals Close, Radlett, WD7 8NQ

STEPHEN ISEMAN & CO
30 Oakridge Avenue, Radlett, WD7 8ER

STUART VINE & CO
Innerview Limited, Station House, 2 Station Road, Radlett WD7 8JX

SUTTONS
103 Gills Hill Lane, Radlett, WD7 8PD
Tel: 01923 859939
Resident Partners/Directors: ICAEW Members
R Sabharwal

RADSTOCK

BERNARD WALDRON FCA ◈
Westfield Business Centre, 32 Second Avenue, Radstock, BA3 4BH
Tel: 01761 409125
Email: smartbern@aol.com
Principal: ICAEW Member
B W Waldron
General Description:
Specialising in small business and start-ups. Member of the tax faculty.

KING WATKINS LTD
The Island House, Midsomer Norton, Radstock, BA3 2DZ

MUSKIN GREGORY
Westfield Court, Third Avenue, Westfield, Midsomer Norton, Radstock BA3 4XD

RAMSGATE

BARRAMSGATE LTD
105 London Road, Ramsgate, CT11 0DR

N TATE & CO
42 St Andrews Road, Ramsgate, CT11 7EQ
Tel: 01227 713787

PETER BARRATT
105 London Road, Ramsgate, CT11 0DR

RAYLEIGH

DEBRA CLARK & CO
128 Rawreth Lane, Rayleigh, SS6 9RR
Tel: 01268 786754
Principal: ICAEW Member
D Clark

ESW LTD
Vantage House, 6-7 Claydons Lane, Rayleigh, SS6 7UP
Tel: 01268 776969
Resident Partners/Directors: ICAEW Members
S J Cracknell, S Wills

M.J. CHURCHILL
5 Bracken Dell, Rayleigh, SS6 8LP
Tel: 01268 779777
Principal: ICAEW Member
M J Churchill

R.V. KENT
Philpot House, Station Road, Rayleigh, SS6 7HH
Tel: 01268 770434
Fax: 01268 772409
Email: wkent@tiscali.co.uk
Principal: ICAEW Member
R V Kent

SCOTT TEMPLE WILSHER & CO
50 Great Wheatley Road, Rayleigh, SS6 7AP

SEARLE INSKIP FREED & CO
Beke Lodge, Beke Hall Chase North, Rawreth, Rayleigh SS6 9EZ
Tel: 01268 780381
Principal: ICAEW Member
R Inskip

READING

A R AVANN & CO
33 Wood Lane, Sonning Common, Reading, RG4 9SJ

A R AVANN AND CO LTD
33 Wood Lane, Sonning Common, Reading, RG4 9SJ

AIMS - DAVID NORRIS
Tidmarsh House, Tidmarsh Lane, Pangbourne, Reading RG8 8HA

AIMS PANGBOURNE - DAVID NORRIS
Tidmarsh House, Tidmarsh Lane, Pangbourne, Reading RG8 8HA

ALAN GOOLD
16 Bayliss Road, Wargrave, Reading, RG10 8DR
Tel: 0118 940 2385
Principal: ICAEW Member
A C W Goold

ALAN J HARLAND
380 Wokingham Road, Earley, Reading, RG6 7HX
Tel: 0118 926 2910
Principal: ICAEW Member
A J Harland

ASSETS LTD
Chiltern Chambers, St Peters Avenue, Caversham, Reading RG4 7DH
Tel: 0118 946 4700
Fax: 0118 946 4880
Email: mail@assets.ltd.uk
Resident Partners/Directors: ICAEW Members
D D Patel, A J Wilson
Registered by the ICAEW to carry out company audit work

AVALON ACCOUNTING
Equity House, 4-6 School Road, Tilehurst, Reading RG31 5AL
Tel: 0118 942 3537
Fax: 0118 941 2822
Email: taxavalon@aol.com
Website: http://www.avalonaccountants.co.uk
Principal: ICAEW Member
J M North
Registered by the ICAEW to carry out company audit work

SPECIALISATIONS – AUDIT & ASSURANCE
Audit

SPECIALISATIONS – BUSINESS & GENERAL ADVICE
Book-keeping
Company Secretarial Service

SPECIALISATIONS – FINANCIAL REPORTING
Accounts Preparation
Limited Companies
Limited Company Accounts
Partnership/Sole Trader Accounts

continued

AVALON ACCOUNTING *cont*

SPECIALISATIONS – INVESTMENT BUSINESS

Planning

SPECIALISATIONS – SECTOR

Corporate

SPECIALISATIONS – TAXATION

Capital Gains — Limited Companies
Capital Gains — Personal
Employee
Partnerships and Sole Traders
Payroll Service and Advice
Personal
Self Assessment Advice
Small Traders
Value Added Tax

General Description: Small general practice with extensive experience in a wide range of industries; covering all aspects of accounting and taxation for individuals, sole traders, small and medium-sized companies. Fees are agreed in advance of work undertaken, and the practice does not charge extra for telephone calls and meetings. An initial consultation is free of charge and without obligation, and can be arranged outside standard office hours if more convenient.
See display advertisement near this entry.

BAKER TOMLINSON ◈
Copse Mead House, Scarletts Lane, Kiln Green, Reading RG10 9XD
Tel: 0118 940 1897
Principal: ICAEW Member
C R Baker

BARRETT & CO ◈
Cheriton, Basingstoke Road, Riseley, Reading RG7 1QL
Tel: 0118 988 3518
Principal: ICAEW Member
S M Barrett

BDO STOY HAYWARD LLP
Kings Wharf, 20-30 Kings Road, Reading, RG1 3EX
Tel: 0118 925 4400
Fax: 0118 925 4470
Resident Partners/Directors: ICAEW Members
R J Beckley, S W Brooker, D Brookes, R M Cantor, R W Frett, J I Parkinson, C Pooles, A Porter, A J Robinson, S D Watson
Resident Partners (Non-ICAEW Members):
M H C Thompson

BILL FONE
Bear Place Farm, Blakes Lane, Hare Hatch, Reading RG10 9TA

BMS (SILCHESTER) LTD
Brookfields, Little London Road, Silchester, Reading RG7 2PP

BRIDGEMAN MENDES LTD
23 Prospect Street, Caversham, Reading, RG4 8JB

CAMERON BROWNE
3a Headley Road, Woodley, Reading, RG5 4JB

THE CAMPBELL PARKER PARTNERSHIP LTD
2 City Limits, Danehill, Lower Earley, Reading RG6 4PB

CAROLINE MEREDITH
9 Bowling Green Lane, Purley on Thames, Reading, RG8 8EJ
Tel: 0118 9845538
Principal: ICAEW Member
C L Meredith

CARROLL & CO
6 Willow Drive, Twyford, Reading, RG10 9DD
Tel: 0118 934 4074
Principal: ICAEW Member
J M Carroll

CHANTREY VELLACOTT DFK LLP
Prospect House, 58 Queens Road, Reading, RG1 4RP
Tel: 0118 952 4700
Fax: 0118 959 8532
Email: info@cvdfk.com
Website: http://www.cvdfk.com
Resident Partners/Directors: ICAEW Members
I B Johnson, R S Parker
Resident Partners (Non-ICAEW Members):
D M Clements
Other Offices: Brighton & Hove, Colchester, Croydon, Leicester, London, Northampton, Stevenage, Watford
Registered by the ICAEW to carry out company audit work
Regulated by the ICAEW for a range of investment business activities

INVESTOR IN PEOPLE

CJM CONSULTANCY LTD
Oriel House, Thames Road, Goring, Reading RG8 9AH

COGNITORES LTD ◈
200 Brook Drive, Green Park, Reading, RG2 6UB
Tel: 0118 959 2100
Resident Partners/Directors: ICAEW Members
D C Turner

COLIN HAWKINS
Hambrook, Bethesda Street,Upper Basildon, Pangbourne, Reading RG8 8NT

COOK SUTTON
Tay Court, Blounts Court Road, Sonning Common, Reading RG4 9RS

CRAWFORD & CO
10 Worsley Place, Theale, Reading, RG7 5QP

CRYER SANDHAM LTD
Epping House, 55 Russell Street, Reading, RG1 7XG

D.J. JONES
10 Beacon Court, Southcote Road, Reading, RG30 2ER
Tel: 0118 958 4870
Principal: ICAEW Member
D J Jones

DAVID GRIMWADE
Watermead, St Mary's Road, Mortimer, Reading RG7 3UE

DAVID WEBB & CO
54 Norcot Road, Tilehurst, Reading, RG30 6BU
Tel: 0118 941 0501
Website: http://www.davidwebbandco.co.uk
Principal: ICAEW Member
D Webb
Registered by the ICAEW to carry out company audit work

DELOITTE & TOUCHE LLP ◈
Abbots House, Abbey Street, Reading, RG1 3BD
Tel: 0118 950 8141
Website: http://www.deloitte.co.uk
Resident Partners/Directors: ICAEW Members
S J Barratt, I R Barton, P Biddle, A J Bowers, J Clennett, G Culshaw, J Davies, T R Davis, W H Harvey, P R Kaye, A M Martin, K J Mitchell, M A M Mullins, D C Norton, P D E Richards, L J Stott, H W Veary, P Waldron, B H White, N Yeomans

EDWIN SMITH
32 Queens Road, Reading, RG1 4AU
Tel: 0118 958 1956
Resident Partners/Directors: ICAEW Members
D L Barnes, P J Nixon, J D Print
Registered by the ICAEW to carry out company audit work
Regulated by the ICAEW for a range of investment business activities

ERNST & YOUNG LLP
Apex Plaza, Forbury Road, Reading, RG1 1YE
Tel: 0118 928 1100
Resident Partners/Directors: ICAEW Members
W A Appleby, I S Beer, D M Hales, K J Havers, N J Hutt, G L Nattrass, P.M. O'Neill, N C Powell, M Thorne, R C Walker

FINDLAY JAMES
2a Butts Hill Road, Woodley, Reading, RG5 4NH

GEOFF WILKINSON
Pickwick House, Bunces Lane, Burghfield Common, Reading RG7 3DL
Tel: 0118 983 1319
Principal: ICAEW Member
G R Wilkinson

GEOFFREY COLE & CO LTD
4 Reading Road, Pangbourne, Reading, RG8 7LY

GOLDSTAR FINANCIAL SERVICES LTD
85 Southampton Street, Reading, RG1 2QU

GRANT THORNTON UK LLP
Ground Floor, Kennet House, 80 Kings Road, Reading RG1 3BJ
Resident Partners/Directors: ICAEW Members
A H Smith

GREENHOW & CO
Montague House, 258 Kings Road, Reading, RG1 4HP

GRIFFINS
Wyvols Court, Swallowfield, Reading, RG7 1WY

H B MISTRY & CO LTD
Tudor House, Mill Lane, Calcot, Reading RG31 7RS

HANCOCK & CO
2-12 Whitchurch Road, Pangbourne, Reading, RG8 7BP

HOLLAND MACLENNAN & CO
115 Crockhamwell Road, Woodley, Reading, RG5 3JP
Tel: 0118 969 8833
Email: mail@hollandmaclennan.co.uk
Resident Partners/Directors: ICAEW Members
R P Holland, R E MacLennan
Registered by the ICAEW to carry out company audit work

SPECIALISATIONS – BUSINESS & GENERAL ADVICE

Company Formation

SPECIALISATIONS – FINANCIAL REPORTING

Accounts Preparation

SPECIALISATIONS – TAXATION

Payroll Service and Advice
Taxation

HORWATH CLARK WHITEHILL LLP
Aquis House, 49-51 Blagrave Street, Reading, RG1 1PL
Tel: 0118 959 7222
Resident Partners/Directors: ICAEW Members
J S Cooper, W I C Dale, B J Hughes, A C Lazda, A R Lyon, J

L Mitchell, P.E.F. O'Neill, J L Stalker

HOWES & CO
27 Eldon Square, Reading, RG1 4DP

HUNTER KANE PROFESSIONAL SERVICES LTD
4 Beech Court, Wokingham Road, Hurst, Reading RG10 0RQ

HW ◈
7-11 Station Road, Reading, RG1 1LG
Tel: 0118 958 4111
Resident Partners/Directors: ICAEW Members
J E Bailey, G C Fairclough, V A Fox, P I Wright

HW CORPORATE FINANCE LLP
7-11 Station Road, Reading, RG1 1LG
Tel: 02380 111310

IDG ACCOUNTANCY
59 St Marys Avenue, Purley on Thames, Reading, RG8 8BJ

JAMES COWPER LLP ◈
3 Wesley Gate, Queens Road, Reading, RG1 4AP
Tel: 0118 959 0261
Fax: 0118 939 3385
Email: info@jamescowper.co.uk
Website: http://www.jamescowper.co.uk
Training Contracts Available.
Resident Partners/Directors: ICAEW Members
J Armitage, M N Farwell, D J Fawcus, T J Goodsell, A R Peal, N A Rogers
Resident Partners (Non-ICAEW Members):
C J Lee
Other Offices: Newbury, Oxford

INVESTOR IN PEOPLE

JANE JENNINGS ACA
28 Barbaras Meadow, Tilehurst, Reading, RG31 6YF

JJ (EMPLOYMENT) TAX UNRAVELLED
28 Barbara's Meadow, Tilehurst, Reading, RG31 6YF
Tel: 0118 941 8744
Email: jane@jjtaxunravelled.com
Principal: ICAEW Member
J A Jennings

JMG ACCOUNTANCY SERVICES LTD
7 The Brookmill, Coley Park Farm, Reading, RG1 6DD
Tel: 0118 958 2561
Resident Partners/Directors: ICAEW Members
J M Godsell

JOHN JENKINS & CO
Seal Lodge, Simms Lane, Mortimer, Reading RG7 2JP
Tel: 0118 933 1430
Principal: ICAEW Member
J M Jenkins

JOHN PLOWS
30 Carlton Road, Caversham Heights, Reading, RG4 7NT
Tel: 0118 946 2200
Principal: ICAEW Member
J G Plows

JOHN S. MORRIS
Rowan House, New Lane Hill, Tilehurst, Reading RG30 4JJ

JOHN TURNER
Berkshire House, 252/256 Kings Road, Reading, RG1 4HP
Tel: 0118 951 9534
Principal: ICAEW Member
J J Turner

KIRKPATRICK & HOPES LTD
Overdene House, 49 Church Street, Theale, Reading RG7 5BX

KPMG LLP
Arlington Business Park, Theale, Reading, RG7 4SD
Tel: 0118 964 2000
Resident Partners/Directors: ICAEW Members
S C Barker, A J L Cottam, A C Dray, N R P Gibb, R J Hampshire, D I McAllan, A R J Morgan, V J Stevens, C J Wilson
Resident Partners (Non-ICAEW Members):
A J Coles, G J O'Brien, R Pygott

LOGAN & BREWERTON
27 Eldon Square, Reading, RG1 4DP

MA HAWKINS BA ACA
212 Norcot Road, Tilehurst, Reading, RG30 6AE

MCNAUGHT & CO
189 Wokingham Road, Earley, Reading, RG6 1LT

NICHOLAS JENNER & CO
PO Box 4001, Pangbourne, Reading, RG8 7FN

NORTONS GROUP
Highlands House, Basingstoke Road, Spencers Wood, Reading RG7 1NT

OUTRAM BUSINESS AND ACCOUNTING SERVICES LTD
10 Bird Wood Court, Sonning Common, Reading, RG4 9RF

OWEN C MORRELL
Fairacre, Cleeve Road, Goring, Reading RG8 9BU

PATRICIA RIZAN
21 Chervil Way, Burghfield Common, Reading, RG7 3YX

PATRICK J. MANNERS
16 Sheridan Avenue, Caversham, Reading, RG4 7QD
Tel: 0118 947 9162
Principal: ICAEW Member
P J Manners

POOLE & CO
90 London Street, Reading, RG1 4SJ

PRICEWATERHOUSE-COOPERS
9 Greyfriars Road, Reading, RG1 1JG

PRICEWATERHOUSE-COOPERS LLP
9 Greyfriars Road, Reading, RG1 1JG
Tel: 0118 959 7111
Resident Partners/Directors: ICAEW Members
R A Hartley, J B G Maitland, R W H McGregor, R J Moore, A R Morgan, M A Saunders, I P Smith, J C Wakelam

R.A. HUBBARD
C/o James Cowper, 3 Wesley Gate, Queens Road, Reading RG1 4AP

R.A. HUBBARD
9 Kelmscott Close, Caversham, Reading, RG4 7DG

R.B. HULL
24 Millers Grove, Calcot, Reading, RG31 7PH

R. BICKNELL & CO
71 Bedford Road, Reading, RG1 7EY

R J BENTLEY
8 Old Stocks Court, Upper Basildon, Reading, RG8 8TD

R.KERRIDGE
32 Queens Road, Reading, RG1 4AU
Tel: 0118 957 7453
Principal: ICAEW Member
R Kerridge

R LEARMONTH DICK
3a Headley Road, Woodley, Reading, RG5 4JB

R. MULLICK ◈
10 Chatteris Way, Lower Earley, Reading, RG6 4JA

REIDWILLIAMS
Prince Regent House, 108 London Street, Reading, RG1 4SJ

RICHARDSONS
99 London Street, Reading, RG1 4QA
Tel: 0118 957 3118
Principal: ICAEW Member
E A Richardson

ROGER BELL & CO
25 Purfield Drive, Wargrave, Reading, RG10 8AP

ROGER LEVEY & CO
26 Conifer Drive, Tilehurst, Reading, RG31 6YU

SINNETT & CO
61-63 Church Street, Caversham, Reading, RG4 8AX

SINNETT & TANSLEY LTD
3 Richfield Place, Richfield Avenue, Reading, RG1 8EQ

SMITH & WILLIAMSON LTD
Citygate Business Centre, Southampton Street, Reading, RG1 2QW
Tel: 0118 922 7227

SRE ASSOCIATES LTD
15 Ryeish Green Cottages, Hyde End Lane, Spencers Wood, Reading RG7 1ET

TARGET
6th Floor, Reading Bridge House, Reading Bridge, Reading RG1 8LS
Tel: 0118 958 1331
Fax: 0118 958 6922
Email: target@target-accountants.com
Website: http://www.target-accountants.com
Date Established: 1998
Registered by the ICAEW to carry out company audit work
Regulated by the ICAEW for a range of investment business activities
General Description: A leading business and accounting firm with offices in Reading, Rugby, Bath and London. Authorised provision of financial services.

TAYLOR COCKS ◈
Atlantic House, Imperial Way, Reading, RG2 0TD
Tel: 0870 770 8111
SPECIALISATIONS – AUDIT & ASSURANCE
Audit
Audit — Private Company

continued

TAYLOR COCKS *cont*

SPECIALISATIONS – BUSINESS & GENERAL ADVICE

Book-keeping
Management Advice to Business
Management Consultancy

SPECIALISATIONS – FINANCIAL REPORTING

Accounts Preparation
Limited Company Accounts

SPECIALISATIONS – SECTOR

Doctors
Solicitors

SPECIALISATIONS – TAXATION

Estate and Inheritance
Investigations
Taxation

TENON LTD
The Aquarium Building, 1-7 King Street, Reading, RG1 2AN
Tel: 0118 953 0350

TENON RECOVERY
23 Duke Street, Reading, RG1 4SA

THROGMORTON UK LTD
42-44 Portman Road, Reading, RG30 1EA

TURNER BARRATT CORPORATE FINANCE LTD ◈
200 Brook Drive, Green Park, Reading, RG2 6UB
Tel: 01189 509200
Email: enquiries@turnerbarratt.co.uk
Website: http://www.turnerbarratt.co.uk
Resident Partners/Directors: ICAEW Members
D C Turner

SPECIALISATIONS – BUSINESS & GENERAL ADVICE

Acquisitions and Mergers
Disposal of Businesses

VALE & WEST ◈
Victoria House, 26 Queen Victoria Street, Reading, RG1 1TG
Tel: 0118 957 3238
Fax: 0118 956 7282
Email: mail@valewest.com
Website: http://www.valewest.com
Training Contracts Available.
Resident Partners/Directors: ICAEW Members
K M Cutts, J M James, P R W Ringrow
Resident Partners (Non-ICAEW Members):
J Pyke
Registered by the ICAEW to carry out company audit work
Regulated by the ICAEW for a range of investment business activities

SPECIALISATIONS – AUDIT & ASSURANCE

Assurance Services
Audit

SPECIALISATIONS – BUSINESS & GENERAL ADVICE

Company Secretarial Service
Management Consultancy

SPECIALISATIONS – FINANCIAL REPORTING

Accounts Preparation
Limited Companies
Partnership/Sole Trader Accounts

SPECIALISATIONS – IT

Computer Systems and Consultancy

SPECIALISATIONS – SECTOR

Clubs/Associations
Corporate
Property
Solicitors

SPECIALISATIONS – TAXATION

Customs Duty
Executorship
Partnerships and Sole Traders
Payroll Service and Advice
Self Assessment Advice
Taxation
Trusts
See display advertisement near this entry.

WELSBY ASSOCIATES LTD
Sintra, Bethesda Street, Upper Basildon, Reading RG8 8NU

WIGGIN'S
Soane Point, 6-8 Market Place, Reading, RG1 2EG
Tel: 0118 925 5232
Fax: 0118 925 5233
Email: charles@wigginco.com
Website: http://www.accountingservicesonline.net
Principal: ICAEW Member
A C D Wiggin
Other Offices: London, Midlands
General Description: Visit our award winning online accounting service at www.accountingservicesonline.net.
Languages Spoken:
German

WILKINS KENNEDY
6c Church Street, Reading, RG1 2SB

REDCAR

ARGOT ACCOUNTING AND BUSINESS SERVICES ◈
16 Queen Street, Redcar, TS10 1AF
Tel: 01642 497100
Principal: ICAEW Member
J Owens

PROUDLER HISER & CO
46/48 Coatham Road, Redcar, TS10 1RS

REDDITCH

ALAN W. DOCKER
8 Milton Close, Headless Cross, Redditch, B97 5BQ

ALISON ROGERS LTD
4 Longborough Close, Redditch, B97 5QN

BROOKFIELD REALISATION LTD
50 Brookfield Close, Hunt End, Redditch, B97 5LL
Tel: 01527 544446
Resident Partners/Directors: ICAEW Members
R C Perkins

BURMAN & CO
Brunswick Hse, Birmingham Rd, Redditch, B97 6DY
Tel: 01527 69667
Resident Partners/Directors: ICAEW Members
D R Burman, N Farmer
Registered by the ICAEW to carry out company audit work

DEREK PAYNE
Alwynne, 48 The Ridgeway, Astwood Bank, Redditch B96 6LT

DEREK YOUNG & CO
Estate House, Evesham Street, Redditch, B97 4HP

HAYWARD WRIGHT LTD ◈
Prospect House, Church Green West, Redditch, B97 4BD
Tel: 01527 69321
Resident Partners/Directors: ICAEW Members
A G Hayward-Wright

KITE & CO
9 Clive House, 80 Prospect Hill, Redditch, B97 4BS

MALCOLM WOOD & CO
Shrubbery House, 47 Prospect Hill, Redditch, B97 4BS

MILLS PYATT
Unit 11, Kingfisher Business Park, Arthur Street, Redditch B98 8LG

MILLS PYATT LTD
Unit 11, Kingfisher Business Park, Arthur Street, Redditch B98 8LG

MITCH CASTLE
30 Radway Close, Church Hill North, Redditch, B98 8RZ
Tel: 01527 69776
Principal: ICAEW Member
M Castle

PHILIP J. HODGES FCA
123 Birchfield Road, Headless Cross, Redditch, B97 4LE

RICHARD PERKINS & CO
50 Brookfield Close, Hunt End, Redditch, B97 5LL
Tel: 01527 544446

RIGBEY HARRISON
4 Church Green East, Redditch, B98 8BT
Tel: 01527 62345
Email: mail@rigbeyharrison.co.uk
Resident Partners/Directors:
ICAEW Members
D Collett, M J Holder, J Smith

REDHILL

ALEXANDERS PROFESSIONAL SERVICES LTD ◈
Redhill Chambers, High Street, Redhill, RH1 1RJ
Tel: 01737 779500
Resident Partners/Directors:
ICAEW Members
C R G Tomaszewski

THE BAILEY PARTNERSHIP ★
Sterling House, 27 Hatchlands Road, Redhill, RH1 6RW

D'CRUZ & CO
21 Hanworth Road, Redhill, RH1 5HS

DAVID A. THOMAS
Castle Villa, Millers Lane, Outwood, Redhill RH1 5QB

DEREK LEE & CO
Unit 4 The Stable Yard, Brewer Street, Bletchingley, Redhill RH1 4QP

GBJ
Sterling House, 27 Hatchlands Road, Redhill, RH1 6RW

GBJ LLP ◈
Sterling House, 27 Hatchlands Road, Redhill, RH1 6RW
Tel: 01737 778848
Email: info@gbjfinancial.co.uk
Website: http://www.gbjfinancial.co.uk
Resident Partners/Directors:
ICAEW Members
N I Green

GJ DUDA ◈
Snatts Hill Cottage, Rabies Heath Road, Bletchingley, Redhill RH1 4NB
Tel: 01883 742753
Resident Partners/Directors:
ICAEW Members
G J Duda

GORMLEY & CO
Brookside Farm, Woodhatch Road, Salfords, Redhill RH1 5JJ

I.C. MATTHEWS
Ivor House, 200 London Road North, Merstham, Redhill RH1 3BG
Tel: 01737 646272
Principal: ICAEW Member
I C Matthews

J F WHITE LTD
36 Cotland Acres, Redhill Surrey, Redhill, RH1 6JZ

J.F. WHITE
36 Cotland Acres, Redhill, RH1 6JZ

JOHN MANKELOW FCA
Holly Cottage, Millers Lane, Outwood, Redhill RH1 5PZ
Tel: 07802 827792
Principal: ICAEW Member
J S Mankelow

KINGSTON SMITH LLP
Surrey House, 36-44 High Street, Redhill, RH1 1RH
Tel: 01737 779000
Fax: 01737 781555
Email: ks@kingstonsmith.co.uk
Website: http://www.kingstonsmith.co.uk
Resident Partners/Directors:
ICAEW Members
P Chadda, K E Halstead, D J Montgomery, P E M Samrah
Registered by the ICAEW to carry out company audit work
Regulated by the ICAEW for a range of investment business activities

R.D. RANGELEY FCA
Abbey House, 25 Clarendon Road, Redhill, RH1 1QZ
Tel: 01737 852170
Principal: ICAEW Member
R D A Rangeley

SERVICE INDUSTRY SUPPORT LTD
Covertside, Kings Mill Lane, South Nutfield, Redhill RH1 5JX

VENTHAMS LTD ◈
The Old Tannery, Oakdene Road, Redhill, RH1 6BT
Tel: 01737 773796
Resident Partners/Directors:
ICAEW Members
M S Cragg
Other Offices: Lincoln's Inn Fields, London, Rochford, Essex

VISTA AUDIT LLP
Chancery House, 3 Hatchlands Road, Redhill, RH1 6AA

VISTA PARTNERS LLP ◈
Chancery House, 3 Hatchlands Road, Redhill, RH1 6AA
Tel: 01737 762728
Fax: 01737 768584
Email: enq@vistapartners.co.uk
Website: http://www.vistapartners.co.uk
Resident Partners/Directors:
ICAEW Members
S Jones
Resident Partners (Non-ICAEW Members):
G Proudlock
Regulated by the ICAEW for a range of investment business activities

WATSON LENNEY
Pendell Court Farmhouse, Pendell Road, Bletchingley, Redhill RH1 4QH

REDRUTH

GRAHAM SMITH
11 Green Lane, Redruth, TR15 1JY
Tel: 01209 213281
Principal: ICAEW Member
M T Staddon

M.E. GREENHALGH FCA
Endsleigh House, Carn Marth Lane, South Carn Marth, Redruth TR16 5TA
Tel: 01209 217271

MEIG LTD
Endsleigh House, Carn Marth Lane, South Carn Marth, Redruth TR16 5TA
Tel: 01209 217271
Resident Partners/Directors:
ICAEW Members
M E Greenhalgh

STONHAM.CO
Chynoweth, Chapel Street, Redruth, TR15 2BY

WALKER MOYLE
3 Chapel Street, Redruth, TR15 2BY
Tel: 01209 214221
Website: http://www.walker-moyle.co.uk
Resident Partners/Directors:
ICAEW Members
D G W Bishop

WESTON UNDERWOOD
63 Agar Road, Illogan Highway, Redruth, TR15 3EJ

REIGATE

ALAN B HIGGS
9 Redwood Mount, Reigate, RH2 9NB
Tel: 01737 222955
Principal: ICAEW Member
A B Higgs

COLE MARIE
Priory House, 45-51 High Street, Reigate, RH2 9AE

COMPETEX LTD
Orchard House, Park Lane, Reigate, RH2 8JX

COVENEY NICHOLLS
The Old Wheel House, 31/37 Church Street, Reigate, RH2 0AD
Tel: 01737 223388
Fax: 01737 241010
Email: johnmabey@coveneynicholls.co.uk
Website: http://www.coveneynicholls.co.uk
Resident Partners/Directors:
ICAEW Members
J N Kelly, J Mabey

COVENEY NICHOLLS LTD
The Old Wheel House, 31/37 Church Street, Reigate, RH2 0AD
Tel: 01737 223388
Resident Partners/Directors:
ICAEW Members
S Beaton, M Bennett, J N Kelly, J Mabey

E.CHAPMAN LTD
Clearways, Colley Way, Reigate, RH2 9JH

EC ACCOUNTANCY
Clearways, Colley Way, Reigate, RH2 9JH
Tel: 01737 240739
Email: enquiries@ecaccountancy.co.uk
Website: http://www.ecaccountancy.co.uk

SPECIALISATIONS – BUSINESS & GENERAL ADVICE
Book-keeping

SPECIALISATIONS – FINANCIAL REPORTING
Accounts Preparation

SPECIALISATIONS – SECTOR
Corporate

SPECIALISATIONS – TAXATION
Payroll Service and Advice
Self Assessment Advice
Taxation

General Description: Chartered tax advisors. Small business tax and accounts.

FOWLER & CO
Orchard House, Park Lane, Reigate, RH2 8JX

G & CO BIRMINGHAM LTD ◈
Ringley Park House, 59 Reigate Road, Reigate, RH2 0QT

J.C. WOODBRIDGE
Ringley Park House, 59 Reigate Road, Reigate, RH2 0QT

JOHN WILLIAMS & CO
41a Bell Street, Reigate, RH2 7AQ
Tel: 01737 225509
Principal: ICAEW Member
J R Williams

LINDSEY-RENTON & CO
43 Waterlow Road, Reigate, RH2 7EY

P.J. LINDSAY
13 Beech Rd, Reigate, RH2 9LS
Tel: 01737 248672
Principal: ICAEW Member
P J Lindsay
SPECIALISATIONS – TAXATION
Taxation

PAMELA J LEGG
Glovers Farm, Reigate Hill, Reigate, RH2 9PN

ROBERT BOOT & CO
Cotleigh, 6A Windermere Way, Reigate, RH2 0LW

RUSHTON OSBORNE & CO
Ringley Park House, 59 Reigate Road, Reigate, RH2 0QJ

RUSHTON OSBORNE & CO LTD
Ringley Park House, 59 Reigate Road, Reigate, RH2 0QJ

S A V BUCHANAN
Heathfield, 49 Raglan Road, Reigate, RH2 0DY

SAMUELS CORPORATE LTD ◈
The Old Forge, 36 West Street, Reigate, RH2 9BX
Tel: 01737 241414
Website: http://www.samcorp.co.uk
Resident Partners/Directors: ICAEW Members
P T Samuels
Regulated by the ICAEW for a range of investment business activities
SPECIALISATIONS – BUSINESS & GENERAL ADVICE
Acquisitions and Mergers

RETFORD

GILDERSON & CO
1 The Stables, Manor Business Park, East Drayton, Retford DN22 0LG
Tel: 01777 249144

RICHARD DAVISON ASSOCIATES LTD
Yorkshire Bank Chambers, Market Square, Retford, DN22 6DQ

ROSEMARY A MOONEY & CO LTD
33 Lime Tree Avenue, Retford, DN22 7BB
Tel: 01777 703145
Resident Partners/Directors: ICAEW Members
R A Mooney

SAUL FAIRHOLM ◈
24 Exchange Street, Retford, DN22 6DT
Tel: 01777 861170
Email: enquiries@saulfairholm.co.uk
Registered by the ICAEW to carry out company audit work
Regulated by the ICAEW for a range of investment business activities

STREETS LLP ◈
Churchgate House, 33 Churchgate, Retford, DN22 6PA
Tel: 01777 869955
Email: info@streetsweb.co.uk
Website: http://www.streetsweb.co.uk
Resident Partners/Directors: ICAEW Members
R C Lee

TERRY J. WILLIAMS & CO
12 Stonehill Close, Ranskill, Retford, DN22 8NG

WIGGLESWORTH HEPWORTH & CO
47 Grove Street, Retford, DN22 6LA

WRIGHT VIGAR LTD ◈
12 Exchange Street, Retford, DN22 6BL
Tel: 01777 707373
Website: http://www.wrightvigar.co.uk
Resident Partners/Directors: ICAEW Members
N M Roberts
SPECIALISATIONS – AUDIT & ASSURANCE
Audit — Private Company
SPECIALISATIONS – SECTOR
Charities

RICHMOND

ASTON BUSINESS CONSULTANCY
69 Bolton Avenue, Richmond, DL10 4BA

C.J. BEESTON ◈
The Laurels, Reeth, Richmond, DL11 6TX
Tel: 01748 884535
Email: cjbeeston-fca@uk2.net
Principal: ICAEW Member
C J Beeston

DAVID N WILLIAMS
Chapel Lodge, Langthwaite, Richmond, DL11 6RE
Tel: 01748 884650
Principal: ICAEW Member
D N Williams

G.D. DEVERELL
Asthill House, Aldbrough St John, Richmond, DL11 7ST

NEEDHAM, CHIPCHASE, MANNERS & CO ◈
30b Market Place, Richmond, DL10 4QG
Tel: 01748 822091
Fax: 01748 850015
Email: ncm@fsmail.net
Date Established: 1966
Resident Partners/Directors: ICAEW Members
R I Crisop, M E Needham
Registered by the ICAEW to carry out company audit work

NIGEL HERRING & CO
Finkle Street Chambers, Finkle Street, Richmond, DL10 4QB

CARPENTER KEEN LLP
Grand Prix House, 102-104 Sheen Road, Richmond, TW9 1UF

DAVID K MEGGITT
5 Parkside, 172 Kew Road, Richmond, TW9 2AS

DE FREITAS & CO
39 Berwyn Road, Richmond, TW10 5BU

E-ACCOUNTANTS LTD
36 Bardolph Road, Richmond, TW9 2LH
Tel: 0845 072 2977
Fax: 0845 0722978
Email: kim@e-accountants.net
Website: http://www.e-accountants.net
Date Established: 1994
Resident Partners/Directors: ICAEW Members
P K Teh
Registered by the ICAEW to carry out company audit work

FELTONPUMPHREY
1 The Green, Richmond, TW9 1PL
Tel: 020 8940 0963
Email: info@fpca.co.uk
Website: http://www.fpca.co.uk
Training Contracts Available.
Other Offices:12 Sheet Street, Windsor, Berkshire, SL4 1BG (Tel: 01753 840111)
Licensed by another DPB to carry on investment business
SPECIALISATIONS – AUDIT & ASSURANCE
Audit
SPECIALISATIONS – BUSINESS & GENERAL ADVICE
Book-keeping
Outsourcing - Financial Services
SPECIALISATIONS – FINANCIAL REPORTING
Financial Reporting
SPECIALISATIONS – TAXATION
Payroll Service and Advice
Personal
Taxation

H A HYATT & CO
H A Hyatt & Co Limited, 4-5 King Street, Richmond, TW9 1ND
Tel: 020 8948 9118

H A HYATT & CO LTD
4-5 King Street, Richmond, TW9 1ND
Tel: 020 8948 9118
Resident Partners/Directors: ICAEW Members
H A Hyatt

THE HUGHES CONSULTANCY ◈
4a Church Court, Richmond, TW9 1JL
Tel: 020 8288 7733
Email: info@thehughesconsultancy.co.uk
Principal: ICAEW Member
D S Hughes
SPECIALISATIONS – BUSINESS & GENERAL ADVICE
Management Advice to Business
Outsourcing - Financial Services
SPECIALISATIONS – FINANCIAL REPORTING
Accounts Preparation
SPECIALISATIONS – SECTOR
Advertising/Design Agencies
Architects/Surveyors
Construction
Entertainers
Insurance Brokers
Travel Industry
SPECIALISATIONS – TAXATION
Payroll Service and Advice
Taxation

J.F. ADAMS
29 Pensford Avenue, Richmond, TW9 4HR
Tel: 020 8876 5583
Principal: ICAEW Member
J F Adams

NIGEL ARNOLD & CO
18 Norfolk House, Courtlands, Sheen Road, Richmond, TW10 5AT
Tel: 020 8948 4766
Principal: ICAEW Member
N W Arnold

P.J.I. LOWTHER
15 Duncan Road, Richmond, TW9 2JD

PERKINS & CO
20 Taylor Avenue, Kew, Richmond, TW9 4ED
Tel: 020 8392 8654
Principal: ICAEW Member
C H Perkins

PK AUDIT LLP
22 The Quadrant, Richmond, TW9 1BP
Tel: 020 8334 9953
Resident Partners/Directors: ICAEW Members
P W Kennedy, M J C Penny, K Shah, J M Waller

PK AUDIT LONDON
22 The Quadrant, Richmond, TW9 1BP

PK GROUP ◈
22 The Quadrant, Richmond, TW9 1BP
Tel: 020 8334 9953

PK PARTNERS LLP
22 The Quadrant, Richmond, TW9 1BP
Tel: 020 8334 9953
Website: http://www.pkgroup.co.uk
Resident Partners/Directors: ICAEW Members
P W Kennedy, M J C Penny, K Shah, J M Waller
Resident Partners (Non-ICAEW Members):
I H Brockwell, S C Coles, D J Truscott

SPECIALISATIONS – AUDIT & ASSURANCE

Audit

SPECIALISATIONS – BUSINESS & GENERAL ADVICE

Acquisitions and Mergers
Book-keeping
Company Formation
Company Secretarial Service
Data Processing Services
Management Accounting Consultancy
Management Advice to Business
Outsourcing - Financial Services

SPECIALISATIONS – FINANCIAL REPORTING

Accounts Preparation
Financial Reporting
Limited Company Accounts
Limited Liability Partnership
Partnership/Sole Trader Accounts

SPECIALISATIONS – FORENSIC ACCOUNTING

Forensic Accounting

SPECIALISATIONS – TAXATION

Capital Gains — Personal
Foreign Nationals in the UK
Partnerships and Sole Traders
Payroll Service and Advice
Personal
Trusts

General Description: PK Partners is the respected accountancy arm of PK Group - the fast growing, London-based, firm of financial architects that assist both individuals and their businesses to protect and grow their wealth.

POCOCKS
3 Thamesgate Close, Ham, Richmond, TW10 7YS
Tel: 020 8948 1509
Fax: 020 8948 0129
Email: pococks@hotmail.com
Mobile: 07801 78848
Date Established: 1994
Principal: ICAEW Member
M Pocock
Individual(s) licensed for insolvency work by the ICAEW

SPECIALISATIONS – BUSINESS & GENERAL ADVICE

Acquisitions and Mergers
Company Formation
Debt Counselling
Disposal of Businesses
Feasibility Studies
Management Advice to Business
Management Consultancy

SPECIALISATIONS – BUSINESS RECOVERY & INSOLVENCY

Bankruptcies
Corporate Recovery
Liquidations

RANDALL & CO
21 Clarence Road, Kew Gardens, Richmond, TW9 3NL

V KAPADIA & CO ◈
9 Beechwood Avenue, Richmond, TW9 4DD
Tel: 020 8392 1099

V KAPADIA & CO LTD ◈
9 Beechwood Avenue, Richmond, TW9 4DD
Tel: 020 8392 1099

WEILER & CO
14 Denbigh Gardens, Richmond, TW10 6EN

RICKMANSWORTH

A.M. GRIFFIN
Ladyacre, Stag Lane, Chorleywood, Rickmansworth WD3 5HD

AIMS - WILLIAM HALL
Sarratt House, Bridle Lane, Loudwater, Rickmansworth WD3 4JA

ANDREW TODD
Highcroft, Deadmans Ash Lane, Sarratt, Rickmansworth WD3 6AL

COX COSTELLO & HORNE LTD ◈
Langwood House, 63-81 High Street, Rickmansworth, WD3 1EQ

CRIPPS & CO
8-10 Heronsgate Road, Chorleywood, Rickmansworth, WD3 5BW

D.E. JONES
22 The Drive, Chorleywood, Rickmansworth, WD3 4EB

DALY, HOGGETT & CO
112-114 High Street, Rickmansworth, WD3 1AQ
Tel: 01923 896831
Email: info@dalyhoggett.co.uk
Website: http://www.dalyhoggett.co.uk
Other Offices: London W1

DAY, SMITH & HUNTER ◈
Batchworth House, Batchworth Place, Church Street, Rickmansworth WD3 1JE
Tel: 01923 771010
Email: info@dsh.co.uk
Website: http://www.dsh.co.uk
Resident Partners/Directors: ICAEW Members
A Bell, M Cassidy, D Jones, R Lim
Other Offices: Maidstone, Kent
Registered by the ICAEW to carry out company audit work
Regulated by the ICAEW for a range of investment business activities

DICKINSONS ◈
Enterprise House, Beesons Yard, Bury Lane, Rickmansworth WD3 1DS
Tel: 01923 776818
Fax: 01923 725825
Email: info@dickinsons.co.uk
Website: http://www.dickinsons.co.uk
Resident Partners/Directors: ICAEW Members
P G Abbott, P Bayes, J Birch, N S Spalton, P D Tucker
Registered by the ICAEW to carry out company audit work
Regulated by the ICAEW for a range of investment business activities

SPECIALISATIONS – FINANCIAL REPORTING

Foreign Subsidiary Companies

SPECIALISATIONS – TAXATION

UK Subsidiaries of Overseas Multinationals

Languages Spoken:
French, German, Finnish

EBRAHIM
252 Uxbridge Road, Rickmansworth, WD3 8EA
Tel: 01923 776198
Principal: ICAEW Member
A Ebrahim

F KELLY & CO
43 Carpenters Wood Drive, Chorleywood, Rickmansworth, WD3 5RN

GRIFFIN & ASSOCIATES
312 Uxbridge Road, Rickmansworth, WD3 8YL

GRIFFIN & ASSOCIATES LTD
312 Uxbridge Road, Rickmansworth, WD3 8YL

GUARDIANS
24 Spencer Walk, Rickmansworth, WD3 4EE

HOCKMANS
Cardinal Point, Park Road, Rickmansworth, WD3 1RE

HOWARD ATKINS LTD
49 The Drive, Rickmansworth, WD3 4EA

J.D. RIMER & CO
The Court House, Chenies, Rickmansworth, WD3 6EU
Tel: 01923 283667
Principal: ICAEW Member
J D Rimer

J.R. KNIGHT
4 Beechwood Avenue, Chorleywood, Rickmansworth, WD3 5RL

K.A. JOHNSON
Norfolk House, Norfolk Rd, Rickmansworth, WD3 1RD
Tel: 01923 771277
Principal: ICAEW Member
K A Johnson

LEE & CO ◈
26 High Street, Rickmansworth, WD3 1ER
Tel: 01923 897975

LEE ACCOUNTING SERVICES LTD ◈
26 High Street, Rickmansworth, WD3 1ER
Tel: 01923 897975
Resident Partners/Directors: ICAEW Members
J D Lee

MARGARET BRYANT CONSULTING LTD
6 Pheasants Way, Rickmansworth, WD3 7ES

NICOLA ANDERSON FCA FCIE
189 Baldwins Lane, Croxley Green, Rickmansworth, WD3 3LL
Tel: 01923 776056
Principal: ICAEW Member
N J Anderson

SPECIALISATIONS – SECTOR

Charities

NICOLA J RUSSELL
27 Valley Road, Rickmansworth, WD3 4DT

PAUL GOODMAN
Mortons Cottage, The Green, Sarratt, Rickmansworth WD3 6BH
Tel: 01923 271010
Principal: ICAEW Member
P J Goodman

PAYNE ALLEN
45 Whitelands Avenue, Chorleywood, Rickmansworth, WD3 5RE

RAMSAY & CO
28 Carpenters Wood Drive, Chorleywood, Rickmansworth, WD3 5RJ

RICHARD D. WARMAN
Silver Birches, Heronsgate, Rickmansworth, WD3 5DN

RPM ASSOCIATES
22 Chestnut Avenue, Rickmansworth, WD3 4HB

S.M.C BRUCE
28 Pheasants Way, Rickmansworth, WD3 7ES
Tel: 01923 720253
Principal: ICAEW Member
S M C Bruce

SQUARE CIRCLE CONSULTING
95 Valley Road, Rickmansworth, WD3 4BL

SUMMERS MORGAN
Sheraton House, Lower Road, Chorleywood, Rickmansworth WD3 5LH
Tel: 01923 284212
Resident Partners/Directors: ICAEW Members
N Corden, D J Manning

THE SWILLETT PORTFOLIO LTD ◈
Berry Cottage, Bullsland Lane, Chorleywood, Rickmansworth WD3 5BD
Tel: 01923 286507
Resident Partners/Directors: ICAEW Members
P R Willey

RIDING MILL

JANICE LIGHTLEY
Beechtree Corner, Sandy Bank, Riding Mill, NE44 6HU

RINGWOOD

BEVIS ACCOUNTANTS LTD
32-34 High Street, Ringwood, BH24 1AG

DAVID A. THOMAS & CO
Garden Reach, 5 Hurn Close, Ashley, Ringwood BH24 2AD

DAVID J MUSKER ◈
Tullich, Forest Lane, Hightown Hill, Ringwood BH24 3HF
Tel: 01425 474756
Principal: ICAEW Member
D J Musker

GRAHAM LATHAM LTD ◈
Hedge House, Hangersley Hill, Hangersley, Ringwood BH24 3JW
Tel: 01425 470900
Email: graham@grahamlatham.co.uk
Resident Partners/Directors: ICAEW Members
G W Latham

Regulated by the ICAEW for a range of investment business activities

SPECIALISATIONS – SECTOR

Agriculture

HARVEY & CO
7 Dryden Close, Ashley Heath, Ringwood, BH24 2JB
Tel: 01425 471103
Principal: ICAEW Member
M Harvey

HENRY PRITCHET
5 Conifer Close, St Leonards, Ringwood, BH24 2RF
Tel: 01425 476246
Principal: ICAEW Member
W H Pritchet

JACKIE PRITCHET
17 Ashley Close, Hightown, Ringwood, BH24 1QX
Tel: 01425 470213
Principal: ICAEW Member
J A Pritchet

JENNY BARNES & CO LTD
1st Floor Offices, 2A Highfield Road, Ringwood, BH24 1RQ
Tel: 01425 476520
Resident Partners/Directors: ICAEW Members
J C Barnes

LEWIS & CO (FINANCIAL MANAGEMENT) LTD ◈
2 Doughty Buildings, Crow Arch Lane, Ringwood, BH24 1NZ
Tel: 01425 470730
Website: http://www.finmgt.co.uk
Resident Partners/Directors: ICAEW Members
P J Lewis

MICHELE WEBB
Woodpecker, Fir Tree Close, St Leonards, Ringwood BH24 2QW
Tel: 01202 895354
Principal: ICAEW Member
M Webb

RINGWOOD ACCOUNTING
1 Folly Farm Lane, Ashley, Ringwood, BH24 2NN

RINGWOOD ACCOUNTING LTD
1 Folly Farm Lane, Ashley, Ringwood, BH24 2NN

ROTHMAN PANTALL & CO
114 Christchurch Road, Ringwood, BH24 1DP
Tel: 01425 479977
Fax: 01425 480514
Email: ringwood@rothman-pantall.co.uk
Resident Partners/Directors: ICAEW Members
G J B Corlett

ROWENA M MARSH FCA MAE
9 St Ives Park, Ashley Heath, Ringwood, BH24 2JX

SHASENS & RE10 (SOUTH EAST) LTD
The Buckman Building, 43 Southampton Road, Ringwood, BH24 1HE

VINCENT CLEMAS ◈
Cornerways House, School Lane, Ringwood, BH24 1LG
Tel: 01425 470908
Email: mailbox@vincentclemas.com
Website: http://www.vincentclemas.com
Principal: ICAEW Member
V E Clemas

Registered by the ICAEW to carry out company audit work

Regulated by the ICAEW for a range of investment business activities

SPECIALISATIONS – FORENSIC ACCOUNTING

Expert Witnesses in Litigation

SPECIALISATIONS – SECTOR

Barristers
Charities
Solicitors

General Description: A team of 8 professionals dedicated to financial excellence.

VINCENT CLEMAS LLP
Cornerways House, School Lane, Ringwood, BH24 1LG

W H. LEVINGS
46 College Road, Ringwood, BH24 1NX

RIPLEY

BUTLER COOK
30/32 High Street, Codnor, Ripley, DE5 9QB

BUTLER COOK ACCOUNTANTS LTD
30/32 High Street, Codnor, Ripley, DE5 9QB
Tel: 01773 749702
Email: info@butler-cook.co.uk
Website: http://www.butler-cook.co.uk
Resident Partners/Directors: ICAEW Members
A F Butler

MABE ALLEN LLP
3 Derby Road, Ripley, DE5 3EA

P.R.A PALFREYMAN
83 Nottingham Road, Codnor, Ripley, DE5 9RH

RIPON

THE BARKER PARTNERSHIP
44 Kirkgate, Ripon, HG4 1PB
Tel: 01765 603501
Fax: 01765 605554
Email: charles@barkersripon.co.uk
Resident Partners/Directors: ICAEW Members
C Gill

Registered by the ICAEW to carry out company audit work

Regulated by the ICAEW for a range of investment business activities

BROUGH KIRKMAN ★ ◈
8 High Skellgate, Ripon, HG4 1BA
Tel: 01765 604441
Resident Partners/Directors: ICAEW Members
C J Wright

EURA AUDIT UK
John Aislabie Wing, Eva Lett House, 1 South Crescent, Ripon HG4 1SN

EURA AUDIT UK ★
Eva Lett House, 1 South Crescent, Ripon, HG4 1SN

F E METCALFE & CO ★
40A Market Place, Ripon, HG4 1BZ
Tel: 01765 604215
Resident Partners/Directors: ICAEW Members
J L Crabtree

HOBBS & CO ◈
18 Marton-Le-Moor, Ripon, HG4 5AT
Tel: 01423 324966
Principal: ICAEW Member
R K Hobbs

LAM
Oakwood, The Paddock, Melmerby, Ripon HG4 5HW

LISHMAN SIDWELL CAMPBELL & PRICE LLP
John Aislabie Wing, Eva Lett House, 1 South Crescent, Ripon HG4 1SN

LSCP LLP
Eva Lett House, 1 South Crescent, Ripon, HG4 1SN

T.F. BROWN & CO
West Farm, Eavestone, Ripon, HG4 3HD

ROBERTSBRIDGE

ALISON STEVENS & CO
5 Kemps Way, Salehurst, Robertsbridge, TN32 5PD
Tel: 01580 880237
Principal: ICAEW Member
A M Stevens

ROCHDALE

A FIELDING & CO
5 Seymour Grove, Rochdale, OL16 4RB

ALAN FIELDING
18 The Walk, Rochdale, OL16 1EP

BRIAN G. SWAIN & CO
55 Dale Street, Milnrow, Rochdale, OL16 3NJ

D.J. COLEMAN ◈
2 Redcar Street, Rochdale, OL12 0PU
Tel: 01706 649808
Principal: ICAEW Member
D J Coleman

FINO LTD
29 Cleveleys Avenue, Rochdale, OL16 4PD

FINO ACCOUNTING
29 Cleveleys Avenue, Rochdale, OL16 4PD

G.M. DINGLE
8 Broad Acre, Norden, Rochdale, OL12 7RP
Principal: ICAEW Member
G M Dingle

GEE & ROBINSON
Eagle House, Eagle Technology Park, Eagle Way (Off Queensway), Rochdale OL11 1TQ
Tel: 01706 631161
Resident Partners/Directors: ICAEW Members
M Kershaw, A C Page

GREENWOOD & CO
5 Cherry Grove, Rochdale, OL11 5YT
Tel: 01706 649457
Principal: ICAEW Member
J Greenwood

HWSEG LTD
Medicount House, 156 Manchester Road, Rochdale, OL11 4JQ
Tel: 01706 353800
Resident Partners/Directors: ICAEW Members
S A McLernon

JOHN A EDGAR
2 Oak View, Shawforth, Rochdale, OL12 8NS

JOHN LAWSON WILD & CO ◈
Cloth Hall, 150 Drake Street, Rochdale, OL16 1PX
Tel: 01706 632554
Resident Partners/Directors: ICAEW Members
M J Pickup, J L Wild

KENNETH P SHEA & CO
25 Durnford Close, Norden, Rochdale, OL12 7RX

LORD & CO
114 Drake Street, Rochdale, OL16 1PN
Tel: 01706 643044

MAURICE BLAND & CO
Suite One, First Floor, Blue Pit Business Centre, Queensway, Rochdale OL11 2PG
Tel: 01706 345070
Principal: ICAEW Member
M N Bland

PETER P BLOMELEY FCA
6 Christopher Acre, Norden, Rochdale, OL11 5FE
Tel: 01706 357861
Principal: ICAEW Member
P P Blomeley

SPL ASSOCIATES
Office Suite 8, 3 Fieldhouse Road, Rochdale, OL12 0AD

TALUKDAR & CO
158 Whitworth Road, Rochdale, OL12 0JG
Tel: 01706 640341
Principal: ICAEW Member
M N H Talukdar

TENON LTD
Lewis House, 12 Smith Street, Rochdale, OL16 1TX
Tel: 01706 355505

TENON AUDIT LTD
Lewis House, 12 Smith Street, Rochdale, OL16 1TX
Tel: 01706 355505

WYATT, MORRIS, GOLLAND & CO ◈
Park House, 200 Drake Street, Rochdale, OL16 1PJ
Tel: 01706 655117
Website: http://www.e-wmg.co.uk
Resident Partners/Directors: ICAEW Members
D Bentley, S N Chadwick, N K Greenhalgh, J B Hoyle, C P J Morris, G Morris, P A Richards
Registered by the ICAEW to carry out company audit work

ROCHESTER

ARKADIA LTD
159 Rochester Road, Burham, Rochester, ME1 3SF
Tel: 01634 869900
Resident Partners/Directors: ICAEW Members
R Kiralfy

ATHAWES & COMPANY LTD ◈
Stirling House, Sunderland Quay, Culpeper Close, Rochester ME2 4HN
Tel: 01634 290210
Resident Partners/Directors: ICAEW Members
A K Athawes

BRADLEY & CO ◈
4b Christchurch House, Beauford Court, Rochester, ME2 4FX

CONTROL ACCOUNTANCY SERVICES
1 Hawkwood Close, St Margaret's Banks, Rochester, ME1 1HW

CROSSLEY & CO
Star House, Star Hill, Rochester, ME1 1UX
Tel: 01634 840440
Email: info@crossley.co.uk
Website: http://www.crossley.co.uk
Resident Partners/Directors: ICAEW Members
R A Brown, T Rose
Registered by the ICAEW to carry out company audit work

FRIEND & GRANT LTD ◈
Bryant House, Bryant Road, Strood, Rochester ME2 3EG
Tel: 01634 731390
Resident Partners/Directors: ICAEW Members
M A Friend, A I Grant

HILARY ADAMS LTD
Unit 5, Rochester Court, Anthony's Way, Medway City Estate, Rochester ME2 4NW
Tel: 01634 722000
Email: hilary@hilaryadams.co.uk
Website: http://www.hilaryadams.co.uk
Other Offices:158 High Street, Herne Bay, 30 The Square, Birmingham

KENT ACCOUNTANCY ◈
20 York Road, Rochester, ME1 3DP

M W DODD & ASSOCIATES LTD
26 High Street, Rochester, ME1 1PT
Tel: 01634 828503
Fax: 01634 407040
Resident Partners/Directors: ICAEW Members
M W Dodd
Registered by the ICAEW to carry out company audit work

THE SINDEN THACKERAY PARTNERSHIP
23 Star Hill, Rochester, ME1 1XF
Tel: 01634 844793
Principal: ICAEW Member
V A Thackeray

WILLIAMS GILES ◈
Empire House, Sunderland Quay, Culpeper Close, Rochester ME2 4HN

WOOLMER & KENNEDY
30 Star Hill, Rochester, ME1 1XB
Tel: 01634 406166
Resident Partners/Directors: ICAEW Members
J F M Kennedy, P T Woolmer

ROCHFORD

DARREN WILLIAMS & CO LTD
32 Ashcombe, Rochford, SS4 1SL

HOWARD & STAPLETON ◈
1st Floor Offices, Natwest Bank, Market Square, Rochford SS4 1AJ
Tel: 01702 549288
Principal: ICAEW Member
G M Stapleton

MURPHY BRITT WOOD ★
Sovereign House, 82 West Street, Rochford, SS4 1AS

SANDERSON J.M.
29 Village Green, Canewdon, Rochford, SS4 3QF

VENTHAMS LTD ◈
Millhouse, 32-38 East Street, Rochford, SS4 1DB
Tel: 01702 209600
Website: http://www.venthams.com
Resident Partners/Directors: ICAEW Members
S R Baldwin, A Mathers, S A Rowson
Resident Partners (Non-ICAEW Members):
A G Godfrey
Other Offices: Lincoln's Inn Fields, London, Redhill, Surrey
Registered by the ICAEW to carry out company audit work

ROMFORD

THE ACCOUNTS PEOPLE ★
5 Princess Road, Romford, RM1 2SR

ALISON MCGINN
5 Academy Fields Road, Gidea Park, Romford, RM2 5UN

CHEGWIDDEN & CO ◈
Priestley House, Priestley Gardens, Chadwell Heath, Romford RM6 4SN
Tel: 020 8597 2531
Resident Partners/Directors: ICAEW Members
B T Buckley, C Otter
Registered by the ICAEW to carry out company audit work

SPECIALISATIONS – BUSINESS & GENERAL ADVICE

Acquisitions and Mergers
Disposal of Businesses
Takeovers

SPECIALISATIONS – SECTOR

Architects/Surveyors
Doctors

CLAY RATNAGE DAFFIN & CO LTD
Suite D, The Business Centre, Faringdon Avenue, Romford RM3 8EN

CLAY RATNAGE STREVENS & HILLS ★
Suite D, The Business Centre, Faringdon Avenue, Romford RM3 8EN

CLEMENCE HOAR CUMMINGS
Riverside House, 1-5 Como Street, Romford, RM7 7DZ

CONRICH & CO
65 Castellan Avenue, Gidea Park, Romford, RM2 6EB
Tel: 01708 748274
Principal: ICAEW Member
L M Conrich

CONRICH & ASSOCIATES ★
65 Castellan Avenue, Gidea Park, Romford, RM2 6EB
Tel: 01708 748274
Resident Partners/Directors: ICAEW Members
L M Conrich

FOOT & ELLIS-SMITH ◈
Abacus House, 68A North Street, Romford, RM1 1DA
Tel: 01708 766922
Resident Partners/Directors: ICAEW Members
I E Foot, S P Mitchell

FOOT & ELLIS-SMITH LTD ◈
Abacus House, 68A North Street, Romford, RM1 1DA
Tel: 01708 766922
Resident Partners/Directors: ICAEW Members
I E Foot, S P Mitchell

GIESS WALLIS CRISP
109a Main Road, Romford, RM2 3SL

JAMES CARPENTER & CO
Guardian House, 5 Conqueror Court, Spilsby Road, Harold Hill, Romford RM3 8SB

JARVIS & CO
75 Main Road, Gidea Park, Romford, RM2 5EL

JOHN S MCCUIN BSC FCA
21 Repton Gardens, Romford, RM2 5LS

K.P. DOHERTY & CO
22 Harlesden Walk, Romford, RM3 9HS

K.P. DOHERTY & CO
118 Collier Row Road, Collier Row, Romford, RM5 2BB

KINGSTON SMITH LLP
Orbital House, 20 Eastern Road, Romford, RM1 3PJ
Tel: 01708 759759
Fax: 01708 759758
Email: ks@kingstonsmith.co.uk
Website: http://www.kingstonsmith.co.uk
Resident Partners/Directors: ICAEW Members
D A Benton, S L Bright, D T Martine, B R Pope, M N Sinclair, R N Surman
Registered by the ICAEW to carry out company audit work
Regulated by the ICAEW for a range of investment business activities

P.M. RANDALL & CO
PO Box 131, Harold Hill, Romford, RM3 9LZ

R VORA & CO LTD ◈
6 Carlton Road, Romford, RM2 5AA
Tel: 01708 736644
Resident Partners/Directors: ICAEW Members
R S Vora

VORA & CO
6 Carlton Road, Romford, RM2 5AA

ROMSEY

ACCOUNTS2TAX LTD
3 Middlebridge Street, Romsey, SO51 8HJ

BELL & CO
4 Jermyns Lane, Ampfield, Romsey, SO51 0QA

BELL & CO (ACCOUNTANCY SERVICES) LTD
4 Jermyns Lane, Ampfield, Romsey, SO51 0QA
Tel: 01794 368954
Resident Partners/Directors: ICAEW Members
J D Bell

BOLER WISEMAN
8 Toll Gate, Stanbridge Earls, Romsey, SO51 0HE

BOLER WISEMAN LTD
8 Tollgate, Stanbridge Earls, Romsey, SO51 0HE

BOLER WISEMAN FINANCIAL SERVICES LTD
8 Tollgate, Stanbridge Earls, Romsey, SO51 0HE

CHRISTOPHER E.J. BURMAN FCA
Ardmhor House, 3 The Paddocks, Ampfield, Romsey SO51 9BG
Tel: 01794 368081
Principal: ICAEW Member
C E J Burman

COOLBELL LTD
Wigley Manor, Romsey Road, Ower, Romsey SO51 6AF
Tel: 02380 814113
Resident Partners/Directors: ICAEW Members
R S Gale, S L Moore

DAVID GAMBLIN
71 The Hundred, Romsey, SO51 8BZ
Tel: 01794 522620
Principal: ICAEW Member
D M Gamblin

HALFORD & CO
Unit 14, Home Farm Business Centre, East Tytherley Road, Lockerley, Romsey SO51 0JT

HOLMES & CO ◈
3a Bell Street, Romsey, SO51 8GY
Tel: 01794 515998
Principal: ICAEW Member
A Holmes

LAWRENCE P. COPPOCK
The Close, Church Lane, Braishfield, Romsey SO51 0QH

MARK HOOTON
2 Butlers Close, Lockerley, Romsey, SO51 0LY

MOORGATE
Wigley Manor, Romsey Road, Ower, Romsey SO51 6AF
Tel: 02380 814113

TBW
E3 The Premier Centre, Abbey Park, Romsey, SO51 9DG

WILKINS KENNEDY ◈
3-4 Eastwood Court, Broadwater Road, Romsey, SO51 8JJ
Tel: 01794 515441
Website: http://www.wilkinskennedy.com
Resident Partners/Directors: ICAEW Members
J R Natt, M R Tizard
Other Offices: Amersham, Ashford, Egham, Guildford, Hertford, London, Orpington, Reading, Southend, Winchester
Overseas Offices: Stanley, Falkland Islands
Registered by the ICAEW to carry out company audit work
SPECIALISATIONS – BUSINESS & GENERAL ADVICE
Acquisitions and Mergers
Disposal of Businesses
Outsourcing - Financial Services
SPECIALISATIONS – SECTOR
Charities
Construction
Property

ROSS-ON-WYE

ANNE COLVIN
Hollendene, Goodrich, Ross-on-wye, HR9 6JA

AUBREY & CO
19 Church Street, Ross-on-wye, HR9 5HN
Tel: 01989 765547
Resident Partners/Directors: ICAEW Members
N R Lewis

HALE JACKSON KNIGHT
Montague House, 4 St Marys Street, Ross-on-Wye, HR9 5HT
Tel: 01989 567500
Resident Partners/Directors: ICAEW Members
L Hale, S L Jackson, P E Knight

J. BARNARD
Brelston Court, Marstow, Ross-on-Wye, HR9 6HF
Tel: 01600 890957
Principal: ICAEW Member
J C Barnard

MARTYN DAVY ◈
North Pole, Gorsley, Ross-on-wye, HR9 7BJ
Tel: 01989 720121
Principal: ICAEW Member
M G Davy

P.J FRAY
Keepers Cottage, Upton Bishop, Ross-on-wye, HR9 7UE
Tel: 01989 780383
Principal: ICAEW Member
P J Fray

PETER J C METCALFE
Hildersley Cottage, Ross-on-wye, HR9 7NJ

PETER WATTS & CO
Berrylands, Hawthorne Lane, Ross-on-Wye, HR9 5BG
Tel: 01989 562088
Principal: ICAEW Member
P M Watts

R.A BODOANO
Rowanberries, Linton, Ross-on-wye, HR9 7RY

THORNE & CO (ROSS-ON-WYE) LTD
1 St Marys Street, Ross-on-Wye, HR9 5HT
Tel: 01989 763636

ROSSENDALE

ASHWORTH MOULDS
1 Grange Crescent, Rawtenstall, Rossendale, BB4 7QT
Tel: 01282 432171
Fax: 01282 412510
Email: accountants@ashworthmoulds.co.uk
Resident Partners/Directors: ICAEW Members
C Harrison
Other Offices:11 Nicholas Street, Burnley, Lancashire BB11 2AL

CASSONS ◈
St Crispin House, St Crispin Way, Haslingden, Rossendale BB4 4PW
Tel: 0845 337 9409
Fax: 0845 337 9408
Email: welcome@cassons.co.uk
Website: http://www.cassons.co.uk
Resident Partners/Directors: ICAEW Members
C G Cooper, S Greenwood, L Nutter, C Tice
Other Offices: Manchester
Registered by the ICAEW to carry out company audit work
Authorised and regulated by the Financial Services Authority for investment business

SPECIALISATIONS – BUSINESS & GENERAL ADVICE
Investment Appraisal
SPECIALISATIONS – FORENSIC ACCOUNTING
Expert Witnesses in Litigation
Forensic Accounting
SPECIALISATIONS – INVESTMENT BUSINESS
Pensions Advice
SPECIALISATIONS – SECTOR

Barristers
Dentists/Opticians
Doctors
Entertainers
Solicitors
SPECIALISATIONS – TAXATION
Estate Planning

H. BINGHAM & CO ◈
39 Andrew Avenue, Rawtenstall, Rossendale, BB4 6EU
Tel: 07970 826667
Principal: ICAEW Member
H Bingham

HALLIWELL & HORTON
29 Burnley Road East, Waterfoot, Rossendale, BB4 9AG

HOWARTH & CO
49 Fields Road, Haslingden, Rossendale, BB4 6QA

JM ACCOUNTANTS LTD
137 Cherry Crescent, Rossendale, BB4 6DS

ROTHERHAM

A.M. ALLWOOD
73 Hallam Road, Moorgate, Rotherham, S60 3ED

ALCO AUDIT LTD
12-14 Percy Street, Rotherham, S65 1ED

ALLOTTS
The Old Grammar School, 13 Moorgate Road, Rotherham, S60 2EN
Tel: 01709 828400
Website: http://www.allotts.co.uk
Resident Partners/Directors: ICAEW Members
A E Grice, N S Highfield, J N Saunders, M S Watson
Resident Partners (Non-ICAEW Members):
K Williamson

DEAN & CO
100 Wellgate, Rotherham, S60 2LP
Tel: 020 8679 7630
Principal: ICAEW Member
M A Mohiuddin

FOSTER & CO
5 South Terrace, Moorgate, Rotherham, S60 2EU

HARDWICKS
Sarsfield House, Gillott Lane, Wickersley, Rotherham S66 1EH
Tel: 01709 545265

HARDWICKS ACCOUNTANTS LTD
Sarsfield House, Gillott Lane, Wickersley, Rotherham S66 1EH
Tel: 01709 545265
Resident Partners/Directors: ICAEW Members
N A Hardwick

HAYWOOD & CO
24-26 Mansfield Road, Rotherham, S60 2DR

MALTBY ACCOUNTANCY SERVICES LTD
63 Bawtry Road, Bramley, Rotherham, S66 2TN

MICHAEL A. JARVIS & CO
Edenthorpe, Grove Road, Rotherham, S60 2ER
Tel: 01709 820360
Resident Partners/Directors: ICAEW Members
J A Cawley, M A Jarvis

MONTGOMERY & CO ◈
Norham House, Mountenoy Road, Moorgate, Rotherham S60 2AJ
Tel: 01709 376313
Principal: ICAEW Member
S A Bell

PKN
63 Bawtry Road, Bramley, Rotherham, S66 2TN

ROBERT OGLE
6 The Elms, Doncaster Road, Rotherham, S65 1DY
Tel: 01709 830725
Email: info@robertogle.co.uk
Website: http://www.robertogle.co.uk
Principal: ICAEW Member
R C Ogle
Registered by the ICAEW to carry out company audit work
Regulated by the ICAEW for a range of investment business activities

THORPES
61 Wickersley Road, Rotherham, S60 3PX

THORPES LTD
61 Wickersley Road, Rotherham, S60 3PX

TREVOR BILLARD AND COMPANY LTD
1 Webster Crescent, Kimberworth, Rotherham, S61 2BS

WALTERS HAWSON LTD ◈
26 Percy Street, Rotherham, S65 1ED
Tel: 01709 369680
Resident Partners/Directors: ICAEW Members
K D Hawson, D I Walters

WATS LTD
63 Bawtry Road, Bramley, Rotherham, S66 2TN

WICKERSLEY ACCOUNTANCY & TAXATION SERVICES
5 Beech Avenue, Brecks, Rotherham, S65 3HN

ROWLANDS GILL

ANDREW R HALL & CO
71 Dominies Close, Rowlands Gill, NE39 1PB

ROWLEY REGIS

E R GROVE & CO
4 Halesowen Street, Rowley Regis, B65 0HG

F.E. SIDAWAY, SON & CO
5-6 Long Lane, Rowley Regis, B65 0JA

ROBERT BILLINGHAM LTD
The Maltings, Ross, Rowley Regis, B65 8DZ

ROYSTON

A.J.WATTS
54 Beldam Avenue, Royston, SG8 9UW
Tel: 01763 241187
Principal: ICAEW Member
A J Watts

AUSTRAL CROSBY
20 Norgetts Lane, Melbourn, Royston, SG8 6HS

BLANCHE & CO
The Lanterns, 16 Melbourn Street, Royston, SG8 7BX
Tel: 020 8317 9633
Resident Partners/Directors: ICAEW Members
J E Gill, J W Jewson

COMPTON BUSINESS SERVICES LTD
Wyndermere House, Ashwell Road, Steeple Morden, Royston SG8 0NZ

FOURWAYS
1a Melbourn Street, Royston, SG8 7BP

FOURWAYS 4 BUSINESS LTD
1a Melbourn Street, Royston, SG8 7BP

HARDCASTLE BURTON LLP
Lake House, Market Hill, Royston, SG8 9JN

N.T.BUTLER
26 Rose Lane, Melbourn, Royston, SG8 6AD
Tel: 01763 263127
Principal: ICAEW Member
N T Butler

NANKIVELLS
45 Green Drift, Royston, SG8 5BX
Tel: 01763 231631
Principal: ICAEW Member
G D Nankivell

NIGEL SPENCE & CO
Tan House, 15 South End, Bassingbourn, Royston SG8 5NJ

QUANTUM FINANCIAL SOLUTIONS LTD
Ellerslie, Crawley End, Chrishall, Royston SG8 8QJ

WKH ◈
22/24 Kneesworth Street, Royston, SG8 5AA
Tel: 01763 247321
Website: http://www.wkhca.co.uk
Training Contracts Available.
Resident Partners/Directors: ICAEW Members
T R Maris, D H Smyth
Registered by the ICAEW to carry out company audit work
Regulated by the ICAEW for a range of investment business activities

INVESTOR IN PEOPLE

SPECIALISATIONS – AUDIT & ASSURANCE
Audit
SPECIALISATIONS – BUSINESS & GENERAL ADVICE
Acquisitions and Mergers
SPECIALISATIONS – SECTOR

Agriculture
SPECIALISATIONS – TAXATION
Payroll Service and Advice

RUGBY

AIMS - JOHN STARLEY
Moonrakers, Back Lane, Birdingbury, Rugby CV23 8EN

AKHTAR & CO
11 Regent Place, Rugby, CV21 2PJ

AKHTAR & CO LTD
11 Regent Place, Rugby, CV21 2PJ

ASTUTE SERVICES
4 Daventry Road, Dunchurch, Rugby, CV22 6NS

ASTUTE SERVICES LTD
4 Daventry Road, Dunchurch, Rugby, CV22 6NS

ATKINSON FINCH & CO
Central Chambers, 45-47 Albert St, Rugby, CV21 2SG
Tel: 01788 543164
Resident Partners/Directors: ICAEW Members
G R Bolton, S G Bolton

BARKER & CO
Street Ashton Farm House, Stretton Under Fosse, Rugby, CV23 0PH
Tel: 01788 833760
Principal: ICAEW Member
K Barker
General Description:
Established 1978, specialising in farming and agriculture.

BOTTOMLEY AND CO
Glenwood House, 5 Arundel Way, Cawston, Rugby CV22 7TU

C H IVENS & CO ◈
50 Regent Street, Rugby, CV21 2PU
Tel: 01788 576166
Fax: 0871 661 3020
Email: info@chivens.co.uk
Website: http://www.chivens.co.uk

SPECIALISATIONS – AUDIT & ASSURANCE
Audit

SPECIALISATIONS – FINANCIAL REPORTING
Accounts Preparation

SPECIALISATIONS – INVESTMENT BUSINESS
Financial Planning and Advice

SPECIALISATIONS – TAXATION
Taxation

CASHMORE & CO
Third Floor, The Robbins Building, Albert Street, Rugby CV21 2SD
Tel: 01788 570424
Principal: ICAEW Member
M J Cashmore

CLIFFORD TOWERS (ACCOUNTANTS) LTD ◈
9 North Street, Rugby, CV21 2RA
Tel: 01788 578488
Resident Partners/Directors: ICAEW Members
S G C Towers

COTTONS
26 Albert Street, Rugby, CV21 2RS

DNA ACCOUNTANTS
2 Toft Villas, Kites Hardwick, Rugby, CV23 8AD

DNA LOGISTICS LTD
2 Toft Villas, Kites Hardwick, Rugby, CV23 8AD

GRAHAM W. LUCKMAN
Park Fields, Birdingbury Lane, Frankton, Rugby CV23 9QR
Tel: 01926 632733
Principal: ICAEW Member
G W Luckman

INDEPENDENT DRIVERS LTD
Suite 22, Dunsmore Business Centre, Spring Street, Rugby CV21 3HH

IVENSCO LTD ◈
50 Regent Street, Rugby, CV21 2PU

J.R. WATSON & CO
Sir Frank Whittle Business, Centre, Great Central Way, Rugby CV21 3XH

JA WALTERS LTD
The Dairy, Buckwell Lane, Clifton-Upon-Dunsmore, Rugby CV23 0BJ

K R CAHILL & CO
Fitzjohns Lodge, Barby Road, Rugby, CV22 5QB

K R CAHILL & CO LTD
Fitzjohns Lodge, Barby Road, Rugby, CV22 5QB

LAWRENCE WEBSTER ASSOCIATES LTD
Eastlands Court, St Peters Road, Rugby, CV21 3QP
Tel: 01788 555088
Resident Partners/Directors: ICAEW Members
L A Webster

MCCOLM CARDEW LTD
10 Main Street, Bilton, Rugby, CV22 7NB

S.J. HUNT & CO
4 Paddox Court, Rugby, CV23 8XX

TARGET CONSULTING LTD
Bloxam Court, Corporation Street, Rugby, CV21 2DU
Tel: 01788 539000
Fax: 01788 539039
Email: target@target-accountants.com
Website: http://www.target-accountants.com
Date Established: 1998
Registered by the ICAEW to carry out company audit work
Regulated by the ICAEW for a range of investment business activities
General Description: A leading business and accounting firm with offices in Rugby, Bath, Reading and London. Authorised provision of financial services.

WRIGHT & CO
2 Longrood Road, Bilton, Rugby, CV22 7RG

RUGELEY

AIMS - MICHAEL BALL
Apartment 2, Howell Mews, Wolseley Road, Rugeley WS15 2GJ

DAINS LLP
The Hollies, Church Street, Rugeley, WS15 2AB
Tel: 0845 555 8844
Fax: 01889 583878
Email: rugeley@dains.com
Website: http://www.dains.com
Date Established: 1926
Resident Partners/Directors: ICAEW Members
A R Massey
Non-resident Partners (ICAEW Members):
N D Smith, M F P Smith, H M P Reynolds, A R Massey, A P Morris, S G Wright, P D Bradshaw
Non-resident Partners (Non-ICAEW Members):
M Castree, N Hawksley, A McQuillian, R C McNeilly, S C Bursell
Other Offices: Burton, Lichfield, Coleshill, Swadlincote, Birmingham
Registered by the ICAEW to carry out company audit work
Regulated by the ICAEW for a range of investment business activities

JONATHAN G. SIMONS
Office No 1, Paris House, Market Square, Rugeley WS15 2BL

PJW ACCOUNTING LTD
Suite 15, Hawkesyard Hall, Armitage Park, Armitage, Rugeley WS15 1PU
Tel: 01889 586431
Resident Partners/Directors: ICAEW Members
P J Woodcock

WALLETTS ★
Rydal House, Colton Road, Rugeley, WS15 3HF

WYNNIATT-HUSEY LTD ◈
Beckett House, 31 Upper Brook Street, Rugeley, WS15 2DP
Tel: 01889 583211
Email: alan@wynniatt-huseyltd.com
Date Established: 1983
Training Contracts Available.
Resident Partners/Directors: ICAEW Members
I A McIntosh, R J Wynniatt-Husey
Resident Partners (Non-ICAEW Members):
A Durose
Registered by the ICAEW to carry out company audit work
Regulated by the ICAEW for a range of investment business activities

RUISLIP

ALLEN ACCOUNTING
57 Dartmouth Road, Ruislip, HA4 0DE

ASHBURNS ◈
79 Victoria Road, Ruislip, HA4 9BH

COLLYER & CO
17A Fairacres, Ruislip, HA4 8AN

DHARSI & CO
Woodview, 92a Broadwood Avenue, Ruislip, HA4 7XT

DIVERSET LTD ◈
Canada House, 272 Field End Road, Ruislip, HA4 9NA

DUNCAN MACAREE
153 Cornwall Road, Ruislip, HA4 6AG
Tel: 01895 632916
Principal: ICAEW Member
D MacAree

THE FOUR PAGES LTD
Canada House, 272 Field End Road, Ruislip, HA4 9NA
Tel: 020 8582 0400
Resident Partners/Directors: ICAEW Members
C P Davis

GRANT HARROD
49a High Street, Ruislip, HA4 7BD
Tel: 01895 624321
Fax: 01895 624123
Email: solutions@grantharrodparkinson.com
Resident Partners/Directors: ICAEW Members
A H Grant, J B Grant

SPECIALISATIONS – FINANCIAL REPORTING
Accounts Preparation
Limited Liability Partnership
Partnership/Sole Trader Accounts

SPECIALISATIONS – SECTOR
Charities
Dentists/Opticians
Doctors

SPECIALISATIONS – TAXATION
Capital Gains — Personal
Partnerships and Sole Traders
Personal
Self Assessment Advice
Small Traders

GRANT HARROD PARKINSON ★
49a High Street, Ruislip, HA4 7BD

HUNT BLAKE
Jubilee House, The Oaks, Ruislip, HA4 7LF

HUNT BLAKE LTD
Jubilee House, The Oaks, Ruislip, HA4 7LF

KOSHAL ASSOCIATES
Gautam House, 1-3 Shenley Avenue, Ruislip Manor, Ruislip HA4 6BP

MG ACCOUNTANTS & CO
Audit House, 260 Field End Road, Ruislip, HA4 9LT

MG AUDIT (LONDON) LTD
31 Westholme Gardens, Ruislip, HA4 8QJ

OVERDRAFT LTD
Canada House Business Centre, 272 Field End Road, Eastcote, Ruislip HA4 9NA

PITMAN COHEN LLP
Great Central House, Great Central Avenue, Ruislip, HA4 6TS

RA & CO
Audit House, 260 Field End Road, Ruislip, HA4 9LT

WARNEFORD GIBBS ★ ◈
College House, 17 King Edwards Road, Ruislip, HA4 7AE
Tel: 01895 677011
Email: warneford.gibbs@virgin.net
Resident Partners/Directors: ICAEW Members
B R Warneford

SPECIALISATIONS – FINANCIAL REPORTING

Accounts Preparation

SPECIALISATIONS – SECTOR

Clubs/Associations
Solicitors

SPECIALISATIONS – TAXATION

Capital Gains — Personal
Payroll Service and Advice
Self Assessment Advice

RUNCORN

AGP
Sycamore House, Sutton Quays Business Park, Sutton Weaver, Runcorn WA7 3EH
Tel: 01244 325511
Email: chester@agp-accountants.co.uk
Resident Partners/Directors: ICAEW Members
P Chesters
Non-resident Partners (ICAEW Members):
R S Gamwell, S McLean, I Black, R Lloyd, L Thomas
Other Offices: Warrington, Sutton Quays

Registered by the ICAEW to carry out company audit work

Regulated by the ICAEW for a range of investment business activities

RUSHDEN

JERVIS & PARTNERS
3 Market Square, Higham Ferrers, Rushden, NN10 8BP
Tel: 01933 356633

P.J. NARRAMORE
3 Williams Way, Higham Ferrers, Rushden, NN10 8AJ
Tel: 01933 316734
Principal: ICAEW Member
P J Narramore

P. WILLSON & CO ★ ◈
Carlton House, High Street, Higham Ferrers, Rushden NN10 8BW
Tel: 01933 357319
Resident Partners/Directors: ICAEW Members
T D Kirk

PETER ARROWSMITH FCA
Office 4 Knights Farm, Newton Road, Rushden, NN10 0SX
Tel: 01933 411941
Website: http://www.niconsultancy.co.uk
Principal: ICAEW Member
P Arrowsmith

SPECIALISATIONS – TAXATION

National Insurance Advice

ROGER DENTON
8A Church Street, Rushden, NN10 9YT
Tel: 01933 311198
Principal: ICAEW Member
R Denton

TREVOR L. NEWELL & CO ◈
155 Wellingborough Road, Rushden, NN10 9TB
Tel: 01933 312950
Resident Partners/Directors: ICAEW Members
T L Newell
Resident Partners (Non-ICAEW Members):
P A Knight

RYDE

DAVID HILLIAM
The Lodge, Oak Lawn, Woodside, Wootton, Ryde PO33 4JR

GEORGE CASSELL
Old Abbey Farm House, Quarr Lane, Ryde, PO33 4ER

MARK WYNTER ◈
Thornton Cottage, Puckpool Hill, Ryde, PO33 1PJ

SOLENT ACCOUNTANCY SERVICES LTD
88 Amherst Place, Ryde, PO33 1FF

WHITMILL WILSON & CO ◈
40 Union St, Ryde, PO33 2LF
Tel: 01983 562964
Principal: ICAEW Member
A J Wilson

RYE

BA TAXATION SERVICES LTD
Lyndhurst, Main Street, Peasmarsh, Rye TN31 6YA

GIBBONS MANNINGTON
6 Lion Street, Rye, TN31 7LB

K.R. FORD
Brook House, Main Street, Beckley, Rye N31 6RL
Tel: 01797 260226
Principal: ICAEW Member
K R Ford

PHIPPS & CO (SOUTH EAST) LLP
Landgate Chambers, 24 Landgate, Rye, TN31 7LJ

SAFFRON WALDEN

BACKHOUSE YONG PARTNERSHIP
Broomwood, Cambridge Road, Quendon, Saffron Walden CB11 3YN

CHARTWELL ◈
79 High Street, Saffron Walden, CB10 1DZ
Tel: 01799 526531
Fax: 01799 523107
Email: rogerevans.chartwell@gmail.com
Mobile: 07701 005098
Date Established: 2005
Principal: ICAEW Member
R Evans
General Description: We specialise in management account reporting, fund raising, capital restructuring and provision of non executive directors.

CHRISTINE SHARPE FCA
2-4 London Road, Saffron Walden, CB11 4ED
Tel: 01799 527531
Principal: ICAEW Member
S C Sharpe

DAVID TURNER & CO
Church Farm, Elmdon, Saffron Walden, CB11 4LT

DEACON'S
The Stables, Shipton Bridge Farm, Widdington, Saffron Walden CB11 3SU

DISCLOSURE SOLUTIONS LTD
The Old Smithy, Radwinter Road, Ashdon, Saffron Walden CB10 2ET
Tel: 01799 584053
Resident Partners/Directors: ICAEW Members
S G Hastie

HILLYATES
Hill House, 27 Meadowford, Newport, Saffron Walden CB11 3QL

HSA PARTNERSHIP ◈
Lewis House, Great Chesterford Court, Great Chesterford, Saffron Walden CB10 1PF

LANHAM AND CO
9 Great Chesterford Court, London Road, Great Chesterford, Saffron Walden CB10 1PF

LANHAM AND COMPANY LTD
9 Great Chesterford Court, London Road, Gt Chesterford, Saffron Walden CB10 1PF

NEWSTONE & CO
3 Pepper Court, Great Chesterford, Saffron Walden, CB10 1NZ
Tel: 01799 530554
Principal: ICAEW Member
R E Newstone

PAUL D. CAMP
Jarrards, Church Hill, Radwinter, Saffron Walden CB10 2SX
Tel: 07801 596506
Principal: ICAEW Member
P D Camp

R M CHANCELLOR & COMPANY LTD ◈
Lewis House, Great Chesterford Court, Great Chesterford, Saffron Walden CB10 1PF

SHIPLEYS LLP
Market House, 10 Market Walk, Saffron Walden, CB10 1JZ
Tel: 01799 521301
Fax: 01799 523854
Email: saffron@shipleys.com
Website: http://www.shipleys.com
Resident Partners/Directors: ICAEW Members
A W Mein
Resident Partners (Non-ICAEW Members):
G Haselton
Other Offices: London, Godalming

Registered by the ICAEW to carry out company audit work

Regulated by the ICAEW for a range of investment business activities

SUE CLARK BA ACA
Labrey Cottage, 14 Victoria Gardens, Saffron Walden, CB11 3AF

THP LTD
24 High Street, Saffron Walden, CB10 1AX

VICTOR KIRBY & CO LTD
Business & Technology Centre, Shire Hill, Saffron Walden, CB11 3AQ
Tel: 01799 525508
Resident Partners/Directors: ICAEW Members
V G Kirby

WHITMILL PRESCOTT & CO
The Green Garages, Cambridge Road, Newport, Saffron Walden CB11 3TN
Tel: 01799 543317
Principal: ICAEW Member
S F L Bulling

SALCOMBE

MICHAEL LOCKE & CO LTD
C/O Salcombe Company Ltd, Fore Street, Salcombe, TU8 8JG

ROBERT FARQUHAR
17 Beadon Road, Salcombe, TQ8 8LX
Tel: 01548 842557
Principal: ICAEW Member
R M Farquhar

SALE

A ALLCOCK CORPORATE FINANCE
59 Granary Way, Sale, M33 4GF

ACCENT CAPITAL LLP ◈
The Moorings, Dane Road Industrial Estate, 1 Dane Road, Sale M33 7BP
Tel: 0161 976 5999
Resident Partners/Directors: ICAEW Members
P A Teasdale

ANDREW OLESIUK & CO
9 Norley Drive, Sale Moor, Sale, M33 2JE

ARMITT & CO
Marsland Chambers, 1a Marsland Road, Sale Moor, Sale M33 3HP
Tel: 0161 962 1855
Email: info@armitt.net
Website: http://www.armitt.net
Date Established: 1989
Training Contracts Available.
Principal: ICAEW Member
P Hoszowskyj

SPECIALISATIONS – BUSINESS & GENERAL ADVICE
Book-keeping
Management Accounting
Consultancy

SPECIALISATIONS – FINANCIAL REPORTING
Accounts Preparation

SPECIALISATIONS – TAXATION
Payroll Service and Advice
Self Assessment Advice
Taxation
Value Added Tax

BARBER & CO
19A Green Lane, Ashton on Mersey, Sale, M33 5PN

CALDWELL CROMPTON
Alderley, 35 Whitehall Road, Sale, M33 3NL

CHARLES & CO ◈
66 Cross Street, Sale, M33 7AN
Tel: 0161 962 8089

CHARLES & CO ACCOUNTANCY SERVICES LTD
66 Cross Street, Sale, M33 7AN

CLEWORTH BEARDSLEY
107-109 Washway Road, Sale, M33 7TY

CLEWORTH BEARDSLEY LTD
107-109 Washway Road, Sale, M33 7TY

DALE PICKARD & CO
Bank House, 4 Wharf Rd, Sale, M33 2AF
Tel: 0161 969 2017
Principal: ICAEW Member
D Pickard

DAVID CHAPMAN ACCOUNTANCY LTD
18 Stoneleigh Avenue, Sale, M33 5FF
Tel: 0161 962 5048
Resident Partners/Directors: ICAEW Members
D L Chapman

THE DEBT PEOPLE
Marsland House, Marsland Road, Sale, M33 3AQ

THE DEBT PEOPLE LTD
Marsland House, Marsland Road, Sale, M33 3AQ

HAROLD SHARP ◈
Holland House, 1-5 Oakfield, Sale, M33 6TT
Tel: 0161 905 1616
Website: http://www.freedomtogrow.co.uk
Resident Partners/Directors: ICAEW Members
A C Copping, H R Cunningham, R M Evans, A J Lane, C A Wrighton
Registered by the ICAEW to carry out company audit work
Authorised and regulated by the Financial Services Authority for investment business

JULIE K HEWER
17 Arran Avenue, Sale, M33 3NQ

KAO FINANCIAL MANAGEMENT SERVICES
16 Buckfast Road, Sale, M33 5QB

PHILIP DYKES & CO
1 Roebuck Lane, Sale, M33 7SY

RIDGETOWN LLP
4 Fernacre, Sale, M33 2BA

SAXON & CO
Crowley, 85 Hope Road, Sale, M33 3AW
Tel: 0161 973 8999
Principal: ICAEW Member
J C Saxon

TWJ
The Moorings, Dane Road Industrial Estate, Sale, M33 7BP

TWJ PARTNERSHIP LLP
The Moorings, Dane Road Industrial Estate, Sale, M33 7BP

WALMSLEY & CO ACCOUNTANTS LTD
8 Eastway, Sale, M33 4DX

WILLIAM H. CHETHAM
10 Arnesby Avenue, Sale, M33 2WJ

SALFORD

ABBOT & CO
35 Cavendish Road, Salford, M7 4WP
Tel: 0161 708 8480
Principal: ICAEW Member
M Epstein

B. OLSBERG & CO
2nd Floor Newbury House, 401 Bury New Road, Salford, M7 2BT

B P & CO
6 Bexley Square, Salford, M3 6BZ

CASTLEFIELD ACCOUNTANCY SERVICES LTD
4 Castlefield Avenue, Salford, M7 4GQ

CRAWFORDS
Stanton House, 41 Blackfriars Road, Salford, M3 7DB

D. HALL & CO
46 Broom Lane, Salford, M7 4FJ

EDWARDS VEEDER LLP
Alex House, 260-268 Chapel Street, Salford, M3 5JZ

FORD CAMPBELL CORPORATE FINANCE LLP ◈
City Wharf, New Bailey Street, Salford, M3 5ER

FORD CAMPBELL LLP
City Wharf, New Bailey Street, Salford, M3 5ER
Tel: 0161 819 2500
Fax: 0161 839 9990
Email: mail@ford-campbell.co.uk
Website: http://www.ford-campbell.co.uk
Resident Partners/Directors: ICAEW Members
J R Butcher, A S Campbell, A J Ford, G C F Travis
Resident Partners (Non-ICAEW Members):
A Woolley
Other Offices: Leeds

FREEMAN JONES LTD
Carlton House, Vere Street, Salford, M50 2GQ

H.KERSHNER
18 New Hall Road, Salford, M7 4EL
Tel: 0161 792 1777
Principal: ICAEW Member
H Kershner

LORD & CO
31 Waterpark Road, Salford, M7 4FT
Tel: 0161 740 1396
Principal: ICAEW Member
M Silver

M. SEITLER & CO ◈
Unit 4, The Cottages, Deva Centre, Trinity Way, Salford M3 7BE
Tel: 0161 832 6600
Principal: ICAEW Member
M P Seitler

MAGINNIS AND CO
24 Broad Street, Salford, M6 5BY

P. DAVID LEVINSON ◈
20 Moor End Avenue, Salford, M7 3NX
Tel: 0161 792 4097
Fax: 0161 792 4097
Email: pdavidl@hotmail.co.uk
Principal: ICAEW Member
P D Levinson
Registered by the ICAEW to carry out company audit work

SPECIALISATIONS – AUDIT & ASSURANCE
Audit

SPECIALISATIONS – FINANCIAL REPORTING
Accounts Preparation
Limited Companies
Limited Company Accounts
Partnership/Sole Trader Accounts

SPECIALISATIONS – TAXATION
Personal
Taxation

R. BLACK & CO
11 Vernon Road, Salford, M7 4NW

RICHARDS & CO
1 Daisy Bank Avenue, Salford, M6 7NT

RPG HOLDINGS LTD
The Copper Room, Deva Centre, Trinity Way, Salford M3 7BG

S. SAMUELS & CO
2nd Floor, Enfield House, Bury Old Road, Salford M7 4QX

TAXPRAC LTD
2nd Floor Newbury House, 401 Bury New Road, Salford, M7 2BT

TOPPING PARTNERSHIP
9th Floor, 8 Exchange Quay, Salford, M5 3EJ

TOPPING PARTNERSHIP LTD
9th Floor, 8 Exchange Quay, Salford, M5 3EJ

SALISBURY

A.R. CLAVELL
2 Whitbred Road, Salisbury, SP2 9PE
Tel: 01722 323584
Principal: ICAEW Member
A R Clavell

ABC 123 LTD
Rechabite House, 91 Crane Street, Salisbury, SP1 2PU

ABC 123 LTD
Forest Edge, Nomansland, Salisbury, SP5 2BP

ACCOUNTS BY FAX LTD
61 Netherhampton Road, Harnham, Salisbury, SP2 8HD

ADJE LTD
Orchard Lea, High Street, Tisbury, Salisbury SP3 6HF

ATKINSONS (BISHOPSTONE) LTD
The Old Chapel, Chapel Lane, Bishopstone, Salisbury SP5 4BT
Tel: 01722 780208
Email: ja@atkinsonsltd.co.uk
Resident Partners/Directors: ICAEW Members
C J Atkinson

BEGBIES TRAYNOR
65 St Edmunds Church Street, Salisbury, SP1 1EF
Tel: 01722 435190
Resident Partners (Non-ICAEW Members):
J Palmer

SPECIALISATIONS – BUSINESS RECOVERY & INSOLVENCY
Bankruptcies
Corporate Recovery
Liquidations

BROADWAY & CO
Nadder House, Lower Road, Bemerton, Salisbury SP2 9NB

CLIFFORD FRY & CO
St Marys House, Netherhampton, Salisbury, SP2 8PU

CLIFFORD FRY & CO LLP
St Marys House, Netherhampton, Salisbury, SP2 8PU

DAVID A. CLARKE
20 Longhill Drive, Salisbury, SP2 8TD
Tel: 01722 503600
Principal: ICAEW Member
D A Clarke

DAVID EDMONDS LTD
Land Court Lane House, Tytherley Road, Winterslow, Salisbury SP5 1PZ
Tel: 01980 862281
Resident Partners/Directors: ICAEW Members
D K Edmonds

EMAMY.COM
61 Netherhampton Road, Harnham, Salisbury, SP2 8HD

FAWCETTS
Windover House, St Ann Street, Salisbury, SP1 2DR
Tel: 01722 420920
Fax: 01722 411375
Email: partners@fawcetts.co.uk
Website: http://www.fawcetts.co.uk
Resident Partners/Directors: ICAEW Members
R M V Allen, T Austreng, S J L Ellingham
Resident Partners (Non-ICAEW Members):
N D Jones
Registered by the ICAEW to carry out company audit work
Regulated by the ICAEW for a range of investment business activities
General Description: Member of the UK 200 Group.

FLETCHER & PARTNERS
Crown Chambers, Bridge Street, Salisbury, SP1 2LZ
Tel: 01722 327801
Fax: 01722 323839
Email: mail@fletchpart.co.uk
Website: http://www.fletchpart.co.uk
Training Contracts Available.
Resident Partners/Directors: ICAEW Members
M J Fisher, J Fletcher, N A Halls, C E Macey, P A Proctor, M F Tompsett, M S Wylie
Registered by the ICAEW to carry out company audit work
Regulated by the ICAEW for a range of investment business activities

FRANCIS CLARK ◈
Hitchcock House, Hilltop Business Park, Devizes Road, Salisbury SP3 4UF
Tel: 01722 337661
Website: http://www.francisclark.co.uk
Resident Partners/Directors: ICAEW Members
P.M. Douglas-Pennant, P C Giessler, N H W Gooch
Authorised and regulated by the Financial Services Authority for investment business

HAMILTON & CO
The White Cottage, Stock Lane, Landford Wood, Salisbury SP5 2ER
Tel: 01794 390310
Principal: ICAEW Member
D N P Hamilton

HEXTALL MEAKIN LTD
Beckett House, 4 Bridge Street, Salisbury, SP1 2LX

THE HOPKINS PARTNERSHIP
1 South Newton Trading Estate, Warminster Road, South Newton, Salisbury SP2 0QW
Tel: 01722 742233
Resident Partners/Directors: ICAEW Members
N L Hopkins
Resident Partners (Non-ICAEW Members):
J Curtis
Registered by the ICAEW to carry out company audit work
Regulated by the ICAEW for a range of investment business activities

HUGH DAVIES & CO LTD
35 Chequers Court, Brown Street, Salisbury, SP1 2AS

J. MATTHIAE & CO
The Tythings, The Plantation, West Winterslow, Salisbury SP5 1RE
Tel: 01980 862892
Principal: ICAEW Member
J Matthiae

J.R. HOARE & CO ◈
8 Wyndham Road, Salisbury, SP1 3AA
Tel: 01722 334740
Principal: ICAEW Member
J R Hoare

J&S ACCOUNTANTS LTD
The Hall, 4 New Street, Salisbury, SP1 2PH

JN OSWELL
Church View House, Becketts Lane, Chilmark, Salisbury SP3 5BD
Tel: 01722 716393
Principal: ICAEW Member
J N Oswell

JOHN BARRETT
Heckfield House, Lower Road, Churchfields, Salisbury SP2 7PN

KING & CO ◈
Oakfield House, Clarendon Road, Alderbury, Salisbury SP5 3AT

MALCOLM FOWLER
21 St Johns Square, Wilton, Salisbury, SP2 0DW

MARK MERRILL ◈
PO Box 2164, 142 The Borough, Downton, Salisbury SP2 2ES
Tel: 01722 446130
Email: mark@merrillconsult.com
Website: http://www.merrillconsult.com
Principal: ICAEW Member
M Merrill

SPECIALISATIONS – SECTOR
Charities

MARSHAL CLARKE & CO
Lloyds Bank Chambers, 4 Salisbury Street, Amesbury, Salisbury SP4 7HD

MIDDLETON PARTNERS ★
The Hall, 4 New Street, Salisbury, SP1 2PH

MOORE STEPHENS (SOUTH) LLP
33 The Clarendon Centre, Salisbury Business Park, Dairy Meadow Lane, Salisbury SP1 2TJ

MSLTA LTD
Milford House, 43-55 Milford Street, Salisbury, SP1 2BP

MYNOTT'S ◈
Long Cottage, Homington Road, Coombe Bissett, Salisbury SP5 4LR
Tel: 07796 695877
Email: tim.mynott@mynotts.co.uk
Principal: ICAEW Member
T J Mynott

SPECIALISATIONS – BUSINESS & GENERAL ADVICE
Acquisitions and Mergers
Disposal of Businesses

NEXIA SMITH & WILLIAMSON AUDIT LTD
Old Library Chambers, 21 Chipper Lane, Salisbury, SP1 1BG
Tel: 01722 411881
Resident Partners/Directors: ICAEW Members
S E Shaw

SPECIALISATIONS – AUDIT & ASSURANCE
Audit

PHILIP DE NAHLIK
Jerrards Farmhouse, Fonthill Gifford, Salisbury, SP3 6QW

RAWLENCE & BROWNE SMALL BUSINESS CENTRES LTD
2nd Floor, Crosskeys House, Queen Street, Salisbury SP1 1EY

ROTHMAN PANTALL & CO
10 St Ann Street, Salisbury, SP1 2DN

SMITH & WILLIAMSON LTD
Old Library Chambers, 21 Chipper Lane, Salisbury, SP1 1BG
Tel: 01722 411881
Fax: 01722 411438
Email: firstname.lastname@smith.williamson.co.uk
Website: http://www.smith.williamson.co.uk
Resident Partners (Non-ICAEW Members):
A Hunt, A S Lockwood
General Description: Smith & Williamson is an independent professional and financial services group employing over 1400 people. We are leading providers of investment management, financial advisory and accountancy services to private clients, professional practices and mid-sized companies. Nexia Smith & Williamson Audit (Bristol) LLP provides audit services to complement the specialist financial advisory services provided by Smith & Williamson.

STEPHENSON SHEPPARD & CO LTD
Albany House, 5 New Street, Salisbury, SP1 2PH
Tel: 01722 334888
Fax: 01722 415130
Email: sailsbury@stepshep.com
Website: http://www.stepshep.com
Resident Partners/Directors: ICAEW Members
G G Stone
Resident Partners (Non-ICAEW Members):
J P Baggot
Registered by the ICAEW to carry out company audit work

WILKS & ASSOCIATES
19 Church Lane, West Tytherley, Salisbury, SP5 1JY
Tel: 01794 341774
Principal: ICAEW Member
H C Wilks

SALTASH

STEVEN CAREY & CO ◈
Countrywide House, 166 Fore Street, Saltash, PL12 6JR
Tel: 01752 841162
Principal: ICAEW Member
S H Carey

THIRD MILLENNIUM CONSULTANTS LTD ◈
Kelly Park, St Dominick, Saltash, PL12 6SQ
Tel: 01579 351353
Resident Partners/Directors: ICAEW Members
G D Wilkins

SANDBACH

ACHILLES ACCOUNTANCY LTD
7 Radbroke Close, Sandbach, CW11 1YT

BARRY HARK FCA
The Canal Centre, Hassall Green, Sandbach, CW11 4YB
Tel: 01270 762292
Principal: ICAEW Member
B Hark

DOUBLEDAY & CO
The Swallows, Marsh Green Farm, Vicarage Lane, Elworth, Sandbach CW11 3BU

J.V. BOTTERELL
4a Hightown, Sandbach, CW11 1AB
Tel: 01270 763434
Principal: ICAEW Member
J V Beeston

PETER W. SEAMAN
32 Offley Road, Sandbach, CW11 1GY

SANDHURST

FULLER HARVEY LTD ◈
90 High Street, Sandhurst, GU47 8EE
Tel: 01252 877477
Fax: 01252 875115
Email: mail@fuller-spurling.co.uk

MARK RILEY & CO
4 Cruikshank Lea, Sandhurst, GU47 0FX

SYMONS
Willow Corner, 7 Ackrells Mead, Sandhurst, GU47 8JJ
Tel: 01252 872151
Email: paul@2symons.com
Resident Partners/Directors: ICAEW Members
K D Symons, P Symons
Registered by the ICAEW to carry out company audit work
SPECIALISATIONS – SECTOR

Charities
Church

TRESISE & CO
Brockhurst, 28 Evesham Walk, Sandhurst, Sandhurst GU47 0YU

SANDWICH

BATCHELOR COOP LTD
The New Barn, Mill Lane, Eastry, Sandwich CT13 0JW
Tel: 01304 620600
Resident Partners/Directors: ICAEW Members
M A Batchelor, R C Coop

SANDY

DAVID BEAGENT & CO
The Old Rectory, Mill Lane, Tempsford, Sandy SG19 2AT

JUDITH KINGSTON
7 The Manor, Potton, Sandy, SG19 2RN

PARLOW ASSOCIATES LTD
16 Brockwood Close, Gamlingay, Sandy, SG19 3EG
Tel: 01767 652924
Resident Partners/Directors: ICAEW Members
I G Parker

WHITMARSH STERLAND
Green End, Gamlingay, Sandy, SG19 3LB

SAWBRIDGEWORTH

BARRY DWYER & CO
25 Pishiobury Drive, Sawbridgeworth, CM21 0WT

CANFIELD & CO,
Bankfield, 38 The Orchards, Sawbridgeworth, CM21 9BB
Tel: 01279 722498
Principal: ICAEW Member
G T Canfield

DONGWORTH LTD
First Floor, 30 London Road, Sawbridgeworth, CM21 9JS

ELIZABETH BURDEN ◈
Church Chambers, Church Street, Sawbridgeworth, CM21 9AB
Tel: 01279 600045

FRANK P DONGWORTH & CO
First Floor, 30 London Road, Sawbridgeworth, CM21 9JS

LEARMONTH & CO LTD
The Granary, 39 Bell Street, Sawbridgeworth, CM21 9AR

SAXMUNDHAM

ENSORS ◈
Blyth House, Rendham Road, Saxmundham, IP17 1WA
Tel: 01728 603005
Resident Partners/Directors: ICAEW Members
A J Hawes
Resident Partners (Non-ICAEW Members):
C Page

HUGH COCHRANE AND CO
26B High Street, Saxmundham, IP17 1AJ
Tel: 01728 602102
Principal: ICAEW Member
H J Cochrane

SCARBOROUGH

ASHBY, BERRY & CO
48/49 Albemarle Crescent, Scarborough, YO11 1XU

COULSONS
P O Box 17, 2 Belgrave Crescent, Scarborough, YO11 1UD
Tel: 01723 364141
Email: postmaster@coulsons.co.uk
Website: http://www.coulsons.co.uk
Resident Partners/Directors: ICAEW Members
D J Bryden, P B Hodgson
Registered by the ICAEW to carry out company audit work
Regulated by the ICAEW for a range of investment business activities
General Description: Member UK 200 Group of practising chartered accountants.

D.J. OATES & CO
Ensley House, 43 Newby Farm Road, Newby, Scarborough YO12 6UJ

DAVID MANSELL BA ACA
4 Castlegate, East Ayton, Scarborough, YO13 9EJ

HARRISON INGHAM & CO
Riggs House, Riggs Head, Scarborough, YO12 5TG

INGHAM & CO ◈
George Stanley House, 2 West Parade Road, Scarborough, YO12 5ED

IQ ACCOUNTANTS LTD
1 Seamer Road Corner, Scarborough, YO12 5BB

J J COOK & CO
50-51 Albemarle Crescent, Scarborough, YO11 1XX
Tel: 01723 503504
Principal: ICAEW Member
J J Cook

JOHN ARMISTEAD
9 West Park Road, Scalby, Scarborough, YO13 0PX
Tel: 01723 367139
Principal: ICAEW Member
J G H L Armistead

JOLLIFFE CORK WYATT
50-51 Albemarle Crescent, Scarborough, YO11 1XX

JOLLIFFE CORK WYATT LTD ◈
50-51 Albemarle Crescent, Scarborough, YO11 1XX
Tel: 01723 503504
Resident Partners/Directors: ICAEW Members
J J Cook, M C Husler, I E A Wyatt

M. WASLEY CHAPMAN & CO
17 York Place, Scarborough, YO11 2NP

MOORE STEPHENS
12/13 Alma Square, Scarborough, YO11 1JU

ONE STOP BUSINESS ADVISERS LTD
Ensley House, 43 Newby Farm Road, Scarborough, YO12 6UJ

PETER HARRISON
Riggs House, Riggs Head, Scarborough, YO12 5TG

RAYNER & CO ★
6 Arundel Place, Scarborough, YO11 1TX

RM LOCKING & CO
50 Norwood Street, Scarborough, YO12 7ER

ROWLEY WARD ◈
13 York Place, Scarborough, YO11 2NP

WALKER & CO
Belgrave House, 15 Belgrave Crescent, Scarborough, YO11 1UB
Tel: 01723 379979
Resident Partners/Directors: ICAEW Members
A Walker
Registered by another RSB to carry out company audit work
Licensed by another DPB to carry on investment business

WINN & CO (YORKSHIRE) LTD ◈
62/63 Westborough, Scarborough, YO11 1TS
Tel: 01723 364341
Resident Partners/Directors: ICAEW Members
S K Clipperton, S R Lloyd

WYATT & CO
50-51 Albemarle Crescent, Scarborough, YO11 1XX

WYATT & CO (SCARBOROUGH) LTD ◈
50-51 Albemarle Crescent, Scarborough, YO11 1XX

SCUNTHORPE

ANDREW G BINNS
5 Kings Croft, Ealand, Scunthorpe, DN17 4GA

C.H. JEFFERSON & CO ★
108 Oswald Road, Scunthorpe, DN15 7PA

FORRESTER BOYD
66-68 Oswald Road, Scunthorpe, DN15 7PG
Tel: 01724 863105
Resident Partners/Directors: ICAEW Members
M T Barnard, S A Fields

GLOVER & CO ◈
50A Oswald Road, Scunthorpe, DN15 7PQ
Tel: 01724 842573
Principal: ICAEW Member
B Campbell

HW
23 Wells Street, Scunthorpe, DN15 6HL

JAMES F COOPER LTD
23 Well Street, Messingham, Scunthorpe, DN17 3RT

R.N. STORE & CO ◈
50-54 Oswald Road, Scunthorpe, North Lincolnshire, DN15 7PQ
Tel: 01724 842713
Resident Partners/Directors: ICAEW Members
A J Clayton, J P Heeney, R F Marris, I M Pounder, R A Smith, P Stapleton

STEPHENSON, SMART & CO ★
80a Oswald Road, Scunthorpe, DN15 7PA

TURNER WARRAN (SCUNTHORPE) LTD
26-28 Laneham Street, Scunthorpe, DN15 6PB
Tel: 01724 842448
Resident Partners/Directors: ICAEW Members
S J Warran

SEAFORD

C.B. HAYMAN
9 Sutton Road, Seaford, BN25 1RU
Tel: 01323 873888
Principal: ICAEW Member
C B Hayman

GRAHAM P THOMPSON
Beaufoys, Firle Road, Seaford, BN25 2HU
Tel: 01323 897483
Principal: ICAEW Member
G P Thompson

IAN S YOUNG
35 Fitzgerald Avenue, Seaford, BN25 1AU
Tel: 01323 491022
Principal: ICAEW Member
I S Young

PAUL JAMES ASSOCIATES
Turnstile Cottage, Firle Road, Seaford, BN25 2JD

ROY F. GENTRY
67 Broad Street, Seaford, BN25 1NR
Tel: 01323 898532
Principal: ICAEW Member
R F Gentry

SWINDELLS & GENTRY ◈
20-21 Clinton Place, Seaford, BN25 1NP
Tel: 01323 892549
Fax: 01323 896279
Email: seaford@swindellsandgentry.co.uk
Website: http://www.swindellsandgentry.co.uk
Resident Partners/Directors: ICAEW Members
J Fackler, I K Jenkins, P I Moorey, J M Terry, R L Thompson
Other Offices: Uckfield (Tel: 01825 763366)
Registered by the ICAEW to carry out company audit work
Licensed by another DPB to carry on investment business

SEAHAM

ROBERT GALE & CO
8 Adelaide Row, Seaham, SR7 7EF

SEASCALE

ALAN R. GREY & CO
The Old Forge, Beck Place, Gosforth, Seascale CA20 1AT

SEATON

CHRIS HAMMETT & ASSOCIATES
8-10 Queen Street, Seaton, EX12 2NY

GEOFFREY R BUTLER
The Mullions, New Road, Beer, Seaton EX12 3EB

HAMMETT ASSOCIATES LTD
8-10 Queen Street, Seaton, EX12 2NY

LENTELLS LTD
Kingsway, 50 Fore Street, Seaton, EX12 2AD
Tel: 01297 20584
Resident Partners (Non-ICAEW Members):
M A Griffiths
Registered by the ICAEW to carry out company audit work
Regulated by the ICAEW for a range of investment business activities

THOMAS WESTCOTT ★
Salcombe House, 25 Fore Street, Seaton, EX12 2LE
Tel: 01297 21467
Resident Partners/Directors: ICAEW Members
S J Carrington

SEDBERGH

JACKSON & GRAHAM ◈
4 Finkle Street, Sedbergh, LA10 5BZ
Tel: 01539 620775
Resident Partners/Directors: ICAEW Members
J M R Hague

R LEWES
15 Guldrey Lane, Sedbergh, LA10 5DS
Tel: 015396 20088
Email: rosel@rlewes.freeserve.co.uk
Principal: ICAEW Member
R Lewes

SELBY

B C HOGG & CO
2 Market Lane, Selby, YO8 4QA

H R ACCOUNTANCY LTD
2 Market Lane, Selby, YO8 4QA

JWPCREERS ★ ◈
20-24 Park Street, Selby, YO8 4PW
Tel: 01757 703731
Fax: 01757 210358
Website: http://www.jwpcreers.co.uk
Training Contracts Available.
Resident Partners/Directors: ICAEW Members
S R Headley, D A Ingall, R Smith
Registered by the ICAEW to carry out company audit work
Regulated by the ICAEW for a range of investment business activities

O'BRIEN & CO ◈
31A Finkle Street, Selby, YO8 4DT
Tel: 01757 213873
Principal: ICAEW Member
S.W. O'Brien

S WALKER
93 Leeds Road, Selby, YO8 4JG

TOWNENDS ★ ◈
11 The Crescent, Selby, YO8 4PD
Tel: 01757 702602
Resident Partners/Directors: ICAEW Members
B J Barker

TOWNENDS ACCOUNTANTS LTD
11 The Crescent, Selby, YO8 4PD
Tel: 01757 702602

SETTLE

HAWORTHS LTD
8 Station Road, Settle, BD24 9AA
Tel: 01729 825755

MILFORD & CO
Duke Street, Settle, BD24 9DJ
Tel: 01729 823576
Principal: ICAEW Member
K Morton

PHIL DODGSON & PARTNERS LTD
Cragdale, Greenfoot, Settle, BD24 9HR

THE SHEPHERD PARTNERSHIP LTD
Kingsley, Station Road, Settle, BD24 9AA
Tel: 01729 823950
Email: skipton@shepherdpartnership.com

SEVENOAKS

A.G. EASTWOOD & CO
2 Brook Place Cottages, Ide Hill, Sevenoaks, TN14 6BL
Tel: 01732 750309
Principal: ICAEW Member
A G Eastwood

A S MUNDY
73 High Street, Shoreham, Sevenoaks, TN14 7TB

A4G ACCOUNTING LLP
Kings Lodge, London Road, West Kingsdown, Sevenoaks TN15 6AR

AH PARTNERSHIP
Stanley House, 49 Dartford Road, Sevenoaks, TN13 3TE

AH PARTNERSHIP LTD
Stanley House, 49 Dartford Road, Sevenoaks, TN13 3TE

AIM - RUSSELL THOMAS FCA
9 Bullfinch Lane, Sevenoaks, TN13 2DY
Tel: 01732 463078
Principal: ICAEW Member
R L Thomas

ALLAN AS LTD ◈
15 Quarry Hill Road, Borough Green, Sevenoaks, TN15 8RQ
Tel: 01732 885444
Resident Partners/Directors: ICAEW Members
D G Allan

B.J. BONE
14 Hurst Farm Road, Weald, Sevenoaks, TN14 6PE

BARBARA M H READE & CO
May Tree Hollow, 10 Crownfields, Sevenoaks, TN13 1EF

BETA WAYS LTD
May Tree Hollow, 10 Crownfields, Sevenoaks, TN13 1EF

BOWLES & CO
14 Westerham Road, Sevenoaks, TN13 2PU

BREBNERS
Tubs Hill House, London Road, Sevenoaks, TN13 1BL
Tel: 01732 457676
Fax: 01732 740432
Email: partners@brebners.com
Website: http://www.brebners.com
Resident Partners/Directors: ICAEW Members
P J Hedges, A C Nicholl, C N Pomeroy, A J S Sturgeon
Non-resident Partners (ICAEW Members):
P J Heath, M N Widdowson
Resident Partners (Non-ICAEW Members):
G J Palmer
Other Offices: The Quadrangle, 180 Wardour Street, London W1F 8LB
Registered by the ICAEW to carry out company audit work
Authorised and regulated by the Financial Services Authority for investment business
Individual(s) licensed for insolvency work by the ICAEW

SPECIALISATIONS – AUDIT & ASSURANCE
Audit

SPECIALISATIONS – BUSINESS & GENERAL ADVICE
Book-keeping
Management Accounting Consultancy

SPECIALISATIONS – BUSINESS RECOVERY & INSOLVENCY
Liquidations

SPECIALISATIONS – FINANCIAL REPORTING
Accounts Preparation
Limited Company Accounts
Limited Liability Partnership
Partnership/Sole Trader Accounts

SPECIALISATIONS – SECTOR
Media
Traders — General

SPECIALISATIONS – TAXATION
Taxation

CAMERON CUNNINGHAM LLP
145 High Street, Sevenoaks, TN13 1XJ
Tel: 01732 468670
Resident Partners/Directors: ICAEW Members
D T Cunningham

COPLESTONS ★
Suite 2, 9 West End, Kemsing, Sevenoaks TN15 6PX

CREASEY SON & WICKENDEN
Hearts of Oak House, 4 Pembroke Road, Sevenoaks, TN13 1XR
Tel: 01732 450744
Resident Partners/Directors: ICAEW Members
A N Davies, N Deverson, M K Lunt

DRAGE & CO
62 The Rise, Sevenoaks, TN13 1RN

GREENAWAY
150 High Street, Sevenoaks, TN13 1XE
Tel: 01732 450088
Resident Partners/Directors: ICAEW Members
B H Greenaway, R J C Lovitt

HELEN GRAY ACCOUNTING SERVICES
53 Woodfields, Chipstead, Sevenoaks, TN13 2RB

THE HHC PARTNERSHIP ★
Suite 2, 9 West End, Kemsing, Sevenoaks TN15 6PX

J A E SIMMONDS & COMPANY LTD
24 Garth Road, Sevenoaks, TN13 1RU

J.B. SHEPPARD & CO
206 Chesterfield Drive, Riverhead, Sevenoaks, TN13 2EH
Tel: 01732 454070
Principal: ICAEW Member
S J Rudden

J M H FINANCIALS LTD
Cumbrae, Brittains Lane, Sevenoaks, TN13 2NF

JAMES PERCIVAL
The Old Orchard, Otford Lane, Halstead, Sevenoaks TN14 7EE

JOHN WINLO HOAR
Spinney Cottage, 68 Brattlewood, Sevenoaks, TN13 1QU

JOHNCOLLETT.COM
36 Amherst Road, Sevenoaks, TN13 3LS

LEE, DICKETTS & CO
York House, 37 High Street, Seal, Sevenoaks TN15 0AW
Tel: 01732 762655
Email: info@leedicketts.com
Resident Partners/Directors: ICAEW Members
G M Cufley, G C Lee, R B Lugg
Resident Partners (Non-ICAEW Members):
M D Bushell
Registered by the ICAEW to carry out company audit work

LEWIS MEAD
The Mead, 143 Pilgrims Way, Kemsing, Sevenoaks TN15 6TR

M.J. READ & CO ◈
1 Cobden Road, Sevenoaks, TN13 3UB
Tel: 01732 452207
Fax: 01732 779220
Email: nigel@mjraccountants.co.uk
Principal: ICAEW Member
N J Wharton
Registered by the ICAEW to carry out company audit work
Regulated by the ICAEW for a range of investment business activities

MCCAMBRIDGE DUFFY LLP ★
1a St James's Road, Sevenoaks, TN13 3NH

ML ACCOUNTANCY SERVICES
West Barn, Elses Farm, Morleys Road, Weald, Sevenoaks TN14 6QX

O.M. HOLMES
Holly Cottage, Main Road, Knockholt, Sevenoaks TN14 7LT

P.J. DICKERSON
133 Marlborough Crescent, Riverhead, Sevenoaks, TN13 2HN
Tel: 01732 457184
Principal: ICAEW Member
P J Dickerson

PALMARIUS LTD
36 Hillydeal Road, Otford, Sevenoaks, TN14 5RU

PERRYS
The Square, Wrotham, Sevenoaks, TN15 7AA

PORRITT RAINEY
9 Pembroke Road, Sevenoaks, TN13 1XR
Tel: 01732 452125
Email: mail@porritt-rainey.co.uk
Resident Partners/Directors: ICAEW Members
R S Holland, A R E Peal

ROBIN LONG
73 Pilgrims Way, Kemsing, Sevenoaks, TN15 6TD
Tel: 01732 761778
Principal: ICAEW Member
R Long

ROBINSON & CO
5 Pinehurst, Sevenoaks, TN14 5AQ

RUSSELL THOMAS & CO
9 Bullfinch Lane, Sevenoaks, TN13 2DY
Tel: 01732 463078

SAMUELS ◈
3 Locks Yard, High Street, Sevenoaks, TN13 1LT
Tel: 01732 742089

SPECIALISATIONS – FORENSIC ACCOUNTING
Expert Witnesses in Litigation
Forensic Accounting

SPECIALISATIONS – SECTOR
Solicitors

SPECIALISATIONS – TAXATION
Investigations

SAMUELS LLP ◈
3 Locks Yard, High Street, Sevenoaks, TN13 1LT

STEPHEN HILL LTD
Kings Lodge, London Road, West Kingsdown, Sevenoaks TN15 6AR

THAIN OSBORNE & CO
47A London Road, Sevenoaks, TN13 1AR
Tel: 01732 460896
Principal: ICAEW Member
C A Thain

THOMPSON & HUNTER
43/45 High Street, Sevenoaks, TN13 1JF
Tel: 01732 740575
Email: stewart@thompsonandhunter.com

Date Established: 1989
Principal: ICAEW Member
W S A Hunter
Registered by the ICAEW to carry out company audit work
Regulated by the ICAEW for a range of investment business activities

TRIQUETRA LTD
3 Meadow Close, Sevenoaks, TN13 3HZ

TURPIN BARKER ARMSTRONG ★
The Old Town Jail, 14-18 London Road, Sevenoaks, TN13 1AJ

W R LOWE MA FCA
48 Copperfields, Kemsing, Sevenoaks, TN15 6QG
Tel: 01732 763863
Principal: ICAEW Member
W R Lowe

SHAFTESBURY

ASHDENS
Pennyroyal, Stour Lane, Stour Row, Shaftesbury SP7 0QJ

GEOFFREY M. SPENCER
The Wincombe Centre, Wincombe Business Park, Shaftesbury, SP7 9QJ
Tel: 01747 854556
Principal: ICAEW Member
G M Spencer

LANHAM & FRANCIS ▽
54a High Street, Shaftesbury, SP7 8AS
Tel: 01747 852524
Resident Partners/Directors: ICAEW Members
R L Machin
Other Offices: Sherborne, Dorset; Yeovil, Somerset
Registered by the ICAEW to carry out company audit work
Regulated by the ICAEW for a range of investment business activities
See display advertisement near this entry.

NICOLA BROOKES
Mole End, Shorts Green Lane, Motcombe, Shaftesbury SP7 9PA

NICOLA BROOKES LTD
Mole End, Shorts Green Lane, Motcombe, Shaftesbury SP7 9PA

PETER R MILLIKEN-SMITH ◈
Meaders Farm, Motcombe, Shaftesbury, SP7 9NX
Tel: 01747 854772
Principal: ICAEW Member
P R Milliken-Smith

PETER R MILLIKEN-SMITH FCA
Meaders Farm, Motcombe, Shaftesbury, SP7 9NX

SHANKLIN

J.R. GRACE & CO
Tanglin, 3A Highfield Road, Shanklin, PO37 6PP
Tel: 01983 864222
Principal: ICAEW Member
J R Grace

SHARON R RYAN
1 The Limes, Priory Road, Shanklin, PO37 6SB
Tel: 01983 861153
Principal: ICAEW Member
S R Ryan

SHEERNESS

W.H.FOREMAN & CO
4 Trinity Road, Sheerness, ME12 2PJ
Tel: 01795 663087
Principal: ICAEW Member
W H Foreman

W. ROWLAND WALLER & CO
6 Trinity Rd, Sheerness, ME12 2PJ
Tel: 01795 580642
Principal: ICAEW Member
P M Taylor

SHEFFIELD

A.I.M.S. SHEFFIELD
82 Upper Hanover Street, Sheffield, S3 7RQ

A M J BALL
75 Banner Cross Road, Ecclesall, Sheffield, S11 9HQ
Tel: 0114 236 1471
Principal: ICAEW Member
A M J Ball

ALI QADAR & CO
60 Abbeydale Road, Sheffield, S7 1FD
Tel: 0114 258 8267
Principal: ICAEW Member
A Qadar

ALTMAN, SMITH & CO
Leverton House, 461-463 London Road, Heeley, Sheffield S2 4HL

ANTONY NORRIS
31 Vicarage Crescent, Grenoside, Sheffield, S35 8RE

ASHRAF & CO
30 Crescent Road, Sheffield, S7 1HL
Tel: 0114 250 9322
Principal: ICAEW Member
M Ashraf

ATKIN MACREDIE & CO LTD ◈
Westbourne Place, 23 Westbourne Road, Sheffield, S10 2QQ
Tel: 0114 268 0200
Resident Partners/Directors: ICAEW Members
S L Brock, S J Hartley, N C Oates

AUKER RHODES LTD
The Masters House, 92a Arundel Street, Sheffield, S1 4RE

AVN WICKERSHAMS ◈
Unit 114, Westthorpe Business Innovation Centre, Westthorpe Fields Road, Killamarsh, Sheffield S21 1TZ
Tel: 0114 218 0610

BARBER HARRISON & PLATT ◈
2 Rutland Park, Sheffield, S10 2PD
Tel: 0114 266 7171
Email: info@bhp.co.uk
Website: http://www.bhp.co.uk
Training Contracts Available.
Resident Partners/Directors: ICAEW Members
P C Allsop, David Charlton, P Cross, M J Ferreday, D Forrest, D H Gray, S Ingram, C King, L A Leighton, J E Marshall, C H Ringrose, G Stuart-Harris, J Warner
Other Offices: Chesterfield
Registered by the ICAEW to carry out company audit work
Regulated by the ICAEW for a range of investment business activities

SPECIALISATIONS – AUDIT & ASSURANCE
Audit
Pension Scheme Auditors

SPECIALISATIONS – BUSINESS RECOVERY & INSOLVENCY
Corporate Recovery

SPECIALISATIONS – FINANCIAL REPORTING
Accounts Preparation

SPECIALISATIONS – FORENSIC ACCOUNTING
Forensic Accounting

SPECIALISATIONS – SECTOR
Charities
Dentists/Opticians
Doctors
Solicitors

SPECIALISATIONS – TAXATION
Payroll Service and Advice
Taxation
Trusts
Value Added Tax

BERRY & HOTSON
Cherrytree Suite 2, Union Road, Nether Edge, Sheffield S11 9EF
Tel: 0114 255 3155

BERRY & HOTSON LLP ◈
Cherrytree Suite 2, Union Road, Nether Edge, Sheffield S11 9EF
Tel: 0114 255 3155
Resident Partners/Directors: ICAEW Members
I Berry

BODEN & CO
342 Glossop Road, Sheffield, S10 2HW
Tel: 0114 272 2737
Principal: ICAEW Member
P S Boden

BODSWORTH & CO
55 Mowbray Street, Sheffield, S3 8EZ
Tel: 0114 275 3471
Principal: ICAEW Member
P Bodsworth

BRAMLEYS
380 Ecclesall Rd South, Sheffield, S11 9PY
Tel: 0114 236 9444
Principal: ICAEW Member
W N Bramley

BRIAN BENNETT
38 Spring House Road, Crookes, Sheffield, S10 1LT

BROWN MCLEOD LTD
51 Clarkegrove Road, Sheffield, S10 2NH
Tel: 0114 268 4747
Email: bmc@brownmcleod.co.uk
Website: http://www.brownmcleod.co.uk
Date Established: 1980
Resident Partners/Directors: ICAEW Members
J Roddison, P P Wilson
Other Offices:10 Three Kings Yard, London W1K 4JR

BRYAN GREY & CO LTD
Broadfield House, 18 Broadfield Road, Sheffield, S8 0XJ

BRYDONE & CO
65 Meersbrook Road, Sheffield, S8 9HU

C F MCBOYLE LTD
Omega Court, 370 Cemetery Road, Sheffield, S11 8FT
Tel: 0114 267 8672
Resident Partners/Directors: ICAEW Members
C F McBoyle

C.J. LANSDOWN & CO LTD
7 Terrey Road, Sheffield, S17 4DD
Tel: 0114 335 0279
Resident Partners/Directors: ICAEW Members
C J Lansdown

C J WOODHEAD & CO LTD
158 Hemper Lane, Greenhill, Sheffield, S8 7FE

CARTLIDGE & CO LTD
137 Laughton Road, Dinnington, Sheffield, S25 2PP

CHAIMEL LTD
55 Longford Road, Bradway, Sheffield, S17 4LP

CHAMBERLAIN & CO
Aizlewood Mill, Nursery Street, Sheffield, S3 8GG

CLB COOPERS ★
Walsh Court, 10 Bells Square, Sheffield, S1 2FY

D.A. POULSOM
81 Brooklands Crescent, Fulwood, Sheffield, S10 4GF

D.W. CHARLTON
20 Canterbury Avenue, Sheffield, S10 3RT
Tel: 0114 229 5208
Principal: ICAEW Member
David Charlton

DALY & CO
The Portergate, Ecclesall Road, Sheffield, S11 8NX

DAVID BOOKER & CO
98 Trippet Lane, Sheffield, S1 4EL

DAVIS & CO
Belmayne House, 99 Clarkehouse Road, Sheffield, S10 2LN

DAVIS & CO
Belmayne House, 99 Clarkehouse Road, Sheffield, S10 2LN

DAVIS & CO (MANAGEMENT CONSULTANTS) LTD
Belmayne House, 99 Clarkehouse Road, Sheffield, S10 2LN

DIMBLEBY & DALE
Junction House, 58 High Street, Beighton, Sheffield S20 1ED

DOBCROFT FINANCIAL SERVICES LTD
750 City Road, Sheffield, S2 1GN

EURA AUDIT UK
16-18 Station Road, Chapeltown, Sheffield, S35 2XH

EURA AUDIT UK ★
16-18 Station Road, Chapeltown, Sheffield, S35 2XH

FAWTHROP WILLIAMS ◈
Old Buttermere Works, 15 Buttermere Road, Sheffield, S7 2AX
Tel: 0114 255 8777
Principal: ICAEW Member
R H Fawthrop

GOODBAND VINER TAYLOR ◈
Ellin House, 42 Kingfield Road, Sheffield, S11 9AS
Tel: 0114 280 2930
Website: http://www.gvt-sheffield.co.uk
Resident Partners/Directors: ICAEW Members
E M C Goodband, M D Viner
Registered by the ICAEW to carry out company audit work
Authorised and regulated by the Financial Services Authority for investment business

GORDON & HOOD
2 Rotunda Business Centre, Thorncliffe Road, Chapeltown, Sheffield S35 2PG
Tel: 0114 246 1722
Resident Partners/Directors: ICAEW Members
R M Hood
SPECIALISATIONS – SECTOR

Dentists/Opticians
Doctors

GRANT THORNTON UK LLP
2 Broadfield Court, Sheffield, S8 0XF
Tel: 0114 255 3371
Resident Partners/Directors: ICAEW Members
D I H Campbell, P R Houghton, M Redfern
Non-resident Partners (ICAEW Members):
R B Thornton
Resident Partners (Non-ICAEW Members):
G Meakin, N Messenger
Non-resident Partners (Non-ICAEW Members):
J C Griffin

HALLIDAY & CO
Victoria House, 45 Rutland Park, Botanical Gardens, Sheffield S10 2PB

HART SHAW LLP ◈
Europa Link, Sheffield Business Park, Sheffield, S9 1XU
Tel: 0114 251 8850
Resident Partners/Directors: ICAEW Members
P Dawson, A J Maybery, M McDonagh, J H Robinson, C Sellars, S Vickers, M Wharin

HAWSONS ◈
Pegasus House, 463a Glossop Road, Sheffield, S10 2QD
Tel: 0114 266 7141
Fax: 0114 266 1456
Email: email@hawsons.co.uk
Website: http://www.hawsons.co.uk
Training Contracts Available.
Resident Partners/Directors: ICAEW Members
R A Frost, C I Hill, P J Kennan, M J Weatherall
Non-resident Partners (ICAEW Members):
R J Powell, P G Lomas, R W Marsh, M A Wilmott, D T Cairns
Resident Partners (Non-ICAEW Members):
K Gregory
Other Offices: Doncaster, Northampton
Registered by the ICAEW to carry out company audit work
Regulated by the ICAEW for a range of investment business activities

INVESTOR IN PEOPLE

HAYWOOD & CO
18 Stalker Walk, Sheffield, S11 8NF
Tel: 01142 681441
Resident Partners/Directors: ICAEW Members
P Hebblethwaite

HEATHER LEA BUSINESS SERVICES
49 Heather Lea Avenue, Sheffield, S17 3DL
Tel: 0114 236 0725
Principal: ICAEW Member
D K P Mangles

HEBBLETHWAITES
Westbrook Court, Sharrow Vale Road, Sheffield, S11 8YZ
Tel: 0114 266 4518
Resident Partners/Directors: ICAEW Members
R Brennan, K G Gosling, R W Murdoch, A Throssell

HEWITTS ★
11 Venture One Business Park, Long Acre Close, Sheffield, S20 3FR
Tel: 0114 276 4440
Resident Partners/Directors: ICAEW Members
B Clegg

HEWSON AND HOWSON
8 Shepcote Office Village, Shepcote Lane, Sheffield, S9 1TG

HODGSON & CO ◈
Knowle Lodge, 27 Carterknowle Road, Sheffield, S7 2DW
Tel: 0114 250 8181
Website: http://www.hodgsonandco.co.uk
Principal: ICAEW Member
J B Hodgson

HODGSON & OLDFIELD ★
3 Paradise Square, Sheffield, S1 2DE

HOLLIS AND CO ◈
35 Wilkinson Street, Sheffield, S10 2GB
Tel: 0114 281 6166
Website: http://www.hollisco.co.uk
General Description: Sage specialists.

HOLLIS AND CO LTD ◈
35 Wilkinson Street, Sheffield, S10 2GB
Tel: 0114 2816 166
Resident Partners/Directors: ICAEW Members
P J Hollis

HOLMES WIDLAKE
3 Sharrow Lane, Sheffield, S11 8AE

HOPKINS ALLEN PROCTER
342 Glossop Road, Sheffield, S10 2HW
Tel: 0114 273 7617

HOPKINS ALLEN PROCTER LTD
342 Glossop Road, Sheffield, S10 2HW
Tel: 0114 273 7617
Resident Partners/Directors: ICAEW Members
J F B Hopkins, S Procter

HUTCHINS & CO ◈
371 Wood Lane, Stannington, Sheffield, S6 5LR
Tel: 0114 233 6391
Principal: ICAEW Member
T Hutchins

HW ◈
Sterling House, 11 Omega Court, 350 Cemetery Road, Sheffield S11 8FT
Tel: 0114 267 1172
Resident Partners/Directors: ICAEW Members
L W Davies, P J Eardley

IAN B THOMPSON LTD ◈
259 Abbeydale Road, Sheffield, S7 1FJ
Tel: 0114 321 5531

IAN SMITH
54 Cockshutts Lane, Oughtibridge, Sheffield, S35 0FX
Tel: 0114 286 2138
Principal: ICAEW Member
I Smith

INGRAM FORREST CORPORATE FINANCE ★ ◈
2 Rutland Park, Sheffield, S10 2PD
Tel: 0114 268 1000
Resident Partners/Directors: ICAEW Members
D Forrest, D H Gray, S Ingram, L A Leighton

J A TOMLINSON
6 Endcliffe Edge, Sheffield, S10 3EH

J S BETHELL & CO
70 Clarkehouse Road, Sheffield, S10 2LJ
Tel: 0114 2682361
Fax: 0114 267 0310
Email: info@jsbethell.co.uk
Resident Partners/Directors: ICAEW Members
T J Day, J A Thompson
Registered by the ICAEW to carry out company audit work
Regulated by the ICAEW for a range of investment business activities

JAMES KING
5 Ashmore Avenue, Eckington, Sheffield, S21 4AH

JOHNSON WALKER
The Masters House, 92a Arundel Street, Sheffield, S1 4RE

THE JOHNSON WALKER PARTNERSHIP LTD
The Masters House, 92a Arundel Street, Sheffield, S1 4RE

KIRTLEY QURESHI & CO
75 Herries Road, Sheffield, S5 7AS

KNOWLES WARWICK LTD ◈
183 Fraser Road, Sheffield, S8 0JP

LABURNUM CONSULTANTS LTD ◈
20 Laburnum Close, Chapeltown, Sheffield, S35 1QU
Tel: 07976 797366
Resident Partners/Directors: ICAEW Members
D Plummer

LANDIN WILCOCK & CO ◈
Queen St Chmbrs, 68 Queen St, Sheffield, S1 1WR
Tel: 0114 275 4321
Website: http://www.landin-wilcock.co.uk
Resident Partners/Directors: ICAEW Members
R M Grierson, J Markham, G Marshall, K J Parkes

M. BALDRIDGE
240 Abbey Lane, Beauchief, Sheffield, S8 0BW

M J HARDING
7 Broad Elms Lane, Ecclesall, Sheffield, S11 9RQ
Tel: 0114 236 3840
Principal: ICAEW Member
M J Harding

M. P. BEAHAN & CO
57 Laughton Road, Dinnington, Sheffield, S25 2PN

MCBOYLE & CO
Omega Court, 370 Cemetery Road, Sheffield, S11 8FT
Tel: 0114 267 8672

MCBROOM & CO
Knowle Lodge, 27 Carterknowle Road, Sheffield, S7 2DW
Tel: 0114 255 4855
Principal: ICAEW Member
A I McBroom

MARTIN D. FLOWERS ◈
1 Paradise Square, Sheffield, S1 2DE

MARTIN MILNER & CO
5 Broadfield Court, Sheffield, S8 0XF
Tel: 0114 250 7150
Website: http://www.martinmilner.co.uk
Principal: ICAEW Member
M P Milner
See display advertisement near this entry.

MICHAEL BALDRIDGE FCA
240 Abbey Lane, Beauchief, Sheffield, S8 0BW

MIKE BRAMALL & CO LTD
Mayfield View, 60 School Green Lane, Sheffield, S10 4GR
Tel: 0114 263 0830
Resident Partners/Directors: ICAEW Members
G M Bramall

MILLINGTON & RUSSELL LTD
Sovereign House, 4 Machon Bank, Sheffield, S7 1GP

MONTPELIER AUDIT LTD
56 Shoreham Street, Sheffield, S1 4SP

MONTPELIER PROFESSIONAL (SHEFFIELD) LTD
56 Shoreham Street, Sheffield, S1 4SP

MORTONS
7A Brooklands Avenue, Sheffield, S10 4GA
Tel: 0114 230 6161
Fax: 0114 230 5788
Principal: ICAEW Member
C B Cotton
Registered by the ICAEW to carry out company audit work

NICOLA A BIRCH
91 Greaves Lane, Stannington, Sheffield, S6 6BD

OLDFIELD & CO
160 Abbeydale Road South, Sheffield, S7 2QS

THE P&A PARTNERSHIP ★ ◈
93 Queen Street, Sheffield, S1 1WF
Tel: 0114 275 5033
Fax: 0114 276 8556
Email: name@thepandapartnership.com
DX: 10616 SHEFFIELD
Website: http://www.thepandapartnership.com
Date Established: 1884
Resident Partners/Directors: ICAEW Members
P A Revill, C M White
Non-resident Partners (ICAEW Members):
B Guilfoyle
Resident Partners (Non-ICAEW Members):
J Priestley, J Russell, D Woolley, A Woods, G Rusling
Other Offices: 1 Whitehall, Whitehall Road, Leeds, LS1 4HR
Individual(s) licensed for insolvency work by the ICAEW
Individual(s) licensed for insolvency work by another RPB

SPECIALISATIONS – BUSINESS & GENERAL ADVICE
Administration

SPECIALISATIONS – BUSINESS RECOVERY & INSOLVENCY
Bankruptcies
Corporate Recovery
Liquidations

SPECIALISATIONS – TAXATION
Investigations

General Description: Our associated company, P&A Receivables Services plc, provides an integrated service to support businesses receivables management - debt recovery, consulting, investigations, lender services, asset recovery, process serving, recruitment and training.

PAUL C. SINGLETON ◈
Riverdale, 89 Graham Road, Sheffield, S10 3GP

PAUL HORTON & ASSOCIATES
86 Stannington View Road, Crookes, Sheffield, S10 1SR

PAUL KIRBY & COMPANY LTD ◈
39 Wellington Street, Sheffield, S1 1XB
Tel: 0114 275 0055
Resident Partners/Directors: ICAEW Members
P Kirby

PEACH WILKINSON LTD
78 Cross Hill, Ecclesfield, Sheffield, S35 9TU

PHILIP HOWES
37 Heather Lea Avenue, Sheffield, S17 3DL

PHILIP M TUCKER
58 Park Grange Croft, Sheffield, S2 3QL

PKF (UK) LLP
2nd Floor, Fountain Precinct, Balm Green, Sheffield S1 2JA
Tel: 0114 276 7991
Email: info.sheffield@uk.pkf.com
Website: http://www.pkf.co.uk
Resident Partners/Directors: ICAEW Members
C P Humphreys, R H M Plews, D J Pownall, E M Shepherd
Resident Partners (Non-ICAEW Members):
P J M Abel

PRICEWATERHOUSE-COOPERS
1 East Parade, Sheffield, S1 2ET

PRICEWATERHOUSE-COOPERS LLP
1 East Parade, Sheffield, S1 2ET
Tel: 0114 272 9141
Resident Partners/Directors: ICAEW Members
P A Gregory

R L & ASSOCIATES LTD
Unit 9, Acorn Business Park, Woodseats Close, Sheffield, S8 0TB
Tel: 0114 258 8888
Resident Partners/Directors: ICAEW Members
K Fretwell, S Sequerra

R ROSE & CO LTD
213 Derbyshire Lane, Norton Lees, Sheffield, S8 8SA
Tel: 0114 281 2331
Resident Partners/Directors: ICAEW Members
B S Duncan, R Rose

MARRIOTT GIBBS REES WALLS ★
13-15 Paradise Square, Sheffield, S1 2DE

RHODES CLARKE & CO
42 Market Street, Eckington, Sheffield, S21 4JH

RICHARD MAWHOOD
9 Far Lane, Wadsley, Sheffield, S6 4FA

RODDIS TAYLOR ROBINSON ◈
275 Glossop Road, Sheffield, S10 2HB

ROYSTON PARKIN ★ ◈
95 Queen Street, Sheffield, S1 1WG
Tel: 0114 272 0306
Fax: 0114 272 6158
Email: sheffield@roystonparkin.co.uk
Non-resident Partners (ICAEW Members):
L C Pridmore
Resident Partners (Non-ICAEW Members):
A Froggatt
Registered by another RSB to carry out company audit work
Licensed by another DPB to carry on investment business

S BURGESS & CO ★
11 Slayleigh Avenue, Fulwood, Sheffield, S10 3RA
Tel: 0114 274 9789
Resident Partners/Directors: ICAEW Members
S Burgess

S.R. DAWSON
37 Adelaide Road, Sheffield, S7 1SQ

SHORTS
912 Ecclesall Road, Sheffield, S11 8TR

SIMPSON WOOD
10a Market Street, Penistone, Sheffield, S36 6BZ

SMITH CRAVEN
2 Queens Road, Sheffield, S2 4DG

SOCHALL SMITH LTD
4 Park Square, Newton Chambers Road, Thorncliffe Park Estate, Chapeltown, Sheffield S35 2PH
Tel: 0114 257 7677
Fax: 0114 257 0075
Email: mjenkinson@sheffield.sochallsmith.co.uk
Website: http://www.sochallsmith.co.uk

STARTUP CONSULTANCY
67 Endowood Road, Millhouses, Sheffield, S7 2LY

STRATEGIC ACCOUNTANTS
P1 Sheffield Airport Business Park, Europa Link, Sheffield, S9 1XU

STRATEGIC ACCOUNTANTS LTD
Omega Court, 370 Cemetery Road, Sheffield, S11 8FT
Tel: 0114 268 4141
Resident Partners/Directors: ICAEW Members
A M Coates, K G Shaw

STRATEGIC CORPORATE FINANCE PARTNERS LLP
Omega Court, 370 Cemetery Road, Sheffield, S11 8FT
Tel: 0114 268 4141
Resident Partners/Directors: ICAEW Members
A M Coates, K G Shaw

STRATOM LTD
25 Haugh Lane, Sheffield, S11 9SA

SUSAN SINGLETON
475 Whirlowdale Road, Whirlow, Sheffield, S11 9NH
Tel: 0114 235 6319
Principal: ICAEW Member
S L Singleton

SUTTON MCGRATH LTD
5 Westbrook Court, Sharrow Vale Road, Sheffield, S11 8YZ

T D G KEYWORTH & CO LTD
158 Hemper Lane, Greenhill, Sheffield, S8 7FE

TINGLE ASHMORE LTD
Enterprise House, Broadfield Court, Sheffield, S8 0XF
Tel: 0114 255 5767
Resident Partners/Directors: ICAEW Members
B P Ashmore, K A Tingle

TURNER BEAUMONT & CO LTD
Thorncliffe Mews, Thorncliffe Park Estate, Newton Chambers Road, Chapeltown, Sheffield S35 2PH

UHY WINGFIELD SLATER ◈
Wellington House, 39 Wellington Street, Sheffield, S1 1XB
Tel: 0114 275 1544
Fax: 0114 275 1366
Email: info@uhy-wingfieldslater.com
Website: http://www.uhy-wingfieldslater.com
Resident Partners/Directors: ICAEW Members
R J Givans, D N Hemmingfield, P F Newsam, J L Wingfield

INVESTOR IN PEOPLE

Languages Spoken:
French

VOICE & CO ◈
Unit 14, Jessops Riverside, 800 Brightside Lane, Sheffield S9 2RX

VOICE & CO ACCOUNTANCY SERVICES LTD ◈
14 Jessops Riverside, 800 Brightside Lane, Sheffield, S9 2RX
Tel: 0114 243 2888
Resident Partners/Directors: ICAEW Members
H A Voice

WELLS RICHARDSON
Cannon House, Rutland Road, Sheffield, S3 8DP
Tel: 0114 275 3030
Email: info@wellsrichardson.co.uk

Resident Partners/Directors: ICAEW Members
A I T Ostrowski, G Wade
Resident Partners (Non-ICAEW Members):
M D Hepworth, J Clarke
Registered by the ICAEW to carry out company audit work

WEST & FOSTER ◈
2 Broomgrove Road, Broomhill, Sheffield, S10 2LR
Tel: 0114 268 9950
Fax: 0114 268 9951
Email: info@westandfoster.co.uk
Resident Partners/Directors: ICAEW Members
S P Dawson, J M G Foster, P J P Miles
Resident Partners (Non-ICAEW Members):
P Middleton
Registered by the ICAEW to carry out company audit work
Regulated by the ICAEW for a range of investment business activities

WESTONS
Queens Buildings, 55 Queen Street, Sheffield, S1 2DX

WESTONS BUSINESS SOLUTIONS LTD
Queens Buildings, 55 Queen Street, Sheffield, S1 2DX

WICKERSHAM LTD ◈
Unit 114, Westthorpe Business Innovation Centre, Westthorpe Fields Road, Killamarsh, Sheffield S21 1TZ
Tel: 0114 243 1668
Resident Partners/Directors: ICAEW Members
S E Key

SHEFFORD

ELBOURNE & CO
5 St Marys Place, Meppershall, Shefford, SG17 5NL
Tel: 01462 817409
Principal: ICAEW Member
C W Elbourne

JOHN NEEDHAM & CO
Shefford Business Centre, 71 Hitchin Road, Shefford, SG17 5JB

R.C. TURNER ◈
Almond House, Grange Street, Clifton, Shefford SG17 5EW
Tel: 01462 813885
Principal: ICAEW Member
R C Turner

SHEPPERTON

ALAN JAMES & CO
Shepperton Marina, 16 Felix Lane, Shepperton, TW17 8NS
Tel: 01932 240540
Fax: 01932 254899
Email: general@alanjames.co.uk
Website: http://www.alanjames.co.uk
Resident Partners/Directors: ICAEW Members
K G Edwards, A G James
Registered by the ICAEW to carry out company audit work
Regulated by the ICAEW for a range of investment business activities

BILLINGE BLEND AND CO
58A High Street, Shepperton, TW17 9AU

DAVID LLOYD & CO
Pembroke Lodge, 12 Broadlands Avenue, Shepperton, TW17 9DQ

F.W.P. LEA & CO
Shepperton Marina, Felix Lane, Shepperton, TW17 8NJ
Tel: 01932 230880
Email: plea@fwplea.co.uk

S.L. CATER
6 Terminal House, Station Approach, Shepperton, TW17 8AS
Tel: 01932 230404
Principal: ICAEW Member
S L Cater

SUE WOODGATE
42 St Nicholas Drive, Shepperton, TW17 9LD
Tel: 01932 247735
Principal: ICAEW Member
S M Woodgate

SUZANNE CATER
6 Terminal House, Station Approach, Shepperton, TW17 8AS

SHEPTON MALLET

A.J. ALLEN & CO
The Orchards, Alhampton, Shepton Mallet, BA4 6PZ

AVON & SOMERSET ACCOUNTANCY SERVICES
PO Box 3161, Shepton Mallet, BA4 5WB

BURTON SWEET ◈
Cooper House, Lower Charlton Estate, Shepton Mallet, BA4 5QE
Tel: 01749 342255
Resident Partners/Directors: ICAEW Members
G H Cole

LONGHILL ACCOUNTING
1 Longhill Lodge, Ditcheat, Shepton Mallet, BA4 6QR

OLD MILL ◈
The Old Mill, Park Road, Shepton Mallet, BA4 5BS

OLD MILL ACCOUNTANCY LLP ◈
The Old Mill, Park Road, Shepton Mallet, BA4 5BS
Tel: 01749 343366
Website: http://www.oldmillgroup.co.uk
Resident Partners/Directors: ICAEW Members
T C Baines, P W Haugh, J H Jackson, I M Sharpe, P G Treby

TENON LTD
The Old Mill, Park Road, Shepton Mallet, BA4 5BS

SHERBORNE

AFB ACCOUNTANTS LTD ◈
York House, Coldharbour Business Park, Sherborne, DT9 4JW
Tel: 01935 814586
Resident Partners/Directors: ICAEW Members
J Hague

GRAHAM HUNN & CO
Field Walls, The Avenue, Sherborne, DT9 3AH

HOPE SHAW LTD
21 The Old Yarn Mills, Westbury, Sherborne, DT9 3RQ
Tel: 01935 815700
Resident Partners/Directors: ICAEW Members
D J L Robinson

LANHAM & FRANCIS ▽ ◈
77a Cheap Street, Sherborne, DT9 3BA
Tel: 01935 814881
Fax: 01935 816999
Email: iandodds@lanham-francis.co.uk
Non-resident Partners (ICAEW Members):
R L Machin
Resident Partners (Non-ICAEW Members):
I D Dodds
Other Offices: Shaftesbury, Dorset; Yeovil, Somerset
Registered by the ICAEW to carry out company audit work
Regulated by the ICAEW for a range of investment business activities
See display advertisement near this entry.

SIGMA
Vale House, Over Compton, Sherborne, DT9 4QS
Tel: 01935 426 151

THE SIMPLIFIED COMPANY ACCOUNTS SERVICE
21 Old Yarn Mills, Westbury, Sherborne, DT9 3RQ
Tel: 01935 815700

SHIFNAL

EIRA MOORE
1 Church Meadow, Shifnal, TF11 9AD

J.S. SLATER
The Old House, 28 Bradford Street, Shifnal, TF11 8AU
Tel: 01952 462273
Principal: ICAEW Member
J S Slater

JOSEPH LOUIS
Mclineux House, 6A Market Place, Shifnal, TF11 9AZ

JULIAN R GRONOW LTD ◈
Field House, Field Lane, Kemberton, Shifnal TF11 9LR
Tel: 01952 582136
Resident Partners/Directors: ICAEW Members
J R Gronow

M.A. MULLETT
9 Stafford Place, Park Street, Shifnal, TF11 9BH

RICHARD H. HUDSON
Lilyhurst House, Lilyhurst, Shifnal, TF11 8RL

TURNER PEACHEY ◈
Lloyds Bank Chambers, 7 Park Street, Shifnal, TF11 9BE
Tel: 01952 461619
Email: shifnal@turner-peachey.co.uk
Website: http://www.turner-peachey.co.uk
Resident Partners/Directors: ICAEW Members
C R Hemming
Non-resident Partners (ICAEW Members):
C C Perry
Other Offices: Bridgnorth, Oswestry, Shrewsbury, Welshpool
Registered by the ICAEW to carry out company audit work
Regulated by the ICAEW for a range of investment business activities

SHIPLEY

ANN EVERIN
24 Victoria Ave, Saltaire, Shipley, BD18 4SQ
Tel: 01274 585912
Principal: ICAEW Member
A Everin

CHRIS GUMBLEY AND CO ◈
5 Mercury Quays, Ashley Lane, Shipley, BD17 7DB
Tel: 01274 531515
Principal: ICAEW Member
C D Gumbley

DOREEN NOBLE
81 Woodcot Avenue, Baildon, Shipley, BD17 6QR

EURA AUDIT UK
1 Park View Court, St Paul's Road, Shipley, BD18 3DZ

G.M. BENNISON
100 Ridgeway, Wrose, Shipley, BD18 1PN
Tel: 01274 787386
Principal: ICAEW Member
G M Bennison

J.C. ANDERSON
28 Temple Rhydding Drive, Baildon, Shipley, BD17 5PU
Tel: 01274 595563
Principal: ICAEW Member
J C Anderson

M. REYNOLDS
4 Whitelands Crescent, Baildon, Shipley, BD17 6NN

RONKOWSKI & HALL
12 Westgate, Baildon, Shipley, BD17 5EJ
Tel: 01274 531066
Registered by the ICAEW to carry out company audit work
Regulated by the ICAEW for a range of investment business activities

RONKOWSKI & HALL LTD
12 Westgate, Baildon, Shipley, BD17 5EJ

SHARMA BENNISON & CO
133 Bradford Road, Shipley, BD18 3TB

SHIPSTON-ON-STOUR

DAVID J PLUMB ◈
5 Ivy Grounds, Burmington, Shipston-On-Stour, CV36 5BD
Tel: 01608 664385
Principal: ICAEW Member
D J Plumb

OFF THE SQUARE LTD
Wheelwright Cottage, Cherington, Shipston-on-stour, CV36 5HS
Tel: 01608 685095
Resident Partners/Directors: ICAEW Members
C I Owen

SHOREHAM-BY-SEA

BARRETTS
1 St Marys House, St Marys Road, Shoreham-by-sea, BN43 5ZA

C.J. WELLS & CO
31 New Road, Shoreham-By-Sea, BN43 6RB

DALEWOOD LTD
42-44 Brunswick Road, Shoreham-By-Sea, BN43 5WB

SHREWSBURY

A H TUDOR LTD
Belmont House, Shrewsbury Business Park, Shrewsbury, SY2 6LG

ACCOUNTING SOLUTIONS
28 Brackley Drive, Shrewsbury, SY3 8BX
Tel: 01743 247401
Principal: ICAEW Member
S Turner

ANDREWS ORME & HINTON LTD
4 Darwin Court, Oxon Business Park, Shrewsbury, SY3 5AL

B.JAY & CO
51 Porthill Drive, Copthorne, Shrewsbury, SY3 8RS

B N JACKSON NORTON ★
3 College Court, College Hill, Shrewsbury, SY1 1LS

BATES & CO ◈
10 Park Plaza, Battlefield Enterprise Park, Shrewsbury, SY1 3AF
Tel: 01743 462604

BATES & COMPANY SHREWSBURY LTD ◈
10 Park Plaza, Battlefield Enterprise Park, Shrewsbury, SY1 3AF

CAERWYN JONES ◈
Emstrey House, Shrewsbury Business Park, Shrewsbury, SY2 6LG
Tel: 01743 241201
Resident Partners/Directors: ICAEW Members
A J Barker, D C Blofield, I A Painter

CBSL GROUP LTD
Rowan House North, 1 The Professional Quater, Shrewsbury Business Park, Shrewsbury SY2 6LG

COMBINED BUSINESS SOLUTIONS LTD ◈
Roman House North, 1 The Professional Quarter, Shrewsbury Business Park, Shrewsbury SY2 6LG

DRE & CO ◈
6 Claremont Buildings, Claremont Bank, Shrewsbury, SY1 1RJ
Tel: 01743 241581
Resident Partners/Directors: ICAEW Members
C H Hall

DYKE YAXLEY LTD
1 Brassey Road, Old Potts Way, Shrewsbury, SY3 7FA
Tel: 01743 241281
Fax: 01743 235794
Email: dy@dykeyaxley.co.uk
DX: 19717 SHREWSBURY
Website: http://www.dykeyaxley.co.uk
Date Established: 1917
Resident Partners/Directors: ICAEW Members
M Bramwell, H P Bruce, A P Davies, M F Griffiths, W L Riley, C H Thomas, K J Winter, A J Young
Resident Partners (Non-ICAEW Members):
G Davies, A D Key
Registered by the ICAEW to carry out company audit work

INVESTOR IN PEOPLE

General Description:
Accounting for your every need. Please consult our website.

G C MORGAN LTD
Belmont House, Shrewsbury Business Park, Shrewsbury, SY2 6LG
Tel: 01743 273273
Resident Partners/Directors: ICAEW Members
G C Morgan

G MURPHY LTD
Belmont House, Shrewsbury Business Park, Shrewsbury, SY2 6LG

HALL LIVESEY BROWN
5 Claremont Bank, Shrewsbury, SY1 1RW
Tel: 01743 367761
Resident Partners/Directors: ICAEW Members
K W Nicholls

HEYWOODS
Countrywide House, Knights Way, Battlefield Enterprise Park, Shrewsbury SY1 3AB
Tel: 01743 467317
Email: alan@heywoods.com
Resident Partners/Directors: ICAEW Members
A R Payne

I F DAVIES
1 Ellesmere Drive, Shrewsbury, SY1 2QU

INDEPENDENT AUDITORS LLP ★
Emstrey House North, Shrewsbury Business Park, Shrewsbury, SY2 6LG

JAMES HOLYOAK & PARKER
Longden House, 105 Longden Road, Shrewsbury, SY3 9DZ

JAMES HOLYOAK & PARKER LTD
Longden House, 105 Longden Road, Shrewsbury, SY3 9DZ

JR
Avondale, Ellesmere Road, Wem, Shrewsbury SY4 5TU
Tel: 01939 233854
Resident Partners/Directors: ICAEW Members
J D Reeves, R A Reeves

LLOYD,THOMPSON & CARL
41 Eastwood Road, The Mount, Shrewsbury, SY3 8YJ

MOORE STEPHENS
4 Darwin Court, Oxon Business Park, Shrewsbury, SY3 5AL
Tel: 01743 369333
Website: http://www.moorestephens.co.uk

P E M COWDY LTD
Belmont House, Shrewsbury Business Park, Shrewsbury, SY2 6LG

PETER JAMES ◈
71 Washford Road, Shrewsbury, SY3 9HW
Tel: 01743 364100
Principal: ICAEW Member
P R James

ROBERT DAVIES & CO
Marche Manor, Halfway House, Shrewsbury, SY5 9DE

ROBERT S BOWDEN
Apple Tree, White Gritt, Minsterley, Shrewsbury SY5 0JN

STEWART GORMAN EVANS LTD
Emstrey House, Sitka Drive, Shrewsbury Business Park, Shrewsbury SY2 6LG

STUBBS PARKIN & SOUTH
4 High Street, Wem, Shrewsbury, SY4 5AA
Tel: 01939 232457

T J JONES LTD
Belmont House, Shrewsbury Business Park, Shrewsbury, SY2 6LG

TURNER PEACHEY ◈
Column House, London Road, Shrewsbury, SY2 6NN
Tel: 01743 273999
Email: enquiries@turner-peachey.co.uk
Website: http://www.turner-peachey.co.uk
Resident Partners/Directors: ICAEW Members
S Allum, J I Morris, C Perry, E E Turner, R Whitfield
Non-resident Partners (ICAEW Members):
J M Ollier, C R Hemming
Other Offices: Bridgnorth, Oswestry, Telford, Welshpool
Registered by the ICAEW to carry out company audit work
Regulated by the ICAEW for a range of investment business activities
General Description: A local professional firm offering a wide range of accounting, financial and taxation services.

VAUGHAN & CO
Telford House, 1 Claremont Bank, Shrewsbury, SY1 1RW
Tel: 01743 239142
Principal: ICAEW Member
D B Vaughan

WHITTINGHAM RIDDELL LLP ◈
Belmont House, Shrewsbury Business Park, Shrewsbury, SY2 6LG
Tel: 01743 273273
Fax: 01743 273274
Email: wr@whittinghamriddell.co.uk
Website: http://www.whittinghamriddell.co.uk
Resident Partners/Directors: ICAEW Members
A M Malpass, P M Sheppard
Resident Partners (Non-ICAEW Members):
S M Harvey
Other Offices: Ludlow, Newtown, Welshpool
Registered by the ICAEW to carry out company audit work
Regulated by the ICAEW for a range of investment business activities

INVESTOR IN PEOPLE

SIDCUP

COLIN ROFE & CO
12 Hatherley Road, Sidcup, DA14 4BG
Tel: 020 8302 5909
Principal: ICAEW Member
C Rofe

DYER & CO
Onega House, 112 Main Road, Sidcup, DA14 6NG

DYER & CO SERVICES LTD
Onega House, 112 Main Road, Sidcup, DA14 6NG

EDWARD BATTARBEE
195 Longlands Road, Sidcup, DA15 7LB
Tel: 020 8300 0527
Resident Partners/Directors: ICAEW Members
E Battarbee

HLB VANTIS AUDIT PLC
Nexus House, 2 Cray Road, Sidcup, DA14 5DA
Tel: 020 8309 0011
Website: http://www.hlbvantisaudit.com
Training Contracts Available.
Registered by the ICAEW to carry out company audit work
Regulated by the ICAEW for a range of investment business activities

SPECIALISATIONS – AUDIT & ASSURANCE
Audit
Audit — Private Company
Audit — Public Company

SPECIALISATIONS – FINANCIAL REPORTING
Audit Exemption Report

KELLEY & LOWE LTD
Marlowe House, 109 Station Road, Sidcup, DA15 7ET

L.R. HALL-STRUTT
25 Cloudesley Close, Sidcup, DA14 6TF

A & S NORMAN & CO
7 Priestlands Park Road, Sidcup, DA15 7HR

POVEY LITTLE
12 Hatherley Road, Sidcup, DA14 4DT

T.R. STEBBINGS & CO
Onega House, 112 Main Road, Sidcup, DA14 6NE
Tel: 020 8309 1363
Principal: ICAEW Member
T R Stebbings

VANTIS GROUP LTD ◈
Nexus House, 2 Cray Road, Sidcup, DA14 5DA
Tel: 0208 309 0011
Website: http://www.vantisplc.com/sidcup
General Description: ICAEW Registered.

SIDMOUTH

AIMS - GRAHAM BIGGS
Peak View, Stevens Cross, Sidford, Sidmouth EX10 9QL
Tel: 01395 519206
Principal: ICAEW Member
G Briggs

EASTERBROOK EATON LTD
Cosmopolitan House, Old Fore Street, Sidmouth, EX10 8LS

HEDGES & CO
The Leighs, Weston, Sidmouth, EX10 0PH
Tel: 07966 148549
Principal: ICAEW Member
D A R Hedges

K. MORRISON
Cheylesmore, Salcombe Hill Road, Sidmouth, EX10 8JR
Tel: 01395 515615
Principal: ICAEW Member
K Morrison

SUTTON ACCOUNTING SERVICES
Capri, Ice House Lane, Sidmouth, EX10 9DS

THOMAS WESTCOTT ★
Durham House, 50 High Street, Sidmouth, EX10 8EJ
Tel: 01395 516909

SITTINGBOURNE

D.S. WILLIAMS
Beaux Aires Cottage, Yelsted Road, Stockbury, Sittingbourne ME9 7QY

F.D. EARL
3 Harvey Drive, Sittingbourne, ME10 4UR

JENNIFER RICHARDSON
43a High Street, Newington, Sittingbourne, ME9 7UR

LAWSON ACCOUNTING LTD
34 Feldspar Close, Sittingbourne, ME10 5FE

LOGIKA LTD
Mainstream House, Bonham Drive, Sittingbourne, ME10 3RY

MCCABE FORD WILLIAMS
Bank Chambers, 1 Central Ave., Sittingbourne, ME10 4AE

PENN ACCOUNTANTS & TAX CONSULTANTS ★
Swale Folly, The Street, Doddington, Sittingbourne ME9 0BG

SMITH MALHOTRA
40-42 High Street, Newington, Sittingbourne, ME9 7JL

SMITH MALHOTRA LTD
40-42 High Street, Newington, Sittingbourne, ME9 7JL

SPAIN BROTHERS ◈
Thames House, Roman Square, Sittingbourne, ME10 4BJ
Tel: 01795 475363
Website: http://www.spainbrothers.co.uk
Training Contracts Available.
Resident Partners/Directors: ICAEW Members
R Bursey, A Cooper, A R Hickie, E M Jordan
Registered by the ICAEW to carry out company audit work
Regulated by the ICAEW for a range of investment business activities

INVESTOR IN PEOPLE

T.F. RAISHBROOK
28 Highsted Road, Sittingbourne, ME10 4PS

WILLIAMS GILES ◈
1 London Road, Sittingbourne, ME10 1NQ
Tel: 01795 478044
Website: http://www.williamsgiles.co.uk
Resident Partners/Directors: ICAEW Members
P H Giles, M Williams
Registered by the ICAEW to carry out company audit work
Regulated by the ICAEW for a range of investment business activities

SKEGNESS

DUNCAN & TOPLIS
27 Lumley Avenue, Skegness, PE25 2AT
Tel: 01754 899899
Fax: 01754 610193
Email: info@skegness.duntop.co.uk
Website: http://www.duntop.co.uk
Resident Partners/Directors: ICAEW Members
J B Chappelle, M H Cope
Resident Partners (Non-ICAEW Members):
J E Thornley
Registered by the ICAEW to carry out company audit work
Regulated by the ICAEW for a range of investment business activities
General Description: Other offices please see Grantham.

HW SKEGNESS
23 Algitha Road, Skegness, PE25 2AG
Tel: 01754 766991
Resident Partners/Directors: ICAEW Members
C G Dedman, A S Minifie, A T Smyth

J ALEXANDER LTD
11 Derby Avenue, Skegness, PE25 3DH

KATHERINE MOWBRAY
17 High Street, Wainfleet, Skegness, PE24 4BP

MICHAEL GREENHALGH & CO LTD
Elland House, 22 High Street, Burgh le Marsh, Skegness PE24 5JT
Tel: 01754 811500
Resident Partners/Directors: ICAEW Members
M Greenhalgh

MICHAEL MAY
47 Algitha Road, Skegness, PE25 2AJ

REBECCA TAYLOR
11 Sea View Road, Skegness, PE25 1BW

SKELMERSDALE

CRESSWALL ASSOCIATES LTD
West Lancashire Investment Centre, Maple View, White Moss Business Park, Skelmersdale WN8 9TG

DENT & CO
Beacon House, 1 Willow Walk, Woodley Park, Skelmersdale WN8 6UR
Tel: 01695 50047
Principal: ICAEW Member
E A Dent

HOLLOWS & HESKETH
9 Sandy Lane, Skelmersdale, WN8 8LA
Tel: 01695 722303
Resident Partners/Directors: ICAEW Members
M W Dunning, J Keeley

ROBERT KEATS
39 Lyndhurst, Skelmersdale, WN8 6UH

SNELSON & CO ★
26 Denholme, Upholland, Skelmersdale, WN8 0AU
Tel: 01695 625578
Resident Partners/Directors: ICAEW Members
K Snelson

SKIPTON

ARMSTRONG WATSON ◈
Currer House, 34/36 Otley Street, Skipton, BD23 1EW
Tel: 01756 620000
Resident Partners/Directors: ICAEW Members
R M Watson

CW BURTON & CO
3 Meadowcroft, Draughton, Skipton, BD23 6EG
Tel: 01756 711056
Principal: ICAEW Member
C W Burton

GOSTLING LTD
Unit 6, Acorn Business Park, Keighley Road, Skipton BD23 2UE
Tel: 01756 709007
Resident Partners/Directors: ICAEW Members
P J Gostling

H & M LTD
1-5 Alma Terrace, Skipton, BD23 1EJ

HUGH D TURNER
Kirk Syke, High Street, Gargrave, Skipton BD23 3RA
Tel: 01756 748117
Principal: ICAEW Member
H D Turner

JENNINGS & CO
6 New Laithe Close, Skipton, BD23 6AZ

PATRO LTD
Holly House, Burnsall, Skipton, BD23 6BN

PEARSON & ASSOCIATES
North Barn, Broughton Hall, Skipton, BD23 3AE

PHIL DODGSON & PARTNERS LTD
63/65 High Street, Skipton, BD23 1DS

QX LTD
High Corn Mill, Chapel Hill, Skipton, BD23 1NL

ROBERTSHAW & MYERS ◈
Number 3, Acorn Business Park, Keighley Road, Skipton BD23 2UE
Tel: 01756 706611
Fax: 01756 706633
Email: info@robertshawmyers.co.uk
Website: http://www.robertshawmyers.co.uk
Resident Partners/Directors: ICAEW Members
P Bailey, M D Bottomley, T D Lodge, D A Richmond
Resident Partners (Non-ICAEW Members):
A S Mitchell
Registered by the ICAEW to carry out company audit work
Regulated by the ICAEW for a range of investment business activities

THE SHEPHERD PARTNERSHIP LTD
Albion House, Rope Walk, Otley Street, Skipton BD23 1ED
Tel: 01756 799823
Email: skipton@shepherdpartnership.com
Website: http://www.shepherdpartnership.com
Resident Partners/Directors: ICAEW Members
A J McManus, A W Webb
Resident Partners (Non-ICAEW Members):
A J Dutton

WESTON, WHALLEY & JACKSON
12 Skipton House, Thanets Yard, Skipton, BD23 1EE
Tel: 01756 792134
Email: robin@skiptonaccountants.co.uk
Principal: ICAEW Member
C R Worthy

WINDLE & BOWKER LTD ◈
Duke House, Duke Street, Skipton, BD23 2HQ
Tel: 01756 790290
Resident Partners/Directors: ICAEW Members
N P C Stead

SLEAFORD

DEXTER & SHARPE ★
The Old Firestation, 19 Watergate, Sleaford, NG34 7PG

DUNCAN & TOPLIS
18 Northgate, Sleaford, NG34 7BJ
Tel: 01529 303773
Fax: 01529 413926
Email: info@sleaford.duntop.co.uk
Website: http://www.duntop.co.uk
Resident Partners/Directors: ICAEW Members
K Phillips, S N Syddall
Registered by the ICAEW to carry out company audit work
Regulated by the ICAEW for a range of investment business activities
General Description: Other officesm, please see Grantham.

KEITH CHAMBERS
24 Westgate, Sleaford, NG34 7PN
Tel: 01529 302887
Principal: ICAEW Member
K Chambers

W.A. GILMOUR
4 St Gilberts Close, Pointon, Sleaford, NG34 0NG
Tel: 01529 240216
Principal: ICAEW Member
W A Gilmour

WRIGHT VIGAR LTD ◈
5/6 Clover House, Boston Road, Sleaford, NG34 7HD
Tel: 01529 415500
Website: http://www.wrightvigar.co.uk
Resident Partners/Directors: ICAEW Members
J P Sewell

SPECIALISATIONS – AUDIT & ASSURANCE

Audit — Private Company

SPECIALISATIONS – SECTOR

Charities

SLOUGH

A & S ASSOCIATES
PO Box 3310, 126 Fairlie Road, Slough, SL1 0AG

A & S ASSOCIATES LTD ◈
P O Box 3310, 126 Fairlie Road, Slough, SL1 0AG
Tel: 01753 535569
Resident Partners/Directors: ICAEW Members
A Jones, S C Jones

AGHS ◈
14 Progress Business Centre, Whittle Parkway, Slough, SL1 6DQ
Tel: 01628 666208
Principal: ICAEW Member
R K Parsons
Registered by the ICAEW to carry out company audit work

AGM
Burnham Business Centre, Dorney House, 46-48a Burnham High Street, Burnham, Slough SL1 7JP

BEAUMONT TEW & CO
Forsythia Cottage, 4 Sefton Paddock, Stoke Poges, Slough SL2 4PT
Tel: 01753 662171
Principal: ICAEW Member
C C Tew

CHARLES STUART LLP ◈
Riding Court, Riding Court Road, Datchet, Slough SL3 9LE
Tel: 01753 580444
Email: value@csuk.com
Website: http://www.csuk.com
Non-resident Partners (ICAEW Members):
L Penny, R Johnson, A Magagnin
Other Offices: Hounslow
Registered by the ICAEW to carry out company audit work
Regulated by the ICAEW for a range of investment business activities

SPECIALISATIONS – AUDIT & ASSURANCE

Audit — Private Company

SPECIALISATIONS – SECTOR

Doctors
Property Development
Property Investment
Solicitors

SPECIALISATIONS – TAXATION

Investigations
Payroll Service and Advice
UK Subsidiaries of Overseas Multinationals

General Description: Small & medium business specialists. Chartered tax advisers.

D.L. GODLEY & CO
April Cottage, Andrew Hill Lane, Hedgerley, Slough SL2 3UL

DEVINE & CO
242/242a Farnham Road, Slough, SL1 4XE
Tel: 01753 534033
Principal: ICAEW Member
B W J Devine

EACOTTS
Grenville Court, Britwell Road, Burnham, Slough SL1 8DF
Tel: 01628 665432
Resident Partners/Directors: ICAEW Members
N M Curtis, M Gatehouse, J B Smith

EACOTTS LTD ◈
Grenville Court, Britwell Road, Burnham, Slough SL1 8DF
Tel: 01628 665432
Resident Partners/Directors: ICAEW Members
N M Curtis, M Gatehouse, M A Newbold, J B Smith

GRANT THORNTON UK LLP
Churchill House, Chalvey Road East, Slough, SL1 2LS
Tel: 01753 781001
Resident Partners/Directors: ICAEW Members
P M D Etherington, A J Flatt, R F Napper, H D Riley, J N Rogers
Resident Partners (Non-ICAEW Members):
H K Parmar, K A Robb

GRIFFITH, MILES, SULLY & CO ▽
7 Gore Road, Burnham, Slough, SL1 8AA
Tel: 01628 665668
Resident Partners/Directors: ICAEW Members
R F Norman

HAINES WATTS ◈
Sterling House, 177-181 Farnham Road, Slough, SL1 4XP
Tel: 01753 530333
Resident Partners/Directors: ICAEW Members
G M Laughton, J R P Moughton, M Perry, C G Segal, P Simmons, R A Welland
Resident Partners (Non-ICAEW Members):
M Davidson
Registered by the ICAEW to carry out company audit work
Regulated by the ICAEW for a range of investment business activities

HEMSLEY MILLER & CO
Old Telephone Exchange, Kingsway, Farnham Common, Slough SL2 3ST
Tel: 01753 645446
Email: info@hmiller.co.uk
Principal: ICAEW Member
N G Dodd
Registered by the ICAEW to carry out company audit work
Regulated by the ICAEW for a range of investment business activities

J.D. WARE
52 The Fairway, Burnham, Slough, SL1 8DS
Tel: 01628 605968
Principal: ICAEW Member
J D Ware

KETAN PATEL & CO
A L'Avenier, 40a Britwell Road, Burnham, Slough SL1 8AQ

MASONS ★
337 Bath Road, Slough, SL1 5PR
Tel: 01628 559551
Email: team@mason-accountants.com
Website: http://www.mason-accountants.com
Date Established: 1976
Resident Partners/Directors: ICAEW Members
A Jeffries
Resident Partners (Non-ICAEW Members):
F E Harding, M F Chapman, P J Gorman, N J Gadeke
Registered by another RSB to carry out company audit work
Licensed by another DPB to carry on investment business
See display advertisement near this entry.

MORLEY AND SCOTT ◈
Winterton House, Nixey Close, Slough, SL1 1ND
Tel: 01753 759000
Fax: 01753 759100
Email: ms@morleyandscott.co.uk
Website: http://www.morleyandscott.co.uk
continued

MORLEY AND SCOTT *cont*
Resident Partners/Directors:
ICAEW Members
I S Anderson, P J Clark, S E Garland, L L Richardson, D G A Wood
Other Offices: London, Solent, Portsmouth
Registered by the ICAEW to carry out company audit work
Authorised and regulated by the Financial Services Authority for investment business

MORLEY AND SCOTT FINANCIAL PLANNING ◈
Winterton House, Nixey Close, Slough, SL1 1ND
Tel: 01753 518044
Fax: 01753 759100
Email: ms@morleyandscott.co.uk
Website: http://www.morleyandscott.co.uk
Other Offices: London, Portsmouth, Solent
Authorised and regulated by the Financial Services Authority for investment business

OURY CLARK
PO Box 150, Herschel House, 58 Herschel Street, Slough
SL1 1HD
Tel: 01753 551111
Fax: 01753 550544
Email: emma.johnson@ouryclark.com
Website: http://www.ouryclark.com
Training Contracts Available.
Resident Partners/Directors:
ICAEW Members
M J Donougher, I Friend, E H Green, S E Harris, E Johnson, R M Lockwood, A C Oury, R A Oury, I Phipps, D A Smith, D G Taylor Rea
Non-resident Partners (ICAEW Members):
J E Oury
Resident Partners (Non-ICAEW Members):
A Williamson, D Chinn
Other Offices: London
Registered by the ICAEW to carry out company audit work
Authorised and regulated by the Financial Services Authority for investment business
Individual(s) licensed for insolvency work by the ICAEW
General Description: The firm provides a full range of services including corporate finance, business recovery, inward investment, taxation, auditing. The firm works closely with Oury Clark Solicitors.

PENTAGON CONSULTING
Beech Court, Summers Road, Burnham, Slough SL1 7EP

PENTAGON FINANCIAL LTD
Beech Court, Summers Road, Burnham, Slough SL1 7EP
Tel: 01628 664500
Resident Partners/Directors:
ICAEW Members
K Sanghera

R A MCLEOD & CO
10 Portland Business Centre, Manor House Lane, Datchet, Slough SL3 9EG
Tel: 01753 542401
Principal: ICAEW Member
R A McLeod

ROBERT S. DEARING
Meadowbank, Parsonage Lane, Farnham Common, Slough
SL2 3PA
Tel: 01753 644480
Principal: ICAEW Member
R S Dearing

S.K. SHARMA & CO
Gable House, Black Pond Lane, Farnham Common, Slough
SL2 3EN

T.J. HUSSEY
Andrew Hill Cottage, Andrew Hill Lane, Hedgerley, Slough
SL2 3UL

TIM LAWRENCE
Whitethorn, Collinswood Road, Farnham Common, Slough
SL2 3LH

TIM O'BRIEN
The Green, Datchet, Slough, SL3 9AS

SMETHWICK

AURORA & CO
174-176 Cape Hill, Smethwick, B66 4SJ

AURORA ACCOUNTANTS LTD
Capital House, 172-176 Cape Hill, Smethwick, B66 4SJ

AUSTRAL RYLEY LTD
416-418 Bearwood Road, Smethwick, B66 4EZ
Tel: 0121 429 2262
Resident Partners/Directors:
ICAEW Members
G J Ashmore, M J Rose
Registered by the ICAEW to carry out company audit work

AUSTREL RYLEY
416-418 Bearwood Road, Bearwood, Smethwick, B66 4EZ

G & CO BIRMINGHAM LTD
414 Bearwood Road, Smethwick, B66 4EU

GODFREY MANSELL & CO
Kenmore House, 51 Downing Street, Smethwick, B66 2PP

GODFREY MANSELL & CO LLP
Kenmore House, 51 Downing Street, Smethwick, B66 2PP

N.J. PATEL & CO ◈
345 Bearwood Road, Smethwick, B66 4DB
Tel: 0121 429 8067
Principal: ICAEW Member
N J Patel

RANA ACCOUNTANTS LTD
140 High Street, Smethwick, B66 3AP

S.D. MODI & CO
Windsor Chambers, 367a Bearwood Road, Smethwick, B66 4DL

SNODLAND

KAMBO & CO
109-111 Malling Road, Snodland, ME6 5AB

PERRYS
44 High Street, Snodland, ME6 5DA

SOLIHULL

A.J.M. QUY
343 Station Road, Dorridge, Solihull, B93 8EY
Tel: 01564 777521
Principal: ICAEW Member
A J M Quy

A.R. NIELD
114 Brookvale Road, Olton, Solihull, B92 7JB

AIMS - ANTHONY MILLNER
54 Milverton Road, Knowle, Solihull, B93 0HY

AIMS - TIM WRIGHT
Batts Hall, Warwick Road, Knowle, Solihull B93 0DS

ANIZ VISRAM & CO
Pinfold Lodge, 32a Hampton Lane, Solihull, B91 2PY

ANIZ VISRAM ACCOUNTANCY SERVICES LTD
Pinfold Lodge, 32a Hampton Lane, Solihull, B91 2PY

ARUNDALES
Stowe House, 1688 High Street, Knowle, Solihull B93 0LY
Tel: 01564 777726
Fax: 01564 770628
Email: info@arundales.co.uk
Training Contracts Available.
Resident Partners/Directors:
ICAEW Members
P A Beddard, B Pulley
Resident Partners (Non-ICAEW Members):
P Poyner
Registered by the ICAEW to carry out company audit work
Regulated by the ICAEW for a range of investment business activities

AVERY WEST
334 Blossomfield Road, Solihull, B91 1TF

AVERY WEST LTD
334 Blossomfield Road, Solihull, B91 1TF

BAKER-GORDON
23 Lindhurst Drive, Hockley Heath, Solihull, B94 6QD

BREARLEY & CO LTD
8 Oakfield House, 478 Station Road, Dorridge, Solihull
B93 8HG

BREARLEY & CO LTD
334 Blossomfield Road, Solihull, B91 1TF
Tel: 0121 704 3430
Resident Partners/Directors:
ICAEW Members
T Brearley

BRESLINS
Westbury House, 701-705 Warwick Road, Solihull, B91 3DA

BUSINESS WIZARDS LTD
12 Darley Mead Court, Hampton Lane, Solihull, B91 2QA

CARTWRIGHT CONSULTING
18 Naseby Road, Solihull, B91 2DR
Tel: 0121 711 8581
Principal: ICAEW Member
R G Cartwright

CICERO FINANCIAL MANAGEMENT
20 Mirfield Road, Solihull, B91 1JD

CICERO FINANCIAL MANAGEMENT LTD
20 Mirfield Road, Solihull, B91 1JD

D A FRANCIS
125 Widney Lane, Solihull, B91 3LH

DAVID J. TOWNEND
17 Stoneleigh Road, Solihull, B91 1DG
Tel: 0121 240 5888
Principal: ICAEW Member
D J Townend

DAVID LLOYD ◈
148 Lugtrout Lane, Solihull, B91 2RX
Tel: 07831 211410
Principal: ICAEW Member
D E Lloyd

EDEN CURRIE
Pegasus House, Solihull Business Park, Solihull, B90 4GT

EDEN CURRIE LTD ◈
Pegasus House, Solihull Business Park, Solihull, B90 4GT
Tel: 0121 746 4171
Email: mail@edencurrie.co.uk
Website: http://www.edencurrie.co.uk
Resident Partners/Directors: ICAEW Members
P B Bosley, C A Webb, T J Wetton
Resident Partners (Non-ICAEW Members):
P Mannion, W M Williams
Registered by the ICAEW to carry out company audit work
Regulated by the ICAEW for a range of investment business activities

INVESTOR IN PEOPLE

EDWARD REVILLE
28 Newton Road, Knowle, Solihull, B93 9HN
Tel: 01564 774800
Principal: ICAEW Member
E Reville

ELLIS MANAGEMENT SERVICES LTD
29 Hartington Close, Dorridge, Knowle, Solihull B93 8SU

EMPLOYER COVENANT SOLUTIONS
112 School Road, Hockley Heath, Solihull, B94 6RB

F.G. KLUYVER
90 Bryanston Road, Solihull, B91 1BS

GEORGE ROGERS & CO
12 Landor Road, Knowle, Solihull, B93 9HZ

GOSLING CONSULTING
Unit 15, Hockley Court, 2401 Stratford Road, Hockley Heath, Solihull B94 6NW

H.I. ASSOCIATES LTD ◈
17 The Orchards, Cheswick Green, Shirley, Solihull B90 4HP

HARBEN BARKER LTD ◈
Drayton Court, Drayton Road, Solihull, B90 4NG
Tel: 0121 704 4004
Resident Partners/Directors: ICAEW Members
A G Purnell, P Stanford

IAN YARWOOD & CO
2 Station Road, Solihull, B91 3SB
Tel: 0121 705 7077
Principal: ICAEW Member
I R Yarwood

J.C. BREWERTON & CO
Ashcombe House, 4 Morville Close, Dorridge, Solihull B93 8SZ

J H COX
8 Hainfield Drive, Solihull, B91 2PL

J.W. BINSTED & CO ◈
Brueton House, 34 Brueton Avenue, Solihull, B91 3EN
Tel: 0121 705 2581
Principal: ICAEW Member
J W Binsted

JERROMS LLP
The Exchange, Haslucks Green Road, Shirley, Solihull B90 2EL
Tel: 0121 693 5000
Resident Partners/Directors: ICAEW Members
N Currie, R M Jerrom

JOHN TAYLOR
11 Jacobean Lane, Copt Heath, Solihull, B93 9LP
Tel: 01675 442282
Principal: ICAEW Member
H J C Taylor

JONES & CO ◈
333 Station Road, Dorridge, Solihull, B93 8EY
Tel: 01564 770766
Resident Partners/Directors: ICAEW Members
A N Jones, H Jones

LKT ◈
26a Richmond Road, Olton, Solihull, B92 7RP
Tel: 0121 707 7015
Principal: ICAEW Member
A S Tennant

MC-CA
19 Kendrick Close, Solihull, B92 0QD
Tel: 0121 711 1660
Email: martin.cooke@mc-ca.co.uk
Principal: ICAEW Member
M P Cooke
Regulated by the ICAEW for a range of investment business activities

MCA BRESLINS
8 The Courtyard, 707 Warwick Road, Solihull, B91 3DA

MCA BRESLINS SOLIHULL LTD ◈
8 The Courtyard, 707 Warwick Road, Solihull, B91 3DA
Tel: 0121 703 9181
Resident Partners/Directors: ICAEW Members
M C Cox, K M Walsh

MASON + CO
4 Dorridge Croft, Dorridge, Solihull, B93 8QL

MATHER & CO
7 Woodchester Road, Dorridge, Solihull, B93 8EN

MICHAEL JELLICOE
59 Knowle Wood Road, Dorridge, Solihull, B93 8JP
Tel: 01564 777522
Principal: ICAEW Member
M J Jellicoe

MICHAEL W. BEARD
62 Hermitage Road, Solihull, B91 2LP
Tel: 0121 705 8364
Principal: ICAEW Member
M W Beard

MORTIMER S
1 Chilwell Close, Solihull, B91 3YL

NEWMAN JAMES
43 St Francis Avenue, Solihull, B91 1EB

NEWMAN JAMES LTD
43 St Francis Avenue, Solihull, B91 1EB

NOEL GRACE
32 Widney Manor Road, Solihull, B91 3JQ

NOEL GRACE LTD ◈
32 Widney Manor Road, Solihull, B91 3JQ
Tel: 01217 056924
Resident Partners/Directors: ICAEW Members
N A Grace

P.A. BROWN
52 Northbrook Road, Shirley, Solihull, B90 3NP

PETER W SHEPHARD
2 Brinsley Close, Solihull, B91 3FR
Tel: 0121 711 7536
Resident Partners/Directors: ICAEW Members
P W Shephard

POWER & CO ◈
12 Queen Eleanors Drive, Knowle, Solihull, B93 9LY
Tel: 01564 777447
Principal: ICAEW Member
S J Power

PRICE DEACON WITHAM LTD
Central Boulevard, Blythe Valley Park, Shirley, Solihull B90 8AG

PRICE PEARSON WITHAM
Central Boulevard, Blythe Valley Park, Shirley, Solihull B90 8AG

PRIME
Marlborough House, Warwick Road, Solihull, B91 3DA

PRIME
Marlborough House, 679 Warwick Road, Solihull, B91 3DA

PRIME SOLIHULL LTD
Marlborough House, 679 Warwick Road, Solihull, B91 3DA
Tel: 0121 711 2468
Resident Partners/Directors: ICAEW Members
K H Johns, J S McDonald, L P Moore

RENDLE & CO
112 School Road, Hockley Heath, Solihull, B94 6RB

RICHARD ABEL & CO
14 Shelwick Grove, Dorridge, Solihull, B93 8UH

RICHARD C. YATES
16 Arnold Grove, Shirley, Solihull, B90 3JR

RICHARD CROSBY ◈
Shrublands Farmhouse, Barston Lane, Barston, Solihull B92 0JU
Tel: 01675 446100
Principal: ICAEW Member
R W V Crosby

RICHARD THOMPSON & CO
15 Swanswell Road, Olton, Solihull, B92 7ET
Tel: 0121 604 8419
Principal: ICAEW Member
R W G Thompson

RODNEY PITTS
4 Fairways, 1240 Warwick Road, Knowle, Solihull B93 9LL
Tel: 01564 779971
Principal: ICAEW Member
J R G Pitts

RP RENDLE & CO LTD ◈
112 School Road, Hockley Heath, Solihull, B94 6RB

SANDERLINGS LLP
Sanderling House, Springbrook Lane, Earlswood, Solihull B94 5SG

SEARLE & CO ◈
Camelot, 32 Diddington Lane, Hampton in Arden, Solihull B92 0BZ

SHAFFERS
90 Moorlands Drive, Shirley, Solihull, B90 3RE

SHRINIVAS HONAP
178 Kineton Green Road, Solihull, B92 7ES
Tel: 07976 955251
Principal: ICAEW Member
S M Honap

SL ACCOUNTANTS LTD
294 Warwick Road, Solihull, B92 7AF
Tel: 0121 706 3550
Resident Partners/Directors: ICAEW Members
S E Green, L A Hartley

SLATER JOHNSTONE
3 Thimble Lane, Knowle, Solihull, B93 0LY
Tel: 01564 770089
Resident Partners/Directors: ICAEW Members
E R Slater, F C Slater

STUART BRAMPTON
23 Saxon Wood Road, Cheswick Green, Solihull, B90 4JN
Tel: 01564 703929
Principal: ICAEW Member
S R Brampton

STUART K JONES FCA ◈
The Willows, Netherwood Lane, Chadwick End, Solihull
B93 0BD

THOMAS & YOUNG
240 Stratford Road, Shirley, Solihull, B90 3AE

THOMAS & YOUNG LTD
240-244 Stratford Road, Shirley, Solihull, B90 3AE

THOMAS & YOUNG LLP ◈
240-244 Stratford Road, Shirley, Solihull, B90 3AE
Tel: 0121 733 1111
Email: mail@thomasandyoung.co.uk
Resident Partners/Directors: ICAEW Members
M J Blamire-Brown, J Carty, R J Gaunt, C G Thomas, M E Vousden, V J Young
Resident Partners (Non-ICAEW Members):
R J Parry, J Carty
Regulated by the ICAEW for a range of investment business activities

WEST
4 Nailsworth Road, Dorridge, Solihull, B93 8NS
Tel: 01564 230104
Principal: ICAEW Member
S West

SOMERTON

BUTTERWORTH JONES ◈
Church House, West Street, Somerton, TA11 7PS
Tel: 01458 272482
Fax: 01458 272482
Registered by the ICAEW to carry out company audit work
Regulated by the ICAEW for a range of investment business activities

SOUTH BRENT

JOHN BEVAN
Underhill, South Brent, TQ10 9DZ
Tel: 01364 72677
Principal: ICAEW Member
J G Bevan

SOUTH CROYDON

AAKABENI & CO
25 Croham Manor Road, South Croydon, CR2 7BJ

AUDIT TAX ASSOCIATES LTD
Compton House, 20(a) Selsdon Road, South Croydon, CR2 6PA
Tel: 020 8686 7878
Resident Partners/Directors: ICAEW Members
M R S Patel, R Patel, P G Thakrar

BRYAN K H ROGERS
1 Cranleigh Gardens, Sanderstead, South Croydon, CR2 9LD
Tel: 020 8657 3053
Principal: ICAEW Member
B K H Rogers

GORRIE WHITSON
9 Station Approach, Sanderstead Road, Station Approach, South Croydon CR2 0PL

GURYEL & CO ◈
21 Chapel View, South Croydon, CR2 7LG
Tel: 020 8090 2183
Principal: ICAEW Member
S Guryel

JEREMY BENJAMIN
Ground Floor Flat, 47 Bynes Road, South Croydon, CR2 0PY
Tel: 020 8681 2251
Principal: ICAEW Member
J D Benjamin

M.R.S. PATEL & CO
Compton House, 20a Selsdon Road, South Croydon, CR2 6PA
Tel: 020 8256 0537
Principal: ICAEW Member
M R S Patel

MANNOOCH & CO
5 Briton Hill Road, Sanderstead, South Croydon, CR2 0JG
Tel: 020 8657 6886
Principal: ICAEW Member
D J Mannooch

NATHAN MAKNIGHT
326a Limpsfield Road, South Croydon, CR2 9DH

NOVITT BAMFORD LTD
Pennyfarthing House, 560 Brighton Road, South Croydon, CR2 6AW

PATENS & CO
Compton House, 20a Selsdon Road, South Croydon, CR2 6PA
Tel: 020 8256 0530
Principal: ICAEW Member
R Patel

PESTELL & CO
2A Nicola Close, South Croydon, CR2 6NB
Tel: 07778 158913
Principal: ICAEW Member
J P Pestell

PETER KAY
14 Hamond Close, South Croydon, CR2 6BZ

RAYMOND CARTER & CO
1b Haling Road, South Croydon, CR2 6HS
Tel: 020 8686 1686
Principal: ICAEW Member
J A Carter

RICHARD H. SNELLING
9 West Hill, Sanderstead, South Croydon, CR2 0SB

SARGENT & CO
194b Addington Road, Selsdon, South Croydon, CR2 8LD
Tel: 020 8651 2719
Fax: 020 8651 1197
Email: alison@alison-sargent.co.uk
Mobile: 07703 538233
Principal: ICAEW Member
A G Sargent
Registered by the ICAEW to carry out company audit work

SPECIALISATIONS – AUDIT & ASSURANCE

Audit — Private Company

SPECIALISATIONS – FINANCIAL REPORTING

Accounts Preparation
Limited Company Accounts

SPECIALISATIONS – SECTOR

Charities

SPECIALISATIONS – TAXATION

Personal
Self Assessment Advice

SAUNDERS & CO
Mayfield, 122 Mitchley Avenue, Sanderstead, South Croydon CR2 9HH

THAKRAR NAGLE JAMES
Compton House, 20(a) Selsdon Road, South Croydon, CR2 6PA
Tel: 020 8686 9900
Principal: ICAEW Member
P G Thakrar

WHITE CORFIELD & FRY LTD
420 Brighton Road, South Croydon, CR2 6AN
Tel: 020 86860482
Resident Partners/Directors: ICAEW Members
E C Fry

SOUTH MOLTON

DAVISONS LTD
11 South Street, South Molton, EX36 4AA
Tel: 01769 572404
Resident Partners/Directors: ICAEW Members
M F Joslin, J C Ward

SULLY & CO
75 South Street, South Molton, EX36 4AG
Tel: 01769 572171
Resident Partners/Directors: ICAEW Members
J R Kelly, N S L Williams

SOUTH SHIELDS

AUSTIN ELLIOTT
138 Westoe Road, South Shields, NE33 3PF

CHARLTON & CO ◈
Saville Chambers, 4 Saville Street, South Shields, NE33 2PR

G W DICK & CO LLP ◈
Earl Grey House, 11 Beach Road, South Shields, NE33 2QA
Tel: 01914 4553779
Resident Partners/Directors: ICAEW Members
G W Dick, W R A Dick

JM ACCOUNTANCY LTD
5 Beach Road, South Shields, NE33 2QA

THOBURN & CHAPMAN
14 Barrington Street, South Shields, NE33 1AJ

WILLIAM L. THOMPSON & CO ◈
Arbeia Business Centre, 8 Stanhope Parade, South Shields, NE33 4BA

WILLIS SCOTT GROUP ★ ◈
5 Beach Road, South Shields, NE33 2QA

SOUTHALL

AST
16 Craneswater Park, Norwood Green, Southall, UB2 5RR

COOPER DAWN JERROM LTD
Units SCF 1 & 2, Western International Market, Hayes Road, Southall UB2 5XJ

GOODHAVEN LTD
Office No 5, Western International Market centre, Hayes Road, Southall UB2 5XJ

ITACCOUNTING
Office No 5, Western International Market Centre, Hayes Road, Southall, Southall UB2 5XJ

PAUL BABBAR & CO
17 Featherstone Road, Southall, UB2 5AA

SOUTHAM

COTTONS
6 High Street, Southam, CV47 0HA

GRINEAUX ACCOUNTANTS LTD
20 Market Hill, Southam, CV47 0HF

GRINEAUX HAMMERSLEY ★
20 Market Hill, Southam, CV47 0HF
Tel: 01926 814578
Fax: 01926 815026
Email: office@grineaux.co.uk
Training Contracts Available.
Resident Partners/Directors: ICAEW Members
D Hammersley

Resident Partners (Non-ICAEW Members):
M Grineaux
Registered by the ICAEW to carry out company audit work

INVESTOR IN PEOPLE

Languages Spoken:
German

MAHON & CO
Marston House, Priors Marston, Southam, CV47 7RP

SOUTHAMPTON

ABC 123 LTD
The Old Manor, Manor Road, Dibden, Southampton SO45 5TJ

ABC 123 LTD
41 Park Road, Freemantle, Southampton, SO15 3AW

ABRAHAM AND DOBELL
230 Shirley Road, Southampton, SO15 3HR

ACCOUNTABLY LTD
110 Hamble Lane, Hamble, Southampton, SO31 4HT
Tel: 02380 453907
Resident Partners/Directors: ICAEW Members
J Best

AIMS - JONATHAN PORTER
8 Bassett Dale, Southampton, SO16 7GT

AKP
41 Park Road, Freemantle, Southampton, SO15 3AW

ALAN MINSHALL ACCOUNTANTS LTD
222 Woodlands Road, Woodlands, Southampton, SO40 7GL

ALISON BROOKER
19 Calmore Crescent, Calmore, Southampton, SO40 2RJ

ASHFORD READ
Unit 4, Basepoint Enterprise Centre, Andersons Road, Southampton SO14 5FE

AVONGLEN LTD ◈
2 Venture Road, Southampton Science Park, Chilworth, Southampton SO16 7NP
Tel: 02380 762570
Resident Partners/Directors: ICAEW Members
P C Dingley, W S Harris, T J Hilton, T W Ricketts

B.W.J. CRANE
Cherry Tree Cottage, Green Lane, Old Netley, Southampton SO31 8EY

BAILEY PHILPOTT LTD
30 Medlicott Way, Swanmore, Southampton, SO32 2NE
Tel: 01489 891997
Resident Partners/Directors: ICAEW Members
D J Bailey, T J Philpott

BASRA & BASRA LTD
9 London Road, Southampton, SO15 2AE
Tel: 02380 211111
Resident Partners/Directors: ICAEW Members
H Basra

BASSETT ACCOUNTANCY LTD
4 Leaside Way, Southampton, SO16 3DU

BDO STOY HAYWARD LLP
Arcadia House, Maritime Walk, Ocean Village, Southampton SO14 3TL
Tel: 02380 881700
Fax: 02380 881701
Resident Partners/Directors: ICAEW Members
P N Anthony, A H Beckingham, T Bentall, S C Day, C D G Driver, K H Hayward, S R Lisle, P B Russell, M B Thixton
Resident Partners (Non-ICAEW Members):
A P Lines

BEGBIES TRAYNOR (CENTRAL) LLP
41 Castle Way, Southampton, SO14 2BW

BRINSMEAD MADEN
The Loft House, Meadow Lane, Hamble, Southampton SO31 4RB
Tel: 02380 457900
Principal: ICAEW Member
C Maden

BTG MCINNES CORPORATE FINANCE
41 Castle Way, Southampton, SO14 2BW

BUCHANANS ◈
Latimer House, 5 Cumberland Place, Southampton, SO15 2BH
Tel: 02380 221222
Resident Partners (Non-ICAEW Members):
P Hall, S Mundy
Authorised and regulated by the Financial Services Authority for investment business
Individual(s) licensed for insolvency work by the ICAEW

BUCHANANS LTD ◈
Latimer House, 5 Cumberland Place, Southampton, SO15 2BH

BUTLER & CO (BISHOPS WALTHAM) LTD ◈
Claylands Road, Bishops Waltham, Southampton, SO32 1BH
Tel: 01489 896996
Resident Partners/Directors: ICAEW Members
S J Slater

D.A. CREAL
Peterkin House, 76 Botley Road, Swanwick, Southampton SO31 7BA
Tel: 01489 885170.
Principal: ICAEW Member
D A Creal

DAVID EXELL ASSOCIATES
Peterkin House, 76 Botley Road, Swanwick, Southampton SO31 7BA

DAVID GRIST & CO
36 St Johns Road, Locks Heath, Southampton, SO31 6NF

DAVID HANCOCK & CO ◈
Webb House, 20 Bridge Road, Park Gate, Southampton SO31 7GE
Tel: 01489 885772
Email: david@dhonline.co.uk
Website: http://www.dhonline.co.uk
Principal: ICAEW Member
D J C Hancock
Registered by the ICAEW to carry out company audit work
Regulated by the ICAEW for a range of investment business activities

DELOITTE & TOUCHE LLP ◈
Mountbatten House, 1 Grosvenor Square, Southampton, SO15 2BE
Tel: 02380 334124
Website: http://www.deloitte.co.uk
Resident Partners/Directors: ICAEW Members
A E Gordon, T C F Wright

DNB ACCOUNTING
33 Luccombe Road, Southampton, SO15 7RJ

DNB ACCOUNTING LTD
33 Luccombe Road, Southampton, SO15 7RJ
Tel: 02380 788978

ED CONNOLLY & CO
126 Bassett Avenue, Southampton, SO16 7EZ

EH CONSULTING LTD
76 Bassett Green Road, Bassett Green, Southampton, SO16 3DZ

ERNST & YOUNG LLP
Wessex House, 19 Threefield Lane, Southampton, SO14 3QB
Tel: 02380 382000
Resident Partners/Directors: ICAEW Members
J J Gray

FBR MCGARRY HARVEY
38-39 New Forest Enterprise Ctr, Rushington Business Park, Totton, Southampton SO40 9LA

FIANDER TOVELL LLP
Stag Gates House, 63-64 The Avenue, Southampton, SO17 1XS
Tel: 02380 332733
Email: info@fiandertovell.co.uk
Website: http://www.fiandertovell.co.uk
Resident Partners/Directors: ICAEW Members
D Harper, P F Meacher, J C Mills, A C Quicke, C Revis, L M Tovell
Registered by the ICAEW to carry out company audit work

INVESTOR IN PEOPLE

GJCA LTD
9 The South Street Centre, 16-20 South Street, Hythe, Southampton SO45 6EB

GRAHAM JONES
9 The South Street Centre, 16-20 South Street, Hythe, Southampton SO45 6EB

GRANT THORNTON UK LLP
1 Dorset Street, Southampton, SO15 2DP
Tel: 02380 381100
Resident Partners/Directors: ICAEW Members
N M Armstrong, S P Davies, S J Mills, J M Sheppard, D K Swift
Non-resident Partners (ICAEW Members):
A H Smith
Resident Partners (Non-ICAEW Members):
D C Tipple, I P Govier

HALL & CO ◈
59 The Avenue, Southampton, SO17 1XS
Tel: 02380 232306
Fax: 023 8023 2393
Email: mail@hall-accountants.co.uk
Resident Partners/Directors: ICAEW Members
G Hall, I Richardson
Registered by the ICAEW to carry out company audit work
Regulated by the ICAEW for a range of investment business activities

HJS
12-14 Carlton Place, Southampton, SO15 2EA

HOPPER WILLIAMS & BELL LTD ◈
Highland House, Mayflower Close, Chandler's Ford, Southampton SO53 4AR
Tel: 02380 461200
Email: admin@hwb-accountants.com
Website: http://www.hwb-accountants.com
Resident Partners/Directors: ICAEW Members
C R Acreman, A R Bell, R A Hurst, A Williams
Resident Partners (Non-ICAEW Members):
M Rogers, G Rhodes, T Jenkins

SPECIALISATIONS – BUSINESS & GENERAL ADVICE
Management Advice to Business

SPECIALISATIONS – SECTOR
Construction
Hotels/Public Houses
Nursing Homes/Clinics
Property

SPECIALISATIONS – TAXATION
Taxation

General Description: Dynamic independent practice committed to Director led service and the provision of quality business and taxation advice.

HUNT JOHNSTON STOKES LTD
12-14 Carlton Place, Southampton, SO15 2EA

HW CORPORATE FINANCE LLP ◈
Kenneth Dibden House, Enterprise Road, Southampton Science Park, Southampton SO16 7NS
Tel: 02380 111310
Resident Partners/Directors: ICAEW Members
J E Bailey, G C Fairclough, C M Fletcher, A M W Godfrey, R J W Hall, D P Lock, B J Potter, R H Style

J&S ACCOUNTANTS LTD
6 Northlands Road, Southampton, SO15 2FL
Tel: 02380 235887
Resident Partners/Directors: ICAEW Members
E M Jones, B A P Stevenson

JACKY GREGORY
Church Lodge, Church Road, Warsash, Southampton SO31 9GF
Tel: 01489 885491
Principal: ICAEW Member
J A Gregory

JAMES ORAM & CO
Cadoro, Roman Drive, Chilworth, Southampton SO16 7HT

JOHN FOLEY
5 Sedge Mead, Netley Abbey, Southampton, SO31 5EY

KEITH POWERS
P O Box 241, Sarisbury Green, Southampton, SO31 1DF

KPMG LLP
Dukes Keep, Marsh Lane, Southampton, SO14 3EX
Tel: 02380 202000
Resident Partners/Directors: ICAEW Members
P I Claisse, P J Cotton

LYNHAM & CO
9 Hampton Lane, Blackfield, Southampton, SO45 1ZA
Tel: 02380 890111
Principal: ICAEW Member
P J Lynham

MANDAIR LTD
Partnership House, 84 Lodge Road, Portswood, Southampton SO14 6RG
Tel: 02380 332882
Resident Partners/Directors: ICAEW Members
T S Mandair

MATTHEWS, MIST & CO
Westbury House, 14 Bellevue Road, Southampton, SO15 2AY

MAZARS CORPORATE FINANCE LTD
Regency House, 3 Grosvenor Square, Southampton, SO15 2BE

MAZARS LLP ◈
Regency House, 3 Grosvenor Square, Southampton, SO15 2BE
Tel: 02380 232428
Resident Partners (Non-ICAEW Members):
M J Attenborough-Cox, S F Christopher
Registered by the ICAEW to carry out company audit work
Authorised and regulated by the Financial Services Authority for investment business

MERIDIAN CORPORATE FINANCE LLP
3rd Floor, Alleyn House, Carlton Crescent, Southampton SO15 2EU

MOORE & CO
Unit 22, Mountbatten Business Centre, Millbrook Road East, Southampton SO15 1HY

MOORE STEPHENS (SOUTH) LLP
45 Westwood Road, Southampton, SO17 1DH

MR E.C. ABRAHAM FCA
18 Pewsey Place, Shirley, Southampton, SO15 7RX
Tel: 02380 771272
Principal: ICAEW Member
E C Abraham

N.J. DILLOW
Vine Cottage, Hampton Hill, Swanmore, Southampton SO32 2QN
Tel: 01489 896858
Principal: ICAEW Member
N J Dillow

NATALIE POWELL ACA
7 Shorefield Road, Marchwood, Southampton, SO40 4SR

NEXIA SMITH & WILLIAMSON AUDIT LTD
Imperial House, 18-21 Kings Park Road, Southampton, SO15 2AT

NICK FROUD
16 Shorewood Close, Warsash, Southampton, SO31 9LB
Tel: 01489 559184
Principal: ICAEW Member
N E Froud

P.H.J. BRUNTON & CO
14 The Brackens, Locks Heath, Southampton, SO31 6TU
Tel: 01489 573730
Principal: ICAEW Member
P H J Brunton

P R LITTLE ◈
16 Kenwyn Close, West End, Southampton, SO18 3PJ
Tel: 07831 260028
Principal: ICAEW Member
P R Little

PANDEY & CO
Cambridge House, 32 Padwell Road, Southampton, SO14 6QZ

PANDEY & CO LTD
Cambridge House, 32 Padwell Road, Southampton, SO14 6QZ

PETER BRANDL LTD
30 St Cuthberts Lane, Locks Heath, Southampton, SO31 6TE

POWER ACCOUNTAX
8c High Street, Southampton, SO14 2DH

POWER ACCOUNTAX LTD
8c High Street, Southampton, SO14 2DH
Tel: 0844 415 0944
Website: http://www.poweraccountax.co.uk
Resident Partners/Directors: ICAEW Members
R P Kohli

PRICEWATERHOUSE-COOPERS
Savannah House, 3 Ocean Way, Ocean Village, Southampton SO14 3TJ

PRICEWATERHOUSE-COOPERS LLP
Savannah House, 3 Ocean Way, Ocean Village, Southampton SO14 3TJ
Tel: 02380 330077
Resident Partners/Directors: ICAEW Members
K Evans, J C F Hitchins, R M J Marshall, E C McCann, A H McNaughtan, N A Smith, S P Udall

R A JONES & CO ◈
38 Rumbridge Street, Totton, Southampton, SO40 9DS
Tel: 02380 666699
Email: enquiries@rajones.co.uk
Website: http://www.rajones.co.uk
Principal: ICAEW Member
R A Jones
Registered by the ICAEW to carry out company audit work
Regulated by the ICAEW for a range of investment business activities

R.A. MCINERNEY
165 Botley Road, Burridge, Southampton, SO31 1BJ
Tel: 01489 575414
Principal: ICAEW Member
R A McInerney

R.A. VOWLES & CO
148 Commercial Road, Totton, Southampton, SO40 3AA
Tel: 02380 860247
Principal: ICAEW Member
R A Vowles

RALPH CRUMP ACCOUNTANTS LTD ◈
14 Bakers Drove, Rownhams, Southampton, SO16 8AD
Tel: 02380 732452
Resident Partners/Directors: ICAEW Members
R Crump
Registered by the ICAEW to carry out company audit work

RICKETTS & CO LTD ◈
43 Bugle Street, Southampton, SO14 2AG
Tel: 02380 339333
Resident Partners/Directors: ICAEW Members
C M W Ricketts

ROCHES ◈
40 Locks Heath Centre, Centre Way, Locks Heath, Southampton SO31 6DX
Tel: 01489 575659
Website: http://www.roches.co.uk
Principal: ICAEW Member
R A Roche
Registered by the ICAEW to carry out company audit work

SPECIALISATIONS – AUDIT & ASSURANCE
Audit

SPECIALISATIONS – FINANCIAL REPORTING
Accounts Preparation
Limited Companies

SPECIALISATIONS – SECTOR
Solicitors

SPECIALISATIONS – TAXATION

Capital Gains — Personal

Partnerships and Sole Traders

Taxation

ROGER SMALLMAN & CO LTD ◈
30A Bedford Place,
Southampton, SO15 2DG
Tel: 02380 222215
Website: http://www.rogersmallman.co.uk
Resident Partners/Directors: ICAEW Members
R C B Smallman

ROGERS EVANS
20 Brunswick Place,
Southampton, SO15 2AQ
Tel: 02380 335888
Fax: 023 8033 4400
Email: businessrecovery@rogersevans.co.uk
Website: http://www.rogersevans.co.uk
Date Established: 1987
Principal: ICAEW Member
T C Evans
Resident Partners (Non-ICAEW Members):
S J Lowes, D P Meany
Other Offices: Christchurch, Belfast, Bristol
Individual(s) licensed for insolvency work by the ICAEW
General Description: Business recovery and insolvency.

ROTHMAN PANTALL & CO ◈
10 Oxford Street, Southampton, SO14 3DJ
Tel: 02380 211088
Fax: 023 8022 9551
Email: southampton@rothman-pantall.co.uk
Website: http://www.rothman-pantall.co.uk
Resident Partners/Directors: ICAEW Members
S T Elliott
Registered by the ICAEW to carry out company audit work
Regulated by the ICAEW for a range of investment business activities

ROWE FRENCH CONSULTING
52 Spitfire Way, Hamble,
Southampton, SO31 4RT

ROWE FRENCH CONSULTING LTD
52 Spitfire Way, Hamble,
Southampton, SO31 4RT

ROWLES & CO
205 Solent Business Centre,
Millbrook Road West,
Southampton, SO15 0HW

RULE DATLEN MANN ◈
66/70 Oxford Street,
Southampton, SO14 3DL
Tel: 02380 336655
Email: soton@ruledatlenmann.co.uk
Website: http://www.ruledatlenmann.co.uk
Resident Partners/Directors: ICAEW Members
S E Datlen, M Rule
Registered by the ICAEW to carry out company audit work
Regulated by the ICAEW for a range of investment business activities

SPECIALISATIONS – AUDIT & ASSURANCE

Audit

SPECIALISATIONS – FINANCIAL REPORTING

Accounts Preparation

SPECIALISATIONS – INVESTMENT BUSINESS

Planning

SPECIALISATIONS – TAXATION

Taxation

S C MILLER LTD ◈
Clock Offices, High Street,
Bishops Waltham, Southampton
SO32 1AA
Tel: 01489 891122
Resident Partners/Directors: ICAEW Members
S C Miller

SHARMA & CO
5 St Denys Road, Portswood,
Southampton, SO17 2GN
Tel: 02380 586953
Principal: ICAEW Member
S K Sharma

SMITH & WILLIAMSON LTD ◈
Imperial House, 18-21 Kings
Park Road, Southampton,
SO15 2AT
Tel: 02380 827600
Email: firstname.lastname@smith.williamson.co.uk
Website: http://www.smith.williamson.co.uk
Resident Partners (Non-ICAEW Members):
T L Amy, A J Phillips
General Description: Smith and Williamson is an independent professional and financial services group employing over 1400 people. We are leading providers of investment management, financial advisory and accountancy services to private clients, professional practices and mid-sized companies. Nexia Smith & Williamson Audit (Bristol) LLP provides audit services to complement the specialist financial advisory services provided by Smith & Williamson.

SPD ACCOUNTANTS LTD
Suite 28, Royal Mail House,
Terminus Terrace, Southampton
SO14 3FD

SPD ACCOUNTANTS LTD
First Floor Hampshire House,
169 High Street, Southampton,
SO14 2BY

STEPHENSON SHEPPARD & CO LTD
The Old School House, Claypits
Lane, Dibden, Southampton
SO45 5TN
Tel: 02380 844242
Fax: 02380 843799
Email: hythe@stepshep.com
Website: http://www.stepshep.com
Non-resident Partners (ICAEW Members):
G G Stone
Non-resident Partners (Non-ICAEW Members):
J P Baggot

STONHAM.CO
Equity & Law House, 14-15
Brunswick Place, Southampton,
SO15 2AQ

STRINGER & CO
5 Bassett Wood Drive,
Southampton, SO16 3PT
Tel: 02380 767241
Principal: ICAEW Member
D J Stringer
Individual(s) licensed for insolvency work by the ICAEW

SUSAN FINNIMORE
20 Dene Way, Ashurst,
Southampton, SO40 7BX

TIM LYONS & CO
29 Carlton Crescent,
Southampton, SO15 2EW

TONY ROBBINS FCA
8 Redwood Close, West End,
Southampton, SO30 3SG

TONY ROBBINS FCA LTD
8 Redwood Close, West End,
Southampton, SO30 3SG
Tel: 02380 476000
Resident Partners/Directors: ICAEW Members
A T Robbins

WARWICK PENDARVES & CO
38 Hound Road, Netley Abbey,
Southampton, SO31 5FX
Tel: 07971 889246
Principal: ICAEW Member
S Pendarves

WEST END ACCOUNTING
18 Lower New Road, West End,
Southampton, SO30 3FL

WILLCOX & CO
10 Chilcott Court, Southampton,
SO52 9PS

YATES & CO
17 Poplar Drive, Marchwood,
Southampton, SO40 4XH

SOUTHEND-ON-SEA

A.K. VOIGTS
14 Elm Grove, Thorpe Bay,
Southend-on-sea, SS1 3EZ

ANIL & CO
220 Maplin Way North, Thrope
Bay, Southend-on-sea, SS1 3NT
Tel: 01702 588112
Email: anil@jram.demon.co.uk
Website: http://www.anilandco.com
Principal: ICAEW Member
A C Jobanputra

AUSTINS
Pine House, Chandlers Way,
Southend-on-sea, SS2 5SE

BEELAMS
93 Burlescoombe Road, Thorpe
Bay, Southend-on-sea, SS1 3PT

BEGBIES TRAYNOR LTD
The Old Exchange, 234
Southchurch Road, Southend-on-sea, SS1 2EG
Tel: 01702 467255
Resident Partners (Non-ICAEW Members):
J Taylor, L Biscoe, L Baxter, D Hudson, M Fry

SPECIALISATIONS – BUSINESS RECOVERY & INSOLVENCY

Bankruptcies

Corporate Recovery

Liquidations

BRADLEY-HOARE & CO
9 West Street, Southend-on-sea,
SS2 6HH

CAMPLING & CO LTD
4 Burges Close, Southend-on-sea, SS1 3JW
Tel: 01702 296004
Resident Partners/Directors: ICAEW Members
N J Campling

CARTER BACKER WINTER
ConnexionsRutland House, 90-92 Baxter Avenue, Southend-on-sea, SS2 6HZ

DOWNER & CO ASSOCIATES LTD
125 Broadclyst Gardens, Thorpe
Bay, Southend-On-Sea,
SS1 3QY

FINDLAY JAMES
30 Clarence Street, Southend-On-Sea, SS1 1BD

GOLDWYNS
Rutland House, 90-92 Baxter
Avenue, Southend-on-sea,
SS2 6HZ

GOLDWYNS LTD
Rutland House, 90-92 Baxter
Avenue, Southend-on-sea,
SS2 6HZ

I.M. PARLANE
41 Cornworthy, Shoeburyness,
Southend-on-sea, SS3 8AN

KSA
2 Nelson Street, Southend-on-sea, SS1 1EF

KWK LTD ◈
11 Weston Road, Southend-on-sea, SS1 1AS
Tel: 01702 332255
Resident Partners/Directors: ICAEW Members
T H R Waite

KYLES & CO ◈
11 Weston Road, Southend-on-sea, SS1 1AS
Tel: 01702 332255
Principal: ICAEW Member
T H R Waite

LAWFORD & CO
3 Royal Terrace, Southend-on-sea, SS1 1DY

LAWFORDS LTD
3 Royal Terrace, Southend-on-sea, SS1 1DY

MATTHAMS & CO
41 Clarence Street, Southend-on-sea, SS1 1BH

MGI RICKARD KEEN LLP ◈
7-11 Nelson Street, Southend-on-sea, SS1 1EH
Tel: 01702 347 771
Website: http://www.rickardkeen.co.uk
Training Contracts Available.
Resident Partners/Directors: ICAEW Members
W J Gould, R I Sadler, A Worsdale
Resident Partners (Non-ICAEW Members):
K E Bell
Other Offices: Glenny House, Southfields Business Park, Fenton Way, Basildon SS15 6TD
Registered by the ICAEW to carry out company audit work
Regulated by the ICAEW for a range of investment business activities

INVESTOR IN PEOPLE

NEWMAN & PARTNERS
457 Southchurch Road, Southend-on-sea, SS1 2PH
Tel: 01702 466886
Resident Partners (Non-ICAEW Members):
P A Stafford

PARLANE PURKIS & CO
177 London Road, Southend-on-sea, SS1 1PW
Tel: 01702 335681
Resident Partners/Directors: ICAEW Members
J Purkis, N D Smeeton

REYNOLDS & CO
4 Thorpe Hall Close, Thorpe Bay, Southend-on-sea, SS1 3SQ

ROBIN G. FAUTLEY
9 Lynton Road, Thorpe Bay, Southend-on-sea, SS1 3BE
Tel: 01702 588536
Principal: ICAEW Member
R G Fautley

ROY C. MARTIN
7 Hawkridge, Shoeburyness, Southend-on-sea, SS3 8AU

SMB TOTAL ACCOUNTING LTD ◈
34 Ravendale Way, Shoebury, Southend-on-sea, SS3 8YB
Tel: 01702 217027
Resident Partners/Directors: ICAEW Members
S Blitz

THP LTD
Cumberland House, 24-28 Baxter Avenue, Southend-on-sea, SS2 6HZ

WILKINS KENNEDY ◈
1-5 Nelson St, Southend-on-sea, SS1 1EG
Tel: 01702 348646
Website: http://www.wilkinskennedy.com
Resident Partners/Directors: ICAEW Members
D M Fenn, J E Golding, R Howard, M.J. Macdonald, M J Norton
Resident Partners (Non-ICAEW Members):
P R East, D P Garside
Other Offices: Amersham, Egham, London, Orpington, Hertford, Reading, Guildford, Ashford, Ramsey, Winchester
Overseas Offices: Stanley, Falkland Islands
Registered by the ICAEW to carry out company audit work
Regulated by the ICAEW for a range of investment business activities

SPECIALISATIONS – BUSINESS & GENERAL ADVICE

Acquisitions and Mergers
Disposal of Businesses

SPECIALISATIONS – BUSINESS RECOVERY & INSOLVENCY

Bankruptcies
Corporate Recovery
Liquidations
Reorganisations and Company Reconstructions

SPECIALISATIONS – FORENSIC ACCOUNTING

Expert Witnesses in Litigation

SPECIALISATIONS – SECTOR

Charities
Construction
Dentists/Opticians
Doctors
Estate Agents
FSA Members
Hotels/Public Houses
Insurance Brokers
Manufacturing
Property
Solicitors

SOUTHMINSTER

DENMARK FORRESTER LTD ◈
First Floor, 1A High Street, Southminster, CM0 7AA

SOUTHPORT

A J WILLIAMS
39 Trafalgar Road, Southport, PR8 2HF

CAROLINE WILSON ◈
45 Kensington Road, Southport, PR9 0RT
Tel: 01704 546000
Principal: ICAEW Member
C E Kirkwood-Wilson

CHAMPION ACCOUNTANTS LLP ◈
71/73 Hoghton Street, Southport, PR9 0PR

CHAMPION BUSINESS SOLUTIONS LTD
71/73 Hoghton Street, Southport, PR9 0PR
Tel: 01704 535687
Fax: 01704 500855
Email: southport@champion-accountants.co.uk
Website: http://www.champion-accountants.co.uk
Resident Partners/Directors: ICAEW Members
G Cosgrove, D A T Wood
Resident Partners (Non-ICAEW Members):
R W Thompson
Other Offices: Manchester, Chester, Preston, Blackpool

DUNCAN SHEARD GLASS ◈
45 Hoghton Street, Southport, PR9 0PG
Tel: 01704 517333
Fax: 01704 500113
Email: lancashire@dsg.uk.com
Website: http://www.dsg.uk.com
Resident Partners/Directors: ICAEW Members
I Douglas
Non-resident Partners (ICAEW Members):
A D Moss
Other Offices: Liverpool, Flintshire
Registered by the ICAEW to carry out company audit work
Regulated by the ICAEW for a range of investment business activities

EAVES AND CO
11 Part Street, Southport, PR8 1HX
Tel: 01704 548698
Email: peaves@eavesandco.co.uk
Website: http://www.eavesandco.co.uk
Resident Partners/Directors: ICAEW Members
P N T Eaves
Other Offices:12 York Place, Leeds LS1 2DS (Tel: 0113 203 1502)

SPECIALISATIONS – TAXATION

Taxation

THE FOCUS PRACTICE
3 Sandringham Road, Birkdale, Southport, PR8 2JZ

FORSHAWS
Clare House, 166 Lord Street, Southport, PR9 0QA

GRAHAM POTTER & CO LTD
3 Sandringham Road, Birkdale, Southport, PR8 2JZ

HADLEY & CO
Adelphi Chambers, 30 Hoghton Street, Southport, PR9 0NZ
Tel: 01704 534539
Resident Partners/Directors: ICAEW Members
P J Barlow, J R D Gummerson, J G Hyland

HARRISON LATHAM & CO
97 Tulketh Street, Southport, PR8 1AW
Tel: 01704 500960
Fax: 01704 500928
Resident Partners/Directors: ICAEW Members
M Harrison, N A Latham
Registered by the ICAEW to carry out company audit work

HDC
Hoghton Chambers, Hoghton Street, Southport, PR9 0TB

HOLDEN TAX CONSULTING LTD
77 Liverpool Road, Southport, PR8 4DE
Tel: 0845 838 0878
Resident Partners/Directors: ICAEW Members
E J Holden

HOLLOWS DAVIES CRANE
Hoghton Chambers, Hoghton Street, Southport, PR9 0TB

IAN WRIGHT & CO
15 Stretton Drive, Southport, PR9 7DR
Tel: 01704 226160
Principal: ICAEW Member
I Wright

J A FELL & CO ★
11b Hoghton Street, Southport, PR9 0NS
Tel: 01704 500299

J. & D. PENNINGTON
55 Hoghton Street, Southport, PR9 0PG

JAMES KIRKHAM & CO
27 Wright Street, Southport, PR9 0TL
Tel: 01704 550637
Principal: ICAEW Member
J A Kirkham

JBS ACCOUNTANTS LLP
2 Fairfield Road, Ainsdale, Southport, PR8 3LH

K.A.FARR & CO
6-8 Botanic Road, Churchtown, Southport, PR9 7NG
Tel: 01704 211434
Principal: ICAEW Member
K O Farr

KEITH OLDER & CO
8 Barford Close, Ainsdale, Southport, PR8 2RS

LESLIE R. BALL
28 Dunkirk Road, Birkdale, Southport, PR8 4RQ

LOU SIMANS & CO
35 Court Road, Southport, PR9 9ET
Tel: 01704 540590

M.C. BILLINGTON & CO
17 Barford Close, Southport, PR8 2RS

M.D. SALE & CO
7 Carlisle Road, Birkdale, Southport, PR8 4DJ

M.G.G. HADDEN & CO LTD
46A Grosvenor Road, Birkdale, Southport, PR8 2ET

MAREK & CO
Kensington House, 7 Roe Lane, Hesketh Park, Southport PR9 9DT
Tel: 01704 548831
Principal: ICAEW Member
M T Szczesniak

MARTYN G PERKINS
166 Portland Street, Southport, PR8 6RB

P.T.WALSH
11 Griffiths Drive, Southport, PR9 7DP

PENNINGTON SILVER
55 Hoghton Street, Southport, PR9 0PG

PHILIP T JONES & PARTNERS ★
55 Hoghton Street, Southport, PR9 0PG

ROBINSON RICE ASSOCIATES
49 Station Road, Ainsdale, Southport, PR8 3HH
Tel: 01704 575655
Principal: ICAEW Member
B E Rice

STEPHEN PRITCHARD & CO
144 Folkestone Road, Southport, PR8 5PP

STUBBS PARKIN TAYLOR & CO LTD
18a London Street, Southport, PR9 0UE

TOPPING & CO
209 Liverpool Road, Birkdale, Southport, PR8 4PH

TURPIN LUCAS LEES
Eldon Court, Hoghton Street, Southport, PR9 0NS

SOUTHSEA

A.E. MUNDY
39 Suffolk Road, Southsea, PO4 8EH

BARTER DURGAN
10 Victoria Road South, Southsea, PO5 2DA
Tel: 02392 738311
Fax: 02392 825025
Email: accountants@barterdurgan.co.uk
Website: http://www.barterdurgan.co.uk
Resident Partners/Directors: ICAEW Members
K A Green, K J Watkins

JONES AVENS
53 Kent Road, Southsea, PO5 3HU
Tel: 02392 820726
Resident Partners/Directors: ICAEW Members
T P Millett

S.G. TALATI
17 St Georges Road, Southsea, PO4 9PL
Tel: 02392 831644
Principal: ICAEW Member
S G Talati

SEAHURST LTD ◈
156 Bath Road, Southsea, PO4 0HU
Tel: 02392 825453
Resident Partners/Directors: ICAEW Members
S C Griffiths

SOUTHWELL

B.R. DUNN
Manton Cottage, Westhorpe, Southwell, NG25 0NE

BEELEY HAWLEY & CO ◈
52a Westgate, Southwell, NG25 0JX

SOUTHWOLD

JULIAN A HIRST
13 York Road, Southwold, IP18 6AN

SPALDING

BULLEY DAVEY ◈
1-4 London Road, Spalding, PE11 2TA
Tel: 01775 766633
Website: http://www.bulleydavey.co.uk
Resident Partners/Directors: ICAEW Members
A R Atkins
Resident Partners (Non-ICAEW Members):
P R Wright
Registered by the ICAEW to carry out company audit work
Regulated by the ICAEW for a range of investment business activities

BULLEY DAVEY ★
1 - 4 London Road, Spalding, PE11 2TA
Tel: 01775 766633
Resident Partners/Directors: ICAEW Members
A R Atkins

C W BARNES LTD
Tolethorpe House, 49 Pinchbeck Road, Spalding, PE11 1QF

DUNCAN & TOPLIS
Enterprise Way, Pinchbeck, Spalding, PE11 3YR
Tel: 01775 766205
Fax: 01775 710512
Email: info@spalding.duntop.co,uk
Website: http://www.duntop.co.uk
Resident Partners/Directors: ICAEW Members
D A J Gratton
Resident Partners (Non-ICAEW Members):
M N Smith
General Description: Other offices please see Grantham.

HULL MATTHEWSON
33 Boston Road South, Holbeach, Spalding, PE12 7LR

HULL MATTHEWSON LTD ◈
33 Boston Road, Holbeach, Spalding, PE12 7LR
Tel: 01406 423166
Resident Partners/Directors: ICAEW Members
J A Matthewson

J.G. SMITH
74 Knight Street, Pinchbeck, Spalding, PE11 3RB
Tel: 01775 761404
Principal: ICAEW Member
J G Smith

MOORE THOMPSON
Bank House, Broad Street, Spalding, PE11 1TB
Tel: 01775 711333
Fax: 01775 711307
Website: http://www.moorethompson.co.uk
Resident Partners/Directors: ICAEW Members
A P Heskin, K J Maggs, T I Martin, M Price
Non-resident Partners (ICAEW Members):
M D Longley
Resident Partners (Non-ICAEW Members):
C Reid, M A East
Other Offices: Monica House, St Augustine Road, Wisbech, Cambridgeshire PE13 3AD, Bank Chambers, 27a Market Place, Market Deeping, Peterborough, Cambs PE6 8EA
Registered by the ICAEW to carry out company audit work
Regulated by the ICAEW for a range of investment business activities

S J FAULKNER
Willow Farm, Town Dam Road, Quadring Eaudyke, Spalding PE11 4PZ

SALWAY & WRIGHT ◈
32 The Crescent, Spalding, PE11 1AF
Tel: 01775 724753
Resident Partners/Directors: ICAEW Members
A M Smith, A D Wood

SALWAY & WRIGHT ◈
22 Church Street, Holbeach, Spalding, PE12 7LL
Tel: 01406 424680

SPENNYMOOR

ADAMS ★
22 Whitworth Terrace, Spennymoor, DL16 7LD

G D O'HEHIR & CO LTD
22/23 Clyde Terrace, Spennymoor, DL16 7SE
Tel: 01388 819911
Resident Partners/Directors: ICAEW Members
G.D. O'Hehir

SPILSBY

BAXTER & CO
1 Old Tower Hall, Market Street, Spilsby, PE23 5JT

DEXTER & SHARPE ★
3 Cornhill, Spilsby, PE23 5JP

ST. AGNES

JEFFERS & STOCK
The Orchard, Mithian, St Agnes, TR5 0QF

ST ALBANS

A.M. BARKER
1B Singlets Lane, Flamstead, St Albans, AL3 8EN

A.M. DONALD
48 Cherry Tree Avenue, London Colney, St Albans, AL2 1RX

ANDREW YARAS & CO
2 Fishpool Street, St Albans, AL3 4RT
Tel: 01727 862317
Principal: ICAEW Member
A J Yaras
Registered by the ICAEW to carry out company audit work

ANN COLEMAN ACCOUNTANCY LTD
Ground Floor, 6a Parkway, Valley Road, Porters Wood, St Albans AL3 6PA

APPLE LEONARD LTD
PO Box 928, St Albans, AL1 9GB

ATTWOODS
12 Palfrey Close, St Albans, AL3 5RE

C.L. BRIDGES
69 Ramsbury Road, St Albans, AL1 1SN
Tel: 01727 838206
Principal: ICAEW Member
C L Bridges

CCH & CO
PO Box 827, London Colney, St Albans, AL1 9AB
Tel: 01727 823649
Resident Partners/Directors: ICAEW Members
C C Hull, J E Hull

COLIN STACEY ASSOCIATES
39 Silk Mill Road, Redbourn, St Albans, AL3 7GE

DAVID M REES & ASSOCIATES LTD
The White Cottage, 41 High Street, Wheathampstead, St Albans AL4 8BB

DELOITTE & TOUCHE LLP ◈
3 Victoria Square, Victoria Street, St Albans, AL1 3TF
Tel: 01727 839000
Website: http://www.deloitte.co.uk
Resident Partners/Directors: ICAEW Members
H A Bygrave, N R Johnson, R S McCabe, P J Schofield, I J Smith

DMP ACCOUNTING
5a Parkway, Porters Wood, St Albans, AL3 6PA

FISHER NG
2 Kings Road, London Colney, St Albans, AL2 1EN

FISHER NG LTD
2 Kings Road, London Colney, St Albans, AL2 1EN

FOWLER & TREMBLING
24 Forge End, St Albans, AL2 3EQ
Tel: 01727 868228
Resident Partners/Directors: ICAEW Members
M P Trembling

FREEMAN BAKER ASSOCIATES ★
The Old Church, 48 Verulam Road, St Albans, AL3 4DH
Tel: 01727 861335
Fax: 01727 843429
Email: enquiries@freemanbaker.co.uk
Website: http://www.freemanbaker.co.uk
Resident Partners/Directors: ICAEW Members
S C Bird, S L Hay
Resident Partners (Non-ICAEW Members):
V J Hunt, N J Keye
Registered by the ICAEW to carry out company audit work
Regulated by the ICAEW for a range of investment business activities

GILBERTS
Pendragon House, 65 London Road, St Albans, AL1 1LJ
Tel: 01727 750 000
Fax: 01727 750005
Email: office@gilberts.uk.com
Website: http://www.gilberts.uk.com
Resident Partners/Directors: ICAEW Members
R Hatrell, R Keeble, A Lovett, R Lovett, A Ruggles

GLASSMAN & CO
8 Holywell Hill, St Albans, AL1 1BZ
Tel: 01727 846204
Principal: ICAEW Member
D Glassman

GLASSMAN & COMPANY LTD
8 Holywell Hill, St Albans, AL1 1BZ
Tel: 01727 846204
Resident Partners/Directors: ICAEW Members
D Glassman

GRAHAM BROOKER FCA ◈
River Hill Cottage, River Hill, Flamstead, St Albans AL3 8BY
Tel: 01582 849349
Email: gbrookerfca@aol.com
Principal: ICAEW Member
G Brooker

GRAHAM MEAGER
12 Wendover Close, St Albans, AL4 9JW
Tel: 01727 852095
Principal: ICAEW Member
G S Meager

GRIFFINS ★
Faulkner House, Victoria Street, St Albans, AL1 3SE

HARDCASTLE BURTON
Old School, The Common, Redbourn, St Albans AL3 7NG

HARRIS LIPMAN

HARRIS LIPMAN LLP ◈
44 Holywell Hill, St Albans, AL1 1BX
Tel: 01727 899300
Fax: 01727 862860
Email: mail@harris-lipman.co.uk
Website: http://www.harris-lipman.co.uk
Non-resident Partners (ICAEW Members):
B D Lewis, M J Atkins, F Khalastchi
Non-resident Partners (Non-ICAEW Members):
J D Cullen, M Hall
Other Offices: London EC2, London N20, Cardiff, Reading

SPECIALISATIONS – BUSINESS RECOVERY & INSOLVENCY
Bankruptcies
Corporate Recovery
Liquidations

SPECIALISATIONS – FORENSIC ACCOUNTING
Expert Witnesses in Litigation
Forensic Accounting

SPECIALISATIONS – TAXATION
Investigations

General Description:
Specialists in corporate recovery, bankruptcies, expert witness in litigation, forensic accounting, liquidations, investigations.

HLB VANTIS AUDIT PLC
Torrington House, 47 Holywell Hill, St Albans, AL1 1HD
Tel: 01727 838 255
Website: http://www.hlbvantisaudit.com
Training Contracts Available.
Resident Partners/Directors: ICAEW Members
A P Scott
Registered by the ICAEW to carry out company audit work
Regulated by the ICAEW for a range of investment business activities

SPECIALISATIONS – AUDIT & ASSURANCE
Audit
Audit — Private Company
Audit — Public Company

SPECIALISATIONS – FINANCIAL REPORTING
Audit Exemption Report

IAN C CUMMINGS ◈
9 Parkland Drive, St Albans, AL3 4AH
Tel: 01727 868567
Principal: ICAEW Member
I C Cummings

JAMES A HEDGES
Westwood Cottage, Lower Gustard Wood, St Albans, AL4 8RU
Tel: 01582 831049
Principal: ICAEW Member
J A Hedges

JANE M. ANDREWS
9 Nimrod Close, Sandpit Lane, St Albans, AL4 9XY
Tel: 01727 753902
Email: info.janemandrews@ntlworld.com
Principal: ICAEW Member
J M Andrews

SPECIALISATIONS – FINANCIAL REPORTING
Accounts Preparation

SPECIALISATIONS – TAXATION
Payroll Service and Advice

THE JANES PARTNERSHIP ★
32 Hawthorn Way, St Albans, AL2 3BH
Tel: 01727 847946
Resident Partners/Directors: ICAEW Members
J P Janes

JAY & CO
28 Fishpool Street, St Albans, AL3 4RT

K. BARNARD
25 Rosemary Drive, Napsbury Park, St Albans, AL2 1UD

KATE BROWN ACCOUNTANCY LTD
81 Gurney Court Road, St Albans, AL1 4QX
Tel: 01727 838775
Resident Partners/Directors: ICAEW Members
K M Brown

KINGS ACCOUNTANCY SERVICES LTD ◈
23 Porters Wood, St Albans, AL3 6PQ
Tel: 01727 868777
Resident Partners/Directors: ICAEW Members
G G King

KINGSTON SMITH & PARTNERS LLP
105 St Peters Street, St Albans, AL1 3EJ
Tel: 01727 896000
Resident Partners/Directors: ICAEW Members
N M Birch, T J Bramston, M Bridge, I M Defty, D J Goodridge
Individual(s) licensed for insolvency work by the ICAEW

SPECIALISATIONS – BUSINESS RECOVERY & INSOLVENCY

Bankruptcies
Corporate Recovery
Liquidations
Reorganisations and Company Reconstructions

KINGSTON SMITH LLP
105 St Peters Street, St Albans, AL1 3EJ
Tel: 01727 896000
Fax: 01727 896001
Email: ks@kingstonsmith.co.uk
Website: http://www.kingstonsmith.co.uk
Resident Partners/Directors: ICAEW Members
N M Birch, M Bridge, D J Goodridge

Registered by the ICAEW to carry out company audit work

Regulated by the ICAEW for a range of investment business activities

KPMG LLP
Aquis Court, 31 Fishpool Street, St Albans, AL3 4RF
Tel: 01727 733000
Resident Partners/Directors: ICAEW Members
M V Matthewman, M R Woodward

LAMBURN & TURNER
Riverside House, 1 Place Farm, Place Farm, Wheathampstead, St Albans AL4 8SB

LEONARD MANN & CO
28 Marlborough Road, St Albans, AL1 3XQ

THE LK PARTNERSHIP LLP
19 Highfield Hall, Highfield Lane, St Albans, AL4 0LE

LKP
19 Highfield Hall, Highfield Lane, St Albans, AL4 0LE

M.R. ALDRIDGE
40 Crown Street, Redbourn, St Albans, AL3 7PF
Tel: 01582 792375
Email: mike@mraldridge.co.uk
Principal: ICAEW Member
M R Aldridge

SPECIALISATIONS – AUDIT & ASSURANCE

Internal Audit

SPECIALISATIONS – BUSINESS & GENERAL ADVICE

Risk Management

MCBW LTD ◈
55 Furse Avenue, St Albans, AL4 9ND
Tel: 01727 843384
Email: mcbw@mcbw.co.uk
Website: http://www.mcbw.co.uk
Resident Partners/Directors: ICAEW Members
M Wood

MERCER & HOLE ◈
Gloucester House, 72 London Road, St Albans, AL1 1NS
Tel: 01727 869141
Website: http://www.mercerhole.co.uk
Resident Partners/Directors: ICAEW Members
K M Scott, S L Smith, P Webster

MERCER & HOLE TRUSTEES LTD
Gloucester House, 72 London Road, St Albans, AL1 1NS
Tel: 01727 869141
Resident Partners/Directors: ICAEW Members
R E Capon, K M Scott, E M Wood

MICHAEL WILLIS & CO
2 Cymbeline Court, The Lawns, St Albans, AL3 4TZ

NOVITT HARRIS & CO LTD
Unit H, Ver House, London Road, Markyate, St Albans AL3 8JP
Tel: 01582 841040
Resident Partners/Directors: ICAEW Members
M S Novitt

O'CONNELL & CO
The Barn, 12a High Street, Wheathampstead, St Albans AL4 8AA
Tel: 01582 834131
Principal: ICAEW Member
S.P. O'Connell

O M MORGAN & CO
153 Verulam Road, St Albans, AL3 4DN

PEARSON & CO
113 Smug Oak Business Centre, Lye Lane, Bricket Wood, St Albans AL2 3UG

PETER DEW
22 Lattimore Road, Wheathampstead, St Albans, AL4 8QE

PRICEWATERHOUSE-COOPERS
10 Bricket Road, St Albans, AL1 3JX

PRICEWATERHOUSE-COOPERS LLP
Marlborough Court, 10 Bricket Road, St Albans, AL1 3JX
Tel: 01727 844155
Resident Partners/Directors: ICAEW Members
D J Brown, R P Girdlestone, C P Hinds, A P Latham, O Mackney, D R W Walters

R.H. PHILLIPS
Wychwood, 86 Kimpton Road, Blackmore End, Wheathampstead, St Albans AL4 8LX

R.S. HARDING
Mercer House, 15 High Street, Redbourn, St Albans AL3 7LE
Tel: 01582 794864
Principal: ICAEW Member
R S Harding

RAYNER ESSEX
Faulkner House, Victoria Street, St Albans, AL1 3SE
Tel: 01727 833222
Email: fh@rayneressex.com
Website: http://www.rayneressex.com
Resident Partners (Non-ICAEW Members):
A H C Federer, C J Males

Registered by the ICAEW to carry out company audit work

Authorised and regulated by the Financial Services Authority for investment business

RAYNER ESSEX LLP
Faulkner House, Victoria Street, St Albans, AL1 3SE
Tel: 01727 833222
Fax: 01727 864752
Email: fh@rayneressex.com
Website: http://www.rayneressex.com
Training Contracts Available.
Resident Partners/Directors: ICAEW Members
C R Essex, A H C Federer, N M Heyes, C J Males, C A Walters
Other Offices: London WC1

SPECIALISATIONS – AUDIT & ASSURANCE

Audit

SPECIALISATIONS – BUSINESS & GENERAL ADVICE

Acquisitions and Mergers
Book-keeping
Company Formation

SPECIALISATIONS – FINANCIAL REPORTING

Accounts Preparation

SPECIALISATIONS – TAXATION

Investigations
Taxation

ROY PINNOCK & CO
Wren House, 68 London Road, St Albans, AL1 1NG
Tel: 01727 840361

ROY PINNOCK & CO LLP
Wren House, 68 London Road, St Albans, AL1 1NG
Tel: 01727 840361
Resident Partners/Directors: ICAEW Members
N B S Grimson

STACEY AND CO LTD
Prime House, 14 Spring Valley, Porters Wood, St Albans AL3 6PQ
Tel: 01727 884500
Resident Partners/Directors: ICAEW Members
I Stacey

TAX FIRST
Faulkner House, Victoria Street, St Albans, AL1 3SE

THE TAXATION COMPLIANCE COMPANY LTD
9 Manor Road, Wheathampstead, St Albans, AL4 8JG
Tel: 01582 467516
Resident Partners/Directors: ICAEW Members
A B Lovett

TESSA DAVIDSON LTD
34A Market Place, St Albans, AL3 5DG

THWAITES, BLACKWELL, BAILEY & CO
Delaport Coachhouse, Wheathampstead, St Albans, AL4 8RQ
Tel: 01582 834165
Principal: ICAEW Member
S J Williams

TYLER WADDINGTON
The Gables, 15 Old Watling Street, Flamstead, St Albans AL3 8HL
Tel: 01582 841785
Principal: ICAEW Member
E A G Tyler-Waddington

VANTIS BUSINESS RECOVERY SERVICES
49 London Road, St Albans, AL1 1LJ
Tel: 01727 811 111
Website: http://www.vantisplc.com/businessrecovery
Individual(s) licensed for insolvency work by another RPB

SPECIALISATIONS – BUSINESS RECOVERY & INSOLVENCY

Bankruptcies
Corporate Recovery
Liquidations

VANTIS GROUP LTD ◈
Torrington House, 47 Holywell Hill, St Albans, AL1 1HD
Tel: 01727 838 255
Website: http://www.vantisplc.com/stalbans
Resident Partners/Directors: ICAEW Members
A P Scott
General Description: ICAEW Registered.

WARREN CLARE
5-6 George Street, St Albans, AL3 4ER

WILTON MUTLOW & CO
3 College Street, St Albans, AL3 4PW

ST AUSTELL

BARBARA J. RUSSETT
Lamara, 29 Duporth Bay, St Austell, PL26 6AF
Tel: 01726 74794
Principal: ICAEW Member
B J Russett

BENNETT JONES & CO ◈
22 Victoria Road, St Austell, PL25 4QD

CHAPMAN PUGH
4 Tregarne Terrace, St Austell, PL25 4BE
Tel: 01726 71070
Resident Partners/Directors: ICAEW Members
D J Chapman, P B Pugh

ERIC WILLS & CO
St Denys House, 22 East Hill, St Austell, PL25 4TR

ERIC WILLS & CO LTD
St Denys House, 22 East Hill, St Austell, PL25 4TR

EWART ROOTS
Trethullan Cottage, Trethullan, Sticker, St Austell PL26 7EH

G.W. HICKS
Glendale House, 9 Brockstone Road, St Austell, PL25 3DW

H. BENNETT
East Park, Woodland Road, St Austell, PL25 4QZ

MICHAEL HARLAND LTD
35 High Cross Street, St Austell, PL25 4AN

P W OSBORNE & CO
29 Westbridge Road, Trewoon, St Austell, PL25 5TF

PETER WILLIAMS & CO
41 South Street, St Austell, PL25 5BJ
Tel: 01726 66826
Resident Partners/Directors: ICAEW Members
P Williams

PHILLIPS FRITH ◈
9 Tregarne Terrace, St Austell, PL25 4DD
Tel: 01726 75981
Resident Partners/Directors: ICAEW Members
I W Chalmers
Resident Partners (Non-ICAEW Members):
J C Webb
Registered by the ICAEW to carry out company audit work
Regulated by the ICAEW for a range of investment business activities

ROY SANDEY
31 High Cross Street, St Austell, PL25 4AN

WILLIS BINGLEY
St Denys House, 22 East Hill, St Austell, PL25 4TR

ST LEONARDS-ON-SEA

A R RAYMOND & CO LTD
67 London Road, St Leonards-on-sea, TN37 6AR
Tel: 01424 424653
Resident Partners/Directors: ICAEW Members
E J Cruttenden, E H Jenman, C O Jones

COLIN H P SMITH
59 Westfield Lane, St Leonards-on-sea, TN37 7NE
Tel: 01424 751575
Principal: ICAEW Member
C H P Smith

HOBBS & CO
27 Albany Road, St Leonards-on-sea, TN38 0LP

MICHAEL SCARLETT & CO
66 Norman Road, St Leonards-on-sea, TN38 0EJ
Tel: 01424 715200
Principal: ICAEW Member
M Scarlett

RAYMOND & CO
A R Raymond & Co Limited, 67 London Road, St Leonards-on-sea, TN37 6AR

SELLENS FRENCH ◈
93/97 Bohemia Road, St Leonards-on-sea, TN37 6RJ

ST COLUMB

DAVID EXELL ASSOCIATES
The Old Surgery, St Columb, TR9 6AE

WHITAKERS ◈
Lloyds Bank Chambers, 36 Fore Street, St Columb, TR9 6RH
Tel: 01637 880318
Fax: 01637 881364
Email: mail@wrp.uk.com
Website: http://www.wrp.uk.com
Authorised and regulated by the Financial Services Authority for investment business

ST. HELENS

A.M. SHAKESHAFT
35 Westfield Street, St Helens, WA10 1QE
Tel: 01744 22870
Principal: ICAEW Member
A M Shakeshaft

ABRAMS ASHTON
77 Corporation Street, St. Helens, WA10 1SX

ABRAMS ASHTON WILLIAMS LTD ◈
77 Corporation Street, St. Helens, WA10 1SX

AIMS - ROGER OWEN
69 Laurel Drive, Eccleston, St Helens, WA10 5JB

BARRETTE LLP
144 Thatto Heath Road, Thatto Heath, St. Helens, WA9 5PE
Tel: 01744 818111

C.A. HUNTER & PARTNERS
Britannia Chambers, George Street, St. Helens, WA10 1BZ

FINDLAY JAMES
58 Broadway, Eccleston, St. Helens, WA10 5DG

HUNTERS
Britannia Chambers, George Street, St. Helens, WA10 1BZ

LIVESEY SPOTTISWOOD LTD ◈
17 George Street, St Helens, WA10 1DB
Tel: 01744 730901
Website: http://www.lsonline.co.uk
Resident Partners/Directors: ICAEW Members
N Bamber, J E Derbyshire, D J Hudd, H J Jesse
Resident Partners (Non-ICAEW Members):
A R Blank, A McMinnis, J Pendlebury, J Molyneux
Registered by the ICAEW to carry out company audit work
Regulated by the ICAEW for a range of investment business activities

MARTINDALE KINGHAM ▽
Kingham House, 161 College Street, St Helens, WA10 1TY

NORTH WEST ACCOUNTING SERVICES LTD
35 Westfield Street, St Helens, WA10 1QD
Tel: 01744 730888
Resident Partners/Directors: ICAEW Members
E J Shew

R.B. PLATT & CO
35 Westfield Street, St Helens, WA10 1QD

TOM CARROLL ASSOCIATES LTD
166 Prescot Road, St. Helens, WA10 3TS

ST. IVES

C J DYKE & CO
C J Dyke & Company, The Old Police Station, Priory Road, St. Ives PE27 5BB
Tel: 01480 463150
Principal: ICAEW Member
C J Dyke

DENNIS MOTT & CO
6a The Pavement, St Ives, PE27 5AD
Tel: 01480 461516
Email: dennis@dmandco.com
Website: http://www.dmandco.com
Principal: ICAEW Member
D P Mott
Registered by the ICAEW to carry out company audit work

EDWARDS ★
15 Station Road, St. Ives, PE27 5BH

I LANCASTER
108 Needingworth Road, St. Ives, PE27 5JY
Tel: 01480 463224
Principal: ICAEW Member
I Lancaster

KINNAIRD HILL
Norfolk House, 4 Station Road, St. Ives, PE27 5AF
Tel: 01480 465561

NICHOLAS COATES
Rosudgeon, 11 Silver Lane, Needingworth, St. Ives PE27 4SL

OGSTONS
6 Norfolk Road, St. Ives, PE27 3DP
Tel: 01480 393721
Principal: ICAEW Member
A Ogston

PAUL A. HILL & CO ◈
3 Bull Lane, St. Ives, PE27 5AX
Tel: 01480 468931
Principal: ICAEW Member
P A Hill
Registered by the ICAEW to carry out company audit work
Regulated by the ICAEW for a range of investment business activities

TACCONI GREEN & CO ★ ◈
32a East Street, St Ives, PE27 5PD
Tel: 01480 300945
Email: general@tacconigreen.co.uk
Resident Partners/Directors: ICAEW Members
H Tacconi

TACCONI GREEN & CO LTD ◈
32a East Street, St Ives, PE27 5PD
Tel: 01480 300945
Resident Partners/Directors: ICAEW Members
H Tacconi

ST IVES

GODFREY REHAAG LTD
7 Camaret Drive, St Ives, TR26 2BE
Tel: 01736 798071
Resident Partners/Directors: ICAEW Members
G C Rehaag

GREENWOOD WILSON ★
The Old School, The Stennack, St Ives, TR26 1QU
Tel: 01736 795753
Resident Partners/Directors: ICAEW Members
D P Wilson

J.A.H. HOLLOW
1 Ventnor Terrace, St Ives, TR26 1DY

LEDDRA PERRY & CO
The Malakoff, St Ives, TR26 2BH

LEDDRA PERRY & CO LTD
The Malakoff, St Ives, TR26 2BH

MILTON & CO
Cranford, Wheal Venture Road, St Ives, TR26 2PQ

WALKER MOYLE
The Old Post Office, Tregenna Place, St Ives, TR26 1AA
Tel: 01736 795378
Website: http://www.walker-moyle.co.uk
Resident Partners/Directors: ICAEW Members
K W Walker

ST. NEOTS

BRADSHAW JOHNSON
30 Cambridge Street, St Neots, PE19 1JL
Tel: 01480 404000
Email: mail@bjca.co.uk
Registered by another RSB to carry out company audit work
Licensed by another DPB to carry on investment business

DAVEY GROVER ★
4 Fenice Court, Phoenix Business Park, Eaton Socon, St. Neots PE19 8EP

DAVID BROWN & CO
1 Church Walk, High Street, St. Neots, PE19 1JA

FARRAND-LAINE LTD
81 High Street, Little Paxton, St. Neots, PE19 6QH
Tel: 01480 391875
Resident Partners/Directors: ICAEW Members
C M Farrand-Laine

HUGILL GORDON
The Maples, Fydell Court, St. Neots, PE19 1UJ

J.E. WHEELER
The Barn, Duck End, Offord Road, Graveley, St. Neots PE19 6PP

K.E. WILSON & CO
40 The Highway, Great Staughton, St Neots, PE19 5DA
Tel: 01480 860688
Principal: ICAEW Member
K E Wilson

KENT CONSULTANCY
PO Box 261, St Neots, PE19 9DE

PETER J. BURGESS
113 High Street, Yelling, St Neots, PE19 6SB
Tel: 01480 880098
Email: peter@burgess-accountants.freeserve.co.uk
Principal: ICAEW Member
P J Burgess
Regulated by the ICAEW for a range of investment business activities

R.J. LITTLECHILD
5 Tintagel Court, St Neots, PE19 2RZ
Tel: 01480 473369
Principal: ICAEW Member
R J Littlechild

ROUND NUMBERS LTD
The Maples, Fydell Court, St. Neots, PE19 1UJ

STREETS AUDIT LLP
The Shrubbery, Church Street, St. Neots, PE19 2HT

STREETS WHITMARSH STERLAND LLP ◈
The Shrubbery, Church Street, St. Neots, PE19 2HT
Tel: 01480 373000
Email: info@streetsweb.co.uk
Website: http://www.streetsweb.co.uk
Resident Partners (Non-ICAEW Members):
P Chandler

STAFFORD

A GRAHAM ACCOUNTANCY SERVICES LTD
The Vicarage, Church Street, Eccleshall, Stafford ST21 6BY

CASTLE ACCOUNTANCY LTD
Parkfield House, Park Street, Stafford, ST17 4AL

CHEADLE
4a Eastgate Street, Stafford, ST16 2NQ

COLLEEN HAMMOND ACA
41 Weeping Cross, Stafford, ST17 0DG

DEAN STATHAM
Bank Passage, Stafford, ST16 2JS
Tel: 01785 258311
Fax: 01785 252614
Email: stafford@deanstatham.com
DX: 701368 STAFFORD 3
Website: http://www.deanstatham.com
Date Established: 1890
Training Contracts Available.
Resident Partners/Directors: ICAEW Members
M R Heenan, J G Hodgkiss, S J Whiting
Registered by the ICAEW to carry out company audit work
Regulated by the ICAEW for a range of investment business activities

SPECIALISATIONS – SECTOR

Agriculture
Doctors
Solicitors

GERAINT PHILLIPS
12 St Michaels Close, Penkridge, Stafford, ST19 5AD

HITCHENORS
School Farm, Barton Lane, Bradley, Stafford ST18 9EF
Tel: 01785 780764
Resident Partners/Directors: ICAEW Members
R J Hitchenor, T L Hitchenor

HOWARDS ◈
Newport House, Newport Road, Stafford, ST16 1DA
Tel: 01785 243276
Website: http://www.howardsca.co.uk
Resident Partners/Directors: ICAEW Members
C P Archer, A D Longden

HOWARDS LTD
Newport House, Newport Road, Stafford, ST16 1DA

KRUPSKI & KRUPSKI
The Maples, Almshouse Croft, Bradley, Stafford ST18 9DF

LEN DAINTY & CO
10 Glastonbury Close, Stafford, ST17 0PB

NICHOLAS BOSTOCK DL FCA
Tixall Lodge, Tixall, Stafford, ST18 0XS
Tel: 01785 662626
Principal: ICAEW Member
N S G Bostock

NIXONS ◈
Meadowside, Little Onn Road, Church Eaton, Stafford ST20 0AY

RB CHARTERED ACCOUNTANT
48 Grange Crescent, Penkridge, Stafford, ST19 5LU

RB CHARTERED ACCOUNTANT LTD
48 Grange Crescent, Penkridge, Stafford, ST19 5LU

SILVER & CO
9-10 Friars Road, Stafford, ST17 4AA

WINTONS LTD
First Floor, 6 Ferranti Court, Staffordshire Technology Park, Stafford ST18 0LQ

WRIGHT & CO PARTNERSHIP LTD
9 Stafford Street, Brewood, Stafford, ST19 9DX
Tel: 01902 850828
Resident Partners/Directors: ICAEW Members
M Atkinson

STAINES

ACCOUNTANTS YOU CAN TALK WITH LTD
38 Worple Road, Staines, TW18 1EA
Tel: 01784 463031
Resident Partners/Directors: ICAEW Members
C H Jerrett

BROOKS JOHNSON
Northumberland House, Drake Avenue, Staines, TW18 2AP

DAVID LLOYD & CO
100 Church Street, Staines, TW18 4DQ

DAVID RICH
8 Mill Mead, Staines, TW18 4NJ

JERRETT
38 Worple Road, Staines, TW18 1EA
Tel: 01784 463031

JOHNSON SMITH & CO LTD
Burma House, Station Path, Staines, TW18 4LA

L.S. LANNING
2 Eton Court, Staines, TW18 2AF

THE LAWFORD CO
Lawford House, Leacroft, Staines, TW18 4NN

MGX ACCOUNTING SERVICES
14 Bowry Drive, Wraysbury, Staines, Middlesex TW19 5NL

LYNTON CONSULTANCY
Lynton, 48 Park Road, Stanwell, Staines TW19 7NY

S.D. WHITING & CO
76 Ouseley Road, Wraysbury, Staines, TW19 5JH
Tel: 01784 483872
Principal: ICAEW Member
S D Whiting
Registered by the ICAEW to carry out company audit work

STALYBRIDGE

ASCENDANT ACCOUNTING LTD
44 Stamford Street, Stalybridge, SK15 1LQ

GRAHAM GOSLING & CO
1 Fawns Keep, Mottram Rise, Stalybridge, SK15 2UL
Tel: 01457 765493
Principal: ICAEW Member
G M Gosling

J.L. JEPSON
5 Valley Way, Stalybridge, SK15 2QZ

JOHN D. DAWSON
6 Rosehill, Stalybridge, SK15 1UT

MOSS & WILLIAMSON ◈
11 Stamford Street, Stalybridge, SK15 1JP
Tel: 0161 338 5294
Resident Partners/Directors: ICAEW Members
P Lee
See display advertisement near this entry.

PETERS & CO ◈
41A Mottram Old Road, Stalybridge, SK15 2TF
Tel: 0161 303 8902
Principal: ICAEW Member
C Peters

ROBERTS TONER LLP
Melbourne House, 44-46 Grosvenor Street, Stalybridge, SK15 2JN
Tel: 0161 304 9000
Fax: 0161 304 9092
Email: mail@robertstoner.co.uk
Resident Partners/Directors: ICAEW Members
D B Roberts
Resident Partners (Non-ICAEW Members):
J M Toner
Registered by the ICAEW to carry out company audit work
Regulated by the ICAEW for a range of investment business activities
SPECIALISATIONS – AUDIT & ASSURANCE
Audit — Private Company
SPECIALISATIONS – FINANCIAL REPORTING
Accounts Preparation
SPECIALISATIONS – TAXATION
Taxation

STAMFORD

DUNCAN & TOPLIS
14 All Saints Street, Stamford, PE9 2PA
Tel: 01780 750888
Fax: 01780 765223
Email: info@stamford.duntop.co.uk
Website: http://www.duntop.co.uk
Resident Partners/Directors: ICAEW Members
R J Hardy, M T Hindmarch
Registered by the ICAEW to carry out company audit work
Regulated by the ICAEW for a range of investment business activities
General Description: Other offices please see Grantham.

HUNTER STEVENS LTD ◈
5/6 Maiden Lane, Stamford, PE9 2AZ
Tel: 01780 761920
Resident Partners/Directors: ICAEW Members
Michel Stevens

MICHELLE FEASEY & CO LTD
Unit 1, West Street Business Park, West Street, Stamford PE9 2PR
Tel: 01780 751115
Resident Partners/Directors: ICAEW Members
M A E Feasey

MOORE EMMERSON ACCOUNTANTS LTD
69 Main Road, Collyweston, Stamford, PE9 3PQ

PETER J.M. COLLINS
Welland Lodge, 13 Holmes Drive, Geeston, Ketton, Stamford PE9 3YB

PHILBYS LTD
Manor Farmhouse, High Street, Duddington, Stamford PE9 3QE
Tel: 01949 823700
Resident Partners/Directors: ICAEW Members
M Philby

STANFORD-LE-HOPE

ARGENTICA LTD
6 Kathleen Close, Stanford-Le-Hope, SS17 8EA

NAJEFY & CO
273a Southend Road, Stanford-le-hope, SS17 8HD

P BAKER & ASSOCIATES ★
Grover House, Grover Walk, Corringham, Stanford-Le-Hope SS17 7LS

STANLEY

3S ACCOUNTANCY SERVICES
12 The Greenhouse, Greencroft Industrial Park, Stanley, DH9 7XN

B J STRAUGHAN & PARTNERS
Fairview House, 46 Mary Street, Stanley, DH9 0NQ

MURRAY & LAMB ◈
5 Royal Road, Stanley, DH9 8AL
Tel: 01207 234203

THIRD SECTOR ACCOUNTANCY SERVICES LTD
12 The Greenhouse, Greencroft Industrial Park, Annfield House, Stanley DH9 7XN

STANMORE

A. BUTNICK & CO
18 Barn Crescent, Stanmore, HA7 2RY
Tel: 020 8954 1096
Principal: ICAEW Member
A E Butnick

ABACI ACCOUNTANCY LTD
38 Drummond Drive, Stanmore, HA7 3PD

ALLON SCHICK-MAIER
21 Culverlands Close, Stanmore, HA7 3AG

ASARIA & CO
67 Morley Crescent West, Stanmore, HA7 2LL

ASM ACCOUNTING SERVICES LTD
21 Culverlands Close, Stanmore, HA7 3AG

ASM COMPANY FORMATIONS LTD
21 Culverlands Close, Stanmore, HA7 3AG

ASM COMPANY SECRETARIES LTD
21 Culverlands Close, Stanmore, HA7 3AG

BARRY PAYDON & CO
28 Church Road, Stanmore, HA7 4AW

BARRY PAYDON LTD
28 Church Road, Stanmore, HA7 4AW

BURNS & CO
33 The Ridgeway, Stanmore, HA7 4BE

CAPLAN J. & CO
39 Silverston Way, Stanmore, HA7 4HS
Tel: 020 8954 1393
Principal: ICAEW Member
J Caplan

CHANDRA SHAH & CO
64 Belmont Lane, Stanmore, HA7 2PZ
Tel: 020 8954 9079
Principal: ICAEW Member
C L Shah

CHARTERED INTELLIGENCE
2nd Floor, Compton House, 29-33 Church Road, Stanmore HA7 4AR

CROMWELL ACCOUNTANTS
29 Lansdowne Road, Stanmore, HA7 2RX
Tel: 0845 260 0818
Resident Partners/Directors: ICAEW Members
C Haria

D. SHAH & CO ◈
40 Anmersh Grove, Stanmore, HA7 1PA
Tel: 020 8933 6684
Principal: ICAEW Member
D K Shah

D. TANNA & CO
32 Berry Hill, Stanmore, HA7 4XS
Tel: 020 8958 3525
Principal: ICAEW Member
D C Tanna

DAVID FINE & CO ◈
Dolphin House, 16 The Broadway, Stanmore, HA7 4DW
Tel: 020 8385 7060
Fax: 020 8385 7061
Email: david@davidfine.co.uk
Date Established: 1983
Principal: ICAEW Member
S D Fine

DONALD JACOBS & PARTNERS
Suite 2, 1st Floor, Fountain House, 1a Elm Park, Stanmore HA7 4AU
Tel: 020 8420 7970
Resident Partners/Directors: ICAEW Members
A Cohen, C J Taylor

FINN, PARROTT & CO
5 London Road, Stanmore, HA7 4PA

FISHER BERGER & ASSOCIATES
Devonshire House, 582 Honeypot Lane, Stanmore, HA7 1JS

FRIENDS ACCOUNTING SERVICES
51 Elm Park, Stanmore, HA7 4AU

GERROLL & CO
10 Brockley Close, Stanmore, HA7 4QL
Tel: 020 8958 6242
Principal: ICAEW Member
A F Gerroll

H BAKER ASSOCIATES ★
28 Lansdowne Road, Stanmore, HA7 2SA

H. GARRISON
10 Bickley Court, Aran Drive, Stanmore, HA7 4NA

HARRISON REEDS
59 Kynance Gardens, Stanmore, HA7 2QJ

HARVEY MARCUS & CONWAY
30 Dene Gardens, Stanmore, HA7 4TD
Tel: 020 8420 6353
Principal: ICAEW Member
D I Conway

J M KAYE
12 Embry Way, Stanmore, HA7 3AZ
Tel: 020 8954 5054
Principal: ICAEW Member
J M Kaye

JAMEN JONES
Suite 9, 8-14 Church Road, Stanmore, HA7 4AW

JOAN L. FREIWALD & CO
60 Pangbourne Drive, Stanmore, HA7 4RB
Tel: 020 8930 5050
Principal: ICAEW Member
J L Roberts

KIAN & CO
23 Mountside, Stanmore, HA7 2DS

KSEG
Stanmore Towers, 8-14 Church Road, Stanmore, HA7 4AW
Tel: 020 8954 9659
Resident Partners/Directors: ICAEW Members
E S Gudka, K S Shah

L. KAFFEL
Helmsdale, Green Lane, Stanmore, HA7 3AH

LAWRENCE GRANT ◈
37 Stanmore Hill, Stanmore, HA7 3DS
Tel: 020 8954 7636
Email: lgmail@lawrencegrant.co.uk
Website: http://www.lawrencegrant.co.uk
Resident Partners/Directors: ICAEW Members
P G Levy
Resident Partners (Non-ICAEW Members):
G Busch, T Rajah

Registered by the ICAEW to carry out company audit work

Regulated by the ICAEW for a range of investment business activities

SPECIALISATIONS – BUSINESS & GENERAL ADVICE

Company Formation
Europe
Overseas Countries

SPECIALISATIONS – FINANCIAL REPORTING

Foreign Subsidiary Companies

SPECIALISATIONS – IT

Computer Consultants

SPECIALISATIONS – SECTOR

Barristers
Dentists/Opticians
Doctors
Nursing Homes/Clinics
Solicitors

SPECIALISATIONS – TAXATION

Foreign Nationals in the UK
Offshore Companies
Trusts
UK Companies Overseas
UK Nationals Overseas
UK Subsidiaries of Overseas Multinationals

M.M. VEKARIA & CO
36 St Andrews Drive, Stanmore, HA7 2NB

MARCUSFIELD DODIA & CO
19 Cumberland Road, Stanmore, HA7 1EL

MICHAEL KING & CO
Suite 9, Stanmore, 8-14 Church Road, Stanmore HA7 4AW

MICHAEL LEVY & CO ◈
Suite 3, First Floor, Stanmore House, 15-19 Church Road, Stanmore HA7 4AR
Tel: 020 8954 6113
Principal: ICAEW Member
M S Levy

MOUNTSIDES LTD
2 Mountside, Stanmore, HA7 2DT

N.J. PATTNI & CO
1 Ennerdale Avenue, Stanmore, HA7 2LB

N.N. KOTHARI & CO
19 Collins Avenue, Stanmore, HA7 1DL

NIGEL M REESE
48 Dalkeith Grove, Stanmore, HA7 4SF

PARKER CAVENDISH
28 Church Road, Stanmore, HA7 4XR
Tel: 020 8954 2727
Fax: 020 8954 8058
Email: accountants@parkercavendish.co.uk
Website: http://www.parkercavendish.co.uk
Resident Partners/Directors: ICAEW Members
J C C Carruth, R A Rubenstein, P B K Shah
Resident Partners (Non-ICAEW Members):
M R N Beth, E Bahar, M Gazza, R Shah

Registered by the ICAEW to carry out company audit work

SPECIALISATIONS – SECTOR

Property Development
Property Investment

PARKER WOOD ★
28 Church Road, Stanmore, HA7 4XR

PAUL & CO ◈
11-12 Freetrade House, Lowther Road, Stanmore, HA7 1EP
Tel: 020 8204 9911
Principal: ICAEW Member
V K Paul

PAYROLL SERVICES LTD
21 Culverlands Close, Stanmore, HA7 3AG

R D MARTIN & CO
28 Church Road, Stanmore, HA7 4XR
Tel: 020 8954 2727
Principal: ICAEW Member
R D Martin

RICHARD FREEDMAN
Suite 2, Fountain House, 1a Elm Park, Stanmore HA7 4AU

ROSS KIT & CO ◈
Victoria House, 18 Dalston Gardens, Stanmore, HA7 1BU
Tel: 020 8204 7772
Principal: ICAEW Member
K Rossides

ROSS KIT & CO LTD
Victoria House, 18 Dalston Gardens, Stanmore, HA7 1BU
Tel: 020 8204 7772
Resident Partners/Directors: ICAEW Members
K Rossides

SCHICK-MAIER ASSOCIATES LTD
21 Culverlands Close, Stanmore, HA7 3AG

SOMAIYA, TJEN & CO
4 Little Common, Stanmore, HA7 3BZ

STEPHEN M. JOSEPH
29 Bentley Way, Stanmore, HA7 3RR

TRENT, RAYMOND & CO
4 Chartley Avenue, Stanmore, HA7 3QZ

V SOPHER
10 Winscombe Way, Stanmore, HA7 3AU

W.J. PALMER & CO
21 Jesmond Way, Stanmore, HA7 4QR

STANSTED

CONNOR WARIN LTD ◈
Forge House, 39-41 Cambridge Road, Stansted, CM24 8BX

MALCOLM BASS & CO
53 Bentfield Causeway, Stansted, CM24 8HU

STEVENAGE

B.M. WOOD
44b High Street, Stevenage, SG1 3EF
Tel: 01438 743215
Principal: ICAEW Member
B M Wood

BAKER WATKIN ◈
Middlesex House, Rutherford Close, Stevenage, SG1 2EF
Tel: 01438 750555
Resident Partners/Directors: ICAEW Members
R B Baker, C P Craggs, A B Watkin

C. TERRY & CO
The Birches, Todds Green, Stevenage, SG1 2JE

CHANTREY VELLACOTT DFK LLP
73-75 High Street, Stevenage, SG1 3HR
Tel: 01438 741147
Resident Partners/Directors: ICAEW Members
G A Cartwright, M F Stevens
Other Offices: Brighton & Hove, Colchester, Croydon, Leicester, London, Northampton, Stevenage, Reading, Watford
Registered by the ICAEW to carry out company audit work
Regulated by the ICAEW for a range of investment business activities

CLARITY ★
2 Lancaster Close, Weston Heights, Stevenage, SG1 4RX
Tel: 07779 833797
Resident Partners/Directors: ICAEW Members
C J Bush
SPECIALISATIONS – SECTOR

Charities

COOK & PARTNERS LTD ◈
108 High Street, Stevenage, SG1 3DW
Tel: 01438 721877
Email: keith.barker@cookpartners.co.uk
Website: http://www.cookpartners.co.uk
Resident Partners/Directors: ICAEW Members
K D Barker

DERRICK LAMB
113 Chancellors Road, Stevenage, SG1 4TZ
Tel: 01438 740706
Principal: ICAEW Member
D R Lamb

GARY SISMAN
Woodlands, Todds Green, Stevenage, SG1 2JE

LATIF & CO
Chestnut House, 101A High Street, Old Town, Stevenage SG1 3HR

LONG & CO LTD
65A High Street, Stevenage, SG1 3AQ

TICK ACCOUNTANCY LTD
168 Fairview Road, Stevenage, SG1 2NE

W. ENGLISH & CO
52 High Street, Stevenage, SG1 3EF

WAGS LLP ◈
Richmond House, Walkern Road, Stevenage, SG1 3QP

WAGSTAFFS ◈
Richmond House, Walkern Road, Stevenage, SG1 3QP
Tel: 01438 740074
Website: http://www.wags.co.uk

WILDER COE
12th Floor, Southgate House, St Georges Way, Stevenage SG1 1HF
Tel: 01438 847200
Fax: 01438 847150
Email: normanc@wildercoe.co.uk
DX: 6015 STEVENAGE
Website: http://www.wildercoe.co.uk
Mobile: 07785 931944
Date Established: 1975
Resident Partners/Directors: ICAEW Members
R S Berry, N Cowan, A A Levy
Other Offices:233-237 Old Marylebone Road, London, NW1 5QT
(Tel: 020 7724 6060)
Regulated by the ICAEW for a range of investment business activities
Individual(s) licensed for insolvency work by the ICAEW
SPECIALISATIONS – BUSINESS & GENERAL ADVICE
Disposal of Businesses
Risk Management
SPECIALISATIONS – BUSINESS RECOVERY & INSOLVENCY
Bankruptcies
Corporate Recovery
Liquidations
Reorganisations and Company Reconstructions
SPECIALISATIONS – FORENSIC ACCOUNTING
Expert Witnesses in Litigation
Forensic Accounting
General Description: Members of Integra International.

YOUR BUSINESS PARTNERS LTD
Bowmans House, Bessemer Drive, Stevenage, SG1 2DL

STEYNING

BELTONS PUBLIC ACCOUNTANTS LTD
38 High Street, Steyning, BN44 3YE

C. NEATE
15 Mill Road, Steyning, BN44 3LN

HAYES LEA & CO
Staplefields Farm, Horsham Road, Steyning, BN44 3AA

MICHAEL PAIGE
Limeshaw, Wappingthorn, Steyning, BN44 3AB

RUCKLIDGE & CO
Blakes Farm, Ashurst, Steyning, BN44 3AN

STOCKBRIDGE

BRYANT & CO
North Houghton Mill, Stockbridge, SO20 6LF
Tel: 01264 810250
Principal: ICAEW Member
D J Bryant

BRYARS & CO
Cloverfield, Houghton Down, Stockbridge, SO20 6JR
Tel: 01264 810060
Principal: ICAEW Member
M J Bryars

HAZELL MINSHALL
2 Clarendon Court, Overwallop, Stockbridge, SO20 8HU

HAZELL MINSHALL LLP
2 Clarendon Court, Overwallop, Stockbridge, SO20 8HU

STOCKPORT

AARBURG ATKINSON
Oak House, 214 Woodford Road, Woodford, Stockport SK7 1QF

ACADIA ACCOUNTING LTD
77 Woodville Drive, Marple, Stockport, SK6 7QX

ADAM & CO
8 Woodend, Bramhall, Stockport, SK7 3LN

ALLENS
123 Wellington Road South, Stockport, SK1 3TH

ALLENS ACCOUNTANTS LTD
123 Wellington Road South, Stockport, SK1 3TH

APPLETONS
Suite 1, Armcon Business Park, London Road South, Poynton, Stockport SK12 1LQ
Tel: 01625 260990
Resident Partners/Directors: ICAEW Members
E G Appleton, R J Ellerton

ARNOLD HILLIER
Dalkeith, 82 Bridge Lane, Bramhall, Stockport SK7 3AW

ASHALL & CO
4 Locksley Close, Heaton Norris, Stockport, SK4 2LW
Tel: 0161 442 2970
Principal: ICAEW Member
R D Ashall

B.R. JOHNSTONE & CO ◈
29 Queensgate, Bramhall, Stockport, SK7 1JT
Tel: 0161 440 0131
Principal: ICAEW Member
B R Johnstone

BAILEY OSTER ◈
Grosvenor House, St Thomas's Place, Stockport, SK1 3TZ

BENNETT VERBY
7 St Petersgate, Stockport, SK1 1EB

BENNETT VERBY LLP
7 St Petersgate, Stockport, SK1 1EB

BOOTH AINSWORTH LLP
Alpha House, 4 Greek Street, Stockport, SK3 8AB

BRITTON & CO
8 Elmfield Road, Davenport, Stockport, SK3 8SE

BRYN GRIFFITH
24 Carleton Road, Poynton, Stockport, SK12 1TL

C M TAX CONSULTANTS LTD
Prudential Buildings, 61 St Petersgate, Stockport, SK1 1DH
Tel: 0161 476 5549
Resident Partners/Directors: ICAEW Members
C S Mitchell

CAP
6 Holly Road, High Lane, Stockport, SK6 8HW

CAROLINE HARTLEY FCA
21 Anglesey Drive, Poynton, Stockport, SK12 1BT
Tel: 01625 850360
Principal: ICAEW Member
C E Hartley

CHARLES TWEEDALE
P.O. Box 19, 157 Woodford Road, Woodford, Stockport SK7 1QA

CHRISTINE TETLEY
195 Bramhall Lane, Stockport, SK2 6JA
Tel: 0161 483 1116
Fax: 0161 487 4449
Email: christine@leydens.plus.com
Principal: ICAEW Member
C M Tetley
Registered by the ICAEW to carry out company audit work

CLARKE NICKLIN LLP ◈
Grove House, 227-233 London Road, Hazel Grove, Stockport, SK7 4HS
Tel: 0161 483 5284
Resident Partners/Directors: ICAEW Members
A Baggott, G Clarke, S Humphries, A S Jakara, A J Robinson

CLARKES
Shaw House, 54 Bramhall Lane South, Bramhall, Stockport SK7 1AH
Tel: 0161 440 2750
Principal: ICAEW Member
P J Clarke

COLIN WARREN
The Warren, 30 Tewkesbury Close, Poynton, Stockport SK12 1QJ
Tel: 01625 872840
Resident Partners/Directors: ICAEW Members
C Warren

ROBERT H COSGROVE
52 Buxton Road, Stockport, SK2 6NB

THE CROSSGROVE PARTNERSHIP LTD Ⓜ
40 Belmont Road, Bramhall, Stockport, SK7 1LE

CULVER SERVICES LTD
16 St Johns Road, Hazel Grove, Stockport, SK7 5HG

CURWEN & CO
44 Queens Drive, Heaton Mersey, Stockport, SK4 3JW

CURWEN & CO LTD
44 Queens Drive, Heaton Mersey, Stockport, SK4 3JW

DANN & CO
Suite 1, Armcon Business Park, London Road South, Poynton, Stockport SK12 1LQ

DAVID R S WELCH
3 Alvington Grove, Hazel Grove, Stockport, SK7 5LS
Tel: 0161 456 9140
Principal: ICAEW Member
D R S Welch

DAVIDSON & CO ACCOUNTANTS LTD
34 Oakfield Road, Davenport, Stockport, SK3 8SG

DAVIES MCLENNON ★ ◈
93 Wellington Road North, Stockport, SK4 2LR
Tel: 0161 612 0077
Website: http://www.daviesmclennon.co.uk
Resident Partners/Directors: ICAEW Members
G A Davies

DC ACCOUNTING SOLUTIONS LTD ◈
Heron House, 41 Higher Bents Lane, Bredbury, Stockport SK6 1EE
Tel: 0161 494 1074
Resident Partners/Directors: ICAEW Members
D W Counsell

DE LA WYCHE BAKER LTD ◈
7 St Petersgate, Stockport, SK1 1EB
Tel: 0161 476 9000
Resident Partners/Directors: ICAEW Members
C N Jackson, K P McCay, S L Rhodes, J R M Sutcliffe

DEREK HILL
38 Knowsley Road, Hazel Grove, Stockport, SK7 6BW

DOWNHAM MAYER CLARKE & CO
41 Greek Street, Stockport, SK3 8AX

DOWNHAM MAYER CLARKE LTD
41 Greek Street, Stockport, SK3 8AX
Tel: 0161 474 0920
Resident Partners/Directors: ICAEW Members
A Clarke, I C Clarke, J K Dootson

DURCAN & CO
4 Woodend Road, Woodsmoor, Stockport, SK3 8TG

EDMONDSON & CO
170A London Road, Hazel Grove, Stockport, SK7 4DJ
Tel: 0161 285 3955
Principal: ICAEW Member
P R Edmondson
Registered by the ICAEW to carry out company audit work

G. YEOMANS & CO
4 Poplar Way, High Lane, Stockport, SK6 8ES
Tel: 01663 763012
Principal: ICAEW Member
G Yeomans

GEOFFREY HANNAM LTD
103 Castle Street, Stockport, SK3 9AR

GORT & MARCH
308 London Road, Hazel Grove, Stockport, SK7 4RF

HALLIDAYS LTD
14 Ack Lane East, Bramhall, Stockport, SK7 2BY

HOW
52 Buxton Road, Stockport, SK2 6NB

HOWARD LYON FCA
18 Laneside Drive, Bramhall, Stockport, SK7 3AR
Tel: 0161 439 7756
Principal: ICAEW Member
H F Lyon

HURST
Lancashire Gate, 21 Tiviot Dale, Stockport, SK1 1TD

HURST & COMPANY ACCOUNTANTS LLP ◈
Lancashire Gate, 21 Tiviot Dale, Stockport, SK1 1TD
Tel: 0161 4772474
Website: http://www.hurst.co.uk
Resident Partners/Directors: ICAEW Members
P N Barratt, H A Besant-Roberts, H M G Hurst, A Milnes, R Murphy, M P Patt, T J Potter
Non-resident Partners (ICAEW Members):
A R Culpin
Other Offices: Orleans House, Edmund Street, Liverpool L3 9NG
(Tel: 0151 237 5900)
Registered by the ICAEW to carry out company audit work
Regulated by the ICAEW for a range of investment business activities

HURST CORPORATE FINANCE
Lancashire Gate, 21 Tiviot Dale, Stockport, SK1 1TD

IAN AFFLICK
336A Wellington Road North, Chapel, Stockport, SK4 5DA

J A SIMPSON & CO LTD
48 Bredbury Green, Romiley, Stockport, SK6 3DN

J GLYNN & ASSOCIATES LTD
24 Valley Road, Bramhall, Stockport, SK7 2NN
Tel: 0161 439 3685
Resident Partners/Directors: ICAEW Members
J A Glynn

J. HUMPHREY JONES & CO
Suite 3C, St Christopher House, Wellington Road South, Stockport SK2 6NG

JOHN H. NIXON & CO
Athena House, 35 Greek Street, Stockport, SK3 8BA

JOHN MILLINGTON
5 Lingfield Avenue, Hazel Grove, Stockport, SK7 4SL

JOHN W. HIRST & CO
62 Wellington Road South, Stockport, SK1 3SU
Tel: 0161 429 9740
Principal: ICAEW Member
J W Moss

JULIE LUCAS
Woodhouse Farm, Anson Road, Poynton, Stockport SK12 1TD
Tel: 01625 850912
Principal: ICAEW Member
J P Lucas

KATHERINE SCOTT
1 Landseer Drive, Marple Bridge, Stockport, SK6 5BL

KEVIN M PITCHFORD & CO
Building 67, Europa Business Park, Bird Hall Lane, Cheadle Heath, Stockport SK3 0XA
Tel: 0161 428 5511
Principal: ICAEW Member
K M Pitchford

KIDSON
The Harrop, 19 Anglesey Drive, Poynton, Stockport SK12 1BT

KPA & CO
41 Oakfield Road, Poynton, Stockport, SK12 1AS

LACY, WATSON ◈
Carlyle House, 107 Wellington Road South, Stockport, SK1 3TL
Tel: 0161 477 7400
Resident Partners/Directors: ICAEW Members
C F Mellalieu, S M Tattersall

LLOYD PIGGOTT
183 London Road South, Poynton, Stockport, SK12 1LQ

LLOYD PIGGOTT (POYNTON) LTD
Abacus House, 183 London Road South, Poynton, Stockport SK12 1LQ

M.C. CLEGG & CO
51 Priestnall Road, Heaton Mersey, Stockport, SK4 3HW

MCKELLENS
Riverview, The Embankment Business Park, Heaton Mersey, Stockport SK4 3GN

MCKELLENS LTD
11 Riverview, The Embankment Business Park, Heaton Mersey, Stockport SK4 3GN

MARK AINLEY ◈
Regent House, Heaton Lane, Stockport, SK4 1BS
Tel: 0161 429 9988
Principal: ICAEW Member
M W Ainley

MOFFAT & CO
211 Buxton Road, Disley, Stockport, SK12 2LH

NEVILLE T. STANTON
3 Buckingham Road West, Heaton Moor, Stockport, SK4 4AZ

NOLAN JAMES
Suite 1, Armcon Business Park, London Road South, Poynton, Stockport SK12 1LQ

NW ACCOUNTS LTD
40 Buxton Road West, Disley, Stockport, SK12 2LY

P JACKSON LTD
Avtech House, Bird Hall Lane, Cheadle Heath, Stockport SK3 0XX

R.D. GALE FCA
94a Strines Road, Marple, Stockport, SK6 7DU
Tel: 0161 427 5611
Principal: ICAEW Member
R D Gale

R. ROBINSON
Broadstones Farm, Mill Brow, Marple, Stockport SK6 5DG

RICHARD A. CROCKER
181 Chester Road, Hazel Grove, Stockport, SK7 6EN
Tel: 01625 858440
Principal: ICAEW Member
R A Crocker

RICHARD FALKNER & CO
Lowfield House, 222 Wellington Road South, Stockport, SK2 6RS

RICHARD SEDDON
4 Hardy Drive, Bramhall, Stockport, SK7 2BW

ROBERT HAYDEN & CO ◈
195 Bramhall Lane, Davenport, Stockport, SK2 6JA
Tel: 0161 483 7755
Principal: ICAEW Member
R L Hayden

ROXBURGH CONSULTING LTD
9 Valley Court, Craig Road, Stockport, SK4 2AW

ROYLES
18 Heaton Gardens, 25 Heaton Moor Road, Stockport, SK4 4LT

ROYLES (HEATON MOOR) LTD
18 Heaton Gardens, 25 Heaton Moor Road, Stockport, SK4 4LT

S. LLOYDBOTTOM & CO
16 Adelaide Road, Bramhall, Stockport, SK7 1LT

SELIGMAN PERCY ◈
Hilton House, Lord Street, Stockport, SK1 3NA
Tel: 0161 476 0100
Resident Partners/Directors: ICAEW Members
B E Percy, P M Seligman

SELLERS & CO LTD
2a Brookfield Avenue, Bredbury, Stockport, SK6 1DF
Tel: 0161 612 1095
Resident Partners/Directors: ICAEW Members
N D Sellers
General Description: Championing local businesses.

SHACKLETON & CO ◈
8 Huxley Drive, Bramhall, Stockport, SK7 2PH
Tel: 0161 440 0126
Resident Partners/Directors: ICAEW Members
J D Shackleton, M F Shackleton

STARR & CO ◈
76 Wellington Road South, Stockport, SK1 3SU
Tel: 0161 429 8166
Principal: ICAEW Member
L Starr

THE TACS PARTNERSHIP ★
Graylaw House, Mersey Square, Stockport, SK1 1AL
Tel: 0161 429 0006
Fax: 0161 429 0004
Email: experts@tacs.co.uk
Website: http://www.tacs.co.uk
Resident Partners/Directors: ICAEW Members
M D Blake, S A Willcox
Resident Partners (Non-ICAEW Members):
I Roberts
SPECIALISATIONS – SECTOR
Corporate
SPECIALISATIONS – TAXATION
Capital Gains — Limited Companies
Capital Gains — Personal
Employee
Investigations
Taxation
General Description: Tax consultants.

TATTON & FLETCHER
492 Hempshaw Lane, Stockport, SK2 5TL
Tel: 0161 456 6288
Resident Partners/Directors: ICAEW Members
P Howard
SPECIALISATIONS – SECTOR
Dentists/Opticians

TOM MORTON
Carcosa, Forbes Park, Bramhall, Stockport SK7 2RE

TREVOR JONES
Sutton House, Acorn Business Park, Heaton Lane, Stockport SK4 1AS

TSALIKIS & CO ◈
30 Carrwood Avenue, Bramhall, Stockport, SK7 2PY
Tel: 0161 440 7958
Fax: 0161 439 8468
Email: info@tsalikis.com
Principal: ICAEW Member
A Tsalikis
Registered by the ICAEW to carry out company audit work
Regulated by the ICAEW for a range of investment business activities

UPPAL & WARR
452 Manchester Road, Heaton Chapel, Stockport, SK4 5DL

V A MCGOWAN
5 Hartington Road, Bramhall, Stockport, SK7 2DZ

V F MATHER & CO ◈
4 Houldsworth Square, Reddish, Stockport, SK5 7AF
Tel: 0161 442 5233
Principal: ICAEW Member
V F Mather

W. JOHN BAKER
4 Corbar Road, Stockport, SK2 6EP
Tel: 0161 483 4574
Principal: ICAEW Member
W J Baker

WARR & CO
Mynshull House, 78 Churchgate, Stockport, SK1 1YJ

WHITEHEAD & CO
40 Lord Street, Stockport, SK1 3NA

WHITEHEAD ACCOUNTANTS LTD ◈
Whitehead & Co, 40 Lord Street, Stockport, SK1 3NA
Tel: 0161 476 1260
Resident Partners/Directors: ICAEW Members
A G Whitehead

WILLIAMS COOPER
39 Park Lane, Poynton, Stockport, SK12 1RD

WILLIAMS, TAYLOR & CO
37/41 Longshut Lane West, Stockport, SK2 6RX

STOCKTON-ON-TEES

ANDERSON BARROWCLIFF
Waterloo House, Thornaby Place, Thornaby on Trees, Stockton-On-Tees TS17 6SA

ANDERSON BARROWCLIFF LLP
Waterloo House, Thornaby Place, Thornaby on Tees, Stockton-On-Tees TS17 6SA
Tel: 01642 660300
Fax: 01642 660301
Email: theteam@anderson-barrowcliff.co.uk
Website: http://www.anderson-barrowcliff.co.uk
Resident Partners/Directors: ICAEW Members
B S Blakey, J Q J P Bury, D J Robertson, R G Robinson, D R Shawcross, N P Upton
Resident Partners (Non-ICAEW Members):
B H Douglass
Registered by the ICAEW to carry out company audit work
Regulated by the ICAEW for a range of investment business activities

ANN LUKE
15 Richard Hind Walk, Stockton-on-tees, TS18 3LU

BAINES JEWITT ◈
Barrington House, 41-45 Yarm Lane, Stockton-on-tees, TS18 3EA
Tel: 01642 632032
Fax: 01642 632033
Email: info@bainesjewitt.co.uk
Website: http://www.bainesjewitt.co.uk
Resident Partners/Directors: ICAEW Members
D Adams, M R Bigley, T Cook, A L Cowley, J Lester
Resident Partners (Non-ICAEW Members):
J M Holden
Registered by the ICAEW to carry out company audit work
Regulated by the ICAEW for a range of investment business activities

BENSON WOOD LTD ◈
10 Yarm Road, Stockton-On-Tees, TS18 3NA
Tel: 01642 604047
Fax: 01642 614166
Email: enquiries@bensonwood.co.uk
DX: 60610 STOCKTON 3
Website: http://www.bensonwood.co.uk
Date Established: 1971
Resident Partners/Directors: ICAEW Members
G W Thompson, P L Wood
Registered by the ICAEW to carry out company audit work
Regulated by the ICAEW for a range of investment business activities
SPECIALISATIONS – SECTOR
Doctors
Solicitors
SPECIALISATIONS – TAXATION
Estate Planning

CHRIS BARKESS FCA
53 Greens Grove, Hartburn, Stockton-On-Tees, TS18 5AW

DAVIES TRACEY & CO
Newport House, Thornaby Place, Stockton-On-Tees, TS17 6SE

DOUGLAS PARK & CO
8 Bute Close, Thornaby, Stockton-on-tees, TS17 0HL

FERGUSSON & CO LTD
Shackelton House, Falcon Court, Preston Farm Industrial Estate, Stockton-On-Tees TS18 3TS
Tel: 01642 669155
Individual(s) licensed for insolvency work by another RPB

G.R.BELSHAW
The Gables, Tees Bank Ave., Eaglescliffe, Stockton-on-tees TS16 9AY
Tel: 01642 781489
Principal: ICAEW Member
G R Belshaw

HOWARD M BEDFORD & CO ◈
1st Floor, 27 Norton Road, Stockton-On-Tees, TS18 2BW

JOHN BENSON & CO
Swift House, Falcon Court, Preston Farm, Stockton-On-Tees TS18 3TX
Tel: 01642 606053
Resident Partners/Directors: ICAEW Members
J A Benson

LYONS & CO ◈
23 Yarm Road, Stockton-on-tees, TS18 3NJ
Tel: 01642 614385
Email: jrl@lyonsandco.co.uk
Principal: ICAEW Member
J R Lyons
Registered by the ICAEW to carry out company audit work

SPECIALISATIONS – AUDIT & ASSURANCE

Audit — Private Company

SPECIALISATIONS – BUSINESS & GENERAL ADVICE

Disposal of Businesses

SPECIALISATIONS – SECTOR

Charities
Solicitors

RODNEY PANGBOURNE ◈

33 Pennal Grove, Ingleby Barwick, Stockton-On-Tees, TS17 5HP
Tel: 01642 308989
Principal: ICAEW Member
R B Pangbourne

TAIT WALKER

Crutes House, Fudan Way, Teesdale Park, Stockton-On-Tees TS17 6EN
Tel: 0164 267 6888
Fax: 01642 605866
DX: STOCKTON ON TEES 10 723019
Website: http://www.taitwalker.co.uk
Other Offices: Newcastle, Morpeth

Registered by the ICAEW to carry out company audit work

Registered by another RSB to carry out company audit work

Regulated by the ICAEW for a range of investment business activities

Authorised and regulated by the Financial Services Authority for investment business

Individual(s) licensed for insolvency work by the ICAEW
Individual(s) licensed for insolvency work by another RPB

INVESTOR IN PEOPLE

TINDLE'S

Scotswood House, Teesdale South, Thornaby Place, Stockton-On-Tees TS17 6SB
Tel: 01642 878555
Fax: 01642 878585
Email: team@tindles.co.uk
Website: http://www.tindles.co.uk

TINDLE'S LLP ◈

Scotswood House, Teesdale South, Thornaby Place, Stockton-On-Tees TS17 6SB
Tel: 01642 878555
Website: http://www.tindles.co.uk
Resident Partners/Directors: ICAEW Members
A Foster, R R Tindle

STOKE BY NAYLAND

G.A.P. LEIGH-POLLITT LTD

The Old Post Office, Polstead Street, Stoke By Nayland, CO6 4SA
Tel: 01206 262633
Resident Partners/Directors: ICAEW Members
G A P Leigh-Pollitt

STOKE-ON-TRENT

ALAN POOLE & CO

51 Colwyn Drive, Knypersley, Stoke-on-trent, ST8 7BJ
Tel: 01782 522670
Principal: ICAEW Member
J A Poole

BAKER TILLY

Festival Way, Festival Park, Stoke-on-trent, ST1 5BB
Tel: 01782 216000
Resident Partners/Directors: ICAEW Members
C I Barcroft, I Latham, M L Owen

BAKER TILLY

Festival Way, Festival Park, Stoke-on-trent, ST1 5BB
Tel: 01782 216000
Resident Partners/Directors: ICAEW Members
C I Barcroft, M W Barnish, R J Goodwin, A Lakin

BAKER TILLY TAX AND ADVISORY SERVICES LLP

Festival Way, Festival Park, Stoke-on-trent, ST1 5BB
Tel: 01782 216000
Resident Partners/Directors: ICAEW Members
C I Barcroft, M W Barnish, R J Goodwin, A Lakin, I Latham, M L Owen, J S Rushton, J E White

BATES

Wulfrun Chambers, 17 Lawton Road, Alsager, Stoke-on-trent ST7 2AA

BATT & CO ◈

11 Woolaston Drive, Alsager, Stoke-on-trent, ST7 2PL

BEAUMONTS

29-31 Moorland Road, Burslem, Stoke-on-trent, ST6 1DS
Tel: 01782 825707
Fax: 01782 837030
Principal: ICAEW Member
S N Mountford
Registered by the ICAEW to carry out company audit work

BEGBIES TRAYNOR LTD

The Old Barn, Caverswall Park, Caverswall Lane, Stoke-on-trent ST3 6HP
Tel: 01782 394500
Resident Partners (Non-ICAEW Members):
R Young, P Finnity

SPECIALISATIONS – BUSINESS RECOVERY & INSOLVENCY

Bankruptcies
Corporate Recovery
Liquidations

BOND PARTNERS LLP

21 Moorland Road, Burslem, Stoke-on-trent, ST6 1DS

CROPP HAWKINS

720 London Road, Oakhill, Stoke-on-trent, ST4 5NP

THE CURTIS PARTNERSHIP

1 Tape Street, Cheadle, Stoke-on-trent, ST10 1BB
Tel: 01538 755866
Resident Partners/Directors: ICAEW Members
D R Curtis, P Curtis

D. MATLEY & CO

500 Hartshill Road, Hartshill, Stoke-on-trent, ST4 6AD
Tel: 01782 714767
Website: http://www.davidmatley.co.uk
Principal: ICAEW Member
D N Matley
Registered by the ICAEW to carry out company audit work

D W T BIRKIN & CO

Ivy House, Nantwich Road, Audley, Stoke-on-trent ST7 8DW

DAVID W T BIRKIN & CO

Ivy House, Nantwich Road, Audley, Stoke-on-trent ST7 8DW

DAVIES SIGLEY

Dresden House, The Strand, Longton, Stoke-on-trent ST3 2PD

THE DAVISON PARTNERSHIP

Reliance House, Moorland Road, Burslem, Stoke-on-trent ST6 1DP

DPC

Vernon Road, Stoke-on-trent, ST4 2QY
Tel: 01782 744144

DPC ACCOUNTANTS LTD

Vernon Road, Stoke-on-trent, ST4 2QY

THE DPC GROUP LTD

Vernon Road, Stoke-on-trent, ST4 2QY
Tel: 01782 744144
Email: simon.webster@dpcaccountants.com
Website: http://www.dpcaccountants.com
Resident Partners/Directors: ICAEW Members
D Griffiths, C Kane, S J Webster

FORRESTERS

Blythe View, 10 Sperry Close, Meir Park Estate, Blythe Bridge, Stoke-on-trent ST3 7QJ
Tel: 07811 747424
Principal: ICAEW Member
K J Forrester

GEENS

68 Liverpool Road, Stoke-on-trent, ST4 1BG
Tel: 01782 847952
Fax: 01782 744357
Email: info@geens.co.uk
Website: http://www.geens.co.uk
Resident Partners/Directors: ICAEW Members
S J Archer, K V Lowe
Resident Partners (Non-ICAEW Members):
C B V France

GEOFFREY F. STEPHENS ◈

2 Haydock Close, Cheadle, Stoke-on-trent, ST10 1UE
Tel: 01538 751214
Principal: ICAEW Member
G F Stephens

HARDWICKES

Etruria Old Road, Stoke-on-trent, ST1 5PE
Tel: 01782 219555
Resident Partners/Directors: ICAEW Members
D Hall, D R Harper, P L Robinson, D R Shaw

HOWSONS

20 Moorland Road, Burslem, Stoke-on-trent, ST6 1DW

HOWSONS ◈

Winton House, Stoke Road, Stoke-on-trent, ST4 2RW
Tel: 01782 848838
Resident Partners/Directors: ICAEW Members
J P Eyre-Walker
Resident Partners (Non-ICAEW Members):
S Preston
Other Offices: Leek, Burslem, Uttoxeter, Newport, Market Drayton, Alsager
Registered by the ICAEW to carry out company audit work

HOWSONS ◈

Wulfrun Chambers, 17 Lawton Road, Alsager, Stoke-on-trent ST7 2AA
Tel: 01270 884314
Non-resident Partners (ICAEW Members):
J Eyre-Walker
Non-resident Partners (Non-ICAEW Members):
S Preston
Other Offices: Leek, Market Drayton, Stoke-On-Trent, Uttoxeter, Newport, Burslem

HOWSONS ACCOUNTANTS LTD

20 Moorland Road, Burslem, Stoke-on-trent, ST6 1DW

I.T. COPELAND
4 Heather Close, Werrington, Stoke-on-trent, ST9 0LB

J.C. BARKER & CO ★
29 Chapel Street, Cheadle, Stoke-On-Trent, ST10 1DU

J.C. BARKER & CO ★
6 Richmond Terrace, Shelton, Stoke-On-Trent, ST1 4ND

J.S. WILLIAMSON & CO
Gladstone House, 505 Etruria Road, Basford, Stoke-on-trent ST4 6JH

JSW ACCOUNTING SERVICES LTD
Gladstone House, 505 Etruria Road, Stoke-On-Trent, ST4 6JH

K.A. STOKES
52 Liverpool Road, Stoke-on-trent, ST4 1AZ

KELLY MOLYNEUX & CO ★
Security House, 1 Queen Street, Burslem, Stoke-on-trent ST6 3EL

LOUISE GIRVIN
Fieldsway, 4A Pikemere Road, Alsager, Stoke-on-trent ST7 2SB

M TATTON & CO ★
2 Adventure Place, Hanley, Stoke-on-trent, ST1 3AF

MCINTOSH
29 Regent Road, Hanley, Stoke-on-trent, ST1 3BT

MARSHALL & CO
19-21 Crewe Road, Alsager, Stoke-on-trent, ST7 2EP

MITTEN CLARKE
Festival Way, Festival Park, Stoke-on-trent, ST1 5TQ

MOORE STEPHENS ◈
6 Ridge House, Ridgehouse Drive, Festival Park, Stoke-on-trent ST1 5TL
Tel: 01782 201120
Email: john.clough@moorestephens.com
Website: http://www.moorestephens.co.uk/stoke/cr
Resident Partners/Directors: ICAEW Members
M H Abdulali, J D Clough

SPECIALISATIONS – AUDIT & ASSURANCE
Assurance Services

SPECIALISATIONS – BUSINESS & GENERAL ADVICE
Management Advice to Business

SPECIALISATIONS – BUSINESS RECOVERY & INSOLVENCY
Bankruptcies
Corporate Recovery
Liquidations
Reorganisations and Company Reconstructions

SPECIALISATIONS – TAXATION
Taxation

MORRIS GREEN ACCOUNTANTS LTD
443 King Street, Longton, Stoke-on-trent, ST4 3EE
Tel: 01782 595691
Resident Partners/Directors: ICAEW Members
V J S Green

MURRAY
Murray House, 58 High Street, Biddulph, Stoke-on-trent ST8 6AR

NIGEL SMITH
The Old Church, Shelton New Road, Stoke-on-trent, ST4 6DP

P. CHESWORTH
12 Cape Street, Hanley, Stoke-on-trent, ST1 5AZ
Tel: 01782 265317
Principal: ICAEW Member
P L Chesworth

PARGETTERS
19 Church Avenue, Stoke-on-trent, ST2 7DA

PATERSON BRODIE
Cliveden Chambers, Cliveden Place, Longton, Stoke-on-trent ST3 4JB

R BATH & CO LTD
8 Northwood Park Road, Hanley, Stoke-on-trent, ST1 2DT

RFS
The Coach House, 1A Watt Place, Cheadle, Stoke-On-Trent, ST10 1NY

RICHARD WILLOUGHBY
3 Ashlands Grove, Harpfields, Stoke-on-trent, ST4 6QU
Tel: 01782 634901
Principal: ICAEW Member
R G W Willoughby

RSM BENTLEY JENNISON ◈
5 Ridge House, Ridge House Drive, Festival Park, Stoke-on-trent ST1 5SJ
Tel: 01782 262121
Fax: 01782 287246
Email: john.capper@rsmbentleyjennison.com
Website: http://www.rsmbentleyjennison.com
Resident Partners/Directors: ICAEW Members
J A Capper, J Dudley, A J Green, M J Stoddard

Registered by the ICAEW to carry out company audit work

Authorised and regulated by the Financial Services Authority for investment business

TAX RETURNS NATIONWIDE LTD
1 Tape Street, Cheadle, Stoke-on-trent, ST10 1BB
Tel: 01538 755337
Resident Partners/Directors: ICAEW Members
D R Curtis, P Curtis

WALLETTS ★ ◈
2 Adventure Place, Hanley, Stoke-on-trent, ST1 3AF

WALLETTS ★
18 Tunstall Road, Biddulph, Stoke-on-trent, ST8 6HH

WHEELHOUSE HULME
Westfield House, Woodhouse Lane, Biddulph, Stoke-on-trent ST8 7DR

STOKE-SUB-HAMDON

SIMON J. QUANTOCK SHULDHAM
East Stoke House, Stoke-sub-hamdon, TA14 6UF

STONE

CONLONG & CO
Unit 1, Whitebridge Industrial Estate, 2 Whitebridge Lane, Stone ST15 8LQ
Tel: 01785 812244
Principal: ICAEW Member
G F Conlong

J.G. ALLBUT & CO ◈
Mansion House, Lichfield Street, Stone, ST15 8BB

PLANT & CO
17 Lichfield Street, Stone, ST15 8NA

SAGAR & CO
3 Glamis Drive, Stone, ST15 8SP
Tel: 01785 811659
Principal: ICAEW Member
P Sagar

STONEHOUSE

ANDREW G. BISHOP ◈
24 Ebley Road, Ryeford, Stonehouse, GL10 2LQ
Tel: 01453 794070
Principal: ICAEW Member
A G Bishop

BW GALE
Yew Tree House, Penn Lane, Kings Stanley, Stonehouse GL10 3PT

KATRINA DOUGLAS
The Chapel House, The Cross, Nympsfield, Stonehouse GL10 3TU
Tel: 01453 860133
Principal: ICAEW Member
K Douglas

PARCELL & ASSOCIATES
Aldreth, Pearcroft Road, Stonehouse, GL10 2JY

RANDALL & PAYNE ◈
30 Bath Road, Stonehouse, GL10 2JA
Tel: 01453 761889
Resident Partners/Directors: ICAEW Members
W J Abbott

STOURBRIDGE

1A ACCOUNTANCY AND TAX LTD
1a Swindell Road, Pedmore, Stourbridge, DY9 0TN

ALISON ROUGHT & CO
16 Appleton Avenue, Pedmore, Stourbridge, DY8 2JZ
Tel: 01384 372822
Principal: ICAEW Member
A M Rought

ANDREW E.S. SHERREY
Laburnum House, Adams Hill, Clent, Stourbridge DY9 9PS
Tel: 01562 885496
Email: andrew@andrewsherrey.co.uk
Principal: ICAEW Member
A E S Sherrey

ANTHONY ILIFF
Westgate, 55 Milestone Drive, Hagley, Stourbridge DY9 0LH

APLEY ACCOUNTING
4 Apley Road, Wollaston, Stourbridge, DY8 4PA

ARMSTRONG CHASE
Suite 1, Winwood Court, Norton Road, Stourbridge DY8 2AE

D.M. RICHARDS
17 Whittington Road, Norton, Stourbridge, DY8 3DB

DAVID H HOWELL
85 Norton Road, Norton, Stourbridge, DY8 2TB
Tel: 01384 370190
Principal: ICAEW Member
D H Howell

DHH ★ ◈
Wychbury Chambers, 78 Worcester Road, Hagley, Stourbridge DY9 0NJ

FOLKES WORTON LLP ◈
15-17 Church Street, Stourbridge, DY8 1LU
Tel: 01384 376964
Resident Partners/Directors: ICAEW Members
N H Meredith, N C Smith

HEIDI E WEBSTER
1 Stuarts Green, Pedmore, Stourbridge, DY9 0XR

IVERLEY MANAGEMENT SERVICES LTD
Iverley Lodge, 186 Norton Road, Iverley, Stourbridge DY8 2RT

J.D. TRINHAM
30a South Road, Stourbridge, DY8 3YB

JORDAN & CO ◈
Knighton House, 62 Hagley Road, Stourbridge, DY8 1QD
Tel: 01384 443444
Principal: ICAEW Member
M A Jordan

KENNETH J WINFIELD
Sunnybank, Adams Hill, Clent, Stourbridge DY9 9PS
Tel: 01562 885675
Principal: ICAEW Member
K J Winfield

M.J. TIMMIS
45 Meddins Lane, Kinver, Stourbridge, DY7 6BZ
Tel: 01384 873446
Principal: ICAEW Member
M J G Timmis

MORLEY HASWELL
4 St James Court, Bridgnorth Road, Wollaston, Stourbridge DY8 3QG

MORLEY HASWELL CONSULTANTS LTD
4 St James Court, Bridgnorth Road, Wollaston, Stourbridge DY8 3QG

NEWFIELD & CO
2 Broadwaters Drive, Hagley, Stourbridge, DY9 0JU
Tel: 01562 884668
Principal: ICAEW Member
R Shaw

NICK PRITCHARD ◈
76 High Street, Stourbridge, DY8 1DX
Tel: 01384 446081
Website: http://www.eightcentre.co.uk
Principal: ICAEW Member
John Nicholas Dearn Pritchard

SPECIALISATIONS – BUSINESS & GENERAL ADVICE
Acquisitions and Mergers
Disposal of Businesses

NORMAN C SANDS LTD
333 Hagley Road, Pedmore, Stourbridge, DY9 0RF

PAUL JACKSON
Wassell Grove Business Centre, Wassell Grove Lane, Stourbridge, DY9 9JH
Tel: 01562 881021
Principal: ICAEW Member
P D Jackson

PAUL TURNER - AIMS ACCOUNTANTS FOR BUSINESS
14a Farlands Road, Oldswinford, Stourbridge, DY8 2DD

PAUL WOODDISSE
2 Chantry Road, Stourbridge, DY7 6SA

PINFIELDS LTD
10 Hagley Road, Stourbridge, DY8 1PS

POOLE WATERFIELD ★
Lynwood House, Dudley Rd, Lye, Stourbridge DY9 8DU

R.A.B. VINER & CO
The Meads, 6 Bromwich Lane, Pedmore, Stourbridge DY9 0QZ

R.G. JUSTICE & CO
36 Heath Street, Stourbridge, DY8 1SB
Tel: 01384 370205
Principal: ICAEW Member
R G Justice

R.H. BIRD & CO
Spencer House, 114 High Street, Wordsley, Stourbridge DY8 5QR
Tel: 01384 402930
Principal: ICAEW Member
R H Bird

R.K.GROSELEY
Lynwood House, Dudley Road, Lye, Stourbridge DY9 8DU

R.P. DENYER
11 Stuarts Green, Stourbridge, DY9 0XR

ROGER A. BISHOP & CO
Elgar, Worcester Road, Clent, Stourbridge DY9 0HU

ROGER M DARBY LTD
85 High Street, Kinver, Stourbridge, DY7 6HD

T.J. SAXON
43 Hagley Road, Stourbridge, DY8 1QR

WRIGHT ASSOCIATES
First Floor, 56-57 High Street, Stourbridge, DY8 1DE
Tel: 01384 371100
Principal: ICAEW Member
K J Wright

STOURPORT-ON-SEVERN

CATTANEO LLP
35 Areley Court, Stourport-On-Severn, DY13 0AR

DAVID J. COX
45 The Ridgeway, Stourport-on-severn, DY13 8XT
Tel: 01299 826323
Principal: ICAEW Member
D J Cox

DAVID T. GUEST
Woodmeadow, Bishopswood Lnane, Crossway Green, Stourport-on-severn DY13 9SE

HELEN J SENIOR
The Azaleas, Norchard Lane, Crossway Green, Stourport-On-Severn DY13 9SN

RICHARD A. SINCLAIR
122 Lickhill Road, Stourport-on-severn, DY13 8SF

STOWMARKET

B.T. HAGGER ◈
Shirebrook House, Fen Street, Buxhall, Stowmarket IP14 3DQ
Tel: 01449 736494
Principal: ICAEW Member
B T Hagger

BARRY PEEK & CO
Clock House, Stonham Parva, Stowmarket, IP14 5JP

CLAIRE BISSET
Beech Tree Cottage, The Street, Bacton, Stowmarket IP14 4LF

JENNIFER HANLON
Wisteria Cottage, Mendlesham Road, Cotton, Stowmarket IP14 4RB

M.E. BRYAN
Croft House, Gt. Finborough, Stowmarket, IP14 3BG
Tel: 01449 613871
Principal: ICAEW Member
M E Bryan

ORRIN ACCOUNTANCY LTD
12 Tavern Street, Stowmarket, IP14 1PH

S.J. COOKE & CO ◈
Stone Farm, Borough Lane, Great Finborough, Stowmarket IP14 3AS
Tel: 01449 770953
Principal: ICAEW Member
S J Cooke

STRATFORD-UPON-AVON

AIMS - MIKE DRINKWATER
1 Hamlet Way, Stratford-Upon-Avon, CV37 0AL
Tel: 01789 261509
Principal: ICAEW Member
M J Drinkwater

ANDREW MARTIN & CO
Unit 35, Timothys Bridge Road, Stratford-Upon-Avon, CV37 9NQ

C WILTSHIRE & CO STRATFORD LTD
17 Greenhill Street, Stratford-Upon-Avon, CV37 6LF
Tel: 01789 269090
Resident Partners/Directors: ICAEW Members
P A Jones, C Wiltshire

CAROL WATERS
Trefoil, Boucher Close, Shottery, Stratford-upon-avon CV37 9YX
Tel: 01789 297865
Principal: ICAEW Member
C A Waters

COOPER ADAMS
12 Payton Street, Stratford-Upon-Avon, CV37 6UA

COOPER ADAMS LTD
12 Payton Street, Stratford-Upon-Avon, CV37 6UA

CORINNE S. CARVER
Pippin Lodge, Church Road, Snitterfield, Stratford-upon-avon CV37 0LF
Tel: 07958 604870
Principal: ICAEW Member
C S Carver

DAVID EXELL ASSOCIATES
Elta House, Birmingham Road, Stratford-Upon-Avon, CV37 0AQ

GORDON CUTLER & CO
The Maybird Suite, The Maybird Centre, Birmingham Road, Stratford-Upon-Avon CV37 0HZ

GRENFELL JAMES
2 Shottery Brook Office Park, Timothys Bridge Road, Stratford Enterprise Park, Stratford-Upon-Avon CV37 9NR
Tel: 01789 415452
Fax: 01789 415118
Email: grenfell@grenfelljames-accountants.com
Website: http://www.grenfelljames-accountants.com
Principal: ICAEW Member
E G D James

Registered by the ICAEW to carry out company audit work

Regulated by the ICAEW for a range of investment business activities

SPECIALISATIONS – AUDIT & ASSURANCE
Audit

SPECIALISATIONS – BUSINESS & GENERAL ADVICE
Company Secretarial Service
Management Advice to Business

SPECIALISATIONS – FINANCIAL REPORTING
Accounts Preparation
Limited Company Accounts
Partnership/Sole Trader Accounts

SPECIALISATIONS – IT
Computer Systems and Consultancy

SPECIALISATIONS – TAXATION
Taxation

GUARD D'OYLY
16 Church Street, Stratford-upon-avon, CV37 6HB

GUEST WILSON LTD ◈
8 Wolverton Road, Snitterfield, Stratford-upon-avon, CV37 0HB
Tel: 01789 730456
Resident Partners/Directors: ICAEW Members
N G Wilson

H.A. BIRD
Richardson House, Clifford Chambers, Welford-on-Avon, Stratford-upon-avon CV37 8LA

H.L. BARNES & SONS
Barclays Bank Chambers, Bridge Street, Stratford-Upon-Avon, CV37 6AH
Tel: 01789 204185
Email: stratford@hlbarnes.co.uk
Resident Partners/Directors: ICAEW Members
R W P Bowen, D M Buxton, P L Woodward

HATCH
29 Wood Street, Stratford-upon-avon, CV37 6JG

HERBERT W TUCKEY FCA
17 Avonside, Mill Lane, Stratford-upon-avon, CV37 6BJ
Tel: 01789 204547
Principal: ICAEW Member
H W Tuckey

JULIA NEW LTD
Tudor House, Loxley Road, Stratford-Upon-Avon, CV37 7DP

LEIGH GRAHAM ASSOCIATES
10 John Street, Stratford-Upon-Avon, CV37 6UB

MURPHY SALISBURY
15 Warwick Road, Stratford-upon-avon, CV37 6YW

REBECCA L PRIDHAM BA ACA
Rosedale, Norton Gardens, Pebworth, Stratford-Upon-Avon CV37 8YA
Tel: 01789 721815
Principal: ICAEW Member
R L Pridham

T.J. ABREY
2 Swallow Close, Clopton Hill, Stratford-upon-avon, CV37 6TT

STREET

HOWELLS COOK ASSOCIATES LTD
26 High Street, Street, BA16 0EB

M.R.F.MILES
191a High Street, Street, BA16 0NE
Tel: 01458 442901
Principal: ICAEW Member
M R F Miles

STROUD

A.G.SLINGSBY & CO
Quinton Cottage, Kitesnest Lane, Whiteshill, Stroud GL6 6BQ

CRITCHLEY, COLE & CO
20 Lansdown, Stroud, GL5 1BG

DAVID RICHARDSON & CO
4a London Road, Stroud, GL5 2AG
Tel: 01453 764083
Principal: ICAEW Member
D Richardson

EUROPA AUDIT SERVICES LTD
The Coach House, The Snow Mill, Bridge Road, Ebley, Stroud GL5 4TR

GODFREY WILSON LTD
Pike House, George Street, Nailsworth, Stroud GL6 0AG

GRIFFITH CLARKE
Slad Valley House, 203 Slad Road, Stroud, GL5 1RJ
Tel: 01453 751561
Website: http://www.griffithclarke.com
Resident Partners/Directors: ICAEW Members
M O Clarke, P J Griffith
Registered by the ICAEW to carry out company audit work
Regulated by the ICAEW for a range of investment business activities

J.A. HARRIS
Overmead, Cheltenham Road, Painswick, Stroud GL6 6XN

J.O. EVANS
Green Banks, The Hill, Merrywalks, Stroud GL5 4EP
Tel: 01453 750074
Email: joevans@msn.com
Website: http://www.j-o-evans.co.uk
Principal: ICAEW Member
J O Evans
Registered by the ICAEW to carry out company audit work

JONATHAN ORCHARD LTD
2 Ash View, Randwick, Stroud, GL6 6JF
Tel: 01453 762688
Resident Partners/Directors: ICAEW Members
J R Orchard

JONATHAN ORCHARD LTD
4 Cottage Gardens, Nympsfield Road, Nailsworth, Stroud GL6 0ET

MARK ROBINSON
Trullwell, Box, Stroud, GL6 9HD

P.S. LOE & CO
Edgecombe, Amberley, Stroud, GL5 5AB

PEARSON & CO
Endover House, Rodborough Common, Stroud, GL5 5BT

PRICE DAVIS ◈
The Old Baptist Chapel, New Street, Painswick, Stroud GL6 6XH

PRICE DAVIS LTD ◈
The Old Baptist Chapel, New Street, Painswick, Stroud GL6 6XH
Tel: 01452 812491
Resident Partners/Directors: ICAEW Members
H Davis

R.K. SHARMA
22 Bisley Road, Stroud, GL5 1HE

R.S. BENSON
Bell Lane House, Bell Lane, Minchinhampton, Stroud GL6 9BP

RANDALL & PAYNE
Rodborough Court, Walkley Hill, Stroud, GL5 3LR
Tel: 01453 763471
Fax: 01453 753807
Email: rp@randall-payne.co.uk
Website: http://www.randall-payne.co.uk
Resident Partners/Directors: ICAEW Members
M A Anthony, R I Byrd, I Selwood, T J Watkins
Registered by the ICAEW to carry out company audit work
Authorised and regulated by the Financial Services Authority for investment business

REBECCA BENNEYWORTH
Woodhouse, Rodborough Lane, Rodborough, Stroud GL5 2LN

ROLAND J. BOGGON
Moorea, Pitchcombe, Stroud, GL6 6LJ
Tel: 01452 812075
Principal: ICAEW Member
R J Boggon

SARAH FOX
Edgeworth House, Edgeworth, Stroud, GL6 7JQ
Tel: 01285 821278
Principal: ICAEW Member
S F S Fox

SARAH M. GOODWIN
Amber Hill, Amberley, Stroud, GL5 5AN
Tel: 01453 873381
Principal: ICAEW Member
S M Goodwin

SUTTON DIPPLE & CO
8 Wheelwright's Corner, Old Market, Nailsworth, Stroud GL6 0DB
Tel: 01453 833060
Email: info@suttondipple.co.uk
Resident Partners/Directors: ICAEW Members
S T Dipple, I R Sutton

STUDLEY

BRATTON A.J.
2 Priory Court, Priory Farm, Studley, B80 7BB
Tel: 01527 854781
Principal: ICAEW Member
A J Bratton

STURMINSTER NEWTON

ACCOUNTANCY PLUS (DORSET) LTD
4 New Street, Marnhull, Sturminster Newton, DT10 1PY
Tel: 01258 820709
Resident Partners/Directors: ICAEW Members
K P Harden

BIGNOLD & CO
Lester House, 7 Bridge Street, Sturminster Newton, DT10 1AP
Tel: 01258 472543
Principal: ICAEW Member
R C Bignold

JOHN COWLEY
Bramleys, Bath Road, Sturminster Newton, DT10 1EB

SIMON JOHN CHRISTOPHER LTD
First Floor Suite, Drapers House, Market Place, Sturminster Newton DT10 1AS
Tel: 01258 471669
Resident Partners/Directors: ICAEW Members
S J Christopher

SUTCLIFFE & CO LTD
Old Bank House, Sturminster Newton, DT10 1AN
Tel: 01258 472344
Resident Partners/Directors: ICAEW Members
J K A Coward, M Langhelt

SUDBURY

EDMONDSON'S ASSOCIATES LTD
1 Tye Green Paddock, Glemsford, Sudbury, CO10 7TS

EDMONDSONS
1 Tye Green Paddock, Glemsford, Sudbury, CO10 7TS

HARVEY & CO
Albany House, Church Lane, Alpheton, Sudbury CO10 9BL
Tel: 01284 828174
Principal: ICAEW Member
A S J Harvey

M BEADLE & CO
53 Peacocks Close, Cavendish, Sudbury, CO10 8DA
Tel: 01787 280755

M BEADLE & CO LTD
53 Peacocks Close, Cavendish, Sudbury, CO10 8DA
Tel: 01787 280755
Resident Partners/Directors: ICAEW Members
M Beadle

M.J.WILLIAMS
Melford Place Cottage, Liston Lane, Long Melford, Sudbury CO10 9LT

MOORE GREEN ◈
22 Friars St, Sudbury, CO10 2AA

OWERS & CO ◈
Round Maples, Edwardstone, Sudbury, CO10 5PR

PERRY DOUGLASS & CO
4 Market Hill, Clare, Sudbury, CO10 8NN
Tel: 01787 277045
Principal: ICAEW Member
D J Perry

ROWLAND STRATFORD & CO
53 The Mews, Newton Croft, Sudbury, CO10 2RW

STACEY & PARTNERS ◈
9 North Street Parade, Sudbury, CO10 1GL
Tel: 01787 375282
Website: http://www.staceys.co.uk
Resident Partners/Directors: ICAEW Members
M J Nicholls
Registered by the ICAEW to carry out company audit work
Regulated by the ICAEW for a range of investment business activities

STACEY & PARTNERS LTD
9 North Street Parade, Sudbury, CO10 1GL

SUNBURY-ON-THAMES

J.T. KINSLEY
28 Harfield Road, Sunbury-on-thames, TW16 5PT
Tel: 01932 784711
Principal: ICAEW Member
J T Kinsley

UDDIN & CO
12 Fairlawns, Sunbury-on-thames, TW16 6QR

SUNDERLAND

BRIAN THURLBECK
Beechmount, 33 Beechwood Terrace, Sunderland, SR2 7LY

DAVID R. ROBSON
143 Sidecliff Road, Roker, Sunderland, SR6 9NE

KAISER & ASSOCIATES
20 Foyle Street, Sunderland, SR1 1LE

LAVERICK WALTON & CO ◈
10 Grange Terrace, Sunderland, SR2 7DF
Tel: 0191 567 2853
Resident Partners/Directors: ICAEW Members
O E Sandy

MITCHELLS GRIEVSON LTD
Business & Innovation Centre, Wearfield, Sunderland Enterprise Park, Sunderland SR5 2TA

NE ACCOUNTANCY SERVICES LTD
9 Park Parade, Roker, Sunderland, SR6 9LU
Tel: 07914 950526
Resident Partners/Directors: ICAEW Members
S Gibson

NEXT LEVEL FINANCIAL MANAGEMENT LTD ◈
Willow House, 17 East Grange, Sunderland, SR5 1NX
Tel: 0191 548 6000
Resident Partners/Directors: ICAEW Members
Les Hodgson

NORTHFIELD ACCOUNTANCY SERVICES ◈
Unit 2, St Catherines Court, Sunderland Enterprise Park, Sunderland, TYNE AND WEAR SR5 3XJ
Tel: 0191 549 4888
Principal: ICAEW Member
M Snaith

P M STAFFORD
22 Foyle Street, Sunderland, SR1 1LE

ROBERT MILLER & CO
43a Front Street, Cleadon, Sunderland, SR6 7PG

ROBERT MILLER & COMPANY (CLEADON) LTD ◈
43a Front Street, Cleadon Village, Sunderland, SR6 7PG

T.A. MATTERSON
31 Tunstall Terrace, New Silksworth, Sunderland, SR3 1HQ

TENON LTD
Ferryboat Lane, Sunderland, SR5 3JN
Tel: 0191 511 5000

TENON AUDIT LTD
Tenon House, Ferryboat Lane, Sunderland, SR5 3JN
Tel: 0191 511 5000

TONY DOVER FCA
11 Defender Court, Hylton Riverside Enterprise Park, Sunderland, SR5 3PE

TTR BARNES LTD ◈
3-5 Grange Terrace, Stockton Road, Sunderland, SR2 7DG
Tel: 0191 567 0304
Resident Partners/Directors: ICAEW Members
R B Huntley, A Russell

TTR BARNES FINANCIAL SERVICES LTD
3-5 Grange Terrace, Stockton Road, Sunderland, SR2 7DG
Tel: 0191 567 0304
Resident Partners/Directors: ICAEW Members
A Russell

UHY TORGERSENS ◈
Somerford Buildings, Norfolk Street, Sunderland, SR1 1EE
Tel: 0191 567 8611
Resident Partners/Directors: ICAEW Members
B Howells, D M Johnson, P N Newbold, S J Torgersen

WILLIS SCOTT GROUP ★ ◈
27/28 Frederick Street, Sunderland, SR1 1LZ
Tel: 0191 567 5471
Email: kscott@willisscott.co.uk
Resident Partners/Directors: ICAEW Members
S K Hutton, N Mullen, K Scott

SURBITON

AIMS - CHRIS POULLIS
30 Tolworth Rise South, Surbiton, KT5 9NN

ALDERWICK JAMES & CO LTD
4 The Sanctuary, 23 Oak Hill Grove, Surbiton, KT6 6DU

ARMSTRONG & CO
Pegaxis House, Suite 8, 61 Victoria Road, Surbiton KT6 4JX

ATHAWOOD CONSULTING
12 Lower Sand Hills, Surbiton, KT6 6RP

BE ROBERTS & CO
3 Kirkleas Road, Surbiton, KT6 6QJ
Tel: 020 8390 3343
Principal: ICAEW Member
B E Roberts

BILIMORIA & CO LTD
171 Raeburn Avenue, Surbiton, KT5 9DE

BUSINESS ASSURANCE & TAXATION SERVICES LTD ◈
145 Ewell Road, Surbiton, KT6 6AW
Tel: 020 8390 6878
Resident Partners/Directors: ICAEW Members
D A Cane

C. MCDONALD & CO
Ditton Lodge, 16 Southborough Road, Surbiton, KT6 6JN

COHEN & PARTNERS
60 Moresby Avenue, Surbiton, KT5 9DS

DAVID ERRINGTON
The Old Vicarage, 9 Endsleigh Gardens, Surbiton, KT6 5JL

FAIRFAX
12 Malvern Close, Surbiton, KT6 7UG

FALLOWS & CO
Archway House, 81-82 Portsmouth Road, Surbiton, KT6 5PT

GILLIAN BARRETT
34 Greenfield Avenue, Surbiton, KT5 9HR

GUY FALLOWS ENTERPRISES LTD
Archway House, 81-82 Portsmouth Road, Surbiton, KT6 5PT

KERSHEN FAIRFAX LTD
22 Seymour Gardens, Surbiton, KT5 8QE

KYBERT CARROLL LTD
52 Brighton Road, Surbiton, KT6 5PL
Tel: 020 8399 0939
Resident Partners/Directors: ICAEW Members
J P Carroll

LEACH & CO
Ashley House, 136 Tolworth Broadway, Surbiton, KT6 7LA

M ULRICH
24 Highfield Road, Tolworth, Surbiton, KT5 9LP
Tel: 020 8399 7665
Principal: ICAEW Member
M P Ulrich

MADON & CO ◈
8th Floor, Tolworth Tower, Ewell Road, Surbiton KT6 7EL
Tel: 020 8390 4444
Fax: 020 8390 3600
Email: krm@madon.co.uk
Website: http://www.madon.co.uk
Date Established: 1985
Principal: ICAEW Member
K R Madon
Registered by the ICAEW to carry out company audit work
Regulated by the ICAEW for a range of investment business activities
See display advertisement near this entry.

MICHAEL GEORGE & CO
1 Southborough Close, Southborough, Surbiton, KT6 6PU

MJF
23 Oaks Way, Long Ditton, Surbiton, KT6 5DX
Tel: 020 8398 8729
Principal: ICAEW Member
M J Freedman

MOYNIHAN & CO ◈
Suite 7, Claremont House, 22-24 Claremont Road, Surbiton KT6 4QU

NIGEL H. GILROY & CO
6 Broomfield Road, Surbiton, KT5 9AZ

NJHCO
8th Floor, Tolworth Tower, Ewell Road, Surbiton KT6 7EL
Tel: 020 8390 3100

R.K. GUPTA & CO
89 Hook Rise South, Surbiton, KT6 7NA

RICHARD MORGAN AND CO
59 Victoria Road, Surbiton, KT6 4NQ
Tel: 020 8390 6991
Email: info@rmco.ac
Website: http://www.rmco.co.uk
Principal: ICAEW Member
R D Morgan
SPECIALISATIONS – BUSINESS & GENERAL ADVICE
Management Advice to Business
SPECIALISATIONS – SECTOR
Media
SPECIALISATIONS – TAXATION
UK Subsidiaries of Overseas Multinationals

ROSS, EDWARDS
70 Claremont Road, Surbiton, KT6 4RH

STEVENSONS
6 Sylvan Gardens, Surbiton, KT6 6PP
Tel: 020 8339 9690
Email: as@stevensonsfca.co.uk
Principal: ICAEW Member
A L Stevenson
Registered by the ICAEW to carry out company audit work
SPECIALISATIONS – BUSINESS & GENERAL ADVICE
Company Formation
SPECIALISATIONS – FINANCIAL REPORTING
Limited Company Accounts
SPECIALISATIONS – TAXATION
Self Assessment Advice
Taxation

T D BROWN & CO
50 The Ridings, Surbiton, KT5 8HQ
Principal: ICAEW Member
T D Brown

T.H. DOWLING & CO
Suite 2, The Sanctuary, 23 Oakhill Grove, Surbiton KT6 6DU
Tel: 020 8390 8133
Principal: ICAEW Member
T H Dowling

TROTMAN & CO
Queensborough House, 2 Claremont Road, Surbiton, KT6 4QU

SUTTON

ACCOUNTING COMPANY LTD
Unit 3, 40 Kimpton Road, Sutton, SM3 9QP

ASHLEI ASSOCIATES
7 Heath Drive, Sutton, SM2 5RP

BLYTHE & CO
41 Oldfields Road, Sutton, SM1 2NB

BREMAKUMARS LTD
591 London Road, Cheam, Sutton, SM3 9AG

BROOKS & CO
Mid-Day Court, 20-24 Brighton Road, Sutton, SM2 5BN
Tel: 020 8642 8681
Email: mharding@brooksand.co.uk
Resident Partners/Directors: ICAEW Members
R Ferris, M J Harding
Non-resident Partners (ICAEW Members):
K Dixon
Resident Partners (Non-ICAEW Members):
S A Sundaran
Non-resident Partners (Non-ICAEW Members):
F Down
Other Offices: East Grinstead
Registered by the ICAEW to carry out company audit work
Languages Spoken:
French

CLARKSON HYDE
137-143 High Street, Sutton, SM1 1JH
Tel: 020 7022 0050
Email: enquiries@clarksonhyde.com
Website: http://www.clarksonhyde.com
Other Offices: 70 Conduit Street, London W1S 2GF

CLARKSON HYDE LLP
137-143 High Street, Sutton, SM1 1JH

COLIN QUEMBY
43 Devon Road, Sutton, SM2 7PE

E. DAWOOD & CO
27 Wilbury Avenue, Cheam, Sutton, SM2 7DU

G.L. TAYLOR & CO
10 Tudor Close, Cheam, Sutton, SM3 8QS
Tel: 020 8644 4817
Principal: ICAEW Member
G L Taylor

GLOUCESTER TROTMAN & CO
119 Westmead Rd, Sutton, SM1 4JE

GLOUCESTER TROTMAN & CO
31 Devon Road, Cheam, Sutton, SM2 7PE

GRAHAM HUNN & CO
27 Cavendish Road, Sutton, SM2 5EY

H K NG
12 Fairholme Road, Cheam, Sutton, SM1 2EE

HARMER SLATER
Salatin House, 19 Cedar Road, Sutton, SM2 5DA
Tel: 020 8652 2700
Resident Partners/Directors: ICAEW Members
C Harmer, T W Slater

HELEN DRURY
41 Prior Avenue, Sutton, SM2 5HY

I.K. SETHIA ◈
6 Arundel Road, Cheam, Sutton, SM2 7AD
Tel: 020 8643 5492
Principal: ICAEW Member
I K Sethia

JACOB CAVENAGH & SKEET ★
5 Robin Hood Lane, Sutton, SM1 2SW
Tel: 020 8643 1166
Resident Partners/Directors: ICAEW Members
R I Haffenden, A R Hazael, M R Hickson

K CONSULTING
12 Fairholme Road, Sutton, SM1 2EE

L.V. GOUGH & CO ★
7 West Drive, Cheam, Sutton, SM2 7NB
Tel: 020 8642 9354
Resident Partners/Directors: ICAEW Members
P B Gough

LIEW & CO
G/F 7 Mulgrave Chambers, 26-28 Mulgrave Road, Sutton, SM2 6LE

M.A. TOBIN
17 Wilbury Avenue, Cheam, Sutton, SM2 7DU

MAURICE ANDREWS
Grove House, 25 Upper Mulgrave Road, Cheam, Sutton SM2 7BE
Tel: 020 8642 2060
Fax: 020 8643 8913
Email: mail@mauriceandrews.co.uk
Resident Partners/Directors: ICAEW Members
B G Elliott, M J Pettit
Registered by the ICAEW to carry out company audit work
Regulated by the ICAEW for a range of investment business activities

MAZARS CORPORATE FINANCE LTD ◈
Times House, Throwley Way, Sutton, SM1 4JQ

MAZARS LLP ◈
Sixth Floor, Times House, Throwley Way, Sutton SM1 4JQ
Tel: 020 8661 1826
Resident Partners/Directors: ICAEW Members
A J Austin, N H Holmes
Resident Partners (Non-ICAEW Members):
E M C Maxwell
Registered by the ICAEW to carry out company audit work
Authorised and regulated by the Financial Services Authority for investment business

MICHAEL GALLANT & CO
95 Sutton Heights, Albion Road, Sutton, SM2 5TD
Tel: 020 8661 0677
Principal: ICAEW Member
M D Gallant

MICHAEL K ◈
7 Forest Road, Sutton, SM3 9NT

MICHAEL TUCKEY
The Dutch House, 24 The Downsway, Sutton, SM2 5RN

MUSAAMIL & CO
101 Epsom Road, Sutton, SM3 9EY

MYRUS SMITH ◈
Norman House, 8 Burnell Road, Sutton, SM1 4BW
Tel: 020 8661 1625
Fax: 020 8643 3446
Email: contact@myrussmith.co.uk
Website: http://www.myrussmith.co.uk
Resident Partners/Directors: ICAEW Members
K C Fisher, S A Jones
Resident Partners (Non-ICAEW Members):
T Subhan
Registered by the ICAEW to carry out company audit work
Regulated by the ICAEW for a range of investment business activities

INVESTOR IN PEOPLE

PAUL WEBSTER & ASSOCIATES
27 Cavendish Road, Sutton, SM2 5EY

ROTHMAN PANTALL & CO
Second Floor, Old Inn House, 2 Carshalton Road, Sutton SM1 4RA
Tel: 020 8642 1048
Fax: 020 8643 6160
Website: http://www.rothman-pantall.co.uk
Resident Partners/Directors: ICAEW Members
A D Miller

SAMMAR & CO LTD
Baet-Ul-Zafar, 14 Albury Avenue, Cheam, Sutton SM2 7JT
Tel: 020 8786 5885
Resident Partners/Directors: ICAEW Members
S A Farooqi

T. WARREN
51 Barrington Road, Sutton, SM3 9PR
Tel: 020 8644 6952
Principal: ICAEW Member
T Warren

TURPIN BARKER ARMSTRONG ★
Allen House, 1 Westmead Road, Sutton, SM1 4LA

WADE STEVENS
7a The Broadway, Cheam, Sutton, SM3 8BH
Tel: 020 8642 2288
Principal: ICAEW Member
G W Stevens

WILDING, HUDSON & CO ◈
Saxon House, 17 Lewis Road, Sutton, SM1 4BR
Tel: 020 8661 6292
Fax: 020 8643 9321
Email: wildingh@aol.com
Principal: ICAEW Member
J R Wilding
Registered by the ICAEW to carry out company audit work
Regulated by the ICAEW for a range of investment business activities

SUTTON COLDFIELD

A.K. PAPADAMOU & CO
573 Chester Road, Sutton Coldfield, B73 5HU
Tel: 0121 384 4380
Resident Partners/Directors: ICAEW Members
A K Papadamou, J G Simons
See display advertisement near this entry.

A.R.HEYWOOD
36 West View Road, Sutton Coldfield, B75 6AY
Tel: 0121 329 2748
Principal: ICAEW Member
A R Heywood

BISSELL & BROWN ◈
Charter House, 56 High Street, Sutton Coldfield, B72 1UJ

BISSELL & BROWN LTD
Charter House, 56 High Street, Sutton Coldfield, B72 1UJ
Tel: 0121 250 6575
Email: info@bissell-brown.com
Website: http://www.bissell-brown.com
Resident Partners/Directors: ICAEW Members
J M Malkin, B J Matthews, D L Thebridge, P M Tremayne
Resident Partners (Non-ICAEW Members):
J J Taheny
Registered by the ICAEW to carry out company audit work
Regulated by the ICAEW for a range of investment business activities

SPECIALISATIONS – AUDIT & ASSURANCE
Audit

SPECIALISATIONS – BUSINESS & GENERAL ADVICE
Management Advice to Business

SPECIALISATIONS – FINANCIAL REPORTING
Accounts Preparation
Limited Company Accounts

SPECIALISATIONS – TAXATION
Taxation

CARROLL & CO
335 Jockey Road, Sutton Coldfield, B73 5XE

CARROLL BUSINESS CONSULTING LTD
335 Jockey Road, Sutton Coldfield, B73 5XE

COLIN J.B. SPINKS & CO ◈
St James House, 65 Mere Green Road, Four Oaks, Sutton Coldfield B75 5BY
Tel: 0121 308 3379
Principal: ICAEW Member
S A Portman

COLLINS HART
Victoria House, 437 Birmingham Road, Sutton Coldfield, B72 1AX
Tel: 0121 382 4443
Resident Partners/Directors: ICAEW Members
N J Collins

DAGGATT & CO
21 Conchar Road, Sutton Coldfield, B72 1LW

FOTAS
Suite D, Astor House, 282 Lichfield Road, Sutton Coldfield B74 2UG

FOUR OAKS TAXATION & ACCOUNTING SERVICES LTD
Suite D, Astor House, 282 Lichfield Road, Sutton Coldfield B74 2UG

G S GROVE
7 Hillwood Common Road, Four Oaks, Sutton Coldfield, B75 5QJ
Tel: 0121 308 0020
Principal: ICAEW Member
G S Grove

GEORGE H W GRIFFITH LTD
Century House, 31 Gate Lane, Sutton Coldfield, B73 5TR
Tel: 0121 321 4800
Email: info@griffithandgriffith.com
Website: http://www.griffithandgriffith.com
Resident Partners/Directors: ICAEW Members
G H W Griffith
Registered by the ICAEW to carry out company audit work Individual(s) licensed for insolvency work by another RPB

HARWOODS ◈
1 Trinity Place, Midland Drive, Sutton Coldfield, B72 1TX
Tel: 0121 355 0901
Principal: ICAEW Member
R F W Harwood

HASLEHURST RUDD & CO LTD
88 Hill Village Road, Four Oaks, Sutton Coldfield, B75 5BE

HASLEHURSTS
88 Hill Village Road, Four Oaks, Sutton Coldfield, B75 5BE

HASLEHURSTS LTD
88 Hill Village Road, Sutton Coldfield, B75 5BE

HASLEHURSTS CORPORATE FINANCE
88 Hill Village Road, Sutton Coldfield, B75 5BE

HASLEHURSTS CORPORATE FINANCE LTD
88 Hill Village Road, Sutton Coldfield, B75 5BE

HASLESHURSTS
88 Hill Village Road, Sutton Coldfield, B75 5BE

J.F. SOCCI & CO
83 Blackwood Road, Streetly, Sutton Coldfield, B74 3PW
Tel: 0121 353 9282

J.F. SOCCI & CO LTD
83 Blackwood Road, Streetly, Sutton Coldfield, B74 3PW
Tel: 0121 353 9282
Resident Partners/Directors: ICAEW Members
J F Socci

J.M. PAGE & CO
14 Tudor Grove, Sutton Coldfield, B74 2LL

JOHN P. DALLISON & CO
Holmrook, 120 Moor Hall Drive, Sutton Coldfield, B75 6LS

JONESGILES LTD
228 Rectory Road, Sutton Coldfield, B75 7RX

LHK
First Floor Offices, 167 Sutton Road, Wylde Green, Sutton Coldfield B23 5TN
Tel: 0121 382 6711
Principal: ICAEW Member
G Q Khan

LINGER & CO ◈
Barrycliffe House, 2 Park View Road, Four Oaks, Sutton Coldfield B74 4PP
Tel: 0121 353 1919
Principal: ICAEW Member
A C Linger

LTS CONSULTING LTD
18 Aldermore Drive, Sutton Coldfield, B75 7HW

M.J.COOK & CO
Sutton House, 4 Coles Lane, Sutton Coldfield, B72 1NE
Tel: 0121 354 5111
Principal: ICAEW Member
M J Cook

M J ONE LTD
33 Coleshill Street, Sutton Coldfield, B72 1SD

M UNDERWOOD ACCOUNTANCY SERVICES
2 Oakhurst Road, Wylde Green, Sutton Coldfield, B72 1EJ

MURRELL CONSULTANCY LTD
39 Manor Road, Sutton Coldfield, B73 6EE

N.P. SMITH & CO
10 Tudman Close, Walmley, Sutton Coldfield, B76 1GP

N R GILLHESPY
172 Birmingham Road, Sutton Coldfield, B72 1BX

N R GILLHESPY LTD
172 Birmingham Road, Sutton Coldfield, B72 1BX

N.R. GILLHESPY MA FCA LTD
172 Birmingham Road, Sutton Coldfield, B72 1BX

PAUL H. DAWSON ◈
104 Clarence Road, Four Oaks, Sutton Coldfield, B74 4AS
Tel: 0121 308 3705
Principal: ICAEW Member
P H Dawson

PAUL HANDLEY
6 Highbury Road, Streetly, Sutton Coldfield, B74 4TF

PERRY & CO
Foley Lodge, 15 Foley Road East, Streetly, Sutton Coldfield B74 3HN

POTTER MCGREGOR & CO
Masonic Hall Chambers, Mill Street, Sutton Coldfield, B72 1TG
Tel: 0121 354 4211
Resident Partners/Directors: ICAEW Members
M J Holt, J A Potter

QUANTUM SOLUTIONS LTD
1 Trinity Place, Midland Drive, Sutton Coldfield, B72 1TX

RP PAINTING
5 Boultbee Road, Sutton Coldfield, B72 1DW

SHACKLEFORDS LTD ◈
3 Essex Road, Four Oaks, Sutton Coldfield, B75 6NR

SHAREWAY FINANCIAL SERVICES LTD
Penns Grange, 9 Netherdale Close, Wylde Green, Sutton Coldfield B72 1YW
Tel: 01213 846069
Resident Partners/Directors: ICAEW Members
S Bumpsteed

STUBBS & CO
21 Bridle Lane, Streetly, Sutton Coldfield, B74 3QE

W.E. CLARKSON & CO ◈
7 Manor Drive, Sutton Coldfield, B73 6ER
Tel: 0121 354 8717
Principal: ICAEW Member
W E Clarkson

WADEX LTD ◈
11 Richmond Road, Sutton Coldfield, B73 6BJ

WEATHERER BAILEY BRAGG LLP
Victoria Chambers, 100 Boldmere Road, Sutton Coldfield, B73 5UB

SUTTON-IN-ASHFIELD

GREGORY PRIESTLEY & STEWART ★
Alexandra House, 123 Priestsic Road, Sutton-in-ashfield, NG17 4EA

K.L. BREALEY & CO
26 Market Place, Huthwaite, Sutton-in-ashfield, NG17 2QX

KENNETH SMITH
69-71 Outram Street, Sutton-In-Ashfield, NG17 4BG

SWADLINCOTE

BUCKLER SPENCER ◈
Old Police Station, Church Street, Swadlincote, DE11 8LN
Tel: 01283 217256
Resident Partners/Directors: ICAEW Members
J M Buckler, R J Spencer

DAINS LLP
2-6 Hill Street, Swadlincote, DE11 8HL
Tel: 0845 5558844
Fax: 01283 550484
Email: swadlincote@dains.com
Website: http://www.dains.com
Date Established: 1926
Resident Partners/Directors: ICAEW Members
N D Smith
Non-resident Partners (ICAEW Members):
S G Wright, M F P Smith, A R Massey, H M P Reynolds, P D Bradshaw, A P Morris
Non-resident Partners (Non-ICAEW Members):
M Castree, N Hawksley, A McQuillan, R C McNeilly, S C Bursell
Other Offices: Coleshill, Burton, Rugeley, Lichfield, Birmingham
Registered by the ICAEW to carry out company audit work
Regulated by the ICAEW for a range of investment business activities

EVOLUSYS LTD
20 De Ruthyn Close, Moira, Swadlincote, DE12 6ED

SWAFFHAM

AVN ARENA LTD
26 Market Place, Swaffham, PE37 7QH
Tel: 01760 723540
Fax: 01760 723334
Email: enquiries@avnarena.com
Website: http://www.avnarena.com

Non-resident Partners (ICAEW Members):
N C Tunnard
Registered by the ICAEW to carry out company audit work
Regulated by the ICAEW for a range of investment business activities

CLENSHAW MINNS
30 Market Place, Swaffham, PE37 7QH

CLENSHAW MINNS LTD
30 Market Place, Swaffham, PE37 7QH

MARTIN & ACOCK ◈
c/o Kenneth Bush Solicitors, 17 Thornton House, London Street, Swaffham PE37 7DD
Tel: 01760 721788
Website: http://www.martin-acock.com
Registered by the ICAEW to carry out company audit work

SWANAGE

HARDINGREDMANS ◈
Bridge House, Court Road, Swanage, BH19 1DX
Tel: 01929 423311
Email: team@hardingredmans.co.uk
Principal: ICAEW Member
S J Harding
Registered by the ICAEW to carry out company audit work
Regulated by the ICAEW for a range of investment business activities

SWANLEY

ATHAR KHAN & CO
Pixfield, Greencourt Road, Crockenhill, Swanley BR8 8JG

GARY SARGEANT + CO
5 White Oak Square, London Road, Swanley, BR8 7AG
Tel: 01322 614681
Email: info@gary-sargeant.co.uk
Resident Partners/Directors: ICAEW Members
E L Beal, A D Hughes, G A Sargeant
Resident Partners (Non-ICAEW Members):
J Brown
Registered by the ICAEW to carry out company audit work
Regulated by the ICAEW for a range of investment business activities

T.S. BATT
11/13 High Street, Swanley, BR8 8AE

SWINDON

ABACS LTD
Barn Cottage, Brookside Farm, Swan Lane, Leigh, Swindon SN6 6RD

ACCOUNTAX SERVICES (SWINDON) LTD
2 Charnwood Court, Newport Street, Swindon, SN1 3DX
Tel: 01793 421007
Resident Partners/Directors: ICAEW Members
R C Bloomer

ALEXANDER VAUGHAN & CO
Suite E, Hillside House, 167 Victoria Road, Swindon SN1 3BU

AMS ACCOUNTANCY LTD
Delta 606, Walton Road, Delta Office Park, Swindon SN5 7XF

ANDREW LEVENS
6 Happyland, Ashton Keynes, Swindon, SN6 6PN

BANKS
14 Devizes Road, Old Town, Swindon, SN1 4BH

BANKS LTD
14 Devizes Road, Old Town, Swindon, SN1 4BH
Tel: 01793 616284
Website: http://www.banksca.co.uk
Resident Partners/Directors: ICAEW Members
R Bluh, N R Elsden

BARRETT ACCOUNTING AND TAX SERVICES
1 Ellis Barn, The Old Dairy, Badbury, Swindon SN4 0EU
Tel: 01793 741250

BARRETT ATS LTD
1 Ellis Barn, The Old Dairy, Badbury, Swindon SN4 0EU
Tel: 01793 741250
Resident Partners/Directors: ICAEW Members
J B Raymond

BHG
77 Shrivenham Hundred Business Park, Majors Road, Watchfield, Swindon SN6 8TY

BHG LLP
77 Shrivenham Hundred Business Park, Majors Road, Watchfield, Swindon SN6 8TY

BJ ◈
Chapel House, Westmead Drive, Westlea, Swindon SN5 7UN
Tel: 01793 603300
Fax: 01793 511123
Email: david.starbuck@rsmbentleyjennison.com
Website: http://www.rsmbentleyjennison.com
Resident Partners/Directors: ICAEW Members
G J Harbour
Registered by the ICAEW to carry out company audit work

C & S ASSOCIATES LTD
3 Wessex Way, Highworth, Swindon, SN6 7NT

CORNABY & STANLEY
18 Bath Rd, Old Town, Swindon, SN1 4BA
Tel: 01793 695991
Resident Partners/Directors: ICAEW Members
T J Stanley

DAVID HERBERT LTD
Regus Centre, Windmill Hill Business Park, Whitehill Way, Swindon SN5 6QR
Tel: 01793 441740
Resident Partners/Directors: ICAEW Members
D J Herbert

DENNIS & TURNBULL
Swatton Barn, Badbury, Swindon, SN4 0EU

DENNIS & TURNBULL LTD
Swatton Barn, Badbury, Swindon, SN4 0EU
Tel: 01793 741600
Resident Partners/Directors: ICAEW Members
N L Dennis, B P Herbert

DERRICK NEWMAN & CO
29 Bath Road, Old Town, Swindon, SN1 4AS

DERRICK NEWMAN LTD
29 Bath Road, Old Town, Swindon, SN1 4AS
Tel: 01793 615761
Fax: 01793 430477
Email: enquiries@derricknewman.co.uk
Resident Partners/Directors: ICAEW Members
P J Crowley, D J Horne
Resident Partners (Non-ICAEW Members):
R E C Goodfellow, K J Kibble
Registered by the ICAEW to carry out company audit work

DYKE BRADING ★
16 Dorcan Business Village, Murdock Road,Dorcan, Swindon, SN3 5HY
Tel: 01793 610008
Email: enquiries@dykebrading.co.uk
Website: http://www.dykebrading.co.uk
Resident Partners/Directors: ICAEW Members
A D Trowbridge
Resident Partners (Non-ICAEW Members):
A B Ponting
Registered by another RSB to carry out company audit work

GEMS ACCOUNTANCY SERVICES LTD
Regus House, Windmill Hill Business Park, Whitehill Way, Swindon SN5 6QR

HW ◈
Old Station House, Station Approach, Newport Street, Swindon SN1 3DU
Tel: 01793 533838
Resident Partners/Directors: ICAEW Members
G C Fairclough, M S Gurney, S E Plumb

IMMOVATION LTD
2 Greywethers Avenue, Swindon, SN3 1QF
Tel: 01793 615662
Resident Partners/Directors: ICAEW Members
M I Imms

LAWRENCE ROSE LTD
53 Basepoint Business Centre, Rivermead Drive, Swindon, SN5 7EX

MONAHANS ◈
38-42 Newport Street, Swindon, SN1 3DR
Tel: 01793 818300
Resident Partners/Directors: ICAEW Members
D I Black, A J H Cohen, S G Fraser, M Shawyer

MORLEY & CO
2 Cricklade Court, Cricklade Street, Old Town, Swindon SN1 3EY

MORLEY & CO (UK) LTD ◈
2 Cricklade Court, Cricklade Street, Old Town, Swindon SN1 3EY
Tel: 01793 610243
Resident Partners/Directors: ICAEW Members
N Morley

MORRIS OWEN ◈
43-45 Devizes Road, Swindon, SN1 4BG
Tel: 01793 603900
Resident Partners/Directors: ICAEW Members
Robert Beale, D W Bond, R J Harman, Michael Johnson
Resident Partners (Non-ICAEW Members):
I Sumbler, A Barlow
Registered by the ICAEW to carry out company audit work
Authorised and regulated by the Financial Services Authority for investment business

OPTIMA FINANCIAL SOLUTIONS
Suite 20, Cherry Orchard West, Kembrey Park, Swindon SN2 8UP

OPTIMA FINANCIAL SOLUTIONS LTD
Suite 20, Cherry Orchard West, Kembrey Park, Swindon SN2 8UP

P.P.S.
29 Devizes Road, Swindon, SN1 4BG
Tel: 01793 488544
Resident Partners/Directors: ICAEW Members
P A Papworth-Smith, I Willoughby

REEVES & CO
Argyle commercial Centre, Argyle Street, Swindon, SN2 6AR

ROBERT RAYNES
Bridleway Cottage, 85 Priors Hill, Wroughton, Swindon SN4 0RL
Tel: 01793 845370
Principal: ICAEW Member
R V M Raynes

ROGER C BLOOMER
2 Charnwood Court, Newport Street, Swindon, SN1 3DX
Tel: 01793 421007

ROSS BROOKE LTD ◈
23 Wood Street, Old Town, Swindon, SN1 4AN
Tel: 01793 523432

S.J. HAYDON
The Conifers, Stone Lane, Lydiard Millicent, Swindon SN5 3LD

SD KNEE
2nd Floor, Marlborough House, High Street, Old Town, Swindon SN1 3EP

SD KNEE LTD
2nd Floor, Marlborough House, High Street, Old Town, Swindon SN1 3EP

SILBURY BUSINESS ADVISERS LTD
Park House, Church Place, Swindon, SN1 5ED

SIMON DAY & CO
Unit 2, Uffcott Farm, Uffcott, Swindon SN4 9NB

T.B. BOLLEN
89 Groundwell Road, Swindon, SN1 2NA

WATERSHEDS LTD ◈
8 Bath Road, Old Town, Swindon, SN1 4BA
Tel: 01793 719788

TADCASTER

CLAVANE & CO
6 Trans Walk, Church Fenton, Tadcaster, LS24 9RR

EURA AUDIT UK ★
The Fisher-More Chambers, 12/14 Westgate, Tadcaster, LS24 9AB

LSCP LLP
Fisher More Chambers, 12-14 Westgate, Tadcaster, LS24 9AB

SHARON HUFFEN
Woodman House, 18 Main Street, Ryther, Tadcaster LS24 9EE
Tel: 01757 268298
Principal: ICAEW Member
S Huffen

TADLEY

H R HARRIS & PARTNERS LTD ◈
12 Ramptons Meadow, Tadley, RG26 3UR

KEVIN FLAIN ACCOUNTANCY SERVICES
52 Woodlands Road, Baughurst, Tadley, RG26 5NS

SHERIDAN SWALLOW ◈
Brickhill House, North Oakley, Tadley, RG26 5TT
Tel: 07831 657094
Principal: ICAEW Member
J B S Swallow

TADWORTH

BEALES & CO
Oaken Coppice, Bears Den, Kingswood, Tadworth KT20 6PL
Tel: 01737 832907
Principal: ICAEW Member
D Beales

DAVID BECKMAN & CO
The White Cottage, Headley Heath Approach, Boxhill, Tadworth KT20 7LL

DAVID BECKMAN & CO
The White Cottage, Headley Heath Approach, Boxhill, Tadworth KT20 7LL

DAVID BECKMAN & CO LTD
The White Cottage, Headley Heath Approach, Boxhill, Tadworth KT20 7LL

DENYER NEVILL ACCOUNTANTS LTD
Regency House, 61a Walton Street, Walton on the Hill, Tadworth KT20 7RZ

DHL ACCOUNTANCY SERVICES
30 Willowbank Gardens, Tadworth, KT20 5DS
Tel: 01737 277862
Principal: ICAEW Member
D H Lane

ENTERPRISE SOLUTIONS (ENGLAND) LTD
March House, 44 The Avenue, Tadworth, KT20 5AT

HMA ACCOUNTANCY SERVICES
Ranmore, Waterhouse Lane, Kingswood, Tadworth KT20 6DT
Tel: 01737 370273
Principal: ICAEW Member
H M Ainsworth

JAMES JACKSON & CO
Barberry Cottage, Waterhouse Lane, Kingswood, Tadworth KT20 6DT
Tel: 01737 354188
Principal: ICAEW Member
J G Jackson

KIR CONSULTANTS LTD
23 Kingswood Grange, Babylon Lane, Lower Kingswood, Tadworth KT20 6UY

MCCAGNEY & CO LTD
Cranmere, Sandy Lane, Kingswood, Tadworth KT20 6NQ

PATRICK WEBB
17 Tower Road, Tadworth, KT20 5QY

PETER BRADLEY
63 Kingswood Road, Tadworth, KT20 5EF

T. STAPLEHURST ◈
April Cottage, Sturt's Lane, Tadworth, KT20 7RQ
Tel: 01737 819560
Principal: ICAEW Member
T Staplehurst

TAYLOR GILLAM & CO
Arkudi House, Waterhouse Lane, Kingswood, Tadworth KT20 6DT

TILBROOK & CO LTD
The Lawn, 9 Cross Road, Tadworth, KT20 5SP

VAN PELT & CO
Wild Acres House, Forest Drive, Kingswood, Tadworth KT20 6LP

TAMWORTH

ADAMS MOORE LTD ◈
38-39 Albert Road, Tamworth, B79 7JS

ADAMS MOORE AUDIT LTD
38-39 Albert Road, Tamworth, B79 7JS

C.A. WHITEHOUSE & CO
5 Lowdham, Wilnecote, Tamworth, B77 4LX
Tel: 01827 897541
Principal: ICAEW Member
C A Whitehouse

D.A. NAYLOR
Woodthorpe House, Packington Lane, Hopwas, Tamworth B78 3AY
Tel: 01827 53089
Principal: ICAEW Member
D A Naylor

DAVIES
2 Albert Road, Tamworth, B79 7JN

DAVIES & ASSOCIATES LTD ◈
Sherwood House, 2 Albert Road, Tamworth, B79 7JN
Tel: 01827 305900
Email: info@daviesca.com
Resident Partners/Directors: ICAEW Members
G V Davies

HOLLIS & CO
The Rookery, Freasley, Tamworth, B78 2EZ

HW ◈
Sterling House, 97 Lichfield Street, Tamworth, B79 7QF
Tel: 01827 61835
Resident Partners/Directors: ICAEW Members
J Blenkinsop, S P Butler, C M Fletcher, A S Minifie

HW CONTROLS & ASSURANCE LLP ★
Sterling House, 97 Lichfield Street, Tamworth, B79 7QF
Tel: 01827 61835

JOSEPH BROWN ◈
The Mount, Church Lane, Kingsbury, Tamworth B78 2LR
Tel: 01827 872069
Principal: ICAEW Member
J Brown

LISA M STRETTON
9 Felstead Close, Dosthill, Tamworth, B77 1QD

PHILIP BARNES & CO LTD
The Old Council Chambers, Halford Street, Tamworth, B79 7RB

PRACTICAL ACCOUNTING LTD
50 Ashby Road, Tamworth, B79 8AD

ROBINS
Leonard House, 12-14 Silver Street, Tamworth, B79 7NH

SMITH MERCIA ACCOUNTANCY SERVICES
4 Sudeley, Dosthill, Tamworth, B77 1JR

STEPHEN DANIELS
50 Ashby Road, Tamworth, B79 8AD
Tel: 01827 63353

STOKES ACCOUNTANTS
385 Tamworth Road, Amington, Tamworth, B77 4AE
Tel: 01827 65610
Principal: ICAEW Member
G R Stokes

TARPORLEY

BUTLERS
Little Garth, Tirley Lane, Utkinton, Tarporley CW6 0JZ

ELAINE PHILLIPSON
Forest Way, Waste Lane, Kelsall, Tarporley CW6 0PE

HALL LIVESEY BROWN
68 High Street, Tarporley, CW6 0AT
Tel: 01829 733333
Fax: 01829 733342
Email: info@hlbtarp.co.uk
Website: http://www.hlb-group.co.uk

Training Contracts Available.
Resident Partners/Directors: ICAEW Members
N Carr, R Evans, S J Jeffrey, S Welsh
Resident Partners (Non-ICAEW Members):
A J Crank, S A McKee
Other Offices: Chester, Shrewsbury, Wrexham
Registered by the ICAEW to carry out company audit work
Regulated by the ICAEW for a range of investment business activities

P.A. KERSHAW
Meadowbank, Willington Road, Willington, Tarporley CW6 0ND

TAUNTON

A.C. MOLE & SONS ◈
Stafford House, Blackbrook Park Avenue, Taunton, TA1 2PX
Tel: 01823 624450
Fax: 01823 444533
Email: info@acmole.co.uk
Website: http://www.acmole.co.uk
Resident Partners/Directors: ICAEW Members
Paul Aplin, N N Banks, C P Loveluck, M Perry, I Pinder
Resident Partners (Non-ICAEW Members):
R Zelazik
Registered by the ICAEW to carry out company audit work
Regulated by the ICAEW for a range of investment business activities

AIMS - VIRGINIA PEARSON FCA
69 Tyne Park, Taunton, TA1 2RP

ALBERT GOODMAN
Mary Street House, Mary Street, Taunton, TA1 3NW

AMHERST & SHAPLAND
Castle Lodge, Castle Green, Taunton, TA1 4AD

AMHERST & SHAPLAND LTD
Castle Lodge, Castle Green, Taunton, TA1 4AD

ARTUME LTD
30 Nichol Place, Cotford St Luke, Taunton, TA4 1JD

ASPEN-WAITE
43 Bridge Street, Taunton, TA1 1TP

BAKER ACCOUNTING
18 Waterleaze, Taunton, TA2 8PX

C.R. JONES & CO LTD
45 Staplegrove Road, Taunton, TA1 1DG

CALTHORN & CO
Headwell House, Headwell, Curry Mallet, Taunton TA3 6SX

CHEDZOY BUTTERWORTH LTD ◈
2 Chartfield House, Castle Street, Taunton, TA1 4AS
Tel: 01823 353598
Email: cb@chedzoybutterworth.co.uk
Resident Partners/Directors: ICAEW Members
J D Parker, D H Stabbins
Non-resident Partners (ICAEW Members):
J D Parker, D H Stabbins
Resident Partners (Non-ICAEW Members):
A W Larpent
Non-resident Partners (Non-ICAEW Members):
R W Symons
Regulated by the ICAEW for a range of investment business activities

CHURCHILL & CO ◈
HiPoint, Thomas Street, Taunton, TA2 6HB
Tel: 01823 321177
Principal: ICAEW Member
A G Shiffers
Other Offices: Honiton (Tel: 01404 43360)

DIXON WALSH ◈
St Mary's House, Magdalene Street, Taunton, TA1 1SB
Tel: 01823 286111
Resident Partners/Directors: ICAEW Members
S A Cole, M J Jewell, J B Lewis, R A O'Donnell

FRANCIS CLARK ◈
9 The Crescent, Taunton, TA1 4EA
Tel: 01823 275925
Website: http://www.francisclark.co.uk
Resident Partners/Directors: ICAEW Members
R I Kennedy, M P Lock
Authorised and regulated by the Financial Services Authority for investment business
General Description: Largest independent firm in the South West, with particular strengths in taxation, VAT, corporate finance, financial planning, forensic accounting , IT and insolvency.

HERRIOT TURNER ★
Lion House, 2 High Street, Wiveliscombe, Taunton TA4 2JX

LENTELLS LTD
11 The Crescent, Taunton, TA1 4EA
Tel: 01823 286274
Resident Partners/Directors: ICAEW Members
P H Bedford, N J Gamblen, P A Stallard

Registered by the ICAEW to carry out company audit work
Regulated by the ICAEW for a range of investment business activities

MAURICE WHITELEY
8 Mill Lane, Bishops Lydeard, Taunton, TA4 3LN

MILSTED LANGDON
Winchester House, Deane Gate Avenue, Taunton, TA1 2UH

MILSTED LANGDON LLP
Winchester House, Deane Gate Avenue, Taunton, TA1 2UH
Tel: 01823 445566
Resident Partners/Directors: ICAEW Members
T A Close, S M Denton, E M Durrant, N P Fry, S P Horton, J C Langdon

MITCHELLS
St Johns House, Castle Street, Taunton, TA1 4AY
Tel: 01823 333813
Fax: 01823 352662
Email: info@mitchells-accountants.co.uk
Website: http://www.mitchells-accountants.co.uk
Resident Partners/Directors: ICAEW Members
D N Mitchell, S J Vigus
Registered by the ICAEW to carry out company audit work
Regulated by the ICAEW for a range of investment business activities
SPECIALISATIONS – FORENSIC ACCOUNTING
Expert Witnesses in Litigation
SPECIALISATIONS – SECTOR

Agriculture
General Description:
Accountants who understand agriculture.

PHILLIPS DINNES LTD
Lyddons, Nailsbourne, Taunton, TA2 8AF
Tel: 01823 451315
Resident Partners/Directors: ICAEW Members
M C Dinnes, Stephen Phillips

SEAMARK FORENSIC SERVICES LTD
Stella House, 82 Greenway Road, Taunton, TA2 6LE

SPENCE ROBERT PETHICK
Atlantic House, 23 Silver Street, Taunton, TA1 3DH

SUE LEWIS ACCOUNTANCY SERVICES
Dove Cottage, 18 Style Road, Wiveliscombe, Taunton TA4 2LN

SUMMERHAYES ◈
Compass House, 6 Billetfield, Taunton, TA1 3NN
Tel: 01823 282511
Principal: ICAEW Member
J F Rudge
Registered by the ICAEW to carry out company audit work
Regulated by the ICAEW for a range of investment business activities
Individual(s) licensed for insolvency work by the ICAEW

TAVISTOCK

ABACUS ACCOUNTING AND BUSINESS SOLUTIONS
Harbridge, Hardimead, Lamerton, Tavistock PL19 8SE

ANTHONY GOLDING
Anthony Golding Limited, Blue Haze, Down Road, Tavistock PL19 9AG
Tel: 01822 611027

ANTHONY GOLDING LTD
Blue Haze, Down Road, Tavistock, PL19 9AG

AZUR CONSULTANCY ◈
Gouvia Lodge, Chollacott Lane, Whitchurch, Tavistock PL19 9DD
Tel: 01822 611222
Principal: ICAEW Member
M L Nettleton MSc MBA BSc(Econ) FCA FCMA

BARRY J. NORTHCOTT
Langstone Manor Cottage, Brentor, Tavistock, PL19 0NE

CONDY MATHIAS ★
Suite 26, Atlas House, West Devon Business Park, Tavistock PL19 9DP

FINAX LTD
28 Church Lea, Whitchurch, Tavistock, PL19 9PS

FRANCIS CLARK ◈
Ridge Grove, Russell Street, Tavistock, PL19 8BE
Tel: 01822 613355
Website: http://www.francisclark.co.uk
Resident Partners/Directors: ICAEW Members
J G Talbot
Authorised and regulated by the Financial Services Authority for investment business
General Description: Largest independent firm in the South West, with particular strengths in taxation, VAT, corporate finance, financial planning, forensic accounting, IT and insolvency.

MICHAEL G WEEMYS
28 Church Lea, Whitchurch, Tavistock, PL19 9PS

MOORLANDS BOOK KEEPING SERVICES
28 Glanville Road, Tavistock, PL19 0EB

MOORLANDS BUSINESS ADVISORY SERVICES
28 Glanville Road, Tavistock, PL19 0EB
Tel: 01822 612351

MOORLANDS PAYROLL SERVICES
28 Glanville Road, Tavistock, PL19 0EB

POTTER BAKER
Bedford Chambers, Bedford Square, Tavistock, PL19 0AD
Tel: 01822 613167
Email: info@potterbaker.co.uk
Website: http://www.potterbaker.co.uk
Non-resident Partners (ICAEW Members):
A D Baker
Other Offices: Launceston
Registered by the ICAEW to carry out company audit work
Authorised and regulated by the Financial Services Authority for investment business

TAVISTOCK BUSINESS CONSULTANCY LTD
28 Glanville Road, Tavistock, PL19 0EB

TEDDINGTON

BAKER & CO (UK) LTD
6 Marina Way, Teddington, TW11 9PN

BAKER & CO (UK) LTD
Crest House, 102-104 Church Road, Teddington, TW11 8PY
Tel: 0845 094 9871
Resident Partners/Directors: ICAEW Members
R A Chalk

BUTTERS & CO
129 High St, Teddington, TW11 8HJ

DUNCAN GASKELL
8 Dells Close, Teddington, TW11 0LD

GRAYS ACCOUNTANTS LTD
Kings Works, Kings Road, Teddington, TW11 0QB

MARTIN G. LEWIN & CO
35 Thamespoint, Fairways, Teddington, TW11 9PP

THE ORANGE PARTNERSHIP
Churcham House, 1 Bridgeman Road, Teddington, TW11 9AJ

THE ORANGE PARTNERSHIP LTD
Churcham House, 1 Bridgeman Road, Teddington, TW11 9AJ

PAUL BEDFORD
36 Princes Road, Teddington, TW11 0RW

PHAROS ASSOCIATES
PO Box 21, Teddington, TW11 9SW

RICHARD KENDALL & CO
15 Victoria Road, Teddington, TW11 0BB

RICHARD KENDALL & CO LTD
15 Victoria Road, Teddington, TW11 0BB

ROGER SUTTON & CO
Roger Sutton & Co., 79 High Street, Teddington, TW11 8HG
Tel: 020 8943 0972
Website: http://www.rogersutton.com
Resident Partners/Directors: ICAEW Members
P R Garner, R W Sutton
Registered by the ICAEW to carry out company audit work

T.H. GRAVES
73 Fairfax Road, Teddington, TW11 9DA
Tel: 020 8943 1717
Principal: ICAEW Member
T H Graves

YOUNG & CO
10 Lindum Road, Teddington, TW11 9DR

TEIGNMOUTH

ASHLEY DAWES FCA
8 Cleland Court, Manor Road, Bishopsteignton, Teignmouth TQ14 9SX
Tel: 01626 364987
Principal: ICAEW Member
A G Dawes

FISHER BELL (SOUTH WEST) LTD
21 Orchard Gardens, Teignmouth, TQ14 8DJ

FISHER BELL (SOUTH WEST) LTD
12 Orchard Gardens, Teignmouth, TQ14 8DJ

KATE WOOLNER
35 Manor Road, Bishopsteignton, Teignmouth, TQ14 9SU
Tel: 01626 774072
Principal: ICAEW Member
K J Woolner

NIGEL EDWARDS
Cross Gate, Shute Hill, Bishopsteignton, Teignmouth TQ14 9QL

R J SPRINGFIELD ◈
Kelani, 32 Teign View Road, Bishopsteignton, Teignmouth TQ14 9SZ
Tel: 01626 777473
Principal: ICAEW Member
R J Springfield

YANNONS LTD ◈
Yannon Towers, The Yannons, Teignmouth, TQ14 9UE
Tel: 01626 779552
Email: info@yannons.co.uk
Resident Partners/Directors: ICAEW Members
D O'Connor
General Description:
Specialists in owner-managed concerns (turnover £50,000-£5m).

TELFORD

A P CARTER & CO
50 Haygate Road, Wellington, Telford, TF1 1QN

ABT SERVICES (UK) LTD
50 Haygate Road, Wellington, Telford, TF1 1QN

D E BALL & CO LTD
15 Bridge Road, Wellington, Telford, TF1 1EB
Tel: 01952 261016
Resident Partners/Directors: ICAEW Members
R M Ball, A Jefferies

DAVIES GRINDROD & CO ◈
11 Queen Street, Wellington, Telford, TF1 1EH
Tel: 01952 243064
Email: mail@daviesgrindod.com
Principal: ICAEW Member
A M Grindrod
Registered by the ICAEW to carry out company audit work

HOLLINGSWORTH & CO
Coppice House, Halesfield 7, Telford, TF7 4NA

THE INTEGRITY PARTNERSHIP LTD
36 High Street, Madeley, Telford, TF7 5AS

J.G. RHODES
Lodge Park, Hortonwood 30, Telford, TF1 7ET
Tel: 01952 606317
Principal: ICAEW Member
J G Rhodes

KESWORTH
8 Highgate Drive, Telford, TF2 9FE

KESWORTH LTD
8 Highgate Drive, Telford, TF2 9FE

MICHAEL J OWEN AND COMPANY LTD
2 Haygate Drive, Wellington, Telford, TF1 2BY
Tel: 01952 413926
Resident Partners/Directors: ICAEW Members
M J Owen

MORRIS COOK
1 Plough Road, Wellington, Telford, TF1 1ET

PHILLIPS
41 Park Street, Wellington, Telford, TF1 3AE

PHILLIPS LTD
41 Park Street, Wellington, Telford, TF1 3AE

RSM BENTLEY JENNISON ◈
Administration Centre, Unit 1, 3 Hollinswood Court, Stafford Park 1, Telford TF3 3BD
Tel: 01952 231256
Fax: 01952 231187
Email: tony.stockdale@rsmbentleyjennison.com
Website: http://www.rsmbentleyjennison.com
Resident Partners/Directors: ICAEW Members
D G Bentley, C E Copeman, D G Searle, A L C Stockdale, I R Walsh
Registered by the ICAEW to carry out company audit work
Authorised and regulated by the Financial Services Authority for investment business

RSM BENTLEY JENNISON ◈
3 Hollinswood Court, Stafford Park, Telford, TF3 3BD
Tel: 01952 290244
Fax: 01952 290006
Email: dennis.muxworthy@rsmbentleyjennison.com
Website: http://www.rsmbentleyjennison.com
Resident Partners/Directors: ICAEW Members
M W Evans, D Muxworthy
Registered by the ICAEW to carry out company audit work
Authorised and regulated by the Financial Services Authority for investment business

STEPHANIE JAMES
44 Lincoln Hill, Ironbridge, Telford, TF8 7NY

TRANTER LOWE
International House, 6 Market Street, Oakengates, Telford TF2 6EF

TRANTER LOWE (OAKENGATES) LTD
International House, 6 Market Street, Oakengates, Telford TF2 6EF

TENBURY WELLS

CELIA ADAMS ASSOCIATES LTD
Eastham Court, Tenbury Wells, WR15 8NW

DHJH
81 Teme Street, Tenbury Wells, WR15 8AE

DYKE RUSCOE & HAYES LTD ◈
40 Teme St, Tenbury Wells, WR15 8AA
Tel: 01584 810322
Resident Partners/Directors: ICAEW Members
P K Reynolds

E R GROVE & CO
Hunt House Farm, Frith Common, Eardiston, Tenbury Wells WR15 8JY

J.C. GODDARD
The Farm, Eardiston, Tenbury Wells, WR15 8JS

JANE JENNER TAXATION AND ACCOUNTING SERVICES
Redroofs, Berrington Road, Tenbury Wells, WR15 8EN
Tel: 01584 819653
Principal: ICAEW Member
F J Jenner

TENTERDEN

BERRY & CO ◈
24 Ashford Road, Tenterden, TN30 6QU
Tel: 01580 763555
Registered by the ICAEW to carry out company audit work

BUSBYS ◈
3B, Leigh Green Business Park, Appledore Road, Tenterden, TN30 7DE
Tel: 01580 765088
Resident Partners/Directors: ICAEW Members
D J R Meredith

DAVID PAYNE ★
Sportsman Farm, St Michaels, Tenterden, TN30 6SY
Tel: 01233 850980
Resident Partners/Directors: ICAEW Members
D J Payne

GIBBONS MANNINGTON
142 High Street, Tenterden, TN30 6HT

JEREMY MARC ANDREWS
Milroy House, Sayers Lane, Tenterden, TN30 6BW

LIDDIARD & CO ◈
Grange Court Park, Grange Road, St Michaels, Tenterden TN30 6EE
Tel: 01580 765191
Principal: ICAEW Member
S P Liddiard

PHIPPS & CO
82 High Street, Tenterden, TN30 6JG

TETBURY

BERNARD ATKINS LTD
25b Long Street, Tetbury, GL8 8AA

BOATMAN & CO LLP
1 Long Street, Tetbury, GL8 8AA

PHILIP KENDELL ◈
Seaton House, Bagpath, Tetbury, GL8 8YG

TEWKESBURY

AVASSETS LTD
Uplands, Mythe Road, Tewkesbury, GL20 6EA

BENEDICT MACKENZIE
The Grange, Aston-on-Carrant, Tewkesbury, GL20 8HL
Tel: 01684 773799
Resident Partners/Directors: ICAEW Members
V L Neave

CROWTHER BEARD LLP
1a Church Street, Tewkesbury, GL20 5PA

GALLAGHER & CO
Ivydene House, Uckinghall, Tewkesbury, GL20 6ES
Tel: 01684 594755
Principal: ICAEW Member
P R Gallagher

STACEY D CHARLESTON ACA
7 Tug Wilson Close, Northway, Tewkesbury, GL20 8RJ

TIM GILSON
54 Thistle Downs, Northway, Tewkesbury, GL20 8RE

WAUGH HAINES RIGBY ◈
The Old Duke of York, 8 Barton Street, Tewkesbury, GL20 5PP
Tel: 01684 850033
Email: admin@w-h-r.co.uk
Website: http://www.whronline.co.uk
Resident Partners/Directors: ICAEW Members
C Biggs, L W Buchanan, D J Phillips

THAME

CAROL COLINSWOOD & CO
Ground Floor, Dorchester House, 15 Dorchester Place, Thame OX9 2DL

FIZZ ACCOUNTING LTD ◈
31 Ormond Road, Thame, OX9 3XN
Tel: 01844 215682
Resident Partners/Directors: ICAEW Members
G J Lovett

HART NURSE LTD
The Old Coach House, Southern Road, Thame, OX9 2ED

RICHARDSONS
30 Upper High Street, Thame, OX9 3EZ

RICHARDSONS FINANCIAL GROUP LTD
30 Upper High Street, Thame, OX9 3EZ

WELLERS ★
Millweye Court, 73 Southern Road, Thame, OX9 2ED

THAMES DITTON

BIRCH RIDDLE & CO LTD
Pond House, Weston Green, Thames Ditton, KT7 0JX
Tel: 020 8398 3122
Resident Partners/Directors: ICAEW Members
G N Birch, B J Riddle

J.L. WILLIAMS
Apple Tree Cottage, 38 Rushett Close, Thames Ditton, KT7 0UT

MARKS HILLS & CO
52 Warwick Gardens, Thames Ditton, KT7 0RB
Tel: 020 8398 6965
Principal: ICAEW Member
A J Hills

TOMLINSONS ★
2 AC Court, High Street, Thames Ditton, KT7 0SA
Tel: 0870 607 0170

THATCHAM

11TH HOUR ACCOUNTANCY SERVICES LTD
6 Wolsingham Way, Thatcham, RG19 3YW

C.B. HESLOP & CO
1 High Street, Thatcham, RG19 3JG
Tel: 01635 868202
Fax: 01635 871703
Resident Partners/Directors: ICAEW Members
T Allen, S J Coke, C B Heslop, W J Owen
Other Offices: The Old School, 51 Princes Road, Weybridge, KT13 9DA
(Tel: 01932 820612)
Registered by the ICAEW to carry out company audit work

DAVID COX
8 The Burdwood Centre, Station Rd, Thatcham, RG19 4YA

J.M. HANDLEY POTTS
Unit 1, Rivermead, Pipers Way, Thatcham RG19 4EP

P.A. GOULDEN
Beechings, Water Street, Hampstead Norreys, Thatcham RG18 0SB

PAUL D. WELCH
34 Chapel Street, Thatcham, RG18 4QL

RICHARD HOPES LTD
Bell House, Ashford Hill, Thatcham, RG19 8BB

WINTERSTOKE FINANCIAL MANAGEMENT LTD
Unit 1, Rivermead, Pipers Way, Thatcham RG19 4EP

WITCOMBS
Turnfields Gate, Thatcham, RG19 4PT
Tel: 01635 869869
Principal: ICAEW Member
S J Witcomb

THETFORD

GRAHAM J. LODGE & CO
12 Main Road, Brookville, Thetford, IP26 4RB
Tel: 01366 728298
Principal: ICAEW Member
G J Lodge

HAINES WATTS
The Innovation Centre, Croxton Road, Thetford, IP24 1JD
Tel: 01842 768350
Resident Partners/Directors: ICAEW Members
N S Ross

LOVEWELL BLAKE ◈
The Gables, Old Market Street, Thetford, IP24 2EN
Tel: 01842 755032
Fax: 01842 762753
Email: djb@lovewell-blake.co.uk
Website: http://www.lovewell-blake.co.uk
Resident Partners/Directors: ICAEW Members
D J Buller, B J Floringer
General Description: The practice has 21 partners and our other offices are listed under our Norwich entry.

MARTIN & ACOCK ◈
40 High Street, Watton, Thetford, IP25 6AE
Tel: 01953 452077
Website: http://www.martin-acock.com

MIKE HARPER TAX & ACCOUNTANCY SERVICES LTD
58a High Street, Watton, Thetford, IP25 6AH
Tel: 01953 882983
Resident Partners/Directors: ICAEW Members
M A Harper

R.M. MADDERS
4 Melville Road, Croxton, Thetford, IP24 1NG

STACEY & PARTNERS ◈
30 Bridge Street, Thetford, IP24 3AG
Tel: 01284 773400
Website: http://www.staceys.co.uk
Resident Partners/Directors: ICAEW Members
R D Alliban
Registered by the ICAEW to carry out company audit work

continued

STACEY & PARTNERS *cont*
Regulated by the ICAEW for a range of investment business activities

STACEY & PARTNERS LTD
30 Bridge Street, Thetford, IP24 3AG

STUART WRIGHT
79 Churchill Road, Thetford, IP24 2JZ
Tel: 01842 754166
Principal: ICAEW Member
S N H Wright

THIRSK

THE BARKER PARTNERSHIP
Unit A, Thirsk Rural Business Centre, Blakey Lane, Thirsk YO7 3AB

THE BARKER PARTNERSHIP
Bank Chambers, 17 Central Buildings, Market Place, Thirsk YO7 1HD

FORSTER, STOTT & CO
24 Finkle Street, Thirsk, YO7 1DA

GEOFFREY ELLIS & CO
Kirby Grange, Cold Kirby, Thirsk, YO7 2HL

STEAD FLINTOFF & CO ★ ◈
39 Westgate, Thirsk, YO7 1QR
Tel: 01845 526001
Resident Partners/Directors: ICAEW Members
J Cummins, A D Young

THORNTON HEATH

BHARAT SHAH & CO ◈
786 London Road, Thornton Heath, CR7 6JB
Tel: 020 8683 0121
Principal: ICAEW Member
B P M Shah

PK SHAH & CO LTD
60 Fairlands Avenue, Thornton Heath, CR7 6HA

VIRASH BACH & CO
72 Lyndhurst Road, Thornton Heath, CR7 7PW

VIRASH BACH & CO LTD ◈
72 Lyndhurst Road, Thornton Heath, CR7 7PW
Tel: 020 8251 2437
Resident Partners/Directors: ICAEW Members
V Patel

THORNTON-CLEVELEYS

B.N. BEWICK
5 Radway Close, Whiteholme, Thornton-Cleveleys, FY5 3EZ
Tel: 01253 853859
Principal: ICAEW Member
B N Bewick

MA2 ★
5 Crescent East, Thornton-Cleveleys, FY5 3LJ

MICHAEL L TRIPP & CO ◈
29 Nutter Road, Thornton-Cleveleys, FY5 1BQ
Tel: 01253 858600

MICHAEL L. TRIPP & CO LTD
29 Nutter Road, Thornton-Cleveleys, FY5 1BQ

MONTPELIER AUDIT LTD
13 Rossall Road, Thornton-Cleveleys, FY5 1AP

MONTPELIER PROFESSIONAL (FYLDE) LTD
13 Rossall Road, Thornton-Cleveleys, FY5 1AP

MP UK LTD
22 Winston Avenue, Thornton-cleveleys, FY5 2HU

PAUL D. FAULCONBRIDGE
16 Trinity Gardens, Thornton-cleveleys, FY5 2UA
Tel: 01253 827075
Principal: ICAEW Member
P D Faulconbridge

TINTAGEL

CHANTER, BROWNE & CURRY ◈
P O Box 8, Tintagel, PL34 0AW
Tel: 07710 261959
Principal: ICAEW Member
D J Chanter

TIVERTON

APSLEYS
21 Bampton St, Tiverton, EX16 6AA
Tel: 01884 257725
Resident Partners/Directors: ICAEW Members
P A Morrish, D I Wicks

BJCA LTD
Suite 13, Swallow Court, Sampford Peverell, Tiverton EX16 7EJ

ELLAM OXTOBY & PECK LLP ★
Sydeham Farm, Rackenford, Tiverton, EX16 8ER

J.N. WILSON
Grosvenor House, 25 St Peter Street, Tiverton, EX16 6NW
Tel: 01884 252993
Principal: ICAEW Member
J N Wilson

KEY AUDIT (SOUTH WEST) LTD
Key House, Woodward Road, Howden Industrial Estate, Tiverton EX16 5HW

PAUL STEELE
18 Newport Street, Tiverton, EX16 6NL
Tel: 01884 252275

R.A.C. WEST & CO
1 St Peter Street, Tiverton, EX16 6NE

R. FORT
Morgans Bradley, Templeton, Tiverton, EX16 8BJ
Tel: 01884 257309
Principal: ICAEW Member
R Fort

REDDAWAY & CO
30 St Peter Street, Tiverton, EX16 6NR
Tel: 01884 256688
Principal: ICAEW Member
R G Pulsford

ROOKE HOLT LTD
Giffords Farm, Giffords Cross, Bampton, Tiverton EX16 9DR

THOMAS WESTCOTT ★
49 St Peter Street, Tiverton, EX16 6NW
Tel: 01884 252058

WILLIAM WITHERS
Town Farm, Templeton, Tiverton, EX16 8BL

TODMORDEN

BRIAN TAYLOR FCA
4 Lee Lane, Lumbutts, Todmorden, OL14 6HS

BROSNANS
10 Rochdale Road, Todmorden, OL14 5AA

CONNELLY & CO
6 White Hart Fold, Todmorden, OL14 7BD

LATCHFORD CONSULTING
Latchford, Broad Gate, Todmorden, OL14 8DE

R D UTTLEY LTD
Shaw Cottage, Shaw Wood Road, Langfield, Todmorden OL14 6HP

R.D. UTTLEY
Shaw Cottage, Shaw Wood Road, Langfield, Todmorden OL14 6HP

TONBRIDGE

A B M VENTURES LTD
175 High Street, Tonbridge, TN9 1BX

BESPOKES LTD
Hilden Park House, 79 Tonbridge Road, Hildenborough, Tonbridge TN11 9BH
Tel: 01732 838877
Resident Partners/Directors: ICAEW Members
P K Matthews

CANTIUM CONSULTING LTD ◈
162 High Street, Tonbridge, TN9 1BB

CURRIE ACCOUNTANCY LTD
5 Riverside House, River Lawn Road, Tonbridge, TN9 1EP

DG ACCOUNTING & BUSINESS ADMINISTRATION LTD
Orchard House, Three Elm Lane, Golden Green, Tonbridge TN11 0BE

G. WRATTEN & CO
8 Higham Lane, Tonbridge, TN10 4JA
Tel: 01732 351806
Principal: ICAEW Member
G Wratten

GEOFFREY MARCHANT & CO ◈
Rathbond House, High Street, Staplehurst, Tonbridge TN12 0AD
Tel: 01580 890102
Fax: 01580 890106
Email: info@geoffreymarchant.co.uk
Date Established: 1994
Principal: ICAEW Member
G K Marchant
Registered by the ICAEW to carry out company audit work
Regulated by the ICAEW for a range of investment business activities

GILBERT ALLEN & CO
Churchdown Chambers, Bordyke, Tonbridge, TN9 1NR

H.S. KONG & CO
Sovereign Manor, Gover View, Gover Hill, Tonbridge TN11 9SQ

HANAFIN KLEIN
The House, High Street, Brenchley, Tonbridge TN12 7NQ

HATCHE & CO
8 Streamside, Tonbridge, TN10 3PU

IDEN BUSINESS SERVICES LTD Ⓜ
2 Garden Close, Staplehurst, Tonbridge, TN12 0EW

K.J.C. COOK
Cuckoo Cottage, Cuckoo Lane, Tonbridge, TN11 0AG

KERSHEN FAIRFAX
The Wolery, 15 Coldharbour Lane, Hildenborough, Tonbridge TN11 9JT

KERSHEN FAIRFAX LTD
The Wolery, 15 Coldharbour Lane, Hildenborough, Tonbridge TN11 9JT

LINDEYER FRANCIS FERGUSON
North House, 198 High Street, Tonbridge, TN9 1BE
Tel: 01732 360200
Resident Partners/Directors: ICAEW Members
M W Ferguson, J S Francis, P E Reynolds, S Wells

M N JENKS & CO LTD
72 Commercial Road, Paddock Wood, Tonbridge, TN12 6DP
Tel: 01892 836005
Resident Partners/Directors: ICAEW Members
M N Jenks, T Lane

PETER YOUNG
Orchard Cottage, Stanford Lane, Hadlow, Tonbridge TN11 0JP

SANDISON LANG & CO
2 St Mary's Road, Tonbridge, TN9 2LB

SR POOLEY & CO
56 Corner Farm Road, Staplehurst, Tonbridge, TN12 0PS

STEPHEN J. KERRY
90 Hilltop, Tonbridge, TN9 2UP
Tel: 01732 369708
Principal: ICAEW Member
S J Kerry

TREVOR ALDRIDGE
64 Old Hadlow Road, Tonbridge, TN10 4EX
Tel: 01732 773066
Principal: ICAEW Member
T A Aldridge

VANTIS BUSINESS RECOVERY SERVICES
Judd House, East Street, Tonbridge, TN9 1HG
Tel: 01732 378 680
Website: http://www.vantisplc.com/businessrecovery
Individual(s) licensed for insolvency work by another RPB

SPECIALISATIONS – BUSINESS RECOVERY & INSOLVENCY
Bankruptcies
Corporate Recovery
Liquidations

TORPOINT

C.E. TAYLOR ◈
Dolphin Cottage, Heavitree Road, Kingsand, Torpoint PL10 1NP
Tel: 01752 823860
Email: cetaylorfca@msn.com
Principal: ICAEW Member
C E Taylor

SPECIALISATIONS – FORENSIC ACCOUNTING
Forensic Accounting

SPECIALISATIONS – TAXATION
Back Duty

POWELL & CO
6 Fore Street, Torpoint, PL11 2AA

TORQUAY

ANDREW PRICE & CO ◈
8 Vaughan Parade, Torquay, TQ2 5EG
Tel: 01803 296678
Principal: ICAEW Member
A D Price

BISHOP FLEMING ◈
50 The Terrace, Torquay, TQ1 1DD
Tel: 01803 291 100
Website: http://www.bishopfleming.co.uk
Resident Partners/Directors: ICAEW Members
G L Howe, J A O'Sullivan
Resident Partners (Non-ICAEW Members):
T M Godfrey

CC ACCOUNTANTS LTD ◈
Business Suite 5, 3rd Floor, Castle Circus House, 136 Union Street, Torquay TQ2 5QG
Tel: 01803 215550
Resident Partners/Directors: ICAEW Members
I Bradshaw

CHECK BOOK LTD
139 St Marychurch Road, Torquay, TQ1 3HW

CRAMPTONS
Delgrae House, 25A St Matthews Road, Chelston, Torquay TQ2 6JA
Tel: 01803 690047
Principal: ICAEW Member
J R Crampton

CREW & HAMMOND ★
13 Park Hill Road, Torquay, TQ1 2AL

DAVID OSMAN
20 Rougemont Avenue, Torquay, TQ2 7JP
Tel: 01803 612376
Principal: ICAEW Member
D R Osman

FRANCIS CLARK ◈
58 The Terrace, Torquay, TQ1 1DE
Tel: 01803 400000
Website: http://www.francisclark.co.uk
Resident Partners/Directors: ICAEW Members
L M Burnett, P Cliff, R J Hussey, J N Rowe
Authorised and regulated by the Financial Services Authority for investment business
General Description: Largest independent firm in the South West, with particular strengths in taxation, VAT, corporate finance, financial planning, forensic accounting, IT and insolvency.

HAWES RICHARDS & CO
6-7 Victoria Parade, Torquay, TQ1 2AZ
Tel: 01803 293773
Principal: ICAEW Member
A N Lear

JOHN ROUX
25 Old Woods Hill, Torquay, TQ2 7NR

KEITH POLLARD
Provincial House, 1 Strand, Torquay, TQ1 2AA
Tel: 01803 211187
Principal: ICAEW Member
K R Pollard

MG ASSOCIATES LTD ◈
7a Ilsham Road, Torquay, TQ1 2JG
Tel: 01803 297591
Email: mga.ltd1@btinternet.com

NEIL WILSON & CO ◈
42A Walnut Road, Chelston, Torquay, TQ2 6HS
Tel: 01803 607721
Principal: ICAEW Member
N D F Wilson

PEPLOWS ◈
Alderbourne, Greenway Road, St Marychurch, Torquay TQ1 4NJ
Tel: 01803 316144
Email: enquiries@peplows.co.uk
Website: http://www.peplows.co.uk
Resident Partners/Directors: ICAEW Members
M A Atkinson
Other Offices: Newton Abbot, Exeter
Registered by the ICAEW to carry out company audit work
Regulated by the ICAEW for a range of investment business activities

ROGER M. PORTEOUS
10 Windermere Road, Babbacombe, Torquay, TQ1 3RF

SPENCE ROBERT PETHICK
The Old Customs House, Torwood Gardens Rd, Torquay, TQ1 1EG

SR POOLEY & CO
8 The Woods, Higher Lincombe Road, Torquay, TQ1 2HS

TAYLOR & CO
20 Edenhurst Court, Parkhill Road, Torquay, TQ1 2DD
Tel: 01803 215126
Principal: ICAEW Member
H C E Downing

THOMAS WESTCOTT ★
Petitor House, Nicholson Road, Torquay, TQ2 7TD
Tel: 01803 618910
Resident Partners/Directors: ICAEW Members
C H Park, S R Smith

TOTNES

DARNELLS
30 Fore Street, Totnes, TQ9 5RP

GARTH PEDLER & CO
Hay Hill, Totnes, TQ9 5LH

IMPACT TOTNES LTD
2 Warland, Totnes, TQ9 5EL
Tel: 01803 862925
Resident Partners/Directors: ICAEW Members
B K Nicoll

W R FROST & CO
Riversdale, Ashburton Road, Totnes, TQ9 5JU
Tel: 01803 862021

W R FROST & CO LTD
Riversdale, Ashburton Road, Totnes, TQ9 5JU
Tel: 01803 862021
Resident Partners/Directors: ICAEW Members
M J Marriott, P D Vooght

TOWCESTER

C E D ACCOUNTANCY SERVICES LTD ◈
Unit 1, Lucas Bridge Business Park, 1 Old Greens Norton Road, Towcester NN12 8AX

J C TATE
The Oaks, 3 Fosters Booth Road, Pattishall, Towcester NN12 8JU

NEUHOFF & CO
Claydons Barns, 11 Towcester Road, Whittlebury, Towcester NN12 8XU

TRING

C.R. STEVENS
57 Station Road, Tring, HP23 5NW

HOWARD SMITH
Finches, Wigginton Bottom, Tring, HP23 6HW

LANGFORD & CO
93 Western Road, Tring, HP23 4BN

N WHITE & CO
5 Catherine Cottages, Wigginton Bottom, Wigginton, Tring HP23 6HP
Tel: 01442 891813
Principal: ICAEW Member
N White

RMCA LTD ◈
The Counting House, 9 High Street, Tring, HP23 5TE
Tel: 01442 891919
Website: http://www.rm-ca.co.uk
Resident Partners/Directors: ICAEW Members
R Masters

SARAH BUTTARS & CO
Brensham Cottage, Malting Lane, Aldbury, Tring HP23 5RH
Tel: 01442 851962
Principal: ICAEW Member
S L Buttars

SUE WICKHAM
30 Gwynne Close, Tring, HP23 5EN
Tel: 01442 827351
Principal: ICAEW Member
S C Wickham

TROWBRIDGE

I. STOKES & CO
Oxenleaze Farm, 88 Keevil, Trowbridge, BA14 6NH

JAMES TRIMBY
Woodruffs, Wingfield, Trowbridge, BA14 9LE

JOHN B PHEBY
The Grey House, Rood Ashton Park, West Ashton, Trowbridge BA14 6AT

LIZ NOBLE FCA CTA
Yew Cottage, 76 Hill Street, Hilperton, Trowbridge BA14 7RS
Tel: 01225 768030
Principal: ICAEW Member
E Noble

MARGARET MORGAN
60A Church Lane, North Bradley, Trowbridge, BA14 0TA

MONAHANS ◈
Clarks Mill, Stallard Street, Trowbridge, BA14 8HH
Tel: 01225 785520
Resident Partners/Directors: ICAEW Members
L Boss, H M Hilliard, R M Snelus

MUNRO
St Georges Terrace, 31 Stallard Street, Trowbridge, BA14 9AA
Tel: 01225 774742
Resident Partners/Directors: ICAEW Members
D A Oakensen

P.A. TOLLEY
51 Victoria Road, Trowbridge, BA14 7LD

PEARSON MAY
5 Wicker Hill, Trowbridge, BA14 8JS

S FOSTER (BOA) LTD
The Courtyard, 33 Duke Street, Trowbridge, BA14 8EA

STEPHEN FOSTER
Blomfield & Co, The Courtyard, 33 Duke Street, Trowbridge BA14 8EA

THOMAS AND CO
11a Silver Street, Trowbridge, BA14 8AA

TRURO

A J SOLWAY LTD
37 Bosvean Road, Shortlanesend, Truro, TR4 9DX
Tel: 07773 521089
Resident Partners/Directors: ICAEW Members
A J Solway

BALME KITCHEN AND PEARCE LTD
25 Lemon Street, Truro, TR1 2LS
Tel: 01872 321555
Resident Partners/Directors: ICAEW Members
A Gessey

BISHOP FLEMING ◈
Chy Nyverow, Newham Road, Truro, TR1 2DP
Tel: 01872 275651
Website: http://www.bishopfleming.co.uk
Resident Partners/Directors: ICAEW Members
I J Fraser, A Oliver

C MICKLEWRIGHT & CO
High Sheriff's House, Trenowth, Grampound Road, Truro TR2 4EH
Tel: 01726 884374
Principal: ICAEW Member
C M Micklewright

COLLINGS & CO
Treen, Perranwell, Goonhavern, Truro TR4 9PD
Tel: 01872 571233
Principal: ICAEW Member
P N Collings

GREG NELSON LTD
The Anchorage, Malpas Village, Truro, TR1 1SN
Tel: 01872 271609
Resident Partners/Directors: ICAEW Members
G C Nelson

KELSALL STEELE LTD
Woodlands Court, Truro Business Park, Truro, TR4 9NH
Tel: 01872 271655
Fax: 01872 277206
Email: enquiries@kelsallsteele.co.uk
Website: http://www.kelsallsteele.co.uk
Resident Partners/Directors: ICAEW Members
I R Forbes, M D Hutchinson, B B Pooley
Resident Partners (Non-ICAEW Members):
L N Trathen
Other Offices:20 Chapel Street, Camborne, Cornwall TR14 8ED
Registered by the ICAEW to carry out company audit work
Authorised and regulated by the Financial Services Authority for investment business

LANG BENNETTS ◈
The Old Carriage Works, Moresk Road, Truro, TR1 1DG
Tel: 01872 272047
Website: http://www.lang-bennetts.co.uk
Resident Partners/Directors: ICAEW Members
J S Mashen, I D Moores, C R E Truscott
Registered by the ICAEW to carry out company audit work
Regulated by the ICAEW for a range of investment business activities

PEARCE WILLS
1 Riverside House, Heron Way, Truro, TR1 2XN

PETER WILLSON
Bowood, The Ropewalk, Penpol, Point, Truro TR3 6NS
Tel: 01872 865224
Principal: ICAEW Member
P E Willson

POOLEYS ◈
45 Lemon Street, Truro, TR1 2NS
Tel: 01872 276760
Website: http://www.pooleysaccountants.co.uk
Principal: ICAEW Member
D H Pooley

INVESTOR IN PEOPLE

RICHARD J. SMITH & CO ★
Norfolk House, 16 Lemon Street, Truro, TR1 2LS
Tel: 01872 261132
Fax: 01872 261134
Email: info@richardjsmith.com
Non-resident Partners (ICAEW Members):
G R Frampton, H M Adam

SPECIALISATIONS – BUSINESS RECOVERY & INSOLVENCY
Bankruptcies
Corporate Recovery
Liquidations

SPECIALISATIONS – FORENSIC ACCOUNTING
Expert Witnesses in Litigation
Forensic Accounting

General Description: Insolvency and forensic accounting specialists.

ROBINSON REED LAYTON ◈
Peat House, Newham Road, Truro, TR1 2DP
Tel: 01872 276116
Fax: 01872 222172
Email: post@rrl-truro.co.uk
Website: http://www.rrl-truro.co.uk
Date Established: 1995
Resident Partners/Directors: ICAEW Members
G D Boulton, S Gainey, T P Reed, R J A Robinson
Resident Partners (Non-ICAEW Members):
J Bailey
Registered by the ICAEW to carry out company audit work
Regulated by the ICAEW for a range of investment business activities
See display advertisement near this entry.

S.J. SIMPSON ◈
Anchor & Hope Cottage, 1 Cove Hill, Perranarworthal, Truro TR3 7QQ
Tel: 01872 870107
Principal: ICAEW Member
S J Simpson

WINTER RULE ◈
Lowin House, Tregolls Road, Truro, TR1 2NA
Tel: 01872 276477
Website: http://www.winterrule.co.uk
Resident Partners/Directors: ICAEW Members
A G Allen, L M Bennett, R A Brownscombe, R R Cowie, J L Endacott, J P Mitchell, P K Penneycard
Other Offices: Newquay
Registered by the ICAEW to carry out company audit work

TUNBRIDGE WELLS

A.G. BARNES & CO
147 Forest Road, Tunbridge Wells, TN2 5EX
Tel: 01892 513598
Principal: ICAEW Member
A G B Barnes

A.H.P. BARTLETT & CO
The Mill House, Speldhurst, Tunbridge Wells, TN3 0NE
Tel: 01892 861400
Principal: ICAEW Member
A H P Bartlett

A.J. EACERSALL & CO
Cutthorn, Parsonage Lane, Lamberhurst, Tunbridge Wells TN3 8DR
Tel: 01892 890861
Principal: ICAEW Member
B L Wilkes

ACE ASSOCIATES
33 London Road, Southborough, Tunbridge Wells, TN4 0PB
Tel: 01892 539267
Principal: ICAEW Member
P H Conradi

AGB SERVICES LTD
147 Forest Road, Tunbridge Wells, TN2 5EX
Tel: 01892 513598
Resident Partners/Directors: ICAEW Members
A G B Barnes

AIMS - JONATHAN LYNN
Coach House, Warren House, Eridge Green, Tunbridge Wells TN3 9JR

ALAN CHARLES ASSOCIATES ◈
Abacus House, 19 Manor Close, Tunbridge Wells, TN4 8YB

ALLENDALE HARVEY & CO ◈
33 London Road, Southborough, Tunbridge Wells, TN4 0PB
Tel: 01592 539267

APT
44 The Pantiles, Tunbridge Wells, TN2 5TN

APT PARTNERSHIP LLP
44 The Pantiles, Tunbridge Wells, TN2 5TN

AUKER HUTTON ◈
The Stables, Little Coldharbour Farm, Tong Lane, Lamberhurst, Tunbridge Wells TN3 8AD
Tel: 01892 891902
Website: http://www.aukerhutton.co.uk
Date Established: 1971
Principal: ICAEW Member
D A Kirk
Registered by the ICAEW to carry out company audit work

SPECIALISATIONS – BUSINESS & GENERAL ADVICE
Company Formation

SPECIALISATIONS – FINANCIAL REPORTING
Limited Company Accounts
Partnership/Sole Trader Accounts

SPECIALISATIONS – TAXATION
Self Assessment Advice

B J LEWIS & CO LTD ◈
134 London Road, Southborough, Tunbridge Wells, TN4 0PL
Tel: 01892 513515
Email: info@lewisandco.biz
Website: http://www.lewisandco.biz
Resident Partners/Directors: ICAEW Members
B J Lewis
General Description: Personal/ Business Tax & Accounts.

BAKER TILLY
Hanover House, 18 Mount Ephraim Road, Tunbridge Wells, TN1 1ED
Tel: 01892 511944
Resident Partners/Directors: ICAEW Members
W B Owen, G G Purdy, N P Sladden

BAKER TILLY
Hanover House, 18 Mount Ephraim Road, Tunbridge Wells, TN1 1ED

BAKER TILLY TAX AND ADVISORY SERVICES LLP
Hanover House, 18 Mount Ephraim Road, Tunbridge Wells, TN1 1ED
Tel: 01892 511944
Resident Partners/Directors: ICAEW Members
W B Owen, G G Purdy, N P Sladden
Resident Partners (Non-ICAEW Members):
P W Hodge

BALANCED ACCOUNTING
Unit J, The Brewery, Bells Yew Green, Tunbridge Wells TN3 9BD
Tel: 0845 833 6250

BALANCED ACCOUNTING LLP
Unit J, The Brewery, Bells Yew Green, Tunbridge Wells TN3 9BD
Tel: 0845 833 6250
Resident Partners/Directors: ICAEW Members
C R Bendall, H A Wells

BENEDICT MACKENZIE
2nd Floor, Frant House, Coach & Horses Passage, Tunbridge Wells TN2 5TE

BREBNERS
55 Calverley Road, Tunbridge Wells, TN1 2TU

BRIDGE BUSINESS RECOVERY LLP
6 Hanover Road, Tunbridge Wells, TN1 1EY
Tel: 01892 615396
Resident Partners/Directors: ICAEW Members
J P Bradney

BUCKLAND STEADMAN & ROBERTS ◈
7 Linden Close, Tunbridge Wells, TN4 8HH

CECIL KIDBY & CO
76 Farmcombe Road, Tunbridge Wells, TN2 5DH
Tel: 01892 529794
Principal: ICAEW Member
C E Kidby

CHARCROFT BAKER
Prospect House, 11-13 Lonsdale Gardens, Tunbridge Wells, TN1 1NU

CHRIS STRAW
1 Penshurst Road, Speldhurst, Tunbridge Wells, TN3 0PB

CHRISTOPHER C JENKINS & CO
Birchden Corner, Station Road, Groombridge, Tunbridge Wells TN3 9NG

CONRADI MORRISON & CO ◈
33 London Road, Southborough, Tunbridge Wells, TN4 0PB
Tel: 01892 539267
Resident Partners/Directors: ICAEW Members
J Bowen, P H Conradi

THE COUNTING HOUSE PARTNERSHIP LLP
6 Hanover Road, Tunbridge Wells, TN1 1EY
Tel: 01892 500070
Resident Partners/Directors: ICAEW Members
J M G Bradney, J P Bradney, M J Worrall

CREASEYS
12 Lonsdale Gardens, Tunbridge Wells, TN1 1PA
Tel: 01892 546546
Fax: 01892 511232
Email: partners@creaseys.co.uk
DX: 3959 TUNBRIDGE WELLS 1
Website: http://www.creaseys.co.uk
Date Established: 1868
Training Contracts Available.
Resident Partners (Non-ICAEW Members):
E J Roberts, T Page
Overseas Offices: Members of International Group of Accounting Firms
Registered by the ICAEW to carry out company audit work
Regulated by the ICAEW for a range of investment business activities

SPECIALISATIONS – AUDIT & ASSURANCE
Audit — Private Company

SPECIALISATIONS – BUSINESS & GENERAL ADVICE
Europe
Management Advice to Business
Overseas Countries

SPECIALISATIONS – SECTOR
Charities
Property Investment
Solicitors

SPECIALISATIONS – TAXATION
Foreign Nationals in the UK
Offshore Companies
UK Companies Overseas
UK Nationals Overseas
UK Subsidiaries of Overseas Multinationals

continued

CREASEYS *cont*
General Description: Winners of the Butterworths Tolley Award as best tax team in a small to medium sized firm in UK in 2001 and runners up in 2002.
Languages Spoken:
French, German, Polish

CREASEYS IT CONSULTING
12 Lonsdale Gardens, Tunbridge Wells, TN1 1PA

CREASEYS LLP
12 Lonsdale Gardens, Tunbridge Wells, TN1 1PA

CREASEYS TAX CONSULTING
12 Lonsdale Gardens, Tunbridge Wells, TN1 1PA
Tel: 01892 546546

DEEKS EVANS
3 Boyne Park, Tunbridge Wells, TN4 8EN
Tel: 01892 526417
Resident Partners/Directors: ICAEW Members
P J Delaney, J M Fisher, P E Garside, R J Young
Resident Partners (Non-ICAEW Members):
K Braddel, S J Moger

DEREK W MILES
6 Wybourne Rise, Tunbridge Wells, TN2 5JG

ETM CONSULTING LTD
The Old Stables, Hendal Farm, Groombridge, Tunbridge Wells TN3 9NU

FOOT DAVSON
17 Church Road, Tunbridge Wells, TN1 1LG
Tel: 01892 774774
Email: fd@footdavson.co.uk
Website: http://www.footdavson.co.uk
Resident Partners/Directors: ICAEW Members
T T Clay, R W D Foot
Registered by the ICAEW to carry out company audit work
SPECIALISATIONS – AUDIT & ASSURANCE
Audit — Private Company
SPECIALISATIONS – SECTOR
Charities

G. REEVES
11 Percy Terrace, Beltring Road, Tunbridge Wells, TN4 9RH

GOWER-SMITH AND CO
Grosvenor Lodge, 72 Grosvenor Road, Tunbridge Wells, TN1 2AZ
Tel: 01892 522551
Principal: ICAEW Member
N M Gower-Smith

HENDRAWS LTD
23 Blatchington Road, Tunbridge Wells, TN2 5EG
Tel: 01892 531367
Resident Partners/Directors: ICAEW Members
Ian D Morgan

HORWATH CLARK WHITEHILL LLP ◈
Jaeger House, 5 Clanricarde Gardens, Tunbridge Wells, TN1 1PE
Tel: 01892 700200
Email: kent@horwath.co.uk
Website: http://www.horwathcw.co.uk
Training Contracts Available.
Resident Partners/Directors: ICAEW Members
M J Anderson
Registered by the ICAEW to carry out company audit work

JAMES RICHARDSON
Sirama, Little Boundes Close, Tunbridge Wells, TN4 0RS

LAMEY & CO
Ridge Cottage, Speldhurst, Tunbridge Wells, TN3 0LE

LOCK & CO
Silverwood, Withyham Rd, Groombridge, Tunbridge Wells TN3 9QR

MDJORDAN
Timaru, Corseley Road, Groombridge, Tunbridge Wells TN3 9SG

MDJORDAN LTD ◈
Unit 2, Birchden Farm, Broadwater Forest Lane, Groombridge, Tunbridge Wells TN3 9NR
Tel: 01892 864425
Resident Partners/Directors: ICAEW Members
M D Jordan

META CORPORATE FINANCE LTD ◈
Hop House, Lower Green Road, Pembury, Tunbridge Wells TN2 4HS
Tel: 01892 822228
Website: http://www.metacf.co.uk
Resident Partners/Directors: ICAEW Members
P M Counsell, M D Ledger-Beadell
Regulated by the ICAEW for a range of investment business activities

NORMAN COX AND ASHBY
Grosvenor Lodge, 72 Grosvenor Road, Tunbridge Wells, TN1 2AZ
Tel: 01892 522551
Email: chartac@nca72.co.uk
Resident Partners/Directors: ICAEW Members
N M Gower-Smith
Resident Partners (Non-ICAEW Members):
N J Russ
Registered by the ICAEW to carry out company audit work

PERRYS
32-34 St Johns Road, Tunbridge Wells, TN4 9NT

QED TAX CONSULTING
4 Clanricarde Gardens, Tunbridge Wells, TN1 1PE
Tel: 01892 530200

R.C.H. STANLEY
Hoth Framhouse, Danegate, Eridge Green, Tunbridge Wells TN3 9HU

R J M BANBURY
44 Bounds Oak Way, Tunbridge Wells, TN4 0TN
Tel: 01892 531944
Principal: ICAEW Member
R J M Banbury

R.L. HINE
72 Yew Tree Road, Southborough, Tunbridge Wells, TN4 0BN

ROCKWELLS
17 Church Road, Tunbridge Wells, TN1 1LG

ROCKWELLS LTD
17 Church Road, Tunbridge Wells, TN1 1LG

SHAIKH & CO ◈
21 Decimus Park, Tunbridge Wells, TN2 3GP
Tel: 01892 552696

SHARNOCK & CO
First Floor, 8B Lonsdale Gardens, Tunbridge Wells, TN1 1NU

SYNERGEE LTD
2nd Floor, 8 Lonsdale Gardens, Tunbridge Wells, TN1 1NU

T W TAX SERVICES LTD
3 Clanricarde Gardens, Tunbridge Wells, TN1 1HQ

TIM HARRIS
6 Ferndale Point, Ferndale, Tunbridge Wells, TN2 3RN

WAIGHT & CO LTD
8 Lonsdale Gardens, Tunbridge Wells, TN1 1NU

WELLS ASSOCIATES
10 Lonsdale Gardens, Tunbridge Wells, TN1 1NU
Tel: 01892 507280

WELLS PROFESSIONAL PARTNERSHIP LLP
10 Lonsdale Gardens, Tunbridge Wells, TN1 1NU

WYLIE & CO
59 Birling Road, Tunbridge Wells, TN2 5LZ

TWICKENHAM

A.G. ANTIPPA
17 Copthall Gardens, Twickenham, TW1 4HH

ANNA CATHERINE REICHWALD
239 Richmond Road, Twickenham, TW1 2NN

ANTIPPA & CO LTD
17 Copthall Gardens, Twickenham, TW1 4HH

BHATIA, SONNADARA & CO ★
Tower House, 17 Tower Road, Strawberry Hill, Twickenham TW1 4PD

CHL
122a Nelson Road, Twickenham, TW2 7AY

CHRISTOPHER HARDEN LTD
122a Nelson Road, Twickenham, TW2 7AY
Tel: 020 8893 3399
Email: chris@chl-online.com
Resident Partners/Directors: ICAEW Members
C P Harden
Registered by the ICAEW to carry out company audit work
Regulated by the ICAEW for a range of investment business activities

COLLARD ASSOCIATES LTD
26 Orleans Road, Twickenham, TW1 3BL
Tel: 020 88914075
Resident Partners/Directors: ICAEW Members
J G Collard

F.F. LEACH & CO
Kestrel House, 111 Heath Road, Twickenham, TW1 4AH

HORSCROFT TURNER BYRNE & CO
78 The Green, Twickenham, TW2 5AG
Tel: 020 8893 8909
Principal: ICAEW Member
J R Byrne

IAN ROBINSON ◈
Electroline House, 15 Lion Road, Twickenham, TW1 4JH
Tel: 020 8892 9292
Principal: ICAEW Member
I Robinson

J.R. ALLSOP
32 Bryanston Avenue, Whitton, Twickenham, TW2 6HP
Tel: 020 8894 7025
Principal: ICAEW Member
J R Allsop

KHANS
Bishop House, 28 Second Cross Road, Twickenham, TW2 5RF

LESLEY PASRICHA
8 Blanchard House, 28 Clevedon House, Twickenham, TW1 2TD
Tel: 020 8607 9592
Principal: ICAEW Member
L A Pasricha

MALLARD BUSINESS SOLUTIONS ◈
20a London Road, Twickenham, TW1 3RR
Tel: 020 8892 0985
Principal: ICAEW Member
J S Fletcher

MICHAEL F.G. COPE
21 Godfrey Avenue, Whitton, Twickenham, TW2 7PE

NIMBUS ASSOCIATES LTD
PO Box 388, Twickenham, TW1 9EQ

STEPHEN WAXMAN & CO
Canada House, 29 Hampton Road, Twickenham, TW2 5QE
Tel: 020 8755 1523
Principal: ICAEW Member
S A Waxman

TATE & CO
30 Rugby Road, Office Unit 13, Twickenham, TW1 1DG

UCKFIELD

ALAN A.M. ROBINSON
New Glenmore, Sliders Lane, Furners Green, Uckfield TN22 3RU
Tel: 01825 790783
Principal: ICAEW Member
A A M Robinson

ANDREA LAW
Sandrock Farmhouse, Limes Lane, Buxted, Uckfield TN22 4PE
Tel: 01825 733543
Principal: ICAEW Member
A L Law

ARMIDA LTD ◈
Bell Walk House, High Street, Uckfield, TN22 5DQ
Tel: 01825 765077
Training Contracts Available.
Resident Partners/Directors: ICAEW Members
T Maton, B R Stevens
Resident Partners (Non-ICAEW Members):
H Toole

ARMIDA BUSINESS RECOVERY LLP
Bell Walk House, Bell Walk, Uckfield, TN22 5DQ

DIXON & CO
Bird in Eye Farm, Bird in Eye Hill, Framfield, Uckfield TN22 5HA
Tel: 01273 480698
Principal: ICAEW Member
R Dixon

HUNOT & CO LTD
The Gate House, Underhill, Maresfield, Uckfield TN22 3AX

MAITLAND LTD
Office C, Maple Barn, Buckham Hill, Uckfield TN22 5XZ
Tel: 01825 748308
Fax: 01825 748307
Email: info@maitlandcharteredaccountants.co.uk
Website: http://www.maitlandcharteredaccountants.co.uk
Mobile: 07770 763775
Resident Partners/Directors: ICAEW Members
A R C Maitland
Registered by the ICAEW to carry out company audit work
SPECIALISATIONS – IT
Computer Consultants

MICHAEL E MASON FCA
PO Box 268, Uckfield, TN22 9DE

SIMMONS GAINSFORD LLP ◈
52 New Town, Uckfield, TN22 5DE
Tel: 01825 746888
Email: solutions@simmonsgainsford.co.uk
Website: http://www.simmonsgainsford.co.uk
Resident Partners/Directors: ICAEW Members
C G Stebbing
Non-resident Partners (ICAEW Members):
M S Pizer, S M Strauss
Other Offices: Cavendish Square, London W1
Registered by the ICAEW to carry out company audit work
Regulated by the ICAEW for a range of investment business activities

SWINDELLS & GENTRY ◈
New Olives, High Street, Uckfield, TN22 1QE
Tel: 01825 763366
Fax: 01825 768664
Email: uckfield@swindellsandgentry.co.uk
Website: http://www.swindellsandgentry.co.uk
Resident Partners/Directors: ICAEW Members
P J Gale, A Hussey, J Sweeney
Other Offices: Seaford (Tel: 01323 892549)
Registered by the ICAEW to carry out company audit work
Regulated by the ICAEW for a range of investment business activities
General Description: Long established practice providing a personal service specialising in private client and business tax and estate planning, incorporated and unincorporated businesses and start-ups, trust administration.
Languages Spoken:
French

WITTICH & CO LTD
Lake House, Rocks Lane, High Hurstwood, Uckfield TN22 4BL

WORMALD ACCOUNTANTS
5 Field End, Maresfield, Uckfield, TN22 2DJ

ZXCV 27 LTD
1 Naseby Cottages, Fletching, Uckfield, TN22 3TB

ULVERSTON

A.B. MERCER
Broad Dale, Pennington Lane, Ulverston, LA12 7SE
Tel: 01229 586074
Principal: ICAEW Member
A B Mercer

J F HORNBY & CO ◈
The Tower, Daltongate Business Centre, Daltongate, Ulverston LA12 7AJ
Tel: 01229 588077
Fax: 01229 588061
Email: jfh@jfhornby.com
Website: http://www.jfhornby.com
Date Established: 1994
Principal: ICAEW Member
J.F. Hornby
Regulated by the ICAEW for a range of investment business activities

ORWIN OLIVER
24 King Street, Ulverston, LA12 7DZ

ORWIN OLIVER LTD
24 King Street, Ulverston, LA12 7DZ

R.F. MILLER & CO
Bellevue, Princes Street, Ulverston, LA12 7NB
Tel: 01229 582149
Resident Partners/Directors: ICAEW Members
T A Crossley

UPMINSTER

AFT
22 Laburnham Gardens, Upminster, RM14 1HU

ALAN F. TRINDER
22 Laburnham Gardens, Upminster, RM14 1HU

J.P.B. HARRIS & CO
54 St Marys Lane, Upminster, RM14 2QP

J.P.B. HARRIS & CO LTD
Harmile House, 54 St Marys Lane, Upminster, RM14 2QT

KOTEN & CO ◈
Suite 7, Essex House, Station Road, Upminster RM14 2SJ
Tel: 01708 228324
Principal: ICAEW Member
B Koten

MICHAEL SONN & CO
140 Hall Lane, Upminster, RM14 1AL

R C PENFOLD
238 Corbets Tey Road, Upminster, RM14 2BL

UPMINSTER LTD ◈
1 Engayne Gardens, Upminster, RM14 1UY

UTTOXETER

GORDON MARJORAM
Glan Aber, The Square, Marchington, Uttoxeter ST14 8LF

GREENHALGH BUSINESS SERVICES LTD
40 Carter Street, Uttoxeter, ST14 8EU
Tel: 01889 567217
Fax: 01889 567570
Email: uttoxeter@greenhalghco.net
Website: http://www.greenhalghco.net
Non-resident Partners (ICAEW Members):
C Peacock, P Handley, M Henshaw
Resident Partners (Non-ICAEW Members):
G Brockway
Non-resident Partners (Non-ICAEW Members):
N Shaw
Other Offices: Nottingham, Burton upon Trent
Registered by the ICAEW to carry out company audit work

HARDING HIGGINS
36 Church Street, Uttoxeter, ST14 8AD

HOWSONS ◈
14 High Street, Uttoxeter, ST14 7HT
Tel: 01889 563550
Resident Partners/Directors: ICAEW Members
R Sunderland
Other Offices: Alsager, Leek, Market Drayton, Stoke-On-Trent, Newport, Burslem

JOHN W J WRIGHT FCA
13 Market Place, Uttoxeter, ST14 8HY

RICE & CO
14A Market Place, Uttoxeter, ST14 8HP

TAX ASSURED LTD
Threefields, Church Lane, Marchington, Uttoxeter ST14 8LJ
Tel: 01283 820270
Resident Partners/Directors: ICAEW Members
R J Wynniatt-Husey

UXBRIDGE

ALAN W HOOPER FCA CTA
21 Hartshill Close, Hillingdon, Uxbridge, UB10 9LH
Tel: 01895 257507
Principal: ICAEW Member
A W Hooper

ASH WILSON
Redmead House, Uxbridge Road, Hillingdon, Uxbridge UB10 0LT

ASH WILSON LTD
Redmead House, Uxbridge Road, Hillingdon, Uxbridge UB10 0LT

ASHMANS ◈
Zone G, Salamander Quay West, Park Lane, Harefield, Uxbridge UB9 6NZ
Tel: 01895 822551
Principal: ICAEW Member
A M Sodha

B.S. UPPAL & CO
31 Oak Avenue, Ickenham, Uxbridge, UB10 8LR

BARNES ROFFE LLP
3 Brook Business Centre, Cowley Mill Road, Cowley, Uxbridge UB8 2FX
Tel: 01895 256423
Resident Partners/Directors: ICAEW Members
S M Davis, C H Green, M A Parkinson

CHASEBLOCK LTD
Panstar House, 13 Bellamy Close, Ickenham, Uxbridge UB10 8SJ

CHHAYA HARE WILSON LTD
Redmead House, Uxbridge Road, Hillingdon Heath, Uxbridge UB10 0LT

DEREK R JAMES & CO
10 Hercies Road, Hillingdon, Uxbridge, UB10 9NA

DMC ACCOUNTING
Olympic House, 63 Wallingford Road, Uxbridge, UB8 2RW

DPN CONSULTING SERVICES LTD
5 Gravel Hill, Uxbridge, UB8 1PB

HENRY GUY
20 Belmont Close, Uxbridge, UB8 1RF

IAN MURRAY & CO
18 Poplar Road, New Denham, Uxbridge, UB9 4AW

K.J. DALTON
Long Lane Farm, Ickenham, Uxbridge, UB10 8QT

KAMBOJ ASSOCIATES LTD
29 New Broadway, Uxbridge, UB10 0LL
Tel: 01895 273428
Resident Partners/Directors: ICAEW Members
H P Kamboj

L + A BUSINESS RECOVERY LLP
3 Beasleys Yard, 126 High Street, Uxbridge, UB8 1JT
Tel: 01895 819460
Fax: 01895 520096
Email: info@labusinessrecovery.com
Website: http://www.labusinessrecovery.com
Date Established: 2008
Resident Partners/Directors: ICAEW Members
P M Levy
Individual(s) licensed for insolvency work by the ICAEW

SPECIALISATIONS – BUSINESS RECOVERY & INSOLVENCY

Bankruptcies
Corporate Recovery
Liquidations
Reorganisations and Company Reconstructions

General Description: Founded by Peter Levy, having been a senior partner in a firm of chartered accountants founded in 1964, he is a member of the Chartered Institute of Taxation and a member of R3 as well as being a licensed insolvency practitioner.
Languages Spoken:
Welsh, Spanish, German, French

M.J. HARVEY & CO
The Old Mill House, Willow Avenue, New Denham, Uxbridge UB9 4AF

M.W. CONSULTANCY SERVICES
8 James Martin Close, Denham, Uxbridge, UB9 5NN

PINKNEY KEITH GIBBS
35 Belmont Rd, Uxbridge, UB8 1RH
Tel: 01895 236335
Fax: 01895 257641
Email: advisors@pkgaccountants.co.uk
Website: http://www.pkgaccountants.co.uk
Resident Partners/Directors: ICAEW Members
G Crane, M Forsythe, D T French, A Morris
Resident Partners (Non-ICAEW Members):
C R Tribe
Registered by the ICAEW to carry out company audit work

SPECIALISATIONS – AUDIT & ASSURANCE

Audit

SPECIALISATIONS – BUSINESS & GENERAL ADVICE

Book-keeping
Company Secretarial Service

SPECIALISATIONS – FINANCIAL REPORTING

Accounts Preparation
Limited Companies
Limited Company Accounts
Partnership/Sole Trader Accounts

SPECIALISATIONS – TAXATION

Partnerships and Sole Traders
Payroll Service and Advice
Personal
Taxation

PRICEWATERHOUSE-COOPERS
West London Office, The Atrium, 1 Harefield Road, Uxbridge UB8 1EX

PRICEWATERHOUSE-COOPERS LLP
The Atrium, 1 Harefield Road, Uxbridge, UB8 1EX
Tel: 01895 522000
Resident Partners/Directors: ICAEW Members
M Amitrano, F M Bradford, D J H Cooke, S J Couch, R F De Peyrecave, T V Hopcroft, N D Hopes, S T Hyde, D J D Macdougall, M T Martin, W E Nicholls, A Packman, J S Sarai, I R Smith, S R Wootten, A T Yeeles

RICHINGS & CO
9 Ashdown Rd, Hillingdon, Uxbridge, UB10 0HY

SHASENS & RE10 (SOUTH EAST) LTD
F2 Salamander Quay West, Park Lane, Harefield, Uxbridge UB9 6NZ

STEPHEN BOOTH
17 Ivyhouse Road, Ickenham, Uxbridge, UB10 8NF
Tel: 01895 630907
Principal: ICAEW Member
S C E Booth

V.V. PATEL & CO
71a Knighton Way Lane, Denham, Uxbridge, UB9 4EH
Tel: 01895 236702
Principal: ICAEW Member
V V Patel

VENTNOR

TERENCE J. DOWN & CO
Brook House, Park Avenue, Ventnor, PO38 1LE

VERWOOD

GRANT SELLERS LTD
Bank Court, Manor Court, Verwood, BH31 6DY

VIRGINIA WATER

COLIN E JONES
Fernwood, Christchurch Rd, Virginia Water, GU25 4QB
Tel: 01344 843709
Principal: ICAEW Member
C E Jones

GRAHAM PRICE
18 Trotsworth Avenue, Virginia Water, GU25 4AL
Tel: 01344 845359
Principal: ICAEW Member
J G V Price

WENTWORTH ACCOUNTANCY SERVICES LTD
6 Cabrera Close, Virginia Water, GU25 4HB

WADEBRIDGE

BROOKS & JEAL
1 Pityme Business Centre, St Minver, Wadebridge, PL27 6NU
Tel: 01208 862053
Resident Partners/Directors: ICAEW Members
N M Brooks

DAVID V ELSTON & CO
51 Molesworth Street, Wadebridge, PL27 7DR

DAVID V ELSTON & CO LTD
51 Molesworth Street, Wadebridge, PL27 7DR

R.L. STATTON
1st Floor, Regency Arcade, Molesworth Street, Wadebridge PL27 7DH
Tel: 01208 813948
Principal: ICAEW Member
R L Statton

SPECIALISATIONS – SECTOR

Agriculture

ROBERT D. SMITH
Hamilton House, The Platt, Wadebridge, PL27 7AD

TRUDGEON HALLING ◈
The Platt, Wadebridge, PL27 7AE
Tel: 0845 130 0403
Email: solutions@t-h.co.uk
Website: http://www.t-h.co.uk
Resident Partners/Directors: ICAEW Members
J H Anderson-Riley, R G Hatch
Registered by the ICAEW to carry out company audit work

Authorised and regulated by the Financial Services Authority for investment business

WADHURST

CATHERINE METCALFE
October House, Jonas Lane, Wadhurst, TN5 6UJ
Tel: 01892 783949
Principal: ICAEW Member
C H Metcalfe

E.M. MOIR
3 Mount Pleasant, Woods Green, Wadhurst, TN5 6QL

J.L. HASTINGS
3 Bewlbridge Close, Flimwell, Wadhurst, TN5 7NL

JOHN W TIMMIS
Beggars Roost, Whitegates Lane, Wadhurst, TN5 6QG
Tel: 01892 782160

JOHN W TIMMIS LTD
Beggars Roost, Whitegates Lane, Wadhurst, TN5 6QG
Tel: 01892 782160
Resident Partners/Directors: ICAEW Members
J W Timmis

KINGANDCO
The Clock House, High Street, Wadhurst, TN5 6AA
Tel: 01892 784321
Principal: ICAEW Member
M R King

KNIGHTS & CO LTD
7 Eden Court, Church Street, Ticehurst, Wadhurst TN5 7AF

MITCHELLS
The Old Stables, Fox Hole Lane, Wadhurst, TN5 6NB
Tel: 01892 785333
Principal: ICAEW Member
M Turner

WAKEFIELD

AIMS ACCOUNTANTS
4 Folly Hall Mount, Tingley, Wakefield, WF3 1TJ
Tel: 0113 252 9842
Principal: ICAEW Member
I M Anderson

BEAUMONTS
Cross Street Chambers, Cross Street, Wakefield, WF1 3BW
Tel: 01924 372954
Fax: 01924 366622
Resident Partners/Directors: ICAEW Members
J H Beaumont, P M Samuel
Registered by the ICAEW to carry out company audit work
Regulated by the ICAEW for a range of investment business activities

DIX VOGAN LTD
2 Chancery Lane, Wakefield, WF1 2SS
Tel: 01924 384984
Fax: 01924 291412
Website: http://www.dixvogan.co.uk
Resident Partners/Directors: ICAEW Members
C W Dix, I Vogan
Registered by the ICAEW to carry out company audit work
SPECIALISATIONS – AUDIT & ASSURANCE
Audit
SPECIALISATIONS – FINANCIAL REPORTING
Accounts Preparation
SPECIALISATIONS – TAXATION
Estate Planning
Payroll Service and Advice

FINANCIAL CONSULTING SERVICES LTD
81A Stanley Road, Wakefield, WF1 4LH

HARRISON & CO
531 Denby Dale Road West, Calder Grove, Wakefield, WF4 3ND

HARRISON & CO ACCOUNTANTS LTD
531 Denby Dale Road West, Calder Grove, Wakefield, WF4 3ND

HPBS LTD
17 Wren Garth, Sandal, Wakefield, WF2 6SL

IAN PARSONS
17 Milnthorpe Drive, Sandal, Wakefield, WF2 7HU

IMPACT BUSINESS MANAGEMENT LTD
16 Kingfisher Close, Durkar, Wakefield, WF4 3NE

J.E. PAYLING & CO
Quarry Close, 23 Northfield Lane, Horbury, Wakefield WF4 5HZ
Tel: 01924 274366
Principal: ICAEW Member
J E Payling

JOLIFFE CORK
33 George Street, Wakefield, WF1 1LX

JOLLIFFE CORK LLP
33 George Street, Wakefield, WF1 1LX
Tel: 01924 376045
Fax: 01924 290522
Email: wakefield@jolliffecork.co.uk
Website: http://www.jolliffecork.co.uk
Resident Partners/Directors: ICAEW Members
J S Crossley, T Hill, A D Hydes, C L Lawton, A R N Perkin
Resident Partners (Non-ICAEW Members):
N S Petch
Registered by the ICAEW to carry out company audit work
Regulated by the ICAEW for a range of investment business activities

KELVIN BURKE & CO LTD
81a Stanley Road, Wakefield, WF1 4LH
Tel: 01924 383160
Resident Partners/Directors: ICAEW Members
W H Tomlinson

LAMBERT ROPER & HORSFIELD LTD
13 High Street, Horbury, Wakefield, WF4 5AB

M.K. BLUNDELL & CO
34 Charles Roberts Office Park, Charles Street, Horbury Junction, Wakefield WF4 5FH
Tel: 01924 280124
Principal: ICAEW Member
M K Blundell

MURDOCH MANN AND COMPANY LTD
Unit 26, Charles Roberts Office Park, Horbury Junction, Wakefield WF4 5FH

PAYLINGS ★
36 Bond Street, Wakefield, WF1 2QP

PERCY PEMBERTON & CO
11 Sandal Cliff, Sandal, Wakefield, WF2 6AU

R.A. LISTER
Suite 2, 14 Rishworth Street, Wakefield, WF1 3BY
Tel: 01924 291388
Email: richard@ralister.co.uk
Principal: ICAEW Member
R A Lister

R.E. MIDGLEY
189 Shay Lane, Walton, Wakefield, WF2 6NW

R M. MOORE
28 Coppice Close, Pinders Heath, Wakefield, WF1 4TA
Tel: 01924 211646
Principal: ICAEW Member
R M Moore

SANDERS GEESON LTD ◈
Raines Business Centre, Raines House, Denby Dale Road, Wakefield WF1 1HR
Tel: 01924 254802
Resident Partners/Directors: ICAEW Members
J Szczepanski
Languages Spoken:
Polish

TAYLOR, CROFT & WINDER
16 Bond Street, Wakefield, WF1 2QP

TAYLOR CROFT WINDER
PO Box 403, Wakefield, WF1 2WT

TENON LTD
33 George Street, Wakefield, WF1 1LX

TENON LTD
Unit 1, Calder Close, Calder Park, Wakefield WF4 3BA
Tel: 01924 241030

WATERTON PARK ACCOUNTANCY
Holly Cottage, Brockswood Court, Walton, Wakefield WF2 6RU

WALLASEY

ELAINE CHATTERTON
5 Heathbank Avenue, Wallasey, CH44 3AS
Tel: 01516 398278
Principal: ICAEW Member
E Chatterton

R.F. FRAZER & CO
86-88 Wallasey Road, Wallasey, CH44 2AE

WENDY LAWRENSON
52 Rowson Street, Wallasey, CH45 2LX

WALLINGFORD

CARA CHAPMAN
6 Wingfield Close, Ewelme, Wallingford, OX10 6JY

CLEMENTS TAYLOR
19 Page Furlong, Dorchester-on-Thames, Wallingford, OX10 7PU
Tel: 01865 340600
Principal: ICAEW Member
A V Clements

DAVID FOX
Allnuts, The Street, Brightwell-Cum-Sotwell, Wallingford OX10 0RR
Tel: 01491 833522
Principal: ICAEW Member
D H Fox

GORE & CO
The Innovation Centre, Bagnold Wing, Howbery Park, Wallingford OX10 8BA
Tel: 0870 241 7019
Principal: ICAEW Member
K S Girn

JANET HOBBS
Rush Court Nurseries, Wallingford, OX10 8LJ
Tel: 01491 836647
Principal: ICAEW Member
J E Hobbs

R. THIRKETTLE
1 Atwell Close, Wallingford, OX10 0LH

RICHARD MOORE & CO
6 Bridge End, Dorchester on Thames, Wallingford, OX10 7JP

ROWLAND HOGG
11 Wood Street, Wallingford, OX10 0BD

WALLINGTON

B. PREBBLE
272 London Road, Wallington, SM6 7DJ
Tel: 020 8773 1509
Principal: ICAEW Member
B Prebble

ERROL MARTIN
Sussex Lodge, 49 Boundary Road, Wallington, SM6 0SZ

FINERTY BRICE ◈
Endeavour House, 78 Stafford Road, Wallington, SM6 9AY
Tel: 020 8395 9944
Resident Partners/Directors: ICAEW Members
N A Brice, B F Finerty
Registered by the ICAEW to carry out company audit work
Regulated by the ICAEW for a range of investment business activities

LINDSAY & CO
119 Boundary Road, Wallington, SM6 0TE

N. NABI & CO
75 Hillside Gardens, Wallington, SM6 9NX

RICHARDSON, WATSON & CO
Mint House, 6 Stanley Park Road, Wallington, SM6 0HA

TRYHORN & LLOYD
153 Stafford Road, Wallington, SM6 9BN

WESLEY WILSON & ASSOCIATES
44 Stafford Road, Wallington, SM6 9AA

WESLEY WILSON & ASSOCIATES LTD
Park House, 44 Stafford Road, Wallington, SM6 9AA

WALSALL

A. HODSON ◈
40 The Glades, Aldridge, Walsall, WS9 8RN

AMIES & CO ◈
205 High Street, Brownhills, Walsall, WS8 6HE
Tel: 01543 377366
Email: enquiries@amiesandco.com
Principal: ICAEW Member
J S Amies
Regulated by the ICAEW for a range of investment business activities

ANTHONY SLANN
52A Walsall Road, Aldridge, Walsall, WS9 0JL

BAKER (MIDLANDS) LTD
Arbor House, Broadway North, Walsall, WS1 2AN

BAKERS
Baker (Midlands) Limited, Arbor House, Broadway North, Walsall WS1 2AN

C J PETTY LTD
175 High Street, Brownhills, Walsall, WS8 6HG

COX JEROME ★
Churchill House, 59 Lichfield Street, Walsall, WS4 2BX

CROMBIES ◈
16 Birmingham Road, Walsall, WS1 2NA
Tel: 01922 748100
Resident Partners/Directors: ICAEW Members
I J Cattell

CROMBIES CORFIELD ACCOUNTANTS LTD ◈
16 Birmingham Road, Walsall, WS1 2NA
Tel: 01902 773993
Resident Partners/Directors: ICAEW Members
I J Cattell, M Fletcher

EDWARDS
Harmony House, 34 High Street, Aldridge, Walsall WS9 8LZ
Tel: 01922 743100
Resident Partners/Directors: ICAEW Members
R M Hughes, N J Taylor, D C P Webb

G.S. SHERGILL
30 Bell Road, Walsall, WS5 3JW

GRIFFIN & KING
26-28 Goodall Street, Walsall, WS1 1QL

GRIFFIN & KING LTD
26/28 Goodall Street, Walsall, WS1 1QL

HAYWARD & CO
49 Dundalk Lane, Cheslyn Hay, Walsall, WS6 7AZ
Tel: 01922 413552
Email: derek.hayward@tiscali.co.uk
Principal: ICAEW Member
D W Hayward

HORWATH CLARK WHITEHILL LLP
Hatherton House, Hatherton Street, Walsall, WS1 1YB
Tel: 01922 725590
Resident Partners/Directors: ICAEW Members
R F Baker, J G Dudley, P Moore, G J Morgan

KENNETH EMERY
7 Stencills Drive, Walsall, WS4 2HP
Tel: 01922 629834
Principal: ICAEW Member
K J Emery

M D JONES
96 Skip Lane, Walsall, WS5 3LR

MURAS GILL
Thomas House, Croxstalls Place, Bloxwich, Walsall WS3 2PP

MURAS GILL LTD
Thomas House, Croxstalls Place, Bloxwich, Walsall WS3 2PP

NORMAN J. WIGLEY & PARTNERS
12 Birmingham Road, Walsall, WS1 2NA
Tel: 01922 611231
Fax: 01922 723617
Email: mjwigley@virgin.net
Principal: ICAEW Member
M J Wigley
Registered by another RSB to carry out company audit work
Regulated by the ICAEW for a range of investment business activities
Licensed by another DPB to carry on investment business
General Description:
Established 1915. General audit accountancy & taxation practice.

NORMAN R EVANS & CO LTD
25-27 Station Street, Cheslyn Hay, Walsall, WS6 7ED
Tel: 01922 419197
Resident Partners/Directors: ICAEW Members
N R Evans

PETER LICKISS CHARTERED TAX ADVISER LTD
35 Honiton Way, Aldridge, Walsall, WS9 0JS

PROFESSIONAL ACCOUNTANCY & BUSINESS SERVICES LTD
5 Plainview Close, Aldridge, Walsall, WS9 0YY

SILVER & CO ◈
36 High Street, Cheslyn Hay, Walsall, WS6 7AD

STANLEY YULE
Beaconsfield House, 26 Belvidere Road, Walsall, WS1 3AU

STEWART & CO
5 Plainview Close, Aldridge, Walsall, WS9 0YY

WALLACE CROOKE & CO ◈
Wallace House, 20 Birmingham Road, Walsall, WS1 2LT

WHITEHOUSE RIDSDALE
26 Birmingham Road, Walsall, WS1 2LZ

WALTHAM ABBEY

CHARING & CO ◈
6 Sewardstone Road, Waltham Abbey, EN9 1NA
Tel: 01992 762875
Principal: ICAEW Member
S L Charing

CONNOR WARIN LTD ◈
Trinity House, Foxes Parade, Sewardstone Road, Waltham Abbey, EN9 1PH
Tel: 01992 715804
Resident Partners/Directors: ICAEW Members
G H Connor, J Warin
Other Offices: Forge House, 39-41 Cambridge Road, Stansted, Essex CM24 8BX
(Tel: 01279 813294)

J F O'BRIEN TAXATION SERVICES LTD
7 Abbey Court, Waltham Abbey, EN9 1RF
Tel: 01992 711592
Resident Partners/Directors: ICAEW Members
J F O'Brien

JOHN D. COLEMAN
Howards, Middle Street, Nazeing, Waltham Abbey EN9 2LH

KNIGHT WHEELER & CO
54 Sun Street, Waltham Abbey, EN9 1EJ

KNIGHT WHEELER & CO
54 Sun Street, Waltham Abbey, EN9 1EJ
Tel: 01992 769050
Resident Partners/Directors: ICAEW Members
P M P Heywood, S N Ross

KNIGHT WHEELER LTD
54 Sun Street, Waltham Abbey, EN9 1EJ

R.J. DAVEY & CO
Unit 7 Howard Business Park, 47 Howard Close, Waltham Abbey, EN9 1XE

WALTHAM CROSS

A R LEVINE
42 Silverbirch Court, Friends Avenue, Cheshunt, Waltham Cross EN8 8LZ

ALEXANDER ASH & CO LTD
1st Floor, Bristol & West House, 100 Crossbrook Street, Cheshunt, Waltham Cross EN8 8JJ

ALTORFER FINANCIAL MANAGEMENT LTD
5 Regent Gate, Waltham Cross, EN8 7AF

BAILEY PHILLIPS
17 Hanbury Close, Cheshunt, Waltham Cross, EN8 9BZ

BRINDLEY GOLDSTEIN LTD
103 High Street, Waltham Cross, EN8 7AN
Tel: 01992 652222
Resident Partners/Directors: ICAEW Members
C H Goldstein

BRINDLEY MILLEN
167 Turners Hill, Cheshunt, Waltham Cross, EN8 9BH

BRINDLEY MILLEN LTD
167 Turners Hill, Cheshunt, Waltham Cross, EN8 9BH

D J. ROBINSON
58 Peartree Walk, Cheshunt, Waltham Cross, EN7 6RE

LYNDA VIJH
11 Everett Close, Cheshunt, Waltham Cross, EN7 6XD

O'BYRNE & KENNEDY LLP
East Wing, Goffs Oak House, Goffs Lane, Goffs Oak, Waltham Cross EN7 5BW

P.J.SPICER
43 Turners Hill, Cheshunt, Waltham Cross, EN8 8NJ

SOLAZZO & CO LTD
Woodlands, 27 Ferney Road, Cheshunt, Waltham Cross EN7 6XQ

STEWART & PARTNERS
6 Regent Gate, High Street, Waltham Cross, EN8 7AF
Tel: 0845 205 0011
Fax: 0845 205 0033
Email: mail@stewartpartners.co.uk
Website: http://www.stewartpartners.co.uk
Principal: ICAEW Member
S A Lever
Registered by the ICAEW to carry out company audit work
Regulated by the ICAEW for a range of investment business activities

THICKBROOM, COVENTRY
147a High Street, Waltham Cross, EN8 7AP

THE TREVOR JONES PARTNERSHIP LLP ◈
Springfield House, 99-101 Crossbrook Street, Cheshunt, Waltham Cross EN8 8JR

WALTON-ON-THAMES

ANGELA WILLIAMS & ASSOCIATES LTD
Angela Williams & Associates Limited, 1 Meadowside, Walton-on-thames, KT12 3LS

ANGELA WILLIAMS & ASSOCIATES
Angela Williams & Associates Limited, 1 Meadowside, Walton-on-thames, KT12 3LS

BEATY-POWNALL ASSOCIATES LTD
5 Fir Close, Walton-on-Thames, KT12 2SX
Tel: 01932 254829
Resident Partners/Directors: ICAEW Members
M.C. Beaty-Pownall

BYRNE, PALMER & CO
14 Queens Road, Hersham, Walton-on-thames, KT12 5LS
Tel: 01932 241852
Website: http://www.byrnepalmer.co.uk
Resident Partners/Directors: ICAEW Members
P J Cobb
Resident Partners (Non-ICAEW Members):
L Woodward-Thwaites
Registered by the ICAEW to carry out company audit work
Regulated by the ICAEW for a range of investment business activities
SPECIALISATIONS – AUDIT & ASSURANCE
Audit
SPECIALISATIONS – SECTOR
Clubs/Associations
SPECIALISATIONS – TAXATION
Payroll Service and Advice
Taxation

FREEPORT MANAGEMENT LTD
5 Fir Close, Walton-on-Thames, KT12 2SX

J M PITMAN & CO
Dometo House, Molesey Road, Hersham, Walton-on-thames KT12 3PW
Tel: 01932 252644
Email: jet@jmpitman.co.uk
Principal: ICAEW Member
P G Jethwa

K.D. POPAT & CO
Kashi Nivas, 65 Ashley Park Avenue, Walton-on-thames, KT12 1EU

KUMAR & CO ★ ◈
85 Rydens Road, Walton-on-Thames, KT12 3AN
Tel: 01932 247906
Resident Partners/Directors: ICAEW Members
S Kumar

LAWFORD & CO
Union House, Walton Lodge, Bridge Street, Walton-on-thames KT12 1BT

LAWFORDS LTD
Union House, Walton Lodge, Bridge Street, Walton-on-thames KT12 1BT

LEAN, NEWTON & CARY
58 York Gardens, Walton-on-Thames, KT12 3EW

LORELIE STAINES
2 Garrick Close, Walton-on-thames, KT12 5NY
Tel: 01932 248825
Principal: ICAEW Member
L M Staines

MARTIN SCHUMAN ACCOUNTANCY
13 Oakfields, Walton-on-Thames, KT12 1EG

MARTIN SCHUMAN ACCOUNTANCY LTD
13 Oakfields, Walton-on-Thames, KT12 1EG

SCHONHUT CARR & CO
Thames House, Mayo Road, Walton-on-Thames, KT12 2QA

UNION CAPITAL LTD
Union House, Walton Lodge, Bridge Street, Walton-on-thames KT12 1BT

WANTAGE

BEECRAFT & CO
Brook Cottage, The Millham, West Hendred, Wantage OX12 8RN

C.J. DAVIES
64 Charlton Road, Wantage, OX12 8HG

CHAPMAN WORTH GODDARD & BROADLEY LLP
6 Newbury Street, Wantage, OX12 8BS
Tel: 01235 770084
Resident Partners/Directors: ICAEW Members
G J Broadley, A M Chapman, M Chapman, A M Goddard

GOULD & MANSFORD
P O Box 151, Anvil Cottage, Anvil Lane, Letcombe Regis, Wantage OX12 9LA

SMITHS
Unit 114, Boston House, Grove Technology Park, Wantage OX12 9FF
Tel: 01235 766162
Website: http://www.smithsca.co.uk
Principal: ICAEW Member
M R Smith

WARE

A WADE TAX CONSULTANCY
2 Plough Cottages, Great Munden, Ware, SG11 1HS

ARMITAGE DAVIS & CO
81b High Street, Ware, SG12 9AD

CELARBEN VENTURES LTD ◈
PO Box 163, Ware, SG12 0ZN
Tel: 01920 438020
Email: info@celarbenventures.co.uk
Resident Partners/Directors: ICAEW Members
C D Carr
Regulated by the ICAEW for a range of investment business activities

COLIN W. HOY
12 Millfield, Wadesmill, Ware, SG12 0TU
Tel: 01920 463428
Principal: ICAEW Member
C W Hoy

DAVID M. WRIGHT
Woodlands Works, Woodlands Road, Thundridge, Ware SG12 0SP
Tel: 01920 469482
Principal: ICAEW Member
D M Wright

G. DUFTON AND CO
61 Page Hill, Ware, SG12 0RZ

GARETH DUFTON ACA
61 Page Hill, Ware, SG12 0RZ
Tel: 01920 420811
Principal: ICAEW Member
G N Dufton

INTEGA
106 Mill Studio, Crane Mead, Ware, SG12 9PY

INTEGA LTD
106 Mill Studio, Ware, SG12 9PY

JANELLE LANKESTER
The Foundry, 9 Park Lane, Puckeridge, Ware SG11 1RL

M.P. DORLING
The Firs, Levens Green, Old Hall Green, Ware SG11 1HD
Tel: 01920 438673
Principal: ICAEW Member
M P Dorling

MALCOLM HIGH
Pantiles, Braughing Friars, Ware, SG11 2NS
Tel: 01279 771351
Principal: ICAEW Member
M High

N ARMES & CO LTD
1 Pelmark House, 11 Amwell End, Ware, SG12 9HP

R.JACKSON & CO
19 Station Road, Puckeridge, Ware, SG11 1SN
Tel: 01920 821482
Principal: ICAEW Member
R D Jackson

RP ACCOUNTING
Studio 301a, Mill Studio Business Centre, Crane Mead, Ware SG12 9PY

RPFCA LTD
Studio 301a, Mill Studio Business Centre, Crane Mead, Ware SG12 9PY

SOUTHWELL, TYRRELL & CO
41 Baldock Street, Ware, SG12 9DH

TITTENSOR & CO
Fourwinds, Wengeo Lane, Ware, SG12 0EH

W.R. THORLIN & CO
Hill Cottage, Easneye, Ware, SG12 8LY

WAREHAM

A.R. THOMAS
Glanton House, 19 Wyatts Lane, Wareham, BH20 4NH

HENDERSONS ◈
18 West Street, Wareham, BH20 4JX

MICHAEL BUNE & CO
The Old Stables, St Johns Hill, Wareham, BH20 4NB

RICHARD PLACE & CO
22 Worgret Road, Wareham, BH20 4PN

WARLINGHAM

CARTER NICHOLLS CONSULTANTS LTD
415 Limpsfield Road, Warlingham, CR6 9HA

MUSCAT & CO
Kingswood Lodge, Kingswood Lane, Warlingham, CR6 9AB

RJB
Warlingham Court Farm, Tithepit Shaw Lane, Warlingham, CR6 9AT

SGB CONSULTING
Woodridings, Landscape Road, Warlingham, CR6 9JB

WARMINSTER

BERKELEY RANKINE
25 Market Place, Warminster, BA12 9BB

BUCHANANS LTD
40 George Street, Warminster, BA12 8QB

MARSH ACCOUNTANCY ◈
34 Market Place, Warminster, BA12 9AN
Tel: 01985 847075
Principal: ICAEW Member
C T Webb

MUSKIN GREGORY
Unit 21, Deverill Road Trading Estate, Deverill Road, Sutton Veny, Warminster BA12 7BZ

R D OWEN & CO
21A Market Place, Warminster, BA12 9AY

R.D. OWEN & CO
21A Market Place, Warminster, BA12 9AY

WARRINGTON

ABRAXAS CORPORATE FINANCE LTD
4 Croft Gardens, Grappenhall Heys, Warrington, WA4 3LH

ACCOUNTANCY SUMMIT LTD
1 St Wilfrids Drive, Grappenhall, Warrington, WA4 2SH

AGP
Sterling House, Mandarin Court, Centre Park, Warrington WA1 1GG

AIMS - DAVID M. COTTAM
40 Gilderdale Close, Gorse Covert, Birchwood, Warrington WA3 6TH

ANTHONY GRAY & CO
28 Church Lane, Culcheth, Warrington, WA3 5DJ

BAKER TILLY
1210 Centre Park Square, Warrington, WA1 1RU
Tel: 01925 424230
Resident Partners/Directors: ICAEW Members
M C Fairhurst, N J Gowans, C J Humphrey, A A Tranter

BAKER TILLY
1210 Centre Park Square, Warrington, WA1 1RU

BAKER TILLY TAX AND ADVISORY SERVICES LLP
1210 Centre Park Square, Warrington, WA1 1RU
Tel: 01925 424230
Resident Partners/Directors: ICAEW Members
G D Carrington, D Charnock, N Davenport, M C Fairhurst, N J Gowans, C J Humphrey, P J Thorburn, A A Tranter

BRAKEN
28 Edward Gardens, Martinscroft, Warrington, WA1 4QT

BROOKSON LTD
Brunel House, 340 Firecrest Court, Centre Park, Warrington WA1 1RG

DAVID CARTY & CO
234 Manchester Road, Warrington, WA1 3BD

DAVID M. COTTAM
40 Gilderdale Close, Gorse Covert, Birchwood, Warrington WA3 6TH

DAVIES, DOWNS & CO
210 Chester Road, Warrington, WA4 6AR

DAVIES, DOWNS & CO
Kemmel House, 6 Red Lane, Appleton, Warrington WA4 5AD
Tel: 01925 633301
Principal: ICAEW Member
J P Davies

DONNAN CALDERBANK
7 Appleford Close, Appleton, Warrington, WA4 3DP
Tel: 01925 261806

DONNAN CALDERBANK (WARRINGTON) LTD
7 Appleford Close, Appleton, Warrington, WA4 3DP

DOW SCHOFIELD WATTS LLP ◈
7700 Daresbury Park, Warrington, WA4 6H5

FIRS LANE ADVISORY LTD
Firscroft, Firs Lane, Appleton, Warrington WA4 5LD

FOUR J'S
46 Chester Road, Stockton Heath, Warrington, WA4 2RX

FRANK BEBBINGTON ACCOUNTANTS LTD
Bridge House, 9 Fowley Common Lane, Glazebury, Warrington WA3 5JJ

HELEN TOMBS
50 Wellfield Road, Culcheth, Warrington, WA3 4JT

HUNTER HEALEY ◈
Abacus House, 450 Warrington Road, Culcheth, Warrington WA3 5QX
Tel: 01925 767222

ISHERWOOD & CO
15 London Road, Stockton Heath, Warrington, WA4 6SG
Tel: 01925 601679
Email: mail@isherwoodandco.co.uk
Principal: ICAEW Member
R J Isherwood
Registered by the ICAEW to carry out company audit work
Regulated by the ICAEW for a range of investment business activities

J AUSTERBERRY & CO
93 Bewsey Street, Warrington, WA2 7JQ

J. DARBYSHIRE
31 York Road, Grappenhall, Warrington, WA4 2EH

J GIBSON & CO LTD
12 Foxhills Close, Appleton, Warrington, WA4 5DH

JACKSON STEPHEN LLP
35-37 Wilson Patten Street, Warrington, WA1 1PG

JOHN TRAYNOR & CO
35 Stockdale Drive, Whittle Hall, Warrington, WA5 3RU

MARK THOMPSON LTD
59 Beamish Close, Appleton, Warrington, WA4 5RJ

MITCHELL CHARLESWORTH ◈
Victoria House, 488 Knutsford Road, Warrington, WA4 1DX
Tel: 01925 635141
Resident Partners/Directors: ICAEW Members
D Darlington

MOORS ANDREW MCCLUSKY & CO
Halton View Villas, 3-5 Wilson Patten Street, Warrington, WA1 1PG
Tel: 0870 111 8998
Principal: ICAEW Member
A McClusky

MOORS ANDREW THOMAS & CO LLP
94 Wilderspool Causeway, Warrington, WA4 6PU

MRM ACCOUNTING
90 Albert Road, Grappenhall, Warrington, WA4 2PG
Tel: 01925 602366
Principal: ICAEW Member
M R Martin

NICK BRAJKOVICH LTD
29 Withers Avenue, Orford, Warrington, WA2 8EU

P. PATEL
71 Park Road, Great Sankey, Warrington, WA5 3EA

PARKIN S. BOOTH & CO ★
2nd Floor, 20 Winmarleigh Street, Warrington, WA1 1JY

R A FRENCH LTD
12 Lychgate, Higher Walton, Warrington, WA4 6TF

REECE HULME & CO ★
1 Wilson Pattern Street, Warrington, WA1 1PG

RIGBY LENNON & CO
20 Winmarleigh Street, Warrington, WA1 1JY
Tel: 01925 636671
Fax: 01925 411739
Email: rl@rigbylennon.co.uk
Date Established: 1985
Resident Partners/Directors: ICAEW Members
A F Harrison, A Lennon, J P Rigby
Registered by the ICAEW to carry out company audit work

ROBERT BLACAS
6 Beamish Close, Pewters Pear, Warrington, WA4 5RH

STYLES & CO ACCOUNTANTS LTD
Heather House, 473 Warrington Road, Culcheth, Warrington WA3 5QU

VOISEY & CO ◈
8 Winmarleigh Street, Warrington, WA1 1JW
Tel: 01925 650703
Fax: 01925 415295
Email: all@voisey.co.uk
Website: http://www.voisey.co.uk
Training Contracts Available.
Resident Partners/Directors: ICAEW Members
A B Perry, C J Thomson, P Urmston, L M Warburton
Registered by the ICAEW to carry out company audit work
Regulated by the ICAEW for a range of investment business activities
SPECIALISATIONS – BUSINESS & GENERAL ADVICE
Management Accounting Consultancy
SPECIALISATIONS – FINANCIAL REPORTING
Accounts Preparation
SPECIALISATIONS – TAXATION
Payroll Service and Advice

THE WALKER BEGLEY PARTNERSHIP
207 Knutsford Road, Warrington, WA4 2QL
Tel: 01925 210000
Fax: 01925 210003
Email: helen.begley@walkerbegley.co.uk
Website: http://www.walkerbegley.co.uk
Resident Partners/Directors: ICAEW Members
K G Begley, K Walker
Registered by the ICAEW to carry out company audit work
Regulated by the ICAEW for a range of investment business activities

WATKINSON BLACK
113 Orford Lane, Warrington, WA2 7AR

WARWICK

B.C TAYLOR
The Bungalow, The Avenue, Rowington, Warwick CV35 7BX

BRIAN PERKINS FCA
11 Ilmington Close, Hatton Park, Warwick, CV35 7TL
Tel: 01926 494864
Principal: ICAEW Member
B K Perkins

CHAPMAN NASH LLP ◈
1c Tournament Court, Edgehill Drive, Warwick, CV34 6LG
Tel: 01926 483790
Email: advice@chapmannash.co.uk
Website: http://www.chapmannash.co.uk
Resident Partners/Directors: ICAEW Members
J S Chapman, E Nash

CILLA WATTS FCA
Vectis House, Banbury Street, Kineton, Warwick CV35 0JS
Tel: 01926 640403
Principal: ICAEW Member
P C Buxton

E J OWEN
1 Beech Cliffe, Coventry Road, Warwick, CV34 5HY

CLIVE GUMMOW
Cottage Farm, Pinley Green, Claverdon, Warwick CV35 8LX
Principal: ICAEW Member
C F Gummow

J.H. HAYWOOD
10 Smith Street, Warwick, CV34 4HH

JONATHAN W. ROBERTS
Blackford Barn, Pillerton Priors, Warwick, CV35 0PE
Tel: 01789 740407
Principal: ICAEW Member
J W Roberts

MICHAEL HARWOOD & CO ◈
Greville House, 10 Jury Street, Warwick, CV34 4EW

PETER J FISH
Culvers Hill, Rowington, Warwick, CV35 7AB

SANSOM & COMPANY ACCOUNTANTS LTD
2 Church Street, Warwick, CV34 4AB

SILVESTER PARKER & CO
31 Robins Grove, Chase Meadow, Warwick, CV34 6RF

THE TILL MORRIS PARTNERSHIP ★
Redfern House, 29 Jury Street, Warwick, CV34 4EH

TRACY GILL
14 Rogers Way, Warwick, CV34 6PY

V M BAXTER & CO
The Old Vicarage, Southam Street, Kineton, Warwick CV35 0LL

WOOTTON & CO
29 Tidmarsh Road, Leek Wootton, Warwick, CV35 7QP

WASHINGTON

ANDREW W. HUNT & CO
13 Lowthian Terrace, Washington, NE38 7BA

GILLIAN TYERMAN & CO
4th Floor, Pennine House, Washington, NE37 1LY
Tel: 0191 417 3123
Principal: ICAEW Member
G C Tyerman

MALCOLM BENGSTON
27 Partridge Close, Ayton Green, Washington, NE38 0ES
Tel: 0191 416 9804
Principal: ICAEW Member
M Bengston

MITCHELLS
Suite 4, Parsons House, Parsons Road, Washington, TYNE AND WEAR NE37 1EZ

WATCHET

MAURICE WHITELEY
Nash House, Swain Street, Watchet, TA23 0AB

WATERLOOVILLE

ACORN ACCOUNTING SOLUTIONS LTD
9 Wedgwood Way, Cowplain, Waterlooville, PO8 8RW
Tel: 07979 505669
Resident Partners/Directors: ICAEW Members
P J Read

BAYLISS WARE LTD
9 Stratfield Park, Elettra Avenue, Waterlooville, PO7 7XN

C.N. CLARKE
5 St Giles Way, Horndean, Waterlooville, PO8 0EE

FOCUS ACCOUNTING
87 Redwing Road, Waterlooville, PO8 0LX

FOCUS ACCOUNTING LTD
87 Redwing Road, Waterlooville, PO8 0LX

GEMMA AKED ACCOUNTANCY SERVICES
49 Hazleton Way, Cowplain, Waterlooville, PO8 9BP
Tel: 07919 388386
Principal: ICAEW Member
G L Aked

J E R ACCOUNTING SERVICES LTD
32 Ramblers Way, Waterlooville, PO7 8RE
Tel: 02392 263649
Resident Partners/Directors: ICAEW Members
M H Harding

MARSHALL ROCHE LTD
77 London Road, Cowplain, Waterlooville, PO8 8UJ

MMO LTD
Wellesley House, 204 London Road, Waterlooville, PO7 7AN

MURRAY MCINTOSH O'BRIEN
Wellesley House, 204 London Road, Waterlooville, PO7 7AN
Tel: 02392 231006
Resident Partners/Directors: ICAEW Members
G McIntosh, S P Murray, R B Pennington
Resident Partners (Non-ICAEW Members):
T O'Brien

S JOHNSTON & CO
24 Picton House, Hussar Court, Waterlooville, PO7 7SQ

S. JOHNSTON & CO LTD
24 Picton House, Hussar Court, Waterlooville, PO7 7SQ

SALLY GRANT LTD
El Villa, 3 Ladybridge Road, Waterlooville, PO7 5RP
Tel: 02392 253213
Resident Partners/Directors: ICAEW Members
S A Walker

STUART HOARE
87 London Road, Cowplain, Waterlooville, PO8 8XB

TAYLOR ROBERTS
15b Somerset House, Hussar Court, Westside View, Waterlooville PO7 7SG
Tel: 02392 263007

WATFORD

A.G.OSBORN & CO
37 Parkside Drive, Watford, WD17 3AS

A MITRA & CO ◈
137 Cassiobury Drive, Watford, WD17 3AH
Tel: 01923 212687
Website: http://www.amitra.co.uk
Resident Partners/Directors: ICAEW Members
A K Mitra, J G Mitra

ALAN JONES & CO
59 Meadow Road, Kingswood, Watford, WD25 0JB
Tel: 01923 674500
Principal: ICAEW Member
A V Jones

ASHFORD & PARTNERS ◈
2nd Floor, Kings House, 202 Lower High Street, Watford WD17 2EH
Tel: 01923 209859
Resident Partners/Directors: ICAEW Members
C H K Shah, N K Shah

BAKER TILLY
1st Floor, 46 Clarendon Road, Watford, WD17 1JJ
Tel: 01923 816400
Resident Partners/Directors: ICAEW Members
G J Bedingfield, S G Bowles, G J Francies, D Lewis, S E Mason, A C Monteith, M J Nicholas, C W Rowe, S Singh

BAKER TILLY RESTRUCTURING AND RECOVERY LLP
1st Floor, 46 Clarendon Road, Watford, WD17 1JJ
Tel: 01923 816400
Resident Partners/Directors: ICAEW Members
S G Bowles, A J Clifford
Resident Partners (Non-ICAEW Members):
M J Wilson, T E Callaghan

BAKER TILLY TAX AND ADVISORY SERVICES LLP
1st Floor, 46 Clarendon Road, Watford, WD17 1JJ
Tel: 01923 816400
Resident Partners/Directors: ICAEW Members
D R Barton, G J Bedingfield, S G Bowles, A J Clifford, G J Francies, D Lewis, M J List, S E Mason, A C Monteith, M J Nicholas, C W Rowe, S Singh
Resident Partners (Non-ICAEW Members):
S T McCrindle, M J Wilson, T E Callaghan

BARRY ROBACK & CO
JSA House, 110 The Parade, Watford, WD17 1GB
Tel: 01923 474777
Principal: ICAEW Member
B P Roback

BLUEDOME FINANCE LTD
Iveco House, Station Road, Watford, WD17 1TA
Tel: 01923 228300
Resident Partners/Directors: ICAEW Members
R G Marsden, R J Sadler, P J Windmill

BRIAN LEWIS FCA ◈
146 Queens Road, Watford, WD17 2NX
Tel: 01923 243888
Email: b.lewis@brianlewis.org.uk
Principal: ICAEW Member
B J Lewis

BURNHAMS LTD
64 Clarendon Road, Watford, WD17 1DA
Tel: 01923 630796
Resident Partners/Directors: ICAEW Members
P A Burnham, R J Malone, G Sterling

BWH AND CO
Iveco House, Station Road, Watford, WD17 1DL

CAPLAN ASSOCIATES ◈
39 Metro Centre, Tolpits Lane, Watford, WD18 9SB
Tel: 020 8242 6544
Email: office@developyour.biz
Website: http://www.developyour.biz
Principal: ICAEW Member
P M Caplan

CBS ACCOUNTANTS
120 Parkside Drive, Watford, WD17 3BB

CBS ACCOUNTANTS LTD
120 Parkside Drive, Watford, WD17 3BB

CHANTREY VELLACOTT DFK LLP
2nd Floor, 34 Clarendon Road, Watford, WD17 1LR
Tel: 01923 255111
Fax: 01923 241300
Email: info@cvdfk.com
Website: http://www.cvdfk.com
Non-resident Partners (ICAEW Members):
S A Kilbane, C D James
Other Offices: Brighton & Hove, Colchester, Croydon, Leicester, London, Northampton, Reading, Stevenage
Registered by the ICAEW to carry out company audit work
Regulated by the ICAEW for a range of investment business activities

INVESTOR IN PEOPLE

COLLEDGE REDFERN ★
2 Nascot Street, Watford, WD17 4RB

COMPELLING SOLUTIONS CONSULTING
29 Lamb Close, Watford, WD25 0TB
Tel: 01923 680103
Principal: ICAEW Member
R A Toner

DAVID MARSTON & CO
Suite A8 Kebbell House, Delta Gain, Carpenders Park, Watford WD19 5BE

FENLEYS
1st Floor, 168 High Street, Watford, WD17 2EG

G.P. COLE & CO
35 Watford Metro Centre, Tolpits Lane, Watford, WD18 9XN

GRAHAM BRAVO & CO
27 Tudor Manor Gardens, Watford, WD25 9TQ

H.W. FISHER & CO
Acre House, 3-5 Hyde Road, Watford, WD17 4WP

HILLIER HOPKINS LLP ◈
64 Clarendon Road, Watford, WD17 1DA
Tel: 01923 232938
Email: info@hhllp.co.uk
Website: http://www.hillierhopkins.co.uk
Resident Partners/Directors: ICAEW Members
J A Barker, P A Burnham, P Collins, J T Harding, R J Malone, G Sterling, R M Twydle
Other Offices: Aylesbury, Hemel Hempstead, London
Registered by the ICAEW to carry out company audit work
Authorised and regulated by the Financial Services Authority for investment business

INVESTOR IN PEOPLE

General Description: Chartered accountants and tax advisers.

HOWARD WILSON ◈
36 Crown Rise, Watford, WD25 0NE
Tel: 01923 670770
Resident Partners/Directors: ICAEW Members
Gary Howard, John Wilson

J B DAVERN & CO
149-151 Sparrows Herne, Bushey Heath, Watford, WD23 1AQ

JAYES FREED
C P House, Otterspool Way, Watford, WD25 8HP

JENKINS & CO
86 Mildred Avenue, Watford, WD18 7DX

JENKINS & CO 2004 LTD
86 Mildred Avenue, Watford, WD18 7DX

JOHN CLARK ◈
Suite 85, Park House, 15-19 Greenhill Crescent, Watford WD18 8PH

JSA
JSA House, 110 The Parade, Watford, WD17 1GB

JSA BUSINESS SERVICES LLP
JSA House, 110 The Parade, Watford, WD17 1GB
Tel: 01923 474757
Email: newclient@jsagroup.co.uk
Website: http://www.jsagroup.co.uk
Resident Partners/Directors: ICAEW Members
M C J Morley, V R Stanton, A D Yates
Registered by the ICAEW to carry out company audit work

SPECIALISATIONS – AUDIT & ASSURANCE
Audit — Private Company

SPECIALISATIONS – BUSINESS & GENERAL ADVICE
Book-keeping
Data Processing Services
Management Advice to Business

SPECIALISATIONS – FINANCIAL REPORTING
Accounts Preparation

SPECIALISATIONS – TAXATION
Taxation

JSA SERVICES LTD
JSA House, 110 The Parade, Watford, WD17 1GB
Tel: 01923 257200
Email: newclient@jsagroup.co.uk
Website: http://www.jsagroup.co.uk
Date Established: 1989
Resident Partners/Directors: ICAEW Members
B P Roback, V R Stanton, A D Yates

SPECIALISATIONS – BUSINESS & GENERAL ADVICE
Outsourcing - Financial Services

SPECIALISATIONS – FINANCIAL REPORTING
Accounts Preparation
Limited Company Accounts

SPECIALISATIONS – IT
Computer Consultants

SPECIALISATIONS – SECTOR
Engineers

SPECIALISATIONS – TAXATION
Payroll Service and Advice

General Description: Sound advice, affordable solutions for freelance professionals. Specialists in outsourcing and back office services.

KAVANAGH BROWN & CO
30 Wentworth Close, Watford, WD17 4LW
Tel: 01923 255483
Resident Partners/Directors: ICAEW Members
N Q Kavanagh Brown, P Kavanagh Brown

LAURENCE B BUTTERS
28 Elm Avenue, Watford,
WD19 4BE

MGW CONSULTANTS LTD
2 Norbury Avenue, Watford,
WD24 4PJ
Tel: 01923 233342
Resident Partners/Directors:
ICAEW Members
M G Ware

MOORE STEPHENS LLP
3-5 Rickmansworth Road,
Watford, WD18 0GX

MYERS CLARK
CHARTERED ACCOUNTANTS

MYERS CLARK ◈
Iveco House, Station Road,
Watford, WD17 1DL
Tel: 01923 224411
Fax: 01923 235303
Email: enquiries@
myersclark.co.uk
Website: http://
www.myersclark.co.uk
Date Established: 1912
Resident Partners/
Directors:
ICAEW Members
J C Crook, R S Driver, R G
Marsden, R J Sadler, J P
Shaw, P J Windmill

Registered by the ICAEW to carry out company audit work

Regulated by the ICAEW for a range of investment business activities

Individual(s) licensed for insolvency work by the ICAEW

SPECIALISATIONS – BUSINESS & GENERAL ADVICE
Acquisitions and Mergers
Disposal of Businesses
Outsourcing - Financial Services

SPECIALISATIONS – BUSINESS RECOVERY & INSOLVENCY
Bankruptcies
Liquidations

SPECIALISATIONS – IT
Computerised Accounting Systems

SPECIALISATIONS – SECTOR
Architects/Surveyors
Charities
Clubs/Associations
Doctors
Estate Agents
Insurance Brokers
Lloyds Underwriters
Nursing Homes/Clinics
Schools
Solicitors

SPECIALISATIONS – TAXATION
Estate and Inheritance
Executorship
Trusts

General Description: Myers Clark, chartered accountants in Watford, works with many local and well-known national clients, in specialist areas including insolvency and not-for-profit. We work closely with clients to make their lives easier and to help them succeed. See www.myersclark.co.uk for a free initial consultation, seminars and fact sheets. Turnball Associates, part of the Myers Clark partnership, specialises in small businesses, start-ups and outsourced services such as payroll and bookkeeping. See www.turnbull-associates.com.

RAYMOND SENTANCE & CO
4 Dunsmore, The Hoe,
Carpenders Park, Watford
WD19 5AU

RG DAWDA & CO
3 Carew Way, Watford,
WD19 5BG

SIMON GROVES & CO
227 Cassiobury Drive, Watford,
WD17 3AN

STEPHEN STARR
77/79 High Street, Watford,
WD17 2DJ

TENON LTD
54 Clarendon Road, Watford,
WD17 1DU
Tel: 01923 431664

THINKFINE LTD
Team House, St Marys Road,
Watford, WD18 0EE

TURNBULL ASSOCIATES
CHARTERED ACCOUNTANTS & BUSINESS ADVISERS

TURNBULL ASSOCIATES
Iveco House, Station Road,
Watford, WD17 1TA
Tel: 01923 228300
Fax: 01923 226216
Email: info@turnbull-
associates.com
Website: http://
www.turnbull-
associates.co.uk
Date Established: 2007
Resident Partners/
Directors:
ICAEW Members
J C Crook, J P Shaw

Regulated by the ICAEW for a range of investment business activities

SPECIALISATIONS – BUSINESS & GENERAL ADVICE
Book-keeping

SPECIALISATIONS – FINANCIAL REPORTING
Accounts Preparation
Audit Exemption Report
Limited Company Accounts
Partnership/Sole Trader Accounts

SPECIALISATIONS – SECTOR
Artists/Graphic Designers
Doctors
Engineers
New Media
Property
Retailers

SPECIALISATIONS – TAXATION
Capital Gains — Personal
Estate and Inheritance
Foreign Nationals in the UK
Investigations
Partnerships and Sole Traders
PAYE Advice
Payroll Service and Advice
Personal
Self Assessment Advice
Small Traders

General Description: Turnbull Associates, Chartered Accountants in Watford, specialises in small businesses, sole traders and start-ups as well as outsourcing services such as payroll and book-keeping. See www.turnbull-associates.com for a free initial consultation. Turnbull Associates is part of the Myers Clark Partnership.

VISANA
43 Parade House, 135 The
Parade, High Street, Watford
WD17 1NS

WARNERS
12-14 Greenhill Crescent,
Watford Business Park, Watford,
WD18 8JA
Tel: 01923 447600
Principal: ICAEW Member
B D Warner

WRIGHT & CO
51 Oxhey Avenue, Watford,
WD19 4HB

WATLINGTON

THE CHILTERN PARTNERSHIP LTD
4 High Street, Watlington,
OX49 5PS

WEDMORE

IAN FAULKNER & CO
Esker Cottage, Quab Lane,
Wedmore, BS28 4AR

T P LEWIS & PARTNERS
10 Church Street, Wedmore,
BS28 4AB
Tel: 01934 712476
Fax: 01934 712476
Email: wedmore@tplewis.co.uk
Resident Partners/Directors:
ICAEW Members
R H Warren

WEDNESBURY

DARLASTON TAXSHOP LTD
210a-212a Darlaston Road,
Darlaston, Wednesbury,
WS10 7TQ

DARLASTON TAXSHOP LTD
10 Walsall Road, Darlaston,
Wednesbury, WS10 9JL

TREVOR A. BOMBER FCA
59 King Street, Darlaston,
Wednesbury, WS10 8DE

WORLEY PRITCHARD & CO ★
34 Hydes Road, Wednesbury,
WS10 9SY

WRIGHT & CO PARTNERSHIP LTD
The Squires, 5 Walsall Street,
Wednesbury, WS10 9BZ

WELLINGBOROUGH

ALANTHWAITE & CO
The Linden Building, Regent Park, Booth Drive, Wellingborough NN8 6GR

BAC AUDITORS
Beeswing House, 31 Sheep Street, Wellingborough, NN8 1BZ

BEDELLS & CHAMBERS ACCOUNTANTS LTD
Beeswing House, 31 Sheep Street, Wellingborough, NN8 1BZ

BERRY KEARSLEY STOCKWELL LTD
Sterling House, 31/32 High Street, Wellingborough, NN8 4HL

CBAC LTD
Hamelin, Bell Hill, Finedon, Wellingborough NN9 5ND

CLIFFORD ROBERTS ◈
63 Broad Green, Wellingborough, NN8 4LQ
Tel: 01933 443311
Resident Partners/Directors: ICAEW Members
L.J.P. O'Malley, J A Payne

HARISH THAKRAR LTD
29 - 31 Finedon Road, Wellingborough, NN8 4AS
Tel: 01933 273910
Resident Partners/Directors: ICAEW Members
H M Thakrar

JAMES MANDEVILLE
6 Ridgeway, Wellingborough, NN8 4RX

JERVIS & PARTNERS (WELLINGBOROUGH)
45 Oxford Street, Wellingborough, NN8 4JH

MWM ★ ◈
24 Oxford Street, Wellingborough, NN8 4JE

R RAJANI & CO LTD
Midland House, 50-52 Midland Road, Wellingborough, NN8 1LU

R THOMPSON & CO LTD
60 Midland Road, Wellingborough, NN8 1LU

ROBERT BROWN
42 High Street, Irthlingborough, Wellingborough, NN9 5TN
Tel: 01933 388399
Principal: ICAEW Member
R Brown

THOMPSON & CO
Sterling Offices, 60 Midland Road, Wellingborough, NN8 1LU

WELLINGTON

BJCA LTD
Landacre House, Castle Road, Wellington, TA21 8YA

DAVID YOUNG & CO
89 Gillards Close, Rockwell Green, Wellington, TA21 9DX

ROY J. HUTCHINGS
Brenacre, Ford Street, Wellington, TA21 9PE

WELLS

CHALMERS HB LTD
20 Chamberlain Street, Wells, BA5 2PF

DAVID STEPHENS
9 Kidder Bank, Wells, BA5 3JT

MARK SHELTON ◈
32 Chamberlain Street, Wells, BA5 2PJ
Tel: 01749 670300
Email: mark.shelton@markshelton.co.uk
Website: http://www.markshelton.co.uk
Principal: ICAEW Member
M W Shelton

SPECIALISATIONS – BUSINESS & GENERAL ADVICE
Feasibility Studies

SPECIALISATIONS – FORENSIC ACCOUNTING
Expert Witnesses in Litigation
Forensic Accounting

SPECIALISATIONS – SECTOR
Agriculture
Food Industry

PETHERICKS & GILLARD LTD
9-13 High Street, Wells, BA5 2AA

RENDELL & CO
125 Portway, Wells, BA5 2BR
Tel: 01749 677065
Fax: 0845 833 1165
Email: email@rendellthompson.co.uk
Website: http://www.rendellthompson.co.uk
Principal: ICAEW Member
J C Rendell
Other Offices: Fleet, Hampshire (Tel: 01252 816636), Christchurch, Dorset (Tel: 01202 474446)
Individual(s) licensed for insolvency work by the ICAEW

SPECIALISATIONS – BUSINESS RECOVERY & INSOLVENCY
Corporate Recovery
Liquidations

SPECIALISATIONS – FINANCIAL REPORTING
Accounts Preparation

RENDELL THOMPSON ★
125 Portway, Wells, BA5 2BR

WEBB & CO LTD
1 New Street, Wells, BA5 2LA
Tel: 01749 676604
Resident Partners/Directors: ICAEW Members
B Davidson, M F Webb
Resident Partners (Non-ICAEW Members):
G S Webb

WELWYN

AIMS ACCOUNTANTS FOR BUSINESS
13 Warren Way, Welwyn, AL6 0DQ

AIMS - CHRIS BURTON
13 Warren Way, Digswell, Welwyn, AL6 0DQ

BOARDMAN & CO
Lakeside, 36 Reynards Road, Welwyn, AL6 9TP
Tel: 01438 714504
Website: http://www.boardman-co.eu
Principal: ICAEW Member
Susan Boardman

D. LITTLE
1 Orchard Road, Burnham Green, Tewin, Welwyn, AL6 0HE

J D FERRY & CO
52 Parkway, Welwyn Garden City, AL8 6HH
Tel: 01707 320800

JAMES TRIPPETT
12 Bluebells, Welwyn, AL6 0XD

NICHOLSONS
Watermead House, 2 Codicote Road, Welwyn, AL6 9NB
Tel: 01438 714007
Principal: ICAEW Member
P McKay

R.S. PARTNERSHIP ◈
Riverside House, 14 Prospect Place, Welwyn, AL6 9EN
Tel: 01438 718118
Fax: 01438 718018
Email: admin@rspartnership.co.uk
Website: http://www.rspartnership.co.uk
Resident Partners/Directors: ICAEW Members
P A Barr, W Stannard
Registered by the ICAEW to carry out company audit work
Regulated by the ICAEW for a range of investment business activities

SPECIALISATIONS – AUDIT & ASSURANCE
Audit

SPECIALISATIONS – BUSINESS & GENERAL ADVICE
Management Consultancy

SPECIALISATIONS – FINANCIAL REPORTING
Accounts Preparation

SPECIALISATIONS – TAXATION
Payroll Service and Advice
Taxation

RATIO BUSINESS SERVICES LTD
10 Mardley Hill, Welwyn, AL6 0TN

WELWYN GARDEN CITY

AMETAB CONSULTANTS
28 Beehive Lane, Welwyn Garden City, AL7 4BQ

BILL COUZENS
40 Digswell Road, Welwyn Garden City, AL8 7PA

C S POMROY & CO ◈
Unit A1, Weltech Centre, Ridgeway, Welwyn Garden City AL7 2AA
Tel: 01707 377057
Principal: ICAEW Member
C S Pomroy

CG ACCOUNTING LTD
70 Eddington Crescent, Welwyn Garden City, AL7 4SQ

EDF ACCOUNTANCY
78 Brocket Road, Welwyn Garden City, AL8 7TU
Tel: 01707 330270
Principal: ICAEW Member
E D Fisher

EURO CAPITAL VENTURES LTD
26 Cypress Avenue, Welwyn Garden City, AL7 1HN

GEORGE ARTHUR LTD ◈
York House, 4 Wigmores South, Welwyn Garden City, AL8 6PL
Tel: 01707 324163
Website: http://www.georgearthur.co.uk
Resident Partners/Directors: ICAEW Members
J A Rook, P P Rook
Registered by the ICAEW to carry out company audit work
Regulated by the ICAEW for a range of investment business activities

JDF SERVICES LTD
52 Parkway, Welwyn Garden City, AL8 6HH
Tel: 01707 320800
Resident Partners/Directors: ICAEW Members
J D Ferry

PAUL NG & ASSOCIATES
15 Halifax Way, Welwyn Garden City, AL7 2QH

WEMBLEY

A.M. PATEL & CO
215B East Lane, Wembley, HA0 3NG
Tel: 020 8904 2015
Principal: ICAEW Member
A M Patel

ABLEMAN SHAW & CO ◈
Mercury House, 1 Heather Park Drive, Wembley, HA0 1SX
Tel: 020 8900 0722
Resident Partners/Directors: ICAEW Members
P Davda, M S Obaray, S M Suchak
Registered by the ICAEW to carry out company audit work
Individual(s) licensed for insolvency work by the ICAEW

AMEY KAMP ★
310 Harrow Road, Wembley, HA9 6LL

ANDREW SHARMA & CO
Wembley Point, 2nd Floor, 1 Harrow Road, Wembley HA9 6DE

ARCHER ASSOCIATES ◈
1 Olympic Way, Wembley, HA9 0NP
Tel: 020 8434 0423
Principal: ICAEW Member
H S Archer

BEEVER AND STRUTHERS ◈
3rd Floor, Alperton House, Bridgewater Road, Wembley HA0 1EH

BENJAMIN, KAY & BRUMMER
York House, Empire Way, Wembley, HA9 0QL
Tel: 020 8795 9123
Fax: 020 8795 9124
Email: mail@bkbweb.com
Resident Partners/Directors: ICAEW Members
S C P Kapoor, M Mohammadi, R J Morris, J J Rome
Registered by the ICAEW to carry out company audit work
Regulated by the ICAEW for a range of investment business activities

BRAHAM NOBLE DENHOLM & CO ★
York House, Empire Way, Wembley, HA9 0PA

CHARLES VITEZ & CO
37 Preston Road, Wembley, HA9 8JZ

COOPER DAWN JERROM LTD
Ground Floor Offices, Cotterell House, 53-63 Wembley Hill Road, Wembley HA9 8DL

DINESH DESAI & CO
Stanley House, Stanley Avenue, Wembley, HA0 4JB

ERIC KIEL & CO
49 Ravenscroft Avenue, Wembley, HA9 9TE
Tel: 020 8904 4769
Principal: ICAEW Member
E S Kiel

FAROOQ & CO
Wembley Point, 1 Harrow Road, Wembley, HA9 6DE

FAROOQ & CO (LONDON) LTD
Wembley Point, 1 Harrow Road, Wembley, HA9 6DE

FELTON ASSOCIATES
112 Wembley Park Drive, Wembley, HA9 8HS

GODLEY & CO
6 Park Lane, Wembley, HA9 7RP

GORDON FENTON & CO
2 The Avenue, Wembley, HA9 9QJ
Tel: 020 3132 2061
Principal: ICAEW Member
G Khubchandani

H.D. SHAH & CO ◈
2 The Avenue, Wembley, HA9 9QJ
Tel: 020 8904 1117
Email: h.d.shah@talk21.com
Principal: ICAEW Member
H D V Shah

HENDERSON REES
Fulton House, Fulton Road, Wembley, HA9 0TF

JANI TAYLOR ASSOCIATES LTD
Office 6A, Popin Business Centre, South Way, Wembley HA9 0HF

KENT & CO LTD
Ground Floor Offices, Cottrell House, 53-63 Wembley Hill Road, Wembley HA9 8DL

KISHORE L. BAVISHI
258 Harrow Road, Wembley, HA9 6QL

LANDAU MORLEY LLP
Lanmor House, 370-386 High Road, Wembley, HA9 6AX
Tel: 020 8903 5122
Website: http://www.landaumorley.co.uk
Training Contracts Available.
Resident Partners/Directors: ICAEW Members
G B Davies, P Faber, M G Freedman, M Haberfeld, R M Jezierski, P L Kutner, R Lampert, D R Passey, I H Segal, B R Thakrar, L C Williams

INVESTOR IN PEOPLE

M.B. PATEL & CO
310 Harrow Road, Wembley, HA9 6QL

M.S.BUHARIWALLA & CO
35a Norton Road, Wembley, HA0 4RG

MMTI LTD
44 Carlton Avenue West, Wembley, HA0 3QU

N.P. SHAH & CO
59 Tudor Court North, Wembley, HA9 6SF

NAIK & CO
66 Montpelier Rise, Wembley, HA9 8RQ

NATH LUTHRA & CO ◈
Minavil House, 1st Floor, Ealing Road, Wembley HA0 4EL
Tel: 020 8795 3441
Principal: ICAEW Member
V N Luthra

P G. PATEL & CO
48 Clarendon Gardens, Wembley, HA9 7QN

P.S. NAGARAJAH
64 Oakington Avenue, Wembley, HA9 8HZ

R. JAGPAL & CO
51 Harrowdene Road, Wembley, HA0 2JQ

R.K. RATTAN
51 Paxford Road, Wembley, HA0 3RQ

R.R. SHAH & CO
78 Wembley Park Drive, Wembley, HA9 8HB

R.R. SPIEGEL
5 Ledway Drive, Wembley, HA9 9TH

RAVINE & CO ◈
783 Harrow Road, Wembley, HA0 2LP

RE10 (LONDON) LTD
Trinity House, Heather Park Drive, Wembley, HA0 1SU

S.J. PATEL & CO
26 Eagle Road, Wembley, HA0 4SH

S. SHARMA & CO
42 Kathleen Ave, Wembley, HA0 4JH

S. SYEDAIN & CO ★
2nd Floor, Heron House, 109 Wembley Hill Road, Wembley, HA9 8DA
Tel: 020 8903 5593
Resident Partners/Directors: ICAEW Members
A M Bharwani, S Husain
Registered by the ICAEW to carry out company audit work

SPECIALISATIONS – FINANCIAL REPORTING
Partnership/Sole Trader Accounts

SPECIALISATIONS – TAXATION
Payroll Service and Advice

SAJID & SAJID
Wembley Point, 1 Harrow Road, Wembley, HA9 6DE

SHOAIE, ZAHEDI & CO ◈
1 Mayfields, Wembley, HA9 9PW

SOMERS BAKER PRINCE KURZ
45 Ealing Road, Wembley, HA0 4BA

T. RASHID
20 Sundew Court, Elmore Close, Wembley, HA0 1YY

TANNA & CO
6 Ravenscroft Avenue, Wembley, HA9 9TL

THANKI ASSOCIATES LTD
16 Wembley Park Drive, Wembley, HA9 8HA

VINOD SHAH
25 Montpelier Rise, Wembley, HA9 8RG

WALTER SINCLAIR & CO
81 Wembley Park Drive, Wembley, HA9 8HE
Tel: 020 8902 2394
Principal: ICAEW Member
W I Sinclair

WEST BROMWICH

AJ & S ASSOCIATES
289a High Street, West Bromwich, B70 8ND

AJ & S ASSOCIATES LTD
289a High Street, West Bromwich, B70 8ND
Tel: 0121 553 7771
Resident Partners/Directors: ICAEW Members
K Jordanou, S A Savva

HOLDEN & CO
Unit 8, Millard Industrial Estate, Cornwallis Road, West Bromwich B70 9BY
Tel: 0121 553 3821
Principal: ICAEW Member
R Holden

ROBERT J. BASS & CO ◈
339 High Street, West Bromwich, B70 9QG
Tel: 0121 525 7236
Website: http://www.robertjbassandco.co.uk
Principal: ICAEW Member
R J Bass
Registered by the ICAEW to carry out company audit work
Regulated by the ICAEW for a range of investment business activities

WEST BYFLEET

ANCHOR ACCOUNTING SERVICES LTD
67 Old Woking Road, West Byfleet, KT14 6LF
Tel: 01932 340543
Resident Partners/Directors: ICAEW Members
R G Pester

BAKER & CO (UK) LTD
35 Station Approach, West Byfleet, KT14 6NF

GIBSON HEWITT & CO ◈
5 Park Court, Pyrford Road, West Byfleet, KT14 6SD
Tel: 01932 336149
Fax: 01932 336150
Email: accs@gibsonhewitt.co.uk
Training Contracts Available.
Regulated by the ICAEW for a range of investment business activities
Individual(s) licensed for insolvency work by the ICAEW
SPECIALISATIONS – BUSINESS RECOVERY & INSOLVENCY
Bankruptcies
Corporate Recovery
Liquidations
Reorganisations and Company Reconstructions
SPECIALISATIONS – FINANCIAL REPORTING
Accounts Preparation
SPECIALISATIONS – FORENSIC ACCOUNTING
Expert Witnesses in Litigation

GIBSON HEWITT OUTSOURCING LTD ◈
5 Park Court, Pyrford Road, West Byfleet, KT14 6SD
Tel: 01932 336149
Email: accs@gibsonhewitt.co.uk
Training Contracts Available.
Resident Partners/Directors: ICAEW Members
L Gibson, R D Hewitt
Individual(s) licensed for insolvency work by the ICAEW
SPECIALISATIONS – BUSINESS & GENERAL ADVICE
Book-keeping Systems
Outsourcing - Financial Services
SPECIALISATIONS – FORENSIC ACCOUNTING
Expert Witnesses in Litigation
SPECIALISATIONS – TAXATION
Partnerships and Sole Traders
Payroll Service and Advice

HAYES & CO
76 Old Woking Road, West Byfleet, KT14 6HU

INSIDE OUT
5 Park Court, Pyrford Road, West Byfleet, KT14 6SD

KEEBLES
Ivanhoe, Maitland Close, West Byfleet, KT14 6RF

MICHAEL WELFARE & COMPANY LTD
100 High Road, Byfleet, West Byfleet, KT14 7QT

TEMPLE WEST LTD
PO Box 454, West Byfleet, KT14 9BD
Tel: 01932 350711
Email: info@templewest.co.uk
Resident Partners/Directors: ICAEW Members
S M Davies
Registered by the ICAEW to carry out company audit work

WEST DRAYTON

HUNTLEY FARRAR LTD
Bentinck House, Bentinck Road, West Drayton, UB7 7RQ

JACKIE BREWER
86B Otterfield Road, Yiewsley, West Drayton, UB7 8PF

PATRICK SOUREN & CO
47 Maple Avenue, Yiewsley, West Drayton, UB7 8LT

WEST MALLING

BACKTOBUSINESS LTD
5 Wheatfield, Leybourne, West Malling, ME19 5QB
Tel: 01732 870026
Resident Partners/Directors: ICAEW Members
H R Truscott

DAVIS & CO
66 Garner Drive, East Malling, West Malling, ME19 6NF

LIBRA WEALTH MANAGEMENT LTD
18 Mitchell Road, West Malling, ME19 4RF

PERRYS
19/21 Swan Street, West Malling, ME19 6JU

WEST MOLESEY

KUMAR & CO ★ ◈
239 Fleetside, West Molesey, KT8 2NL
Tel: 020 8941 0744
Resident Partners/Directors: ICAEW Members
S Kumar

WEST WICKHAM

ALLAN GEORGE CONSULTANTS
107 The Grove, West Wickham, BR4 9LA

B M DUNK
70 Windermere Road, West Wickham, BR4 9AW

DANIELS & CO ◈
111a Station Road, West Wickham, BR4 0PX
Tel: 020 8777 3135
Website: http://www.danielsandco.me.uk
Principal: ICAEW Member
K B Daniels
Registered by the ICAEW to carry out company audit work
SPECIALISATIONS – FINANCIAL REPORTING
Limited Company Accounts
SPECIALISATIONS – SECTOR
Charities
SPECIALISATIONS – TAXATION
Partnerships and Sole Traders

DANIELS & CO (ACCOUNTANTS) LTD ◈
111a Station Road, West Wickham, BR4 0PX
Tel: 020 8777 3135
Resident Partners/Directors: ICAEW Members
J R Byers

I.P. SCOTT
81 Hawes Lane, West Wickham, BR4 0DF

J.C. SEABROOK
56 Woodland Way, West Wickham, BR4 9LR

MICHAEL COSTA CORREA & CO
7 Windermere Road, West Wickham, BR4 9AN
Tel: 020 8777 9092
Principal: ICAEW Member
M F Costa Correa

N. HAGGART & CO
114 Copse Avenue, West Wickham, BR4 9NP

PAPA & CO
36 Copse Avenue, West Wickham, BR4 9NR
Tel: 020 8777 8181
Principal: ICAEW Member
J S Papa

S.J. ROSE & CO
2 Oak Lodge, 6 Oak Lodge Drive, West Wickham, BR4 0RQ

T.E. CARPENTER
362 Pickhurst Rise, West Wickham, BR4 0AY

WILLIAM HOWELL & CO
2 Seabrook Drive, West Wickham, BR4 9AJ
Tel: 020 8777 7790
Principal: ICAEW Member
W G Howell

WITHALL & CO
Squires House, 205A High Street, West Wickham, BR4 0PH
Tel: 020 8777 0800
Resident Partners/Directors: ICAEW Members
S E Withall

WESTBURY

CHAPPELL ASSOCIATES
Westfield House, Bratton Road, Westbury, BA13 3EP

WESTBURY-ON-SEVERN

DEREK DRAPER
The Glen, Adsett, Westbury-on-severn, GL14 1PH

PHILIP MARSHALL LTD ◈
Gatwick Farm House, Stantway Lane, Westbury-On-Severn, GL14 1QG
Tel: 01452 760301
Resident Partners/Directors: ICAEW Members
P R Marshall

WESTCLIFF-ON-SEA

A I COHEN & ASSOCIATES LTD
61 Crowstone Road, Westcliff-on-Sea, SS0 8BG

BRANNANS ★
617/619 London Road, Westcliff-on-sea, SS0 9PE
Tel: 01702 346600
Fax: 01702 346566
Email: philip@brannans.co.uk
Website: http://www.brannans.co.uk
Resident Partners/Directors: ICAEW Members
P G Warburton
Non-resident Partners (ICAEW Members):
A J Prevett, G R Coia
Resident Partners (Non-ICAEW Members):
S E James
Other Offices: London, Colchester
Registered by the ICAEW to carry out company audit work
Regulated by the ICAEW for a range of investment business activities
SPECIALISATIONS – AUDIT & ASSURANCE
Assurance Services
Audit
Audit — Private Company
Pension Scheme Auditors

SPECIALISATIONS – BUSINESS & GENERAL ADVICE

Administration
Book-keeping
Book-keeping Systems
Company Formation
Company Secretarial Service
Data Processing Services
Debt Counselling
Disposal of Businesses
Divorce/Matrimonial
Feasibility Studies
Franchising
Investment Appraisal
Management Accounting Consultancy
Management Consultancy
Outsourcing - Financial Services
Overseas Countries
Risk Management
Takeovers

SPECIALISATIONS – FINANCIAL REPORTING

Accounts Preparation
Audit Exemption Report
Financial Reporting
Limited Companies
Limited Company Accounts
Limited Liability Partnership
Partnership/Sole Trader Accounts

SPECIALISATIONS – IT

Computer Systems and Consultancy
Computerised Accounting Systems
Information Technology

SPECIALISATIONS – SECTOR

Advertising/Design Agencies
Architects/Surveyors
Artists/Graphic Designers
Catering/Restaurants
Charities
Clothing/Textiles
Clubs/Associations
Construction
Corporate
Dentists/Opticians
Doctors
Engineers
Entertainers
Entertainment Centres
Estate Agents
Food Industry
Higher Education/Research Establishments
Hotels/Public Houses
Human Resources
Insurance Brokers
Journalists/Writers/Copywriters
Leisure Industry
Manufacturing
Media
New Media
Nursing Homes/Clinics
Property
Property Development
Property Investment
Retailers
Road Haulage and Distribution
Schools
Solicitors
Trade Assoc/Unions/Friendly Societies
Traders — General
Traders — Luxury Items
Travel Industry

SPECIALISATIONS – TAXATION

Back Duty
Capital Gains — Limited Companies
Capital Gains — Personal
Employee
Estate and Inheritance
Estate Planning
Executorship
Foreign Nationals in the UK
Investigations
National Insurance Advice
Offshore Companies
Partnerships and Sole Traders
PAYE Advice
Payroll Service and Advice
Personal
Self Assessment Advice
Small Traders
Trusteeship
Trusts
UK Companies Overseas
UK Nationals Overseas
Value Added Tax

BRIDGE BUSINESS RECOVERY LLP
615 London Road, Westcliff-on-Sea, SS0 9PE

EUROPA
617-619 London Road, Westcliff-on-Sea, SS0 9PE

EUROPA AUDIT SERVICES LTD
617-619 London Road, Westcliff-on-Sea, SS0 9PE

FRICKER & CO
155 Prittlewell Chase, Westcliff-on-sea, SS0 0RR

GARY DREWERY
27 Canewdon Road, Westcliff-on-Sea, SS0 7NE

HEDGES & CO LTD
366/368 Hamlet House, London Road, Westcliff-on-Sea, SS0 7HZ

HEDGES CHANDLER (SUDBURY) LTD
Hamlet House, 366-368 London Road, Westcliff-on-Sea, SS0 7HZ

HEDGES CHANDLER (WESTCLIFF) LTD ◈
Hamlet House, 366/368 London Road, Westcliff-on-sea, SS0 7HZ

JOSLIN & CO LTD
30 Milton Road, Westcliff-on-Sea, SS0 7JX

KEITH ENGLISH & CO
Kings Cote, 151B Kings Road, Westcliff-on-Sea, SS0 8PP
Tel: 01702 483953
Principal: ICAEW Member
N K English

M G WALTERS & CO LTD
21 Drake Road, Westcliff-on-Sea, SS0 8LP
Tel: 01702 392008
Resident Partners/Directors: ICAEW Members
M G Walters

M. QIDWAI & CO
29 Highfield Gardens, Westcliff-on-Sea, SS0 0SY
Tel: 01702 338 934
Principal: ICAEW Member
M Qidwai

MAN & CO
114 Hamlet Court Road, Westcliff-on-Sea, SS0 7LP

MWS ◈
Kingsridge House, 601 London Road, Westcliff-on-Sea, SS0 9PE
Tel: 01702 332076
Email: mail@mws-accounts.co.uk
Training Contracts Available.
Resident Partners/Directors: ICAEW Members
J R Gorridge, N P Kleinfeld, D McCartney, F A Read, G R M Simons, C R Smith

Registered by the ICAEW to carry out company audit work

Regulated by the ICAEW for a range of investment business activities

General Description: The firm provides a full range of taxation, accountancy, audit and financial services, placing great emphasis on the ability to provide specialist tax and financial planning advice and advice for new businesses.

PAUL WINSTON LTD ◈
23 Alleyn Place, Westcliff-on-Sea, SS0 8AT
Tel: 01702 304563
Resident Partners/Directors: ICAEW Members
P Winston

RAYMOND HECEK
615 London Road, Westcliff-on-Sea, SS0 9PE

RENTON & CO
Chalkwell Park House, 700 London Road, Westcliff-on-sea, SS0 9HQ

RWP LTD
324 Station Road, Westcliff-on-Sea, SS0 8DZ
Tel: 01702 343968
Resident Partners/Directors: ICAEW Members
D M Flatt

STEPHEN JOSLIN & CO
30 Milton Road, Westcliff-on-Sea, SS0 7JX

TENON LTD
Suite 3, Chalkwell Lawns, 648-656 London Road, Westcliff-on-Sea SS0 9HR
Tel: 01702 433668
Resident Partners/Directors: ICAEW Members
P J Forsey

WESTERHAM

BROWN & CO AUDIT LTD
Brown & Co House, 4 High Street, Brasted, Westerham TN16 1JA

BROWN & CO LLP
Brown & Co House, 4 High Street, Brasted, Westerham TN16 1JA

D.M. KIRKE-SMITH
Springhill House, Pilgrims Way, Westerham, TN16 2DU
Tel: 01959 563247
Principal: ICAEW Member
D M Kirke-Smith

JULIAN PAUL & CO
The Mount House, Brasted, Westerham, TN16 1JB
Tel: 01959 563617
Principal: ICAEW Member
J B Paul

K. ROBINSON
Willowcroft, Brasted Chart, Westerham, TN16 1LX

KEMPSTERS
Prospect House, 20 High Street, Westerham, TN16 1RG

LEE HILLIER
1 Granary Cottages, High Street, Brasted, Westerham, TN16 1JA

WESTON-SUPER-MARE

ATKINS & CO
335 Milton Road, Weston-super-mare, Avon, BS22 8JH

ATKINS ACCOUNTANCY SERVICES LTD
335 Milton Road, Weston-super-mare, Avon, BS22 8JH

BROOKING, RUSE & CO
Charterhouse, 3 Beaconsfield Road, Weston-super-mare, Somerset BS23 1YE
Tel: 01934 622466
Principal: ICAEW Member
L D Cox, R D Orr, M Paphitis, B E Ruse

BURTON SWEET ◈
Spencer House, Morston Court, Aisecombe Way, Weston-super-mare BS22 8NA
Tel: 01934 620011
Resident Partners/Directors: ICAEW Members
T P Wicks

BUTTERWORTH JONES ◈
Tallford House, 38 Walliscote Road, Weston-Super-Mare, Somerset BS23 1LP
Tel: 01934 620428
Fax: 01934 415852
Email: weston@butterworthjones.co.uk
Resident Partners/Directors: ICAEW Members
J D Parker, D H Stabbins, G D Thacker
Resident Partners (Non-ICAEW Members):
A Jackson
Registered by the ICAEW to carry out company audit work
Regulated by the ICAEW for a range of investment business activities

D.W. EDWORTHY BSC FCA ◈
The Old Rectory, Rectory Way, Lympsham, Weston-super-mare BS24 0EW
Tel: 01934 750817
Principal: ICAEW Member
D W Edworthy

DAVID K. HARDIMAN
36-38 Meadow Street, Weston-Super-Mare, Avon, BS23 1QQ

J.J. CLEMENT ◈
57 Boulevard, Weston-Super-Mare, Avon, BS23 1PG
Tel: 01934 416 649
Principal: ICAEW Member
J J Clement

JENKIN & CO
28 Waterloo Street, Weston-Super-Mare, Avon, BS23 1LN

PAULINE M. WHITE
6 Ivy Lane, Weston-super-mare, Avon, BS24 7AX
Tel: 01934 513613
Principal: ICAEW Member
P M White

STUART CARDWELL LTD
9a Alexandra Parade, Weston-super-mare, Avon, BS23 1QT

T P LEWIS & PARTNERS (WSM) LTD
34 Boulevard, Weston-Super-Mare, Avon, BS23 1NF
Tel: 01934 415022
Email: mail@tplewis.co.uk
Website: http://www.tplewis.co.uk
Resident Partners/Directors: ICAEW Members
J R Boswell, N J B Gravell, P K Ison

TOM BURGESS
27 Ellesmere Road, Uphill, Weston-Super-Mare, Avon BS23 4UT

WETHERBY

ALAN BARKER & CO
Barnhill, Wetherby Road, Collingham, Wetherby LS22 5AY

ANDREW ST J ELLIS
1 High Street, Bramham, Wetherby, LS23 6QQ

ARTHUR WIGGLESWORTH & CO LTD ◈
43a High Street, Wetherby, LS22 6LR
Tel: 01937 580093

BECKETTS ◈
17-19 Market Place, Wetherby, LS22 6LQ
Tel: 01937 582038
Website: http://www.becketts-accountants.co.uk
Principal: ICAEW Member
A R H Beckett

BKAS
45 Deerstone Ridge, Wetherby, LS22 7XN

BRAYS LTD
23 Market Place, Wetherby, LS22 6LQ
Tel: 01937 583043
Fax: 01937 580214
Email: wetherby@lesliebray.co.uk
Resident Partners/Directors: ICAEW Members
J Dale, I D Parkinson
Registered by the ICAEW to carry out company audit work

C.M. CLARK
43 Poplar Avenue, Wetherby, LS22 7RA

EURA AUDIT UK ★
1 Highcliffe Court, Greenfold Lane, Wetherby, LS22 6RG

JEAL & CO
Sovereign House, 51 High Street, Wetherby, LS22 6LR

JEAL & CO LTD
Sovereign House, 51 High Street, Wetherby, LS22 6LR

LAVERICK & CO
21 Ullswater Rise, Wetherby, LS22 6YP

MORTIMER & CO
Ashfield Hse., 304 High St, Boston Spa, Wetherby LS23 6AJ

MOULDS & CO LTD
Unit 10, York Road Estate, Wetherby, LS22 7SU

P.L. WOOD
20 Lonsdale Meadows, Boston Spa, Wetherby, LS23 6DQ
Tel: 01937 842708
Principal: ICAEW Member
P L Wood

PETER HOWARD & CO ★ ◈
Wharfe Mews House, 1 Wharfe Mews, Cliffe Terrace, Wetherby LS22 6LX
Tel: 01937 580004
Resident Partners/Directors: ICAEW Members
S C Foreman

PETER HOWARD FOREMAN & CO ★ ◈
1 Wharfe Mews Cliffe Terrace, Wetherby, LS22 6LX
Tel: 01937 580004
Resident Partners/Directors: ICAEW Members
S C Foreman

QUERIPEL AND KETTLEWELL LTD
The Barn, Hall Mews, Boston Spa, Wetherby LS23 6DT
Tel: 01937 541770
Resident Partners/Directors: ICAEW Members
J S Kettlewell, P G Queripel

T.A. PARKINSON
Linton Close, Trip Lane, Linton, Wetherby LS22 4HX

T.M. MCMULLEN FCA
5 Milnthorpe Lane, Bramham, Wetherby, LS23 6SW
Principal: ICAEW Member
T M McMullen

WAITE & HARTLEY ◈
66 North Street, Wetherby, LS22 6NR
Tel: 01937 587188
Principal: ICAEW Member
D N Hartley

WEYBRIDGE

ABG ACCOUNTANCY
1 Mays Close, Weybridge, KT13 0XL

BRUCE MORLEY LTD
The Old Rectory, Church Street, Weybridge, KT13 8DE

C.B. HESLOP & CO
The Old School, 51 Princes Road, Weybridge, KT13 9BN

COLIN WOOD
15 Ronneby Close, Oatlands Chase, Weybridge, KT13 9SB

DAVID HOWARD
47 Queens Road, Weybridge, KT13 9UH
Tel: 01932 855644
Email: accountant@davidhoward.co.uk

DEAN BURROWS STEVENSON
24 Templemere, Oatlands Drive, Weybridge, KT13 9PB

ERNEST ENG
Lynwood, Mayfield Road, Weybridge, KT13 8XD

F C REES
Michaelmas, 13 Oatlands Chase, Weybridge, KT13 9RQ

GCA
Beacon House, South Road, Weybridge, KT13 9DZ
Tel: 01932 833950
SPECIALISATIONS – SECTOR
Hotels/Public Houses
SPECIALISATIONS – TAXATION
Payroll Service and Advice

GCA (SURREY) LTD
Beacon House, South Road, Weybridge, KT13 9DZ

GRAHAM NIGEL CARTER LTD
The Old Rectory, Church Street, Weybridge, KT13 8DE

K.W. GORDON & CO
32 Hillcrest, Baker Street, Weybridge, KT13 8EB

KEVIN KEARNEY ASSOCIATES
Suite 3, Weybridge Business Centre, 66 York Road, Weybridge KT13 9DY

LIVINGSTONE & CO ◈
123 Oatlands Drive, Weybridge, KT13 9LB
Tel: 01932 829369
Website: http://www.livingaccounts.co.uk
Principal: ICAEW Member
A Livingstone
Registered by the ICAEW to carry out company audit work

MGI MIDGLEY SNELLING
Ibex House, 61/65 Baker Street, Weybridge, KT13 8AH
Tel: 01932 853393
Fax: 01932 854323
Email: email@midsnell.co.uk
Website: http://www.midsnell.co.uk
Training Contracts Available.
Resident Partners/Directors: ICAEW Members
J R Beecher, J M Farrow, A P Grout, R G Sewell, S P Yeates
Registered by the ICAEW to carry out company audit work
Regulated by the ICAEW for a range of investment business activities
SPECIALISATIONS – AUDIT & ASSURANCE
Audit
SPECIALISATIONS – BUSINESS & GENERAL ADVICE
Management Advice to Business
Overseas Countries
SPECIALISATIONS – FINANCIAL REPORTING
Foreign Subsidiary Companies
SPECIALISATIONS – TAXATION
Foreign Nationals in the UK
Taxation
UK Subsidiaries of Overseas Multinationals

General Description: MGI is a worldwide association of independent auditing, accounting and consulting firms. Neither MGI nor any member firm accepts responsibility for the activities, work, opinions or service of any other members.
Languages Spoken:
German, French

MUMFORD & CO
The Old Rectory, Church Street, Weybridge, KT13 8DE

NICOLAS GOLLINGS & CO
Haddon Cottage, Victoria Road, Weybridge, KT13 9QH

PEMBROKE CONSULTING
Clive House, 12-18 Queens Road, Weybridge, KT13 9XB

PHILIP MUNK LTD
The Old Rectory, Church Street, Weybridge, KT13 8DE

PIPER THOMPSON
Mulberry House, 53 Church Street, Weybridge, KT13 8DJ

SOUTHWORTH & CO
Unit 2, Investment House, 28 Queens Road, Weybridge, KT13 9UT
Tel: 01932 855322
Principal: ICAEW Member
I G Southworth
Registered by the ICAEW to carry out company audit work

SPECIALISATIONS – AUDIT & ASSURANCE
Audit

SPECIALISATIONS – FINANCIAL REPORTING
Accounts Preparation

SPURLING & CO
Hidden Cottage, Egerton Road, Weybridge, KT13 0PW

TWP ◈
The Old Rectory, Church Street, Weybridge, KT13 8DE
Tel: 01932 704 700
Fax: 01932 855049
Email: service@twpaccounting.co.uk
Website: http://www.twpaccounting.co.uk
Resident Partners (Non-ICAEW Members):
A Goddon
Registered by the ICAEW to carry out company audit work
Regulated by the ICAEW for a range of investment business activities

SPECIALISATIONS – AUDIT & ASSURANCE
Audit

SPECIALISATIONS – BUSINESS & GENERAL ADVICE
Book-keeping
Management Advice to Business

SPECIALISATIONS – FINANCIAL REPORTING
Accounts Preparation

SPECIALISATIONS – INVESTMENT BUSINESS
Financial Planning and Advice

SPECIALISATIONS – SECTOR
Nursing Homes/Clinics
Property Development
Property Investment

SPECIALISATIONS – TAXATION
Estate and Inheritance
Estate Planning
Payroll Service and Advice
Trusts

TWP ACCOUNTING LLP
The Old Rectory, Church Street, Weybridge, KT13 8DE

WARD WILLIAMS
Park House, 25-27 Monument Hill, Weybridge, KT13 8RT

WARD WILLIAMS LTD
Park House, 25 - 27 Monument Hill, Weybridge, KT13 8RT
Tel: 01932 830664
Fax: 01932 830733
Email: paul@wardwilliams.co.uk
Website: http://www.wardwilliams.co.uk
Date Established: 1992
Training Contracts Available.
Resident Partners/Directors: ICAEW Members
P J Grainger, R J Hayward, M.W.McKinnell, R N Warburton
Other Offices: Venture House, 2 Arlington Square, Bracknell, Berkshire RG12 1WA
Registered by the ICAEW to carry out company audit work

SPECIALISATIONS – BUSINESS & GENERAL ADVICE
Acquisitions and Mergers

SPECIALISATIONS – FORENSIC ACCOUNTING
Expert Witnesses in Litigation

SPECIALISATIONS – SECTOR
Charities

SPECIALISATIONS – TAXATION
UK Subsidiaries of Overseas Multinationals

General Description: Based in Weybridge and Bracknell, we are a progressive firm providing wide ranging business solutions for small and medium sized businesses, including financial services and HR. We are dedicated to delivering an exceptional service that will contribute towards your business success.
Languages Spoken:
French, Spanish, Swedish

WEYMOUTH

AIMS - DANIEL RUDD
3 St Andrews Avenue, Weymouth, DT3 5JS
Tel: 01305 782212
Principal: ICAEW Member
D J Rudd

COYNE BUTTERWORTH & CHALMERS
Lupins Business Centre, 1-3 Greenhill, Weymouth, DT4 7SP

COYNE BUTTERWORTH HARDWICKE LTD
The Lupins Business Centre, 1-3 Greenhill, Weymouth, DT4 7SP
Tel: 01305 772458
Resident Partners/Directors: ICAEW Members
A J Goracy, J A Hall, M J Howard, A E Newberry, I W Walton
Registered by the ICAEW to carry out company audit work
Regulated by the ICAEW for a range of investment business activities
Individual(s) licensed for insolvency work by the ICAEW

ELLIOT & CO LLP
84 Portland Road, Wyke Regis, Weymouth, DT4 9AB

HELEN MILLER ACCOUNTANCY SERVICES
5 Bincleaves Road, Weymouth, DT4 8RL

K.J. COUSINS
Apt 17, 2 Corscombe Close, Weymouth, DT4 0UG

L.T.J SMITH
3 Manor Farm Walk, Portesham, Weymouth, DT3 4PH

PETER BURROWS
11 Telford Close, Preston, Weymouth, DT3 6PG
Tel: 01305 832456
Principal: ICAEW Member
P H Burrows

R.W. & CO
Bishops Farm, Coldharbour, Weymouth, DT3 4BG
Tel: 01305 789322
Principal: ICAEW Member
R A J Wood

WHITBY

M. WASLEY CHAPMAN & CO
3 Victoria Square, Whitby, YO21 1EA

PHILIP BURLEY (WHITBY) LTD
28 Bagdale, Whitby, YO21 1QL
Tel: 01947 602577
Resident Partners/Directors: ICAEW Members
A Walker
Registered by another RSB to carry out company audit work
Licensed by another DPB to carry on investment business

SIMON J GIBSON LTD
7 Eskdale Close, Sleights, Whitby, YO22 5EW

WHITCHURCH

WHEELER & CO ◈
The Shrubbery, 14 Church Street, Whitchurch, RG28 7AB

ALAN SALT
Rose Croft, Fauls Green, Fauls, Whitchurch SY13 2AS

COLIN F WHITFIELD & CO
Redbrook View, Redbrook, Whitchurch, SY13 3AD

STUBBS PARKIN & SOUTH
23 St Mary's Street, Whitchurch, SY13 1QZ
Tel: 01948 665344
Resident Partners/Directors: ICAEW Members
J M A Birtles, D J Kelsall

WHITEHAVEN

ARMSTRONG WATSON ◈
25 Lowther Street, Whitehaven, CA28 7DG
Tel: 01946 212000
Resident Partners/Directors: ICAEW Members
G I Hayton

J.F.W. ROBINSON & CO
72 Lowther Street, Whitehaven, CA28 7AH
Tel: 01946 692423
Email: accountancy@jfwr.co.uk
Website: http://www.jfwr.co.uk
Resident Partners/Directors: ICAEW Members
J.D.O'Hare, M A Wood

SAINT & CO ▽ ◈
12-13 Church Street, Whitehaven, CA28 7AY
Tel: 01946 693731
Email: whitehaven@saint.co.uk
Website: http://www.saint.co.uk
Resident Partners/Directors: ICAEW Members
I Scott, E J Southward
Registered by the ICAEW to carry out company audit work
Authorised and regulated by the Financial Services Authority for investment business

SARAH E LAMB BSC ACA
23 Park Drive, Whitehaven, CA28 7RY
Tel: 01946 691269
Principal: ICAEW Member
S E Lamb

WHITLEY BAY

AIMS - ALAN REAY
3 Hartley Avenue, Whitley Bay, NE26 3NS

BELL TINDLE WILLIAMSON SERVICES LTD ◈
Coliseum Building, 248 Whitley Road, Whitley Bay, NE26 2TE

FE LAUGHLIN LTD
23 The Crescent, Whitley Bay, NE26 2JG

HARRISON HUTCHINSON LTD ◈
246 Park View, Whitley Bay, NE26 3QX
Tel: 0191 252 1566
Resident Partners/Directors: ICAEW Members
P Hutchinson

LONEY & CO
13 Berrishill Grove, Red House Farm, Whitley Bay, NE25 9XU

NICHOL GOODWILL BROWN LTD ◈
112 Whitley Road, Whitley Bay, NE26 2NE
Tel: 0191 253 1857
Resident Partners/Directors: ICAEW Members
I G Brown, D Nichol

RYECROFT GLENTON ◈
189 Park View, Whitley Bay, NE26 3RD
Tel: 0191 252 1849
Fax: 0191 297 1204
Email: advice@ryecroft-glenton.co.uk
Website: http://www.ryecroft-glenton.co.uk
Non-resident Partners (ICAEW Members):
D Milligan
Registered by the ICAEW to carry out company audit work
Regulated by the ICAEW for a range of investment business activities

SIRIUS BUSINESS SOLUTIONS LTD
1 Cheldon Close, Whitley Bay, NE25 9XS

WALSH & CO
First Floor Offices, 59 Appletree Gardens, Whitley Bay, NE25 8XD

WHITSTABLE

AUSTIN TAYLOR LTD
Atlas House, Tyler Way, Swalecliffe, Whitstable CT5 2RS
Tel: 01227 794477
Resident Partners/Directors: ICAEW Members
E B Taylor

J C NEAME
The Elders, 52 Ham Shades Lane, Tankerton, Whitstable CT5 1NX

LILLEY & CO
125 John Wilson Business Park, Chestfield, Whitstable, CT5 3QT

PETER ALEXANDER
The Firs, Monkton Court, Molehill Road, Chestfield, Whitstable CT5 3QR

WICKFORD

21ST CENTURY ACCOUNTING SERVICES LTD
12 Silver Way, Wickford, SS11 7AP

ALAN BODDY & CO ◈
Damer House, Meadoway, Wickford, SS12 9HA
Tel: 01268 571466
Principal: ICAEW Member
A D Boddy

CHARTWELLS
Knightlands, North Benfleet, Wickford, SS12 9JR

CLAY RATNAGE DAFFIN & CO LTD
Construction House, Runwell Road, Wickford, SS11 7HQ

CLAY RATNAGE STREVENS & HILLS ★
Construction House, Runwell Road, Wickford, SS11 7HQ

HAMILTON BRADING
1 Sopwith Crescent, Wickford, SS11 8YU
Tel: 01268 561800
Email: admin@hbca.co.uk
Resident Partners/Directors: ICAEW Members
A J Brading, D H Hamilton
Registered by the ICAEW to carry out company audit work
Authorised and regulated by the Financial Services Authority for investment business

SPECIALISATIONS – AUDIT & ASSURANCE
Audit

SPECIALISATIONS – BUSINESS & GENERAL ADVICE
Company Formation

SPECIALISATIONS – FINANCIAL REPORTING
Accounts Preparation
Limited Company Accounts
Partnership/Sole Trader Accounts

SPECIALISATIONS – TAXATION
Payroll Service and Advice
Taxation

NG ACCOUNTANCY SERVICES
36 Sutherland Place, Wickford, SS12 9HD

P.S. VORA & CO
32 Doeshill Drive, Wickford, SS12 9RD

READ & CO
3c Sopwith Crescent, Hurricane Way, Wickford, SS11 8YU
Tel: 01268 560983
Principal: ICAEW Member
S R Read

RM ACCOUNTANCY LTD
8 Harris Close, Wickford, SS12 9QY

SPL ASSOCIATES
2nd Floor, De Burgh House, Market Road, Wickford SS12 0BA

WIDNES

ACCOUNTING CONCEPTS (CHESHIRE) LTD
134 Liverpool Road, Widnes, WA8 7JB

BRAMWELL MORRIS
133 Albert Road, Widnes, WA8 6LB
Tel: 0151 424 5208
Email: info@bramwellmorris.co.uk
Website: http://www.bramwellmorris.co.uk
Training Contracts Available.
Resident Partners/Directors: ICAEW Members
A D Morris
Registered by the ICAEW to carry out company audit work
Regulated by the ICAEW for a range of investment business activities

INVESTOR IN PEOPLE

HOLLAND & CO
102/104 Widnes Road, Widnes, WA8 6AX

MITCHELL CHARLESWORTH ◈
101 Albert Road, Widnes, WA8 6LB
Tel: 0151 423 7500
Resident Partners/Directors: ICAEW Members
R L Davies

MOORE STEPHENS ◈
25 Peel House Lane, Widnes, WA8 6TN

TAXASSIST ACCOUNTANTS
134 Liverpool Road, Widnes, WA8 7JB
Tel: 0151 422 9977

WIGAN

C.E. MURPHY
Hale Bank, 40 Bridgeman Terrace, Wigan, WN1 1TT
Tel: 01942 829314
Principal: ICAEW Member
C E Murphy

ELAINE HORSLEY & CO
Ivy House, 687 Ormskirk Road, Pemberton, Wigan WN5 8AQ
Tel: 01942 219419
Principal: ICAEW Member
E Horsley

FAIRHURST
Douglas Bank House, Wigan Lane, Wigan, WN1 2TB

GEOFF CROFT
28 Hollins Road, Hindley, Wigan, WN2 4JZ
Tel: 01942 253283
Principal: ICAEW Member
G Croft

HAYWARD COOPER & CO ◈
30 Bolton Road, Aspull, Wigan, WN2 1YY
Tel: 01942 833204
Principal: ICAEW Member
M E Hayward

HAYWARDS ★
4 Bridgeman Terrace, Wigan, WN1 1SX

J J FINNEY
4 Chiltern Drive, Winstanley, Wigan, WN3 6DY
Tel: 01942 207383
Principal: ICAEW Member
J J Finney

JOHN WILLIAMS & CO
Westerview, Grimshaw Green Lane, Parbold, Wigan WN8 7BB
Tel: 01257 464259
Principal: ICAEW Member
D J Williams

M DB
14 Trescott Mews, Standish, Wigan, WN6 0AW

N.R. BARTON & CO ★
19-21 Bridgeman Terrace, Wigan, WN1 1TD
Tel: 01942 242245
Fax: 01942 820237
Email: accounts@nrbarton.co.uk
Website: http://www.nrbarton.co.uk
Resident Partners/Directors: ICAEW Members
G H Potter, C M Rogers, J Schofield, D J Shirley
Resident Partners (Non-ICAEW Members):
A Farrimono
Registered by the ICAEW to carry out company audit work
Regulated by the ICAEW for a range of investment business activities
See display advertisement near this entry.

NERO ACCOUNTING LTD ◈
Crows Nest, Ashton Road, Billinge, Wigan WN5 7XY
Tel: 01744 893303
Resident Partners/Directors: ICAEW Members
N J Duncan, R J Palk

P A HULL & CO
41 Bridgeman Terrace, Wigan, WN1 1TT

P A HULL & CO
Beech House, 23 Ladies Lane, Hindley, Wigan WN2 2QA

P HAYWOOD
61 Moxon Way, Manor Park, Ashton-in-Makerfield, Wigan WN4 8SW

PAUL CONRON FCA
4 Robin Hood Lane, Wrightington, Wigan, WN6 9QG
Tel: 01257 254745
Principal: ICAEW Member
P A Conron

WIGSTON

ASHLEY COOLING & CO
170 Leicester Road, Wigston, LE18 1DS

PENNY HOWITT
4 Canvey Close, Wigston, LE18 3WS
Tel: 0116 288 0121
Principal: ICAEW Member
P A Howitt

PETER K BLACKWELL
11 Farndale, Wigston, LE18 3XP
Tel: 07843 050703
Principal: ICAEW Member
P K Blackwell

PKB
11 Farndale, The Meadows, Wigston Magna, Wigston LE18 3XP

POWDRILL & SMITH ◈
120 Bull Head Street, Wigston Magna, Wigston, LE18 1PB
Tel: 0116 288 7029
Fax: 0116 281 2408
Email: peter@powdrillsmith.co.uk
Website: http://www.powdrillsmith.co.uk
Principal: ICAEW Member
P R W Smith

WIGTON

ARMSTRONG WATSON ◈
8 King Street, Wigton, CA7 9DT
Tel: 01697 343451
Resident Partners/Directors: ICAEW Members
H L Utting

CAROLE CARRE ASSOCIATES LTD ◈
Ivy Cottage, Blennerhasset, Wigton, CA7 3QR
Tel: 01697 323296
Resident Partners/Directors: ICAEW Members
C L M Carre

DAVID A TAYLOR ◈
The Old Rectory, Boltongate, Wigton, CA7 1DA
Tel: 01697 371647
Principal: ICAEW Member
D A Taylor

DAVID MOFFATT
Windy Ridge, Station Hill, Wigton, CA7 9BJ
Tel: 01697 344758
Principal: ICAEW Member
M D Moffatt

R.M. SLACK
278 Skinburness Road, Skinburness, Wigton, CA7 4QU

SAINT & CO ▽ ◈
49 High Street, Wigton, CA7 9NJ
Tel: 01697 342173
Email: wigton@saint.co.uk
Website: http://www.saint.co.uk
Resident Partners/Directors: ICAEW Members
D A Gibson, A P Irving
Registered by the ICAEW to carry out company audit work
Authorised and regulated by the Financial Services Authority for investment business

WILLENHALL

BARNETT & CO
19-21 New Road, Willenhall, WV13 2BG

GRAVESTOCK & OWEN LTD
75 New Road, Willenhall, WV13 2DA
Tel: 01902 636111
Resident Partners/Directors: ICAEW Members
K Evans

GRAVESTOCK & OWEN LTD
33 Market Place, Willenhall, WV13 2AA

JPO ASSOCIATES LTD
19-21 New Road, Willenhall, WV13 2BG

WILMSLOW

AARDVARK WILLIAMS
53 Racecourse Road, Wilmslow, SK9 5LJ

ACORN CORPORATE FINANCE LTD
Bollin House, Riverside Park, Wilmslow, SK9 1DP

CHARLES E. SPEIGHT
2 Osbourne House, 73 Alderley Road, Wilmslow, SK9 1DA
Tel: 01625 527822
Principal: ICAEW Member
C E Speight

CLARE FRETTSOME
96 Knutsford Road, Wilmslow, SK9 6JD

DAVID LEDERER
Riverdale, 32 Kings Road, Pownall Park, Wilmslow SK9 5PZ
Tel: 01625 525594
Principal: ICAEW Member
D A Lederer

FENCZUK & CO
6 Sefton Drive, Wilmslow, SK9 4EL
Tel: 01625 536536
Email: ajf@fenczukandco.co.uk
Principal: ICAEW Member
A J Fenczuk

SPECIALISATIONS – FORENSIC ACCOUNTING
Expert Witnesses in Litigation
Forensic Accounting

HORNER CHRISTOPHER
First House, Altrincham Road, Styal, Wilmslow SK9 4JE

JANE FOY & CO
24 Mosswood Road, Wilmslow, SK9 2DR
Tel: 01625 528512
Email: Jane.Foy@btinternet.com
Principal: ICAEW Member
J B Foy

SPECIALISATIONS – BUSINESS & GENERAL ADVICE
Book-keeping
Company Secretarial Service

SPECIALISATIONS – FINANCIAL REPORTING
Accounts Preparation
Limited Company Accounts
Partnership/Sole Trader Accounts

SPECIALISATIONS – TAXATION
Taxation

MICHAEL JAMES KENYON
Ashview, 88A Knutsford Road, Wilmslow, SK9 6JD

MICHAEL MOSS & CO
135 Courthill House, 60 Water Lane, Wilmslow, SK9 5AJ

PHIBBS EDGE ◈
Enterprise House, 97 Alderley Road, Wilmslow, SK9 1PT
Tel: 01625 416380
Email: info@phibbsedge.co.uk
Website: http://www.phibbsedge.co.uk
Principal: ICAEW Member
J E Phibbs
Registered by the ICAEW to carry out company audit work
continued

PHIBBS EDGE *cont*

Regulated by the ICAEW for a range of investment business activities

PHILLIPS PARKINSON & CO
2 Fawns Keep, Wilmslow, SK9 2BQ

QUAY ACCOUNTING LTD
Springfield House, Suite 8, Water Lane, Wilmslow SK9 5AG

ROBIN BLACKBURN
Field House, 29 Adlington Road, Wilmslow, SK9 2BJ

SANDISON EASSON & CO
Rex Buildings, Alderley Road, Wilmslow, SK9 1HY
Tel: 01625 527351
Fax: 01625 539315
Email: info@sandisoneasson.co.uk
Website: http://www.sandisoneasson.co.uk
Resident Partners/Directors: ICAEW Members
M D Murray, A S Thomson, I R Tongue
Resident Partners (Non-ICAEW Members):
H D Rushmer
Authorised and regulated by the Financial Services Authority for investment business

SPECIALISATIONS – FINANCIAL REPORTING
Accounts Preparation
Partnership/Sole Trader Accounts

SPECIALISATIONS – INVESTMENT BUSINESS
Financial Planning and Advice
Pensions Advice
Planning

SPECIALISATIONS – SECTOR
Doctors

SPECIALISATIONS – TAXATION
Employee
Estate and Inheritance
Partnerships and Sole Traders
PAYE Advice
Personal
Taxation

General Description: We specialise in acting for doctors in all areas of the United Kingdom.

TC GREENWOOD
22 Ullswater Road, Handforth, Wilmslow, SK9 3NQ

WIMBORNE

CHRIS CHARLTON LTD
38 Middlehill Road, Colehill, Wimborne, BH21 2SE

FOSKETT & CO
Beechcroft, Northleigh Lane, Colehill, Wimborne BH21 2PN

THE FRIENDLY ACCOUNTANTS
Peartree Business Centre, Cobham Road, Ferndown, Wimborne BH21 7PT

FROST & CO
Magnolia House, 24 West Street, Wimborne, BH21 1JS
Tel: 01202 840225

FROST & COMPANY (CA) LTD
Magnolia House, 24 West Street, Wimborne, BH21 1JS
Tel: 01202 840225
Resident Partners/Directors: ICAEW Members
S J Frost

THE GRETTON PARTNERSHIP LTD ◈
9 Brook Lane, Corfe Mullen, Wimborne, BH21 3RD
Tel: 01202 604200
Resident Partners/Directors: ICAEW Members
C W Gretton, R J Gretton

HORSMANS
Stoney Down Farm, Rushall Lane, Corfe Mullen, Wimborne BH21 3RS

HORSMANS LTD
Stoney Down Farm, Rushall Lane, Corfe Mullen, Wimborne BH21 3RS

JENIFER H SIMM
Tun Mead, Gussage All Saints, Wimborne, BH21 5ET

KWG LTD
Arena Business Centre, Unit B1, 9 Nimrod Way, Ferndown Industrial Estate, Ferndown Wimborne Dorset BH21 7SH

MIDDLETON PARTNERS ★
38a Arena, Business Centre, 9 Nimrod Way, Ferndown, Wimborne BH21 7SH

P.A. THOMAS
6 Poole Road, Wimborne, BH21 1QE

PWP ACCOUNTING SERVICES
Number Nine, Nimrod Way, Wimborne, BH21 7SH

THE TAYLOR COCKS PARTNERSHIP LTD ◈
Arena Business Centre, 9 Nimrod Way, Wimborne, BH21 7SH
Tel: 0870 770 8111
Resident Partners/Directors: ICAEW Members
S Beaumont

SPECIALISATIONS – AUDIT & ASSURANCE
Audit
Audit — Private Company

SPECIALISATIONS – BUSINESS & GENERAL ADVICE
Book-keeping
Management Advice to Business
Management Consultancy

SPECIALISATIONS – FINANCIAL REPORTING
Accounts Preparation
Limited Company Accounts

SPECIALISATIONS – SECTOR
Doctors
Solicitors

SPECIALISATIONS – TAXATION
Estate and Inheritance
Investigations
Taxation

TERRY BURRELLS
33 Rectory Avenue, Corfe Mullen, Wimborne, BH21 3EZ
Tel: 01202 694234
Principal: ICAEW Member
T Burrells

THOMAS & WOOLVEN ★
6 Poole Road, Wimborne, BH21 1QE

THOMSON WOOD & COMPANY LTD
Units 7 & 8, The Parade, 147 Wareham Road, Corfe Mullen, Wimborne BH21 3LA
Tel: 01202 601153
Website: http://www.thomsonwood.co.uk
Resident Partners/Directors: ICAEW Members
S J Wood
Resident Partners (Non-ICAEW Members):
B A Wood

WARD GOODMAN ◈
4 Cedar Park, Cobham Road, Ferndown Industrial Estate, Wimborne BH21 7SF

WARD GOODMAN LTD ◈
4 Cedar Park, Cobham Road, Wimborne, BH21 7SF
Tel: 01202 875900
Website: http://www.wardgoodman.co.uk
Resident Partners/Directors: ICAEW Members
G G Ball, D E R Lapthorn, I M Rodd
Resident Partners (Non-ICAEW Members):
R S Duckworth, S Willcox

Registered by the ICAEW to carry out company audit work

INVESTOR IN PEOPLE

SPECIALISATIONS – BUSINESS & GENERAL ADVICE
Acquisitions and Mergers
Divorce/Matrimonial

SPECIALISATIONS – TAXATION
Estate and Inheritance

THE WILCOX PARTNERSHIP ★
Woodside, 6 Queen's Copse Lane, Holtwood, Wimborne BH21 7EF
Tel: 01258 841216
Resident Partners/Directors: ICAEW Members
B H Wilcox

WINCANTON

ANDREW WILKINSON & CO
The Coach House, Rectory Lane, Charlton Musgrove, Wincanton BA9 8ES

FREESTONE & CO
Pine House, 26 High Street, Wincanton, BA9 9JF

WINCHESTER

ANDREW OXENHAM
Pylewell House, Field Way, Compton Down, Winchester SO21 2AF

BRENT KING LTD
113 Greenhill Road, Winchester, SO22 5DX

CHRISTOPHER JENNER & CO LTD
3 Birinus Road, Winchester, SO23 7EG

DAWKINS LEWIS & SOAR ◈
4 Cowdown Business Park, Micheldever, Winchester, SO21 3DN
Tel: 01962 795001
Email: enquiries@dlsa.co.uk
Resident Partners/Directors: ICAEW Members
P Clay, J S Dawkins, A J Sawdon
Registered by the ICAEW to carry out company audit work

HEADY & CO LTD
27 City Business Centre, Hyde Street, Winchester, SO23 7TA
Tel: 01962 850003

J.A. WHITTICK
1 Shepherds Close, Olivers Battery, Winchester, SO22 4HU

JON MILLS FCA
The Old School House, Church Lane, Easton, Winchester SO21 1EH

MCNEILL & CO ◈
The Lilacs, Westhill Road North, South Wonston, Winchester SO21 3HJ
Tel: 01962 882445
Principal: ICAEW Member
H McNeill

MARSHAL CLARKE & CO
Abbots Lodge, Fairfield Road, Shawford, Winchester SO21 2DA

MARTIN AND CO ◈
25 St Thomas Street, Winchester, SO23 9HJ
Tel: 01962 844300
Resident Partners/Directors: ICAEW Members
D J C Barr, J A Burnett, S P McLaughlin
Non-resident Partners (ICAEW Members):
C Griffiths

SPECIALISATIONS – SECTOR

Agriculture

MICHAEL WARNER & CO
37 Southgate Street, Winchester, SO23 9EH

PETER HOWES ASSOCIATES
6 Abbey Hill Close, Winchester, SO23 7AZ

RICHARD NEWTON
15 Manningford Close, Winchester, SO23 7EU

ROTHMAN ACCOUNTANCY SERVICES LTD
The Old Butchery, High Street, Twyford, Winchester SO21 1NH
Tel: 01962 714600
Resident Partners/Directors: ICAEW Members
R L E Rothman

ROTHMAN PANTALL & CO
Avebury House, St Peter Street, Winchester, SO23 8BN
Tel: 01962 842345
Fax: 01962 842346
Website: http://www.rothman-pantall.co.uk
Resident Partners/Directors: ICAEW Members
B Blake, P J Dawson, B Lynch, J Poulter

TEAM 4 ACCOUNTING LTD
Cressfield House, School Lane, Headbourne Worthy, Winchester SO23 7JX
Tel: 01962 881083
Resident Partners/Directors: ICAEW Members
J A Mills

WILKINS KENNEDY ◈
Parmenter House, 57 Tower Street, Winchester, SO23 8TD
Tel: 01962 852263
Website: http://www.wilkinskennedy.com
Resident Partners/Directors: ICAEW Members
J W Beames, A W Brown, I M Talbot
Resident Partners (Non-ICAEW Members):
S A Hollis
Other Offices: Amersham, Ashford, Egham, Guildford, Hertford, London, Orpington, Ramsey, Reading, Southend
Overseas Offices: Stanley, Falkland Islands
Registered by the ICAEW to carry out company audit work

SPECIALISATIONS – BUSINESS & GENERAL ADVICE

Acquisitions and Mergers
Disposal of Businesses
Outsourcing - Financial Services

SPECIALISATIONS – SECTOR

Charities
Construction
Property

WINDERMERE

A. F. MCGHEE & CO ◈
First Floor Offices, 54 Main Road, Windermere, LA23 1DX

ACCOUNTANTS FOR SMALL BUSINESS
Postal Buildings, Ash Street, Bowness-on-Windermere, Windermere LA23 3EB

JACKSON & GRAHAM ◈
Lake Road, Windermere, LA23 2JJ
Tel: 01539 443148
Resident Partners/Directors: ICAEW Members
P C Wood

LAKES ACCOUNTANCY ◈
11 Church Street, Windermere, LA23 1AQ
Tel: 01539 446844
Email: lakesaccountancy@btconnect.com
Principal: ICAEW Member
S A Bloy

WINDLESHAM

BURGE ACCOUNTANCY
Whitecroft House, Hatton Hill, Windlesham, GU20 6AB

BURGE ACCOUNTANCY LTD
Whitecroft House, Hatton Hill, Windlesham, GU20 6AB

DAVID A LEES
8 Fosters Grove, Windlesham, GU20 6JZ

DAVID L. HOHNEN
Cedars Lodge, Church Road, Windlesham, GU20 6BL

HOHNEN DAVID LESLIE
Cedars Lodge, Church Road, Windlesham, GU20 6BL

WINDSOR

C.M.A. SIMON
13 Malt House Close, Old Windsor, Windsor, SL4 2SD

F.P. JOHNSON
Suite 75, 24 St Leonards Road, Windsor, SL4 3BB

FELTON PUMPHREY
Feltons Limited, 12 Sheet Street, Windsor, SL4 1BG

FELTONS LTD
12 Sheet Street, Windsor, SL4 1BG

FELTONS PUMPHREY
12 Sheet Street, Windsor, SL4 1BG

FOREMAN & HILL
5 Curfew Yard, Thames Street, Windsor, SL4 1SN

KEITH ARUNDALE ◈
8 Chestnut Drive, St Leonards Hill, Windsor, SL4 4UT
Tel: 01753 851878
Principal: ICAEW Member
K Arundale

LW FELTONS LTD
12 Sheet Street, Windsor, SL4 1BG

MICHAEL MANN & CO
71 White Horse Road, Windsor, SL4 4PG

NEIL BEATON & CO
4A Albert Street, Windsor, SL4 5BU

STEPHEN LE BRAS
6 Queens Anne's Court, Peascod Street, Windsor, SL4 1DG

TENON LTD
Amberley Place, 107-111 Peascod Street, Windsor, SL4 1TE
Tel: 01753 754400

TENON AUDIT LTD
Amberley Place, 107-111 Peascod Street, Windsor, SL4 1TE
Tel: 01753 754400

WILLIAM J MAYES
Vansittart Estate, Arthur Road, Windsor, SL4 1SE
Tel: 01753 620237
Resident Partners/Directors: ICAEW Members
B W Mayes, W J Mayes

WINSCOMBE

CLEARVIEW BOOK KEEPING & ACCOUNTANCY SERVICES
Little Brockley, Broadway, Shipham, Winscombe BS25 1UF
Tel: 01934 844106
Principal: ICAEW Member
A D Read

CRAIGWEST CONSULTING LTD
Hilltop Meadow, Cuck Hill, Shipham, Winscombe, AVON BS25 1RB
Tel: 01934 844191
Email: craigwestcns@aol.com
Resident Partners/Directors: ICAEW Members
K S Chalk
Individual(s) licensed for insolvency work by the ICAEW

JAMES STEWART & CO
72 Church Road, Winscombe, BS25 1BJ
Tel: 01934 844426
Principal: ICAEW Member
J A H Stewart

MAXWELLS
12 Woodborough Road, Winscombe, BS25 1AA
Tel: 01934 843211
Principal: ICAEW Member
B S Hawkins

PAUL VENN MA FCA
40 Woodborough Road, Winscombe, Somerset, BS25 1AG
Tel: 01934 842828
Email: paul@paulvenn.co.uk
Principal: ICAEW Member
P B Venn
Registered by the ICAEW to carry out company audit work

WHITE ADAMS & CO ◈
1 Famona House, Bridgwater Road, Winscombe, Somerset BS25 1NA
Tel: 01934 844854
Principal: ICAEW Member
C J White-Adams

WINSFORD

A.D.SMITH & CO
112-114 High Street, Winsford, CW7 2AP

GEORGE SNAPE
214 High Street, Winsford, CW7 2AU

HURST & CO
74/76 High St, Winsford, CW7 2AP
Tel: 01606 558552
Principal: ICAEW Member
G Hurst

MURRAY SMITH LLP ◈
Grange House, Grange Lane, Winsford, CW7 2BP
Tel: 01606 868570
Resident Partners/Directors: ICAEW Members
C R Johnson

PAUL BROADHURST & CO
74-76 High Street, Winsford, CW7 2AP

WIRRAL

ACCOUNTS AND TAX LTD ◈
Wellswood, 2 Highfields, Heswall, Wirral CH60 7TF
Tel: 0151 348 4479
Resident Partners/Directors: ICAEW Members
P Owen

AIMS - WILLIAM JUKES ◈
30 Parkway, Meols, Wirral, CH47 7BT

AINLEY COOKSON & CO
Elm Grove Cottage, 4 Bridge Road, West Kirby, Wirral CH48 5EX

ALL ON THE WEB LTD
51 Hambledon Drive, Wirral, CH49 2QH

ANTHONY P. LINTON
8 Croome Drive, West Kirby, Wirral, CH48 8AH

ASHVILLE ACCOUNTANCY LTD
33-35 Old Chester Road, Bebington, Wirral, CH63 7LE

ASHVILLE HENDERSON
33-35 Old Chester Road, Bebington, Wirral, CH63 7LE
Tel: 0151 645 5656

BAILEY PAGE & ROPER
93 Banks Road, West Kirby, Wirral, CH48 0RB

BENNETT BROOKS
33 Allport Lane Precinct, Bromborough, Wirral, CH62 7HH

BERTRAM BURROWS ◈
10 Grange Road, West Kirby, Wirral, CH48 4HA
Tel: 0151 625 2332
Fax: 0151 625 9961
Email: mail@bertramburrows.co.uk
Website: http://www.bertramburrows.co.uk
Date Established: 1962
Principal: ICAEW Member
C N Burrows
Registered by the ICAEW to carry out company audit work
Regulated by the ICAEW for a range of investment business activities
General Description: A small firm with a personal approach providing a comprehensive accounting and taxation service and help and advice for growing businesses.

BIRCHALL & CO ◈
5 Penrhos Road, Hoylake, Wirral, CH47 1HU
Tel: 07714 695948
Principal: ICAEW Member
F J Birchall

CALDWELL CROMPTON
Egerton Chambers, 14 Pensby Road, Heswall, Wirral CH60 7RE

COOKS
61 Thurstaston Road, Heswall, Wirral, CH60 6SA

CS ACCOUNTING
7 Thingwall Road, Irby, Wirral, CH61 3UA

CS ACCOUNTING LTD
7 Thingwall Road, Irby, Wirral, CH61 3UA

DAWPOOL ACCOUNTANCY SERVICES LTD
48 Brimstage Road, Heswall, Wirral, CH60 1XG

DONNAN CALDERBANK
12 Kingsway, Heswall, Wirral, CH60 3SW

DUFTON KELLNER LTD
Barnston House, Beacon Lane, Heswall, Wirral CH60 0EE

EDWARDS, ROWLEY & CO ◈
168A Hoylake Road, Moreton, Wirral, CH46 8TQ

ELPIZO LTD ◈
50 Bickerton Avenue, Higher Bebington, Wirral, CH63 5NB
Tel: 0151 641 9871
Resident Partners/Directors: ICAEW Members
M J Wright

FORRESTERS
8 Gayton Road, Lower Heswall, Wirral, CH60 8PE

GWATKIN & CO ◈
98 Meols Parade, Meols, Wirral, CH47 5AY
Tel: 0151 632 3582
Principal: ICAEW Member
P Gwatkin

HAILWOOD & CO ◈
377-379 Hoylake Road, Moreton, Wirral, CH46 0RW
Tel: 0151 677 7729

HAILWOOD ACCOUNTANTS LTD
377-379 Hoylake Road, Moreton, Wirral, CH46 0RW
Tel: 0151 677 7729
Resident Partners/Directors: ICAEW Members
Danny French

HASTIES
48 Brimstage Road, Heswall, Wirral, CH60 1XG

HORNER DOWNEY & CO
30 Bromborough Village Road, Bromborough, Wirral, CH62 7ES

HORNER DOWNEY & COMPANY LTD
30 Bromborough Village Road, Bromborough, Wirral, CH62 7ES

JOHN GRAHAM & CO
30 Birkenhead Road, Hoylake, Wirral, CH47 3BW
Tel: 0151 632 3361
Fax: 0151 632 5795
Email: mail@johngraham.co.uk
Website: http://www.johngraham.co.uk
Resident Partners/Directors: ICAEW Members
A S Fisher, J M Graham
Registered by the ICAEW to carry out company audit work
Regulated by the ICAEW for a range of investment business activities

JOHN WILLIAMS & CO
1 The Royal, Hoylake, Wirral, CH47 1HS
Tel: 0151 632 6212
Principal: ICAEW Member
J B Williams

JON C ENDEACOTT
66 Meols Drive, Hoylake, Wirral, CH47 4AW

LOUGHREY & CO
38 Market Street, Hoylake, Wirral, CH47 2AF

LOUGHREY & CO LTD
38 Market Street, Hoylake, Wirral, CH47 2AF
Tel: 0151 632 3298
Resident Partners/Directors: ICAEW Members
M J Loughrey

M B NORONHA
15 Sandy Lane, West Kirby, Wirral, CH48 3HY

M C MICHAEL
32 Avondale Road, Hoylake, Wirral, CH47 3AS

MCEWAN WALLACE ◈
68 Argyle Street, Birkenhead, Wirral, CH41 6AF

MARTIN BLOOR & CO
Woodlands, 16 Barnston Towers Close, Heswall, Wirral CH60 2UJ

MORRIS & CO
Ashton House, Chadwick Street, Moreton, Wirral CH46 7TE
Tel: 0151 678 7979
Fax: 0151 606 0909
Email: pjh@moco.co.uk
Website: http://www.moco.co.uk
Date Established: 1975
Resident Partners/Directors: ICAEW Members
P J Harrison, D D Lea
Other Offices: 1 Heritage Court, Lower Bridge Street, Chester CH11 1RD
Registered by the ICAEW to carry out company audit work
Regulated by the ICAEW for a range of investment business activities

SPECIALISATIONS – BUSINESS & GENERAL ADVICE
Franchising

SPECIALISATIONS – SECTOR
Charities
Dentists/Opticians
Doctors

SPECIALISATIONS – TAXATION
Payroll Service and Advice

PENNINGTON HUNTER LTD ◈
Stanhope House, Mark Rake, Bromborough, Wirral CH62 2DN
Tel: 0151 334 2444
Fax: 0151 334 5056
Email: enquiries@penningtonwilliams.co.uk
Website: http://www.penningtonwilliams.co.uk
Resident Partners/Directors: ICAEW Members
G P Cullen, D I H Hunter, M R Pennington, L B Webster
Resident Partners (Non-ICAEW Members):
L B Webster

PENNINGTON WILLIAMS ◈
Stanhope House, Mark Rake, Bromborough, Wirral CH62 2DN
Tel: 0151 334 2444
Fax: 0151 334 5056
Email: enquiries@penningtonwilliams.co.uk
Website: http://www.penningtonwilliams.co.uk
Date Established: 1975
Resident Partners (Non-ICAEW Members):
L B Webster

PLATINUM CAPITAL PARTNERS LLP
James House, Prenton Way, North Cheshire Trading Estate, Wirral CH43 3DU

PROACTIVE CONSULTANTS FOR PROFESSIONALS LTD
1 Grangewood Grammar School, West Kirby, Wirral, CA48 8BU

RACHEL KEENAN & CO LTD
16 Thornfield Hey, Spital, Wirral, CH63 9JT

RICHARD TAYLOR & CO
Orchard Chambers, 4 Rocky Lane, Heswall, Wirral CH60 0BY
Tel: 0151 342 5232
Principal: ICAEW Member
R C C Taylor

ROBSON WELSH
4 The Goose Green, Wirral, CH47 6BQ

ROY GRESHAM FCA ◈
40 Barcombe Road, Barnston, Heswall, Wirral, CH60 1UZ
Tel: 0151 342 4256
Principal: ICAEW Member
R Gresham

S.W.M. REYNOLDS
Morar, 20 Delavor Road, Heswall, Wirral CH60 4RW

STONEBRIDGE STEWART ◈
Daryl House, 76a Pensby Road, Heswall, Wirral CH60 7RF
Tel: 0151 342 4875
Resident Partners/Directors: ICAEW Members
S G Lawrence, C Williams

T.M.J. NORTON
10 Poll Hill Road, Heswall, Wirral, CH60 7SN

TONY HAILWOOD LTD
14 Davenport Road, Heswall, Wirral, CH60 9LF

TREVOR J MATHEW-JONES
30 Bertram Drive, Hoylake, Wirral, CH47 0LQ

WISBECH

ADD ACCOUNTING SERVICES
16 Clarkson Avenue, Wisbech, PE13 2EG

ANTHONY N. BRISTOW
84 Wisbech Road, Outwell, Wisbech, PE14 8PF

BRUCH & CO LTD
1 School Lane, Wisbech, PE13 1AW

BULLEY DAVEY
9-10 The Crescent, Wisbech, PE13 1EH
Tel: 01945 464711
Website: http://www.bulleydavey.co.uk
Resident Partners/Directors: ICAEW Members
M A Burden
Registered by the ICAEW to carry out company audit work
Regulated by the ICAEW for a range of investment business activities

ELIZABETH A. MATTHEWS & CO
Parklands, Barton Road, Wisbech, PE13 1LE

LEIGHTON & CO
40 Alexandra Road, Wisbech, PE13 1HQ
Tel: 01945 581581
Principal: ICAEW Member
R Leighton

MELLOR BELLAMY ★
2 The Crescent, Wisbech, PE13 1EH

MOORE THOMPSON ◈
Monica House, St Augustines Road, Wisbech, PE13 3AD
Tel: 01945 465767
Fax: 01945 476692
Website: http://www.moorethompson.co.uk
Resident Partners/Directors: ICAEW Members
M D Longley, C W Wright

T & I (WISBECH) LTD
16 Clarkson Avenue, Wisbech, PE13 2EG

TURNER & PARTNERS
8 The Crescent, Wisbech, PE13 1EN

WHEELERS ◈
16 North Street, Wisbech, PE13 1NE
Tel: 01945 582547
Website: http://www.wheelers-accountants.co.uk
Resident Partners/Directors: ICAEW Members
M R Baker, A J Cave, H Garrett
Resident Partners (Non-ICAEW Members):
M A Plant, R J Booty

WHITING & PARTNERS ◈
12/13 The Crescent, Wisbech, PE13 1EP
Tel: 01945 584113
Resident Partners/Directors: ICAEW Members
R C Meadows

WITHAM

A.D. KIDDLE
Newlands Farm, Wickham Bishops, Witham, CM8 3JH

BAVERSTOCKS
Dickens House, 3-7 Guithavon Street, Witham, CM8 1BJ

BAVERSTOCKS LTD
Dickens House, Guithavon Street, Witham, CM8 1BJ

CONWAY FIELDEN GOUGH
Colne House, 19 Guithavon Street, Witham, CM8 1BL
Tel: 01376 513177
Website: http://www.vgc.co.uk
Registered by the ICAEW to carry out company audit work
Regulated by the ICAEW for a range of investment business activities

CONWAY FIELDEN GOUGH LTD
Colne House, Guithavon Street, Witham, CM8 1BL
Tel: 01376 513177
Fax: 01376 513447
Email: mail@vgc.co.uk
Website: http://www.vgc.co.uk
Resident Partners/Directors: ICAEW Members
P Conway, D J Verney
Resident Partners (Non-ICAEW Members):
Y M Gough
Registered by the ICAEW to carry out company audit work
Regulated by the ICAEW for a range of investment business activities

IAN SMITH & CO
Lockram Villas, 7 Collingwood Road, Witham, CM8 2DY
Tel: 01376 510511
Principal: ICAEW Member
I D S Smith

INTEGER
72/72a Newland Street, Witham, CM8 1AH

INTEGER ACCOUNTANTS LTD
72a Newland Street, Witham, CM8 1AH

WITHERNSEA

LARSEN AND CO
2 High Brighton Street, Withernsea, HU19 2HL
Tel: 01964 615430
Principal: ICAEW Member
R A Larsen

WITNEY

ACCOUNTANCY PLUS
Unit 7, Thorney Leys Park, Witney, OX28 4GH

ACCOUNTING CENTRE EYNSHAM LTD
26 High Street, Eynsham, Witney, OX29 4HB

BRONSENS ◈
14 Langdale Court, Witney, OX28 6FQ
Tel: 01993 776593

C.S. WILKINSON ◈
49B Market Square, Witney, OX28 6AG

CAMERONS ACCOUNTANCY CONSULTANTS LTD
9 Worton Park, Worton, Witney, OX29 4SX
Tel: 01865 882621
Resident Partners/Directors: ICAEW Members
E O'Donnell

CARTER A.J. & CO
22B High Street, Witney, OX28 6RB
Tel: 01993 703414
Resident Partners/Directors: ICAEW Members
A J Carter, M D A Gyde, N C Williams

FISCALIS MANAGEMENT LTD
4 Meadow Court, 41-43 High Street, Witney, OX28 6RN

FISCALIS MANAGEMENT LTD
1st Floor, 4 Meadow Court, 41-43 High Street, Witney, OX28 6ER

JAMESONS LTD ◈
Jamesons House, Compton Way, Witney, OX28 3AB

JULIE LEWIS
The Cottage, Fordwells, Witney, OX29 9PP
Tel: 01993 878573

LANDTAX
Mitre House, Lodge Road, Hanborough Business Park, Long Hanborough, Witney OX29 8SS

M.R. BEAUMONT & CO ◈
The Birches, 28A High Street, Standlake, Witney OX29 7RY
Tel: 01865 300184
Principal: ICAEW Member
M R Beaumont
General Description:
Management accounting, taxation.

MARK ANDERSON
68 Crawley Road, Witney, OX28 1HU
Tel: 01993 705580
Principal: ICAEW Member
M R Anderson

MORGAN CAMERON
Wittas House, Two Rivers, Station Lane, Witney, OX28 4BL

MORGAN CAMERON LTD ◈
Wittas House, Two Rivers, Station Lane, Witney, OX28 4BH
Tel: 01993 700900
Email: alan.thornton@morgancameron.com
Resident Partners/Directors: ICAEW Members
A F Thornton, M R Thornton
Registered by the ICAEW to carry out company audit work
Regulated by the ICAEW for a range of investment business activities

PETER EDWARDS & CO
1st Floor, 4 Meadow Court, 41/43 High Street, Witney OX28 6ER

PETERSONS
Harvestway House, 28 High Street, Witney, OX28 6RA

PETERSONS ACCOUNTANTS LTD ◈
Harvestway House, 28 High Street, Witney, OX28 6RA
Tel: 01993 776476
Website: http://www.petersons.co.uk
Resident Partners/Directors: ICAEW Members
P J Hellawell, M J Sinfield

REESRUSSELL LLP ◈
37 Market Square, Witney, OX28 6RE
Tel: 01993 702418
Resident Partners/Directors: ICAEW Members
J M Russell

REESRUSSELL TAXATION SERVICES LTD ◈
37 Market Square, Witney, OX28 6RE
Tel: 01993 702418
Resident Partners/Directors: ICAEW Members
J M Russell

SMITH KENNEDY LTD
14 Stanton Harcourt Road, Witney, OX28 3LD

SNEDKERS
Angel House, Hardwick, Witney, OX29 7QE
Tel: 01865 303079
Principal: ICAEW Member
N D Snedker

STONHAM.CO
1st Floor, 4 Meadow Court, 41-43 High Street, Witney OX28 6ER

TADMANS
Blandford House, Church Walk, Combe, Witney OX29 8NQ
Tel: 01993 898040
Principal: ICAEW Member
M R Tadman

TERRY R. WELLSTOOD & CO
Copse Lodge, Cogges Lane, Stanton Harcourt, Witney OX29 5AJ

WILLIAMSON WEST
10 Langdale Gate, Witney, OX28 6EX
Tel: 01933 774555
Resident Partners/Directors: ICAEW Members
D Horton, A R Matthews, A P Spokes, J A West, S Williamson

SPECIALISATIONS – SECTOR

Doctors

WINDRUSH AEC LTD
The Cottage, Fordwells, Witney, OX29 9PP
Tel: 01993 878573
Resident Partners/Directors: ICAEW Members
J Lewis

WOKING

A.C.CRIPPS
5 Kingcup Drive, Bisley, Woking, GU24 9HH

ACUMEN
Unit 4k, 102 Lower Guildford Road, Knaphill, Woking GU21 2EP

AIMS - JACKIE BONELLA LTD
Avonlea, Bush Lane, Send, Woking GU23 7HP
Tel: 01483 211123
Resident Partners/Directors: ICAEW Members
J A Bonella

AJ ROWLANDS & CO ◈
Suite 17, 4th Floor, 1 Crown Square, Church Street East, Woking GU21 6HR
Tel: 01483 776007
Email: accounts@ajrowlands.com
Principal: ICAEW Member
A J Rowlands

AMANDA THORNTON
Saltwood, Onslow Crescent, Woking, GU22 7AU

AUGHTERSONS ◈
1 Wheatsheaf Close, Woking, GU21 4BL
Tel: 01483 841015
Principal: ICAEW Member
J R Aughterson

BARNBROOK SINCLAIR LTD ◈
1 High Street, Knaphill, Woking, GU21 2PG
Tel: 01483 797337
Email: mail@barnbrooksinclair.com
Website: http://www.barnbrooksinclair.com
Resident Partners/Directors: ICAEW Members
G N Barnbrook, A S Holmes, M E Sinclair
Registered by the ICAEW to carry out company audit work

SPECIALISATIONS – BUSINESS & GENERAL ADVICE

Company Formation

SPECIALISATIONS – TAXATION

Investigations

BUTLERS
4 Oakwood Gardens, Knaphill, Woking, GU21 2RX
Tel: 01483 486042
Principal: ICAEW Member
J D Butler

C.E. PETTY & CO
1 Effingham Court, Constitution Hill, Woking, GU22 7RX
Tel: 01483 773326
Principal: ICAEW Member
C E Petty

SPECIALISATIONS – BUSINESS & GENERAL ADVICE

Book-keeping

SPECIALISATIONS – FINANCIAL REPORTING

Accounts Preparation

Limited Company Accounts

SPECIALISATIONS – TAXATION

Personal

C.M. WILSON
7 Saunders Copse, Saunders Lane, Mayford, Woking GU22 0NS
Tel: 01483 767495
Principal: ICAEW Member
C M Wilson

CHAPMAN & CO
Spinnaker House, Horsell Park, Woking, GU21 4LY

COHEN CORKERY
30 Chertsey Road, Woking, GU21 5AJ

COHEN CORKERY LTD
30 Chertsey Road, Woking, GU21 5AJ

COUSSENS
Chimneys, Boughton Hall Avenue, Send, Woking GU23 7DD
Tel: 01483 225400
Email: mail@coussens.co.uk
Date Established: 1988
Resident Partners/Directors: ICAEW Members
M C Coussens

CROOK & CO (ACCOUNTS) LTD
Pencoed, Sheets Heath Lane, Brookwood, Woking GU24 0EL
Tel: 01483 472391
Resident Partners/Directors: ICAEW Members
J Crook

DAVID EXELL ASSOCIATES
Green Umbrella, 4 The Links, Old Woking Road, Old Woking, Woking GU22 8BF

DAVIES ROWBOTHAM & CO
1 St Lawrence Court, 81 High Street, Chobham, Woking GU24 8LX

THE DYER PARTNERSHIP
The Dyer Partnership Limited, 17 Westminster Court, Hipley Street, Woking GU22 9LG

THE DYER PARTNERSHIP LTD
17 Westminster Court, Hipley Street, Woking, GU22 9LG
Tel: 01483 215060
Resident Partners/Directors: ICAEW Members
M E Dyer
Resident Partners (Non-ICAEW Members):
S E Dyer

ELLY SAUNDERS
15 St Marthas Avenue, Woking, GU22 9BN

FOLEY & CO ◈
44A Oriental Road, Woking, GU22 7AR
Tel: 01483 768058
Principal: ICAEW Member
M J M Foley

GRAHAM WORSFOLD
102 Hawthorn Road, Woking, GU22 0BG

GUY & CO
Beechwood, 5 Hale End, Hook Heath, Woking GU22 0LH

HAMLYNS
Sundial House, 98 High Street, Horsell, Woking GU21 4SU

HERBERT PARNELL
Kingsway House, 123 Goldsworth Road, Woking, GU21 6LR

HERBERT PARNELL
Kingsway House, 123 Goldsworth Road, Woking, GU21 6LR

HPCA LTD ◈
Kingsway House, 123 Goldsworth Road, Woking, GU21 6LR
Tel: 01483 885700
Email: partners@herbertparnell.com
Website: http://www.herbertparnell.com
Resident Partners/Directors: ICAEW Members
A W Hodgetts, A M Peckham, L G Redman
Registered by the ICAEW to carry out company audit work
Regulated by the ICAEW for a range of investment business activities
General Description:
Specialisms: SME's; Owner Managed; Businesses; Dentists; Charities; UK Subsidiaries; Full Outsourcing.
Languages Spoken:
German, French

J A CINI
6 Birnam Close, Ripley, Woking, GU23 6JH

JAFFERIES
134A Maybury Road, Woking, GU21 5JR
Tel: 01483 762632
Email: info@jafferies.co.uk
Principal: ICAEW Member
R U Shah

JOANNE ADOLPHUS FCA
Aigburth, 1 Seymour Place, Mile Path, Woking GU22 0JX
Tel: 01483 751077
Principal: ICAEW Member
J Adolphus

JOHN CRACKNELL
Mark House, Aviary Road, Pyrford, Woking GU22 8TH

JOHN WATKINS
67 Park Road, Woking,
GU22 7DH

JS2 LTD
1 Crown Square, Church Street East, Woking, GU21 6HR
Tel: 0845 022 4466
Resident Partners/Directors: ICAEW Members
J R Sanders, J A B Speed

K.A. YOUNG
2A Fenwick Close, Goldsworth Park, Woking, GU21 3BY

KAY & CO
Suite C, Aston House, Portsmouth Road, Ripley, Woking GU23 6EW

KEY, PEARSON & CO
12a The Broadway, Woking, GU21 5AP
Tel: 01483 723952
Principal: ICAEW Member
G H Pearson

L E MARSHALL & CO
Unit D1C, Fairoaks Airport, Chobham, Woking GU24 8HX
Tel: 01276 488091
Principal: ICAEW Member
L E Marshall

MAURICE DAWES
Glen View, Boughton Hall Avenue, Send, Woking
GU23 7DF

MENZIES
Woking Office, Midas House, 62 Goldsworth Road, Woking
GU21 6LQ
Tel: 01483 755000

MENZIES LLP
Woking Office, Midas House, 62 Goldsworth Road, Woking
GU21 6LQ

MORRISON & CO
The Tile House, Bagshot Road, Worplesdon Hill, Woking
GU22 0QY

NOBLE ACCOUNTANCY LTD
41 Guildford Road, West End, Woking, GU24 9PW

NORTHERN ALLIANCE ◈
47 White Rose Lane, Woking, GU22 7LB

NORTHERN ALLIANCE LTD ◈
47 White Rose Lane, Woking, GU22 7LB

P.G. FRY & CO
Hatherley House, Bisley Green, Bisley, Woking GU24 9EW
Tel: 01483 475073
Principal: ICAEW Member
P G Fry

PETER J.W. STANGER
171 Old Woking Road, Pyrford, Woking, GU22 8NU
Tel: 01932 346401
Principal: ICAEW Member
P J W Stanger

PIERCY & CO
Tudor Lodge, The Drive, Hook Heath, Woking GU22 0JS
Tel: 01483 727768
Principal: ICAEW Member
M W Piercy

R & S BUSINESS SERVICES LTD
60 Kingsway, Woking, GU21 6NT

R J BARWICK
Maybury Copse, The Ridge, Woking, GU22 7EQ
Tel: 01483 763298
Principal: ICAEW Member
R J Barwick

RAWLINGS PROFESSIONALS LTD
Unit 4K, 102 Lower Guildford Road, Knaphill, Woking
GU21 2EP

S.F. BROCKLEHURST & CO
Forest Lodge, Forest Road, Pyrford, Woking GU22 8NA

SALEPORT LTD
Greenwood House, Cedar Road, Woking, GU22 0LF

SAM MERCHANT
73 Gorsewood Road, St John's, Woking, GU21 8XG

SCOVELLS
Mennadews, Windlesham Road, Chobham, Woking GU24 8SY

SMITH PEARMAN & CO
Hurst House, High Street, Ripley, Woking GU23 6AY

SMITH PEARMAN LTD
Hurst House, High Street, Ripley, Woking GU23 6AY
Tel: 01483 225457
Fax: 01483 211023
Email: general@smithpearman.com
Website: http://www.smithpearman.com
Resident Partners/Directors: ICAEW Members
K J Hardy

TILBURY YOUNG LTD
Almac House, Church Lane, Bisley, Woking GU24 9DR

VERNON & CO
Fairfields, Pennypot Lane, Chobham, Woking GU24 8DJ

W ACCOUNTANCY LTD
74 Victoria Road, Knaphill, Woking, GU21 2AA

WOKINGHAM

A.M. ACCOUNTING LTD
191A Finchampstead Road, Wokingham, RG40 3HE

ACCOUNTWISE LTD
19 Woosehill Lane, Wokingham, RG41 2TR
Tel: 01189 623702
Resident Partners/Directors: ICAEW Members
R J Melhuish

ALAN REYNOLDS & CO LTD
Walnut House, Walnut Court, Rose Street, Wokingham
RG40 1XU
Tel: 01189 787561
Resident Partners/Directors: ICAEW Members
J A Reynolds

ALUN G HICKS ◈
Westways, Tintagel Road, Finchampstead, Wokingham
RG40 3JJ
Tel: 0118 977 3712
Email: alun@westways42.freeserve.co.uk
Mobile: 07748 962849
Principal: ICAEW Member
A G Hicks

BERTRAM TODD
5 Oxford House, Oxford Road, Wokingham, RG41 2YE
Tel: 0118 977 0944
Principal: ICAEW Member
N A Nicolaou-Todd

BETTRIDGE & CO ◈
5 Magnolia Way, Wokingham, RG41 4BN
Tel: 0118 978 9226

BROWNING HOTCHKISS & PARTNERS
Buckhurst Chambers, Coppid Beech Hill, London Road, Wokingham RG40 1PD
Tel: 0118 978 9020
Fax: 0118 977 2531
Email: info@browninghotchkiss.com
Website: http://www.browninghotchkiss.com
Resident Partners/Directors: ICAEW Members
C R Browning, A J Hotchkiss
Registered by the ICAEW to carry out company audit work
General Description: Company Accounts Fixed Fee Initiative. Our CAFFI scheme fixes the fee for preparation of annual accounts where turnover is under £1m. Please contact 0118 978 9020 for details.

ELLIS & CO ◈
1 Peach Street, Wokingham, RG40 1XJ
Tel: 0118 977 0700
Fax: 0118 997 0701
Email: john@ellis-co.demon.co.uk
Principal: ICAEW Member
J R Ellis
Registered by the ICAEW to carry out company audit work
Regulated by the ICAEW for a range of investment business activities

EVANS & CO
28 Booth Drive, Wokingham, RG40 4HL

GERALD F HAYTER
32 Broad Street, Wokingham, RG40 1AB

GRANARY ACCOUNTING LTD
The Granary, Wheatlands Manor, Park Lane, Finchampstead, Wokingham
RG40 4QL

THE HUNTERS WOOD PARTNERSHIP LTD
Hunters Wood, Heath Ride, Finchampstead, Wokingham
RG40 3QJ
Tel: 0118 973 3517
Resident Partners/Directors: ICAEW Members
R D F Clarke

IAN HARROWER
Fleet Rise, Fleet Hill, Finchampstead, Wokingham
RG40 4LE
Tel: 01189 737333
Principal: ICAEW Member
I Harrower

PPK PROFESSIONAL SERVICES
Oaklands Business Centre, Oaklands Park, Fishponds Road, Wokingham RG41 2FD

PPK PROFESSIONAL SERVICES LTD
Oaklands Business Centre, Oaklands Park, Fishponds Road, Wokingham RG41 2FD

RBS ACCOUNTANCY & BOOKKEEPING
32 Broad Street, Wokingham, RG40 1AB

ROBERT H. NELSON
15 South Drive, Wokingham, RG40 2DH

ROBERT J TUCKER & CO
4 Limmerhill Road, Wokingham, RG41 4BU
Tel: 0118 989 2269
Principal: ICAEW Member
R J Tucker

STEPHANIE BRASS
12 Snowdrop Grove, Winnersh, Wokingham, RG41 5UP

T J LOUGHNANE
Albany House, 14 Shute End, Wokingham, RG40 1BJ

T J LOUGHNANE LTD
Albany House, 14 Shute End, Wokingham, RG40 1BJ

TITCHENERS
The Elms, 26 Broad Street, Wokingham, RG40 1AB
Tel: 0118 989 2005
Resident Partners/Directors: ICAEW Members
P D Kelly

TITCHENERS LTD
The Elms, 26 Broad Street, Wokingham, RG40 1AB
Tel: 0118 989 2005
Resident Partners/Directors: ICAEW Members
A M Beet
See display advertisement near this entry.

TJ LELLIOTT FCA
7 The Lilacs, Barkham, Wokingham, RG41 4UT

WOLVERHAMPTON

A.M. SMITH
5 Corns Grove, Wombourne, Wolverhampton, WV5 0BZ
Tel: 01902 896655
Principal: ICAEW Member
A M Smith

AIMS - DAVID GREENSILL
63 Farrington Road, Ettingsall Park, Wolverhampton, WV4 6QJ

AIMS - SURRINDER KALIRAI ACA ◈
2 Pinfold Lane, Penn, Wolverhampton, WV4 4EE
Tel: 01902 343200
Email: surrinder.kalirai@aims.co.uk
Resident Partners/Directors: ICAEW Members
S S Kalirai

AKM
10 Deyncourt Road, Wednesfield, Wolverhampton, WV10 0SQ

ALAN CORBETT
45 Rooker Avenue, Parkfields, Wolverhampton, WV2 2DT
Tel: 01902 402444
Principal: ICAEW Member
A Corbett

ANDREW HOBBS
17 Suckling Green Lane, Codsall, Wolverhampton, WV8 2BL
Tel: 01902 843735
Principal: ICAEW Member
A R Hobbs

APPLEBY MALL
86 Tettenhall Road, Wolverhampton, WV1 4TF

ATP ASSOCIATES
7 Upper Aston, Claverley, Wolverhampton, WV5 7EE

ATTWOOD & CO
Harrison House, Marston Road, Wolverhampton, WV2 4NJ

BAXTERS ◈
3 Nightingale Place, Pendeford Business Park, Wobaston Road, Wolverhampton WV9 5HF
Tel: 01902 787171
Email: info@baxters-ca.co.uk
Website: http://www.baxters-ca.co.uk
Principal: ICAEW Member
A G Baxter

BHATTI & CO
60 Waterloo Road, Wolverhampton, WV1 4QP
Tel: 01902 771071
Principal: ICAEW Member
P Bhatti

CLAVERLEY ACCOUNTANCY SERVICES
22 The Wold, Claverley, Wolverhampton, WV5 7BD

COTTERELL & CO
The Chubb Buildings, Fryer Street, Wolverhampton, WV1 1HT

COTTERELL PARTNERSHIP LTD
The Chubb Buildings, Fryer Street, Wolverhampton, WV1 1HT

CROMBIES
34 Waterloo Road, Wolverhampton, WV1 4DG
Tel: 01902 773993
Resident Partners/Directors: ICAEW Members
M Fletcher, P G Taylor

CROWTHER JORDAN LTD ◈
39 High Street, Wednesfield, Wolverhampton, WV11 1ST
Tel: 01902 738333
Resident Partners/Directors: ICAEW Members
S Gray

DAW WHITE MURRALL
1 George Street, Wolverhampton, WV2 4DG

DTE LEONARD CURTIS
Regent House, Bath Avenue, Wolverhampton, WV1 4EG
Tel: 01902 810102

E R LLOYD & COMPANY LTD ◈
Regent House, Bath Avenue, Wolverhampton, WV1 4EG
Tel: 01902 810056
Resident Partners/Directors: ICAEW Members
E R Lloyd

FOSTER & CO
Foxbourne Business Centre, Heath Mill Close, Wombourne, Wolverhampton WV5 8EX

GARRATTS ◈
29 Waterloo Road, Wolverhampton, WV1 4DJ
Tel: 01902 773658

GARRATTS WOLVERHAMPTON LTD
29 Waterloo Road, Wolverhampton, WV1 4DJ

GILBERT & CO ★
Suite 2, Hilton Hall, Hilton Lane, Essington, Wolverhampton WV11 2BQ
Tel: 01902 737768
Resident Partners/Directors: ICAEW Members
B J Gilbert

H DAVIES & CO ◈
37a Birmingham New Road, Wolverhampton, WV4 6BL

H.E. PRESSEY
16 Dovecote Close, Tettenhall, Wolverhampton, WV6 8NA
Tel: 01902 752112
Principal: ICAEW Member
H E Pressey

HEDLEY S. WORWOOD
8 Showell Lane, Penn, Wolverhampton, WV4 4UA

HENN & WESTWOOD
Bradford House, 41 Commercial Road, Wolverhampton, WV1 3RQ
Tel: 01902 870700

HIRONS & CO
2 Corfton Drive, Wolverhampton, WV6 8NR
Tel: 01902 746 285
Principal: ICAEW Member
D R Jones

HOWELL DAVIES LTD ◈
37a Birmingham New Road, Wolverhampton, WV4 6BL
Tel: 01902 331117
Resident Partners/Directors: ICAEW Members
R Jebb, R G Jeff, C J Pole
Resident Partners (Non-ICAEW Members):
J E Peasley

HW ◈
Keepers Lane, The Wergs, Wolverhampton, WV6 8UA
Tel: 01902 793333
Resident Partners/Directors: ICAEW Members
M P Brown, A K Gardner, G T Hopwood, A S Minifie, D M Oliver

HW FORENSIC
Keepers Lane, The Wergs, Wolverhampton, WV6 8UA
Tel: 01902 793333
Resident Partners/Directors: ICAEW Members
A S Minifie, D M Oliver

IAN RICHMOND LTD
Chapel Ash House, 6 Compton Road, Wolverhampton, WV3 9PH

J.M. RUDDY
Long Acre, Pattingham, Wolverhampton, WV6 7AD
Tel: 01902 700265
Principal: ICAEW Member
J M Ruddy

J MORGAN & CO ◈
3 Woodford Way, Wombourne, Wolverhampton, WV5 8HD

JAMES E. CONWAY
12 Marchant Road, Wolverhampton, WV3 9QG

JAN G GROMADZKI
4 Bilbrook Road, Codsall, Wolverhampton, WV8 1EZ

JANE HATTON
Harrison House, Marston Road, Wolverhampton, WV2 4NJ
Tel: 01902 310930
Principal: ICAEW Member
C J Hatton

LANCASTER & CO ◈
Granville House, 2 Tettenhall Rd, Wolverhampton, WV1 4SB
Tel: 01902 424261
Resident Partners/Directors: ICAEW Members
S N Beesley, B D Nicholson, E G M Thompson

M FULLWOOD & CO
8 Histons Drive, Codsall, Wolverhampton, WV8 2ET
Tel: 01902 844543
Principal: ICAEW Member
M Fullwood

MURAS BAKER JONES ◈
Regent House, Bath Avenue, Wolverhampton, WV1 4EG
Tel: 01902 393000
Fax: 01902 393010
Email: enquiries@muras.co.uk
Website: http://www.muras.co.uk
Resident Partners/Directors: ICAEW Members
D J Baker, M J Botwood, T Brueton, J H Marks, C A Morris, M H Parker, O Ross, S Ross
Registered by the ICAEW to carry out company audit work
Regulated by the ICAEW for a range of investment business activities
Individual(s) licensed for insolvency work by the ICAEW

NICHOLAS BARWELL & CO LTD
Stirling House, Carriers Fold, Church Road, Wombourne, Wolverhampton WV5 9DJ

ONE STOP SMALL BUSINESS CENTRE
5 Lane Green Shopping Parade, Duck Lane, Codsall, Wolverhampton WV8 1JA

PARTON & CO
2 Lime Tree Avenue, The Dippons,Tettenhall Wood, Wolverhampton, WV6 8HB

PHILIP GEE & COMPANY LTD
15-16 Bond Street, Wolverhampton, WV2 4AS
Tel: 01902 771294
Resident Partners/Directors: ICAEW Members
P W S Gee

R.J. WHITTAKER
Rivelin Cottage, Wynne Cresent, Lower Penn, Wolverhampton WV4 4SW
Tel: 01902 330719
Principal: ICAEW Member
R J Whittaker

R. TENNANT & CO
3A Newton Court, West Strand, Pendeford Business Park, Wobaston Road, Wolverhampton WV9 5HB
Tel: 01902 788661
Principal: ICAEW Member
R Tennant

ROBERT E. PERRY
Parkside House, Old Stafford Road, Slade Heath. Near Coven, Wolverhampton WV10 7PH

ROCHE & CO
Barnswood, 64 Orton Lane, Wombourne, Wolverhampton WV5 9AW

SILVER & CO ◈
41 Graisley Lane, Wednesfield, Wolverhampton, WV11 1PE

SOUTHERNS & CARTER
Harrison House, Marston Road, Wolverhampton, WV2 4NJ

THORPE THOMPSON
1st Floor, Lincoln Lodge, 2 Tettenhall Road, Wolverhampton, WV1 4SA
Tel: 01902 421103
Principal: ICAEW Member
C J Thompson
Registered by the ICAEW to carry out company audit work
General Description: We are registered auditors and chartered accountants.

TILDESLEY & TONKS LTD ◈
Unit 8, Pendeford Place, Pendeford Business Park, Wobaston Road, Wolverhampton WV9 5HD
Tel: 01902 783172
Fax: 01902 789274
Email: enquiries@tildesley-tonks.co.uk
Website: http://www.tildesley-tonks.co.uk
Mobile: 07850 385198
Resident Partners/Directors: ICAEW Members
M J Evans
Registered by the ICAEW to carry out company audit work
Regulated by the ICAEW for a range of investment business activities

VICTOR S. GREEN & CO
7 Inchlaggan Road, Fallings Park, Wolverhampton, WV10 9QX

WEST HOUSE ACCOUNTANTS LTD ◈
14 High Street, Tettenhall, Wolverhampton, WV6 8QT
Tel: 01902 759800
Website: http://www.westhouseaccountants.co.uk
Resident Partners/Directors: ICAEW Members
J B Guy

WOODBRIDGE

C. COOPER
24 Haughgate Close, Woodbridge, IP12 1LQ

CONGRAVE & CO ◈
Maple Court, Hacheston, Woodbridge, IP13 0DS
Tel: 01728 748496
Resident Partners/Directors: ICAEW Members
A J Gravelius

DIGBY & CO
5 Rendlesham Mews, Rendlesham, Woodbridge, IP12 2SZ
Tel: 01394 461 463
Fax: 01394 420760
Email: robertdigby@rendlesham.me.uk

JEREMY STEWART
16 Mayhew Road, Rendlesham, Woodbridge, IP12 2GT
Tel: 01394 421700
Principal: ICAEW Member
J D Stewart

KENNETH T. MOORE
Longmeadow, Broomheath, Woodbridge, IP12 4DL

MICHAEL LISTER ASSOCIATES
Buttons Barn, Magpie Street, Charsfield, Woodbridge IP13 7QE

NIJHAWAN
23a Bridge Street, Framlingham, Woodbridge, IP13 9AH
Tel: 01728 720143
Principal: ICAEW Member
S Nijhawan

ROBERT DIGBY LTD
5 Rendlesham Mews, Rendlesham, Woodbridge, IP12 2SZ
Tel: 01394 461463
Resident Partners/Directors: ICAEW Members
R R Digby

SAXBYS
Maple House, Rookery Road, Monewden, Woodbridge IP13 7DD

SAXBYS LTD
Maple House, Rookery Road, Monewden, Woodbridge IP13 7DD

T.J. MOORBY
1 Fitzgerald Road, Woodbridge, IP12 1EN
Tel: 01394 383227
Principal: ICAEW Member
T J Moorby

TURNER & ELLERBY
The Guildhall, Framlingham, Woodbridge, IP13 9AZ

WOODFORD GREEN

ALAN PARDOE ◈
52 Owen Gardens, Woodford Green, IG8 8DJ
Tel: 020 8504 4690
Principal: ICAEW Member
A P Pardoe

BALFOUR SANSON
17 Bourne Court, Southend Road, Woodford Green, IG8 8HD

BRASSINGTON & CO ◈
600 High Rd, Woodford Green, IG8 0PS
Tel: 020 8559 0556
Email: brassington@lineone.net
Principal: ICAEW Member
I R Brassington
Registered by the ICAEW to carry out company audit work
Regulated by the ICAEW for a range of investment business activities

COOPER YOUNG
Hunter House, 109 Snakes Lane West, Woodford Green, IG8 0DY

GREAVES & CO
White Lodge, 33 Woodside Road, Woodford Green, IG8 0TW
Tel: 020 8506 1002
Principal: ICAEW Member
C M Greaves

HITESH PATEL
14 Denehurst Gardens, Woodford Green, IG8 0PA

JEFFREYS LIVEMORE
114 Kings Avenue, Woodford Green, IG8 0JG

LINDSEY & CO ★
11 The Boulevard, Repton Park, Woodford Green, IG8 8GW
Tel: 020 8501 4500
Resident Partners/Directors: ICAEW Members
B Lindsey

NIEMAN WALTERS NIMAN ★
7 Bourne Court, Southend Road, Woodford Green, IG8 8HD

P.D. KATZ
Apartment 8, Alexandra House, Richmond Drive, Repton Park, Woodford Green IG8 8RF

PETER KATZ & CO
Flat 8, Alexandra House, Richmond Drive, Woodford Green IG8 8RF

RAFFINGERS STUART ★
19-20 Bourne Court, Southend Road, Woodford Green, IG8 8HD

SANSON LTD
17 Bourne Court, Southend Road, Woodford Green, IG8 8HD

STUART DUNSTAN & CO
105 Oak Hill, Woodford Green, IG8 9PF

VICTOR KIRBY & CO LTD
82 Snakes Lane East, Woodford Green, IG8 7QQ
Tel: 020 8559 1660

WISE & CO
24 Woodside Road, Woodford Green, IG8 0TR

WOODSTOCK

COX & BROWNING ★
35 Manor Road, Bladon, Woodstock, OX20 1RU

DAVID TAYLOR
15 Hill Rise, Woodstock, OX20 1AA

KBDR ★
The Old Tannery, Hensington Road, Woodstock, OX20 1JL

WORCESTER

A J MILLARD AND CO LTD
The Granary, Grange Lane, Lower Broadheath, Worcester WR2 6RW
Tel: 01905 333510
Fax: 01905 333536
Email: bdwm.worcester@btconnect.com
Resident Partners/Directors: ICAEW Members
A J Millard
Registered by the ICAEW to carry out company audit work

A J PEACH & CO LTD
104 Grasshopper Avenue, Worcester, WR5 3TB

ANN MASSEY FCA
229 Ombersley Road, Worcester, WR3 7BY
Tel: 01905 456720
Principal: ICAEW Member
A Massey

BHPG LTD ◈
50 New Street, Worcester, WR1 2DL
Tel: 01905 724666
Resident Partners/Directors: ICAEW Members
R M Pritchard

BOUNDARY ACCOUNTING LTD
Bank Farm, Leigh, Worcester, WR6 5LA
Tel: 01886 833933
Resident Partners/Directors: ICAEW Members
G K Corbett

CHRISTOPHER M. STEPHEN-HAYNES
Malvern View Barn, Shrawley, Worcester, WR6 6TS
Tel: 01905 621266
Principal: ICAEW Member
C M Stephen-Haynes

CROWTHER BEARD LLP ◈
Suite 1A, Shire Business Park, Wainwright Road, Worcester WR4 9FA
Tel: 01905 454854
Email: worcester@crowtherbeard.com
Website: http://www.crowtherbeard.com
Resident Partners/Directors: ICAEW Members
J H Painter

ELIZABETH R DEAN
West Lodge, Hall Court, Bishops Frome, Worcester WR6 5BY
Tel: 01885 490659

GARDINER FOSH ◈
31 St Johns, Worcester, WR2 5AG
Tel: 01905 748073
Website: http://www.gardinerfosh.co.uk
Registered by the ICAEW to carry out company audit work
Regulated by the ICAEW for a range of investment business activities

GARDINER FOSH LTD ◈
31 St Johns, Worcester, WR2 5AG

GRETTON & CO LTD
Middle Bouts Farm, Bouts Lane, Inkberrow, Worcester WR7 4HP

HAMILTON PRITCHARD & CO
50 New Street, Worcester, WR1 2DL
Tel: 01905 724666

HARRISON, PRIDDEY & CO
6 College Yard, Worcester, WR1 2LA

HOWARD PAINTER & COMPANY LTD
26 Sansome Walk, Worcester, WR1 1LX
Tel: 01905 21236
Resident Partners/Directors: ICAEW Members
H N Painter

IMOGEN TAYLOR
38 Beech Avenue, Worcester, WR3 8PY
Tel: 01905 458498
Principal: ICAEW Member
Mrs I.C. Taylor

J.C. GODDARD
30 Sansome Walk, Worcester, WR1 1LX

J EVANS
10 Walmer Crescent, Worcester, WR4 0ES

JAMES A. SADLER
13 Fountain Place, Barbourne, Worcester, WR1 3HW

JFA
24 Foregate Street, Worcester, WR1 1DN

JFA ACCOUNTANCY LTD
24 Foregate Street, Worcester, WR1 1DN
Tel: 01905 611833
Resident Partners/Directors: ICAEW Members
J P Flanaghan

JOHN HUBBARD LTD ◈
3 St Marys Street, Worcester, WR1 1HA
Tel: 01905 29827
Resident Partners/Directors: ICAEW Members
J M Hubbard

JOHN YELLAND & CO
22 Sansome Walk, Worcester, WR1 1LS
Tel: 01905 612822
Principal: ICAEW Member
J A Yelland

KENDALL WADLEY LLP ◈
Merevale House, 27 Sansome Walk, Worcester, WR1 1NU
Tel: 01905 26215
Website: http://www.kwca.co.uk
Resident Partners/Directors: ICAEW Members
T C P Calder, J T Marston
Registered by the ICAEW to carry out company audit work

KSURE LTD
Four Winds, Nunnery Lane, Worcester, WR5 1RQ

LCCA LTD
Hopton Corner House, Alfrick, Worcester, WR6 5HP
Tel: 01886 832392
Resident Partners/Directors: ICAEW Members
L A Cotterill

LINDA COTTERILL
Hopton Corner House, Alfrick, Worcester, WR6 5HA

MG WRIGHT FCA FINSTD ◈
The Old Schoolhouse, Church Road, Strensham, Worcester WR8 9LW
Tel: 01386 751309
Principal: ICAEW Member
M G Wright

P.F.HOPE
17 Agatha Gardens, Fernhill Heath, Worcester, WR3 8PB

PAUL CUMMING ◈
Warwick House, Church Lane, Little Witley, Worcester WR6 6LP

PETER J. HEARNSHAW & CO
2 Sankyns Green, Little Witley, Worcester, WR6 6LQ
Tel: 01299 896695
Principal: ICAEW Member
P J Hearnshaw

POTTER THOMPSON
7 Malvern Road, St Johns., Worcester, WR2 4ZH

R.R. HALLETT ◈
Orleton Grange, Orleton, Stanford Bridge, Worcester WR6 6SU

RABJOHNS LLP
1-3 College Yard, Worcester, WR1 2LB

THE RICHARDS SANDY PARTNERSHIP LTD
6 Edgar Street, Worcester, WR1 2LR

ROSEMARY A CAMPBELL
Butterscotch House, 32 Besford Court Estate, Besford, Worcester WR8 9LZ

SANDISON & CO
Church End Court, Queenhill, Upton-on-Severn, Worcester WR8 0RE

SANDISON ROUSE & CO
Richmond House, 48 Bromyard Road, St Johns, Worcester WR2 5BT

SMITH & WILLIAMSON LTD
1 St Swithin Street, Worcester, WR1 2PY

STANSFIELD & CO
2 Fountain Place, Barbourne, Worcester, WR1 3HW
Tel: 01905 723794
Principal: ICAEW Member
S M Stansfield

TAMBLYN & CO LTD
Kinnersley House, Kinnersley, Nr Severn Stoke, Worcester WR8 9JR
Tel: 01905 371454
Resident Partners/Directors: ICAEW Members
S E Tamblyn

TENON LTD
Alexander House, High St, Inkberrow, Worcester WR7 4DT
Tel: 01386 793445

TENON LTD
6 College Yard, Worcester, WR1 2LA
Tel: 01905 745779

TWY LTD
20 Sansome Walk, Worcester, WR1 1LR

WIGGIN'S
1a Shaw Street, Worcester, WR1 3QQ

WORCESTER PARK

FAIRMAN DAVIS
Fairman Law House, 1-3 Park Terrace, Worcester Park, KT4 7JZ

FAIRMAN LAW ★ ◈
Fairman Law House, Park Terrace, Worcester Park, KT4 7JZ
Tel: 020 8408 7500
Resident Partners/Directors: ICAEW Members
I E Mawji, F Meghani, F G Ramji

JOHN LLOYD & CO
Coles House, 64d Central Road, Worcester Park, KT4 8HY
Tel: 020 8337 1276
Fax: 020 8335 0632
Email: enquiries@johnlloydco.co.uk
Date Established: 1984
Principal: ICAEW Member
J C Lloyd
Registered by the ICAEW to carry out company audit work

KAMAL HOSSAIN & CO
Suite 24, Fitzroy House, Lynwood Drive, Worcester Park KT4 7AT
Tel: 020 8337 8963
Principal: ICAEW Member
M M Hossain

PROTO & CO
41 Kingsmead Avenue, Worcester Park, KT4 8XA

STANTON PARTNERSHIP
55 Lynwood Drive, Worcester Park, KT4 7AE
Tel: 020 8335 5530
Resident Partners/Directors: ICAEW Members
M J Stanton

STEPHENS PAUL
24 Cuddington Avenue, Worcester Park, KT4 7DA

VIKRAM PATEL
49 Forest Side, Worcester Park, KT4 7PA

WORKINGTON

GIBBONS & CO
Carleton House, 136 Gray Street, Workington, CA14 2LU

HILARY BELL
North Mosses, Asby, Workington, CA14 4RP

HILARY BELL LTD
North Mosses, Asby, Workington, CA14 4RP

HOWARD H. BOUCH
Grove House, 13 Low Seaton, Seaton, Workington CA14 1PR

J.F.W. ROBINSON & CO
Oxford Chambers, New Oxford Street, Workington, CA14 2LR
Tel: 01900 603623
Email: accountancy@jfwr.co.uk
Resident Partners/Directors: ICAEW Members
P E Ellwood, J D Plaskett, J Spires, R Troughton
Resident Partners (Non-ICAEW Members):
D Hopkinson, V Bishop
Other Offices:72 Lowther Street, Whitehaven
Registered by the ICAEW to carry out company audit work
Authorised and regulated by the Financial Services Authority for investment business

LAMONT PRIDMORE
Milburn House, 3 Oxford Street, Workington, CA14 2AL
Tel: 01900 65955
Fax: 01900 65999
Email: lamont.pridmore@virgin.net
Website: http://www.lamontpridmore.com
Resident Partners/Directors: ICAEW Members
G W Lamont
Other Offices: Kendal, Cumbria, Keswick, Cumbria, Barrow-in-Furness, Cumbria, Carlisle, Cumbria
Registered by the ICAEW to carry out company audit work
Authorised and regulated by the Financial Services Authority for investment business

INVESTOR IN PEOPLE

MONTPELIER PROFESSIONAL (BORDERS) LTD
19 Lillyhall Business Centre, Jubilee Road, Workington, CA14 4HA

WORKSOP

ALCO AUDIT LTD
1 Overend Road, Worksop, S80 1QG

GERALD BAILEY
6 St Martins Close, Firbeck, Worksop, S81 8JU
Tel: 01709 819956
Principal: ICAEW Member
G Bailey

JOHN HARRISON & CO
78 Carlton Road, Worksop, S80 1PH

SLANEY & CO ◈
Portland House, 3 Queen Street, Worksop, S80 2AW
Tel: 01909 472105
Email: worksop@slaneyandco.co.uk
Resident Partners/Directors: ICAEW Members
C G H Jubb, R K Ryder

WILLIAMS KNOWLES & CO ◈
Lloyd Chambers, 139 Carlton Road, Worksop, S81 7AD
Tel: 01909 500232
Principal: ICAEW Member
N M Knowles

WORTHING

A.B. CANNEAUX
Lis House, 11 Anscombe Close, Worthing, BN11 5EW

ATHERTON BAILEY
1 Liverpool Terrace, Worthing, BN11 1TA

ATHERTON BAILEY LLP ◈
1 Liverpool Terrace, Worthing, BN11 1TA
Tel: 01903 217712

BADCOCK BUSINESS SOLUTIONS LTD
4 Prince William Close, Worthing, BN14 0AZ

BOLDEN & LONG
36a Goring Road, Goring-by-Sea, Worthing, BN12 4AD

CARPENTER BOX
15 Grafton Road, Worthing, BN11 1QR

CARPENTER BOX LLP ◈
15 Grafton Road, Worthing, BN11 1QR
Tel: 01903 234094
Fax: 01903 534591
Email: info@carpenterbox.com
Website: http://www.carpenterbox.com
Resident Partners/Directors: ICAEW Members
P M Archer, J G Billings, K N Blake, R W Dowling, M R Godsmark, E M Goff, S R Noakes
Resident Partners (Non-ICAEW Members):
A Edwards, E Goff, C Coopey
Registered by the ICAEW to carry out company audit work

SPECIALISATIONS – AUDIT & ASSURANCE
Audit

SPECIALISATIONS – BUSINESS & GENERAL ADVICE
Company Formation

SPECIALISATIONS – FINANCIAL REPORTING
Accounts Preparation

SPECIALISATIONS – TAXATION
Taxation

DEREK LONGDEN
47 West Parade, Worthing, BN11 5EF

GORDON SPENCER
70A Victoria Road, Worthing, BN11 1UN

THE HIGHGROVE PRACTICE ◈
6 Highgrove Gardens, Worthing, BN11 4SN
Tel: 01903 218654
Principal: ICAEW Member
R C Matthews

HODSON & CO
Wiston House, 1 Wiston Avenue, Worthing, BN14 7QL
Tel: 01903 238628
Resident Partners/Directors: ICAEW Members
B F Hodson, M J Hodson

IVOR G. QUINCEY
50 Offington Avenue, Worthing, BN14 9PJ

L.E.V. MASTERS & CO
46A Goring Road, Worthing, BN12 4AD

THE MARTLET PARTNERSHIP LLP
12 Liverpool Terrace, Worthing, BN11 1TA
Tel: 01903 600555
Resident Partners/Directors: ICAEW Members
F E McIlwee, T V Wolstenholme

NAJEFY & CO
46 Victoria Road, Worthing, BN11 1XE
Tel: 01903 238664
Principal: ICAEW Member
S Najefy

PAUL MARSHALL & CO ◈
138 George V Avenue, Worthing, BN11 5RX
Tel: 01903 504728
Email: paul.marshall2@btconnect.com
Principal: ICAEW Member
P F Marshall

QUEST DUTHOIT LTD
19 Farncombe Road, Worthing, BN11 2AY

R.F. GEORGE & CO
110 Ferring Street, Ferring, Worthing, BN12 5JP

RICHARD HEWS
C P L House, Ivy Arch Road, Worthing, BN14 8BX
Tel: 01903 230999
Principal: ICAEW Member
R A F Hews

SHOAIE, ZAHEDI & CO
10 Clive Avenue, Goring-by-Sea, Worthing, BN12 4SG

SMART & CO
17 Liverpool Road, Worthing, BN11 1SU
Tel: 01903 201940
Principal: ICAEW Member
D M Smart

SPOFFORTHS ◈
A2 Yeoman Gate, Yeoman Way, Worthing, BN13 3QZ
Tel: 01903 828728
Resident Partners/Directors: ICAEW Members
J R Frean, J Haulkham, P J W Hussey, M A Nicholson, P J H B Thatcher, C J Took
Resident Partners (Non-ICAEW Members):
I G Burrows

VANTIS BUSINESS RECOVERY SERVICES
Southfield House, 11 Liverpool Gardens, Worthing, BN11 1RY
Tel: 01903 222 500
Website: http://www.vantisplc.com/businessrecovery
Individual(s) licensed for insolvency work by another RPB
SPECIALISATIONS – BUSINESS RECOVERY & INSOLVENCY
Bankruptcies
Corporate Recovery
Liquidations

W.Y.THOMSON & CO
7 Telgarth Road, Ferring, Worthing, BN12 5PX
Tel: 01903 501620
Principal: ICAEW Member
R G Snook

WOLSTENHOLME MCILWEE LTD ◈
12 Liverpool Terrace, Worthing, BN11 1TA
Tel: 01903 600555
Resident Partners/Directors: ICAEW Members
F E McIlwee, T V Wolstenholme

WOTTON-UNDER-EDGE

BURTON SWEET ◈
9b Long Street, Wotton-Under-Edge, GL12 7ES
Tel: 01453 844721

WEST COUNTRY ACCOUNTING SERVICES LTD
The Paddocks, Duck Street, Tytherington, Wotton-Under-Edge GL12 8QB

WILLOW ACCOUNTANCY
Willow Cottage, Valley Road, Wotton-Under-Edge, GL12 7NP

WYMONDHAM

CHAPPELL & CO
Baysfield House, Silfield Road, Wymondham, NR18 9AZ

P SHANE MCGUIRE BA (ECON) FCA
97 Norwich Road, Wymondham, NR18 0SJ
Tel: 01953 603180
Principal: ICAEW Member
P S McGuire

PAUL TAYLOR
22 Middleton Street, Wymondham, NR18 0AD

YARM

J.MARTIN JAMES
101A High Street, Yarm, TS15 9BB

J S CARLING ACCOUNTANCY
41 Knaith Close, Yarm, TS15 9TL
Tel: 01642 889019
Principal: ICAEW Member
J S Carling

TAYLOR ROWLANDS
8 High Street, Yarm, TS15 9AE

W.A. SHERET
Meadowcroft, Yarm Road, Hilton, Yarm TS15 9LF

YARMOUTH

PETER M N JENNINGS FCA
Mariners, Longs Wharf, Yarmouth, PO41 0PW

YATELEY

ELLAY
Maple Court, Quarry Lane, Cricket Hill, Yateley GU46 6XW

IAIN MCGRORY
2 The Studio, 24 Pond Croft, Reading Road, Yateley GU46 7UR

J.E. BENNEYWORTH
7 Broome Close, Yateley, GU46 7SY

JAMES BORTHWICK FCA
4 Hawkins Close, Yateley, GU46 6LS

LEFEVRES
4 Huddington Glade, Yateley, GU46 6FG

LEFEVRES LTD
4 Huddington Glade, Yateley, GU46 6FG

YELVERTON

JOHN LYDDON LTD
Uplands, Manor Estate, Horrabridge, Yelverton PL20 7RS

KEANE & CO
1-2 Moorside Court, Yelverton Business Park, Crapstone, Yelverton PL20 7PE
Tel: 01822 855467
Email: consult@keaneco.demon.co.uk
Date Established: 1984
Resident Partners/Directors: ICAEW Members
R H Keane
Registered by the ICAEW to carry out company audit work
Regulated by the ICAEW for a range of investment business activities

PAUL CREASY
St Davids, Meavy Bourne, Yelverton, PL20 6AR

SIMON MURRAY & CO
Woburn House, Yelverton, PL20 6BS
Tel: 01822 853485
Principal: ICAEW Member
S A Murray

SYNERGY
17 Torbridge Road, Horrabridge, Yelverton, PL20 7SD

YEOVIL

ALBERT GOODMAN
Hendford Manor, Yeovil, BA20 1UN

CHALMERS & CO ◈
Magnolia House, Princes Street, Yeovil, BA20 1EP

IVAN RENDALL & CO
Torre Lea House, 33 The Avenue, Yeovil, BA21 4BN

LANHAM & FRANCIS ▽ ◈
Church House, Church Street, Yeovil, BA20 1HB
Tel: 01935 476401
Fax: 01935 433534
Email: iandodds@lanhamandfrancis.co.uk
Website: http://www.lanhamandfrancis.co.uk
Non-resident Partners (ICAEW Members):
R L Machin
Non-resident Partners (Non-ICAEW Members):
I D Dodds
Other Offices: Shaftesbury, Dorset; Sherborne, Dorset
Registered by the ICAEW to carry out company audit work
Regulated by the ICAEW for a range of investment business activities
See display advertisement near this entry.

MILSTED LANGDON LLP
Motivo House, Alvington, Yeovil, BA20 2FG
Tel: 01935 383500
Resident Partners/Directors: ICAEW Members
N P Moysey, G Salter

MJT ACCOUNTANCY SERVICES
9 Elmleigh, Yeovil, BA21 3UJ

NURSEN PRIEST
3 Watercombe Heights, Yeovil, BA20 2TQ

OLD MILL
Number One, Goldcroft, Yeovil, BA21 4DX
Tel: 01935 426181
Website: http://www.oldmillgroup.co.uk
Resident Partners/Directors: ICAEW Members
M J Butler, C H Howes, D J Maslen, J R G Stonehouse

R.J. DENNIS
Kerian, Corkscrew Lane, Woolston, Yeovil BA22 7BP

TENON LTD
Number One, Goldcroft, Yeovil, BA21 4DX

TOMSETT & CO
Marsh Hill Farm, Marsh Lane, Yeovil, BA21 3QA

WHITES
99 Preston Grove, Yeovil, BA20 2DB
Tel: 01935 433708
Fax: 01935 433645
Email: plevey@whites-chartac.co.uk
Principal: ICAEW Member
P L Levey

YORK

A J BROWN LTD
91 Front Street, Acomb, York, YO24 3BU
Tel: 01904 792226
Resident Partners/Directors: ICAEW Members
A J Brown

A.J. BROWN
91 Front Street, Acomb, York, YO24 3BU

AIMS - PAUL WHELAN FCA
Ashby House, Bernard Lane, Green Hammerton, York YO26 8BP

ASHBY, BERRY & CO
8 Bondgate, Helmsley, York, YO62 5BR

ASSURED ACCOUNTANCY
14 Market Place, Pocklington, York, YO42 2AR

ATKINSONS ◈
The Innovation Centre, Innovation Way, Heslington, York YO10 5DG

BARRON & BARRON
Bathurst House, 86 Micklegate, York, YO1 6LQ
Tel: 01904 628551
Fax: 01904 623533
Email: info@barronyork.co.uk
Resident Partners/Directors: ICAEW Members
R C Bailey, G S Ward
Other Offices: Easingwold
Registered by the ICAEW to carry out company audit work
Regulated by the ICAEW for a range of investment business activities

BARRON & BARRON
Windross Square, Market Place, Easingwold, York YO61 3AL
Tel: 01347 822055
Fax: 01347 822055
Email: info@barronyork.co.uk
Other Offices: York
Registered by the ICAEW to carry out company audit work
Regulated by the ICAEW for a range of investment business activities

BOTTING & CO
8 Clifton Moor Business Village, James Nicolson Link, York, YO30 4XG
Tel: 01904 692888
Principal: ICAEW Member
A E W Botting

BOTTING & CO LTD
8 Clifton Moor Business Village, James Nicolson Link, York, YO30 4XG
Tel: 01904 692888
Resident Partners/Directors: ICAEW Members
A E W Botting

BRODERICKS ◈
1 Heslington Court, Heslington, York, YO10 5EX
Tel: 01904 430603
Fax: 01904 411763
Email: mike@brodericksyork.com
Principal: ICAEW Member
J M Broderick
Regulated by the ICAEW for a range of investment business activities

C & S CHRISTIE LTD
1 Nalton Close, Copmanthorpe, York, YO23 3YY

C.S. FENTON & CO ★
2 Clifton Moor, Business Village, James Nicolson Link, York YO30 4XG
Tel: 01904 692120
Resident Partners/Directors: ICAEW Members
C S Fenton

CAERUS
23 Larch Rise, Easingwold, York, YO61 3RZ

CLIVE OWEN & CO LLP
Oak Tree House, Harwood Road, Northminster Business Park, Upper Poppleton, York YO26 6QU

FISHER & COMPANY LTD ◈
Kingfisher House, 65 Market Place, Market Weighton, York YO43 3AN

FORSTER, STOTT & CO
Langton House, 124 Acomb Road, Holgate, York YO24 4EY
Tel: 01904 799499
Resident Partners/Directors: ICAEW Members
L P Bean, S J Kilmartin, I W Wallace

G & E (HOLDINGS) LTD
Garbutt & Elliott, Arabesque House, Monks Cross Drive, Huntington, York YO32 9GW

G.S. COOK ◈
26 Southdown Road, Huntington, York, YO32 9RW

GARBUTT & ELLIOTT LTD ◈
Arabesque House, Monks Cross Drive, Huntington, York YO32 9GW
Tel: 01904 464100
Fax: 01904 464111
Website: http://www.garbutt-elliott.co.uk
Training Contracts Available.
Resident Partners/Directors: ICAEW Members
D J Dickson, C Manson, S M Reid, N J Scull, A M Sidebottom, I C Smith, A Widdowson
Resident Partners (Non-ICAEW Members):
J Oliver, R Turner, A Tarpey
Registered by the ICAEW to carry out company audit work
Regulated by the ICAEW for a range of investment business activities

GARDINERS LTD ◈
Hutton House, Dave Road, Sheriff Hutton, York YO60 6RZ
Tel: 01347 878305
Resident Partners/Directors: ICAEW Members
B Cleaver, S J R Roy

GRAHAM WALKER ◈
1 Westfield Cottages, Newton on Derwent, York, YO41 4DG
Tel: 01904 607496
Resident Partners/Directors: ICAEW Members
G B Walker

HARRIS, LACEY AND SWAIN
19 Railway Street, Pocklington, York, YO42 2QR

HARRIS, LACEY AND SWAIN LTD ◈
19 Railway Street, Pocklington, York, YO42 2QR
Tel: 01759 305969

HARRISON HOLT
High Park Farm, Kirkbymoorside, York, YO62 7HS

HPH
54 Bootham, York, YO30 7XZ
Tel: 01904 611164
Resident Partners/Directors: ICAEW Members
P A Thake, C M S Walker, R W Woolley

HUNTER GEE HOLROYD
Club Chambers, Museum Street, York, YO1 7DN
Tel: 01904 655202
Fax: 01904 623456
Email: enquiries@hghyork.co.uk
Resident Partners/Directors: ICAEW Members
N P Atkinson, N C Everard, M R Grewer
Other Offices: Easingwold, Filey
Registered by the ICAEW to carry out company audit work
Regulated by the ICAEW for a range of investment business activities
General Description: A long established firm providing audit, taxation, accountancy, strategic business planning and financial services to individuals, partnerships and director-controlled companies.

HUNTER GEE HOLROYD
Bradgate House, Chapel Street, Easingwold, York YO61 3AE

INGHAM & CO
All Saints Church House, High Market Place, Kirkbymoorside, York YO6 6AT

INMAN & CO ACCOUNTANTS LTD
24 Green Lane, Clifton, York, YO30 5QX

J B NORFOLK & CO
12 Chatsworth Grove, Boroughbridge, York, YO51 9BB
Tel: 01423 322151
Principal: ICAEW Member
J B Norfolk

JOHN CUNNINGHAM
Cortigan, Main Street, Bishop Wilton, York YO42 1SR

JOHN MINFORD ASSOCIATES
Market Place, Easingwold, York, YO61 3AG

JOHN MINFORD ASSOCIATES ◈
London House, Mill Lane Corner, 31 Hawthorn Grove, York YO31 7UA
Tel: 01904 658865
Principal: ICAEW Member
A J Minford

JONES & CO OF YORK LTD
Prospect House, 148 Lawrence Street, York, YO10 3EB
Tel: 01904 430830
Fax: 01904 424499
Email: info@jonesandco.co.uk
Website: http://www.jonesandco.co.uk
Mobile: 07904 394608
Resident Partners/Directors: ICAEW Members
N Jones
Registered by the ICAEW to carry out company audit work
See display advertisement near this entry.

JWPCREERS ★ ◈
Foss Place, Foss Islands Road, York, YO31 7UJ
Tel: 01904 624155
Fax: 01904 612347
Website: http://www.jwpcreers.com
Training Contracts Available.
Resident Partners/Directors: ICAEW Members
D E Dorman, J A Farmer, F A Johnson, J A G Latimer, J W Machin
Resident Partners (Non-ICAEW Members):
J Jesty, N Clemit
Registered by the ICAEW to carry out company audit work
Regulated by the ICAEW for a range of investment business activities

KAYE MIDDLETON & CO
19 Railway Street, Pocklington, York, YO42 2QR

KIM BOWLER & CO LTD
32 Clarence Street, York, YO31 7EW
Tel: 01904 651955
Resident Partners/Directors: ICAEW Members
K D Bowler

MARCH:ENGENUS
Ornhams Hall, Boroughbridge, York, YO51 9JH

MARY MATTHEWS ◈
140 Clifton, York, YO30 6BH
Tel: 01904 640848
Principal: ICAEW Member
L M C Matthews
Regulated by the ICAEW for a range of investment business activities
SPECIALISATIONS – TAXATION
Personal

MICHAEL C. JEFFERY
7 Chalfonts, York, YO24 1EX
Tel: 01904 707624
Principal: ICAEW Member
M C Jeffery

MJS ACCOUNTANCY SERVICES (FANGFOSS) LTD
Hillcroft, Fangfoss, York, YO41 5QJ

MOORE STEPHENS
1 Church Street, Kirkbymoorside, York, YO62 6AZ

PCLG
Equinox House, Clifton Park Avenue, Shipton Road, York YO30 5PA
Tel: 01904 558300
Resident Partners/Directors: ICAEW Members
I P Broadley, A M Clarkson, L R Elliot, M Lester

PD HUGHES CONSULTANCY SERVICES
Unit K6 The Raylor Centre, James Street, York, YO10 3DW
Tel: 01904 425025
Principal: ICAEW Member
P D Hughes

PEARSON JONES PLC
21 Davygate, York, YO1 8QT

PECKITT OGDEN & CO
8 Marsden Business Park, James Nicolson Link,Clifton, York, YO30 4WX
Tel: 01904 691616
Email: phil@peckittogden.co.uk
Website: http://www.peckittogden.co.uk
Resident Partners/Directors: ICAEW Members
P J Ogden, K Peckitt
Registered by the ICAEW to carry out company audit work
General Description:
Specialists in business development work.

PETER SMITH & CO
12 Bonneycroft Lane, Easingwold, York, YO61 3AR

POSITIVE ACCOUNTANTS
Elmwood House, York Road, Kirk Hammerton, York YO26 8DH
Tel: 0800 097 0093
Resident Partners/Directors: ICAEW Members
A D Lock

ROWLEY WARD ◈
Tower House, 4 Tower Street, York, YO1 9SB

S. C. TELFER
24 High Street, Holme-on-Spalding Moor, York, YO43 4HL
Tel: 01430 861616
Principal: ICAEW Member
S C Richardson

SYCAMORE ACCOUNTING SERVICES
42 New Lane, Huntington, York, YO32 9NT

TENON LTD
Suite 5c, Tower Business Centre, Fishergate, York YO10 4UA
Tel: 01904 652100

TOWNEND ENGLISH ◈
93 Market Street, Pocklington, York, YO42 2AE
Tel: 01759 305989
Principal: ICAEW Member
F D Townend

TOWNENDS ★
Harlington House, 3 Main Street, Fulford, York YO10 4HJ

TOWNENDS ACCOUNTANTS LTD
Harlington House, 3 Main Street, Fulford, York YO10 4HJ
Tel: 01904 687500
Resident Partners/Directors: ICAEW Members
B B Davis, S M Green, J Williamson

UHY CALVERT SMITH
31 St Saviourgate, York, YO1 8NQ
Tel: 01904 557570
Fax: 01904 557571
Email: info@uhy-calvertsmith.com
Website: http://www.uhy-calvertsmith.com
Resident Partners/Directors: ICAEW Members
J M Judson Smith, N J Pearce, H L Priest, K W Ward
Registered by the ICAEW to carry out company audit work
Regulated by the ICAEW for a range of investment business activities

General Description: The practice has been established for over 30 years and provides practical advice on all aspects of financial and fiscal matters arising in family, sole trader businesses educational establishments, charities and limited companies.

WALKER & ASSOCIATES LTD
47 Orrin Close, Woodthorpe, York, YO24 2RA

WHITE KITE
8 Forest Farm Business Park, Fulford, York, YO19 4RE

WILD & CO
34 Dringthorpe Road, Dringhouses, York, North Yorkshire YO24 1LG
Tel: 01904 707227
Principal: ICAEW Member
C B Wild

SPECIALISATIONS – BUSINESS & GENERAL ADVICE
Management Advice to Business

SPECIALISATIONS – FINANCIAL REPORTING
Accounts Preparation
Limited Company Accounts

SPECIALISATIONS – TAXATION
Partnerships and Sole Traders

WILLIAMS & CO LTD.
Ebor House, 1 Knott Lane, Easingwold, York YO61 3LX

THE OFFICIAL ICAEW DIRECTORY OF FIRMS 2009

ISLE OF MAN

BALDRINE

CORLETT & CO LTD
Ellan Vannin, Baldrine, Isle Of Man, IM4 6HA
Tel: 01624 861060
Resident Partners/Directors: ICAEW Members
J K Corlett

BALLASALLA

CROSSLEYS LLC
Portland House, Station Road, Ballasalla, Isle Of Man IM9 2AE

FOWLER & CO
1st Floor Norton House, 41 Arbory Street, Castletown, Isle Of Man IM9 1LL
Tel: 01624 827848
Principal: ICAEW Member
V Steer-Fowler

BRADDAN

TENON LTD
Skanco Court, Cooil Road, Braddan, Isle Of Man IM2 2SR
Tel: 01624 695560

CASTLETOWN

AHS & CO LTD
1 Castle Street, Castletown, Isle Of Man, IM9 1LF

FOXDALE CONSULTING LTD
PO Box 2, Castletown, Isle Of Man, IM99 5YJ

LAWFORDS LTD
6 Hope Street, Castletown, Isle Of Man, IM9 1AS

MICHAEL TURNER & CO
Ballanorris Court, Douglas Road, Castletown, Isle Of Man IM9 4EF

COLBY

DAVID J. HILL & CO
Museum Buildings, Church Road, Port Erin, Isle Of Man IM9 6AH
Tel: 01624 833776
Email: hill@manx.net
Principal: ICAEW Member
D J Hill

SPECIALISATIONS – SECTOR

Doctors

DOUGLAS

ALDER DODSWORTH & CO
22 Athol Street, Douglas, Isle Of Man, IM1 1JA
Tel: 01624 622865
Principal: ICAEW Member
S G Alder

ASHGROVES
14 Albert Street, Douglas, Isle Of Man, IM1 2QA

BAKER TILLY BENNETT ROY
2a Lord Street, Douglas, Isle Of Man, IM1 2BD

BAKER TILLY ISLE OF MAN LLC
2a Lord Street, Douglas, Isle Of Man, IM1 2BD
Fax: 01624 693901
Email: mail@bakertilltiom.com
Website: http://www.bakertilly.com
Date Established: 1979
Training Contracts Available.
Resident Partners/Directors: ICAEW Members
D Bailey, W L Bennett, A J Collister, F J Radford, R J Kirkham, I M Lawrence, Ian Radford, A S Roy
Registered by the ICAEW to carry out company audit work

SPECIALISATIONS – AUDIT & ASSURANCE

Audit

SPECIALISATIONS – BUSINESS RECOVERY & INSOLVENCY

Liquidations

SPECIALISATIONS – FINANCIAL REPORTING

Accounts Preparation

SPECIALISATIONS – FORENSIC ACCOUNTING

Forensic Accounting

SPECIALISATIONS – TAXATION

Investigations
Offshore Companies
Taxation
Value Added Tax

General Description: As a general practice in an island community we have wide experience in all areas from new resident tax planning to executorships and from company acquisitions to liquidations. We also specialise in offshore company and trust services through our licensed corporate service provider.

BDO CREG LHEA LLC
18 Athol Street, Douglas, Isle Of Man, IM1 1JA
Tel: 01624 620711
Resident Partners/Directors: ICAEW Members
I A Cook

BOOTHMANS
Millennium House, Summerhill Business Park, Victoria Road, Douglas, Isle Of Man IM2 4RW
Tel: 01624 611926
Website: http://www.boothmans.com
Principal: ICAEW Member
D A Boothman

BOWERS & CO
71 Circular Road, Douglas, Isle Of Man, IM1 1AZ

BROWNE CRAINE ASSOCIATES LTD
Burleigh Manor, Peel Road, Douglas, Isle Of Man IM1 5EP
Tel: 01624 629369
Email: office@burleigh.co.im
Website: http://www.brownecraine.com
Resident Partners/Directors: ICAEW Members
D P Craine, M Singer
Resident Partners (Non-ICAEW Members):
B D Bielich, C Mitchell
Registered by the ICAEW to carry out company audit work

CALLIN & CO
6-7 Fort William, Head Road, Douglas, Isle Of Man IM1 5BG
Tel: 01624 675528
Fax: 01624 670666
Email: callin@manx.net
Principal: ICAEW Member
G C Boyde

CALLOW MATTHEWMAN & CO,
Atholl House, 29-31 Hope Street, Douglas, Isle Of Man IM1 1AR
Tel: 01624 622752
Resident Partners/Directors: ICAEW Members
D M Callin, C Matthewman, R G Woolley

CHARLES FARGHER
Ballafreer House, Union Mills, Douglas, Isle Of Man IM4 4AT
Tel: 01624 851190
Email: jcfargher@manx.net
Date Established: 1990
Principal: ICAEW Member
J C Fargher

SPECIALISATIONS – BUSINESS & GENERAL ADVICE

Book-keeping
Management Advice to Business
Management Consultancy

SPECIALISATIONS – FINANCIAL REPORTING

Accounts Preparation
Limited Company Accounts
Partnership/Sole Trader Accounts

SPECIALISATIONS – TAXATION

Taxation

General Description: General practice specialising in local business consultancy.

CROWE MORGAN
8 St George's Street, Douglas, Isle Of Man, IM1 1AH
Tel: 01624 665100
Fax: 01624 665166
Email: admin@crowemorgan.com
Website: http://www.crowemorgan.com
Resident Partners/Directors: ICAEW Members
M F G Crowe, D J Morgan, A L Slee
Resident Partners (Non-ICAEW Members):
J Barry McCarney
Registered by the ICAEW to carry out company audit work

SPECIALISATIONS – AUDIT & ASSURANCE

Audit

SPECIALISATIONS – BUSINESS & GENERAL ADVICE

Administration
Company Formation
Company Secretarial Service

SPECIALISATIONS – FINANCIAL REPORTING

Accounts Preparation

SPECIALISATIONS – TAXATION

Trusteeship

DAVID WILCOCK
Pine View, Glen Vine Road, Glen Vine, Isle Of Man IM4 4HG

DELOITTE & TOUCHE ◈
Grosvenor House, 66/67 Athol Street, Douglas, Isle Of Man IM99 1XJ
Tel: 01624 672332
Website: http://www.deloitte.co.uk
Resident Partners/Directors: ICAEW Members
N D Evans

DOUGLAS & CO LTD
Broadway House, 8-10 Broadway, Douglas, Isle Of Man IM2 4EL
Tel: 01624 628571
Resident Partners/Directors: ICAEW Members
F D Newton

EDWARDS & HARTLEY
PO Box 237, Peregrine House, Peel Road, Douglas, Isle Of Man IM99 1SU

EIS ADVSORS LTD
3rd Floor, Goldie House, 1-4 Goldie Terrace, Upper Church Street, Douglas Isle of Man IM1 1EB

ERNST & YOUNG
Rose House, 51-59 Circular Road, Douglas, Isle Of Man IM1 1AZ
Tel: 01624 691800

ERNST & YOUNG LLC
Rose House, 51-59 Circular Road, Douglas, Isle Of Man IM1 1AZ

FRYERS BELL & CO
27 Athol Street, Douglas, Isle Of Man, IM1 1LB
Tel: 01624 639850
Fax: 01624 639869
Email: fryers_bell@manx.net
Date Established: 1977
Resident Partners/Directors: ICAEW Members
G A Bell, K W Fryers

GALLOWAY SMITH & CO
9 Hope Street, Douglas, Isle Of Man, IM1 1AQ

GRANT THORNTON
PO Box 307, 3rd Floor Exchange House, 54-58 Athol Street, Douglas, Isle Of Man IM1 1JD
Tel: 01624 639494
Principal: ICAEW Member
D A McGurgan, R C Ratcliffe

HARDING LEWIS LTD
4 Upper Church Street, Douglas, Isle Of Man, IM1 1EE
Tel: 01624 679524
Fax: 01624 677524
Email: a.gerrard@hardinglewis.com
Website: http://www.hardinglewis.com
Resident Partners/Directors: ICAEW Members
D L Cooper, M J Estella, A M Gerrard
Registered by the ICAEW to carry out company audit work

HORWATH CLARK WHITEHILL AUDIT LLC
6th Floor, Victory House, Prospect Hill, Douglas, Isle Of Man IM1 1EQ
Tel: 01624 627335
Resident Partners/Directors: ICAEW Members
R G Barrs, P S Bird, J A Cowan

HORWATH CLARK WHITEHILL LLC
6th Floor, Victory House, Prospect Hill, Douglas, Isle Of Man IM1 1EQ
Tel: 01624 627335
Email: mail@horwath.co.im
Website: http://www.horwath.co.im
Resident Partners/Directors: ICAEW Members
R G Barrs, P S Bird, J A Cowan
Resident Partners (Non-ICAEW Members):
E Corrin

INDEPENDENT TAX CONSULTANTS LTD
Eaglehurst, Belmont Hill, Douglas, Isle Of Man IM1 4NY

JESSUP & CO
44 Athol Street, Douglas, Isle Of Man, IM1 1JB

JOHN CLARKE & CO
Ragnall House, 18 Peel Road, Douglas, Isle Of Man IM1 4LZ

JONATHAN T COX
26 Anagh Coar Close, Douglas, Isle Of Man, IM2 2BG

JONES & CO
Analyst House, Penthouse Suite, Peel Road, Douglas, Isle Of Man IM1 4LZ

MANNAC
Mgs House, Circular Road, Douglas, Isle Of Man IM1 1BL
Tel: 01624 675245
Resident Partners/Directors: ICAEW Members
J B Shooter

MATTHEW EDWARDS & CO
Clinch's House, Lord Street, Douglas, Isle Of Man IM1 4LN
Tel: 01624 663166
Fax: 01624 677108
Email: audit@matthew-edwards.com
Resident Partners/Directors: ICAEW Members
N R Morris, M J Wickers
Registered by the ICAEW to carry out company audit work
Regulated by the ICAEW for a range of investment business activities

SPECIALISATIONS – AUDIT & ASSURANCE

Audit
Audit — Private Company

SPECIALISATIONS – FINANCIAL REPORTING

Accounts Preparation
Limited Company Accounts
Partnership/Sole Trader Accounts

MICHAEL TURNER & CO
17 Hope Street, Douglas, Isle Of Man, IM1 1AQ
Tel: 01624 629619
Fax: 01624 629620
Email: mbturner@manx.net
Principal: ICAEW Member
M B Turner

MOORE STEPHENS ◈
P O Box 25, 26-28 Athol Street, Douglas, Isle Of Man IM99 1BD
Tel: 01624 662020
Email: mail@moorestephens.co.im
Website: http://www.moorestephens.co.im
Training Contracts Available.
Resident Partners/Directors: ICAEW Members
C N S Barton, C O L Dixon, B L Hazell, A T J Moll, J T B Pickles, D J Shadwell
Registered by the ICAEW to carry out company audit work

INVESTOR IN PEOPLE

NOBLE & CO
Abacus House, Mona Street, Douglas, Isle Of Man IM1 3AE
Tel: 01624 624633
Principal: ICAEW Member
G C Noble

PETER D. LACE
First Floor, 18 Hope Street, Douglas, Isle Of Man IM1 1AQ
Tel: 01624 661640
Principal: ICAEW Member
P D Lace

PKF (ISLE OF MAN) LLC
PO Box 16, Analyst House, Douglas, Isle Of Man IM99 1AP
Tel: 01624 652000
Fax: 01624 652001
Email: mail@pkfiom.com
Website: http://www.pkfiom.com
Training Contracts Available.
Resident Partners/Directors: ICAEW Members
M H Crowe, J M Cryer, P E Dearden, D A R Drewett, P A Seaward, A Wild
Resident Partners (Non-ICAEW Members):
J H Nugent
Individual(s) licensed for insolvency work by the ICAEW

SPECIALISATIONS – AUDIT & ASSURANCE

Assurance Services
Audit
Audit — Private Company
Audit — Public Company
Internal Audit
Pension Scheme Auditors

SPECIALISATIONS – BUSINESS & GENERAL ADVICE

Acquisitions and Mergers
Book-keeping
Book-keeping Systems
Company Formation
Company Secretarial Service
Investment Appraisal
Management Accounting Consultancy
Management Consultancy
Takeovers

SPECIALISATIONS – BUSINESS RECOVERY & INSOLVENCY

Corporate Recovery
Liquidations

SPECIALISATIONS – FINANCIAL REPORTING

Accounts Preparation
Audit Exemption Report
Financial Reporting
International Reporting Standards (IFRS)
Limited Companies
Limited Company Accounts
Partnership/Sole Trader Accounts

SPECIALISATIONS – FORENSIC ACCOUNTING

Expert Witnesses in Litigation
Forensic Accounting

SPECIALISATIONS – IT

Computerised Accounting Systems

SPECIALISATIONS – SECTOR

Charities
Corporate
Hotels/Public Houses
Leisure Industry
Manufacturing
Property Development
Property Investment
Solicitors
Transport

SPECIALISATIONS – TAXATION

Estate and Inheritance
Estate Planning
Executorship
Foreign Nationals in the UK
Investigations
Offshore Companies
Self Assessment Advice
Taxation
Trusteeship
Trusts
UK Companies Overseas
UK Nationals Overseas
UK Subsidiaries of Overseas Multinationals
Value Added Tax

PRICEWATERHOUSE-COOPERS ▽
Sixty Circular Road, Douglas, Isle Of Man, IM1 1SA

R.P. HARKER
9 Circular Road, Douglas, Isle Of Man, IM1 1AF

RADFORD BAILEY
First Floor, 2a Lord Street, Douglas, Isle Of Man IM99 1HP

ROGER & CO
18 St Georges Street, Douglas, Isle Of Man, IM1 1PL

SABRE MANAGEMENT SERVICES LTD
Anglo International House, Lord Street, Douglas, Isle Of Man IM1 4LN

SHIMMIN WILSON & CO ◈
13-15 Hope Street, Douglas, Isle Of Man, IM1 1AQ
Tel: 01624 627744
Fax: 01624 629666
Email: mail@shimminwilson.com
Date Established: 1991
Resident Partners/Directors: ICAEW Members
A J Clark-Wilson, A P Shimmin
Registered by the ICAEW to carry out company audit work

SMP ACCOUNTING AND TAX LTD
PO Box 227, Clinch's House, Lord Street, Douglas, Isle Of Man IM99 1RZ

T.P. WINNELL & CO
7 Hill Street, Douglas, Isle Of Man, IM1 1EF
Tel: 01624 670022
Principal: ICAEW Member
T P Winnell

THOMAS AND CO
2a Lord Street, Douglas, Isle Of Man, IM1 2BD

WOOLFORD & CO LLP
69 Athol Street, Douglas, Isle Of Man, IM1 1JE

LAXEY

COLIN D CLARK
Riverside House, Off Glen Road, Laxey, Isle Of Man IM4 7AT

NICOLA BOWKER & CO LTD
The Commissioners Offices, 35 New Road, Laxey, Isle Of Man IM4 7BG
Tel: 01624 861271
Resident Partners/Directors: ICAEW Members
N J Bowker

SAMANTHA FRIZE
Fairy Cottage House, Fairy Cottage, Laxey, Isle Of Man IM4 7HR

LONAN

SIMM ASSOCIATES
Hillside Cottage, Agneash, Lonan, Isle Of Man IM4 7NS
Tel: 01624 861 627
Principal: ICAEW Member
M Simm

ONCHAN

ACADIA & CO
14a Village Walk, Onchan, Isle Of Man, IM3 4EB

ERNIE THORN
47 Buttermere Drive, Onchan, Isle Of Man, IM3 2EB

T.A. CORKISH
34 Alberta Drive, Onchan, Isle Of Man, IM3 1LS
Tel: 01624 622440
Principal: ICAEW Member
T A Corkish

PEEL

J P FORBES
Croit-E-Ferish, Tynwald Road, Peel, Isle Of Man IM5 1JL

PORT ERIN

JH MADDRELL ACA
1 Meadowfield, Port Erin, Isle Of Man, IM9 6PH
Tel: 01624 833535
Principal: ICAEW Member
J H Maddrell

RICHARD W.J. WALKER
Bracken Hills, Surby Road, Port Erin, Isle Of Man IM9 6TD

PORT ST. MARY

YOUNG AND ASSOCIATES LTD
St Georges House, Bay View Road, Port St Mary, Isle Of Man IM9 5AE
Tel: 01634 838808
Fax: 01624 837808
Email: iain.wood@youngassociates.co.im
Resident Partners/Directors: ICAEW Members
I D Wood, P A Young
Non-resident Partners (ICAEW Members):
P A Smith

SPECIALISATIONS – TAXATION
Offshore Companies

General Description: Licensed by the Isle of Man Financial Supervision Commission as a Corporate Service Provider.

RAMSEY

C.R. NEEDHAM
Watersmeet, Westfield Drive, Ramsey, Isle Of Man IM8 3ER

CALLOW MATTHEWMAN & CO,
West House, Auckland Terrace, Ramsey, Isle Of Man IM8 1AE
Tel: 01624 814494

SHANNON CALLISTER & CO
Shannon Court, Bowring Road, Ramsey, Isle Of Man IM8 2LQ

UNION MILLS

JULIE OATES ACA
2 Camlork Place, Union Mills, Isle Of Man, IM4 4NY
Tel: 01624 852552
Principal: ICAEW Member
J Oates

SOUTHWINDS CONSULTING LTD
Southwinds, Trollaby Lane, Union Mills, Isle Of Man IM4 4AW

THE OFFICIAL ICAEW DIRECTORY OF FIRMS 2009

WALES

ABERAERON

HATFIELD & JOHN LTD
2 Market Street, Aberaeron, SA46 0AS

PATTERSON, JONES & EVANS
3 Market Street, Aberaeron, SA46 0AS

ABERDARE

BARLOW, MENDHAM & CO ★
Glandover House, 67 Bute Street, Aberdare, South Glamorgan CF44 7LD

H.MARTIN SMITH & CO
40 Springfield Gardens, Hirwaun, Aberdare, CF44 9LY
Tel: 01685 811949
Principal: ICAEW Member
H M Smith

KTS OWENS THOMAS LTD
18a Whitcombe Street, Aberdare, CF44 7AU
Tel: 01685 872028

ABERGAVENNY

ASHMOLE & CO ★
7a Nevill Street, Abergavenny, NP7 5AA

CATHERINE A WILLIAMS LTD
Ciderbank Cottage, Brynderi, Abergavenny, NP7 8UE
Tel: 01600 780111
Resident Partners/Directors:
ICAEW Members
C A Williams

DEREK F. PARKHOUSE ◈
10 Plas Derwen Close, Abergavenny, NP7 9SQ
Tel: 01873 855611
Principal: ICAEW Member
D F Parkhouse

DORRELL OLIVER LTD
26 Monk Street, Abergavenny, NP7 5NF
Tel: 01873 852113
Fax: 01873 858523
Email: admin@dorrells.co.uk
Website: http://www.dorrells.co.uk
Resident Partners/Directors:
ICAEW Members
P E Lea, E A Moore

Registered by the ICAEW to carry out company audit work

Regulated by the ICAEW for a range of investment business activities

SPECIALISATIONS – AUDIT & ASSURANCE
Audit

SPECIALISATIONS – FINANCIAL REPORTING
Accounts Preparation

SPECIALISATIONS – INVESTMENT BUSINESS
Financial Planning and Advice

See display advertisement near this entry.

PEACHEYS CA LTD
21 Nevill Street, Abergavenny, NP7 5AA
Tel: 01873 852124

SPENCER-SMITH & CO
The Old Rectory, Llanvetherine, Abergavenny, NP7 8RG
Tel: 01873 821216
Principal: ICAEW Member
T P Spencer-Smith

ABERGELE

ASTON, HUGHES & CO ▽
First Floor, 26 Market Street, Abergele, LL22 7AA

COPTHORNE ◈
Copthorn House, The Broadway, Abergele, LL22 7DD
Tel: 01745 825779
Resident Partners/Directors:
ICAEW Members
R D Atack, J Payne

ABERTILLERY

G.T BASFORD
62A Somerset Street, Abertillery, NP13 1DP

THEO JONES
49 Somerset Street, Abertillery, NP13 1DL

ABERYSTWYTH

FRANCIS, JONES & DAVIES LTD
57 North Parade, Aberystwyth, SY23 2JN

KYFFIN & CO ★
The Old Convent, Llanbadarn Road, Aberystwyth, SY23 1EY

PATTERSON, JONES & EVANS ◈
8 The Science Park, Aberystwyth, SY23 3AH
Tel: 01970 617917
Resident Partners/Directors:
ICAEW Members
S A Longworth

PROF. R.H. MACVE FCA
Bronwydd, 3 Trefor Road, Aberystwyth, SY23 2EH
Tel: 01970 624586
Principal: ICAEW Member
R H Macve

AMLWCH

I.G. JONES & CO ◈
12 Salem Street, Ynys Mon, Amlwch, LL68 9BP
Tel: 01407 830409
Resident Partners/Directors:
ICAEW Members
D G Williams

AMMANFORD

ASHMOLE & CO ★
Castle House, High Street, Ammanford, SA18 2NB

BALA

HILL & ROBERTS ◈
87 High Street, Bala, LL23 7AE
Tel: 01678 520662
Resident Partners/Directors:
ICAEW Members
D V Evans

BANGOR

HUGHES PARRY & CO
121 High Street, Bangor, LL57 1NT
Tel: 01248 362198
Principal: ICAEW Member
J G Pritchard

J.EMYR THOMAS & CO
Tegfan, 7 Deiniol Road, Bangor, LL57 2UR
Tel: 01248 353487
Resident Partners/Directors:
ICAEW Members
E Orwig, M L Owen, P G Thomas, E R Williams

WILLIAMS DENTON CYF ★ ◈
Glaslyn, Ffordd y Parc, Parc Menai, Bangor LL57 4FE

BARRY

HAYWARD WILLIAMS LTD ◈
79 High Street, Barry, CF62 7DZ
Tel: 01446 747373
Resident Partners/Directors:
ICAEW Members
M B Hayward

IMPACT ACCOUNTING SERVICES LTD
The Gatehouse, Llanvithyn, Llancarfan, Barry CF62 3AT

JOHN GRAHAM & CO
209 Holton Road, Barry, CF63 4HR
Tel: 01446 733286
Principal: ICAEW Member
J Graham

LEWIS VAN EMDEN LTD
174 Westward Rise, Barry, CF62 6NQ

MARTIN HAYWARD
79 High Street, Barry, CF62 7DZ
Tel: 01446 747373
Principal: ICAEW Member
M B Hayward

NAUNTON JONES LE MASURIER ★
Hamilton House, 123 Broad Street, Barry, CF62 7AL

BEAUMARIS

MACAULAY SUMMERS ★
Regent House, Church Street, Beaumaris, LL58 8AB
Tel: 01248 811333
Resident Partners/Directors:
ICAEW Members
R J Macaulay

BLACKWOOD

UK TAXATION SERVICES
221 High Street, Blackwood, NP12 1AL

UKTS AUDIT LTD
221 High Street, Blackwood, NP12 1AL

BLAENAU FFESTINIOG

GARETH JONES
Ger-y-garth, Tyddyngwyn, Manod, Blaenau Ffestiniog LL41 4AL

M. RICHARDSON & CO
Unit 15, Glanypwll Workshops, Blaenau Ffestiniog, LL41 3NW

BRECON

JOHN MORGAN (ACCOUNTANCY) LTD
Ivy Cottage, Sennybridge, Brecon, LD3 8PG
Tel: 01874 636738
Resident Partners/Directors:
ICAEW Members
J J Morgan

KING, MORTER, PROUD & CO
Kings Arms Vaults, The Watton, Brecon, LD3 7EF

MITCHELL MEREDITH LTD
34 High Street, Brecon, LD3 7AN

ROCHE-SAUNDERS & CO
34 The Watton, Brecon, LD3 7EF

W J JAMES & CO LTD ◈
Bishop House, 10 Wheat Street, Brecon, LD3 7DG
Tel: 01874 622381
Website: http://www.wjjamesaccountants.co.uk
Resident Partners/Directors:
ICAEW Members
J Morrell, N J Morrell, W Williams

Registered by the ICAEW to carry out company audit work

Regulated by the ICAEW for a range of investment business activities

BRIDGEND

ANDREW SINGER & CO
Singer House, 10 Court Road, Bridgend, CF31 1BN

CLAY SHAW THOMAS LTD

Ty Atebion, 2 Ffordd Yr Hen Gae, Bocam Park, Bridgend CF35 5LJ
Tel: 01656 867167
Email: enquiries@clayshawthomas.com
Website: http://www.clayshawthomas.com
Resident Partners/ Directors:
ICAEW Members
D R Thomas, D G J Williams
Registered by the ICAEW to carry out company audit work
Regulated by the ICAEW for a range of investment business activities

INVESTOR IN PEOPLE

General Description: Audit, tax, corporate finance and business consulting.

COWDERY BRAWN & COMPANY LTD

Cradoc House, Heol-y-Llyfrall, Aberkenfig, Bridgend CF32 9PL

DAVID WRIGHT ACCOUNTANTS LTD ◈

1st Floor, Nathaniel House, David Street, Bridgend CF31 3SA
Tel: 01656 646444
Resident Partners/Directors:
ICAEW Members
D J Wright

GRAHAM PAUL

10-12 Dunraven Place, Bridgend, CF31 1JD

GRAHAM PAUL LTD ◈

10-12 Dunraven Place, Bridgend, CF31 1JD
Tel: 01656 679800
Resident Partners/Directors:
ICAEW Members
D G Paul, B G Scott, J D Squire, I G Washbourne

H R HARRIS & PARTNERS LTD

7 Dunraven Place, Bridgend, CF31 1JF

HARRIES WATKINS & JONES LTD

16 Coychurch Road, Pencoed, Bridgend, CF35 5NG

HUW THOMAS

HHPG House, Coity Road, Bridgend, CF31 1LT

MEDRUS UK LTD ◈

43 Parkfields, Penyfai, Bridgend, CF31 4NQ
Tel: 07866 461439
Resident Partners/Directors:
ICAEW Members
C E Byrne

SPECIALISATIONS – BUSINESS & GENERAL ADVICE

Management Accounting Consultancy
Management Advice to Business
Outsourcing - Financial Services

SPECIALISATIONS – SECTOR

Construction
Media

MORRIS & THOMAS LLP

9 Court Road, Bridgend, CF31 1BE

PHILLIP JENKINS LTD ◈

16 Parkfields, Pen-Y-Fai, Bridgend, CF31 4NQ
Tel: 01656 766691
Resident Partners/Directors:
ICAEW Members
P Jenkins

WALLACE WILLIAMS & CO

4 Island Farm Close, Bridgend, CF31 3LY
Tel: 01656 660584
Principal: ICAEW Member
R F King

WOODLAND & WOODLAND LTD ◈

Dragon House, Princes Way, Bridgend Industrial Estate, Bridgend CF31 3AQ
Tel: 01656 668886
Resident Partners/Directors:
ICAEW Members
A M Woodland, D B Woodland

BUILTH WELLS

CLARK & CO

4 Broad Street, Builth Wells, LD2 3DT
Tel: 01982 553604
Principal: ICAEW Member
A Clark

COLVILLE & CO

Rhoscwm, Builth Wells, LD2 3PT

KING, MORTER, PROUD & CO

Bank House, 11 West Street, Builth Wells, LD2 3AH

CAERNARFON

A. HUGHES-JONES, DYSON & CO

Bryn Afon, Segontium Terrace, Caernarfon, LL55 2PN
Tel: 01286 672525
Resident Partners/Directors:
ICAEW Members
B Hughes, I R Parry, E Pursglove

GWENNO MAIR WYN ACA

2 Tan y Ffynnon, Bethel, Caernarfon, LL55 1AX

OWAIN BEBB A'I GWMNI

32 Y Maes, Caernarfon, LL55 2NN
Tel: 01286 675916
Fax: 01286 677634
Email: post@owainbebb.net
Resident Partners/Directors:
ICAEW Members
A E Evans, R R Harris
Other Offices: Cerrigydrudion, Pwllheli
Registered by the ICAEW to carry out company audit work
Regulated by the ICAEW for a range of investment business activities
Languages Spoken:
Welsh, English

W.J. MATTHEWS & SON

11 - 15 Bridge Street, Caernarfon, LL55 1AB
Tel: 01286 673555
Resident Partners/Directors:
ICAEW Members
D A Chidley, B O Jones, J M Pritchard

CAERPHILLY

BRIAN BELL MEYER & CO LTD ◈

Plymouth Chambers, 23 Bartlett Street, Caerphilly, CF83 1JS
Tel: 02920 867131
Resident Partners/Directors:
ICAEW Members
A G Howell, P J H Meyer

CLYNE & CO LTD

3 Mountain Road, Caerphilly, CF83 1HG

CONWAY DAVIS LTD

4 Station Terrace, Caerphilly, CF83 1HD

RILY ACCOUNTANCY AND BUSINESS SOLUTIONS LTD

Rily House, 55 Stryd Hywel Harris, Ystrad Mynach, Hengoed CF82 7DN

ZDP LTD

4 Station Terrace, Caerphilly, CF83 1HD

CALDICOT

CONWAY DAVIS LTD

Greenfield, The Causeway, Undy, Caldicot NP26 3DP
Tel: 01633 882699
Resident Partners/Directors:
ICAEW Members
G Conway

CUCKOO ◈

2 Station Road, Portskewett, Caldicot, NP26 5SF
Tel: 07811 349858
Resident Partners/Directors:
ICAEW Members
L Thomas

CARDIFF

A.E. JONES

51 Kelston Road, Whitchurch, Cardiff, CF14 2AH

A.J. FOLEY ◈

Gwylfa, 16 Cefn Mably Park, Cardiff, CF3 6AA
Tel: 07813 200337
Principal: ICAEW Member
A J Foley

A.P. BAKER & CO

191 Whitchurch Road, Gabalfa, Cardiff, CF14 3JR

A.W.G.WARREN & SON ◈

74 Wyndham Crescent, Cardiff, CF11 9EF
Tel: 02920 220162
Website: http://www.awgw.co.uk
Principal: ICAEW Member
M J G Warren

AGINCOURT PRACTICE LTD

Sophia House, 28 Cathedral Road, Cardiff, CF11 9LJ

AHMAD & CO

Ahmad Accountancy Services Limited, 232 Whitchurch Road, Cardiff, CF14 3ND

AHMAD ACCOUNTANCY SERVICES LTD

232 Whitchurch Road, Cardiff, CF14 3ND

AIMS - STEVE HALLETT

5 Chargot Road, Llandaff, Cardiff, CF5 1EW
Tel: 02920 302165

ALEX EMBIRICOS & CO

Sophia House, 28 Cathedral Road, Cardiff, CF11 9LJ

ALEXANDER STEINBECK

27 Cressy Road, Penylan, Cardiff, CF23 5BE

ALLYSON MORRIS

1 Alltmawr Road, Cyncoed, Cardiff, CF23 6NQ

ARIAN ACCOUNTANTS LTD

19 Sundew Close, Radyr Cheyne, Cardiff, CF5 2SE

B.J. ROBINSON
10 Bishops Avenue, Llandaff, Cardiff, CF5 2HJ

B N JACKSON NORTON ★
3rd Floor South, West Gate House, Womanby Street, Cardiff CF10 1DD

BALDHU CONSULTING ◈
20 Pantbach Road, Birchgrove, Cardiff, CF14 1UA
Tel: 08456 3488743
Principal: ICAEW Member
A K Denton

BEGBIES TRAYNOR LTD
5th Floor, Riverside House, 31 Cathedral Road, Cardiff CF11 9HB
Tel: 02920 225022
Resident Partners/Directors: ICAEW Members
P R Dewey, D Hill

SPECIALISATIONS – BUSINESS RECOVERY & INSOLVENCY
Bankruptcies
Corporate Recovery
Liquidations

BEST, DAVIES HAMILTON
476a Cowbridge Road East, Victoria Park, Cardiff, South Glamorgan CF5 1BL

BEVAN & BUCKLAND
11 Richmond Road, Cardiff, CF24 3AQ

BPU LTD ◈
Radnor House, Greenwood Close, Cardiff Gate Business Park, Pontprennau, Cardiff CF23 8AA
Tel: 02920 734100
Fax: 02920 734345
Website: http://www.bpuaccountants.co.uk
Resident Partners/Directors: ICAEW Members
M D Bishop, J H Palin, C Russell, N M Toye, E P Umbleja
Other Offices: The Counting House, Pound Field, Llantwit Major, Vale of Glamorgan, CF61 1DL
(Tel: 01446 796313)
Registered by the ICAEW to carry out company audit work
Regulated by the ICAEW for a range of investment business activities

BRIAN ROBERTS & CO
6 Raleigh Walk, Brigantine Place, Cardiff, CF10 4LN

BRIAN T. WILLIAMS
11 Westminster Drive, Cyncoed, Cardiff, CF23 6RD
Tel: 02920 756759
Principal: ICAEW Member
B T Williams

BROOMFIELD & ALEXANDER ◈
Pendragon House, Caxton Place, Pentwyn, Cardiff CF23 8XE
Tel: 02920 549939
Fax: 02920 739430
Email: info@broomfield.co.uk
Website: http://www.broomfield.co.uk
Resident Partners (Non-ICAEW Members):
S Gates
Other Offices: Newport

BROOMFIELD & ALEXANDER LTD ◈
Pendragon House, Caxton Place, Pentwyn, Cardiff CF23 8XE
Tel: 02920 549939
Resident Partners/Directors: ICAEW Members
M Jones, R S Preece, L J Reed, I Thomas, M Thomas

C.J. LLEWELLYN
69 Heol Don, Whitchurch, Cardiff, CF14 2AT

C.J. LLEWELLYN & CO
69 Heol Don, Cardiff, CF14 2AT

C.S. COCKS
45 Rannoch Drive, Lakeside, Cardiff, CF23 6LP

CARSTON
Tudor House, 16 Cathedral Road, Cardiff, CF11 9LJ

CARSTON & CO (CARDIFF) LTD
First Floor, Tudor House, 16 Cathedral Road, Cardiff CF11 9LJ

CHRIS MADGE & CO
Sophia House, 28 Cathedral Road, Cardiff, CF11 9LJ
Tel: 02920 660110
Website: http://www.chris-madge.co.uk

SPECIALISATIONS – FORENSIC ACCOUNTING
Expert Witnesses in Litigation
Forensic Accounting

SPECIALISATIONS – TAXATION
Back Duty
Customs Duty
Investigations
PAYE Advice
Value Added Tax

CLIFTON HOUSE PARTNERSHIP
Clifton House, Four Elms Road, Cardiff, CF24 1LE

COTSEN & CO
8 Columbus Walk, Brigantine Place, Cardiff, CF10 4BY

COWDERY BRAWN & CO
Unit 11, Cardiff Business Park, Lambourne Crescent, Llanishen, Cardiff CF14 5GF

COWDERY BRAWN & COMPANY LTD
Unit 11, Cardiff Business Park, Lambourne Crescent, Llanishen, Cardiff CF14 5GF

DAVIES WILLIAMS ◈
21 St Andrews Crescent, Cardiff, CF10 3DB
Tel: 02920 829800
Fax: 029 2039 7130
Email: brian@davieswilliams.co.uk
Website: http://www.davieswilliams.co.uk
Resident Partners/Directors: ICAEW Members
S Johns, B A Minton, P Williams
Registered by the ICAEW to carry out company audit work
Regulated by the ICAEW for a range of investment business activities

DELOITTE & TOUCHE LLP ◈
Blenheim House, Fitzalan Court, Newport Road, Cardiff CF24 0TS
Tel: 02920 481111
Website: http://www.deloitte.co.uk
Resident Partners/Directors: ICAEW Members
J L Antoniazzi, J Foster Thomas, R M Hawes, N J Thomas

DEWEY & CO
17 St Andrews Crescent, Cardiff, CF10 3DB

DFC
Grove House, 3 Park Grove, Cardiff, CF10 3BL
Tel: 02920 228845
Fax: 02920 342545
Email: enq@dfcand.co.uk
Resident Partners/Directors: ICAEW Members
P G Dennis, S M H Lewis
Registered by the ICAEW to carry out company audit work
Regulated by the ICAEW for a range of investment business activities

DOWLE HORRIGAN ◈
110 Whitchurch Road, Cardiff, CF14 3LY

DOWLE HORRIGAN LTD
110 Whitchurch Road, Cardiff, CF14 3LY

EDMONDS & CO
9 Clun Terrace, Cathays, Cardiff, CF24 4RB

ELEMENT CONSULTING
Woodlands, Home Farm, Cefn Mably, Cardiff CF3 6LP

ELEMENT CORPORATE FINANCE
Woodlands, Home Farm, Cefn Mably, Cardiff CF3 6LP

ELEMENT LEADERSHIP CONSULTING LTD
Woodlands, Home Farm, Cefn Mably, Cardiff CF3 6LP

EPIPHANY BUSINESS SOLUTIONS LTD
4 Ynys Bridge Court, Gwaelod-y-Garth, Cardiff, CF15 9SS

EVANS HUGHES ◈
Regus House, Falcon Drive, Cardiff, CF10 4RU

EVANS HUGHES LTD ◈
Regus House, Falcon Drive, Cardiff, CF10 4RU
Tel: 02920 504025
Resident Partners/Directors: ICAEW Members
W E Evans

G.MALCOLM PEARCE
Whitefriars, 22 Westminster Crescent, Cyncoed, Cardiff CF23 6SE

GAMBIT CORPORATE FINANCE ★ ◈
Kenneth Pollard House, 5-19 Cowbridge Road East, Cardiff, CF11 9AQ
Tel: 02920 667799
Resident Partners/Directors: ICAEW Members
G H H Ainsworth, J F Holmes, G A Rowe
Authorised and regulated by the Financial Services Authority for investment business

GAPFILLERS LTD
5 Chargot Road, Llandaff, Cardiff, South Glamorgan CF5 1EW

GEOFFREY N. BURFORD & CO
Eaglehurst, 110 Cyncoed Road, Cyncoed, Cardiff CF23 6BL

GEORGE A. KITCHER & CO
1 Cyncoed Crescent, Cyncoed, Cardiff, CF23 6SW
Tel: 02920 750245
Principal: ICAEW Member
G A Kitcher

GORDON DOWN & PARTNERS ★
275 Cowbridge Road East, Cardiff, CF5 1JB
Tel: 02920 395342
Resident Partners/Directors: ICAEW Members
L S Cohen
Registered by the ICAEW to carry out company audit work

GORDON MOSS
159 Pencisely Road, Llandaff, Cardiff, CF5 1DN

GRAHAM PAUL LTD ◈
372-374 Cyncoed Road, Cardiff, CF23 6SA
Tel: 02920 681980
Resident Partners/Directors: ICAEW Members
A S Lee

GRANT THORNTON UK LLP
11-13 Penhill Road, Cardiff, CF11 9UP
Tel: 02920 235591
Resident Partners/Directors: ICAEW Members
J G Davies, W H W Davies, A G Wardell

GRIFFITH, WILLIAMS & CO
Temple Court, Cathedral Road, Cardiff, CF11 9HA

GROVES & CO
141 Cyncoed Road, Cardiff, CF23 6AF

GROVES DAVEY LTD ◈
34 Wellfield Road, Cardiff, CF24 3PB
Tel: 02920 482622
Fax: 029 2048 7672
Email: info@grovesdavey.co.uk
Website: http://www.grovesdavey.co.uk
Resident Partners/Directors: ICAEW Members
J L Davey
Registered by the ICAEW to carry out company audit work

SPECIALISATIONS – AUDIT & ASSURANCE
Audit — Private Company

SPECIALISATIONS – BUSINESS & GENERAL ADVICE
Company Formation
Company Secretarial Service
Management Advice to Business

SPECIALISATIONS – FINANCIAL REPORTING
Accounts Preparation
Limited Company Accounts

SPECIALISATIONS – IT
Computer Systems and Consultancy
Computerised Accounting Systems

SPECIALISATIONS – TAXATION
Estate Planning
Payroll Service and Advice
Taxation

General Description: A friendly people-based practice committed to providing comprehensive business advice and support.

GWYTHER B PERSEUS & CO
4 Heath Halt Court, Heath Halt Road, Cardiff, CF23 5QB
Tel: 02920 759458
Principal: ICAEW Member
H Gwyther

HAMILTON & CO
7 Greave Close, The Grange,Wenvoe, Cardiff, CF5 6BU
Tel: 02920 594440
Principal: ICAEW Member
R C Hamilton

HANDYSIDE & CO
Bank Chambers, 92 Newport Road, Cardiff, CF24 1DG

HARALED CONSULTANCY LTD ◈
54 Bettws-y-Coed Road, Cyncoed, Cardiff, CF23 6PN
Resident Partners/Directors: ICAEW Members
A J Williams

HARRIS
LIPMAN

HARRIS LIPMAN LLP ◈
Coptic House, 4-5 Mount Stuart Square, Cardiff, CF10 5EE
Tel: 02920 495444
Fax: 029 2049 5744
Email: mail@harris-lipman.co.uk
DX: 200767 CARDIFF BAY
Website: http://www.harris-lipman.co.uk
Non-resident Partners (ICAEW Members):
B D Lewis, M J Atkins, F Khalastchi
Resident Partners (Non-ICAEW Members):
J D Cullen
Non-resident Partners (Non-ICAEW Members):
M Hall
Other Offices: London EC1, London N20, Reading, St Albans
Individual(s) licensed for insolvency work by another RPB

SPECIALISATIONS – BUSINESS RECOVERY & INSOLVENCY
Bankruptcies
Corporate Recovery
Liquidations

SPECIALISATIONS – FORENSIC ACCOUNTING
Expert Witnesses in Litigation
Forensic Accounting

SPECIALISATIONS – TAXATION
Investigations

General Description:
Specialists in corporate recovery, bankruptcies, expert witness in litigation, forensic accounting, liquidations, investigations.

HAYVENHURSTS
Fairway House, Links Business Park, St Mellons, Cardiff CF3 0LT

HAYVENHURSTS
Lermon Court, Fairway House, Links Business Park, St Mellons, Cardiff CF3 0LT

HAYVENHURSTS LTD
Fairway House, Links Business Park, St Mellons, Cardiff CF3 0LT

HODGE BAKSHI ◈
Churchgate House, Church Road, Whitchurch, Cardiff CF14 2DX
Tel: 02920 529529
Principal: ICAEW Member
P S Bakshi

HOUGHTON STONE DE CYMRU LTD
The Executive Centre, Temple Court, Cathedral Road, Cardiff CF11 9HA

HOWARD J WEARE & CO
34 Llwyn y Pia Road, Lisvane, Cardiff, CF14 0SY
Tel: 02920 747011

HOWARD J WEARE & CO LTD
34 Llwyn y Pia Road, Lisvane, Cardiff, CF14 0SY

HUW J EDMUND LTD
Garth House, 7 Ty-Nant Court, Morganstown, Cardiff CF15 8LW
Tel: 02920 814084
Resident Partners/Directors: ICAEW Members
H J Edmund
Resident Partners (Non-ICAEW Members):
A Williams

HW CORPORATE FINANCE ◈
Ground Floor, 19 Neptune Court, Vanguard Way, Cardiff CF24 5PJ
Tel: 02920 313390
Resident Partners/Directors: ICAEW Members
G C Fairclough, A M W Godfrey, N S Williams

HWCA LTD ◈
7 Neptune Court, Vanguard Way, Cardiff, CF24 5PJ
Tel: 02920 300101

IKON
Penrhos, 203 Heathwood Road, Cardiff, CF14 4HQ

IKON ACCOUNTANCY LTD
Penrhos, 203 Heathwood Road, Cardiff, CF14 4HQ

INNOVATION PROFESSIONAL SERVICES LLP
Sophia House, 28 Cathedral Road, Cardiff, CF11 9LJ
Tel: 02920 660273
Resident Partners/Directors: ICAEW Members
P J Moroz

ISIS FINANCIAL CONSULTANCY LTD
95 Blackoak Road, Cyncoed, Cardiff, CF23 6QW

J.CLIVE SLOCOMBE FCA, CTA
3 Cyncoed Crescent, Cyncoed, Cardiff, CF23 6SW
Tel: 02920 754928
Principal: ICAEW Member
J C Slocombe

J.H. REYNOLDS
2 Insole Gardens, Cardiff, CF5 2HW
Tel: 02920 567786
Principal: ICAEW Member
J H Reynolds

J JONES & CO
30 Woodvale Avenue, Cardiff, CF23 6SQ

J.S. WEBER & CO
29 Woodvale Avenue, Cyncoed, Cardiff, CF23 6SP

JENEFER M HUTTON
85 St Johns Crescent, Whitchurch, Cardiff, CF14 7AG

JFM GROWING BUSINESS SOLUTIONS LTD ◈
38 Triscombe Drive, Cardiff, South Glamorgan, CF5 2PN

JOHN HAM
114 Heol Llanishen Fach, Rhiwbina, Cardiff, CF14 6LG

JOHN JONES
30 Woodvale Avenue, Cyncoed, Cardiff, CF23 6SQ

JOHNS JONES & LO
14 Lambourne Crescent, Cardiff Business Park, Llanishen, Cardiff CF14 5GF

JOHNS JONES & LO LTD
14 Lambourne Crescent, Cardiff Business Park, Llanishen, Cardiff CF14 5GF

JONESGILES LTD
11 Coopers Yard, Curran Road, Cardiff, CF10 5NB

KEANE & CO
Tudor House, 16 Cathedral Road, Cardiff, CF11 9LJ

KIDDY & CO
61 Cowbridge Road East, Cardiff, CF11 9AE
Tel: 02920 396051
Principal: ICAEW Member
A Kiddy

KPMG LLP
Marlborough House, Fitzalan Court, Fitzalan Road, Cardiff CF24 0TE
Tel: 02920 468000
Resident Partners/Directors: ICAEW Members
S R Jones, G C Lloyd

KTS OWENS THOMAS ◈
The Counting House, Celtic Gateway, Cardiff, CF11 0SN

KTS OWENS THOMAS LTD ◈
The Counting House, Celtic Gateway, Cardiff, CF11 0SN

LAMBERT LEWIS
401 Cowbridge Road East, Canton, Cardiff, CF5 1JG

LEWIS BALLARD ★
Celtic House, Caxton Place, Pentwyn, Cardiff CF23 8HA
Tel: 02920 735502
Resident Partners/Directors: ICAEW Members
M D Lewis

LINGHAMS
6 Raleigh Walk, Waterfront 2000, Atlantic Wharf, Cardiff CF10 4LN

LLANDAFF ACCOUNTANCY & BUSINESS SERVICES
5 Insole Close, Cardiff, CF5 2HQ

LYNNE GITTENS ACA
5 Crystal Wood Road, Heath, Cardiff, CF14 4HU

M. LYNNE THOMAS FCA
7 Rambler Close, Thornhill, Cardiff, CF14 9FH

MARGARET E. GREGORY
5 Bryn Castell, Radyr, Cardiff, CF15 8RA

MARGARET THOMAS
7 Rambler Close, Thornhill, Cardiff, CF14 9FH

MEDINA LYNCH ★
252 Cowbridge Road East, Canton, Cardiff, CF5 1GZ

MICHAEL SINGLETON
7 Rudry Road, Lisvane, Cardiff, CF14 0SN

MM ACCOUNTANCY SERVICES
Lychgate House, Tyr Winch Road, Old St Mellons, Cardiff CF5 5UW
Tel: 02920 778640
Principal: ICAEW Member
M C Milsom

NAUNTON JONES LE MASURIER ★
5 St Andrews Crescent, Cardiff, CF10 3DA

P. GREENSMITH & CO ◈
35 Pinecrest Drive, Thornhill, Cardiff, CF14 9DS
Tel: 02920 747427
Principal: ICAEW Member
P Greensmith

P.J. REED
20a Pantbach Road, Birchgrove, Cardiff, CF14 1UA
Tel: 02920 617004
Principal: ICAEW Member
P J Reed

P.M. HUMPHREYS & CO
82a Whitchurch Road, Cardiff, CF14 3LX
Tel: 02920 664746
Email: pmh2@pmhumphreys.co.uk
Principal: ICAEW Member
P M Humphreys
Registered by the ICAEW to carry out company audit work

PAUL EDDINS
214 Whitchurch Road, Cardiff, CF14 3ND
Tel: 02920 529435
Fax: 029 2061 3306
Email: peddins@baynet.co.uk
Principal: ICAEW Member
P F R Eddins
General Description: General practice, though specialising in business start up, forecasting and management accounting.

PAUL R MARSHALL
4 Coed Briwnant, Rhiwbina, Cardiff, CF14 6QU

PC ACCOUNTING SOLUTIONS LTD
61 Cowbridge Road East, Cardiff, CF11 9AE

PETER WILKINS & CO ◈
Clare House, 68 Tudor Street, Cardiff, CF11 6AL
Tel: 02920 340207
Email: peter-wilkins@breathe.com
Website: http://www.peter-wilkins.co.uk
Principal: ICAEW Member
P J D Wilkins
Registered by the ICAEW to carry out company audit work
Regulated by the ICAEW for a range of investment business activities

PHILIP THOMAS & CO
72 Station Road, Llanishen, Cardiff, CF14 5UT

PKF (UK) LLP
18 Park Place, Cardiff, CF10 3PD
Tel: 02920 646200
Email: info.cardiff@uk.pkf.com
Website: http://www.pkf.co.uk
Resident Partners/Directors: ICAEW Members
K R Morgan, T D Smith
Resident Partners (Non-ICAEW Members):
D Roberts

PRICEWATERHOUSE-COOPERS
One Kingsway, Cardiff, CF10 3PW

PRICEWATERHOUSE-COOPERS LLP
One Kingsway, Cardiff, CF10 3PW
Tel: 02920 237000
Resident Partners/Directors: ICAEW Members
J Clarke, G J Davies, M C Ellis, L M Hine

RCA CORPORATE FINANCE
80 Beulah Road, Cardiff, CF14 6LZ

RICHARD ALSEPT ◈
20 Greenwich Road, Victoria Park, Cardiff, CF5 1EU

RICHARD COPPOCK ASSOCIATES LTD
80 Beulah Road, Cardiff, CF14 6LZ

AIMS - RICHARD NOBLE
4 Butterbur Place, Cardiff, CF5 4QZ
Tel: 02920 598879

RLJ ◈
Chapel Cottage, Michaelston-y-Fedw, Cardiff, CF3 6XT

RN CONSULTANCY LTD ◈
5 Butterbur Place, Cardiff, CF5 4QZ

ROBERT HUGH
15 Dan-y-Bryn Avenue, Radyr, Cardiff, CF15 8DD
Tel: 02920 844098

ROBERT HUGH LTD
15 Dan-y-Bryn Avenue, Radyr, Cardiff, CF15 8DD
Tel: 02920 844098
Resident Partners/Directors: ICAEW Members
R Hugh

ROBLINS
3 Deryn Court, Wharfedale Road, Pentwyn, Cardiff CF23 7HA
Tel: 02920 540024
Resident Partners/Directors: ICAEW Members
A J Prankerd, L A Roblin

RON COATES & CO LTD
374 Cowbridge Rd East, Cardiff, CF5 1JJ

S D CAVELL & CO
17 Cae Garw, Thornhill, Cardiff, CF14 9DX

SHEWRINGS
17 Tynewydd Drive, Castleton, Cardiff, CF3 2SB

SJB ACCOUNTANCY LTD
41 Lochaber Street, Roath, Cardiff, CF24 3LS
Tel: 02920 451771
Resident Partners/Directors: ICAEW Members
S J Bastable

STEVEN TURNER ACCOUNTANCY SERVICES LTD
11 Marguerites Way, St Fagans, Cardiff, CF5 4QW

STREET & BERG LTD ◈
8 Columbus Walk, Cardiff, CF10 4BY
Tel: 02920 494604

SUSAN J ARTHUR & CO
8 Columbus Walk, Brigantine Place, Cardiff, CF10 4BY
Tel: 02920 473316
Principal: ICAEW Member
S J Arthur

TRENCHARD CARNIE LTD
3 Rhododendron Close, Cardiff, CF23 7HS
Tel: 02920 252310
Resident Partners/Directors: ICAEW Members
N J Carnie

WALLACE WILLIAMS AUSTIN LTD
57 Cowbridge Road East, Cardiff, CF11 9AE
Tel: 02920 220217
Email: mail@wwa-online.co.uk
Resident Partners/Directors: ICAEW Members
T J Robinson

WATTS GREGORY LLP ◈
Elfed House, Oak Tree Court, Mulberry Drive, Cardiff Gate Business Park, Pontprennau, Cardiff CF23 8RS
Tel: 02920 546600
Email: all@watts-gregory.co.uk
Website: http://www.watts-gregory.co.uk
Resident Partners/Directors: ICAEW Members
D P Challenger, A P Embiricos, C D Hatcher, N Pugh, K Reid, K A Smith, D C Williams
Resident Partners (Non-ICAEW Members):
L T Hogg

WILLIAMS ROSS LTD
4 Ynys Bridge Court, Gwaelod-y-Garth, Cardiff, CF15 9SS

WILLMOTT
6 Parc y Fro, Creigiau, Cardiff, CF15 9SA

CARDIGAN

ASHMOLE & CO ★
Manchester House, Bridge Street, Cardigan, SA43 1HY
Tel: 01239 612162

DMB DAVIES LTD
Broyan House, Priory Street, Cardigan, SA43 1BU

PRITCHARD & CO ★
47 St Mary Street, Cardigan, SA43 1HA

R.E. MATTHEWS
Garn Hebogydd, Gwbert on Sea, Cardigan, SA43 1PR

CARMARTHEN

A LANSDOWN FCA
Newton Lodge, Cynwyl Elfed, Carmarthen, SA33 6SP
Tel: 01267 281252
Principal: ICAEW Member
A J C Lansdown

ASHMOLE & CO ★
9 Station Road, St Clears, Carmarthen, SA33 4BL

ASHMOLE & CO ★
The Old School, Coracle Way, Carmarthen, SA31 3JP

BEVAN & BUCKLAND
20 Blue Street, Carmarthen, SA31 3LE

CLAY SHAW BUTLER
24 Lammas Street, Carmarthen, SA31 3AL

CLAY SHAW BUTLER LTD ◈
24 Lammas Street, Carmarthen, SA31 3AL
Tel: 01267 228500
Email: info@clayshawbutler.com
Training Contracts Available.
Resident Partners/Directors: ICAEW Members
D G Butler
Registered by the ICAEW to carry out company audit work
Regulated by the ICAEW for a range of investment business activities

INVESTOR IN PEOPLE

SPECIALISATIONS – BUSINESS & GENERAL ADVICE
Management Consultancy

SPECIALISATIONS – SECTOR
Charities
Construction
Solicitors

General Description: Audit, tax planning, mentoring, business consultancy, grants, Sage business partners.

D I DAVIES FCA
3 Gwynfan, Nantycaws, Carmarthen, SA32 8HF

DONALD OWEN LTD
34 Quay Street, Carmarthen, Carmarthenshire, SA31 3JT
Tel: 01267 236225
Website: http://www.donaldowen.co.uk
Resident Partners/Directors: ICAEW Members
G P G Jones
Registered by the ICAEW to carry out company audit work

H & W JONES & CO
6 Barn Road, Carmarthen, SA31 1DE

HAROLD D. PRITCHARD & CO
Old Oak House, 49-51 Lammas Street, Carmarthen, SA31 3AL
Tel: 01267 237340
Resident Partners/Directors: ICAEW Members
B C Carroll, T J Evans, R D Thomas

JONES WARD LTD
6 St Catherine Street, Carmarthen, SA31 1RE

L.H. PHILLIPS & CO
29/30 Quay St, Carmarthen, SA31 3JT
Tel: 01267 237534
Resident Partners/Directors: ICAEW Members
H M W Thomas, M J Williams
Registered by the ICAEW to carry out company audit work
Regulated by the ICAEW for a range of investment business activities

LLYR JAMES
25 Bridge Street, Carmarthen, SA31 3JS
Tel: 01267 237754
Principal: ICAEW Member
C L James

MARTIN WATERWORTH LTD
Bronwylfa, Llangunnor Road, Carmarthen, SA31 2PB
Tel: 01267 223444
Resident Partners/Directors: ICAEW Members
M Waterworth

PRICE JENKINS & CO
53 King Street, Carmarthen, SA31 1BD

PRITCHARD JONES ACCOUNTANCY SERVICES LTD
3 Quay Street, Carmarthen, SA31 3JT

PRITCHARD ROBERTS & CO
108A Lammas Street, Carmarthen, SA31 3AP

TSW INTERNATIONAL TAXATION CONSULTING
4 Clos y Ffynnon, Wellfield Road, Carmarthen, SA31 1DU

CHEPSTOW

C. JOHN SAGE
Orchard House, Mathern, Chepstow, NP16 6JA

GUY RASTALL (FINANCIAL SERVICES) LTD
Crestacre House, Sedbury Lane, Tutshill, Chepstow NP16 7DU

MACARIO LEWIN
Bellarmine House, 14 Upper Church Street, Chepstow, NP16 5EX

MACARIO LEWIN LTD
Bellarmine House, 14 Upper Church Street, Chepstow, NP16 5EX

MALCOLM WILTON & CO
Ty Gwyn, Catbrook, Chepstow, NP16 6ND
Tel: 01600 860341
Principal: ICAEW Member
M C Wilton

OXLEY ACCOUNTANTS LTD ◈
Top Floor, The Greyhound Building, 17 Moor Street, Chepstow, NP16 5DB

ROSEMARY CHICKEN
11 Moor Street, Chepstow, NP16 5DD

W.G.RASTALL
Crest Acre House, Sedbury Lane, Tutshill, Chepstow NP16 7DU
Tel: 01291 622680
Principal: ICAEW Member
W G Rastall

COLWYN BAY

ASTON, HUGHES & CO ▽
Selby Towers, 29 Princes Drive, Colwyn Bay, LL29 8PE

E.G. JONES & CO
2 Colwyn Avenue, Rhos-on-Sea, Colwyn Bay, LL28 4RB
Tel: 01492 547345
Principal: ICAEW Member
E G Jones

M.W. HORNER & CO
Cilgerran, Eglwysbach, Colwyn Bay, LL28 5UA

M W ROBERTS & CO LTD
8 Kings Oak, Colwyn Bay, LL29 6AJ
Tel: 01492 535553
Resident Partners/Directors: ICAEW Members
M W Roberts

O. EVANS-JONES
Bod Marian, Glan Conwy, Colwyn Bay, LL28 5SY
Tel: 01492 580284
Principal: ICAEW Member
O Evans-Jones

PRITCHETT & CO
16 Wynnstay Road, Colwyn Bay, LL29 8NB

SHAW AUSTIN ◈
49 Conway Road, Colwyn Bay, LL29 7AN
Tel: 01244 400244

SPEECHLEYS
Princes Chambers, 23 Wynnstay Road, Colwyn Bay, LL29 8NT

CONWY

MARK VICKERS FCA
Eagles View, Castle Quay Mews, Conwy, LL32 8DF

COWBRIDGE

AIMS - STEVEN KAVANAGH ◈
Aeolian House, Piccadilly, Llanblethian, Cowbridge CF71 7JL
Tel: 01446 771687
Principal: ICAEW Member
S P Kavanagh

BEMAN & CO
The Bungalow, Llantrithyd House, Llantrithyd, Cowbridge CF71 7UB
Tel: 01446 781069
Principal: ICAEW Member
D G Beman

CARSTON & CO (CARDIFF) LTD
Sycamore House, Vale Business Park, Llandow, Cowbridge CF71 7PF

COWBRIDGE TAX SERVICES
Mill Brow, Brookfield Park Road, Cowbridge, CF71 7HJ
Tel: 01446 771536

O'SHEA & OWEN
5 Willow Walk, Cowbridge, CF71 7EE
Tel: 01446 772804
Principal: ICAEW Member
M Owen

R. H BRADSHAW ◈
Mill Brow, Brookfield Park Road, Cowbridge, CF71 7HJ
Tel: 01446 771536
Principal: ICAEW Member
R H Bradshaw

RJ & CA PERKINS
Clemenstone Court, Clemenstone, Cowbridge, CF71 7PZ

SAMANTHA JAMES
Pippins, Trerhyngyll, Cowbridge, CF71 7TN

CRICCIETH

HAROLD SMITH
29 High Street, Criccieth, LL52 0BS

J.T. THOMAS & CO
70 High Street, Criccieth, LL52 0HB
Tel: 01766 522141
Principal: ICAEW Member
J T Thomas

CRICKHOWELL

C.DIANA WILDING
Heathfield, Ffawyddog, Crickhowell, NP8 1PY

HUW JONES & CO
Larchfield, Pregge Lane, Crickhowell, NP8 1SE

IAN F. FLETCHER LTD ◈
49 High Street, Crickhowell, NP8 1BH
Tel: 01873 810285
Resident Partners/Directors: ICAEW Members
I F Fletcher

MICHAEL N. DANIEL & CO
4 Mill Street, Crickhowell, NP8 1BA
Tel: 01873 812625
Principal: ICAEW Member
M N Daniel

PAUL PHILLIS & CO LTD
4 Dan y Gollen, Crickhowell, NP8 1TN

ROB JONES & CO
The Forge, Glanusk Park, Crickhowell, NP8 1LP

ROBERT JONES (WALES) LTD
The Forge, Glanusk Park, Crickhowell, NP8 1LP

CWMBRAN

DAVID EXELL ASSOCIATES
11 New Street, Pontnewydd, Cwmbran, NP44 1EE

DAVID F. EDWARDS
Victoria House, Victoria Street, Cwmbran, NP44 3JS
Tel: 01633 873414
Principal: ICAEW Member
D F Edwards

GREEN & CO ★
7 New Street, Pontnewydd, Cwmbran, NP44 1EE

GRIFFITHS & JAMES LTD ◈
Suite 5, Brecon House, Llantarnam Park, Cwmbran NP44 3AB
Tel: 01633 877900
Resident Partners/Directors: ICAEW Members
D P Griffiths

GRIFFITHS, GREEN, ARNOLD ★ ◈
11 New Street, Pontnewydd, Cwmbran, NP44 1EE
Tel: 01633 838222
Resident Partners/Directors: ICAEW Members
R Arnold, K Davies

DEESIDE

CLARE F. RIMMER FCA
Fir Tree House, Truemans Way, Hawarden, Deeside CH5 3LS
Tel: 01244 533349
Principal: ICAEW Member
C F Rimmer

DUNCAN SHEARD GLASS ◈
Unit 5, Evolution House, Lakeside Business Village, St Davids Park, Ewloe, Deeside CH5 3XP
Tel: 01244 526030
Fax: 01244 529517
Email: northwales@dsg.uk.com
Website: http://www.dsg.uk.com
Resident Partners/Directors: ICAEW Members
C Wheatley
Non-resident Partners (ICAEW Members):
J Ellis
Other Offices: Liverpool, Southport
Registered by the ICAEW to carry out company audit work
Regulated by the ICAEW for a range of investment business activities

GLYN HEWITT
Network House, St Ives Way, Sandycroft, Deeside CH5 2QS
Tel: 01244 526019
Principal: ICAEW Member
R G Hewitt

HENRY R. DAVIS & CO
33 Chester Road West, Queensferry, Deeside, CH5 1SA
Tel: 01244 831277
Principal: ICAEW Member
A H Travers

NOEL POPPLEWELL & CO
18 Vaughan Way, Connah's Quay, Deeside, CH5 4NG
Tel: 01244 831923
Principal: ICAEW Member
N Popplewell

RIMMER CASE PARTNERSHIP
Fir Tree House, Truemans Way, Hawarden, Deeside CH5 3LS
Tel: 01244 533349
Resident Partners/Directors: ICAEW Members
B E Case, C F Rimmer

ROBERT PARRY & CO LTD
Nat. Westminster Bank Chambers, 2 Dundas Street, Queensferry, Deeside CH5 1SZ

DENBIGH

AD HOC ACCOUNTANCY SERVICES
6 Lon Nant, Denbigh, LL16 4BE

ANN BITCON
6 Lon Nant, Denbigh, LL16 4BE

D.C. EVANS ◈
Cae Nant, Llandyrnog, Denbigh, LL16 4HB
Tel: 01824 790344
Principal: ICAEW Member
D C Evans

IONA EDWARDS
Hen Dy, Plas Madoc, Llansannan, Denbigh LL16 5LF

PARRY, SCHOLES & CO ◈
Parry Scholes & Co, 5a Vale Street, Denbigh, LL16 3AF
Tel: 01745 812245
Principal: ICAEW Member
P T Scholes

PETER WARBURTON & CO
Gwalia, Llangynhafal, Denbigh, LL16 4LN
Tel: 01824 790489
Principal: ICAEW Member
P Warburton

DINAS POWYS

ALFRED E REDDEN FCA
42 Drylla, Dinas Powys, CF64 4UL

CARSTON & CO (CARDIFF) LTD
24 Cardiff Road, Dinas Powys, CF64 4JS

G.G. WALL
Brynglas, St Andrews Road, Dinas Powys, CF64 4AT

GSR CONSULTANCY (UK) LTD
Leigh Cottage, Mount Road, Dinas Powys, CF64 4DG

HOURIHAN LTD
21 Millbrook Road, Dinas Powys, CF64 4BZ
Tel: 02920 515325
Resident Partners/Directors: ICAEW Members
A Hourihan

MICHAEL G WILTSHIRE
39 Cardiff Road, Dinas Powys, CF64 4DH

STEPHEN MAYLED & ASSOCIATES
Stephen Mayled & Associates Ltd, Cottage Farm, Michaelston-le-Pit, Dinas Powys CF64 4HE

STEPHEN MAYLED & ASSOCIATES LTD
Cottage Farm, Michaelston-le-Pit, Dinas Powys, CF64 4HE

STEPHEN MAYLED & ASSOCIATES BUSINESS DEVELOPMENT SPECIALISTS
Stephen Mayled & Associates Ltd, Cottage Farm, Michaelston-le-Pit, Dinas Powys CF64 4HE

STEPHEN MAYLED & ASSOCIATES DENTAL BUSINESS SPECIALISTS
Stephen Mayled & Associates Ltd, Cottage Farm, Michaelston-le-Pit, Dinas Powys CF64 4HE

DOLGELLAU

GRIFFITH, WILLIAMS & CO ◈
Heol Glyndwr, Dolgellau, LL40 1BB

FISHGUARD

PRITCHARD & CO ★
74 High Street, Fishguard, SA65 9AU
Tel: 01348 873263
Resident Partners/Directors: ICAEW Members
I R Williams

GOODWICK

PRESELI MANAGEMENT ACCOUNTING
Ranelagh, Precelly Crescent, Goodwick, SA64 0HF

HAVERFORDWEST

ASHMOLE & CO ★
Williamston House, 7 Goat Street, Haverfordwest, SA61 1PX

BEVAN & BUCKLAND
45 High Street, Haverfordwest, SA61 2BP

BEVAN & BUCKLAND
2a Cross Square, St Davids, Haverfordwest, SA61 2BP

PRITCHARD & CO ★
15 Victoria Place, Haverfordwest, SA61 2JX

HOLYHEAD

THOMAS R. KNOWLES & WILLIAMS
Stanley House, Market Square, Holyhead, LL65 1UF
Tel: 01407 763237
Principal: ICAEW Member
C D Williams

HOLYWELL

CHRISTIAN & CO LTD
26 High Street, Holywell, Flintshire, CH8 7LH
Tel: 01352 713337
Resident Partners/Directors: ICAEW Members
N E Christian, N H G Christian

GARDNER SALISBURY LTD ◈
Brynford House, Brynford Street, Holywell, CH8 7RD

MR MELLOR & CO LTD
Panton House, Panton Place, High Street, Holywell CH8 7LD

KIDWELLY

WILLIAMS & CO
Longmead, 3 Heol Gwermont, Llansaint, Kidwelly SA17 5JA

KILGETTY

P.A.N. GRIMLEY ◈
Hillcrest, Lawrenny Road, Cresselly, Kilgetty SA68 0TB

KNIGHTON

CAERWYN JONES
8 Broad Street, Knighton, LD7 1BL

D.R.E. & CO (AUDIT) LTD
Wylcwm Place, Knighton, LD7 1AE

DRE & CO
3 West Street, Knighton, LD7 1EN
Tel: 01547 528383

DRE & CO LTD
3 West Street, Knighton, LD7 1EN

LAMPETER

DAVID UPTON & CO
Felinsych, Cwmann, Lampeter, SA48 8EA

H & W JONES & CO
81 Bridge Street, Lampeter, SA48 7AB

PATTERSON, JONES & EVANS ◈
23 College Street, Lampeter, SA48 7DY
Tel: 01570 422451
Resident Partners/Directors: ICAEW Members
D R Patterson
Languages Spoken:
Welsh

LLANDEILO

PRITCHARD EVANS & CO LTD
21 Carmarthen Street, Llandeilo, SA19 6AN

LLANDOVERY

PETER PRICE & CO
9 Broad Street, Llandovery, SA20 0AR
Tel: 01550 720890
Principal: ICAEW Member
P G Price

LLANDRINDOD WELLS

A J ACCOUNTANCY LTD
The Old Surgery, Spa Road, Llandrindod Wells, LD1 5EY
Tel: 01597 825777
Resident Partners/Directors: ICAEW Members
A C Jones

ANDREW JONES & CO ◈
The Old Surgery, Spa Road, Llandrindod Wells, LD1 5EY
Tel: 01597 825777
Principal: ICAEW Member
A C Jones

MITCHELL MEREDITH
The Exchange, Fiveways, Temple Street, Llandrindod Wells LD1 5HG

MITCHELL MEREDITH LTD
The Exchange, Fiveways, Temple Street, Llandrindod Wells LD1 5HG

MOORE SCOTT & CO
Aden Chambers, South Crescent, Llandrindod Wells, LD1 5DH
Tel: 01597 824041
Website: http://www.moore-scott.co.uk
Resident Partners/Directors: ICAEW Members
J W Bean, I P McNair

LLANDUDNO

ASTON, HUGHES & CO ▽ ◈
Livingstone House, Llewelyn Avenue, Llandudno, Conwy LL30 2ER

BREEZE & CO
9 Lloyd Street, Llandudno, LL30 2UU
Tel: 01492 870680

BREEZE & CO (LLANDUDNO) LTD
9 Lloyd Street, Llandudno, Conwy, LL30 2UU

BUTTERWORTHS
Windsor House, 26 Mostyn Avenue, Llandudno, LL30 1YY

BUTTERWORTHS ACCOUNTANTS LTD
Windsor House, 26 Mostyn Avenue, Craig-y-Don, Llandudno LL30 1YY

BUTTERWORTHS PAYROLL SERVICES
Windsor House, 26 Mostyn Avenue, Craig-y-Don, Llandudno LL30 1YY

GARETH HUGHES & COMPANY LTD
The Round House, Glan-y-Mor Road, Llandudno Junction, LL31 9SG
Tel: 01492 593345
Fax: 01492 593930
Email: gareth@garethhughes.co.uk
Website: http://www.garethhughes.co.uk
Resident Partners/Directors: ICAEW Members
G W Hughes
Resident Partners (Non-ICAEW Members):
M J Wilkes

SPECIALISATIONS – IT
Computerised Accounting Systems

SPECIALISATIONS – TAXATION
Taxation

H.E. DUNNING
Highleigh,Nant-Y-Gamar Road, Craig-Y-Don, Llandudno, Clwyd, LL30 3BD

HAWLEY AND CO ◈
First Floor Suite, 23 Trinity Square, Llandudno, LL30 2RH
Tel: 01492 863970
Principal: ICAEW Member
G S Hawley

J.T. THOMAS & CO ◈
Natwest Chamberse, 62 Mostyn Street, Llandudno, LL30 2SN
Tel: 01492 874543

J.V. BANKS
Banks House, Ty Isa Road, Llandudno, LL30 2PL

JOHN PRATT & CO
Basford House, 29 Augusta Street, Llandudno, Clwyd LL30 2AE
Tel: 01492 870575
Principal: ICAEW Member
J P Pratt

MARK BUTTERWORTH LTD
Windsor House, 26 Mostyn Avenue, Llandudno, LL30 1YY

PARKIN S. BOOTH & CO ★
24 Trinity Square, Llandudno, LL30 2RH

TIERNAYFEDRICK
Tiernay Fredrick, 19 Trinity Square, Llandudno, LL30 2RD
Tel: 01492 860055
Resident Partners/Directors: ICAEW Members
S Roberts, N F Tiernay, P J B Tiernay

WILLIAMS DENTON CYF ★
San Remo, 13 Trinity Square, Llandudno, LL30 2RB
Tel: 01492 879375

LLANELLI

AIMS - ERIC ANDERSON
Rhos Fach Farm, Cross Hands, Llanelli, SA14 6DG

ALEXANDER PARTNERSHIP
5/6A West End, Llanelli, SA15 3DN

COLIN P THOMAS
16 Penyfai Lane, Furnace, Llanelli, SA15 4EN

RIMMER & MAY ★ ◈
19 Murray Street, Llanelli, SA15 1AQ
Tel: 01554 773525
Resident Partners/Directors: ICAEW Members
A M Evans, E Truman

STEVE ELLUM & ASSOCIATES LTD
18 Bryn Terrace, Llanelli, SA15 2PD

LLANFAIRPWLLGWYNGYLL

A.E.M. JONES
Tai Cochion, Brynsiencyn, Llanfairpwllgwyngyll, LL61 6TQ

LLANGEFNI

FOWLER & HARE
Pennant House, Glyndwr, Llangefni, LL77 7EF

I.G. JONES & CO ◈
Cefni Chambers, 10a High Street, Llangefni, LL77 7LT
Tel: 01248 750140
Resident Partners/Directors: ICAEW Members
D L Jones

O. LEWIS
Cefni Chambers, 10A High Street, Llangefni, LL77 7LT

O. LEWIS & CO
Cefni Chambers, 10A High Street, Llangefni, LL77 7LT

W GLYNNE OWEN & CO LTD
6a Church Street, Llangefni, LL77 7DU
Tel: 01248 750484
Resident Partners/Directors: ICAEW Members
W G Owen

LLANGOLLEN

MORRIS COOK ◈
Brynestyn, East Street, Llangollen, LL20 8RB
Tel: 01978 860376
Resident Partners/Directors: ICAEW Members
W P Cooper

LLANIDLOES

MOORE SCOTT & CO
Town Hall, Great Oak Street, Llanidloes, SY18 6BN

PETER GEARY & CO
4 Great Oak Street, Llanidloes, SY18 6BN

R.D.I. SCOTT & CO
4a China Street, Llanidloes, SY18 6AB

LLANRWST

J LLYWELYN HUGHES & CO
Ty'r Bont, Llanrwst, LL26 0EY
Tel: 01492 640391
Fax: 01492 641930
Email: david@jlhughes.co.uk
Resident Partners/Directors: ICAEW Members
D E Thomas, R A Thomas

Registered by the ICAEW to carry out company audit work

Regulated by the ICAEW for a range of investment business activities

LLANTWIT MAJOR

BPU
The Counting House, Pound Field, Llantwit Major, CF6 1DL

LLANYBYDDER

GLYNIS D. MORRIS
Cae Ceffylau, Drefach, Llanybydder, SA40 9SX
Tel: 01570 481161
Principal: ICAEW Member
G D Morris

LLANYMYNECH

ANDREW R Q MORGAN LTD
Oaklea, Llansantffraid, SY22 6TE
Tel: 01691 829212
Resident Partners/Directors: ICAEW Members
A R Q Morgan

C.J. WAREHAM
Breidden, Greenfield Cottages, Four Crosses, Llanymynech SY22 6RF
Tel: 01691 831481
Principal: ICAEW Member
C J Wareham

GERAINT HUMPHREYS & CO
Bridge Street, Llanfyllin, SY22 5AU
Tel: 01691 648414

MACHYNLLETH

G J TAGGART LTD
Fach Uchaf, Cwmllinau, Machynlleth, SY20 9PF

MENAI BRIDGE

WAYNE T. KING & CO
2 High Street, Menai Bridge, LL59 5EE
Tel: 01248 716258
Principal: ICAEW Member
W T King

MERTHYR TYDFIL

BTP ASSOCIATES
84-86 High Street, Merthyr Tydfil, CF47 8UG

BTP ASSOCIATES LTD
84-86 High Street, Merthyr Tydfil, CF47 8UG

E WAYNE PULMAN & CO LTD
19 Church Street, Merthyr Tydfil, CF47 0AY

MORGAN & MORGAN
9 Lakeside Gardens, Merthyr Tydfil, CF48 1EN
Tel: 01685 71040
Principal: ICAEW Member
J E Morgan

PHILIP MORGAN
9 Lakeside Gardens, Merthyr Tydfil, CF48 1EN
Tel: 01685 371040
Principal: ICAEW Member
P Morgan

Y DRYDEDD DDRAIG CYF
86 High Street, Merthyr Tydfil, CF47 8UG

MILFORD HAVEN

DAVIDSON & CO ◈
17 Temeraire House, Nelson Quay, Milford Haven, SA73 3BN
Tel: 01646 694996
Fax: 01646 697157
Email: davidson.company@virgin.net
Principal: ICAEW Member
B J Davidson
Registered by the ICAEW to carry out company audit work

EVENS & CO LTD ◈
Hamilton House, Hamilton Terrace, Milford Haven, SA73 3JP

MOLD

BENNETT BROOKS
First Floor Offices, 42 High Street, Mold, Flintshire CH7 1BH

H.D. LLOYD
Pen Y Graig, Cilcain Road, Pantymwyn, Mold CH7 5NJ
Tel: 01352 740260
Principal: ICAEW Member
H D Lloyd

HICKS RANDLES LTD
100 High Street, Mold, CH7 1BH

HILL & ROBERTS
50 High Street, Mold, CH7 1BH
Tel: 01352 700086
Resident Partners/Directors: ICAEW Members
H P Baines

JDH BUSINESS SERVICES LTD
94a Wrexham Street, Mold, CH7 1HQ

KATHARINE WILDING BA(HONS) ACA
Oldfield, Forestry Road, Llanferres, Mold CH7 5SH

PAUL E. WILDERMUTH
Pentre Farm, Pentre, Cilcain, Mold CH7 5PF

MONMOUTH

AGINCOURT PRACTICE LTD
6 Agincourt Street, Monmouth, NP25 3DZ

ELGAN
Wyastone Business Park, Wyastone Leys, Monmouth, NP25 3SR
Tel: 01600 891531
Email: info@elgan.co.uk
Principal: ICAEW Member
J M Humby

HONEYWELL & CO
9 Whitecross Street, Monmouth, NP25 3BY

HONEYWELL (MONMOUTH) LTD
9 Whitecross Street, Monmouth, NP25 3BY

HUSBANDS & CO ◈
Forge House, Forge Road, Osbaston, Monmouth NP25 3AZ
Tel: 01600 716461
Principal: ICAEW Member
C M W Husbands

J.T. BARTER
2 Howard Bowen Close, Osbaston, Monmouth, NP25 3AU

W.GLYN EVANS & CO
Ashmead, Llangovan, Monmouth, NP25 4BT

MONTGOMERY

MONTGOMERY TAX SERVICES LTD
Hendomen Farmhouse, Hendomen, Montgomery, SY15 6HB

MOUNTAIN ASH

E WAYNE PULMAN & CO LTD
F19, Enterprise House, Navigation Park, Abercynon, Mountain Ash, Mid Glamorgan CF45 4SN

NARBERTH

LLEWELYN DAVIES ◈
Bank House, St James Street, Narberth, Pembrokeshire SA67 7BX
Tel: 01834 860291
Resident Partners/Directors: ICAEW Members
K J Randall
Registered by the ICAEW to carry out company audit work

NEATH

C S JAMES & CO LTD
88 New Road, Skewen, Neath, SA10 6HG
Tel: 01792 817439
Resident Partners/Directors: ICAEW Members
C S James

J GARETH MORGAN & CO
13a Victoria Gardens, Neath, SA11 3AY

M.J. HAZEL & CO
30 Brookfield, Neath, SA10 7EH
Tel: 01639 637186
Principal: ICAEW Member
M J Hazel

PCP LTD
Bronleigh, 88 Main Road, Crynant, Neath SA10 8NT

PROACTIVE CONSULTANTS FOR PROFESSIONALS LTD
Bronleigh, 88 Main Road, Crynant, Neath SA10 8NT

WATKINS, BRADFIELD & CO
Woodfield House, Castle Walk, Neath, SA11 3LN

NEWCASTLE EMLYN

MICHAEL S RAMSEY LTD
Y Ddol, Llandyfriog, Newcastle Emlyn, SA38 9HB
Tel: 01239 711326
Resident Partners/Directors: ICAEW Members
M S Ramsey

TOPLINE LTD
Y Ddol, Llandyfriog, Newcastle Emlyn, SA38 9HB
Tel: 01239 711326
Resident Partners/Directors: ICAEW Members
M S Ramsey

NEWPORT

A. HURLEY
4 Friars Crescent, Newport, NP20 4EY

ANDREW TURFORD & CO LTD
33 Stow Park Avenue, Newport, NP20 4FN
Tel: 01633 214658
Fax: 01633 250176
Email: andrew@andrewturford.co.uk
Resident Partners/Directors: ICAEW Members
A J Turford

ARTHUR GAIT & CO
18 Gold Tops, Newport, NP20 5WJ
Tel: 01633 262352
Website: http://www.arthurgait.co.uk
Resident Partners/Directors: ICAEW Members
D E Hayes, C J Pritchard
Registered by the ICAEW to carry out company audit work

BROOMFIELD & ALEXANDER LTD
Waters Lane Chambers, Water Lane, Newport, NP20 1LA
Tel: 01633 265828
Website: http://www.broomfield.co.uk
Resident Partners/Directors: ICAEW Members
S Case, B Morgan

C.J.JONES
45 Cwm Cwddy Drive, Rhiwderin Heights, Newport, NP10 8JN

CLARK R. DURBIN & CO
92 Western Avenue, Newport, NP20 3QZ

CS TAXATION AND ACCOUNTANCY LTD
41 High Cross Drive, Rogerstone, Newport, NP10 9AB
Tel: 01633 895870
Resident Partners/Directors: ICAEW Members
C Sage

ELLIS LLOYD JONES LLP
2 Risca Road, Newport, NP20 4JW

G.THOMAS & CO
12 Llwynderi Road, Newport, NP20 4LW

GREENS ACCOUNTANCY & TAX SERVICES LTD
106a Commercial Street, Risca, Newport, NP11 6EE

GUILFOYLE, SAGE & CO
21 Gold Tops, Newport, NP20 4PG

HSJ ACCOUNTANTS LTD
Severn House, Hazell Drive, Newport, NP10 8FY

HUGHES & CO
Severn House, Hazell Drive, Newport, NP10 8FY

HWCA LTD ◈
Pagefield House, 24 Gold Tops, Newport, NP20 4PG
Tel: 01633 222881
Resident Partners/Directors: ICAEW Members
J P Crowley, A S Cunningham, D T Green

INNOVATION PROFESSIONAL SERVICES LLP
Merlin House, Priory Drive, Langstone, Newport NP18 2HJ
Tel: 02920 660273
Resident Partners/Directors: ICAEW Members
J S Messore, R J Powis

J.S. NOTLEY
195 Caerleon Road, Newport, NP19 7HA

J.W. APPLEBEE
2 Oaklands Park Drive, Rhiwderin, Newport, NP10 8RB

KEVIN WHATLEY & CO
25 Newport Road, Cwmcarn, Newport, NP11 7ND

KILSBY & WILLIAMS LLP ◈
Cedar House, Hazell Drive, Newport, NP10 8FY
Tel: 01633 810081
Email: simon.tee@kilsbywilliams.com
Website: http://www.kilsbywilliams.com
Resident Partners/Directors: ICAEW Members
A Kilsby, S R Tee, N Williams

MINTY JONES & BECKETT ★
Churchgate House, Clytha Park Road, Newport, NP20 4PB

NEIL HODGE & CO LTD
106A Commercial Street, Risca, Newport, NP11 6EE

PBM (AUDITORS) LTD
Summit House, 5 Gold Tops, Newport, NP20 4PG

PBM (AUDITORS) LTD
Churchgate House, Clytha Park Road, Newport, NP20 4PB

PEACHEYS ◈
Lanyon House, Mission Court, Newport, NP20 2DW
Tel: 01633 213318

PEACHEYS CA LTD
Lanyon House, Mission Court, Newport, NP20 2DW

R. WEARE & CO
Brook House, Llandevaud, Newport, NP18 2AA

SHEPHERD & CO
Melbourne House, 58 St Mary Street, Risca, Newport NP11 6GQ

SHERRINGTON & CO
16 Gold Tops, Newport, NP20 4PH

WALTER HUNTER & CO LTD ◈
24 Bridge Street, Newport, NP20 4SF
Tel: 01633 265323
Resident Partners/Directors: ICAEW Members
J Rhodes, D R Thomas

THE WORKHOUSE
4 Arthur Street, Caerleon, Newport, NP18 1BJ

NEWTOWN

D.R.E. & CO
20 Broad Street, Newtown, SY16 2NA

DRE & CO LTD
20 Broad Street, Newtown, SY16 2NA

MITCHELL MEREDITH LTD
30 Short Bridge Street, Newtown, SY16 2LN
Tel: 01686 628748

MORGAN GRIFFITHS LLP
Cross Chambers, 9 High Street, Newtown, SY16 2NY

RD ACCOUNTANCY SOLUTIONS LTD
18 Poplar Road, Newtown, SY16 2AQ

WHITTINGHAM RIDDELL LLP ◈
Hafren House, 5 St Giles Business Park, Newtown, SY16 3AJ
Tel: 01686 626230
Email: wr@whittinghamriddell.co.uk
Resident Partners (Non-ICAEW Members):
F G Bennett
Other Offices: Shrewsbury, Ludlow, Welshpool

PEMBROKE

BEVAN & BUCKLAND
Castle Chambers, 6 Westgate Hill, Pembroke, SA71 4LB

GEOFF DAVIES ASSOCIATES LTD
27 Main Street, Pembroke, SA71 4JS
Tel: 01646 685656
Resident Partners/Directors: ICAEW Members
G M Davies

MICHAEL A COLLEY
Leicester House, 6 Hamilton Terrace, Main Street, Pembroke SA71 4DE
Tel: 01646 682582
Principal: ICAEW Member
M A Colley

RICHARD CALEY LTD
Havenside, Trewent Hill, Freshwater East, Pembroke SA71 5LJ

PEMBROKE DOCK

GILL ORCHARD ACA
Warreston House, Slade Cross, Cosheston, Pembroke Dock SA72 4SX

LLEWELYN DAVIES ◈
50 Queen Street, Pembroke Dock, SA72 6JE
Tel: 01646 683341
Email: pdock@llewelyndavies.co.uk
Registered by the ICAEW to carry out company audit work

LUCY JONES
First Floor, Pier House, Pier Road, Hobbs Point, Pembroke Dock SA72 6TR
Tel: 01646 650000
Principal: ICAEW Member
L J Jones

PENARTH

IAN MCCANN & CO
4 Rowan Close, The Paddocks, Penarth, CF64 5BU

JOHN PRICE & CO ◈
18 Archer Road, Penarth, CF64 3HW
Tel: 02920 70 4585
Principal: ICAEW Member
J L Price

NAUNTON JONES LE MASURIER ★ ◈
3 Herbert Terrace, Penarth, CF64 2AH

PENTRE

CURTIS BOWDEN & THOMAS
The Woodlands, Pentre Road, Pentre, CF41 7DJ

PONTYCLUN

MACE AND PARTNERS
52 Talbot Road, Talbot Green, Pontyclun, CF72 8AF
Tel: 01443 222058
Principal: ICAEW Member
R A Huckridge

STUART ANDERSON
Newland, Ely Valley Road, Talbot Green, Pontyclun CF72 8AP
Tel: 01443 223384

STUART ANDERSON ACCOUNTANTS LTD
Newland, Ely Valley Road, Talbot Green, Pontyclun CF72 8AP
Tel: 01443 223384
Resident Partners/Directors: ICAEW Members
S Anderson

PONTYPOOL

BARRY MITCHELL & CO
Pentre Farm House, Mamhilad, Pontypool, NP4 0JH
Tel: 01495 785511
Principal: ICAEW Member
B G Mitchell

PETER PRICE & COMPANY (PONTYPOOL) LTD
Park Royal House, Hanbury Road, Pontypool, NP4 6LL

STEPHEN NAPIER & CO
First Floor, Hodges Chambers, Crane Street, Pontypool NP4 6LY
Tel: 01495 762962
Principal: ICAEW Member
S Napier

WM. E. PRICE & CO
Nyth Glyd, Ffrwd Road, Abersychan, Pontypool NP4 8PF

PONTYPRIDD

ACCOUNTING FOR CHARITIES LTD
26-27 Park Street, Pontypridd, CF37 1SN

HARRIES WATKINS & JONES LTD
85 Taff Street, Pontypridd, CF37 4SL

HUW JOHN & CO LTD ◈
Upper Floor, 5-7 Mill Street, Pontypridd, CF37 2SN

JAMES DE FRIAS LTD ◈
Llanover House, Llanover Road, Pontypridd, CF37 4DY
Tel: 01443 491551
Resident Partners/Directors: ICAEW Members
D R Bowden, P R de Frias, D A James

JOHN SMART
Delfan, New Park Terrace, Trefforest, Pontypridd CF37 1TH

KENNETH LEWIS & CO ◈
22 Gelliwastad Rd, Pontypridd, CF37 2BW
Tel: 01443 493118
Principal: ICAEW Member
K R Lewis

O'BRIEN & PARTNERS
Highdale House, 7 Centre Court, Main Av, Treforest Ind Estate, Pontypridd CF37 5YR

R.H. JEFFS & ROWE ◈
27-28 Gelliwastad Road, Pontypridd, CF37 2BW
Tel: 01443 402116
Website: http://www.accountancywales.com
Date Established: 1908
Resident Partners/Directors: ICAEW Members
H T W Jones, R E Thomas

INVESTOR IN PEOPLE

R LEACH
12 Fothergill Street, Treforest, Pontypridd, CF37 1SG
Tel: 01443 402394
Principal: ICAEW Member
R Leach

RH JEFFS & ROWE LTD
27-28 Gelliwastad Road, Pontypridd, CF37 2BW
Tel: 01443 402116
Website: http://www.accountancywales.com
Resident Partners/Directors: ICAEW Members
H T W Jones, R E Thomas

SULLIVANS
14 Gelliwastad Road, Pontypridd, CF37 2BW

SULLIVANS ASSOCIATES LTD
14 Gelliwastad Road, Pontypridd, CF37 2BW

YOUNG & PHILLIPS LTD
Inspiration House, Williams Place, Cardiff Road, Pontypridd CF37 5BH

PORT TALBOT

BARRY PAGE & CO
72 Pentyla Baglan Road, Port Talbot, SA12 8AD

PORTHCAWL

ALWYN THOMAS ◈
Glenaub House, Old School Road, Porthcawl, CF36 3AW
Tel: 01656 771000
Principal: ICAEW Member
A Thomas

ANDREW SINGER & CO
39 John Street, Porthcawl, CF36 3AP
Tel: 01656 783420
Principal: ICAEW Member
A B Singer

BOWEN-JONES, WATKINS & PARTNERS
17 Dan-Y-Graig Avenue, Newton, Porthcawl, CF36 5AA
Tel: 01656 773990
Principal: ICAEW Member
A J Watkins

G T OWENS
41 Severn Road, Porthcawl, CF36 3LN

HUW THOMAS ◈
14 Severn Road, Porthcawl, CF36 3LN

J BRIAN HARRISON
4 Locks Common, Porthcawl, CF36 3HU

J BRIAN HARRISON
4 Locks Common Road, Porthcawl, CF36 3HU

J BRIAN HARRISON LTD
4 Locks Common Road, Porthcawl, CF36 3HU

PORTHMADOG

DUNN & ELLIS ◈
7 High Street, Porthmadog, LL49 9LR
Tel: 01766 512361
Fax: 01766 514373
Email: mail@dunnandellis.co.uk
Resident Partners/Directors: ICAEW Members
C T Brown, P Roberts
Resident Partners (Non-ICAEW Members):
S Roberts
Registered by the ICAEW to carry out company audit work

LAUD MEREDITH & CO ★
94 High Street, Porthmadog, LL49 9NW

PRESTATYN

HAROLD SMITH
5 Nant Hall Rd, Prestatyn, LL19 9LR
Tel: 01745 864447

M.I MURRAY F.C.A
The Hollins, Manor Close, Prestatyn, LL19 9PH

PWLLHELI

GRIFFITH, WILLIAMS & CO ◈
36 Stryd Fawr, Pwllheli, LL53 5RT

GWYN THOMAS & CO ◈
1 Thomas Buildings, New Street, Pwllheli, LL53 5HH
Tel: 01758 701770
Email: gwynthomas-co@tiscali.co.uk
Principal: ICAEW Member
G T Thomas
Registered by the ICAEW to carry out company audit work

OWAIN BEBB A'I GWMNI
20 Penlan, Pwllheli, LL53 6AP
Tel: 01758 612646
Website: http://www.owainbebb.net
Resident Partners (Non-ICAEW Members):
I Hughes
Other Offices:32 Y Maes Caernarfon (Tel: 01286 675916)
Registered by the ICAEW to carry out company audit work
Regulated by the ICAEW for a range of investment business activities
Languages Spoken:
Welsh

RHAYADER

MOORE SCOTT & CO
The Beehive, West Street, Rhayader, LD6 5AB
Tel: 01597 810818

RHOSNEIGR

PARRY & CO ◈
Ynys Hir, Sandy Lane, Rhosneigr, LL64 5XA
Tel: 01407 811120
Principal: ICAEW Member
W Parry

RHYL

J.V. BANKS
Banks House, Paradise Street, Rhyl, LL18 3LW

M.G. FELLOWS
1 Rhodfa Heilyn, Gwelfor Park, Dyserth, Rhyl LL18 6LW
Tel: 01745 570868
Principal: ICAEW Member
M G Fellows

RUTHIN

D.R.E. & CO (AUDIT) LTD
The Gallery, Park Road, Ruthin, LL15 1NB

DE LONGA & CO ◈
Birch House, Hen Lon Parcwr, Ruthin, LL15 1NA
Tel: 01824 702205
Resident Partners/Directors: ICAEW Members
P C De Longa, R H De Longa

DRE & CO
The Gallery, Park Road, Ruthin, LL15 1NB
Tel: 01824 702999

HICKS RANDLES LTD ◈
4 Record Street, Ruthin, LL15 1DS
Tel: 01824 702403

HILL & ROBERTS
1 Tan-Y-Castell, Dog Lane, Ruthin, LL15 1DQ
Tel: 01824 704545
Resident Partners/Directors: ICAEW Members
R A Roberts

J D 2000 LTD
Glan-yr-Afon, Clocaenog, Ruthin, LL15 2BB

RETOUT CAPEL & CO ◈
Plas Uchaf, Graigadwywynt, Ruthin, LL15 2TF
Tel: 01824 704535
Principal: ICAEW Member
P G Retout

SP KELL
Clwyd House, 3c Clwyd Street, Ruthin, LL15 1HF
Tel: 01824 707747
Resident Partners/Directors: ICAEW Members
S P Kell

SAUNDERSFOOT

YOUNG & CO ◈
Bay View, Frances Road, Saundersfoot, SA69 9AH
Other Offices: Hereford, Herefordshire

ST. ASAPH

GARDNER SALISBURY
Irish Square, Upper Denbigh Road, St. Asaph, LL17 0RN

HAROLD SMITH
Unit 32, Llys Edmund Prys, St Asaph Business Park, St Asaph LL17 0JA
Tel: 01745 538000
Fax: 01745 538111
Email: nickashton@haroldsmith.co.uk
Website: http://www.haroldsmith.co.uk
Resident Partners/Directors: ICAEW Members
L C Archer, N L Ashton, P R Cato, N J Hulson, C I Jones, S Murray-Williams, B J M Shields

JOHN LYONS & CO
Office 21, Optic Tecnium, Ffordd William Morgan, St Asaph Business Park, St. Asaph LL17 0JD
Tel: 0845 644 4194
Principal: ICAEW Member
J G Lyons

PKF (UK) LLP
10 Hanover Business Centre, Hanover House, The Roe, St. Asaph LL17 0LT
Tel: 01745 585345
Non-resident Partners (Non-ICAEW Members):
K Bailey

SAGE & COMPANY BUSINESS ADVISORS LTD ◈
102 Bowen Court, St Asaph Business Park, St. Asaph, LL17 0JE
Tel: 01745 586360
Resident Partners/Directors: ICAEW Members
M F Gilmartin, C N Porter, D C Thomas

SWANSEA

A.C. EVANS
27 Knoll Avenue, Uplands, Swansea, SA2 0JE

AIMS - TIM TAYLOR FCA
24 Brynfield Road, Langland, Swansea, SA3 4SX

ALUN WALTERS & CO
Llandewi Castle, Llandewi, Reynoldston, Swansea SA3 1AU
Tel: 01792 390667
Principal: ICAEW Member
A J Walters

ASHMOLE & CO ★
60 St Teilo Street, Pontarddulais, Swansea, SA4 8SY

ASHMOLE & CO ★
Abertawe House, 115 Ystrad Road, Fforestfach, Swansea SA5 4JB
Tel: 01792 585757
Resident Partners/Directors: ICAEW Members
C H Rees, D R Vaughan

B N JACKSON NORTON ★
Abertawe House, Ystrad Road, Fforestfach, Swansea SA5 4JS

BEVAN & BUCKLAND
Russell House, Russell Street, Swansea, SA1 4HR
Tel: 01792 410100
Fax: 01792 648105
Email: mail@bevanbuckland.co.uk
Website: http://www.bevanbuckland.co.uk
Training Contracts Available.
Resident Partners/Directors: ICAEW Members
J McLellan, R.K.C. O'Shea, A Vickers

Registered by the ICAEW to carry out company audit work
Authorised and regulated by the Financial Services Authority for investment business

SPECIALISATIONS – AUDIT & ASSURANCE
Audit

SPECIALISATIONS – FINANCIAL REPORTING
Accounts Preparation
Limited Companies

SPECIALISATIONS – INVESTMENT BUSINESS
Pensions Advice

SPECIALISATIONS – TAXATION
Estate and Inheritance
Taxation
Trusts

BRUCE G.T.REES & CO
60 Mansel Street, Swansea, SA1 5TF
Tel: 01792 464842
Fax: 01792 646603
Email: brucegtrees@tiscali.co.uk
Principal: ICAEW Member
B G T Rees
Individual(s) licensed for insolvency work by the ICAEW

BUSINESS INFORMATION SYSTEMS ◈
11 Upper Church Park, Mumbles, Swansea, SA3 4DD
Tel: 01792 361121
Principal: ICAEW Member
P W Bates

BUTTERFIELD MORGAN LTD
Druslyn House, De La Beche Street, Swansea, SA1 3HJ

C. DUSGATE & CO ◈
Fir Tree Cottage, Llanmadoc, Gower, Swansea SA3 1DB
Tel: 01792 386343
Principal: ICAEW Member
C I Dusgate

CARR, JENKINS & HOOD
Redwood Court, Tawe Business Village, Swansea Enterprise Park, Swansea SA7 9LA
Tel: 01792 794588

CLEMENTS JONES
Second Floor, 64-65 The Kingsway, Swansea, SA1 5HW
Tel: 01792 643713
Resident Partners/Directors: ICAEW Members
T J Clements

CLEMENTS JONES LTD
Second Floor, 64-65 The Kingsway, Swansea, SA1 5HW
Tel: 01792 643713
Resident Partners/Directors: ICAEW Members
J S Clements

CLIVE ATKINS & CO LTD
60 Mansel Street, Swansea, SA1 5TF

CONTE DAVIES & CO LTD
Ground Floor, Frigate House, Quay West, Quay Parade, Swansea SA1 1SR

CROSS & BOWEN
11 Calvert Terrace, Swansea, SA1 6AT
Tel: 01792 655138
Resident Partners/Directors: ICAEW Members
T P Hopkins, R G Margetts

D.J. LEWIS
23 Heol Eglwys, Ystradgynlais, Swansea, SA9 1EY

DEXTER MATTHEWS LTD
99 Walter Road, Swansea, SA1 5QE

DM
99 Walter Road, Swansea, SA1 5QE

DRP & CO ◈
6 St Johns Court, Upper forest Way, Swansea, SA6 8QQ
Tel: 01792 791591
Resident Partners/Directors: ICAEW Members
E Davies
Resident Partners (Non-ICAEW Members):
M Poptani
Registered by the ICAEW to carry out company audit work

GERALD THOMAS & CO ◈
Furze Bank, 34 Hanover Street, Swansea, SA1 6BA
Tel: 01792 465155
Email: enquiries@geraldthomas.co.uk
Training Contracts Available.
Resident Partners/Directors: ICAEW Members
J M Evans, B G Garland, M E Jones, P S Jones, G Lewis
Resident Partners (Non-ICAEW Members):
P J Williams
Registered by the ICAEW to carry out company audit work
Authorised and regulated by the Financial Services Authority for investment business

SPECIALISATIONS – AUDIT & ASSURANCE
Audit

SPECIALISATIONS – FINANCIAL REPORTING
Accounts Preparation
Limited Companies

SPECIALISATIONS – INVESTMENT BUSINESS
Pensions Advice

SPECIALISATIONS – TAXATION
Estate and Inheritance
Taxation

GORDON DOWN & PARTNERS ★ ◈
144 Walter Road, Swansea, SA1 5RW

GRIFFITH & MILES
Charter Court, Phoenix Way, Enterprise Park, Swansea SA7 9FS

GRIFFITH & MILES LTD ◈
Charter Court, Phoenix Way, Enterprise Park, Swansea SA7 9FS
Tel: 01792 790444
Resident Partners/Directors: ICAEW Members
J H T Aylward, D L George, J F Spencer

H R HARRIS & PARTNERS ◈
44 St Helens Road, Swansea, SA1 4BB
Tel: 01792 643311
Fax: 01792 458706
Email: info@hrharrispartners.co.uk
Website: http://www.hrharrispartners.co.uk
Registered by the ICAEW to carry out company audit work
Regulated by the ICAEW for a range of investment business activities
Individual(s) licensed for insolvency work by another RPB

H R HARRIS & PARTNERS LTD
44 St Helens Road, Swansea, SA1 4BB
Tel: 01792 643311
Email: geoff.muxworthy@hrharrispartners.co.uk
Resident Partners/Directors: ICAEW Members
S J Burkinshaw
Resident Partners (Non-ICAEW Members):
G W Muxworthy, M J Hammond
Registered by the ICAEW to carry out company audit work
Regulated by the ICAEW for a range of investment business activities
Individual(s) licensed for insolvency work by the ICAEW

H W VAUGHAN & CO ◈
33 Heathfield, Swansea, SA1 6HD
Tel: 01792 652108
Resident Partners/Directors: ICAEW Members
R J Halliday

HARRIS BASSETT & CO
5 New Mill Court, Phoenix Way, Swansea, SA7 9FG

I.D. BOWEN & CO
19 Alexandra Road, Gorseinon, Swansea, SA4 4NW

J DAVIES FCA
96 Belgrave Road, Gorseinon, Swansea, SA4 6RE

JAMES & UZZELL ★
Axis 15, Axis Court, Mallard Way, Riverside Business Park, Swansea Vale Swansea SA7 0AJ

JANE E. CLAYTON
Dolgoy House, 49 West Cross Lane, West Cross, Swansea SA3 5LS

JOHN F HARVEY
Dynevor House, 5-6 De la Beche Street, Swansea, SA1 3HA
Tel: 01792 468006
SPECIALISATIONS – SECTOR

Agriculture

KEITH B FERGUSON LTD
First Floor, 95 High Street, Gorseinon, Swansea SA4 4BL

KEITH VINCENT LTD
Y Felin, Fforest, Pontardulais, Swansea SA4 0YJ

M J BEYNON & CO
7 Pennard Drive, Pennard, Swansea, SA3 2BL

M J BEYNON LTD
7 Pennard Drive, Pennard, Swansea, SA3 2BL

MACARIO LEWIN
Unit 20, J Shed, Kings Road, Swansea SA1 8PL

MAVIS LUCAS
Bolgoed Isaf, Bolgoed Road, Pontardulais, Swansea SA4 8JP

MB CONSULTING
21 Oakland Close, Glais, Swansea, SA7 9EW

N.R. BACON & CO
19 Queens Road, Sketty, Swansea, SA2 0SD

OWEN A. PARRY & CO
14 Tavistock Road, Sketty, Swansea, SA2 0SL
Tel: 01792 204744
Principal: ICAEW Member
O A Parry

OWEN JOHN & CO LTD
Mardy Chambers, 6 Wind Street, Swansea, SA1 1DH

PRICEWATERHOUSE-COOPERS
Princess House, Princess Way, Swansea, SA1 5LH

PRICEWATERHOUSE-COOPERS LLP
Princess House, Princess Way, Swansea, SA1 5LH
Tel: 01792 473691
Resident Partners/Directors: ICAEW Members
P W Jenkins

REDWOOD WALES LTD
Redwood Court, Tawe Business Village, Swansea Enterprise Park, Swansea SA7 9LA
Tel: 01792 794588
Resident Partners/Directors: ICAEW Members
P E Carr, J C Hood

REES BEAUFORT & CO
38 Beaufort Avenue, Langland, Swansea, SA3 4PB

ROBERTS & BALL
Minyrafon, 4 High Street, Pontardawe, Swansea SA8 4HU

ROBERTS & BALL LTD
Minyrafon, 4 High Street, Pontardawe, Swansea SA8 4HU

STEPHEN KENT & COMPANY LTD ◈
456 Gower Road, Killay, Swansea, SA2 7AL
Tel: 01792 290366
Resident Partners/Directors: ICAEW Members
S M Kent

SUMMERS ACCOUNTANCY AND BOOK KEEPING SERVICES
Office Above, Red Lion Hotel, 49 Sway Road, Morriston, Swansea SA6 6JA
Tel: 01792 793040
Principal: ICAEW Member
R N Lewis

THOMAS & CO ◈
Oxwich Green Farmhouse, Oxwich, Swansea, SA3 1LX
Tel: 01792 390411
Principal: ICAEW Member
N J Thomas

TIM TAYLOR & CO LTD
24 Brynfield Road, Langland, Swansea, SA3 4SX
Tel: 01792 363444
Resident Partners/Directors: ICAEW Members
T M Taylor

WILLIAMS NAYLOR
1st Floor, 454 Gower Road, Killay, Swansea SA2 7AL
Tel: 01792 280872
Principal: ICAEW Member
M S Williams

WILLIS JONES ◈
64 Walter Road, Swansea, SA1 4PT

TENBY

ALEXANDER PARTNERSHIP
Barclays Bank Chambers, 18 High Street, Tenby, Pembrokeshire SA70 7HD
Tel: 01834 844743
Email: info@thealexanderpartnership.co.uk
Resident Partners/Directors: ICAEW Members
M S Dashfield, P W Griffiths
Registered by the ICAEW to carry out company audit work

LLEWELYN DAVIES ◈
County Chambers, Warren Street, Tenby, SA70 7JS
Tel: 01646 683341
Email: tenby@llewelyndavies.co.uk
Registered by the ICAEW to carry out company audit work

TONYPANDY

CURTIS BOWDEN & THOMAS
101 Dunraven Street, Tonypandy, CF40 1AR
Tel: 01443 431012
Fax: 01443 433547

CURTIS BOWDEN & THOMAS LTD
First Floor, 101 Dunraven Street, Tonypandy, CF40 1AR

TREDEGAR

CAMBRIAN PARTNERSHIP
100A Commercial Street, Tredegar, NP22 3XJ

J GARETH MORGAN & CO
100A Commercial Street, Tredegar, NP22 3DW

MITCHELL MEREDITH LTD
Beacon House, Red Lion Square, Tredegar, NP22 3PW

TREFRIW

M K PARR & CO LTD
8 Coed Gwydyr, Trefriw, LL27 0JR

TREGARON

JENNY REGAN
Ffoslas, Penuwch, Tregaron, SY25 6RA

PATTERSON, JONES & EVANS
3 Station Road, Tregaron, SY25 6HU

TREHARRIS

MECO ACCOUNTANCY SERVICES
Holmwood, Pentwyn, Treharris, CF46 5BS

TREORCHY

YOUNG & PHILLIPS LTD
77 Bute Street, Treorchy, CF42 6AH

TYN-Y-GONGL

MITCHELL BRITTAIN
6 Lon Farchog, Upper Breeze Hill, Benllech, Tyn-y-Gongl LL74 8UL

USK

DAYKINS
6 Abergavenny Road, Usk, Monmouthshire, NP15 1SB

WELSHPOOL

CADWALLADER & CO LLP
Eagle House, 25 Severn Street, Welshpool, SY21 7AD
Tel: 01938 552625
Website: http://www.cadwalladerllp.co.uk
Resident Partners/Directors: ICAEW Members
M J Cadwallader

CAERWYN JONES
38B Broad Street, Welshpool, SY21 7RR

GERAINT HUMPHREYS & CO
37 Broad Street, Welshpool, SY21 7RR
Tel: 01938 555393

TURNER PEACHEY ◈
Stone House, 17 High Street, Welshpool, SY21 7JP
Tel: 01938 552078
Email: welshpool@turner-peachey.co.uk
Website: http://www.turner-peachey.co.uk
Non-resident Partners (ICAEW Members):
J M Ollier
Other Offices: Bridgnorth, Oswestry, Shrewsbury, Telford
Registered by the ICAEW to carry out company audit work
Regulated by the ICAEW for a range of investment business activities
General Description: A local professional firm offering a wide range of accounting, financial & taxation services.
Languages Spoken:
Welsh

WHITTINGHAM RIDDELL LLP ◈
23 Severn Street, Welshpool, SY21 7AD
Tel: 01938 553361
Email: wr@whittinghamriddell.co.uk
Resident Partners/Directors: ICAEW Members
G C Morgan
Other Offices: Shrewsbury, Ludlow, Newtown

WHITLAND

LLEWELYN DAVIES
Yelerton House, St John Street, Whitland, SA34 0AW
Tel: 01994 240254
Fax: 01994 240103
Email: whitland@llewelyndavies.co.uk

Resident Partners/Directors: ICAEW Members
H I Bowen
Registered by the ICAEW to carry out company audit work
Languages Spoken:
Welsh

WREXHAM

A C GRACE & COMPANY LTD
Brook Lane House, 1a Rossett Business Village, Rossett, Wrexham LL12 0AY

ACG
Bridge House, 1 Station Road, Rossett, Wrexham LL12 0HE

ADAM REEVES
Redwither Business Centre, Wrexham Industrial Estate, Wrexham, LL13 9XR

ALLEN ACCOUNTANCY SERVICES
Croesnewydd Hall, Wrexham Technology Park, Wrexham, LL13 7YP
Tel: 01978 265365
Fax: 01978 265526
Email: tanya@allenaccountancyservices.co.uk
Website: http://www.allenaccountancyservices.co.uk
Principal: ICAEW Member
T L Allen

BRUCE ROBERTS & CO LTD
18 Ruabon Road, Wrexham, LL13 7PB
Tel: 01978 357545
Resident Partners/Directors: ICAEW Members
B S S Roberts

CAROL JONES
35 Dean Close, Rhosnesni, Wrexham, LL13 9EP

COLIN FOWLER
The Woodlands, Mold Road, Cefn-y-Bedd, Wrexham LL12 9YG

COXEYS ◈
25 Grosvenor Road, Wrexham, LL11 1BT

D.A. HOPKINS
7 King Street, Wrexham, LL11 1HF

DILLAMORE & CO
The Stables Offices, Stansty Park, Summerhill Road, Wrexham LL11 4YW

DILLAMORE & CO LTD
The Stables Offices, Stansty Park, Summerhill Road, Wrexham LL11 4YW
Tel: 01978 752000
Resident Partners/Directors: ICAEW Members
R M Dillamore

ELLIS & CO
63 Regent Street, Wrexham, LL11 1PF

GODFREY EDWARDS
Park Lodge, Rhosddu Road, Wrexham, LL11 1NF

GREYS ACCOUNTANTS LTD
5 Whiteoaks, Bwlchgwyn, Wrexham, LL11 5UJ

GUY WALMSLEY & CO
3 Grove Road, Wrexham, LL11 1DY
Tel: 01978 265760
Website: http://www.guywalmsley.co.uk
Resident Partners/Directors: ICAEW Members
J D Bevan, N Fryer, A S Griffiths, M D Lindley
Resident Partners (Non-ICAEW Members):
N P Wynne

SPECIALISATIONS – AUDIT & ASSURANCE
Audit

SPECIALISATIONS – BUSINESS & GENERAL ADVICE
Company Secretarial Service

SPECIALISATIONS – FINANCIAL REPORTING
Accounts Preparation
Limited Company Accounts
Partnership/Sole Trader Accounts

SPECIALISATIONS – TAXATION
Payroll Service and Advice
Taxation

HALL LIVESEY BROWN
Wingett House, 25 Chester Street, Wrexham, LL13 8BG
Tel: 01978 290285

HICKS RANDLES LTD ◈
7 Grove Park Road, Wrexham, LL12 7AA
Tel: 01987 261579
Resident Partners/Directors: ICAEW Members
I V Roberts, P A Selwyn-Smith

HILLS ★
Eddystone House, Aberderfyn, Johnstown, Wrexham LL14 1PB

JOHN DAVIES AND CO ★
St Andrews House, Yale Business Village, Ellice Way, Wrexham LL13 7YL

M. D. COXEY & CO LTD ◈
25 Grosvenor Road, Wrexham, LL11 1BT
Tel: 01978 355477
Resident Partners/Directors: ICAEW Members
G H Atkinson, M D Coxey, P W McVeigh
Resident Partners (Non-ICAEW Members):
A J Lewis, M Browning

SJR ASSOCIATES
5 Rodens Close, Rossett, Wrexham, LL12 0EZ
Tel: 01244 579054
Principal: ICAEW Member
S J Roberts

T A GITTINS & CO
63 King Street, Wrexham, LL11 1HR
Tel: 01978 264846

UHY HACKER YOUNG
First Floor, Pembroke House, Ellice Way, Wrexham Technology Park, Wrexham LL13 7YT

THE OFFICIAL ICAEW DIRECTORY OF FIRMS 2009

CHANNEL ISLANDS

GUERNSEY

A. G. ACCOUNTING SERVICES LTD
24 Mount Durand, St Peter Port, Guernsey, GY1 1ED
Tel: 01481 720217
Email: andygill@guernseyaccounting.com
Website: http://www.guernseyaccounting.com
Resident Partners/Directors: ICAEW Members
A D Gill

ADRIAN LEOPARD & CO
Adrian Leopard & Co Chartered Accounts L, PO Box 27, Alderney, Guernsey GY9 3AS

ALDERNEY OFFSHORE LTD
Adrian Leopard & Co Chartered Accounts L, PO Box 27, Alderney, Guernsey GY9 3AS

ALEX PICOT
1 Pier Steps, St Peter Port, Guernsey, GY1 2LF

ALEX PICOT GUERNSEY LTD
1 Pier Steps, St Peter Port, Guernsey, GY1 2LF

ANDY GILL ACCOUNTING SERVICES
24 Mount Durand, St Peter Port, Guernsey, GY1 1ED

ARTEMIS
PO Box 100, Sydney Vane House, Admiral Park, St Peter Port, Guernsey GY1 3EL

BDO NOVUS LTD
PO Box 180, Elizabeth House, St Peter Port, Guernsey GY1 3LL
Tel: 01481 724561
Resident Partners/Directors: ICAEW Members
P M Burnard, I R Damarell, R M Searle

BDO NOVUS (AUDIT) LTD
PO Box 180, Guernsey, GY1 3LL
Tel: 01481 724561
Resident Partners/Directors: ICAEW Members
I R Damarell, J M Hallett, R P Jackson, R M Searle

BREHON LTD
Mayfield House, Grand Rue, St Martin, Guernsey GY4 6AA

BWCI GROUP ★
Albert House, South Esplanade, St Peter Port, Guernsey GY1 1AW

CENTURY ACCOUNTING LTD
PO Box 56 Century House, Victoria Street, Alderney, Guernsey GY9 3UF

CHANDLER BACKER & CO
PO Box 63, 1st Floor, Filton House, Clifton, St Peter Port, Guernsey GY1 4BH
Tel: 01481 739900
Fax: 01481 739911
Email: info@chandlerbacker.com
Mobile: 07781 105099
Principal: ICAEW Member
M Mahe
Registered by another RSB to carry out company audit work

CHANDLERS LTD ◈
PO Box 313, Anson Court, La Route des Camps, St Martin, Guernsey GY1 3TF
Tel: 01481 234411
Individual(s) licensed for insolvency work by another RPB

CLELAND & CO LTD
1st Floor, Harbour Court, Les Amballes, St Peter Port, Guernsey GY1 1WU
Tel: 01481 740205
Resident Partners/Directors: ICAEW Members
A H G Dick-Cleland

COLIN PICKARD & CO ◈
PO Box 511, Borough House, Rue de Pre, St Peter Port, Guernsey GY1 6DU
Tel: 01481 715669
Email: cpickard@cpco.gg
Principal: ICAEW Member
C J Pickard

COLLENETTE JONES LTD
Crossways Centre, Braye Road, Vale, Guernsey GY3 5PH
Tel: 01481 246324
Resident Partners/Directors: ICAEW Members
J P Collenette, M J Collenette, C S Falla

DELOITTE & TOUCHE LLP ◈
PO Box 137, Regency Court, Glategny Esplande, St Peter Port, Guernsey GY1 3HW
Tel: 01481 724011
Website: http://www.deloitte.co.uk
Resident Partners/Directors: ICAEW Members
J G Clacy, R A Garrard

DUNNING J.MICHAEL & CO
Pacifica, Colborne Road, St Peter Port, Channel Islands, Guernsey GY1 1BF

ERNST & YOUNG LLP
PO Box 9, 14 New Street, St Peter Port, Guernsey GY1 4AF
Tel: 01481 717400
Resident Partners/Directors: ICAEW Members
M R Bane, A J Offen, G W Parrott, S M Phillips

GRANT THORNTON LTD
PO Box 313, Anson Court, La Route des Camps, St Martin, Guernsey GY1 3TF
Tel: 01481 230455

GRANT THORNTON LTD ◈
Anson Court, La Route des Camps, St Martin, Guernsey GY1 3TF
Tel: 01481 230455

J.A. HAYES
Les Chalumaux, Val Au Bourg, St Martins, Guernsey GY4 6EP

JOHN F. PETERS
Tcherant Chinq, York Way, Fort George, St Peter Port, Guernsey GY1 2SY

JOHN HAYES FCA
Les Chalumaux, Val Au Bourg, St Martins, Guernsey GY4 6EP

JOHN LUCAS
Clos des Monts, Les Brayes, St Martin, Guernsey GY4 6XG

KEMP LE TISSIER LTD
Suite 2 Houmet House, Rue Des Houmets, Castel, Guernsey GY5 7XZ

KPMG CHANNEL ISLANDS LTD
20 New Street, St Peter Port, Guernsey, GY1 4AN
Tel: 01481 721000
Resident Partners/Directors: ICAEW Members
R A Hutchinson, N D Jehan, A C Paxton, M R Thompson
Resident Partners (Non-ICAEW Members):
E Monkhouse, D Smith, A Mancini

LINCE SALISBURY LTD
Avenue House, St Julians Avenue, St Peter Port, Guernsey GY1 1WA
Tel: 01481 735000
Resident Partners/Directors: ICAEW Members
M J Fattorini, G G Robert, N C White

LINCE, SALISBURY
Avenue House, St Julian's Ave, St Peter Port, Guernsey GY1 1WA
Tel: 01481 735000
Resident Partners/Directors: ICAEW Members
M J Fattorini, G G Robert, N C White

MICOL AND PARTNERS
P O Box 616, Newport House, 15 The Grange, St Peter Port, Guernsey GY1 2QL

MOORE STEPHENS
PO Box 146, Town Mills South, La Rue Du Pre, St Peter Port, Guernsey GY1 3HZ

MS&CO ◈
First Floor, Park Court, Park Street, St Peter Port, Guernsey GY1 1EE

NORMANDIE & CO
Les Petits Forts, La Rue de la Hougue, Castel, Guernsey GY5 7EA

PERFITT CONSULTANTS LTD
Le Manoir, Havilland Road, St Peter Port, Guernsey GY1 1ER

PERKINS ★
The Albany, South Esplanade, St Peters Port, Guernsey GY1 1AE

PKF (GUERNSEY) LTD
Sarnia House, PO Box 296,Le Truchot, St Peter Port, Guernsey GY1 4NA

PRICEWATERHOUSE-COOPERS ▽
P O Box 321, National Westminster House, Le Truchot, St Peter Port, Guernsey GY1 4ND

PRICEWATERHOUSE-COOPERS CI LLP
PO Box 321, National Westminster House, Le Truchot, St Peter Port, Guernsey GY1 4ND

RAWLINSON & HUNTER
Trafalgar Court, 3rd Floor, West Wing, St Peter Port, Guernsey GY1 2JA

RAWLINSON & HUNTER LTD
Trafalgar Court, 3rd Floor, West Wing, St Peter Port, Guernsey GY1 2JA
Tel: 01481 711166
Resident Partners/Directors: ICAEW Members
J Heaume, S A James, A D M Morgan

RICHARD STAPLEY
PO Box 349, Maison de Haut, La Grande Rue, St Saviours, Guernsey GY1 3UZ

RICHARD STAPLEY LTD
PO Box 349, Maison de Haut, La Grande Rue, St Saviours, Guernsey GY1 3UZ

S J BALL
PO Box 587, St Peter Port, Guernsey, GY1 6LS
Tel: 01481 710449

SAFFERY CHAMPNESS
P O Box 141, La Tonnelle House, Les Banques, St Sampson, Guernsey GY1 3HS
Tel: 01481 721374
Fax: 01481 722046
Email: info@saffery.gg
Website: http://www.saffery.gg
Date Established: 1977
Resident Partners/Directors:

continued

SAFFERY CHAMPNESS *cont*
ICAEW Members
R A Angliss, R T Elliott, S J Garrard, H F Green, M P Johnson, C A H Nicholson
Non-resident Partners (ICAEW Members):
R T Elliott, S J Garrard, M P Johnson, C A H Nicholson
Registered by the ICAEW to carry out company audit work
SPECIALISATIONS – AUDIT & ASSURANCE
Audit
SPECIALISATIONS – INVESTMENT BUSINESS
Financial Planning and Advice
SPECIALISATIONS – TAXATION
Taxation

SPHERE MANAGEMENT LTD
PO Box 587, St Peter Port, Guernsey, GY1 6LS
Tel: 01481 710449
Fax: 01481 736974
Email: steve@sphereman.com
Mobile: 07781 146847
Date Established: 1995
Resident Partners/Directors: ICAEW Members
S J Ball
SPECIALISATIONS – TAXATION
Offshore Companies

STAFFORD CHALLIS & CO
PO Box 344, Longue Houge House, St Sampson, Guernsey GY1 3US

WOOLFORD & CO LLP
PO Box 161, Dixcart House, Sir William Place, St Peter Port, Guernsey GY1 4EZ

JERSEY

A & T ACCOUNTING SERVICES LTD
The Office, Oaklands, La Rue Du Coin Varin, St Peter, Jersey JE3 7ZG

A. J. SALSAC & CO
PO Box 625, Commercial House, Commercial Street, St Helier, Jersey JE4 5YL

A L R MORTON FCA
Hawk House, Park Estate, La Route Des Genets, St Brelade, Jersey JE3 8EQ

AJH LTD ◈
Trinity House, Bath Street, St Helier, Jersey JE2 4ST
Tel: 01534 858540
Resident Partners/Directors: ICAEW Members
M A Assman, S D Hall

ALEX PICOT
95-97 Halkett Place, St Helier, Jersey, JE1 1BX
Tel: 01534 753753
Fax: 01534 753754
Email: mail@alexpicot.com
Website: http://www.alexpicot.com
Resident Partners/Directors: ICAEW Members
A D Le Cheminant, S J Phillips, D J Picot, J D Rhodes
Resident Partners (Non-ICAEW Members):
D R Connolly
Other Offices: Guernsey
Registered by the ICAEW to carry out company audit work
SPECIALISATIONS – AUDIT & ASSURANCE
Audit
SPECIALISATIONS – BUSINESS & GENERAL ADVICE
Administration
Company Formation
Company Secretarial Service
Overseas Countries
SPECIALISATIONS – FINANCIAL REPORTING
Accounts Preparation
SPECIALISATIONS – TAXATION
Estate Planning
Trusteeship
General Description: Member of GMN International.

ALEX PICOT LTD
95/97 Halkett Place, St Helier, Jersey, JE1 1BX
Tel: 01534 753753
Resident Partners/Directors: ICAEW Members
A D Le Cheminant, S J Phillips, D J Picot, C Purcell, J D Rhodes

ALEX PICOT TRUST CO LTD & SUBSIDIARIES
95-97 Halkett Place, St Helier, Jersey, JE1 1BX

BAKER HOMYARD
Ingouville House, Ingouville Lane, St Helier, Jersey JE2 4SG

BAKER TILLY CHANNEL ISLANDS LTD
PO Box 437, 13 Castle Street, St Helier, Jersey JE4 0ZE
Tel: 01534 755150
Resident Partners/Directors: ICAEW Members
B M Le Claire

BBA LTD
Beachside Business Centre, La Rue du Hocq, St Clement, Jersey JE2 6LF
Tel: 01534 858490
Resident Partners/Directors: ICAEW Members
R S Behan, M J Godel, C R Le Marquand

BDO ALTO LTD
First Floor, 28-30 The Parade, St Helier, Jersey JE1 1BG

BRIAN J COUTANCHE
Egret House, Mount Bingham, St Helier, Jersey JE2 4XY
Tel: 01534 720387
Principal: ICAEW Member
B J Coutanche

BUXTON & CO
Le Pallion, La Route Des Landes, St Ouen, Jersey JE3 2AA

BWCI GROUP ★
Kingsgate House, 55 Esplanade, St Helier, Jersey JE2 3QB

CAVERSHAM ★
Harbour Reach, PO Box 258, Rue De Carteret, St Helier, Jersey JE4 8TY
Tel: 01534 874707
Website: http://www.caversham.com
Resident Partners/Directors: ICAEW Members
R P Surcouf, S Whale
Resident Partners (Non-ICAEW Members):
J Ramsden
SPECIALISATIONS – TAXATION
Foreign Nationals in the UK
Offshore Companies
Trusteeship
Trusts

CLIVE TOMES & CO ◈
PO Box 771, Ground Floor, Colomberie Close, St Helier, Jersey JE4 0RX

CONSACC ACCOUNTING & TAX SERVICES
PO Box 643, Ground Floor Office Suite, Colomberie Close, Jersey JE4 0YS

CQ ACCOUNTANCY SERVICES LTD
First Floor Centre Office, Charles House, Charles Street, St Helier, Jersey JE2 4SF

CRICHTON ASSOCIATES
P.O. Box 218, 45 La Motte Street, St Helier, Jersey JE4 8SD

DELOITTE & TOUCHE LLP ◈
PO Box 403, Lord Coutanche House, 66-68 Esplanade, St Helier, Jersey JE4 8WA
Tel: 01534 824200
Website: http://www.deloitte.co.uk
Resident Partners/Directors: ICAEW Members
G J Branch, C D Leck

EDWARD HAMON
Mirador, 1 Rue de L'Est, St Helier, Jersey JE2 4UD

ERNST & YOUNG LLP
Liberation House, Castle Street, St Helier, Jersey JE1 1EY

Resident Partners/Directors: ICAEW Members
A J Dann, G C B Davies, D R J Moore

FOXLEIGH KNIGHT & CO LTD ◈
PO BOX 162, Ground Floor, Anley House, 5 Anley Street, St Helier Jersey JE4 5NZ

GRANT THORNTON LTD
Le Sueur, Ireson & Co, 46/50 Kensington Place, Jersey JE1 1ET

GS LTD
Shiraz Loft Suite, Belvedere Hill, St Saviour, Jersey JE2 7RP

HLB JACKSON FOX
8th Floor, Union House, Union St, St Helier, Jersey JE2 3RF
Tel: 01534 511700
Fax: 01534 511701
Email: reception@hlbjacksonfox.com
Resident Partners/Directors: ICAEW Members
G P Angus, L M M Bracken-Smith, A J Rothwell, N F Walker
Registered by the ICAEW to carry out company audit work
SPECIALISATIONS – TAXATION
Offshore Companies
Trusts

HOLL CAMERON & CO LTD
Ground Floor, Beresford House, Bellozanne Road, St Helier, Jersey JE2 3JW
Tel: 01534 629700
Resident Partners/Directors: ICAEW Members
D J Holl

HUGH DURELL ASSOCIATES
1st Floor, 17 Bond Street, St Helier, Jersey JE2 3NP

I.C.N. TOOLE & CO ★
Augres House, 16 Dumaresq Street, St Helier, Jersey JE2 3RL
Tel: 01534 759372
Fax: 01534 722630
Email: itoole@icntooleco.com
Resident Partners/Directors: ICAEW Members
I C N Toole
Resident Partners (Non-ICAEW Members):
D J P Thérézien

K A JENKINS
Maison De Bas, La Rue De La Ville Au Bas, St Lawrence, Jersey JE3 1EW

KATHRINE STEWART
Fieldview, La Rue de Samares, St Clement, Jersey JE2 6LZ

KPMG CHANNEL ISLANDS LTD
5 St Andrew's Place, Charing Cross, St Helier, Jersey JE4 8WQ
Tel: 01534 888891
Resident Partners/Directors: ICAEW Members
E J Bertrand, S D Hunt, J S Laity, Mrs M J MacCallum, A P Quinn

LANGTRY INTERNATIONAL
IFG House, 15 Union Street, St Helier, Jersey JE1 1FG

LE ROSSIGNOL, SCOTT WARREN AND PARTNERS
Thomas Edge House, Tunnell Street, St Helier, Jersey JE2 4LU
Tel: 01534 785200
Principal: ICAEW Member
C H Taylor
SPECIALISATIONS – AUDIT & ASSURANCE
Audit

LE SUEUR, IRESON & CO
Kensington Chambers, 46/50 Kensington Place, St Helier, Jersey JE1 1ET
Tel: 01534 885885
Fax: 01534 885775
Email: mail@gt-ci.com
Website: http://www.gt-ci.com
Date Established: 1975
Resident Partners/Directors: ICAEW Members
D De Ste Croix, R E G Ireson
Resident Partners (Non-ICAEW Members):
H J F Taverner, C Q Swale, J R Toynton, D I Clark
Other Offices: Anson Court, La Route des Champs, St Martin, Guernsey, GY1 3TF
Individual(s) licensed for insolvency work by another RPB
SPECIALISATIONS – AUDIT & ASSURANCE
Audit
SPECIALISATIONS – FINANCIAL REPORTING
Accounts Preparation
Limited Company Accounts
SPECIALISATIONS – TAXATION
Offshore Companies

LUBBOCK, FINE
Harbour Reach, Rue De Carteret, St Helier, Jersey JE4 8TY
Tel: 01534 874707
Resident Partners/Directors: ICAEW Members
G G Goodyear, R Majithia, R P Surcouf, S Whale

MARTIN EDWARDS & CO
La Fantaisie, St Martin, Jersey, JE3 6HE
Tel: 01534 857800
Principal: ICAEW Member
M W Edwards

MAYNE & CO
Beach House, Petit Port, St Brelade, Jersey JE3 8HL

M MAZARS

MAZARS CHANNEL ISLANDS LTD
23-27 Charter Place, Seaton Place, St Helier, Jersey JE2 2QL
Tel: 01534 758700
Fax: 01534 888869
Email: enquiries@mazarsjersey.com
Website: http://www.mazarsjersey.com
Training Contracts Available.
Resident Partners/Directors: ICAEW Members
A T Budworth, D R P Herbinet, B H Morris
Non-resident Partners (ICAEW Members):
D Herbinet
Resident Partners (Non-ICAEW Members):
J R Lees-Baker
Registered by the ICAEW to carry out company audit work
SPECIALISATIONS – AUDIT & ASSURANCE
Assurance Services
Audit
SPECIALISATIONS – BUSINESS & GENERAL ADVICE
Book-keeping
Risk Management
SPECIALISATIONS – FINANCIAL REPORTING
Accounts Preparation
SPECIALISATIONS – FORENSIC ACCOUNTING
Forensic Accounting
SPECIALISATIONS – TAXATION
Taxation

MICHAEL RUSSELL
P O Box 460, Waterloo House, Don Street, Jersey JE4 5RS
Tel: 01534 836666
Principal: ICAEW Member
M C Russell

MJM ACCOUNTING SERVICES
Fremont House, La Rue de Fremont, St John, Jersey JE3 4DA

MOORE STEPHENS
P O Box 236, First Island House, Peter Street, St Helier, Jersey JE4 8SG

PAUL G. LEWIS
First Floor, 17 Bond Street, St Helier, Jersey JE2 3NP
Tel: 01534 733232
Principal: ICAEW Member
P G Lewis

PRICEWATERHOUSE-COOPERS ▽
Twenty Two Colomberie, St Helier, Jersey, JE1 4XA

PRICEWATERHOUSE-COOPERS CI LLP
Twenty Two Colomberie, St Helier, Jersey, JE1 4XA

R.H. HENKHUZENS & CO
PO Box 643, Ground Floor Office Suite, Colomberie Close, Jersey JE4 0YS

R.H. HENKHUZENS LTD
PO Box 643, Ground Floor Office Suite, Colomberie Close, Jersey JE4 0YS

RABET & CO
2 Old Farm Close, La Route Du Mont Mado, St John, Jersey JE3 4DS

RAWLINSON & HUNTER ★
PO Box 83, Ordnance House, 31 Pier Road, St Helier, Jersey JE4 8PW
Tel: 01534 825200
Resident Partners/Directors: ICAEW Members
D G Goar, M W Richardson

READS & CO
PO Box 179, 40 Esplanade, St Helier, Jersey JE4 9RJ
Tel: 01534 816000
Email: info@readsco.com
Website: http://www.readsco.com

READS & CO
PO Box 179, 40 Esplanade, St Helier, Jersey JE4 9RJ
Tel: 01534 816000

READS & CO LTD
PO Box 179, 40 Esplanade, St Helier, Jersey JE4 9RJ
Tel: 01534 816000
Resident Partners/Directors: ICAEW Members
P J Crosby, C J Moulder

READS (AUDIT) LTD
PO Box 179, 40 Esplanade, St Helier, Jersey JE4 9RJ
Tel: 01534 816000
Resident Partners/Directors: ICAEW Members
P J Crosby, C J Moulder

READS & CO GROUP LTD
PO Box 179, 40 Esplanade, St Helier, Jersey JE4 9RJ
Tel: 01534 816000
Resident Partners/Directors: ICAEW Members
P J Crosby, C J Moulder

RJF HAMON FCA
Le Mahier, La Rue Mahier, St Ouen, Jersey JE3 2DW

ROBERT TAYLOR ASSOCIATES LTD ◈
L'Abordage, La Rue Du Crocquet, St Brelade, Jersey JE3 8BZ

ROSSCOT LTD
Thomas Edge House, Tunnell Street, St Helier, Jersey JE2 4LU
Tel: 01534 785200
Fax: 01534 785299
Email: accounts@rosscot.com
Date Established: 1997
Resident Partners/Directors: ICAEW Members
K G Bates, P J S Ingram, A J Keites, C H Taylor
Resident Partners (Non-ICAEW Members):
D Stuart, S P O'Flaherty
SPECIALISATIONS – AUDIT & ASSURANCE
Assurance Services
Audit
SPECIALISATIONS – BUSINESS & GENERAL ADVICE
Company Formation
Company Secretarial Service
Management Advice to Business
SPECIALISATIONS – FINANCIAL REPORTING
Accounts Preparation
SPECIALISATIONS – FORENSIC ACCOUNTING
Forensic Accounting
SPECIALISATIONS – IT
Computerised Accounting Systems
SPECIALISATIONS – TAXATION
Estate Planning
Offshore Companies
Taxation
Trusts

RTA LTD ◈
PO Box 851, 2nd Floor, 24-26 Broad Street, Jersey JE4 0XE

T.A. JEHAN & CO
Ingouville House, Ingouville Lane, St Helier, Jersey JE4 8SP

TELEOLOGICA
Egret House, Mount Bingham, St Helier, Jersey JE2 4XY

TSAVO ACCOUNTS LTD
Amador, Tower Road, St Helier, Jersey JE2 3HR

TWO PLUS TWO ACCOUNTING LTD
Malgre Tout, La Rue de Haut, St Lawrence, Jersey JE3 1JQ

THE OFFICIAL ICAEW DIRECTORY OF FIRMS 2009

SCOTLAND

ABERDEEN

ACCORD TAX AND ACCOUNTANCY LTD
16a Bon Accord Square, Aberdeen, AB11 6DJ

BARBARA CRESSWELL
7 Baillieswells Grove, Bieldside, Aberdeen, AB15 9BH
Tel: 01224 861833
Principal: ICAEW Member
B Cresswell

COHEN & PARTNERS
236 Abbotswell Crescent, Aberdeen, AB12 3JT

DELOITTE & TOUCHE LLP ◈
2 Queens Terrace, Aberdeen, AB10 1XL
Tel: 01224 625888
Website: http://www.deloitte.co.uk
Resident Partners/Directors: ICAEW Members
G T Hollis

ERNST & YOUNG LLP
Blenheim House, Fountainhall Road, Aberdeen, AB15 4DT
Tel: 01224 653000

FORBES-CABLE
8 Albert Place, Aberdeen, AB25 1RG

KPMG LLP
37 Albyn Place, Aberdeen, AB10 1JB
Tel: 01224 591000
Resident Partners/Directors: ICAEW Members
D Macaskill
Resident Partners (Non-ICAEW Members):
M G Findlay

MALCOLM MARSH & CO
77 John Street, Aberdeen, AB25 1LP
Tel: 01224 658200
Resident Partners/Directors: ICAEW Members
M R Marsh

MALCOLM MARSH & CO LTD
77 John Street, Aberdeen, AB25 1LP
Tel: 01224 658200
Resident Partners/Directors: ICAEW Members
M R Marsh

PRICEWATERHOUSE-COOPERS
32 Albyn Place, Aberdeen, AB10 1YL

PRICEWATERHOUSE-COOPERS LLP
32 Albyn Place, Aberdeen, AB10 1YL
Tel: 01224 210100
Resident Partners/Directors: ICAEW Members
M A Higginson

TENON LTD
39 Queens Road, Aberdeen, AB15 4ZN
Tel: 01224 209666

ABOYNE

C.D. WRIGHT
Mains of Balfour, Birse, Aboyne, AB34 5DB
Tel: 013398 86168
Principal: ICAEW Member
C D Wright

ACHARACLE

A. GREEN
Dal Ghorm House, Ardtoe, Acharacle, PH36 4LD

ALFORD

KEITH S JOHNSON CONSULTING LTD
Brookside, Smiddyhill, Alford, AB33 8NA

ANNAN

SAINT & CO ▽ ◈
26 High Street, Annan, DG12 6AJ
Tel: 01461 202732
Email: annan@saint.co.uk
Website: http://www.saint.co.uk
Resident Partners/Directors: ICAEW Members
Marion Nolan

Registered by the ICAEW to carry out company audit work

Authorised and regulated by the Financial Services Authority for investment business

AVOCH

TIM PHILLIPS
The Steading, Knockmuir, Avoch, IV9 8RD

AYR

MCADAM AND CO
7 Chalmers Road, Ayr, KA7 2RQ

WILLIAM DUNCAN & CO ▽
30 Miller Road, Ayr, KA7 2AY

BALLACHULISH

CHRISTOPHER WILLIAMS
Carnoch House, Glencoe, Ballachulish, PH49 4HS

BANCHORY

PETER COPP
Tullymet, Kincardine Road, Torphins, Banchory AB31 4GH

WILLIAMSONS
Rosewood, Raemoir Road, Banchory, AB31 4ET
Tel: 01330 823981
Principal: ICAEW Member
M N Williamson

BIGGAR

HARRISON & CO
St Johns Kirk, Symington, Biggar, ML12 6JU

BONNYRIGG

MORGAN & CO
Dalhousie Grange House, Cockpen, Bonnyrigg, EH19 3HX

BRECHIN

WALKER HARRIS
27 St David Street, Brechin, DD9 6EG
Tel: 01356 622389

BRIDGE OF WEIR

CHEETHAM & CO
Holmlea House, Quarrier's Village, Bridge of Weir, PA11 3SX

BUCKIE

RITSONS ▽
1a Cluny Square, Buckie, AB56 1AH

CARLUKE

PETER WALTON
23 Castleknowe Gardens, Kirkton Park, Carluke, ML8 5UX
Tel: 01555 752164
Principal: ICAEW Member
P Walton

CARNOUSTIE

WALKER,DUNNETT & CO ▽
24 High Street, Carnoustie, DD7 6AQ

CASTLE DOUGLAS

BELL OGILVY ▽
36 King Street, Castle Douglas, DG7 1AF
Tel: 01556 502377
Resident Partners/Directors: ICAEW Members
J E Moffat

MONTPELIER PROFESSIONAL (BORDERS) LTD
226 King Street, Castle Douglas, DG7 1EA

COATBRIDGE

PKF (UK) LLP
Fountain Business Centre, Ellis Street, Coatbridge, ML5 3AA
Tel: 01236 423144
Email: info.coatbridge@uk.pkf.com
Website: http://www.pkf.co.uk
Resident Partners (Non-ICAEW Members):
F R Paterson

CRIEFF

KELLY ACCOUNTING LTD
42 Comrie Street, Crieff, PH7 4AX

MCLACHLAN & TIFFIN
Clifton House, Craigard Road, Crieff, PH7 4BN
Tel: 01764 652371
Principal: ICAEW Member
R C Tiffin

CUMNOCK

WILLIAM DUNCAN & CO ▽
31 The Square, Cumnock, KA18 1AT

DALKEITH

SPRINGFORDS LLP
Dundas House, Westfield Park, Eskbank, Dalkeith EH22 3FB

DUMFRIES

ARMSTRONG WATSON
51 Rae Street, Dumfries, DG1 1JD
Tel: 01387 269726

BARBARA E.THORP
Newtonrigg House, Holywood, Dumfries, DG2 0RA

MONTPELIER PROFESSIONAL (BORDERS) LTD
23 George Street, Dumfries, DG1 1EA

SAINT & CO ▽ ◈
26 Castle Street, Dumfries, DG1 1DU
Tel: 01387 255477
Email: dumfries@saint.co.uk
Website: http://www.saint.co.uk

Registered by the ICAEW to carry out company audit work

Authorised and regulated by the Financial Services Authority for investment business

DUNBAR

C A CAMERON ACA
4 Temple Mains, Innerwick, Dunbar, EH42 1SE

G. SPRATT & CO ◈
3 Abbeylands, High Street, Dunbar, EH42 1EH
Tel: 01368 863565
Principal: ICAEW Member
P A Ronan

DUNDEE

ATK ACCOUNTS
5 Invergowrie Drive, Dundee, DD2 1RD

ATK ACCOUNTS LTD
5 Invergowrie Drive, Dundee, DD2 1RD

I G. HUSSEIN & CO
3 Magdalen Place, Dundee, DD1 4NN

WALKER,DUNNETT & CO ▽
29 Commercial Street, Dundee, DD1 3DG

DUNS

M. ST. J. WRIGLEY
36 Castle Street, Duns, TD11 3DP
Tel: 01361 883529
Principal: ICAEW Member
M S J Wrigley

EDINBURGH

ANDREW HAMILTON & CO ▽
38 Dean Park Mews, Edinburgh, EH4 1ED

ANDREW PD CRAMB BSC
26/7 Eildon Terrace, Edinburgh, EH3 5LU
Tel: 0131 558 1599
Email: andrewdcramb@aol.com
Principal: ICAEW Member
A P D Cramb
SPECIALISATIONS – TAXATION
Taxation

ANNE DOBSON
23 Littlejohn Avenue, Edinburgh, EH10 5TG
Tel: 0131 447 9981
Principal: ICAEW Member
A E Dobson

ATHENA & CO
Room 9, Leith Walk Business Centre, 130 Leith Walk, Edinburgh EH6 5DT

BAKER TILLY
First Floor, Quay 2, 139 Fountainbridge, Edinburgh, EH3 9QG
Tel: 0131 659 8300
Resident Partners (Non-ICAEW Members):
J M Hamblin, D S Morton, A Tait

BAKER TILLY
First Floor Quay 2, 139 Fountainbridge, Edinburgh, EH3 9QG

BAKER TILLY CORPORATE FINANCE LLP
First Floor, Quay 2, 139 Fountainbridge, Edinburgh, EH3 9QG
Resident Partners (Non-ICAEW Members):
M J Davidson, D M Russell, M S Stewart

BAKER TILLY RESTRUCTURING AND RECOVERY LLP
First Floor, Quay 2, 139 Fountainbridge, Edinburgh, EH3 9QG
Tel: 0131 659 8300
Resident Partners (Non-ICAEW Members):
K V Anderson, D M Menzies

BAKER TILLY TAX AND ADVISORY SERVICES LLP
First Floor, Quay 2, 139 Fountainbridge, Edinburgh, EH3 9QG

BAYLEY MILLER LTD
16b Queen Street, Edinburgh, EH2 1JE
Tel: 0131 220 2010
Resident Partners/Directors: ICAEW Members
C Bayley

BEGBIES TRAYNOR LTD
Atholl Exchange, 6 Canning Street, Edinburgh, EH3 8EG
Tel: 0131 222 9060
Resident Partners (Non-ICAEW Members):
K Pattullo, S McGregor
SPECIALISATIONS – BUSINESS RECOVERY & INSOLVENCY
Bankruptcies
Corporate Recovery
Liquidations

BROWN R S ◈
4 Straiton View, Straiton Business Parc, Edinburgh, EH20 9QZ
Tel: 0131 440 3894
Principal: ICAEW Member
R S Brown

CLIFFE CATTERALL LTD
21 Dick Place, Edinburgh, EH9 2JU
Tel: 0131 667 4404
Resident Partners/Directors: ICAEW Members
S J C Catterall

CRITICAL PATH SOLUTIONS
The Mews, Canaan Lane, Edinburgh, EH10 4SG

DANZIG & CO ★
8-12 Torphichen Street, Edinburgh, EH3 8JQ

DELOITTE & TOUCHE LLP ◈
Saltire Court, 20 Castle Terrace, Edinburgh, EH1 2DB
Tel: 0131 221 0002
Website: http://www.deloitte.co.uk
Resident Partners/Directors: ICAEW Members
J W F Baird, J C Reid, F Salzen, R J Topley

ERNST & YOUNG LLP
Ten George Street, Edinburgh, EH2 2DZ
Tel: 0131 777 2000
Resident Partners/Directors: ICAEW Members
H W Ball, R Laverick, G M Reid

FROST & CO
51 Bernard Street, Edinburgh, EH6 6SL

GILLESPIE INVERARITY & CO ★
41/43 Constitution Street, Edinburgh, EH6 7BG

GRANT THORNTON UK LLP
1-4 Atholl Crescent, Edinburgh, EH3 8LQ
Tel: 0131 229 9181
Resident Partners (Non-ICAEW Members):
N Goode, R K Hannah, G S McCracken, J E A Watt, W McWilliams

HAFEEZ & CO
2 Minto Street, Edinburgh, EH9 1RG
Tel: 0131 667 2125
Principal: ICAEW Member
M Hafeez

HW EDINBURGH ◈
Q Court, 3 Quality Street, Davidsons Mains, Edinburgh EH4 5BP
Tel: 0131 625 5151
Resident Partners/Directors: ICAEW Members
S J Hodgson, A S Minifie

IFRS 2009 LTD ◈
Heron House, 45 Riversdale Grove, Edinburgh, EH12 5QS
Tel: 0131 622 0152
Email: stephen.muncaster@ifrs2009.co.uk
Resident Partners/Directors: ICAEW Members
S Muncaster
SPECIALISATIONS – AUDIT & ASSURANCE
Assurance Services
SPECIALISATIONS – BUSINESS & GENERAL ADVICE
Company Formation
Company Secretarial Service
Management Consultancy
SPECIALISATIONS – FINANCIAL REPORTING
Financial Reporting
International Reporting Standards (IFRS)
SPECIALISATIONS – SECTOR
Banks/Financial Institutions
Corporate
Oil/Petroleum Industries
General Description: IFRS thought leadership, UK-wide.

INVOCAS BUSINESS RECOVERY AND INSOLVENCY LTD
2nd Floor, Capital House, 2 Festival Square, Edinburgh EH3 9SU
Tel: 0131 222 2460
Resident Partners/Directors: ICAEW Members
S J Lightley
Individual(s) licensed for insolvency work by the ICAEW
Individual(s) licensed for insolvency work by another RPB

INVOCAS GROUP PLC
2nd Floor, Capital House, 2 Festival Square, Edinburgh EH3 9SU
Tel: 0131 222 2460
Resident Partners/Directors: ICAEW Members
S J Lightley, I J Macneil, C A A Murdoch

KPMG LLP
Saltire Court, 20 Castle Terrace, Edinburgh, EH1 2EG
Tel: 0131 222 2000
Resident Partners/Directors: ICAEW Members
G L T Bainbridge, A W S Barbour, R S Hills, J P Meeten
Resident Partners (Non-ICAEW Members):
L M S Bennett, U F Cameron, B R Drummond, C A Graham

L & J LAWRIE ★
23 Buckingham Terrace, West End, Edinburgh, EH4 3AE
Tel: 0131 343 2043
Resident Partners/Directors: ICAEW Members
J L Lawrie

M.L. COWAN & CO
32 Moray Place, Edinburgh, EH3 6BZ

MAZARS CORPORATE FINANCE LTD
Donaldson House, 97 Haymarket Terrace, Edinburgh, EH12 5HD

MAZARS LLP ◈
Donaldson House, 97 Haymarket Terrace, Edinburgh, EH12 5HD
Tel: 0131 313 7900
Resident Partners (Non-ICAEW Members):
D C Marshall
Registered by the ICAEW to carry out company audit work
Authorised and regulated by the Financial Services Authority for investment business

NEIL H MACGREGOR
177-4 Craigmillar Castle Ave, Edinburgh, EH16 4DN

NWHI LTD
20 Trafalgar Street, Edinburgh, EH6 4DF

OGILVIE & COMPANY LTD ◈
25 Rutland Square, Edinburgh, EH1 2BW
Tel: 0131 656 0563
Resident Partners/Directors: ICAEW Members
D C N Ogilvie
Languages Spoken:
French

OWEN & CO ◈
41 Ashley Terrace, Edinburgh, EH11 1RY
Tel: 0131 313 4471
Principal: ICAEW Member
A G Owen

PKF (UK) LLP
17 Rothesay Place, Edinburgh, EH3 7SQ
Tel: 0131 225 3688
Email: info.edinburgh@uk.pkf.com
Website: http://www.pkf.co.uk
Resident Partners/Directors: ICAEW Members
M J Gill
Resident Partners (Non-ICAEW Members):
N Whyte, A Rae

PRICEWATERHOUSE-COOPERS
Erskine House, 68-73 Queen Street, Edinburgh, EH2 4NH

PRICEWATERHOUSE-COOPERS LLP
Erskine House, 68-73 Queen Street, Edinburgh, EH2 4NH
Tel: 0131 226 4488
Resident Partners/Directors: ICAEW Members
M E W Hoskyns-Abrahall, D J A Law

ROBERT MACLAREN LTD
16 Ainslie Place, Edinburgh, EH3 6AU

ROSS FINANCIAL CONSULTANCY LTD
33 Campbell Road, Edinburgh, EH12 6DT

RSM BENTLEY JENNISON ◈
The Merchants Hall, 22 Hanover Street, Edinburgh, EH2 2EP
Tel: 0131 225 0660
Registered by the ICAEW to carry out company audit work

SAFFERY CHAMPNESS ◈
Edinburgh Quay, 133 Fountainbridge, Edinburgh, EH3 9BA
Tel: 0131 221 2777
Fax: 0131 221 2778
Website: http://www.saffery.com
Training Contracts Available.
Resident Partners/Directors: ICAEW Members
M J Floydd, D Hughes
Resident Partners (Non-ICAEW Members):
R Ludwig, E McInroy
Registered by the ICAEW to carry out company audit work
Regulated by the ICAEW for a range of investment business activities
Authorised and regulated by the Financial Services Authority for investment business

INVESTOR IN PEOPLE

General Description: See London office entry.
Languages Spoken:
French, Danish, Welsh

SCHOFIELD SMITH
69 East Craigs Rigg, Edinburgh, EH12 8JA
Tel: 0131 317 1269
Principal: ICAEW Member
J S R Smith

SCOTT-MONCRIEFF ▽
17 Melville Street, Edinburgh, EH3 7PH

SYSTEMATIC TAX & ACCOUNTANCY
Hudson House, 8 Albany Street, Edinburgh, EH1 3QB

TENON LTD
160 Dundee Street, Edinburgh, EH11 1DQ
Tel: 0131 221 8820

TENON AUDIT LTD
160 Dundee Street, Edinburgh, EH11 1DQ
Tel: 0131 221 8820

WAGNER ASSOCIATES LTD
39 Barclay Place, Edinburgh, EH10 4HW
Tel: 0800 081 1567
Other Offices:39 Barclay Place Edinburgh EH10 4HW

WHITELAW WELLS ▽
9 Ainslie Place, Edinburgh, EH3 6AT
Tel: 0131 226 5822
Resident Partners/Directors: ICAEW Members
S C Jarvie

ELGIN

RITSONS ▽
The Tower, 103 High Street, Elgin, IV30 1EB

ELLON

ALPHA BUSINESS SERVICES ◈
Inverebrie, Ellon, AB41 8PX
Tel: 01358 761444
General Description: Accounts, tax & business advice.

ALPHA BUSINESS SERVICES LTD ◈
Inverebrie, Ellon, AB41 8PX
Tel: 01358 761444
Resident Partners/Directors: ICAEW Members
C S Hall

EYEMOUTH

G. SPRATT & CO
Northburn, Eyemouth, TD14 5ER
Tel: 01890 750645

J.C. GIBSON & CO
The Rest, Murrayfield, St Abbs, Eyemouth TD14 5PP
Tel: 018907 71312
Principal: ICAEW Member
J C Gibson

FORFAR

THE SURREY PRACTICE LTD
Canmore Park, 29 Canmore Street, Forfar, DD8 3HT

FORRES

RITSONS ▽
103 High Street, Forres, IV36 1AA

FORTROSE

TIM WICKENS
6 Academy Street, Fortrose, IV10 8TW

GALASHIELS

THE JRW GROUP ▽
Riverside House, Ladhope Vale, Galashiels, TD1 1BT

GLASGOW

ASHRAF BADAR & CO
219 Allison Street, Glasgow, G42 8RU

BAKER TILLY
Breckenridge House, 274 Sauchiehall Street, Glasgow, G2 3EH
Tel: 0141 307 5000
Resident Partners (Non-ICAEW Members):
W M Blyth, D W Lemay, J A Lockhart, J L McLaren, R G Murray, P J Norris

BAKER TILLY TAX AND ADVISORY SERVICES LLP
Brecekenridge House, 274 Sauchiehall Street, Glasgow, G2 3EH
Tel: 0141 307 5000
Resident Partners (Non-ICAEW Members):
W M Blyth, J A Lockhart, J L McLaren, R G Murray, P J Norris, R M Ross

BDO STOY HAYWARD LLP
4 Atlantic Quay, 70 York Street, Glasgow, G2 8JX
Tel: 0141 248 3761
Fax: 0141 248 1653
Resident Partners (Non-ICAEW Members):
N A Craig, J A E Fingland, D J Hill, A D Knox, R A Ralston, E D Turner, J B Stephen, J C Cairns, J Collins, A J McNamara

BEGBIES TRAYNOR LTD
2nd Floor, Finlay House, 10-14 West Nile Street, Glasgow G1 2PP
Tel: 0141 222 2230
Website: http://www.begbies-traynor.com
Resident Partners (Non-ICAEW Members):
K Pattullo, S McGregor
SPECIALISATIONS – BUSINESS RECOVERY & INSOLVENCY
Bankruptcies
Corporate Recovery
Liquidations

CARRINGTON DEAN
135 Buchanan Street, Glasgow, G1 2JA

CARRINGTON DEAN GROUP LTD
135 Buchanan Street, Glasgow, G1 2JA

THE DEBT EXPERTS
135 Buchanan Street, Glasgow, G1 2JA

DELOITTE & TOUCHE LLP ◈
Lomond House, 9 George Square, Glasgow, G2 1QQ
Tel: 0141 204 2800
Website: http://www.deloitte.co.uk
Resident Partners/Directors: ICAEW Members
D N Claxton, N S Cruickshanks

EASY DEBT SOLUTIONS
135 Buchanan Street, Glasgow, G1 2JA

ERNST & YOUNG LLP
George House, 50 George Square, Glasgow, G2 1RR
Tel: 0141 626 5000

F H TAKAHASHI
2/2 287 Wilton Street, Glasgow, G20 6DD

FIONA CURRY & CO
9 Crookfur Road, Newton Mearns, Glasgow, G77 6DY
Tel: 0141 639 2879
Principal: ICAEW Member
F A Curry

FT ACCOUNTS
2/2 287 Wilton Street, Glasgow, G20 6DD

GRANT THORNTON UK LLP
95 Bothwell Street, Glasgow, G2 7JZ
Tel: 0141 223 0000
Resident Partners (Non-ICAEW Members):
R Caven, A P Godfrey, A Howie

HAINES WATTS GLASGOW LTD
231-233 St Vincent Street, Glasgow, G2 5QY
Tel: 0141 227 4700
Resident Partners/Directors: ICAEW Members
A S Minifie

HW
231 - 233 St Vincent Street, Glasgow, G2 5QY

HW FORENSIC (SCOTLAND) LTD
231 - 233 St Vincent Street, Glasgow, G2 5QY

IAIN D SIM & CO ▽
Gainsborough House, 151 West George Street, Glasgow, G2 2JJ

IMOGEN BEATTIE & CO
5 Douglas Drive, Cambuslang, Glasgow, G72 8NG
Tel: 0141 643 9875
Principal: ICAEW Member
I M Beattie

INVOCAS BUSINESS RECOVERY AND INSOLVENCY LTD ◈
James Miller House, 98 West George Street, Glasgow, G2 1PJ

INVOCAS GROUP PLC
98 West George Street, Glasgow, G2 1PJ

J.A. MCELHOLM
71 Beech Avenue, Newton Mearns, Glasgow, G77 5QR

K.A. KHOKHAR & CO LTD
60 Kingston Street, Glasgow, G5 8BP

KPMG LLP
191 West George Street, Glasgow, G2 2LJ
Tel: 0141 226 5511
Resident Partners/Directors: ICAEW Members
S M Pashby
Resident Partners (Non-ICAEW Members):
C Anderson, G A Deans, B C Nimmo, M Ross

MARTIN AITKEN & CO ★
Caledonia House, 89 Seaward Street, Glasgow, G41 1HJ

MAZARS CORPORATE FINANCE LTD ◈
90 St Vincent Street, Glasgow, G2 5UB

MAZARS LLP ◈
90 St Vincent Street, Glasgow, G2 5UB
Tel: 0141 226 4924
Resident Partners (Non-ICAEW Members):
P B Jibson, R M Downie, H M Bowman, R Mackenzie
Registered by the ICAEW to carry out company audit work
Authorised and regulated by the Financial Services Authority for investment business

MOORE STEPHENS LLP
Allan House, 25 Bothwell Street, Glasgow, G2 6NL

NEILSON RENTON & CO ▽
101 Main Street, Uddingston, Glasgow, G71 7EW

PKF (UK) LLP
78 Carlton Place, Glasgow, G5 9TH
Tel: 0141 429 5900
Email: info.glasgow@uk.pkf.com
Website: http://www.pkf.co.uk
Resident Partners (Non-ICAEW Members):
C D Barnett, A Buchanan, G Cassells, B A Jackson, D M Jenkins, F R Paterson, F Thomson

PRICEWATERHOUSE-COOPERS
Kintyre House, 209 West George Street, Glasgow, G2 2LW

PRICEWATERHOUSE-COOPERS LLP
Kintyre House, 209 West George Street, Glasgow, G2 2LW
Tel: 0141 248 2644
Resident Partners/Directors: ICAEW Members
A C Sturgess

RJ CROMAR LTD ◈
7 Kinnaird Avenue, Newton Mearns, Glasgow, G77 5EL

ROBERTSON CRAIG & CO ▽
3 Clairmont Gardens, Glasgow, G3 7LW

SCOTT-MONCRIEFF ▽ ◈
25 Bothwell Street, Glasgow, G2 6NL

SMITH & WILLIAMSON LTD
21 Blythswood Square, Glasgow, G2 4BL
Tel: 0141 222 1100

SOMERFORD ACCOUNTANTS
11 Somerford Road, Bearsden, Glasgow, G61 1AS

STEELE ROBERTSON GODDARD
Turnberry House, 175 West George Street, Glasgow, G2 2LB

STUART RAMSDEN
12 Station Road, Bardowie, Glasgow, G62 6ET

TENON LTD
2-4 Blythswood Square, Glasgow, G2 4AD
Tel: 0141 272 8000

TENON AUDIT LTD
2 Blythswood Square, Glasgow, G2 4AD
Tel: 0141 272 8000

WAGNER ASSOCIATES LTD
34 West George Street, Glasgow, G2 1DA

WHITELAW WELLS ▽
9 Royal Crescent, Glasgow, G3 7SP

WILSON ANDREWS
151 West George Street, Glasgow, G2 2JJ

GLENROTHES

CAMERON CLARK
Prinlaws House, 12 Walkerton Drive, Leslie, Glenrothes KY6 3BT

D.K. GARDINER & CO
15F Postgate, Glenrothes, KY7 5LH
Tel: 01592 758135
Principal: ICAEW Member
D K Gardiner

PATERSON BOYD & CO ◈
18 North Street, Glenrothes, KY7 5NA

GRANGEMOUTH

TENON LTD
Unit 3, Gateway Business Park, Beancross Road, Grangemouth FK3 8WX
Tel: 01324 475700

TENON AUDIT LTD
Unit 3, Gateway Business Park, Beancross Road, Grangemouth FK8 8WX
Tel: 01324 475700

HAMILTON

ANDERSON BROWNLIE LTD
53 Wellhall Road, Hamilton, ML3 9BY
Tel: 01698 303552
Resident Partners/Directors: ICAEW Members
T A Anderson

WILLIAM DUNCAN & CO ▽
Silverwells House, 114 Cadzow Street, Hamilton, ML3 6HP

WILLIAM DUNCAN & CO ▽
104 Quarry Street, Hamilton, ML3 7AX

HAWICK

THE JRW GROUP ▽
19 Buccleuch Street, Hawick, TD9 0HL

P A BISHOP
13 Maxton Court, Hawick, TD9 7QN

HELENSBURGH

HAMMOND & CO
69 Sinclair Street, Helensburgh, G84 8TG

INVERNESS

C J SEDGWICK & CO ◈
34 Cherry Park, Balloch, Inverness, IV2 7HG
Tel: 01463 791000
Principal: ICAEW Member
C J Sedgwick

EASTBURY ACCOUNTING SOLUTIONS LTD
Beechwood, Balnain, Drumnadrochit, Inverness IV63 6TJ

ERNST & YOUNG LLP
Barony House, Stoneyfield Business Park, Inverness, IV2 7PA
Tel: 01463 667000

RITSONS ▽
27 Huntly Street, Inverness, IV3 5PR

SAFFERY CHAMPNESS ◈
Kintail House, Beechwood Park, Inverness, IV2 3BW
Tel: 01463 246300
Fax: 01463 246 301
Website: http://www.saffery.com
Training Contracts Available.
Resident Partners/Directors: ICAEW Members
S W Swift
Resident Partners (Non-ICAEW Members):
S A Mathieson
Other Offices: Bournemouth, Bristol, Edinburgh, Geneva, Guernsey, Harrogate, High Wycombe, London, Manchester, Peterborough
Registered by the ICAEW to carry out company audit work
Regulated by the ICAEW for a range of investment business activities

INVESTOR IN PEOPLE

General Description: See London office entry.

TENON LTD
10 Ardross Street, Inverness, IV3 5NS
Tel: 01463 235321

TENON AUDIT LTD
10 Ardross Street, Inverness, IV3 5NS

INVERURIE

LETHENTY ACCOUNTS
Burnside, Lethenty, Inverurie, AB51 0HQ

IRVINE

ADAM & CO
151 High Street, Irvine, KA12 8AD

ISLE OF ISLAY

ROLAND WORTHINGTON-EYRE
Quartz Lodge, Kildalton, Port Ellen, Isle Of Islay PA42 7EF

KEITH

RITSONS ▽
17 Regent Street, Keith, Banffshire, AB55 5DY

KELSO

DOUGLAS HOME & CO
47-49 The Square, Kelso, TD5 7HW

DOUGLAS HOME & CO LTD
47-49 The Square, Kelso, TD5 7HW
Tel: 01573 225082
Resident Partners/Directors: ICAEW Members
L C Mark

MONKTON ACCOUNTING SERVICES
Yetholmlaw House, Town Yetholm, Kelso, TD5 8SH
Tel: 01573 420209
Principal: ICAEW Member
C P Grindell

KILMARNOCK

IAIN D SIM & CO ▽ ◈
38 Beansburn, Kilmarnock, KA3 1RL
Tel: 01563 525599
Resident Partners/Directors: ICAEW Members
G Groom

MILLIKEN & CO
9 Vennel Street, Stewarton, Kilmarnock, KA3 5HL
Tel: 01560 482203
Principal: ICAEW Member
T J Milliken

KINLOCHLEVEN

ARTHUR C CUSTANCE
Tigh na Bruaich, Garbhein Road, Kinlochleven, PH50 4SE
Tel: 01855 831590
Principal: ICAEW Member
A C Custance

KIRKCALDY

TENON LTD
44 Victoria Road, Kirkcaldy, KY1 1DH

KIRKWALL

THE LONG PARTNERSHIP
1 Castle Street, Kirkwall, KW15 1HD
Tel: 01856 878600
Resident Partners/Directors: ICAEW Members
A E Long

LANGHOLM

THE JRW GROUP ▽
46 High Street, Langholm, DG13 0JH

LAUDER

WHITTAKER & ASSOCIATES ◈
Inchkeith House, Lauder, TD2 6TE
Tel: 01578 722671
Principal: ICAEW Member
I P Whittaker

LEVEN

PATERSON BOYD & CO
8 Mitchell Street, Leven, KY8 4HJ

LOCKERBIE

ARMSTRONG WATSON ◈
27 High Street, Lockerbie, DG11 2JL
Tel: 01576 202540

LONGNIDDRY

DOUGLAS & REAVES ★
Loanshiel, Haddington Road, Aberlady, Longniddry EH32 0RX

MONTROSE

WALKER HARRIS
9a George Street, Montrose, DD10 8EN
Tel: 01674 673306
Email: enquiries@walkerharris.co.uk
Principal: ICAEW Member
D H Harris

NAIRN

JOHN SUTTON & CO
Heaton House, 4 Gordon Street, Nairn, IV12 4DQ
Tel: 01667 456889
Principal: ICAEW Member
J E Sutton

STEPHEN C RANSCOMBE & CO
Tigh Ceilidh, Nairn, IV12 5NX

NEWTON STEWART

MONTPELIER AUDIT LTD
1 Dashwood Square, Newton Stewart, DG8 6EQ

MONTPELIER PROFESSIONAL (GALLOWAY) LTD
1 Dashwood Square, Newton Stewart, DG8 6EQ

NORTH BERWICK

PETER O'CONNELL FCA
Bickley, Westerdunes Park, North Berwick, EH39 5HJ

OBAN

JACK MACDONALD & CO ◈
Ar Baile, Clachan Seil, Oban, PA34 4TJ
Tel: 01852 300511
Principal: ICAEW Member
J M MacDonald

PATHHEAD

FALA ACCOUNTING LTD
Haughhead House, Fala Dam, Pathhead, Midlothian EH37 5SW

PEEBLES

ALAN M CRAWFORD & CO LTD ◈
10 Frankscroft, Peebles, EH45 9DX
Tel: 01721 720801
Email: alan@alanmcrawford.co.uk
Resident Partners/Directors: ICAEW Members
A M Crawford

THE JRW GROUP ▽
2 Rowan Court, Cavalry Park, Peebles, EH45 9BU

PENICUIK

THE ROSEBERY COMPANY LTD
Bush House, Bush Estate, Penicuik, EH26 0BB

PERTH

BELL & CO ★
Moray House, 39 St John Street, Perth, PH1 5HQ
Tel: 01738 632081
Fax: 01738 630989
Email: admin@bellandcompany.co.uk
Website: http://www.bellandcompany.co.uk
Date Established: 1945
Resident Partners/Directors: ICAEW Members
R M Howes
Resident Partners (Non-ICAEW Members):
J H Dewar, N W Fraser, C Carnegie
Registered by another RSB to carry out company audit work
Licensed by another DPB to carry on investment business

FIONA
33 Talisker Place, Perth, PH1 3GW

GILLESPIE INVERARITY & CO ★
33 Leslie Street, Blairgowie, Perth, PH10 6AW

TENON LTD
5 Kings Place, Perth, PH2 8AA
Tel: 01738 636069

TENON AUDIT LTD
5 Kings Place, Perth, PH2 8AA
Tel: 01738 636069

PORTREE

RITCHIE BURGE & CO
14 Earlish, Portree, Isle Of Skye, IV51 9XL
Tel: 01470 542227
Principal: ICAEW Member
N D R Burge

SHETLAND

BAKER TILLY
122 Commercial Street, Lerwick, Shetland, ZE1 0HX
Tel: 01595 693384

BAKER TILLY
122 Commercial Street, Lerwick, Shetland, ZE1 0HX

BAKER TILLY TAX AND ADVISORY SERVICES LLP
122 Commercial Street, Lerwick, Shetland, ZE1 0HX
Tel: 01595 693384
Resident Partners (Non-ICAEW Members):
I Hambleton

SKELMORLIE

R.A. WOOLLARD
19 Annetyard Drive, Skelmorlie, PA17 5BN
Tel: 01475 520699
Principal: ICAEW Member
R A Woollard

STIRLING

MRS N J WOODBURN
100 Station Road, Bannockburn, Stirling, FK7 8JP
Tel: 01786 815695
Principal: ICAEW Member
N J Woodburn

STONEHAVEN

BUCHANAN BONDS LTD
39 Braehead Crescent, Stonehaven, Kincardineshire, AB39 2PP

STRANRAER

CRAIG, MCINTYRE & PEACOCK ▽
33 Lewis Street, Stranraer, DG9 7LB
Tel: 01776 703539
Resident Partners/Directors: ICAEW Members
K A Cox

STRATHDON

MORAG REID
Blackhillock, Glenbuchat, Strathdon, AB36 8TQ

STRATHPEFFER

COLIN CLARK
Cloverhome, Heights of Inchvannie, Strathpeffer, IV14 9AF

KARIBU LTD
Cloverhome, Heights of Inchvannie, Strathpeffer, IV14 9AF

MACWILLIAMS CONSULTING LTD
2 Ardival East, Strathpeffer, IV14 9DY

TARBERT

WILLIAM DUNCAN & CO ▽
Loch Awe House, Barmore Road, Tarbert, PA29 6TW

THURSO

THE LONG PARTNERSHIP
3a Princes Street, Thurso, Caithness, KW14 7BQ

TILLICOULTRY

ATKINSON & CO
Victoria House, 87 High Street, Tillicoultry, FK13 6AA

ATKINSON & CO LTD
Victoria House, 87 High Street, Tillicoultry, FK13 6AA

THE OFFICIAL ICAEW DIRECTORY OF FIRMS 2009

NORTHERN IRELAND

ARMAGH

PRICEWATERHOUSE-COOPERS
3-5 Market Street, Armagh, BT61 7BW

PRICEWATERHOUSE-COOPERS LLP
3-5 Market Street, Armagh, BT61 7BW
Tel: 02837 522695

BALLYCLARE

STEPHEN CUNNINGHAM & CO
Silversprings, 140 The Burn Road, Templepatrick, Ballyclare BT39 0DQ

BELFAST

BDO STOY HAYWARD ▽
Lindsay House, 10 Callender Street, Belfast, BT1 5BN

DELOITTE & TOUCHE LLP ◈
19 Bedford Street, Belfast, BT2 7EJ
Tel: 02890 322861
Website: http://www.deloitte.co.uk
Resident Partners/Directors: ICAEW Members
L G Russell

ERNST & YOUNG LLP
Bedford House, 16-22 Bedford Street, Belfast, BT2 7DT
Tel: 02890 443500

GRANT THORNTON UK LLP
Waters Edge, Clarendon Dock, Belfast, BT1 3BH
Tel: 02890 315500
Resident Partners (Non-ICAEW Members):
M R Allen, T T Blayney, R J M Gibson, C Kerlin, G W Neill

MCCAMBRIDGE DUFFY LLP ★
20 Adelaide Street, Belfast, BT2 8GB

PGM
405 Lisburn Road, Belfast, County Antrim, BT9 7EW

PRICEWATERHOUSE-COOPERS
Waterfront Plaza, 8 Laganbank Road, Belfast, BT1 3LR

PRICEWATERHOUSE-COOPERS LLP
Waterfront Plaza, 8 Laganbank Road, Belfast, BT1 3LR
Tel: 02890 245454
Resident Partners/Directors: ICAEW Members
M C Fleetwood, C I Tenner

ROGERS EVANS
Regus House, 33 Clarendon Dock, Laganside, Belfast BT1 3BG

SMITH & WILLIAMSON LTD
Cunningham Coates Stockbrokers, 19 Donegall Street, Belfast, BT1 2HA
Tel: 02890 323456

T MURPHY & CO
43 Lockview Road, Belfast, BT9 5FJ

COLERAINE

J.E.M. CALDWELL
105 Carrowreagh Road, Garvagh, Coleraine, BT51 5LH

CRAIGAVON

PRICEWATERHOUSE-COOPERS
12 High Street, Portadown, Craigavon, BT62 1HY

PRICEWATERHOUSE-COOPERS LLP
12 Church Street, Portadown, Craigavon, BT62 3LQ
Tel: 02838 333718
Resident Partners/Directors: ICAEW Members
A R Wylie

DUNGANNON

PRICEWATERHOUSE-COOPERS
18 Northland Row, Dungannon, BT71 6AP

PRICEWATERHOUSE-COOPERS LLP
18 Northland Row, Dungannon, BT71 6AP
Tel: 02887 722726

HOLYWOOD

BURKE WALLACE ★
146 High Street, Holywood, BT18 9HS

FITZPATRICK
88 Church Road, Holywood, BT18 9BX

LONDONDERRY

JOHN WARD & CO
10 Steelstown Road, Londonderry, BT48 8EU

MCCAMBRIDGE DUFFY LLP ★
Templemore Business Park, Northland Road, Derry, Londonderry BT48 0LD

MCCARTNEY & CO ◈
Grove House, 27 Hawkin Street, Londonderry, BT48 6RE
Tel: 02871 261271
Principal: ICAEW Member
A M McCartney

PRICEWATERHOUSE-COOPERS
1-3 Guildhall Street, Londonderry, BT48 6BB

PRICEWATERHOUSE-COOPERS LLP
Guild House, 1-3 Guildhall Street, Londonderry, BT48 6BB
Tel: 02871 266104

MAGHERA

MARTIN MCCULLAGH ACA
45 Ballymacilcurr Road, Maghera, BT46 5HR

NEWRY

FITZPATRICK & KEARNEY ▽ ◈
20 Newry Street, Kilkeel, Newry, BT34 4DN
Tel: 02841 762178

FITZPATRICK & KEARNEY ▽ ◈
10 Marcus Square, Newry, BT34 1AE
Tel: 02830 262344
Resident Partners/Directors: ICAEW Members
M Reynolds

G P BOYLE & CO
Old Fire Station, Cecil Street, Newry, BT35 6AU
Tel: 02830 250296
Principal: ICAEW Member
G P Boyle

NEWTOWNARDS

ISCA ACCOUNTANCY SERVICES
40 Ballymartin Road, Killinchy, Newtownards, BT23 6QR

OMAGH

PRICEWATERHOUSE-COOPERS
43 Market Street, Omagh, BT78 1EE

PRICEWATERHOUSE-COOPERS LLP
43 Market Street, Omagh, BT78 1EE
Tel: 02882 246100

STRABANE

MCCARTNEY & CO
4 Railway Street, Strabane, BT82 8EF

THE OFFICIAL ICAEW DIRECTORY OF FIRMS 2009

OVERSEAS

ANDORRA

ANDORRA LA VELLA

MOORE STEPHENS ▼
Prat de la Creu, 92 1er despatx 11, Andorra La Vella

ANGOLA

LUANDA

ERNST & YOUNG ▼
Rua Major Kanyangulo, 59-1st Floor D.T., Luanda, P-1003

PRICEWATERHOUSE-COOPERS ▼
Rue Eca de Queiroz 17, Alvalade, Luanda

ANTIGUA

ST. JOHNS

PANNELL KERR FORSTER ▼
Redcliffe Street, St Johns

PRICEWATERHOUSE-COOPERS ★
P O Box 1531, Old Parham Road, St Johns

ARGENTINA

BUENOS AIRES

BDO INTERNATIONAL ▽
Av. Cordoba 1318-9th Floor, Buenos Aires, 1055

ERNST & YOUNG ▼
Maipu 942 Ground Floor, Buenos Aires, 1340

FINSTERBUSH PICKENHAYN SIBIL ▼
Montevideo 496, 10th Floor, Buenos Aires, 1019

FINSTERBUSH PICKENHAYN SIBIL ▼
Avenida Leandro N. Alem, 1050, Buenos Aires, 1001

KPMG ▼
Audicont S.A., Bouchard 710, 1st Floor, Buenos Aires C1106ABL

MOORE STEPHENS ▼
Maipu 942, 12th Floor, Buenos Aires, 1340

PRICEWATERHOUSE-COOPERS ▼
Avenida A moreau de Justo 270, Piso 2, Puerto Madero, Buenos Aires, C1107AAF

PRICEWATERHOUSE-COOPERS ▼
Cerrito 268, Buenos Aires, C1010AAF

PRICEWATERHOUSE-COOPERS ▼
Tucuman 117, 7th Floor, Buenos Aires, C1049AAC

VILLAGARCIA & ASOCIADOS ▼
Villagarcia & Ascoiados, Esmeralda 625, 1 er Piso, Buenos Aires C1007 ABE

VILLAGARCIA Y ASOCIADOS ▼
Esmeralda 625-ler Piso, Buenos Aires, 1007

CORDOBA

PRICEWATERHOUSE-COOPERS ▼
Boulevard Chacabuco 492, Cordoba, X5000IIR

MENDOZA

PRICEWATERHOUSE-COOPERS ▼
9 de julio 1140, Piso 2, Mendoza, M5500DOX

ROSARIO

PRICEWATERHOUSE-COOPERS ▼
Calle Cordoba 1452,Piso 2, Oficina 'C', Rosario, S2000AWV

ARUBA

ORANJESTAD

KPMG CROES & CROES ▼
Wayaka 31-D, 2nd Floor, Nassaustraat 85, Oranjestad

PRICEWATERHOUSE-COOPERS
LG Smithboulevard 62, Oranjestad

AUSTRALIA

ADELAIDE

TIMOTHY DUBENS
1a Young Street, Glenelg East, Adelaide, SA 5045

BDO INTERNATIONAL ▽
G.P.O. Box 2018, Adelaide, SA 5001

DELOITTE TOUCHE TOHMATSU ★
PO Box 1969, Adelaide, SA 5001

ERNST & YOUNG ★
21 King William Street, Adelaide, SA 5000
Tel: 00 61 884171600

HALL WILSON ▼
191 Flinders Street, Adelaide, SA 5000

J.S.G. MARTIN ◈
3rd Floor, 117 King William Street, Adelaide, SA 5000

KPMG ▽
115 Grenfell Street, (GPO Box 2499), Adelaide, SA 5000

MACINTYRE STRATER INTERNATIONAL LTD ▼
253 Sturt Street, Adelaide, SA 5000

MCLEAN DELMO HALL CHADWICK ▼
191 Flinders Street, G.P.O.Box 1171, Adelaide, SA 5001

PKF ▼
GPO Box 2505, Adelaide, SA 5001

PRICEWATERHOUSE-COOPERS ★
91 King William Street, Level 14, GPO Box 418, Adelaide, SA 5001

ALBURY

KPMG ▽
Peat Marwick Center, 545-549 Kieaw Street, (P.O. 500), Albury, NSW 2640

ALICE SPRINGS

DELOITTE TOUCHE TOHMATSU ★
P O Box 1796, Alice Springs, NT 0871

ATHERTON

HALL WILSON ▼
Suite 9, Barletta's Arcade, 1 Robert Street, Atherton, QLD 4883

BELMONT

COLLETT & CO
PO Box 467, Belmont, VIC 3216

BRISBANE

BDO INTERNATIONAL ▽
G.P.O. Box 2751, Brisbane, QLD 4001

DELOITTE TOUCHE TOHMATSU ★
307 Queen Street, (G.P.O. Box 1463, 4001), Brisbane, QLD 4001

ERNST & YOUNG ★
PO Box 7878, Waterfront Place, 1 Eagle Street, Brisbane, QLD 4001

GRANT THORNTON ▼
Level 30, MLC Center, 239 George Street, Brisbane, QLD 4000

HALL WILSON ▼
12th level, 46 Edward Street, Brisbane, QLD 4000

KPMG ▽
Level 30, Central Plaza One, 345 Queen Street, Brisbane, QLD 4000

MCLEAN DELMO HALL CHADWICK ▼
12th Level, Hall Chadwick Centre,46 Edward Street, Brisbane, QLD 4001

MOORE STEPHENS ★
GPO Box 1144, 5th Floor, 255 Adelaide Street, Brisbane, QLD 4001

MOORES ROWLAND ▼
Level 26, AMP Place, 10 Eagle Street, Brisbane, QLD 4000

PKF ▼
Level 6, 120 Edward Street, Brisbane, QLD 4000

PRICEWATERHOUSE-COOPERS ★
Riverside Centre, 123 Eagle Street, GPO Box 150, Brisbane, QLD 4001

BUNDALL

ERNST & YOUNG ★
Level 5, 2 Corporate Court, Bundall, QLD 4217

CABOOLTURE

HALL WILSON ▼
7 James Street, Caboolture, QLD 4510

MCLEAN DELMO HALL CHADWICK ▼
7 James Street, Caboolture, QLD 4510

CAIRNS

AUDITORS & FORENSIC ACCOUNTANTS
7/345 Sheridan Street, Cairns North, PO Box 428H, Edge Hill Q 4870, Cairns, QLD 4870

GRANT THORNTON ▼
242 Sheridan Street, Cairns, QLD 4870

HALL WILSON ▼
1st Floor, 74 Abbott Street, Cairns, QLD 4870

KPMG ▽
Level 13, 15 Lake Street, P.O. Box 7200, Cairns, QLD 4870

MCLEAN DELMO HALL CHADWICK ▼
1st Floor, 74 Abbott Street, Cairns, QLD 4870

PRICEWATERHOUSE-COOPERS ★
Cairns Corporate Tower, 15 Lake Street, Level 11, GPO Box 814, Cairns, QLD 4870

CANBERRA

PKF ▼
Level 7, 28 University Avenue, Canberra, ACT 2600

DELOITTE TOUCHE TOHMATSU ★
8 Brindabella Circuit, Brindabella Business Park, Canberra Airport, Canberra, ACT 2609

ERNST & YOUNG ★
Ernst & Young House, 51 Albura Street, GPO Box 281, Canberra, ACT 2601

GRANT THORNTON ▼
7th Floor, 60 Marcus Clarke Street, Canberra, ACT 2601

KPMG ▽
5th Floor, 80 Northbourne, Avenue, GPO Box 796, Canberra, ACT 2601

PKF DI BARTOLO DIAMOND & MIHAILAROS ▼
Level 7, 28 University Avenue, Canberra, ACT 2600

PRICEWATERHOUSE-COOPERS ★
64 Northbourne Avenue, Level 5, Canberra, ACT 2601

CARINGBAH

HALL WILSON ▼
Suite 4, Centre Court, 307-309 The Kingsway, Caringbah, NSW 2229

CARLTON NORTH

UK EXPAT LTD
5/491 Nicholson Street, Carlton North, VIC 3054

CHATSWOOD

A.C.K. WONG TOO YUEN
P.O.Box 5184, Chatswood, NSW 1515

CHERRYBROOK

PN PHILIS & CO
16 Macquarie Drive, Cherrybrook, NSW 2126

CIVIC SQUARE

D.L. THOMPSON
c/- P O Box 294, Civic Square, ACT 2608

DARWIN

DELOITTE TOUCHE TOHMATSU ★
GPO Box 4296, Darwin, NT 0801

ERNST & YOUNG ★
2nd Floor, 9-11 Cavenagh St, Darwin, NT 0800

KPMG ▽
18 Smith Street, Darwin, NT 0800

MCLEAN DELMO HALL CHADWICK ▼
85 Cavenagh Street, Darwin, NT 0801

PKF BOB COWLING ▼
Ground Floor, Tem House, 5 Edmunds Street, Darwin, NT 0800

DOVER HEIGHTS

WIKRAMANAYAKE & CO ▽
50 Hardy Street, Dover Heights, NSW 2030

E BENTLEIGH

GEORGE TAVARES
55 Purtell Street, East Bentleigh, VIC 3165

ELANORA HEIGHTS

JOANNE MARSH & CO
8 Wilga Street, Elanora Heights, NSW 2101

ESSENDON

DELOITTE TOUCHE TOHMATSU ★
P.O.Box 289, 707 Mount, Alexander Rd., Moonee Ponds, Essendon, VIC 3039

FORREST

PRICEWATERHOUSE-COOPERS ★
Level 1, 25 National Circuit, GPO Box 447, Forrest, ACT 2603

GLEN IRIS

MOORE STEPHENS ★
14 Audrey Crescent, Glen Iris, VIC 3146

GOLD COAST

BDO INTERNATIONAL ▽
P.O. Box 7717, Gold Coast Mail Centre, Gold Coast, QLD 4217

GOSFORD

BDO INTERNATIONAL ▽
99 Mann Street, Gosford, NSW 2250

PANNELL KERR FORSTER ▼
79 Mann Street, Gosford, NSW 2250

HOBART

DELOITTE TOUCHE TOHMATSU ★
P.O.Box 250, Level 6, Reserve Bank, 111 Macquarie Street, Hobart, TAS 7000

PKF ▼
AMP Building, 27 Elizabeth Street, Hobart, TAS 7000

PKF ▼
30 Davey Street, Hobart, TAS 7000

PRICEWATERHOUSE-COOPERS ★
AMP Building, Level 6, 86 Collins Street, GPO Box 2138, Hobart, 7000

HORNSBY

LEE FINANCIAL MANAGEMENT P/L
18 Grevillea Cresent, Hornsby, NSW 2077

HURSTVILLE

HALL WILSON ▼
578 Railway Parade, Hurstville, NSW 2220

KELVIN GROVE

PANNELL KERR FORSTER ▼
AMA House, 88 L'Estrange Terrace, Kelvin Grove, QLD 4059

KENMORE

J. MARTIN
P O Box 695, Kenmore, QLD 4069

KEW

DARRELL H. WEBB
1st Floor, 88 Charles Street, Kew, VIC 3101

KILLARNEY HEIGHTS

STROTHER ALEXANDER
5 Ballyshannon Road, Killarney Heights, NSW 2087

LAUNCESTON

DELOITTE TOUCHE TOHMATSU ★
P.O.Box 770, 49-51 Elizabeth Street, Launceston, TAS 7250

KPMG ▽
33 George Street, Launceston, TAS 7250

MAREEBA

GRANT THORNTON ▼
188 Byrnes Street, Mareeba, QLD 4880

MELBOURNE

AHEAD FOR BUSINESS PTY LTD
Level 10, 420 St Kilda Road, Melbourne, VIC 3004

DELOITTE TOUCHE TOHMATSU ★
180 Lonsdale Street, Melbourne, VIC 3000

DELOITTE TOUCHE TOHMATSU ★
505 Bourke Street, (P.O.Box 78B), Melbourne, VIC 3001

ERNST & YOUNG ★
Ernst & Young Building, 8 Exhibition Street, Melbourne, VIC 3000

GRANT THORNTON ▼
555 Lonsdale Street, Melbourne, VIC 3000

GRANT THORNTON ★
Level 35, North Tower, Riaito Towers, 525 Collins St, Melbourne VIC 3000
Tel: 00 61 039611 6611

GREENWOODS & FREEHILLS ★
Level 44, 101 Collins Street, Melbourne, VIC 3000

HALL WILSON ▼
12th level, Capita Centre,459 Collins Street, Melbourne, VIC 3000

KPMG ▽
147 Collins Street, Melbourne, VIC 3000

KPMG ▽
161 Collins Street, Melbourne, VIC 3000

MACINTYRE STRATER INTERNATIONAL LTD ▼
50 Burwood Road, Hawthorn, Melbourne, VIC 3122

MCLEAN DELMO HALL CHADWICK ▼
Level 12, Capita Centre, 459 Collins Street, Melbourne, VIC 3000

MOORE STEPHENS ▼
Level 14, 607 Bourke Street, Melbourne, VIC 3000

PAUL TAY & CO
63 Stead Street, Melbourne, VIC 3205

PKF ▼
Level 11, CGU Tower, 485 LaTrobe Street, Melbourne, VIC 3000

PRICEWATERHOUSE-COOPERS ★
2 Southbank Boulevard, Southbank, Melbourne, VIC 3006

PRICEWATERHOUSE-COOPERS ★
GPO Box 1331L, Melbourne, VIC 3001

PRICEWATERHOUSE-COOPERS ★
215 Spring Street, GPO Box 1331L, Melbourne, VIC 3000

PRICEWATERHOUSE-COOPERS ★
2 Lonsdale Street, GPO Box 1331L, Melbourne, VIC 3000

MELTON

HALL WILSON ▼
147 High Street, Melton, VIC 3337

MIRANDA

BDO INTERNATIONAL ▽
Suite 10, 50-52 Urunga Parade, Miranda, NSW 2228

MOUNT BARKER

HALL WILSON ▼
39 Gawler Street, Mount Barker, SA 5251

PKF ▼
33 Hutchinson Street, Mount Barker, SA 5251

NEWCASTLE

PRICEWATERHOUSE-COOPERS ★
26 Honeysuckle Drive, PO Box 798, Newcastle, NSW 2300

PRICEWATERHOUSE-COOPERS ★
8 Auckland Street, PO Box 798, Newcastle, NSW 2300

PARRAMATTA

DELOITTE TOUCHE TOHMATSU ★
35 Smith Street, (P.O.Box 38, 2124), Parramatta, NSW 2150

KPMG ▽
KPMG Centre, 111 Phillip Street, Parramatta, NSW 2150

MOORE STEPHENS ▼
Level 6, Spruson & Ferguson Centre, 460 Church Street, Parramatta, NSW 2124

PERTH

DELOITTE TOUCHE TOHMATSU ★
Woodside Plaza Level 14, 240 St Georges Terrace, Perth, WA 6000

GRANT THORNTON ▼
Level 1, 10 Kings Park Road, West Perth, Perth, WA 6005
Tel: 00 61 0894802000

BDO INTERNATIONAL ▽ ◈
P.O. Box 7426, Cloisters Square, Perth, WA 6850
Tel: 00 61 893604200

CASEY YOON & CO
Level 5, 231 Adelaide Terrace, Perth, WA 6000

ERNST & YOUNG ★
GPO Box M939, Perth, WA 6843

HALL WILSON ▼
18th level, AMP Tower,140 St George's Terrace, Perth, WA 6000

KPMG ▽
30th Floor Central Park, 152-158 St George's Terrace, Perth, WA 6000

MACINTYRE STRATER INTERNATIONAL LTD ▼
9th Floor, 55 St George's Terrace, Perth, WA 6000

MCLEAN DELMO HALL CHADWICK ▼
20th Level, AMP Tower, 140 St Georges Terrace, P.O. Box W2106, Perth, WA 6846

PICKUP INVESTIGATIVE ACCOUNTING & FORENSICS PTY LTD
23 Emerald Tce, Perth, WA 6005

PKF ▼
Level 7, BGC Centre, 28 The Esplanade, Perth, WA 6000

PRICEWATERHOUSE-COOPERS ★
QVI Building, 250 St George's Terrace, GPO Box D198, Perth, WA 6000

SANCTUARY COVE

DAVID S. BROOKS
PO Box 852, Sanctuary Cove, QLD 4212

SCONE

GRANT THORNTON ▼
196 Kelly Street, Scone, NSW 2337

SOUTHPORT

PANNELL KERR FORSTER ▼
Level 3, 1 Lawson Street, Queensland, Southport, QLD 4215

SUBIACO

GRANT THORNTON ▼
128 Hay Street, Subiaco, WA 6008

SURFERS PARADISE

PANNELL KERR FORSTER ▼
Level 5, RSL Centre, 9 Beach Road, Surfers Paradise, QLD 4217

PKF GOLD COAST SURFERS PARADISE ▼
Level 5, RSL Centre, 9 Main Beach Parade, Surfers Paradise, QLD 4217

SYDNEY

BDO BINDER ▼
Level 19, 2 Market Street, Sydney, NSW 2000

BDO INTERNATIONAL ▽
G.P.O. Box 2551, Sydney, NSW 2001

COOPER & CO
Level 15, Lumley House, 309 Kent Street, Sydney, NSW 2000

DELOITTE TOUCHE TOHMATSU ★
Grosvenor Place, 225 George Street, P.O. Box N 250, Sydney, NSW 2000

DUESBURYS MAREEBA ▼
Grant Thornton, 52 Phillip Street, Sydney, NSW 2000

ERNST & YOUNG ★
The Ernst & Young Building, 680 George Street, Sydney, NSW 2000

GRANT THORNTON ★
Level 17, 383 Kent Street, Sydney, NSW 2000
Tel: 00 61 2829 72400
Resident Partners/Directors:
ICAEW Members
P A Billingham

HALL WILSON ▼
20th Level, 1 York Street, Sydney, NSW 2000

KFPW PTY LTD (KNIGHT FRANK PRICE WATERHOUSE ★
John Hunter Bldg, Level 16, 9 Hunter Street, Sydney, NSW 2000

KPMG ▽
10 Shelley Street, Sydney, NSW 2000

MACINTYRE STRATER INTERNATIONAL LTD ▼
Anz Bank Building, 68 Pitt Street, Sydney, NSW 2000

MCLEAN DELMO HALL CHADWICK ▼
20th Level, 1 York Street, Sydney, NSW 2000

MOORE STEPHENS ▼
Level 15, 309 Kent Street, Sydney, NSW 2000

MOORES ROWLAND ▼
Level 2, 32 Martin Place, Sydney, NSW 2001

PKF ▼
Level 10, 1 Margaret Street, Sydney, NSW 2000

PRICEWATERHOUSE-COOPERS ★
Darling Park Tower 2, 201 Sussex Street, GPO Box 2650, Sydney, NSW 2000

RGL INTERNATIONAL (AUSTRALASIA) PTY LTD
Suite 3.01, Level 3, 56 Pitt Street, Sydney, NSW 2000

STIRLING INTERNATIONAL ★
11th Floor, St James Centre, 111 Elizabeth Street, GPO Box 7019, Sydney, NSW 2001
Tel: 00 61 282367500
Resident Partners/Directors:
ICAEW Members
R C Williams

TROOD PRATT & CO
GPO Box 3437, Sydney, NSW 1043

THIRROUL

HUSSAIN A. HASHAMBHOY
244 Lawrence Hargrave Drive, Thirroul, NSW 2515

TOWNSVILLE

ERNST & YOUNG ★
62 Walker Street, Townsville, QLD 4810

PKF ▼
Commonwealth Bank Building, 5th Floor, 370 Flinders Mall, Townsville, QLD 4810

PRICEWATERHOUSE-COOPERS ★
51 Sturt Street, PO Box 1047, Townsville, QLD 4810

WAHROONGA

MAYA'S
11 Bunyana Avenue, Wahroonga, NSW 2076

WANTIRNA SOUTH

N M NARIELVALA
8B Kingsley Terrace, 430 Burwood Highway, Wantirna South, VIC 3152

WAYVILLE

GRANT THORNTON ▼
67 Greenhill Road, Wayville, SA 5034

WEST PENNANT HILLS

K M YAP & CO
34 Peartree Circuit, West Pennant Hills, NSW 2125

AUSTRIA

BADEN

OSTERREICHISCHE REVISIONS UND TREUHANGESLELSCHAF T M.B.H ▼
Wassergasse 3, A2500 Baden

PANNELL KERR FORSTER ▼
Wassergasse 3, A 2500 Baden

PANNELL KERR FORSTER ▼
Wasserstrasse 3, A-2500 Baden

BREGENZ

KPMG ALPEN-TREUHAND ▼
Wolfeggstrasse 11, A-6900 Bregenz

DORNBIRN

COOPERS & LYBRAND GMBH ▼
Markstrasse 30, A-6850 Dornbirn

INNSBRUCK

COOPERS & LYBRAND GMBH ▼
Andreas-Holer-Strasse 43, A-6020 Innsbruck

KLAGENFURT

KPMG ALPEN-TREUHAND ▼
Krassinggstrasse 36, A-9020 Klagenfurt

LINZ

COOPERS & LYBRAND GMBH ▼
Goethestrasse 7, A-4020 Linz

KPMG ALPEN-TREUHAND ▼
Kudlichstrasse 48, A-4021 Linz

KPMG ALPEN-TREUHAND ▼
Kudlichstrasse 43, A-4021 Linz

SALZBURG

KPMG ALPEN-TREUHAND ▼
Klessheimer Allee 47, A-5020 Salzburg

MOORE STEPHENS GMBH ▼
Leonhard-Posch-Weg 11, A-5026 Salzburg

VIENNA

BDO INTERNATIONAL ▽
Gloriettegasse 31, 1130 Vienna

COOPERS & LYBRAND GMBH ▼
Berggasse 31, (Postfach 161), A-1092 Vienna

COOPERS & LYBRAND GMBH ▼
Liechtensteinstrasse 23, A-1092 Vienna

MOORE STEPHENS CITY TREUHAND GMBHGMBH ▼
Graben 20, A-1010, 1130 Vienna

MOORES ROWLAND GMBH ▼
1180 Wien, Hockegasse 22, 22 Vienna

PANNELL KERR FORSTER ▼
Hegelgsse 8, 1010 Vienna

PRICE WATERHOUSE AG ▼
Prinz-Eugen-Strasse 72, A-1040 Vienna

AZERBAIJAN

BAKU

ERNST & YOUNG ▼
Mardonov Qardashlar(ex Gogo), 11 Apt 32, Baku

PRICEWATERHOUSE-COOPERS
The Landmark Office Plaza, 5th Floor, 96 Nizami Street, Baku 370010

AZORES

PONTA DELGADA

ERNST & YOUNG ▼
Rua do Melo, 44-2, 9500 Ponta Delgada

BAHAMAS

FREEPORT

ANDREAE & FINGLAND ★
Chancery House, The Mall, (P.O. Box F2415), Freeport

DELOITTE & TOUCHE ▼
P.O.Box F-3746, Sylvia Gill Building, East Sunrise Highway, Freeport

KPMG ★
International Building, (P.O. Box F25), Freeport

PANNELL KERR FORSTER ▼
Room 22A, Kipling Building, Freeport

PRICEWATERHOUSE-COOPERS ★
Regent Centre, The Mall, Suite A, Freeport

NASSAU

ANDREAE & FINGLAND ★
E.D. Sassoon Bldg, Providence House,East Hill, Street, P.O. Box N3910, Nassau

BDO MANN JUDD ★
P.O. Box N10144, East Street, Nassau

DELOITTE & TOUCHE ▼
P.O.Box 7120, Dehands House, 2nd Terrace West, Collins Avenue, Nassau

ERNST & YOUNG ▼
(P.O. Box N3231), Sassoon House, Shirley & Victoria, Nassau

GRAHAM M. COOPER & CO
Peek Building, George St, P.O. Box N8160, Nassau

KPMG ★
Montague Sterling Centre, East Bay Street, PO Box N123, Nassau

KPMG PEAT MARWICK ★
PO Box N123, Montague Sterling Centre, East Bay Street, Nassau

MICHAEL H FIELDER
Sutie One The Gomez Building, PO Box N1608, Nassau

MOORE STEPHENS BUTLER & TAYLOR ▼
P O Box N-7777, 29 Retirement Road, Off Albury, Lane, Shirley Street, Nassau
Tel: 00 1 242 3930224

PANNELL KERR FORSTER ▼
Pannell House, Elizabeth Avenue Apt 44, P.O.Box N 8335, Nassau

PRICEWATERHOUSE-COOPERS ★
Providence House, East Hill Street,PO Box N3910, Nassau

BAHRAIN

MANAMA

ERNST & YOUNG ▽ ◈
P.O. Box 140, Manama
Tel: 00 973 17535455
Resident Partners/Directors: ICAEW Members
N R Abid, A Adil, P J Griffiths, J M Mower, A A H Rudman, M T Sadiq Akbar, J K Sanderson

PANNELL KERR FORSTER & PARTNERS - BAHRAIN ▼
14th Flower, Bahrain Tower, Office No 102, Building 20, Al Khalifa Avenue, Manama 305

PRICEWATERHOUSE-COOPERS ▼
PO Box 21144, BMB Centre, 4th Floor, Diplomatic Area, Manama

BANGLADESH

CHITTAGONG

KHAN WAHAB SHAFIQUE RAHMAN & CO ★
923/A Sk. Mujib Road, Chittagong

S.F.AHMED & CO ★
Ispahani Bldg., Sk. Mujib Road, Agrabad, Chittagong

DHAKA

A QASEM & CO ▽
Gulshan Pink City, Suites 01-03 Level 7, Plot No. 15 Road No. 103, Gulshan Avenue, Dhaka 1212

ATA KHAN & CO
67 Motijheel Commercial Area, Dhaka 1000

BAREE PEAR & KHAN
4/3 Iqbal Road (2nd Floor), Mohammadpur, Dhaka 1207

KHAN WAHAB SHAFIQUE RAHMAN & CO ★
55 Dilkusha, Commercial Area, Dhaka 1000

M.HUQUE & CO
70/C Purana Paltan Line, 3rd Floor, Dhaka 1000

OCTOKHAN
2nd Floor, Hosna Centre, 106 Gulshan Ave, Dhaka

RAHMAN RAHMAN HUQ
9 Mohakhali Commercial Area, Dhaka 1212
Tel: 00 880 298864502
Resident Partners/Directors: ICAEW Members
A Ashfaq, S A Hafiz, A H Khan, A N A H Siddiqui

S.F.AHMED & CO ★
House No 25D, Road No 13A, Block D, Banani, Dhaka 1213

KHULNA

KHAN WAHAB SHAFIQUE RAHMAN & CO ★
33 Lower Jessore Road, Khulna

BARBADOS

BANNATYNE

P.A. WALFORD
Bannatyne Cottage, Bannatyne

BRIDGETOWN

ERNST & YOUNG ★
PO Box 261, Bridgetown

KPMG ★
P O Box 690C, Bridgetown

PRICEWATERHOUSE-COOPERS ★
Financial Services Centre, Bishop's Court Hill, Bridgetown

SINGH & CO
Apartment F, Banyan Court, P.O. Box 427, Bridgetown

WARD, PATEL & CO
The Gables, Haggatt Hall, St Michael, Bridgetown

ST MICHAEL

PANNELL KERR FORSTER ▼
First Floor, Building 2, Chelston Park, Collymore Rock, St Michael

BELGIUM

ANTWERP

BDO INTERNATIONAL ▽
Uitbreidingstraat 66, Bus 13, 2600 Antwerp

KPMG CORPORATE FINANCE ▼
Prins Boudewijnlaan 24d, Kontich, 2550 Antwerp

PANNELL KERR FORSTER ▼
Potvlietlaan 6, B-2600 Antwerp

PKF ▼
Potvlietlaan 6, 2600 Antwerp

PKF BEDRIFSREVISION (AUDITORS) ▼
PKF, Potviliet Laan 6, 2600 Antwerp

PRICEWATERHOUSE-COOPERS ▼
General Lemastraat 67, B-2018 Antwerp

PRICEWATERHOUSE-COOPERS ▼
Generaal Lemanstraat 55, B-2018 Antwerp

TINNEMANS,POURBAIX VAES & CO ▼
Albion Building, Britslei 23-25, 2000, Antwerp

VAN DER STEEN, RISKE, DE WEERDT, LEFEBVRE & PARTNERS ▼
Kipdorpvest 40, 2000 Antwerp

BRUSSELS

A.B. COULSON
30 Rue Aux Fleurs, 1380 Brussels

BDO INTERNATIONAL ▽
International Office, Boulevard de la Woluwe 60, B-1200 Brussels

CHRISTOPHER THUBRON
Avenue Louise 251, Bte 14, B 1050 Brussels

HERMANT - DODEMONT & CO
Boulevard Du Souverain 191, 1160 Brussels

KPMG ADVISORY ▼
Accounts Department, Avenue du Bourget 40, 1130 Brussels

KPMG PEAT MARWICK ▼
Avenue du Bourgetlaan 40, B-1130 Brussels

MICHAEL J. RIDGWAY
Avenue du Maelbeek 7 bte 11, 1000 Brussels
Tel: 00 32 22800494
Principal: ICAEW Member
M A J Ridgway

MOORE STEPHENS EUROPEAN AFFAIRS OFFICE ▼
Avenue Louise 251, 1050 Brussels

PANNELL KERR FORSTER ▼
Metrologicelaan 10 B 15, 1130 Brussels

PHILIP P. COULDREY
93 Avenue Besme, 1190 Brussels

PKF BEDRIJFSREVISOREN ▼
Maastrichtersteenweg 8 B/5,6, 3500 Hasselt, 3500 Brussels

PRICEWATERHOUSE-COOPERS ▼
Avenue de Cortenbergh 75, B-1000 Brussels

PRICEWATERHOUSE-COOPERS ▼
Woluwe Garden, Woluwedal 18, Sint-Stevens-Woluwe, B-1932 Brussels

DIEGEM

DELOITTE & TOUCHE CORPORATE FINANCE
Berkenlaan 8C, 1831 Diegem

DRT EUROPE SERVICES S.A. ▼
Brussels Airport Business Park, Berkenlaan 6, 1831 Diegem

TINNEMANS,POURBAIX VAES & CO ▼
Brussels Airport Park, Berkenlaan 6, B-1831 Diegem

GHENT

BDO INTERNATIONAL ▽
MP-Center, Brouwerijstraat 1, Drongen, 9031 Ghent

ERNST & YOUNG ★
Residentie Lieven Bauwens, Martelaarslaan 53-5515, B-9000 Ghent

PRICEWATERHOUSE-COOPERS ▼
Kuiperskaai 55i, B-9000 Ghent

PRICEWATERHOUSE-COOPERS ▼
Wilsonplein 5G, B-9000 Ghent

HASSELT

MOORE STEPHENS VAN HAVERMAET ▼
Kasteel Ter Poorten, Diepenbekerweg 65/1, Hasselt

PKF BEDRIJFSREVISOREN (AUDITORS) ▼
Maastrichterseenweg, 8B/5-6, 3500 Hasselt

KNOKKE-HEIST

FLAMLAND & PARTNERS ▼
T Walletje 18, 8300 Knokke-Heist

LASNE

ALGONQUIN TRUST S.A.
Cour du Moulin, 5-9 Route de L'Etat, 1380 Lasne

LEUVEN

PRICEWATERHOUSE-COOPERS ▼
Interleuvenlaan 15i, Greenhill Campus, B-3001 Leuven

LIEGE

BDO INTERNATIONAL ▽
Rue Waucomont 51, Battice, 4651 Liege

PRICEWATERHOUSE-COOPERS ▼
Avenue Maurice Destenay 13, B-4000 Liege

LOUVAIN LA NEUVE

CHRISTOPHER HARVEY
Rue de la Neuville 58, 1348 Louvain La Neuve

VERVIERS

JULIAN TODD
Rue De France 36, B4800 Verviers
Tel: 00 32 473774844
Principal: ICAEW Member
J Todd

BELIZE

BELIZE CITY

HORWATH BELIZE ★ ◈
35a Regent Street, P O Box 756, Belize City

PANNELL KERR FORSTER ▼
Regent House, 35 Regent Street, Belize City

PANNELL KERR FORSTER ▼
Island Plaza, Barrier Reef Drive, San Pedro, Ambergris Caye, Belize City

BERMUDA

HAMILTON

ARTHUR MORRIS & CO ★
P.O. Box HM 1806, Century House, 16 Par La Ville Road, Hamilton HM HX

BUTTERFIELD & STEINHOFF ▼
P.O. Box 247, Vallis Building, Hamilton

DELOITTE & TOUCHE ▼
P.O.Box HM 1556, Corner House, Church & Parliament Streets, Hamilton HM FX

ERNST & YOUNG ▼
Reid Hall, 3 Reid Street, Hamilton HM11

ERNST & YOUNG ▼
Reid Hall, P.O. Box HM 463, Hamilton HM BX

KPMG ★
PO Box HM 897, Hamilton

KPMG ★
Crown House, 4 Par-la-Ville Road, Hamilton HM 08
Tel: 00 1 441 295 5063
Resident Partners/Directors: ICAEW Members
J L C Carne, S Green, D J Henderson, R Lightowler

MAZARS ▼ ◈
The Williams Building, 2nd Fl., 20 Reid Street, Hamilton HM11
Tel: 00 1 441 2923862
SPECIALISATIONS – FINANCIAL REPORTING
Accounts Preparation

MOORE STEPHENS & CO
Vallis Building, P.O.Box HM 1816, Hamilton HM HX

MOORE STEPHENS & BUTTERFIELD ★
Suite 600, 12 Church Street, Hamilton HM11

MORRIS SNELLING & CO ★
P.O. Box HM 1806, Century House, Richmond Road, Hamilton HM HX

PRICEWATERHOUSE-COOPERS ★
Dorchester House, 7 Church Street West, PO Box HM1171, Hamilton HM EX

RAWLINSON & HUNTER ▼
P.O.Box HM 1556, Corner House, Church and Parliament Streets, Hamilton HM FX
Tel: 00 1 441 2953180

BOLIVIA

LA PAZ

BDO INTERNATIONAL ▽
P.O. Box 3760, La Paz

MORENO, MUNOZ Y CIA ▼
Avenida Mariscal Santa Cruz, Esquina Yanacocha, Edificio Hansa-Piso 18, La Paz

PANNELL KERR FORSTER ▼
Avenida 20 De Octubre No 6, Edificio Zafiro, Piso, La Paz

PANNELL KERR FORSTER ▼
Avenida 20 de Octubre No. 6, Edifiao Zafiro, La Paz, PSO 5

PRICEWATERHOUSE-COOPERS
Avenida Mariscal Santa Cruz, con Yanacocha, Edificio Hansa, 19th Floor, La Paz

SANTA CRUZ DE LA SIERRA

PANNELL KERR FORSTER ▼
Equipetrol, Calle 8 Oeste (La Plata) No 6, Santa Cruz

PRICEWATERHOUSE-COOPERS
Calle Ciro Torres No 9, Barrio Equipetrol, PO Box 568, Santa Cruz De La Sierra

BOSNIA AND HERZEGOVINA

SARAJEVO

DELOITTE D.O.O SARAJEVO
Obala Kulina bana 2/111, Sarajevo, 71000

BOTSWANA

GABORONE

BDO INTERNATIONAL ▽
PO Box 1839, Gaborone

ERNST & YOUNG ★
P.O. Box 41015, Gaborone

PKF (GABORONE) INC GABORONE (BOTSWANA) ▼
P O Box 1308, Gaborone

PRICEWATERHOUSE-COOPERS ★
Plot 50371, Fair Ground Office Park, Show Grounds, PO Box 1453, Gaborone

BRAZIL

BELEM

PANNELL KERR FORSTER ▼
Rua Castelo Branco 811, Para, Belem, 66063-080

BELO HORIZONTE

KPMG AUDITORES INDEPENDENTES ★
Rua Paraiba 1122, 13th Floor, 30130-918 Belo Horizonte

PANNELL KERR FORSTER ▼
Rua da Bahia No 916-Sala 1007, MG CEP, Belo Horizonte, 30160-011

PRICEWATERHOUSE-COOPERS ★
Rua dos Inconfidentes 1190, 9th Floor, 30140-120 Belo Horizonte

BLUMENAU

WALTER HEUER AUDITORES INDEPENDENTES ▼
Rua Oswaldo Hesse 1420, Blumenau, 774

BRASILIA

PRICEWATERHOUSE-COOPERS ★
SCS Sector Comercial Sul, Quadra 6, Edificio Bandeirante, 4th Floor, 70300-968 Brasilia

CAMPINAS

PRICEWATERHOUSE-COOPERS ★
Edificio Hannover Tower, Av Jose de Souza Campos 243, 10th Floor, 13025-320 Campinas

CURITIBA

PANNELL KERR FORSTER ▼
Rua Ermiliano Pernetta, 297-18 - Sala 181, 80010-050 Curitiba

PRICEWATERHOUSE-COOPERS ★
Curitaba Trade Centre, Al Dr Carlos Carvalho 417, 10th Floor, 80410-180 Curitiba

PORTO ALEGRE

KPMG AUDITORES INDEPENDENTES ★
Rua Dos Andradas, 1001, 17th Floor, RS 90020 Porto Alegre

PRICEWATERHOUSE-COOPERS ★
Rua General Bento Martins 24, 8th Floor, 90010-080 Porto Alegre

RECIFE

BDO INTERNATIONAL ▽
Av. Conselheiro Aguiar, 4635 sl. 107, Boa Viagem, 51021-020 Recife

DELOITTE TOUCHE TOHMATSU ★
Cxa Postal 248,CEP 50001, PE, Avenida Dantas Barreto, 1200, Recife

ERNST & YOUNG ▼
Av. Dantus Barreto 1090, P.O. Box 853, 50020 Recife

PANNELL KERR FORSTER ▼
Rua das Ninfas, 254-1 Andar, Boa Vista, Recife 50070-050

PRICEWATERHOUSE-COOPERS ★
Edificio Empresarial Center 1, Rua Padre Carapuceiro 733, 8th Floor, 51020-280 Recife

RIBEIRAO PRETO

PRICEWATERHOUSE-COOPERS ★
Rua Rui Barbosa 1145, 12th Floor, 14015-120 Ribeirao Preto

RIO DE JANEIRO

BDO INTERNATIONAL ▽
Rua de Quitanda, 52-5th Floor, 20011-030 Rio De Janeiro

DELOITTE TOUCHE TOHMATSU ★
Caixa Postal 1338, CEP 20001-970, Rio De Janeiro

ERNST & YOUNG ▼
Avenida Rio Branco 128, 15-17th Floors, 20042 Rio De Janeiro

KPMG AUDITORES INDEPENDENTES ★
Av Almirante Barroso 52 4th, Rio De Janeiro, 20031-000

PANNELL KERR FORSTER ▼
Av. Almirante Barroso, No. 3-14 Piso, Rio De Janeiro, 20031-000

PRICEWATERHOUSE-COOPERS ★
Rua da Candelaria 65, 20091-020 Rio De Janeiro

SALVADOR

DELOITTE TOUCHE TOHMATSU ★
Avenida Tancrdo Neves 1.283, -4 andar, Edificio,Empresarial Omega, CEP 4182 Salvador

KPMG AUDITORES INDEPENDENTES ★
Caxia Postal 1903, 40001-970 Salvador

PANNELL KERR FORSTER ▼
Travessa Sao Joao 2-S/405, Edifficio Regente Feijo, Salvador

PRICEWATERHOUSE-COOPERS ★
Edificio Citibank, Rua Miguel Calmon 555, 9th Floor, 40015-010 Salvador

SAO CARLOS

KPMG AUDITORES INDEPENDENTES ★
Rue Sete de Setembro, 1950 Centro, 13560-180 Sao Carlos

SAO PAULO

BDO INTERNATIONAL ▽
Rua Senador Felico dos Santos, 392, 01511-010 Sao Paulo

DELOITTE TOUCHE TOHMATSU ★
Cxa Postal 2922,CEP 01051, SP, Avenida Ipiranga, 324-6,andar, Sao Paulo

ERNST & YOUNG ▼
Condominio Sao Luiz, Torre 1 Floors 5-8, Av. Pres Juscelino Kubitschek, 04543-900 Sao Paulo

KPMG AUDITORES INDEPENDENTES ★
Rua Dr Renato Paes de Barros33, Itaim Bibi, CEP 04530-904, Sao Paulo

PRICEWATERHOUSE-COOPERS ★
Avenida Francisco Matarazzo 1400, Torre Torino, Aqua Branca, Sao Paulo 05001-903

PRICEWATERHOUSE-COOPERS ★
Edificio Independencia, Rua General Jardim 36, 01223-906 Sao Paulo

PRICEWATERHOUSE-COOPERS ★
Avenida Ipiranga 324, 11th Floor, Bloco C, 01046-010 Sao Paulo

PRICEWATERHOUSE-COOPERS ★
Centro Empresarial Agua Branca, Avenida Francisco Matarazzo, 1700, Torre Milano, 16/F, 05001-400 Sao Paulo

RICHARD HANMER
Rua Ambrizette 180-11, 05704-020 Sao Paulo

VILLAGARCIA & ASCOIADOS ▼
Rua Dom Jose de Barros, 264-11 Piso, Sao Paulo

SOROCABA

PRICEWATERHOUSE-COOPERS ★
Edificio Trade Tower, Rua Riachuelo, 460-11 Andar, Salas 1104 & 1105, 18035-330 Sorocaba

UBERLANDIA

WALTER HEUER AUDITORES INDEPENDENTES ▼
AV Rio Branco 198, Uberlandia

VITORIA

PRICEWATERHOUSE-COOPERS ★
Avenida Nossa Senhora de Penha, 699 8th Floor, Edificio Century, Towers, Torre B, Santa Lucia, 29055-131 Vitoria

BRITISH VIRGIN ISLANDS

ROAD TOWN

BAKER TILLY (BVI) LTD
P O Box 650, Tropic Isle Building, Nibbs Street, Road Town

BDO INTERNATIONAL ▽
PO Box 34, Road Town

DELOITTE & TOUCHE ★
James Frett Building, Wickhams Cay 1, P O Box 3083, Road Town

KROLL (BVI) LTD
2nd Floor Palm Grove House, Wickhams Cay, PO Box 4571, Road Town
Tel: 00 1 284 4949600
Resident Partners/Directors: ICAEW Members
W R Tacon

PRICEWATERHOUSE-COOPERS ▼
Geneva Place, 2nd Floor, 333 Waterfront Drive, Wickham's Cay, Road Town

RAWLINSON & HUNTER LTD
P.O.Box 3162, Road Town

RAWLINSON & HUNTER LTD
Woodbourne Hall, P.O. Box 3162, Road Town, VG1110
Tel: 00 1 284 4945414

VIGILATE FINANCIAL SERVICES LTD
PO Box 417, 2nd Floor, Abbott Building, Waterfront Drive, Road Town

TORTOLA

KPMG ★
P O Box 4467, 3rd Floor, Flemming House, Road Town, Tortola

BRUNEI

BANDAR SERI BEGAWAN

DELOITTE & TOUCHE ★
P.O.Box 1965, 22/23 Jalan Sultan, Bandar Seri Begawan

ERNST & YOUNG ▼
Room 408B, 4th Floor, Wisma Jaya, Jalan Pemancha, Bandar Seri Begawan 1921

FOO KON & TAN
No 17 C7-1, First Floor, Block C, Lot 56646, Bangunan Haji Lajim Dan Anak-anak Kampong Kiarong, PO Box 140 Seri Complex Bandar Seri Begawan BE1318

KPMG ▼
Unit 402/403A, Wisma Jaya, Jalan Pemancha, Bandar Seri Begawan BS 8811

KPMG ★
Unit 402-403A, Wisma Jaya, Jalan Pemancha, Bandar Seri Begawan

LEE CORPORATEHOUSE ASSOCIATES ▼
No 11, 1st Floor, Regent Square, Simpang 150, Bandar Seri Begawan
Tel: 00 673 2223341
Resident Partners/Directors:
ICAEW Members
K Y Lee

DARUSSLAM

ERNST & YOUNG ▼
4th Fl, Hong Kong Bank Cmbrs,Jalan Sultan Pemencha,NEGARA, Darusslam, 2085

ERNST & YOUNG ▼
2nd Fl, Foh Building, Lot 308,Jalan Bunga Raya, Darusslam, 6082

KUALA BELAIT

FOO KON & TAN
1st Floor, Unit No 15, Lot 7191, Bgn Haji Hassa, Hj Abd. Ghani Dan Anak-anak Jalan Jaya Negara Kg Pandan Kuala Belait KA 1931

LEE CORPORATEHOUSE ASSOCIATES ▼
Rm S7 2nd Floor, HongKong Bank Chambers, Jalan McKerron, Kuala Belait KA1131
Tel: 00 673 3331406

BULGARIA

SOFIA

KPMG BULGARIA OOD ▼
37 Fridtjof Nansen Street, 1142 Sofia

PANNELL KERR FORSTER ▼
12 Macedonia Boulevard, 1606 Sofia

BURUNDI

BUJUMBURA

MPMG KLYNVELD ▼
BP 2995, Bujumbura

CAMEROON

DOUALA

AKINTOLA WILLIAMS ADETONA ISICHEI & CO ★
Socar Building, Entrance C. Block A, 1st Floor, Douala, BP 5393

ERNST & YOUNG ▼
B.P. 443, Douala

PANNELL KERR FORSTER ★
797 rue Vasnitex, Bonapriso, Douala

PETITEAU SCACCHI ET ASSOCIES ▼
Immeuble Le Cauris, Rue Alfred Saker, Akwa, Douala

PRICEWATERHOUSE-COOPERS ▼
BP 5689, Avenue de General de Gaulle, Immeuble BICEC, Bonanjo, Douala

YAOUNDE

PRICEWATERHOUSE-COOPERS ▼
Immeuble SNI, 11e etage, 34 Rue du Mfoundi, BP 1010, Yaounde

CANADA

ABBOTSFORD

KPMG LLP
32575 Simon Avenue, Abbotsford V2T 4W6

ALEXANDRIA

BDO INTERNATIONAL ▽
431 Main Street South, Alexandria K0C 1A0

AMOS

DELOITTE & TOUCHE LLP
101 1re Avenue est, Amos J9T 1H4, QUE

KPMG LLP
4 rue Principale Nord, bureau 103, Amos J9T 2K6, QUE

BAIE COMEAU

DELOITTE & TOUCHE LLP
859 Rue Bosse, Baie Comeau G5C 3P8, QUE

BARRIE

BDO INTERNATIONAL ▽
Cedar Pointe Business Park, 15 Cedar Pointe Drive, Unit 11, Barrie L4N 5R7

BRADFORD

BDO INTERNATIONAL ▽
P.O. Box 729, Bradford L3Z 2B2

BROCKVILLE

BDO INTERNATIONAL ▽
P.O. Box 175, Brockville K6V 5V2

BROSSARD

L.R. FONG
1050 Schubert Street, Brossard J4X 1X1, QUE

BURNABY

KPMG LLP
Metrotower II, Suite 2400 - 4720 Kingsway, Burnaby V5H 4N2

CALGARY

CHATUR L. ALI
601, 1088 - 6 Avenue SW, Calgary T2P 5N3

DELOITTE & TOUCHE LLP
3000 Scotia Centre, 700-2nd Street S.W., Calgary T2P 0S7

ERNST & YOUNG ★
Ernst & Young Tower, 1000, 440-2nd Avenue, South West, Calgary T2P 5E9

KPMG LLP
Bow Valley Square II, 205-5th Avenue SW Suite 1200, Calgary T2P 4B9

KPMG MANAGEMENT CONSULTING ▼
Bow Valley Square II, 205-5th Avenue SW, Suite 1200, Calgary T2P 4B9

PRICEWATERHOUSE-COOPERS ★
111, 5th Avenue SW, Suite 3100, Calgary T2P 5L3

WGD LLP
900 Elveden House, 717-7 Seventh Avenue SW, Calgary T2P 0Z3

CAMBRIDGE

KPMG LLP
19 Thorpe Street, Cambridge N1R 1J3

CAMPBELLTON

BARRY.R. COLEMAN
28 Dufferin Street, Campbellton E3N 2N2

CHARLOTTETOWN

PRICEWATERHOUSE-COOPERS ★
Prince Edward Place, 18 Queen Street, Suite 100, Charlottetown C1A 4A2

CHATHAM

BDO INTERNATIONAL ▽
375 St Clair Street, Chatham N7L 3K3

CHIBOUGAMAU

DELOITTE & TOUCHE LLP
552 3e Rue, Chibougamau G8P 1N9, QUE

CHILLIWACK

KPMG LLP
200 9123 Mary Street, Chilliwack V2P 4H7

COBOURG

BDO INTERNATIONAL ▽
P.O. Box 627, Cobourg K9A 4L3

CORNWALL

BDO INTERNATIONAL ▽
P.O. Box 644, Cornwall K6H 5T3

DELOITTE & TOUCHE LLP
The Deloitte & Touche, Building, 55 Water Street West Suite 200, Cornwall K6J 1A1

CRANBROOK

BDO INTERNATIONAL ▽
200-25 10th Avenue South, Cranbrook V1C 2M9

DARTMOUTH

DELOITTE & TOUCHE LLP
P.O.Box 23, Royal Bank, Tower, 202 Brownlow Avenue, Dartmouth B2Y 3Y2

DELTA

A.S. BUBBER & ASSOCIATES INC
6420 Sunshine Drive, Delta V4E 1P2

DRYDEN

BDO INTERNATIONAL ▽
37 King Street, Dryden P8N 3G3

EDMONTON

COLIN REES PROFESSIONAL CORPORATION
101 14020-128th Avenue, Edmonton T5L 4M8

DELOITTE & TOUCHE LLP
2000 ManuLife Place, 10180-101 Street, Edmonton T5J 4E4

ERNST & YOUNG ★
1800 Esso Tower, Scotia Place,10060 Jasper Avenue, Edmonton J5J 3R8

GARDINER KARBANI AUDY & PARTNERS
4107-99 Street, Edmonton T6E 3N4

KPMG LLP
Commerce Place, 10125-102 Street, Edmonton T5J 3V8

KPMG MANAGEMENT CONSULTING ▼
Commerce Place, 10125-102 Street, Edmonton T5J 3V8

MOORE STEPHENS ▼
500 West Tower, Coronation Plaza, Edmonton T5M 3Z7

MOORE STEPHENS ▼
9797 45th Avenue, Edmonton T6E 5V8

PRICEWATERHOUSE-COOPERS ★
Toronto Dominion Tower, Edmonton Centre, Suite 1501, 10088 102 Avenue, Edmonton T5J 2Z1

S.D. JANMOHAMED ◈
235-2903 Rabit Hill Road, Edmonton T6R 3A3
Tel: 00 1 780 235 8139
Principal: ICAEW Member
S D H Janmohamed

STUART COWEN PROF CORP'N
11148-81 Avenue, Edmonton T6G 0S5

ELLIOT LAKE

KPMG LLP
11 Manitoba Road, PO Box 151 Stn Main, Elliot Lake P5A 2J7

SMYTHE RATCLIFFE CA ▼
No. 205, 15117 101st Avenue, Surrey B.C., Canada, Elliot Lake V3R 8P7

EMBRUN

BDO INTERNATIONAL ▽
P.O. Box 128, Embrun K0A 1W0

ESSEX

BDO INTERNATIONAL ▽
14 Victoria Street, Essex N8M 1M3

FARNHAM

DELOITTE & TOUCHE LLP
149 rue Desjardins Est, Farnham J2N 2W6, QUE

FREDERICTON

KPMG LLP
Frederick Square, 77 Westmorland Street, Suite 700, Fredericton E3B 6Z3

GATINEAU

DELOITTE & TOUCHE LLP
144 Blvd. de l'Hopital, Gatineau J8T 7S7, QUE

GLOUCESTER

SAABIR & CO
6078 Ridgelea Place, Orleans, Gloucester K1C 5P8

GRANBY

DELOITTE & TOUCHE LLP
74 rue Court, Granby J2G 4Y5, QUE

ERNST & YOUNG ★
35 Duffin Street, Granby J2G 4W5, QUE

GRIMSBY

KPMG LLP
Grimsby Place Plaza, 76 Main Street West, PO Box 68 Stn Main, Grimsby L3M 4G1

GUELPH

BDO INTERNATIONAL ▽
600 Speedvale Ave. W., Suite 201, Guelph N1K 1E5

DELOITTE & TOUCHE LLP
98 Macdonnell Street, Suite 400, Guelph N1H 8L1

HALIFAX

ERNST & YOUNG ★
1959 Upper Water Street, Halifax B3J 3N2

KPMG LLP
Purdy's Wharf Tower One, 1959 Upper Water Street, Suite 1600, Halifax B3J 3N2

KPMG MANAGEMENT CONSULTING ▼
Purdy's Wharf, Tower One, 1959 Upper Water Street, Suite 1505, Halifax B3J 3N2

PRICEWATERHOUSE-COOPERS ★
1809 Barrington Street, Suite 600, Halifax B3J 3K8

HAMILTON

BDO INTERNATIONAL ▽
505 York Boulevard, Suite 2, Hamilton L8R 3K4

BDO INTERNATIONAL ▽
Insolvency Unit, 805, 25 Main Street West, Hamilton L8P 1H1

KPMG LLP
Commerce Place, 21 King Street West Suite 700, PO Box 976 Stn LCD1, Hamilton L8P 3R1

KPMG MANAGEMENT CONSULTING ▼
Commerce Place, 21 King Street West Suite 690, PO Box 976 Stn LCD1, Hamilton L8N 3R1

PRICEWATERHOUSE-COOPERS ★
21 King Street West, Main Floor, Hamilton L8P 4W7

HANOVER

BDO INTERNATIONAL ▽
485-10th Street, Hanover N4N 1R2

HAWKESBURY

DELOITTE & TOUCHE LLP
250 Rue Principale Est, Hawkesbury K6A 1A5

HUDSON BAY

MOORE STEPHENS ▼
103 Churchill Street, Box 1300, Hudson Bay S0E 0Y0

HULL

DELOITTE & TOUCHE LLP
25 Rue Laurier, Hull J8X 4C8, QUE

HUNTSVILLE

BDO INTERNATIONAL ▽
2 Elm Street, Huntsville P0A 1K0

JONQUIERE

DELOITTE & TOUCHE LLP
2433 Rue St-Dominique, Jonquiere G7X 6L1, QUE

KAMLOOPS

BDO INTERNATIONAL ▽
300, 272 Victoria Street, Kamloops V2C 1Z6

KELOWNA

G.A. MAILE
3021B Pandosy Street, Kelowna V1Y 1W3

KPMG LLP
300-1674 Bertram Street, Kelowna V1Y 9G4

KENORA

BDO INTERNATIONAL ▽
Suite 300, 301 First Avenue South, Kenora P9N 4E9

KINGSTON

BDO INTERNATIONAL ▽
480 Bath Road, Kingston K7M 4X6

KPMG LLP
863 Princess Street Suite 400, PO Box 1600 Stn Main, Kingston K7L 5C8

KITCHENER

DELOITTE & TOUCHE LLP
Canada Trust Centre, 55 King Street West, Suite 700, Kitchener N2G 4W1

ERNST & YOUNG ★
515 Riverbend Drive, (P.O. Box 9458 Station C), Kitchener N2G 4W9

PRICEWATERHOUSE-COOPERS ★
Suite 900, 55 King Street W, Kitchener N2G 4W1

LA SHARPE

KPMG LLP
226 2e rue est, La Sharpe J9Z 2G9, QUE

LANGLEY

BDO INTERNATIONAL ▽
220-19916-64th Avenue, Langley V2Y 1A2

DELOITTE & TOUCHE LLP
20316-56th Avenue, Langley V3A 3Y7

LAVAL

ERNST & YOUNG ★
Bureau 400, Edifice Cumis, 3080, boul. le Carrefour, Laval H7T 2K9, QUE

LETHBRIDGE

KPMG LLP
Lethbridge Centre Tower, 400-4th Avenue South, Suite 500, Lethbridge T1J 4E1

LINDSAY

BDO INTERNATIONAL ▽
P.O. Box 358, Lindsay K9V 4S3

LONDON

BDO INTERNATIONAL ▽
495 Richmond Street, Suite 900, London N6A 5A9

ERNST & YOUNG ★
1 London Place, Suite 1700,255 Queens, Ave, P.O. Box 5332, London N6A 5S7

PRICEWATERHOUSE-COOPERS ★
275 Dundas Street, Suite 1500, London N6B 3L1

LONGUEUIL

DELOITTE & TOUCHE LLP
1111 Rue St-Charles Ouest, Tour Est, Longueuil J4K 5G4, QUE

MANOTICK

BDO INTERNATIONAL ▽
1136 Clapp Lane, Box 291, Manotick K4M 1A3

MARKHAM

ANTOINE S CALFA
18 Crown Steel Drive, Suite 201, Markham L3R 9X8

BDO INTERNATIONAL ▽
60 Columbia Way, Suite 400, Markham L3R 0C9

LLOYD G RASKINA CA
5 McIntosh Drive, Suite 218, Markham L3R 8C7

R.W. DAVIDSON
47 Squire Bakers Lane, Markham L3P 3G8

MATANE

DELOITTE & TOUCHE LLP
750 Rue du Phare Ouest, Matane G4W 3N2, QUE

MEDICINE HAT

MOORE STEPHENS ▼
666 - 4th Street, Box 580, Medicine Hat T1A 7G5

MELFORT

MOORE STEPHENS ▼
609 Main Street, Box 2020, Melfort S0E 1A0

MISSISSAUGA

BDO INTERNATIONAL ▽
4255 Sherwoodtowne Boulevard, Mississauga L4Z 1Y5

DELOITTE & TOUCHE LLP
1 City Centre Drive, Suite 1100, Mississauga L5B 1M2

PRICEWATERHOUSE-COOPERS ★
Mississauga Executive Centre, 1 Robert Speck Parkway, Suite 1100, Mississauga L4Z 3M3

S.S SINGH
7560 Airport Road, Suite 12, Mississauga L4T 4H4

MONCTON

KPMG LLP
Place Marvens, One Factory Lane, PO Box 827 Stn Main, Moncton E1C 9M3

MONTREAL

BDO INTERNATIONAL ▽
4150 Ste Catherine West, 6th Floor, Montreal H3Z 2Y5, QUE

DELOITTE & TOUCHE LLP
1 Place Ville-Marie, Bureau 3000, Montreal H3B 4T9, QUE

HAREL DOURIN-PKF ▼
215 Saint Jacques, Suite 1200, Montreal H2Y 1M6, QUE

KPMG LLP
Bureau 1500, 600 boul De Maisonneuve Ouest, Montreal H3A OA3, QUE

PANNELL KERR FORSTER ▼
1100 Cremazie Boulevard East, Suite 805, Montreal H2P 2X2, QUE

PRICEWATERHOUSE-COOPERS ★
1250 Rene Levesque Blvd West, Bureau 3500, Montreal H3B 2G4, QUE

RICHTER, USHER & VINEBERG ▼
2 Place Alexis Nihon, 3500 de Maisonniuve, Montreal H3Z 3C2, QUE

RICHTER, USHER & WINEBERG ▼
2 Place Alexis Nihon, 3500 de Maisonneuve, Montreal H3Z 2C2, QUE

MOUNT FOREST

BDO INTERNATIONAL ▽
P.O. Box 418, Mount Forest N0G 2L0

NANAIMO

SMYTHE RATCLIFFE CA ▼
8C-2220 Bowen Road, Nanaimo V9S 1H9

NEW WESTMINSTER

DELOITTE & TOUCHE LLP
300 First Capital Place, 960 Quayside Drive, New Westminster V3M 6G2

KPMG LLP
400-625 Agnes Street, New Westminster V3M 5Y4

NORTH BAY

BDO INTERNATIONAL ▽
P.O. Box 20001, North Bay P1B 9N1

KPMG LLP
925 Stockdale Road, Suite 300, P O Box 990, North Bay P1B 8K3

NORTH VANCOUVER

MATTHEW WRIGHT
Apt 201, 1650 Chesterfield Avenue, North Vancouver V7M 2N7

NORTH YORK

AUNDHIA & PARIKH
265 Rimrock Road, Suite 1, North York M3J 3C6

DELOITTE & TOUCHE LLP
North York City Centre, 5140 Yonge St, North York M2N 6L7

KPMG LLP
Yonge Corporate Centre, 500-4120 Yonge Street, North York MP2 2B8

PRICEWATERHOUSE-COOPERS ★
5700 Yonge Street, North York M2M 4K7

OAKVILLE

BDO INTERNATIONAL ▽
151 Randall Street, Oakville L6J 1P5

ORANGEVILLE

BDO INTERNATIONAL ▽
77 Broadway Avenue, 2nd Floor, Orangeville L9W 1K1

ORILLIA

BDO INTERNATIONAL ▽
Box 670, Orillia L3V 6K5

OSHAWA

BDO INTERNATIONAL ▽
Oshawa Executive Centre, 502-419 King Street West, Oshawa L1J 2K5

OTTAWA

BDO INTERNATIONAL ▽
301 Moodie Drive, Suite 400, Nepean, Ottawa K2H 9C4

DELOITTE & TOUCHE LLP
1000 Royal Bank Centre, 90 Sparks St, Ottawa K1P 5T8

ERNST & YOUNG ★
Suite 1600, 100 Queen Street, Ottawa, K1P 1K1

KPMG LLP
World Exchange Plaza, 45 O'Connor Street, Suite 1000, Ottawa K1P 1A4

KPMG MANAGEMENT CONSULTING ▼
11th Floor, World Exchange Plaza, 45 O'Connor Street, Ottawa K1P 1A4

PRICEWATERHOUSE-COOPERS ★
99 Bank Street, Suite 800, Ottawa K1P 1E4

OWEN SOUND

BDO INTERNATIONAL ▽
P.O. Box 397, Owen Sound N4K 5P7

PENTICTON

KPMG LLP
2nd Floor, 498 Ellis Street, Penticton V2A 4M2

PETERBOROUGH

BDO INTERNATIONAL ▽
P.O. Box 1026, Peterborough K9J 7A5

POINTE CLAIRE

ANDREWS & ASSOCIE CA SENC
151 Hymus Boulevard, Pointe Claire H9R 1E9

PORT ELGIN

BDO INTERNATIONAL ▽
P.O. Box 1390, Port Elgin N0H 2C0

PORTAGE LA PRAIRIE

KPMG LLP
Bell Building, 32 Tupper Street North, Suite 201, Portage La Prairie V2L 4Y2

MOORE STEPHENS ▼
14 Tupper Street S, Portage La Prairie R1N 1W6

PRINCE ALBERT

DELOITTE & TOUCHE LLP
P.O.Box 1990, 5-15th Street East, Prince Albert S6V 6K1

PRINCE GEORGE

DELOITTE & TOUCHE LLP
299 Victoria Street, Prince George V2L 5B8

DERECK C. SALE
4015 Cormack Crescent, Prince George V2N 5K8

SCHMITZ & DE GRACE ★
1116 Sixth Avenue, Prince George V2L 3M6

PRINCE RUPERT

VOHORA & CO ★
P.O. Box 728, 607 West Second Avenue, Prince Rupert V8J 3S1

QUEBEC CITY

DELOITTE & TOUCHE LLP
5400 Boulevard des Galeries, Quebec City G2K 2B5

ERNST & YOUNG ★
140 Grande Allee East, Bureau 200, Quebec City GIR 5P2

RED DEER

MOORE STEPHENS ▼
102 Sun Centre, 4922 - 53rd Street, Red Deer T4N 2E9

RED LAKE

BDO INTERNATIONAL ▽
P.O. Box 234, Red Lake P0V 2M0

REGINA

DELOITTE & TOUCHE LLP
1874 Scarth Street, Regina S4P 4B3

PRICEWATERHOUSE-COOPERS ★
Royal Bank Building, Suite 900, 2010 11th Avenue, Regina S4P 0J3

REVELSTOKE

BDO INTERNATIONAL ▽
P.O. Box 2100, Revelstoke V0E 2S0

RICHMOND

LOK KI HO & CO ★
Suite No 2325, 8888 Odlin Crescent, Richmond V6X 3Z8

PRICEWATERHOUSE-COOPERS ★
5611 Cooney Road, Suite 100, Richmond V6X 3J6

RICHMOND HILL

ARUL & ASSOCIATES
10 Lynngrove Crescent, Richmond Hill L4B 2B7

PABANI & CO
30 Wertheim Court, Suite 14B, Richmond Hill L4B 1B9

RIDGETOWN

BDO INTERNATIONAL ▽
211 Main Street East, Ridgetown N0P 2C0

RIMOUSKI

DELOITTE & TOUCHE LLP
320 rue Saint-German eSt, Rimouski G5L 1C2, QUE

ROBERVAL

DELOITTE & TOUCHE LLP
775 Boulevard St-Joseph, Roberval G8H 2L4, QUE

ROUYN

DELOITTE & TOUCHE LLP
147 boulevard Quebec, Rouyn-Noranda, Rouyn J9X 6M8, QUE

KPMG LLP
155 rue Dallaire, Rouyn J9X 4T3, QUE

SACKVILLE

WILDE TIMMONS MICHAUD INC ★ ◈
32 Glendale Avenue, Lower Sackville B4C 3M1
Tel: 00 1 902 2524101
Resident Partners/Directors: ICAEW Members
P F Wilde

SAINT JOHN

DELOITTE & TOUCHE LLP
P.O.Box 6549, Station A., 44 Chipman Hill, Saint John E2L 4R9

ERNST & YOUNG ★
One Brunswick Square, Saint John E2L 4V1

KPMG MANAGEMENT CONSULTING ▼
Harbour Building, 133 Prince William Street, St John E2L 2B5

PRICEWATERHOUSE-COOPERS ★
Brunswick House, Suite 300, 44 Chipman Hill, Saint John E2L 4B9

SAINT-HYACINTHE

DELOITTE & TOUCHE LLP
2200 Ave. Leon-Pratte, Saint-Hyacinthe J2S 4B6, QUE

SALMON ARM

BDO INTERNATIONAL ▽
P.O. Box 1809, Salmon Arm V1E 4P8

SARNIA

BDO INTERNATIONAL ▽
P.O. Box 730, Sarnia N7T 7J7

DELOITTE & TOUCHE LLP
3301 Front Street North, Sarnia N7T 5S6

SASKATOON

DELOITTE & TOUCHE LLP
122-1st Avenue South, 400, Saskatoon S7K 7E5

ERNST & YOUNG ★
1400 Saskatoon Square, 410/ 22nd Street East, Saskatoon S9K 5T6

KPMG LLP
600-128 Fourth Ave South, Saskatoon S7K 1M8

KPMG MANAGEMENT CONSULTING ▼
600-128 4th Avenue South, Saskatoon S7K 1M8

PRICEWATERHOUSE-COOPERS ★
The Princeton Tower, 123 2nd Avenue South, Suite 200, Saskatoon S7K 7E6

SAULT STE. MARIE

BDO INTERNATIONAL ▽
P.O. Box 1109, Sault Ste. Marie P6A 5N7

KPMG LLP
111 Elgin Street Suite 200, PO Box 578 Stn Main, Sault Ste. Marie P6A 5M6

SCARBOROUGH

AMIR KASSAM
Suite 207, 1911 Kennedy Road, Scarborough M1P 2L9

ANTHONY C J HUMPHREYS
25 Crestwood Drive, Scarborough M1E 1E6
Tel: 00 1 416 269 7870
Principal: ICAEW Member
A C J Humphreys

SENNETERRE

DELOITTE & TOUCHE LLP
660-10e Avenue, Senneterre J0Y 2M0, QUE

SEPT-ILES

DELOITTE & TOUCHE LLP
106 Rue Napoleon, Sept-iles G4R 3L7, QUE

KPMG LLP
421 Rue Arnaud, Bureau 200, Sept-iles G4R 3B3, QUE

SHAWINIGAN

DELOITTE & TOUCHE LLP
704 5e Rue, (CP 910), Shawinigan G9N 7N5, QUE

SQUAMISH

BDO INTERNATIONAL ▽
P.O. Box 168, Squamish V0N 3G0

ST. CATHARINES

BDO INTERNATIONAL ▽
P.O. Box 1237, St Catharines L2R 7A7

KPMG LLP
P O Box 1294 Str Main, St Catharines L2R 7AZ

ST. FELICIEN

DELOITTE & TOUCHE LLP
1133 Rue Notre-Dame, St Felicien G8K 1Z7, QUE

ST.JOHN'S

DELOITTE & TOUCHE LLP
Fort William Bldg, 10 Factory Lane, St John's A1C 6H5

KPMG LLP
Harbour Building, 133 Prince William Street, St John's E2L 2B5

PRICEWATERHOUSE-COOPERS ★
Atlantic Place, 215 Water Street, Suite 802, St John's A1C 6C9

STRATFORD

BDO INTERNATIONAL ▽
150 Huron Street, 2nd Floor, Stratford N5A 5S8

SUDBURY

BDO INTERNATIONAL ▽
Suite 301, 888 Regent Street, Sudbury P3E 6C6

KPMG LLP
Claridge Executive Centre, 144 Pine Street, PO Box 700 Stn B, Sudbury P3C 1X3

SURREY

BDO INTERNATIONAL ▽
202, 15225 - 104 Avenue, Surrey V3R 6Y8

PRICEWATERHOUSE-COOPERS ★
Station Tower, Gateway, 13401 108th Avenue, Suite 1600, Surrey V3T 5T3

SYDNEY

DELOITTE & TOUCHE LLP
164 Charlotte St, (Box 70), Sydney B1P 6G9

KPMG LLP
Commerce Tower, 15 Dorchester Street Suite 600, PO Box 1 Stn A, Sydney B1P 6G9

THORNHILL

JAMES K. LEE
22 Dorian Place, Thornhill L4J 2M3

THUNDER BAY

BDO INTERNATIONAL ▽
1095 Barton Street, Thunder Bay P7B 5N3

KPMG LLP
979 Alloy Drive, Thunder Bay
P7B 5Z8

TORONTO

BDO INTERNATIONAL ▽
P.O. Box 32, Royal Bank Plaza,
Toronto M5J 2J8

CLARK & HORNER LLP
Dundee Place, 1 Adelaide Street
East, Suite 2340, PO Box 181,
Toronto M5C 2V9
Tel: 00 1 416 861 0431
Resident Partners/Directors:
ICAEW Members
R J Horner

CLARKE HENNING LLP ★ ◈
10 Bay Street, Suite 801,
Toronto M5J 2R8
Tel: 00 1 416 364 4421
Resident Partners/Directors:
ICAEW Members
V M Raja

DELOITTE & TOUCHE LLP
Suite 1400, 181 Bay Street,
Toronto M5J 2V1

DELOITTE & TOUCHE LLP
2 Queen Street East, Suite 1200,
Maritime Tower, PO Box 8,
Toronto M5C 3G7

DELOITTE & TOUCHE LLP
79 Wellington Street West, PO
Box 29 TD Centre, Toronto
M5K 1B9

ERNST & YOUNG ★
175 Commerce Valley Drive
West, Suite 600, Toronto
L3T 7P6

ERNST & YOUNG ★
P.O Box 251, Ernst & Young
Tower, Toronto M5K 1J7

GRANT THORNTON LLP
50 Bay Street, 12th Floor,
Toronto M5J 2Z8
Tel: 00 1 416 366 4240
Resident Partners/Directors:
ICAEW Members
J T Holdstock

HEW & HEW
16 Cassandra Boulevard,
Toronto M3A 1S4

KPMG LLP
Suite 3300, Commerce Court
West, 199 Bay Street, Toronto
M5L 1B2

KPMG MANAGEMENT CONSULTING ▼
Commerce Court West, 199 Bay
Street, PO Box 31 Stn
Commerce Court, Toronto
M5L 1B2

KPMG MANAGEMENT CONSULTING ▼
Actuarial Benefits &,
Compensation Inc, 199 Bay
Street, PO Box 31, Toronto
M5L 1B2

M. DEWSHI
233 McKee Avenue, Toronto
M2N 4E2

MARTIN COSTA
55A Glen Road, Toronto
M4W 2V3

MOORE STEPHENS COOPER MOLYNEUX ▼
701 Evans Avenue, 8th Floor,
Toronto M9C 1A3

PANNELL KERR FORSTER ▼
30 St Patrick Street, 8th Floor,
Toronto M5T 3A3

PKF HILL LLP ▼
41 Valleybrook Drive, Suite 200,
Toronto M3B 2S6

PRICEWATERHOUSE-COOPERS ★
145 King Street West, Toronto
M5H 1V8

PRICEWATERHOUSE-COOPERS ★
Royal Trust Tower, Suite 3000
Box 82, Toronto-Dominion
Centre, 77 King Street, Toronto
M5K 1G8

PRICEWATERHOUSE-COOPERS ★
10 York Mills Road, Suite 400,
Toronto M2P 2G7

RICHTER, USHER & VINEBERG ▼
90 Eglinton Avenue East, Suite
700, Toronto M4P 2Y3

RICHTER, USHER & WINEBERG ▼
90 Eglinton Avenue East, Suite
700, Toronto M4P 2Y3

RING ★
339 Eglinton Avenue E, Toronto
M4P 1L7

SBLR LLP
2345 Yonge Street, Suite 300,
Toronto M4P 2E5

TROIS-PISTOLES

DELOITTE & TOUCHE LLP
31 Rue Notre-Dames est, Trois-
pistoles G0L 4K0, QUE

TROIS-RIVIERES

DELOITTE & TOUCHE LLP
1160 Place Royale, Trois-rivieres
G9A 4X3, QUE

TRURO

PRICEWATERHOUSE-COOPERS ★
710 Prince Street, Truro
B2N 5E5

UNIONVILLE

S N POCHKHANAWALA & CO
86 Braeside Square, Unionville
L3R 0A5

SHABIR VELJI
260 Hollingham Rd, Unionville
LR3 8J6

VAL D'OR

KPMG LLP
450 3e Avenue, Val D'or
J9P 1S2, QUE

VANCOUVER

BDO INTERNATIONAL ▽
300-One Bentall Centre, 505
Burrard Street, Vancouver
V7X 1T1

CAMPBELL, SAUNDERS & CO ★
Suite 500-1055, West Broadway,
Vancouver V6H 1E2

COLIN DOWSON ★
1748 West 2nd Avenue,
Vancouver V6J 1H6

DELOITTE & TOUCHE LLP
P.O.Box 49279, Bentall Cntr.,
1055 Dunsmuir Street,
Vancouver V7X 1P4

ERNST & YOUNG ★
700 West Georgia Street, (P.O.
Box 10101), Vancouver
V7Y 1C7

GRANT THORNTON LLP
Grant Thornton Place, Suite
1600 - 333 Seymour Street,
Vancouver V6B 0A4
Tel: 00 1 6046872711

KPMG LLP
Box 10426 Pacific Centre, 777
Dunsmuir Street, Vancouver
V7Y 1K3

KPMG MANAGEMENT CONSULTING ▼
Box 10427 Pacific Centre, 500-
777 Dunsmuir Street, 1177 West
Hastings Street, Vancouver
V7Y 1K5

LANG & YUEN
270-5655 Cambie Street,
Vancouver V5Z 3A4

LIONG KONG
2195 Westhill Wynd, Vancouver
V7S 2Z3

M.R.DESAI
Suite 201-5990 Fraser Street,
Vancouver V5W 2Z7

MOORE STEPHENS ELLIS FOSTER LTD ▼
1650 West First Avenue,
Vancouver V6J 1G1

MOORES ROWLAND ▼
Suite 800, Burrard Bldg, 1030
West Georgia Street, Vancouver
V6E 3B9

N.P.D. SARKARI
Suite 1904, 2075 Comox Street,
Vancouver V6G 1S2

NOORDIN MADATALI
Suite 203, 1571 Bellevue
Avenue, West Vancouver,
Vancouver V7V 1A6

PANNELL KERR FORSTER ▼
800 West Pender Street, Suite
1120, Vancouver V6C 2V6

PRICEWATERHOUSE-COOPERS ★
250 Howe Street, Suite 700,
Vancouver V6C 3S7

RICHTER, USHER & WINEBERG ▼
7th Floor, Marine Building, 355
Burrard Street, Vancouver
V6C 2G8

SMYTHE RATCLIFFE CA ▼
7th Floor, Marine Building, 355
Burrard Street, Vancouver
V6C 2G8

VERNON

KPMG LLP
Credit Union Building, 3205-32
Street, Suite 300, Vernon
V1T 9A2

VICTORIA

GRANT THORNTON LLP
3rd Floor, 888 Fort Street,
Victoria V8W 1H8
Tel: 00 1 250 3934191

KPMG LLP
St Andrews Square II, 800-730
View Street, Victoria V8W 3YZ

PRICEWATERHOUSE-COOPERS ★
777 Broughton Street, Victoria
V8W 1E3

SMYTHE RATCLIFFE CA ▼
207-895 Fort Street, Victoria
V8W 1H7

VILLE SAINT-GEORGES

DELOITTE & TOUCHE LLP
16711 6e Avenue, Ville Saint-
georges G9T 5K8, QUE

VIRDEN

MOORE STEPHENS ▼
233 Queen Street W, Box 670,
Virden R0M 2C0

WAINWRIGHT

MOORE STEPHENS ▼
707 Main Street, Box 1088, Wainwright T0B 4P0

WALKERTON

BDO INTERNATIONAL ▽
P.O. Box 760, Walkerton N0G 2V0

WELLAND

BDO INTERNATIONAL ▽
37 Dorothy Street, Welland L3B 3V6

WEST VANCOUVER

SMYTHE RATCLIFFE CA ▼
Suite 811, 100 South Park Royal, West Vancouver V7T 1A2

WHISTLER

BDO INTERNATIONAL ▽
Box 509, Whistler V0N 1B0

WHITE ROCK

WATKINS ODENDAAL ★
No. 300 Windsor Square, 1959 152nd Street, White Rock V4A 9E3

WIARTON

BDO INTERNATIONAL ▽
P.O. Box 249, Wiarton N0H 2T0

WILLOWDALE

HOGG SHAIN & SCHECK ★
Suite 404, 2255 Sheppard Avenue East, Willowdale M2J 4Y1

WINCHESTER

BDO INTERNATIONAL ▽
P.O. Box 390, Winchester K0C 2K0

WINDSOR

BDO INTERNATIONAL ▽
3630 Rhodes Drive, Windsor N8W 5A4

ERNST & YOUNG ★
Unit 400, 4520 Rhodes Drive, Windsor N8W 5C2

GERALD DUTHIE & CO
525 Windsor Avenue, Windsor N9A 1J4

KPMG LLP
618 Greenwood Centre, 3200 Deziel Drive, Windsor N8W 5K8

PRICEWATERHOUSE-COOPERS ★
245 Quellette Avenue, 3rd Floor, Windsor N9A 7J4

WINNIPEG

DELOITTE & TOUCHE LLP
360 Main Street, Winnipeg R3C 3Z3

ERNST & YOUNG ★
2700 Commodity Exchange, Tower, 360 Main Street, Winnipeg R3C 4G9

KPMG LLP
Suite 2000, One Lombard Place, Winnipeg R3B 0X3

NEWBOUND & CO ★
578 St Mary's Road, Winnipeg R2M 3L5

PRICEWATERHOUSE-COOPERS ★
Richardson Building, 1 Lombard Place, Suite 2300, Winnipeg R3B 0X6

SCARROW & DONALD ▼
100-Five Donald St, Winnipeg R3L 2T4

WOODSTOCK

BDO INTERNATIONAL ▽
P.O. Box 757, Woodstock N4S 8A2

YARMOUTH

KPMG LLP
360 Main Street, PO Box 67 Stn Main, Yarmouth B5A 4B1

YELLOWKNIFE

WONG & ASSOCIATES ★
5403-48 Street, Yellowknife X14 1P8

KPMG MANAGEMENT CONSULTING ▼
4910-50th Street, PO Box 727 Stn Main, Yellowknife X1A 2N5

CAYMAN ISLANDS

GEORGE TOWN

CHRIS JOHNSON ASSOCIATES LTD
PO Box 2499, Elizabethan Square, 80 Shedden Road, George Town KY1-1104

DELOITTE & TOUCHE ★
P.O.Box 1787 GT, One Capital Place, George Town

FINANCIAL CONSULTING & ACCOUNTING LTD
Unit 4, Commerce House, Dr Roy's Drive, PO Box 1976, George Town

KPMG
P O Box 493 GT, Century Yard Building, George Town

MOORE STEPHENS (CAYMAN ISLANDS) LTD
3rd Floor, West Wind Building, PO Box 1782 GT, George Town KY1-1109

MORRIS BRANKIN & CO ▼
3rd Floor, West Wind Building, George Town

PAUL HARRIS & CO
PO Box 61 GT, George Town, KY1 1102

PRICEWATERHOUSE-COOPERS ★
Strathvale House, PO Box 258, George Town, KY1-1103

RAWLINSON & HUNTER ★
One Capital Place, P O Box 897, George Town, KY1-1103
Tel: 00 1 345 9497576
Resident Partners/Directors: ICAEW Members
R E Douglas

CHILE

ANTOFAGASTA

PRICEWATERHOUSE-COOPERS ★
Edificio Segundo Gomez, Prat 461, Oficina 1106, Antofagasta

CONCEPCION

PRICEWATERHOUSE-COOPERS ★
Anibal Pinto 215, 6th Floor, Oficina 607, Concepcion

IQUIQUE

BDO INTERNATIONAL ▽
Mapocho 48 C, Barrio Industrial, Iquique

PUERTO MONTT

PRICEWATERHOUSE-COOPERS ★
Edificio Campanario, Calle Benavente 550, Oficina 314, Puerto Montt

SANTIAGO

BDO INTERNATIONAL ▽
General Del Canto 230, 7th Floor - Of 701, Santiago

ERNST & YOUNG ▼
P.O. Box 50080 & 2186, Santiago

KPMG PEAT MARWICK ▼
Monjitas 527- Piso 15, Santiago

MACINTYRE STRATER INTERNATIONAL LTD ▼
La Sierra No 1438, Providencia, Santiago

PKF CHILE ▼
Santo Domingo 1160-Piso 11, Santiago

PRICEWATERHOUSE-COOPERS ★
Avenida Andres Bello 2711, Torre Costanera, Piso 5, Santiago

TALCA

MACINTYRE STRATER INTERNATIONAL LTD ▼
5 Oriente No 896, Talca

VALDIVIA

PRICEWATERHOUSE-COOPERS ★
Perez Rosales 619, Oficina 304, Valdivia

VINA DEL MAR

PRICEWATERHOUSE-COOPERS ★
Edificio Pleno Centro, Avenida Valparaiso 585, Oficina 902, Vina Del Mar

CHINA

BEIJING

BDO INTERNATIONAL ▽
Suite 601, Beijing Tower, 10 East Changan Avenue, Beijing 100006

DELOITTE TOUCHE TOHMATSU
8-F Tower W2, The Towers, Oriental Plaza, 1 East Chang An Avenue, Beijing 100738

DELOITTE TOUCHE TOHMATSU ★
Suite 130 Scite Tower, 22 Jianguo Men Wai Da Jie, Beijing 100004

ERNST & YOUNG ▼
Level 17 Tower E3, The Towers, Oriental Plaza, Dong Cheng District, Beijing 100738

ERNST & YOUNG ▼
Level 16, Tower E3, Oriental Plaza, No 1 East Chang Avenue, Dong Cheng Street, Beijing

ERNST & YOUNG ▼
Hong Kong Macau Centre, 10/F Office Bldg, Dong Si, Shi Tiao Li Jiao Qiao, Beijing 100027

KPMG ★
Level 16 China World Tower 2, China World Trade Centre, No 1 Jian Guo Men Wai Avenue, Beijing 100004

KPMG ★
8th Floor, Tower E2, Oriental Plaza, 1 East Chang An Avenue, Beijing 100738

PEAT MARWICK ▼
Citic Building, 19 Jianguo Men Wai Da Jie, Beijing 100004

PRICEWATERHOUSE-COOPERS ★
11th Floor, China World Tower 1, 1 Jian Guo Men Wai Avenue, Beijing 100004

PRICEWATERHOUSE-COOPERS ★
26/F Office Tower A, Beijing Fortune Plaza, 23 Dongsanhuan North Road, Chaoyang District, Beijing 100020

PRICEWATERHOUSE-COOPERS ★
Beijing Kerry Centre, 18th Fl, 1 Guang Hua Road, Chao Yang District, Beijing 100020

DALIAN

PRICEWATERHOUSE-COOPERS ★
1705 Gold Name Tower, 68 Renmin Lu, Zhongshan District, Dalian 116001

FUJIAN

MOORE STEPHENS FUZHOU ▼
9th Floor, 106 Guang Da Road, Fuzhou, Fujian 350005

GUANGZHOU

DELOITTE TOUCHE TOHMATSU
Guangzhou Branch, 26/F Teemtower, 208 Tianhe Road, Guangzhou 510620

KPMG ★
29th Floor, Guangzhou International, Electronics Tower, 403 Huang Shi Dong Road, Guangzhou 510095

KPMG HUAZHEN ★
38th Floor, Teem Tower, 208 Tianhe Road, Guangzhou 510620

PRICEWATERHOUSE-COOPERS ★
1808 Yi An Plaza, 33 Jianshe Liu Ma Lu, Guangzhou 510060

NANJING

DELOITTE TOUCHE TOHMATSU
Nangjing Branch, Room B, 11F Golden Eagle Plaza, 89 Hanzhong Road, Nanjing 210029

QINGDAO

KPMG ADVISORY (CHINA) ★
4th Floor, Inter Royal Building, 15 Donghai West Road, Qingdao 266071

SHANGHAI

ANSLEY & ASSOCS INC ▼
4607A Plaza 66, 1266 Nanjing West Road, Shanghai 200040

DELOITTE TOUCHE TOHMATSU ★
30th Floor, Bund Centre, 222 Yan An Road East, Shanghai 20002

DELOITTE TOUCHE TOHMATSU
30/F Bund Center, 222 Yan An Road East, Shanghai 200002

ERNST & YOUNG ★
23/F The Center, 989 Chang Le Road, Shanghai 200031

KP CHENG & CO
Suite 1607, 16/F, Cloud Nine Plaza, 1118 Yan An Xi Road, Shanghai

KPMG ★
50th Floor Plaza 66, 1266 Nanjing West Road, Shanghai 200040

PEAT MARWICK ▼
Zone 3 Yantze New World Hotel, 2099 Yanan Xi Road, Shanghai 200335

PRICEWATERHOUSE-COOPERS ★
11/F PricewaterhouseCoopers Center, 202 Hu Bin Road, Shanghai 200031

PRICEWATERHOUSE-COOPERS ★
12th Floor Shui On Plaza, 333 Huai Hai Zhong Road, Shanghai 200021

PRICEWATERHOUSE-COOPERS ★
Central Plaza, 18th Floor, 381 Huai Hai Zhong Road, Shanghai 200021

SHENZHEN

BDO INTERNATIONAL ▽
3/F, Bldg A, Commercial Centre Seaview Grdn, Shekou, Shenzhen 518067

BDO INTERNATIONAL ▽
3/F, Huaxia Bond Bldg, 8th Zhenhua Road, Shenzhen 518031

DELOITTE TOUCHE TOHMATSU
Shenzhen Branch, 13/F China Resources Building, 5001 Shennan Road East, Shenzhen 518010

PRICEWATERHOUSE-COOPERS ★
Shun Hing Square, Room 3706, Di Wang Commercial Centre, 5002 Shennan Road East, Shenzhen 518008

WUHAN

ERNST & YOUNG ▼
Level 6, Wuhan Urban Commercial Bank Plaza, No 933, Jian She Avenue, Wuhan City 430015

COLOMBIA

BARRANQUILLA

PRICEWATERHOUSE-COOPERS ▼
Edificio Centro Empresarial, des las Americas, Calle 77 B, No 57-141, Piso 8, Barranquilla

BOGOTA

BDO INTERNATIONAL ▽
Tr 21 No 98-45, Bogota

ERNST & YOUNG ▼
Transversal 22 No. 100-15, Apartado Aereo 092638, Bogota

KPMG PEAT MARWICK ▼
Calle 90 No 21-74, Bogota, D C

PANNELL KERR FORSTER ▼
Calle 37 No 22-28, Bogota

PRICEWATERHOUSE-COOPERS ▼
Calle 100, No 11-A-35, Bogota

BUCARAMANGA

BDO INTERNATIONAL ▽
Apartado Aereo 4574, Bucaramanga

CALI

BDO INTERNATIONAL ▽
Apartado Aereo 3048, Cali

KPMG PEAT MARWICK ▼
Calle 19 Norte No 2-N-29, 31st Floor Office 3102, Edificio Torre de Cali, Cali

PRICEWATERHOUSE-COOPERS ▼
Edificio la Torre de Cali, Calle 19, Norte No N-29, 7th Floor, Cali

IBAGUE

BDO INTERNATIONAL ▽
Carrera 4 No. 11-40 Ofc. 302, Ibague

MANIZALES

BDO INTERNATIONAL ▽
Apartado Aereo 944, Manizales

MEDELLIN

PANNELL KERR FORSTER ▼
Torre Empresarial Dann, Carrera 43A No 7-50a Of 1013, Medellin

PRICEWATERHOUSE-COOPERS ▼
Eficidio Colinas del Poblado, Carrera 43A, No 14-27, Piso 9, Medellin

CONGO

BRAZZAVILLE

PETITEAU SCACCHI ET ASSOCIES ▼
Fidafrica BP 1098, Brazzaville

KINSHASA

PRICEWATERHOUSE-COOPERS ▼
Immeuble Midema, 13 Avenue Mongola, Kinshasa

PRICEWATERHOUSE-COOPERS ▼
Immeuble Midema, 13 Avenue Mongala, BP 10195, Kinshasa

LUBUMBASHI

PRICEWATERHOUSE-COOPERS ▼
BCDC Building, 1st Floor, Avenue Kasai 701, Lubumbashi

POINTE NOIRE

PRICE WATERHOUSE ▼
32 Avenue du General De Gaulle, Pointe Noire

PRICEWATERHOUSE-COOPERS ▼
32 avenue du General de Gaulle, Pointe Noire

COOK ISLANDS

RAROTONGA

PEAT, MARWICK, MITCHELL & CO ▼
Parekura Place, Tutakimoa Road, P.O.Box 691, Rarotonga

COSTA RICA

SAN JOSE

PANNELL KERR FORSTER ▼
2nd Ave, 1st & 3rd Streets, San Pedro Montes de Oca, San Jose

PEAT MARWICK MITCHELL & CO ▼
Edificio Rex,4th Floor., Calle Central Avenida 4, Apartado Postal 10208, San Jose

PRICEWATERHOUSE-COOPERS ▼
Apartado 2594-1000, San Jose

COTE D'IVOIRE

ABIDJAN

AKINTOLA WILLIAMS ADETONA ISICHEI & CO ★
01 B.P. 4114, 224 Immeuble Alpha 2000, Abidjan

KPMG ▼
Immeuble Amci, 15 Avenue Joseph Anoma, Abidjan-Plateau, Abidjan, 01

PKF ★
29 Boulevard Clozel, Abidjan, 04

PRICE WATERHOUSE ▼
Immeuble Alpha 2000, 23rd Floor, Rue Gourgas, Abidjan

PRICEWATERHOUSE-COOPERS ▼
Immeuble Colina,2nd Floor, Boulevard Roume, Abidjan, 01

PRICEWATERHOUSE-COOPERS ▼
Alpha 2000, 23rd Floor, Abidjan

RICHARD DIAMOND
01 BP 7168, Abidjan

CROATIA

SPLIT

PRICEWATERHOUSE-COOPERS ▼
Mazuranicevo setaliste 24b, Split, 21000

ZAGREB

KPMG CROATIA D.O.O ▼
Centar Kaptol, Nova Ves 11, Zagreb, 10 000

PANNELL KERR FORSTER ▼
Vlaska 78, Hrvatska, 10000, Zagreb

PRICEWATERHOUSE-COOPERS ▼
A von Humboldta 4, Zagreb, 10000

CYPRUS

LARNACA

ANDREAS PRODROMOU & CO
Prodromou Court, 54 Sittica Hanoum Street, P.O. Box 40163, 6301 Larnaca

BAKER TILLY KLITOU AND PARTNERS
Yiannis Maria Building, Stratigou Timayia Avenue, 2nd Floor, 203, 6308 Larnaca

DELOITTE & TOUCHE LTD ★
Patroclos Tower, 4th Floor, 41-43 Spyrou Kyprianou Avenue, CY 6051 Larnaca

ERNST & YOUNG ★
Christa Court, Second Floor, 16C Arch Makarios III Ave, 6017 Larnaca

GREGORY & CO ◈
12 Kikas & Frosos Sountia Street, 6016 Larnaca
Tel: 00 357 24 656298
Principal: ICAEW Member
M G Gregory

JOANNIDES & CO LTD
Elpa Building, 8 Gr. Afxentiou Avenue, (P O Box 40147), 6301 Larnaca

KOUMETTOU TACKOUSHIS & IOANNOU
Dipa Building 13, P.O. Box 890, Larnaca

KPMG
P O Box 40075, 6300 Larnaca

KPMG ★
P O Box 40075, 6300 Larnaca

LOIZOU & LOIZOU ★
P. Valdaseride 33, PO Box 42501, 6500 Larnaca

MCA PAPADEMETRES LLP
Loukis Pierides Street, Lysion Court, Flat 1, 6021 Larnaca
Tel: 00 357 24658998
Resident Partners/Directors: ICAEW Members
M Papademetris

MGI GREGORIOU & CO LTD
GR. Afxentiou Avenue, Third Floor 307, P.O. Box 712, Larnaca

P HADJIMICHAEL
Office 5, 44 Hakket, 6045 Larnaca

PANAYIOTOU KITTOS SOTERIOU & CO ★
Stratigou Timayia Av, Nicolaides Shopping City, Joanna Ct 2nd Fl PO Box 42529, 6500 Larnaca

PANICOS Y KOMODROMOS & CO
Demetriou Building, 24 Filiou Zannetou, Office 102, Larnaca

PRICEWATERHOUSE-COOPERS LTD
City House, 4 Artemidos Avenue, CY-6030 Larnaca
Tel: 00 357 24555000
Resident Partners/Directors: ICAEW Members
Y A Kaponides, C M Nicolaides, C Themistocleous

LEFKOSA, MERSIN 10

AHMET OZDAL
135 Sht Huseyin Amca, Caddesi, Gonyeli, PO Box 478, Lefkosa Mersin 10

D.K. DENIZ & CO ◈
2 Memduh Asaf Sokak, Lefkosa
Tel: 00 357 90 392 227 3352
Fax: 00 90 39222 86709
Email: deniz@north-cyprus.net
Mobile: 00 90 542 8565009
Date Established: 1985
Principal: ICAEW Member
D K Deniz

SPECIALISATIONS – AUDIT & ASSURANCE
Assurance Services
Audit

SPECIALISATIONS – BUSINESS & GENERAL ADVICE
Book-keeping
Company Formation

SPECIALISATIONS – FINANCIAL REPORTING
Accounts Preparation

SPECIALISATIONS – TAXATION
Offshore Companies
Taxation

General Description: Audit, accounting and taxation.
Languages Spoken:
English, Turkish

DENIZ-GUMUS & CO ★
111/5 Mehmet Aki f Caddesi, Lefkosa MERSIN 10

ERDAL & CO
100 Bedrettin Demirel CAD, PO Box 410, Lefkosa MERSIN 10

FIKRI & CO
Ali Tanner Fikri Building, Kyrenia Avenue No.78, Lefkosa MERSIN 10

RAIF OMER & CO ◈
P.K. 533, Atacag Ishani, 9 Ali Ruhi Sokak, Lefkosa, Mersin 10
Tel: 00 357 392 227 4198
Resident Partners/Directors: ICAEW Members
R Omer

SUMER RUSTEM & CO
Buzcuoglu Apt D/2, Yusuf Kaptan Sokak, Lefkosa MERSIN 10

TATAR & CO
28 Kasim Str, No 12, Lefkosa MERSIN 10

TATAR & CO
11 Hasene Ilgas Str, P.O. Box 768, Lefkosa MERSIN 10
Tel: 00 357 90 392 228 3475
Fax: 00 90 392 2282264
Email: info@tatarandco.com
Website: http://www.tatarandco.com
Date Established: 1976
Resident Partners/Directors: ICAEW Members
E R Tatar, R Z Tatar

LIMASSOL

A. KAKOFENGITIS & CO
Zinas Kanther 4, 3035 Limassol

ABACUS LTD
City House, 2nd Floor, 6 Karaiskakis Street, PO Box 56183, CY 3305 Limassol

AJAY KAUSHIK
Chrysalia Court, 206 Makarios Avenue, P O Box 50465, 3605 Limassol

BDO PHILIPPIDES LTD
146 Arch Makarios III Avenue, Alpha Tower, 4th FLoor, PO Box 51681, CY- 3507 Limassol

C TSIELEPIS & CO LTD
Helios Court, 221 Chr.Haggipavlou Street, PO Box 51631, 3507 Limassol

CHRISTODOULIDES SHAKALLIS & CO ★
Christodoulides Building, 8 Alasias Street, P.O.Box 4428, Limassol

CM ADAMIDES & CO ★
212 Arch. Makarios Avenue, Lordos Seta Court, Block B, Office 16, 3030 Limassol

DELOITTE & TOUCHE ★
Eftapaton Court, 256 Makarios Avenue, P O Box 53180, 3301 Limassol

DELOITTE & TOUCHE LTD ★
319 28th October Street, Kanika Business Centre 2nd Floor, P O Box 58466, 3734 Limassol

DEMETRIOU, KOMODROMOU & CO ★
9 Marathovounou Str, P.O. Box 53159, 3071 Limassol

ERNST & YOUNG ★
P.O. Box 123, Nicolaou Pentadromos, Centre, Office 908 BlockA, 205 Limassol

FIDELICO LTD
G Pavides Court, 5th Floor, 2 Arch Kyprianou & Ayiou Andreou Street, 3036 Limassol

GRANT THORNTON ▼
10 Filiou Zannetou Str, 2nd Floor, PO Box 55299, 3820 Limassol
Tel: 00 357 25878855
Resident Partners/Directors: ICAEW Members
A Papathomas

HASSAPIS & CO ★
Doma Building, 227 Arch Makarios III Avenue, PO Box 53104, 3300 Limassol
Tel: 00 357 25589408
Fax: 00 357 2558 2636
Email: info@hassapis.com
Website: http://www.hassapis.com
Resident Partners/Directors: ICAEW Members
P Hassapis
Non-resident Partners (ICAEW Members):
M Hassapis

HLB AFXENTIOU LTD
Acropolis Court, 6 Aristophanous Street, P.O. Box 3478, Limassol

JOANNIDES & CO LTD
Ayias Zonis Street, Nic. Penp. Centre, (P O Box 53309), 3302 Limassol

KPMG ★
PO Box 50161, 3601 Limassol

KPMG
Berengaria Building, 25 Spyrou Araouzou Street, PO Box 50161, 3036 Limassol

KYPRIANIDES, NICOLAOU & ASSOCIATES
4 Evagora Papachristoforou St, Themis Court, 3rd Floor, PO Box 51771, 3508 Limassol

KYPRIANIDES, NICOLAOU & ECONOMIDES
4 Evagora papachristoforou, Themis Court, Office 301, 3030 Limassol

M. ATHANASIOU
PO Box 4320, 3723 Limassol

MACINTYRE STRATER INTERNATIONAL LTD ▼
Marathovounou 9, PO Box 53159, 3071 Limassol

MGI GREGORIOU & CO LTD
Grivas Dighenis Avenue, Second Floor 202, P.O. Box 3442, Limassol

MOORE STEPHENS ▼
Zako Building, Appt 603, P O Box 7528, 24 Limassol

N A NICOLAIDES
8 Kesarianis Street, 3117 Limassol
Tel: 00 357 99612430
Principal: ICAEW Member
N Nicolaides

N CONSTANTINOU & CO AUDIT LTD
Limassol Centre, PO Box 54039, Block B. Office 508, Rega Fereou St, 3720 Limassol
Tel: 00 357 25368823
Fax: 00 357 253 75173
Email: snic53@logos.cy.net
Website: http://www.nconstantinou.com
Resident Partners/Directors: ICAEW Members
N Constantinou

SPECIALISATIONS – AUDIT & ASSURANCE
Audit

SPECIALISATIONS – BUSINESS & GENERAL ADVICE
Company Formation

SPECIALISATIONS – TAXATION
Offshore Companies

NICOS MOUZOURIS
12 Navarinou Str, 3041 Limassol

PKF SAVVIDES & CO LTD
Meliza Court, 4th & 7th Floors, 229 Arch Makarios III Ave, 3503 Limassol

PRICEWATERHOUSE-COOPERS LTD
City House, 6 Karaiskakis Street, CY-3032 Limassol
Tel: 00 357 25 555 000
Resident Partners/Directors: ICAEW Members
S C Constantinou, V P Hadjivassiliou, T N Nolas, P Petrakis, E Theodorou

SIS
38 Karaiskaki Street, Kanika Alexander Ctr Block 1, 1st Floor, Office 113 CD, PO Box 58532 CY3733 Limassol

MESA GEITONIA

SAVVIDES & SAVVIDES
Loucaides Court, 3 Makarios Avenue, 4th Floor, Mesa Geitonia

NICOSIA

A.N. ATHANASIADES & CO LTD
46 Stassinos Street, 1st Floor Office 28, 2002 Nicosia

A.T.C.O. ★
52 Vyzantiou Street, Rita Court 21, Office 203, CY 2064 Nicosia

ABACUS LTD
P O Box 25549, CY-1310 Nicosia
Tel: 00 357 22555800
Fax: 00 357 225 55801
Email: abacus@abacus.com.cy
Website: http://www.abacus.com.cy
Resident Partners/Directors: ICAEW Members
N C Nicolaides, G Trachonitis, M Georghiou
Non-resident Partners (ICAEW Members):
C Hadjicosti
Resident Partners (Non-ICAEW Members):
P Demetriou
Other Offices: Arianthi Court, 2nd Floor, 50 Agias Zonis Street, CY-3090 Limassol, Cyprus

SPECIALISATIONS – BUSINESS & GENERAL ADVICE
Administration
Book-keeping
Company Formation
Company Secretarial Service

SPECIALISATIONS – FINANCIAL REPORTING
Accounts Preparation

SPECIALISATIONS – TAXATION
Trusteeship

General Description: The firm specialises in the establishment and administration of International businesses operating out of Cyprus and the formation and administration of trusts.

ABACUS LTD
Elenion Building, 2nd Floor, 5 Themistocles Dervis Street, CY-1066 Nicosia

AFXENTIOU & PHILLIPPIDES ▼
Afemia House,3rd Floor, 70 Makarios Avenue, P.O. Box 7171, Nicosia

ALLIOTT PARTELLAS KILIARIS LTD
16 Kyriacou Matsi Avenue, 3rd Floor, 1082 Nicosia

ANTONIOS VRAHIMIS
P O Box 21936, 1515 Nicosia

ASTON DRAYCOTT
57 Kennedy Avenue, 1076 Nicosia, PO Box 22433, 1521 Nicosia

ATHINODOROU & ZEVEDEOU LTD
5 Costi Palama Street, Office Suite 201, 1096 Nicosia
Tel: 00 357 22418814
Email: info@auditaz.com
Resident Partners/Directors: ICAEW Members
A Athinodorou, M Zevedeou

SPECIALISATIONS – TAXATION
Offshore Companies

AUDITPRO SERVICES LTD
Engomi Business Centre, PO Box 2552, Block B, Office 104, 28th October Avenue No 1 Engomi 1310 Nicosia

BAKER TILLY KLITOU AND PARTNERS
11 Bouboulinas Street, 1060 Nicosia

BAKER TILLY KLITOU AND PARTNERS LTD
11 Bouboulinas Street, 1060 Nicosia

BDO INTERNATIONAL ▽
PO Box 22283, K4M 1A3 Nicosia

BDO PHILIPPIDES LTD
75 Prodromou Avenue, Floors 1 & 2, Oneworld Parkview House, PO Box 25277, 1308 Nicosia

CHRISTOU & CO
P.O. Box 5297, Nicosia

DELOITTE & TOUCHE ★
P O Box 27233, 1 Lasonos Street, 1082 Nicosia

DELOITTE & TOUCHE LTD ★
Lambousa Street 1, 1095 Nicosia

DELOITTE & TOUCHE LTD ★
Corner Of Them, Dervis-Florinis Street, P O Box 21675, 1512 Nicosia
Tel: 00 357 22360300
Fax: 00 357 223 60400
Email: infonicosia@deloitte.com
Website: http://www.deloitte.com/cy
Resident Partners/Directors: ICAEW Members
C M Christoforou, M C Lambrou, P Markou, P Papadopoulos, N D Papakyriacou, E N Philippou
Non-resident Partners (ICAEW Members):
N S Kyriakides, C Georghadjis, A Taliotis, A Agathocleous
Resident Partners (Non-ICAEW Members):
A Chrysanthou, P Mallis, C Papamarkides, K Whyte
Non-resident Partners (Non-ICAEW Members):
N Charalambous, N Spanoudis, G Martides
Other Offices:PO Box 40772, CY-6307, Larnaca, Cyprus, PO Box 58466, CY-3734 Limassol, Cyprus, Larnaca: Patroclos Tower, 4th Floor, 41-43 Spyrou Kyprianou Avenue CY-6051 Larnaca, Cyprus, Limassol: Kanika Business Centre, 2nd Floor, 319, 28th October Street, CY-3105, Limassol Cyprus
Registered by another RSB to carry out company audit work
General Description: Audit - Tax - Consulting - Financial Advisory.
Languages Spoken:
Greek, English

DFK DEMETRIOU TRAPEZARIS LTD
59-61 Acropolis Avenue, 3rd Floor, 2012 Nicosia

DKP CONSULTANTS LTD
PO Box 24856, 1304 Nicosia

ERNST & YOUNG ★
Nicosia Tower Centre, 36 Byron Avenue, P.O Box 21656, 1511 Nicosia
Tel: 00 357 22 209999
Fax: 00 357 22 209998
Email: ninos.hadjirousos@cy.ey.com
Website: http://www.ey.com
Resident Partners/Directors: ICAEW Members
A Demetriou, N A Hadjirousou, G Kourris, N Neophytou, G Onisiforou, S Pantzaris, C Stylianou, Y Theoklitou
Other Offices: Nicolaou Pentadromus Centre, Office 908,

continued

ERNST & YOUNG *cont*
Block A, P O Box 50123, 3601 Limassol
(Tel: 00 357 252 0999)
(Fax: 00 357 252 0998)
Registered by another RSB to carry out company audit work

SPECIALISATIONS – AUDIT & ASSURANCE
Assurance Services
Audit
Audit — Private Company
Audit — Public Company
Internal Audit
Pension Scheme Auditors

SPECIALISATIONS – BUSINESS & GENERAL ADVICE
Acquisitions and Mergers
Book-keeping
Company Formation
Company Secretarial Service
Risk Management

SPECIALISATIONS – BUSINESS RECOVERY & INSOLVENCY
Corporate Recovery
Liquidations
Reorganisations and Company Reconstructions

SPECIALISATIONS – FINANCIAL REPORTING
Accounts Preparation

SPECIALISATIONS – INVESTMENT BUSINESS
Financial Planning and Advice

SPECIALISATIONS – SECTOR
Banks/Financial Institutions

SPECIALISATIONS – TAXATION
Taxation
Trusteeship

General Description: A member of Ernst & Young International. Ernst & Young in Cyprus was established in 1989 as a result of the international merger of Arthur Young (Russell & Co established in 1937) and Ernst & Whinney. In addition to the general and specific services mentioned above the firm provides a wide range of financial services to international business companies.
Languages Spoken:
Greek, English

GEORGE A. STROVOLIDES
Hermes Building Office 501, 31 Chr Sozos Street, PO Box 22104, 1517 Nicosia

GRANT THORNTON ▼
P.O. Box 23907, 1687 Nicosia
Tel: 00 357 22600000
Resident Partners/Directors: ICAEW Members
S A Ioannou, S Michaelides, G T Pouros, A A Savva

HLB AFXENTIOU LTD
Synyka Building, Corner of Nikis Avenue &, Kastoros Street, CY-1087 Nicosia
Tel: 00 357 2513533
Email: nicosia@hlb.com.cy
Website: http://www.hlb.com.cy
Resident Partners/Directors: ICAEW Members
C Afxentiou, M F Hadjihannas, P Polyviou, S Prodromitis
Resident Partners (Non-ICAEW Members):
V Theophylactou

SPECIALISATIONS – AUDIT & ASSURANCE
Audit

SPECIALISATIONS – FINANCIAL REPORTING
International Reporting Standards (IFRS)

SPECIALISATIONS – TAXATION
Taxation

JOANNIDES & CO LTD
13 Agiou Prokopiou Street, PO Box 25411, CY-1309 Nicosia
Tel: 00 357 22556556
Resident Partners/Directors: ICAEW Members
C Loizou, E Papakyriacou

JOSEPH KOKKINOS & CO
22 Ajax Street, 1082 Nicosia

K&S QUALITY AUDIT LTD
PO Box 23404, CY 1683 Nicosia

KALLIAS & ASSOCIATES
Office 202, 10 Gregoriou Xenopoulou Street, 1061 Nicosia

KOUMETTOU TACKOUSHIS & IOANNOU
Suites 204/205, 2 Katsoni Street, 150 Nicosia

KPMG
14 Esperidon Street, 1087 Nicosia
Tel: 00 357 220 9000
Resident Partners/Directors: ICAEW Members
M Antoniades, A K Christofides, A M Gregoriades, P A Peleties, A I Shiammoutis, N Syrimis, D S Vakis, C Vasiliou

KPMG ★
P O Box 21121, 1502 Nicosia
Tel: 00 357 2 678700
Resident Partners/Directors: ICAEW Members
M Antoniades, A K Christofides, A M Gregoriades, E Hadjizacharias, M Loizides, P G Loizou, P A Peleties, A I Shiammoutis, S Sofocleous, N Syrimis, D S Vakis, C Vasiliou

KYPRIANIDES, NICOLAOU & ASSOCIATES
9 G Kranidiotis St, Office 201, 1065 Nicosia
Fax: 00 357 227 56595
Email: nicos.nicolaou@kyprianides.com
Date Established: 1955
Training Contracts Available.
Resident Partners/Directors: ICAEW Members
P K Kyprianides, N Nicolaou

KYRIAKOS YIAMBIDES
1 Sophoulis Street, Acropolis, 2008 Nicosia

M KALLIAS & CO LTD
Office 202, 10 Gregoriou Xenapoulou Street, 1061 Nicosia

M. PAPADAKIS & CO
Maria House, 5th Floor, 1 Avlonos Street, 1075 Nicosia

MACINTYRE STRATER INTERNATIONAL LTD ▼
4 Andreas Zakos Street, Engomi, P O Box 5474, Nicosia

MACINTYRE STRATER INTERNATIONAL LTD ▼
Mykalis Street No 2, P O Box 4901, Nicosia

MARIOS ARISTOU KRITICOS & CO
Kriticos House, Corner Kennedy Ave/Araouzos, Street, P.O. Box 4830, Nicosia

MGI GREGORIOU & CO LTD
Greg Tower, 7 Florina Street, P.O. Box 24854, 1304 Nicosia

MICHAEL J. ANTONIOU
Flat 7, 29 Aeschylus Street, 1011 Nicosia

MICHAEL MICHALOPOULOS FCA
70 Kennedy Avenue, Papavasilou Building, 3rd Floor, Office 304, PO Box 28783, CY2083 Nicosia

MOORE STEPHENS STYLIANOU & CO
Iris Tower, Office 602, 5B Archbishop Makarios Avenue, 1302 Nicosia

NEXIA POYIADJIS ★ ◈
2 Sophouli St, Chanteclair House, 8th Flr, P O Box 21814, 1513 Nicosia

NICOS VOSKARIDES
P O Box 25081, 1306 Nicosia
Tel: 00 357 22 356646
Principal: ICAEW Member
N C Voskarides

PANICOS Y KOMODROMOS & CO
Karantokis Building, 16 Zenas De Tyras, Office 6, P.O. Box 27162, Nicosia

PANICOS Y KOMODROMOS & CO
16 Zenas De Tyras Str, Office 6, 3rd Floor, PO Box 27162, 1642 Nicosia

PATSALIDES & CO
60 Larnacos Avenue, Flat 301, Aglantzia, 2101 Nicosia

PKF/ATCO
Leof Lemesou 2, Aluminium Tower 2nd, 3rd, 4th Floor, Strovolos, 2003 Nicosia

PKF/ATCO LTD
2 Limassol Avenue, Aluminium Tower, Floors 3 & 4, 2003 Nicosia

POLYDOROS K. XENOPHONTOS
70 Arsinoes Street, 1010 Nicosia

POLYDOROS K. XENOPHONTOS
Athienitis Building, 8 Kennedy Avenue, Suite 305, 1087 Nicosia

PRICEWATERHOUSE-COOPERS LTD
Julia House, 3 Themistocles Dervis Street, CY-1066 Nicosia
Tel: 00 357 22 555 000
Resident Partners/Directors: ICAEW Members
M S Andreou, N Chimarides, A T Constantinides, C Constantinou, E Eftychiou, E Evgeniou, G K Foradaris, C Hadjiconstantinou, P Y Kaouris, G C Lambrou, A M Loizou, C L Mavrocordatos, C N Papadopoulos, T C Parperis, C Pelekanos, P K Pilides, A S Pittas, C K Santis, P Soseilos, S Stephanides, A Tavitian, N A Theodoulou, C Tsolakis

ROTSAS & CO
2 Ioanni Clerides Street, PO Box 25597, 1310 Nicosia

RUSSELL & CO ★
Nicosia Tower Centre, 36 Byron Avenue, PO Box 21638, 1511 Nicosia

S THEODOROU ACCOUNTANTS LTD ◈
14 Souliou, Aglantzia, 2102 Nicosia
Tel: 00 357 22876570
Resident Partners/Directors: ICAEW Members
S G Theodorou

SAVVAS E SAVVIDES LTD
Pelekanos Court 21, 12 Prometheus Str, Office 102, PO Box 28743, 2082 Nicosia
Tel: 00 357 2245 1030
Fax: 00 357 2245 1031
Email: info@savvides-taxconsultant.com
Resident Partners/Directors:
ICAEW Members
S E Savvides
SPECIALISATIONS – TAXATION
Taxation

SHIAKALLIS & CO AUDIT SERVICES LTD
44-46 Acropolis Avenue, 1st Floor Office 101, CY2012 Nicosia

SNK
13 Machera Street, 2650 Nicosia
Tel: 00 357 99852386
Resident Partners/Directors:
ICAEW Members
S Kazamia

THEMISTOCLEOUS THEMIS
20a Mouson Street, Egkomi, 2412 Nicosia

TIMENIDES & EVANGELI ★
PO Box 21560, 1510 Nicosia

TSERKEZOS SAVVIDES ASSOCIATES LTD
6 Demostheni Severi Avenue, Office 22, 1683 Nicosia

UHY ANTONIS KASSAPIS LTD
89 Kennedy Avenue, Off 201, Floor 2, P O Box 26624, 1640 Nicosia

V. KOMODROMOS & CO ACCOUNTANTS & CONSULTANTS LTD
PO Box 27162, 1642 Nicosia

YAMAKIS & CO ★
Ragaena House, 4A Ragaena Street, PO Box 21082, 1501 Nicosia

YIAKOUMI & PARTNERS LTD
1 Ayias Lavras Street, Office 304, Engomi, 2414 Nicosia
Tel: 00 357 2 591444
Resident Partners/Directors:
ICAEW Members
P N Yiacoumi, I N Yiakoumi

PAPHOS

C. LEVENTIS LTD
33 Apostolou Pavlou Avenue, Andreas - Niki Court, Office 204, 8046 Paphos

CLEARLY READ LTD
18 Neofytou Nicolaidi Avenue, 8011 Paphos
Tel: 00 357 26811313
Resident Partners/Directors:
ICAEW Members
D P S Bedi

ERNST & YOUNG ★
Salamis House, Third Floor, 44 Georgios Grivas, Dhigenis Avenue, 8220 Paphos

KPMG ★
P O Box 60288, 8101 Paphos

PRICEWATERHOUSE-COOPERS LTD
City House, 58 Grivas Dighenis Avenue, CY-8047 Paphos
Tel: 00 357 26555000
Resident Partners/Directors:
ICAEW Members
S C Michail

V. KOMODROMOS & CO ACCOUNTANTS & CONSULTANTS LTD
Tepelenion Tower, 13 Teleleniou Str, Office 106, P O Box 61049, 8130 Paphos

Y P LAZAROU
79 Ellados Avenue, 8020 Paphos

PARALIMNI

KPMG ★
2 Sotiras Street, P O Box 33200, 5280 Paralimni

STROVOLOS

CONSTANTINOS TSIOLAKKIS
Agion Ioxkim 10, Archangelos, Strovolos

K&S QUALITY AUDIT
17A Pavlou Mela Street, CY 2051 Strovolos

CZECH REPUBLIC

BRNO

PANNELL KERR FORSTER ▼
Nove Sady 27, 60200 Brno

PRICEWATERHOUSE-COOPERS ★
namesti Svobody 20, 602 00 Brno

CESKE BUDEJOVICE

PANNELL KERR FORSTER ▼
Zizkova 12, 37000 Ceske Budejovice

HODONIN

PANNELL KERR FORSTER ▼
Plucarna 1, P.O. Box 144, 69501 Hodonin

HRADEC KRALOVE

PANNELL KERR FORSTER ▼
Svatojanske nam. 163, 50003 Hradec Kralove

LADA

HZ CESKA LIPA SRO ▼
47001 Lada

LIBEREC

PANNELL KERR FORSTER ▼
Dr M Horakove 60, 46006 Liberec

OLOMOUC

PANNELL KERR FORSTER ▼
Husitska 4, 77900 Olomouc

OSTRAVA

PANNELL KERR FORSTER ▼
Rybarska 12, 74601 Ostrava

PRICEWATERHOUSE-COOPERS ★
Zamecka 20, 702 00 Ostrava

PLZEN

PANNELL KERR FORSTER ▼
Uslavska 75, 30156 Plzen

PODEBRADY

PANNELL KERR FORSTER ▼
L Dostalove 775, 260 01 Podebrady

PRAGUE

DELOITTE & TOUCHE ★
Nile House, karolinska 654/2, Karlin, 18600 Prague

DELOITTE & TOUCHE ★
Tyn 641/4, 110 00, 1 Prague

ERNST & YOUNG ▼
Karlovo Namesti 10, 12000 Prague

HZ PRAGUE LTD ▼
Kodanska 46, 10010 Prague

KPMG ★
Pobrezni 1a, 186 00 Prague

MOORE STEPHENS SOCIETAETS-TREUHAND ▼
Spolecnost s r o, Narodni 28, 11000 Prague

MOORES ROWLAND LEVEY & JUNG ★
Biskupsky Dvur 8, 110 00 Prague
Tel: 00 420 221722 445
Email: postmaster@mri-lj.cz
Website: http://www.mri-lj.cz
Resident Partners/Directors:
ICAEW Members
M Levey
Registered by another RSB to carry out company audit work
Licensed by another DPB to carry on investment business
Individual(s) licensed for insolvency work by another RPB

PANNELL KERR FORSTER ▼
Kodanska 46, 10010 Prague

PRICEWATERHOUSE-COOPERS ★
BusinessCommunityCenter, Katerinska 40/466, 120 00 Prague

TREBIC

PANNELL KERR FORSTER ▼
Letna 500, Hrotovice, 67555 Trebic

DENMARK

AABENRAA

KPMG C JESPERSEN ▼
Skibbrogade 27, DK 6200 Aabenraa

AALBORG

BDO INTERNATIONAL ▽
Sofiendalsvej 1, 9000 Aalborg

ERNST & YOUNG ▼
Vestre Havnepromendade 5, DK-9000 Aalborg

KPMG C JESPERSEN ▼
Nyhavnsgade 9, DK 9000 Aalborg

PRICEWATERHOUSE-COOPERS
PO Box 69, DK 9100 Aalborg

AARHUS

BDO INTERNATIONAL ▽
Aboulevarden 11-13, 8000 Aarhus

ERNST & YOUNG ▼
Soren Frichs Vej 38A, Aabyhoj, DK-8230 Aarhus

MOORE STEPHENS DENMARK APS ▼
Katrinebjergvej 89f, P O Box 1069, DK-8200 Aarhus

PRICEWATERHOUSE-COOPERS
Nobelparken, Jens Chr Skous Vej 1, DK 8000 Aarhus

ASSENS

ERNST & YOUNG ▼
Ostergade 42, DK-5610 Assens

BJERRINGBRO

BDO INTERNATIONAL ▽
Torvegade 11, 8850 Bjerringbro

BRANDE

BDO INTERNATIONAL ▽
Storegade 5, 7330 Brande

BRONDERSLEV

BDO INTERNATIONAL ▽
Nygade 34, 9700 Bronderslev

COPENHAGEN

ALSO & BREINHOLT A/S ▼
Roskildevej 39, 2000 Copenhagen

BDO INTERNATIONAL ▽
Kristineberg 3, 2100 Copenhagen

ERNST & YOUNG ▼
Tagensvej 86, DK 2200 Copenhagen

MACINTYRE STRATER INTERNATIONAL LTD ▼
Vestergade 11, Kobenhaunk, DK1456 Copenhagen

MOORE STEPHENS DENMARK APS ▼
Noerre Farimagsgade 11, P O Box 1034, DK-1007 Copenhagen

PANNELL KERR FORSTER ▼
Frederiksgade 1, DK-1265 Copenhagen

PANNELL KERR FORSTER ▼
Hovedvejen 56, Glostrup, DK-2600 Copenhagen

PANNELL KERR FORSTER ▼
Dynamovej 11, Herlev, DK 2730 Copenhagen

PRICEWATERHOUSE-COOPERS
Strandvejen 44, P O Box 2709, Hellerup, DK 2900 Copenhagen

PRICEWATERHOUSE-COOPERS
Tuborg Boulevard 1, Hellerup, DK 2900 Copenhagen

EJBY

BDO INTERNATIONAL ▽
Jernbanevej 1, 5592 Ejby

EJSTRUPHOLM

BDO INTERNATIONAL ▽
Ostergade 12, 7361 Ejstrupholm

ESBJERG

ERNST & YOUNG ▼
Fordesgade 70, DK-6700 Esbjerg

KPMG C JESPERSEN ▼
Randersvej 38, DK-6700 Esbjerg

PRICEWATERHOUSE-COOPERS
PO Box 80, 6701 Esbjerg

FAABORG

BDO INTERNATIONAL ▽
Assensvej 4, 5600 Faaborg

FJERRITSLEV

PRICEWATERHOUSE-COOPERS
Postbox 16, DK 9690 Fjerritslev

FREDERICIA

PRICEWATERHOUSE-COOPERS
Smedevaenget 8, DK 7000 Fredericia

FREDERIKSBERG

KPMG C JESPERSEN ▼
Borups Alle 177, P.O.Box 250, 2000 Frederiksberg

FREDERIKSHAVN

BDO INTERNATIONAL ▽
Rimmensalle 89, 9900 Frederikshavn

HAMMEL

ERNST & YOUNG ▼
Ostergade 13, DK-8450 Hammel

HANTSHOLM

MOORE STEPHENS DENMARK APS ▼
Bytorvet 34, DK-7730 Hantsholm

HERNING

BDO INTERNATIONAL ▽
Markedspladsen 2, DK 7400 Herning

PRICEWATERHOUSE-COOPERS
PO Box 399, DK 7400 Herning

HILLEROD

ERNST & YOUNG ▼
Milnersveo 43, DK-3400 Hillerod

HIRTSHALS

BDO INTERNATIONAL ▽
Jorgen Fibigersgade 16, 9850 Hirtshals

HOBRO

BDO INTERNATIONAL ▽
Nytorv 12, 9500 Hobro

HOLBECK

PRICEWATERHOUSE-COOPERS
PO Box 300, DK 4300 Holbeck

HOLSTEBRO

PRICEWATERHOUSE-COOPERS
PO Box 1443, DK 7500 Holstebro

HORSENS

BDO INTERNATIONAL ▽
Lovenornsgade 3, 8700 Horsens

KPMG C JESPERSEN ▼
Holmbues Alte 1, DK 8700 Horsens

PRICEWATERHOUSE-COOPERS
PO Box 471, DK 8700 Horsens

HURUP

MOORE STEPHENS DENMARK APS ▼
Mollevaenget 17, DK-7760 Hurup

IKAST

BDO INTERNATIONAL ▽
Saturnvej 1, 7430 Ikast

KOGE

MOORE STEPHENS DENMARK APS ▼
Torvet 21, DK-4600 Koge

KOLDING

KPMG C JESPERSEN ▼
P.O. Box 205, DK 6000 Kolding

MOORE STEPHENS ▼
Lasbybanke 15, 2, P O Box 451, 6000 Kolding

PRICEWATERHOUSE-COOPERS
Postbox 359, DK 6000 Kolding

MARSTAL

MOORE STEPHENS DENMARK APS ▼
Kongensgade 18, DK-5960 Marstal

MIDDELFART

PRICEWATERHOUSE-COOPERS
Postbox 90, SK 5500 Middelfart

NAESTVED

ERNST & YOUNG ▼
Farvergade 15, DK-4700 Naestved

PRICEWATERHOUSE-COOPERS
Postbox 430, DK 4700 Naestved

NYBORG

BDO INTERNATIONAL ▽
Kongegade 24, 5800 Nyborg

NYKOBING

ERNST & YOUNG ▼
Torvet 2, DK-4800 Nykobing

NYKOBING MORS

MOORE STEPHENS DENMARK APS ▼
Limfjordsvej 42, DK-7900 Nykobing Mors

ODENSE

BDO INTERNATIONAL ▽
Pantheonsgade 10, 5100 Odense

KPMG C JESPERSEN ▼
Borstenbindervej 6, DK-5230 Odense

PRICEWATERHOUSE-COOPERS
Ostre Stationsvej 33, DK 5100 Odense

PADBORG

BDO INTERNATIONAL ▽
Lejrvej 8, 6330 Padborg

RANDERS

BDO INTERNATIONAL ▽
Provstegarden, Provstegade 10, 8900 Randers

PRICEWATERHOUSE-COOPERS
Postbox 98, DK 8900 Randers

RINGKOBING

PRICEWATERHOUSE-COOPERS
Postbox 60, DK 6950 Ringkobing

ROSKILDE

ERNST & YOUNG ▼
Ostergade 11, DK-4000 Roskilde

PRICEWATERHOUSE-COOPERS
Postbox 28, 4000 Roskilde

SAEBY

BDO INTERNATIONAL ▽
Saebygardvej 25, 9300 Saeby

SILKEBORG

BDO INTERNATIONAL ▽ ◈
Godthabsvej 4, 8600 Silkeborg

SKAGEN

BDO INTERNATIONAL ▽
Spliidsvej 25, 9990 Skagen

SKIVE

PRICEWATERHOUSE-COOPERS
Postbox 19, DK 7800 Skive

SKJERN

PRICEWATERHOUSE-COOPERS
Postbox 160, DK 6900 Skjern

SLAGELSE

PRICEWATERHOUSE-COOPERS
PO Box 264, DK 4200 Slagelse

SONDERBORG

ERNST & YOUNG ▼
Ellegaardsvej 25, DK-6400 Sonderborg

KPMG C JESPERSEN ▼
Sundsmarkvej 12, DK 6400 Sonderborg

STRUER

PRICEWATERHOUSE-COOPERS
Postbox 159, DK 7600 Struer

SVENDBORG

KPMG C JESPERSEN ▼
P O Box 209, DK-5700 Svendborg

MOORE STEPHENS DENMARK APS ▼
Klosterplads 9, DK-5700 Svendborg

THISTED

MOORE STEPHENS DENMARK APS ▼
Thyparken 10, DK-7700 Thisted

TONDER

ERNST & YOUNG ▼
Spikergade 19, DK-6270 Tonder

TORSHAVN

KPMG C JESPERSEN ▼
P/F Grannskodarastovan, Staravegur 17, FR 110 Torshavn

VEJLE

ERNST & YOUNG ▼
Damhaven 3C, DK-7100 Vejle

PRICEWATERHOUSE-COOPERS
PO Box 439, DK 7100 Vejle

VIBORG

BDO INTERNATIONAL ▽
Fabrikvej 11, 8800 Viborg

DOMINICAN REPUBLIC

SANTO DOMINGO

GUZMAN TAPIA & CO ▼
Calle 14, No 3 A, Ensache Urbanizacion Fernandez, Santo Domingo

KPMG PEAT MARWICK ▼
Apartado Postal 1467, Santo Domingo

PANNELL KERR FORSTER ▼
Calle 14, No 3A, Ensache Urbanizacion, Fernandez, Santo Domingo

PRICEWATERHOUSE-COOPERS ▼
PO Box 1286, Santo Domingo

ECUADOR

CUENCA

MACINTYRE STRATER INTERNATIONAL LTD ▼
Bolivar 16-78y Miguel Heredia, Cuenca, 01010620

GUAYAQUIL

BDO INTERNATIONAL ▽
P.O. Box 09-01-9131, Guayaquil

DELOITTE & TOUCHE ★
Casilla 5857, Tulcan 803 y Avenida 9, de Octubre, Guayaquil

PANNELL KERR FORSTER ▼
Avenida 9 de Octubre Apt1911, Piso 12 P.O.Box. 09-06-2045, Edificio Finansur, Guayaquil

PEAT, MARWICK, MITCHELL & CO ▼
P. Icaza 220 y Pedro Carbo, (Apartado 3818), Guayaquil

PRICEWATERHOUSE-COOPERS ▼
Carchi 702, 2nd Floor, Guayaquil

QUITO

BDO INTERNATIONAL ▽
P.O. Box 17-11-5058 CCI, Quito

DELOITTE & TOUCHE ★
Casilla 17-01-361, Quito

PANNELL KERR FORSTER ▼
Av Republica Del Salvador, 836 Y Portugal, Edificio Prisma Norte, Piso 4, of 404, Quito

PEAT, MARWICK, MITCHELL & CO ▼
Ed. Del Col. De Ing. Civ de, Pi.,Av.9 de Oct.y Av.Colon, Segundo Piso, Quito

PRICEWATERHOUSE-COOPERS ▼
Casilla 17-21-227, Quito

EGYPT

ALEXANDRIA

BDO INTERNATIONAL ▽
P.O. Box 896, Alexandria, 21519

KPMG HAZEM HASSAN ▼
12 Nouh Affrendi Street, From Soltan Hessein, Alexandria

MOSTAFA SHAWKI & CO ★
78 ABD Al Salam Arefs, El Salam Tower Gleim, Alexandria, 21411

NAWAR & CO
25 Sharia Champilion, Alexandria

PRICEWATERHOUSE-COOPERS ▼
42 Ahmed Shawki Street, Moustafa Kamel, Alexandria

CAIRO

BDO INTERNATIONAL ▽
95C Mirgany Street, Cairo, 11341

BDO INTERNATIONAL ▽
PO Box 110/12655, 1 Wadi El Nil Street, Mohandessin, Giza, Cairo

DR AM HEGAZY & ASSOCIATES ▼
6 Boulos Hanna Street, PO Box 2132, Dokki, Cairo

ERNST & YOUNG ▼ ◈
P.O.Box 97 Dokki, Giza, Cairo
Tel: 00 20 2 3362 000
Resident Partners/Directors: ICAEW Members
A F H Hamouda, A R Tajdeen

KPMG HAZEM HASSAN ▼
Pyramide Heights Office Park, Km 22 Cairo, Alex Dessert Road, P O Box 48, Alahram CAIRO 12556

MAURICE W. MOUSSA
Suite 51, Bourg El Zamalek, 18 Shargarret El Dorr Street, Zamalek, Cairo 11211

MOSTAFA SHAWKI & CO ★
153 Mohamed Farid St, Bank Misr Tower,P.O.Box 2095, Cairo, 11511

NAWAR & CO
21 Sharia Talaat Harb, Cairo

PRICEWATERHOUSE-COOPERS ▼
22 El Nasr Street, New Maadi, Cairo, 11431

RASHED BADR & CO ▼
95 Hafez Ramadan Street, By El Ahly Club, Nasr City, Cairo

RASHED BADR & CO ▼
95 Hafez Ramadan St, By El Ahly Club, Nasr City, Cairo

SALEH, BARSOUM & ABDEL AZIZ ▽
P.O. Box 393, Cairo, 11511

SALEH, BARSOUM & ABDEL AZIZ ▽
15 Sherif Street, Cairo, 11511

GIZA

DR AM HEGAZY & ASSOCIATES ▼
6 Boulos Hannah St, Dokki, Giza, 12311

EL SALVADOR

SAN SALVADOR

AGUIRRE LOPEZ Y ASOCIADOS SC ▼
Edificio Montresor 20 Piso, Local 3-B, Final Avenida Sor No 243, Colonia Roma, San Salvador

KPMG PEAT MARWICK ▼
Avenida Olimpica 3324 & 3330, San Salvador

PRICEWATERHOUSE-COOPERS ▼
Apartado Postal 695, San Salvador

ESTONIA

TALLINN

DU AUDIT EA ▼
44 Mustamae Tee, Tallinn 10621

PRICEWATERHOUSE-COOPERS ▼
Parnu mnt 15, Tallinn 10141

ETHIOPIA

ADDIS ABABA

A.A. BROMHEAD & CO
P.O. Box 709, Addis Ababa
Tel: 00 251 116518170
Fax: 00 251 115 524576
Email: bromhead@ethionet.et
Website: http://www.aabromhead.com
Mobile: 00 251 911 200074
Principal: ICAEW Member
A A Bromhead
Languages Spoken:
English

NAWAR & CO
Ras Desta Damtew Ave, P.O.Box 3349, Addis Ababa

TADDESSE WOLDEGABRIEL & CO
P.O. Box 22848 - Code 1000, Addis Ababa

FALKLAND ISLANDS

STANLEY

WILKINS KENNEDY
Globe Offices, Philomel Street, Stanley
Tel: 00 500 22918
Website: http://www.wilkinskennedy.com
Registered by the ICAEW to carry out company audit work

SPECIALISATIONS – BUSINESS & GENERAL ADVICE

Acquisitions and Mergers
Disposal of Businesses
Outsourcing - Financial Services

SPECIALISATIONS – SECTOR

Charities
Insurance Brokers
Property

FAROE ISLANDS

TORSHAVN

PRICEWATERHOUSE-COOPERS ▼
A Gladsheyggi, Torshavn, 110

FIJI

LAUTOKA

KPMG ▼
157 Vitogo Parade, PO Box 701, Lautoka

PANNELL KERR FORSTER ▼
125 Vitogo Parade, P O Box 867, Lautoka

PRICEWATERHOUSE-COOPERS ▼
52 Narara Parade, Lautoka

PRICEWATERHOUSE-COOPERS ▼
131 Vitogo Parade, Lautoka

SUVA

ERNST & YOUNG ▼ ◈
Pacific House, Level 7, 1 Butt Street, Suva
Tel: 00 679 3314166

KPMG ▼
Ratu Sukuna House, Victoria Parade, (G.P.O Box 32), Suva

PKF ▼
Level 10, FNPF Place, 343 Victoria Parade, Suva

PRICEWATERHOUSE-COOPERS ▼
Civic Tower, Level 8, 262 Victoria Park, Suva

FINLAND

HELSINKI

KPMG WIDERI OY AB ▼
P.O. Box 1037, SF-00101, Helsinki

PANNELL KERR FORSTER ▼
Munkkiniemen Puistotie 25, 00330 Helsinki

PANNELL KERR FORSTER ▼
Paciuksenkatu 21, 00270 Helsinki

PRICEWATERHOUSE-COOPERS OY ▼
Itamerentori 2, PO Box 1015, Helsinki, FIN-00100

PRICEWATERHOUSE-COOPERS OY ▼
Mannerheimintie 16a, Helsinki, FIN-00100

TILINTARKASTAJIEN OY ERNST & YOUNG ▼
Kaivokatu 8, Helsinki, 00100

TUOKKO TILINTARKASTUS OY KHT - YHTEISO ▼
Munkkiniemen Puistotie 25, 00330 Helsinki

JYVASKYLA

PRICEWATERHOUSE-COOPERS OY ▼
Kauppakatu 31 B, Jyvaskyla, FIN-40100

KUOPIO

PRICEWATERHOUSE-COOPERS OY ▼
Vuorikatu 26 A, Kuopio, FIN-70100

LAPPEENRANTA

KPMG WIDERI OY AB ▼
West Post B.O.Box 109, St Petersburg, Lappeenranta, FIN-53101

PRICEWATERHOUSE-COOPERS OY ▼
Valtakatu 38B, Lappeenranta, FIN-53100

OULU

KPMG WIDERI OY AB ▼
Isokatu 32C, Oulu, 90100

PRICEWATERHOUSE-COOPERS OY ▼
Kauppurienkatu 11 B, Oulu, FIN-90100

PORI

PRICEWATERHOUSE-COOPERS OY ▼
Etelakauppatori 4 A, Pori, FIN-28100

SAVONLINNA

PRICEWATERHOUSE-COOPERS OY ▼
Kauppatori 1 A, Savonlinna, FIN-57130

SEINAJOKI

PRICEWATERHOUSE-COOPERS OY ▼
Kauppakatu 20, PO Box 114, Seinajoki, FIN 60101

TAMPERE

KPMG WIDERI OY AB ▼
Kauppakatu 6, Tampere, 33210

PANNELL KERR FORSTER ▼
Rautatienkatu 25, Tampere, SF 33100

PRICEWATERHOUSE-COOPERS OY ▼
Hameenkatu 26a, Tampere, FIN-33200

TURKU

KPMG WIDERI OY AB ▼
Linnankatu 26C, SF-20, Turku, 10

PRICEWATERHOUSE-COOPERS OY ▼
Lantinten Rantakatu 7, Turku, FIN-20100

VAASA

PRICEWATERHOUSE-COOPERS OY ▼
Hovioikeudenpuistikko 13A, Vaasa, FIN-65100

FRANCE

AIX-EN-PROVENCE

BDO INTERNATIONAL ▽
7 Avenue du Marechal Lyautey, 13100 Aix-en-Provence

AMIENS

COOPERS & LYBRAND ▼
BP 24, 80017 Amiens Cedex 1, 14 boulevard Alsace Lorraine, 80000 Amiens

KPMG ▼
77 rue Saint-Fuscien, 80008 Amiens

ANGERS

ERNST & YOUNG S R L ▼
5 bis Boulevard Foch, 49100 Angers

PKF FRANCE ▼
2 Square Gaston, Allard, 49000 Angers

ARGENTEUIL

GROUPE AGORA ★
33 rue de la Folie, 95100 Argenteuil

AVIGNON

BDO INTERNATIONAL ▽
P.O. Box 139, 84007 Avignon

AVON

MACINTYRE STRATER INTERNATIONAL LTD ▼
36 Rue De La Charite, 77210 Avon

BASTIA

GROUPE AGORA ★
Immeuble Cacciari, Avenue de la Liberation, 20600 Bastia

BAYONNE

KPMG ▼
88 rue de Bahinos, 64600 Bayonne

BEAUVAIS

BDO INTERNATIONAL ▽
13 rue de d'Amiens, 60000 Beauvais

BESANCON

KPMG ▼
41 Chemin des Montarmots, 25009 Besancon

BORDEAUX

BORDEAUX JURIS CONSEIL ▼
179 Cours du Medoc, 33300 Bordeaux

COOPERS & LYBRAND ▼
179 Cours du Medoc, 33300 Bordeaux

COOPERS & LYBRAND AUDIT ▼
179 Cours de Medoc, 33300 Bordeaux

KPMG ▼
Le Montesquieu, Av.du President J.F.Kennedy, 33704 Bordeaux

KPMG AUDIT ★
Le Montesquieu, Av President Kennedy, Merignac, 33704 Bordeaux

BOURGES

COOPERS & LYBRAND ▼
5 rue Paul Valery, 01000 Bourges

KPMG ▼
B P 241, 18005 Bourges

CAEN

KPMG ▼
1 rue Claude Bloch, 14042 Caen

CALAIS

KPMG ▼
5 a 9 rue A Brain duet, 62226 Calais

CANNES

PKF FRANCE ▼
32 Boulevard de Lorraine, 06400 Cannes

CARNOET

SMALL DEVELOPMENTS LTD
Pen Ar Vern, 22160 Carnoet

CAROUGE

INTANDEM BUSINESS SERVICES
c/o Fiduciaire Chavaz SA, Rue Jacques-Grosselin 8, Case Postale 1835, CH-1227 Carouge

CHALON-SUR-SAONE

KPMG ▼
3,Ave, de Chalon,Les Chavannes, Saint-Marcel, 71380 Chalon-sur-Saone

CHELLES

GROUPE AGORA ★
184 rue du Tir, 77500 Chelles

CHOLET

PETITEAU SCACCHI ET ASSOCIES ▼
Boulevard de Touraine, ZI Legere BP 7, 49308 Cholet

CLERMONT-FERRAND

KPMG ▼
Parc Technologique le Pardieu, 6 rue Valentin Haiiy, 63000 Clermont-Ferrand

COGNAC

COOPERS & LYBRAND ▼
4 Rue de Segonzac, BP 124, 16104, Cedex, 16100 Cognac

COOPERS & LYBRAND AUDIT ▼
4 rue de Segonzac, 16100 Cognac

CRE-PY-EN-VALOIS

GROUPE AGORA ★
1 rue Sadi Carnot, 60800 Cre-Py-En-Valois

DIJON

COOPERS & LYBRAND ▼
Les Blasons du Chateau, 11 E Boulevard Rembrandt, 21000 Dijon

COOPERS & LYBRAND AUDIT ▼
BP 57024, 21070 Dijon

DURFORT

NEIL CAMERON
Chemin Neuf, 30170 Durfort
Tel: 00 33 4 66770651
Principal: ICAEW Member
N A Cameron

FONTAINEBLEAU

MACINTYRE STRATER INTERNATIONAL LTD ▼
46 Rue Auguste Barbier, F 77300 Fontainebleau

GATHEMO

NEVILLE K. TAYLOR
La Chardiere, 50150 Gathemo

GIRONVILLE

MARIAN WATTS
5 Rue Grande, 77890 Gironville

GRENOBLE

COOPERS & LYBRAND ▼
Immeuble Grenat, 3 avenue du Doyen Louis Weil, 38000 Grenoble

KPMG ▼
9 Avenue du Granier, Meylan, 38244 Grenoble

LANDWELL & ASSOCIES ▼
Immeuble Grenat, 3 avenue du Doyen Louis Weil, 38000 Grenoble

LE MANS

KPMG ▼
160 Avenue Bollee, 72000 Le Mans

LE TEMPLE SUR LOT

BREAVIS CONSULTANTS
Boufferille, 47110 Le Temple Sur Lot
Tel: 00 33 353 402120
Resident Partners/Directors: ICAEW Members
B J Rea-Palmer

LEVALLOIS-PERRET

KPMG AUDIT ★
Les Allees de Valois, 2 bis rue de Villiers, 92300 Levallois-Perret

LILLE

BDO INTERNATIONAL ▽
68 Blvd. du General de Gaulle, Roubaix, 59100 Lille

COOPERS & LYBRAND ▼
37 rue du Vieux Faubourg, 59800 Lille

COOPERS & LYBRAND AUDIT ▼
37 rue du Vieux Faubourg, 59800 Lille

ERNST & YOUNG S R L ▼
14 rue du Vieux Faubourg, Lille Cedex, 59042 Lille

KPMG ▼
159 Avenue de la Marne, Marcq en Baroeul, 59700 Lille

PRICE WATERHOUSE ▼
37 Rue du Vieux Faubourg, 59800 Lille

LIMOGES

COOPERS & LYBRAND ▼
20 rue Banc Leger, 87000 Limoges

COOPERS & LYBRAND AUDIT ▼
20 rue Banc Leger, 87000 Limoges

KPMG ▼
Residence Sylvestre, 34 rue Ferdinand Buisson, 87038 Limoges

LYON

BDO INTERNATIONAL ▽
79 Rue Francois Mermet, Tassin-La-Demi-Lune, 69160 Lyon

COOPERS & LYBRAND ▼
20 Rue Garibaldi, Cedex 06, 69451 Lyon

COOPERS & LYBRAND AUDIT ▼
20 Rue Garibaldi, Cedex 06, 69451 Lyon

DELOITTE & TOUCHE ▼
Park Avenue, 81 Boulevard de Stalingrad, Villeurbanne, 69100 Lyon

KPMG ▼
3 Avenue General Brosset, Tassin La Demie Lune, 69811 Lyon

KPMG AUDIT ★
3 Av General Brosset, Tassin-La-Demi-Lune, 69811 Lyon

PANNELL KERR FORSTER ▼
Le Thelemos, 12 quai du Commerce, CP 202-69336 Cedex 09, 69336 Lyon

PRICE WATERHOUSE ▼
1 rue Garibaldi, Cedex 06, 69451 Lyon

MARSEILLE

AUDIT CONSEIL ▼
71 Chemin Gilbert Charmasson, BP 162, 13016 Marseille

ERNST & YOUNG S R L ▼
485 Avenue du Prado, 13008 Marseille

KPMG ▼
480 Avenue du Prado, Cedex 08, 13272 Marseille

PANNELL KERR FORSTER ▼
2a Boulevard de Louvain, 13008 Marseille

PRICE WATERHOUSE ▼
BP 48, Cedex 2, 13472 Marseille

MILLAC

EDWARD MOORE & PARTNERS ★
Pont De Vaux, 86150 Millac

MONTARGIS

COOPERS & LYBRAND ▼
5 rue Louis Lacroix, 45200 Montargis

MONTPELLIER

COOPERS & LYBRAND ▼
BP 12, Cedex 9, 34935 Montpellier

COOPERS & LYBRAND AUDIT ▼
BP 12, Cedex 9, 34935 Montpellier

KPMG ▼
747 Rue des Apothicaires, Parc Euromedecine, 34000 Montpellier

MORET SUR LOING

MACINTYRE STRATER INTERNATIONAL LTD ▼
30 Avenue Jean Javres, 77250 Moret Sur Loing

MORZINE

CAROLINE DOCKERILL
487 Chemin de la Contettaz, 74110 Morzine

MULHOUSE

BDO INTERNATIONAL ▽
15 Rue de Verdun, 68100 Mulhouse

NANCY

KPMG ▼
Les Hauts de Villers, 523 avenue Andre Malraux, 54600 Villers-les-, Nancy

KPMG AUDIT ★
Les Hauts de Villiers, 523 Av Andre Malraux, 54600 Nancy

NANTES

BDO INTERNATIONAL ▽
P.O. Box 209, 44085 Nantes

COOPERS & LYBRAND ▼
Immeuble Beaumanoir-hall B, 15 rue Lamoriciere, 44100, 44100 Nantes

COOPERS & LYBRAND AUDIT ▼
Immeuble Beaumanoir-Hall B, 15 rue Lamoriciere, 44300 Nantes

ERNST & YOUNG S R L ▼
10 Rue Du President Herriot, 44000 Nantes

KPMG ▼
18 rue du Pin, 44300 Nantes

KPMG AUDIT ★
18 Rue du Pin, BP 1125, 44013 Nantes

PETITEAU SCACCHI ET ASSOCIES ▼
11 rue de Douet-Garnier, Allee Baco, F44015 Nantes

PRICE WATERHOUSE ▼
Immeuble Beaumnaoir-Hall B, 15 rue Lamoriciere, 50522 Nantes

PRICEWATERHOUSE-COOPERS ★
34 Place Viarme, 44000 Nantes

NEUILLY-SUR-SEINE

DELOITTE & TOUCHE ▼
185 avenue Charles De Gaulle, 92200 Neuilly-sur-Seine

ERNST & YOUNG S R L ▼
41 Rue Ybry, 92200 Neuilly-sur-Seine

KPMG AUDIT ★
Les Hauts de Villiers, 2 Bis rue de Villiers, 92200 Neuilly-sur-Seine

PRICEWATERHOUSE-COOPERS ★
Transaction Services, 63 rue de Villiers, 92200 Neuilly-sur-Seine

NICE

BDO INTERNATIONAL ▽
14 rue Fremont, 06200 Nice

COOPERS & LYBRAND ▼
Le Palmeira, 45 rue Saint Philippe, BP 1006, Cedex 1, 06001 Nice

COOPERS & LYBRAND AUDIT ▼
Le Palmeira, 45 rue Saint-Philippe, (B.P.6,06001), 06000 Nice

PANNELL KERR FORSTER ▼
6 Place Garibaldi, D6300 Nice

PARIS

B L CHANCELLOR ◈
132 rue de Longchamp, 75116 Paris

CABINET GALLEY MANTERFIELD
Anatoth, 19 Allee de la Gare, Le Vesinet, 78110 Paris
Tel: 00 33 134800134
Email: anatoth@wanadoo.fr
Principal: ICAEW Member
L M Manterfield

COOPERS & LYBRAND ▼
32 rue Guersant, 75017 Paris

COOPERS & LYBRAND ▼
32 rue Guersant, Cedex 17, 75829 Paris

COOPERS & LYBRAND AUDIT ▼
32 Rue Guersant, 75829 Paris

DELOITTE TOUCHE TOHMATSU AUDIT ★
B.P. 136, 185 Ave. Charles, de Gaulle,Neuilly Sur Seine, F-92201 Paris

DIXON WILSON
19 avenue de L'Opera, 75001 Paris
Tel: 00 33 147031290
Fax: 00 33 1 4703 1285
Email: james.howes@dixonwilson.fr
Website: http://www.dixonwilson.com
Training Contracts Available.
Resident Partners/Directors: ICAEW Members
J R Benford, P J Howes
Resident Partners (Non-ICAEW Members):
S Lemaitre

SPECIALISATIONS – TAXATION

Offshore Companies
Personal
Trusteeship
Trusts
UK Nationals Overseas

General Description: The Paris office of Dixon Wilson is fully qualified in France to carry out all types of accountancy, audit and investigation work. Member of the 'Ordre des Experts Comptables' and of the 'Compagnie des Commissaires aux Comptes'. Bilingual staff. Specialises in advising on investment into France; setting up French companies; company accounting; payroll services, etc. We are used to working with a UK company's existing auditors. French personal tax planning a speciality.
Languages Spoken:
French, English
See display advertisement near this entry.

ERNST & YOUNG S R L ▼
Tour Ernst & Young, Faubourg de l'Arche, La Defense Cedex, 92037 Paris

GROUPE AGORA ★
2 rue Joseph Sansboeuf, 75008 Paris

JOHN F. KENNEDY
Fiteco - Paris, 17 rue Alfred Roll, 75017 Paris

KPMG ▼
54 rue de Courcelles, 75008 Paris

KPMG ▼
Les Hauts de Villiers, 2 Bis rue de Villiers, Levallois-Perret, 92309 Paris

KPMG AUDIT ★
1 Cours Valmy, Paris La Defense, 92923 Paris

PANNELL KERR FORSTER ▼
47 Rue de Liege, 75008 Paris

PETITEAU SCACCHI ET ASSOCIES ▼
98 Rue de Courcelles, 75017 Paris

PRICE WATERHOUSE ▼
Tour AIG, 34 Place Des Corolles, Paris La Defense 2, 92908 Paris

ROBERT J. TWIST
42 Rue de Bassano, 75008 Paris
Tel: 00 33 140170547
Fax: 00 33 140170334
Email: rt@rjtwist.com
Website: http://www.rjtwist.com
Principal: ICAEW Member
R J Twist

S & W ASSOCIES ★
100 Rue De Courcelles, 75017 Paris
Tel: 00 33 1 5621 0303
Resident Partners/Directors: ICAEW Members
D M W Dowse

S & W ASSOCIES ★
Grant Thornton IBS, 10 Place de la Madeleine, 75008 Paris

PAU

COOPERS & LYBRAND ▼
Villa Saint-Michel, 1 Rue Benado, 64000 Pau

COOPERS & LYBRAND AUDIT ▼
Villa Saint-Michel, 1 Rue Benado, 64000 Pau

QUIMPER

COOPERS & LYBRAND ▼
9 Rue President Sadate, 9 BP 1552, Cedex, F-29105 Quimper

COOPERS & LYBRAND AUDIT ▼
BP 1552, 29105 Quimper

KPMG ▼
9 Allee Sully Stang-vihan, 29000 Quimper

REIMS

KPMG ▼
Pole Technologique Henri Farma, 19 rue Clement Ader, 51000 Reims

RENNES

COOPERS & LYBRAND ▼
Centre D'Affaires Alphasis, St Gregoire Cedex, 35769 Rennes

COOPERS & LYBRAND AUDIT ▼
Centre D'Affaires Alphasis, St Gregoire Cedex, 35769 Rennes

KPMG ▼
15 rue du Professeur Jean Pecker, 35000 Rennes

KPMG AUDIT ★
15 rue du Professeur Jean Pecker, 35000 Rennes

PRICEWATERHOUSE-COOPERS ★
Centre d'apparres, Alphasis, 35769 Rennes

RESNY-SUR-SEINE

GROUPE AGORA ★
Residence Gabrielle d'Estrees, 60 Route Nationale 13, 78710 Resny-Sur-Seine

ROUEN

COOPERS & LYBRAND ▼
Parc de la Vatine, 20 rue Aron, Mont Saint Aignan, 76130 Rouen

FEUILLET JOUFFRE ET ASSOCIES SA ▼
Parc de la Vatine, 20 rue Aron, Mont Saint Aignan, 76130 Rouen

KPMG ▼
6 rue Le Verrier, Mont-Saint-Aignan, 76135 Rouen

PRICE WATERHOUSE ▼
Parc de la Vatine, 20 rue Aron, Mont Saint Aignan, 76130 Rouen

RUEIL MALMAISON

ERNST & YOUNG S R L ▼
Immeuble Ariane, 2 Rue Jacques Daguerre, 92565 Rueil Malmaison

SAINT ETIENNE

KPMG ▼
Parc Giron, 6 Allee Drouot, 42031 Saint Etienne

SETE

J I SCOBIE
Apartment 29, Residence Le College, Grande Rue Haute, 34200 Sete

SOPHIA ANTIPOLIS

COOPERS & LYBRAND ▼
Les Bouillides, 55 Allee Pierre Ziller, BP 165, 06903 Sophia Antipolis

COOPERS & LYBRAND AUDIT ▼
55 Allee Pierre Ziller, Les Boullides, BP 165, Cedex, 06903 Sophia Antipolis

ST CLOUD

BDO INTERNATIONAL ▽
25 Quai Carnot, 92210 St Cloud

ST MALO

COOPERS & LYBRAND ▼
18 Avenue Jean Jaures, B.P.15, 35401, Cedex, 35401 St Malo

COOPERS & LYBRAND AUDIT ▼
18 Avenue Jean Juares, B.P.15, 35401 St Malo

ST QUENTIN

COOPERS & LYBRAND ▼
Les Jardins de l'hotel Dieu, 35 Rue Arnaud Bisson, (BO 49), 02100 St Quentin

COOPERS & LYBRAND AUDIT ▼
Les Jardins de L'Hotel Dieu, 35 Rue Arnaud Bisson, (BP 49), 02100 St Quentin

STRASBOURG

ERNST & YOUNG S R L ▼
Le Sebastopol, 3 Quai Kleber, Cedex, 67055 Strasbourg

PANNELL KERR FORSTER ▼
53 rue de General, Offenstein BP3, Cedex, 67023 Strasbourg

PETITEAU SCACCHI ET ASSOCIES ▼
Immeuble Le Sebastopol, 3 Quai Kleber, F67055 Strasbourg

PRICE WATERHOUSE ▼
2 avenue de la Foret-Noire, BP 57, Cedex, 67002 Strasbourg

TOULOUSE

BDO INTERNATIONAL ▽
Toulouse 2000, 2 Esplanade Compan Caffarelli, 31000 Toulouse

COOPERS & LYBRAND ▼
Immeuble Le Sully, 1 place Occitane, BP 836, 31080 Toulouse

COOPERS & LYBRAND AUDIT ▼
Immeuble le Sully, 1 place Occitane, BP 836, 31080 Toulouse

KPMG ▼
B.P. 2351, 31022 Toulouse

PETITEAU SCACCHI ET ASSOCIES ▼
1 Place Alfonse Jourdain, 31000 Toulouse

PRICE WATERHOUSE ▼
BP 836, Cedex 06, 31080 Toulouse

TOURS

KPMG ▼
130 Rue de Rempart, 37000 Tours

TROYES

MACINTYRE STRATER INTERNATIONAL LTD ▼
5 Chemin Des Granges, La Riviere Des Corps, 10300 Troyes

VILLEURBANNE

ERNST & YOUNG S R L ▼
113 Boulevard Stalingrad, 69626 Villeurbanne

WATTRELOS

PANNELL KERR FORSTER ▼
184 rue Jean Lebas BP5, CEDEX59392 Wattrelos

GABON

LIBREVILLE

PRICEWATERHOUSE-COOPERS ▼
366 rue Alfred-Marche, BP 2164, Libreville

PORT GENTIL

PRICEWATERHOUSE-COOPERS ▼
BP 584, Port Gentil

GERMANY

ACHERN

PRICEWATERHOUSE-COOPERS GMBH ★
Eisenbahnstrasse 19-23, D-77855 Achern

AHRENSBURG

MS BERATUNGS-UND-TREUHAND-UNION GMBH ▼
Grosse Strasse 19, 22926 Ahrensburg

AUGSBURG

MS BERATUNGS-UND-TREUHAND-UNION GMBH ▼
Wirtchaftsprufer, Steuerberater, Rechtsanwaelte, Grottenau 6, 8900 Augsburg

BAD SODEN

MS BERATUNGS-UND-TREUHAND-UNION GMBH ▼
Koenigsteiner Strasse 6a, D-6232 Bad Soden

BERLIN

BDO INTERNATIONAL ▽
Kurfurstendamm 182-183, 10707 Berlin

ERNST & YOUNG GMBH ★
Fraunhofer Strasse 33-36, D-10587 Berlin

KPMG DEUTSCHE TREUHAND GROUP ★
Taubenstrasse 44-45, 10117 Berlin

KPMG DEUTSCHE TREUHAND GROUP ★
Klingelhoferstrasse 18, 10785 Berlin

MACINTYRE STRATER INTERNATIONAL LTD ▼
Keithstrasse 2-4, 10787 Berlin

MS BERATUNGS-UND-TREUHAND-UNION GMBH ▼
Knesebeckstrasse 68/69, 1000 Berlin

PANNELL KERR FORSTER ▼
Alt Kopenick 15, 12555 Berlin

PANNELL KERR FORSTER ▼
Platanenallee 11, 14050 Berlin

PRICEWATERHOUSE-COOPERS GMBH ★
Lise-Meitner-Strasse 1, D-10589 Berlin

BIELEFELD

GREIFFENHAGEN GMBH ▼
Viktoriastrasse 16-20, 33602 Bielefeld

KPMG DEUTSCHE TREUHAND GROUP ★
Nikolaus - Durkopp Str, 33602 Bielefeld

PRICEWATERHOUSE-COOPERS GMBH ★
Niederwall 28, D-33602 Bielefeld

BINGEN AM RHEIN

KPMG DEUTSCHE TREUHAND GROUP ★
Veronastrasse 10, D-6530 Bingen Am Rhein

BOCHUM

KPMG DEUTSCHE TREUHAND GROUP ★
Am Alten Stadtpark 35, 44791 Bochum

BONN

BDO INTERNATIONAL ▽
P.O. Box 2955, 53019 Bonn

PRICEWATERHOUSE-COOPERS GMBH ★
Walter-Flex-Str 2, D-53113 Bonn

BREMEN

FIDES ▼
Contrescarpe 97, P.O. Box 10 5727, D-2800 Bremen

KPMG DEUTSCHE TREUHAND GROUP ★
Am Wall 175-177, 28195 Bremen

COLOGNE

BACHEM, JASSEN & MEHRHOFF ▼
Hohenzollernring 57-63, 5000 Cologne

BDO INTERNATIONAL ▽
Konrad-Adenauer-Ufer 79-81, 50668 Cologne

HERFORT VAN KERKOM HOWER STREIT ▼
Gereonstrasse 34-36, 50670 Cologne

KPMG DEUTSCHE TREUHAND GROUP ★
Bibliothek, Barbarossaplatz 1A, 50674 Cologne

PANNELL KERR FORSTER ▼
Gereonstrasse 34-36, 50670 Cologne

DRESDEN

KPMG DEUTSCHE TREUHAND GROUP ★
Ammonstrasse 10, 01069 Dresden

PANNELL KERR FORSTER ▼
Zellescher Weg 24, 01217 Dresden

PRICEWATERHOUSE-COOPERS GMBH ★
Boltenhagener Platz 9, D-01109 Dresden

SOCIETAETS TREUHASND GMBH ▼
P O Box 12 03 05, 01004 Dresden

DUISBURG

FASSELT & PARTNER WIRTSCHAFTSPRUFUNG SGESELLSCHAFT ▼
Schifferstrasse 210, 47059 Duisburg

MS BERATUNGS-UND-TREUHAND-UNION GMBH ▼
Kuhlenwall 8, 4100 Duisburg

DUSSELDORF

BDO INTERNATIONAL ▽
P.O. Box 101464, 40005 Dusseldorf

DELOITTE & TOUCHE GMBH ★
Schwannstrasse 6, 40476 Dusseldorf

ERNST & YOUNG GMBH ★
Wirtschaftspruefungsgesellschaft, Graf-Adolf-Platz 15, 40213 Dusseldorf

ERNST & YOUNG GMBH ★
PO 102252, 40013 Dusseldorf

ERNST & YOUNG GMBH ★
Am Wehrhahn 50, D-40211 Dusseldorf

KPMG DEUTSCHE TREUHAND GROUP ★
Tersteengenstrasse19-31, 40474 Dusseldorf

KPMG DEUTSCHE TREUHAND GROUP ★
Am Bonneshof 35, D-40474 Dusseldorf

KPMG DEUTSCHE TREUHAND GROUP ★
Am Bonneshof 35, 40474 Dusseldorf

MACINTYRE STRATER INTERNATIONAL LTD ▼
Schirmerstrasse 76, 40211 Dusseldorf

PRICEWATERHOUSE-COOPERS GMBH ★
Moskauer Strasse 19, D-40227 Dusseldorf

SOZIETAET DR. MULLER, HAEB & PARTNER ▼
Benrather Schlossallee 85, 40597 Dusseldorf

ERFURT

PRICEWATERHOUSE-COOPERS GMBH ★
Burohaus an der Martinbastion, Maximillan-Welsch-Strasse 4, D-99084 Erfurt

ESCHBORN

ERNST & YOUNG AG ★
Mergenthalerallee 10-12, 65760 Eschborn

KPMG DEUTSCHE TREUHAND GROUP ★
Rahmannstrasse 11, 65760 Eschborn

ESSEN

BDO INTERNATIONAL ▽
P.O. Box 340107, 45073 Essen

PRICEWATERHOUSE-COOPERS GMBH ★
Friedrich-List-Str 20, D-45128 Essen

PRICEWATERHOUSE-COOPERS GMBH ★
Baumstr 25, D-45128 Essen

FLENSBURG

BDO INTERNATIONAL ▽
Dr-Todsen-Strasse 7, 24937 Flensburg

FRANKFURT-AM-MAIN

DELOITTE & TOUCHE
Franklinstrasse 50, 60486 Frankfurt Am Main

DELOITTE & TOUCHE
PO Box 150362, 60063 Frankfurt Am Main

ERNST & YOUNG GMBH ★
Mergenthalerallee 10-12, Eschborn, D65760 Frankfurt Am Main

ERNST & YOUNG GMBH ★
Eschersheimer Landstrasse 14, D-60322 Frankfurt Am Main

KPMG DEUTSCHE TREUHAND-GESELLSCHAFT ▼
Marie-Curie Strasse 30, 60439 Frankfurt Am Main

MOORES ROWLAND GMBH ▼
Grosser Hasenpfad 30, 60598 Frankfurt Am Main

PKF PANNELL KERR FORSTER GMBH ▼
Feuerbachstrasse 8, 60325 Frankfurt Am Main

PRICEWATERHOUSE-COOPERS GMBH ★
Marie-Curie-Strasse 24-28, D-60439 Frankfurt Am Main

PRICEWATERHOUSE-COOPERS GMBH ★
Bockenheimer Anlage 15, Postfach 111842, 60053 Frankfurt Am Main

PRICEWATERHOUSE-COOPERS GMBH ★
Olof-Palme-Strasse 35, 60439 Frankfurt Am Main

PRICEWATERHOUSE-COOPERS GMBH ★
Im Trutz 55, D-60322 Frankfurt Am Main

FREIBURG

BDO INTERNATIONAL ▽
Kaiser-Joseph-Strasse 274, 79098 Freiburg

KPMG DEUTSCHE TREUHAND GROUP ★
Bismarckalle 18-20, 79098 Freiburg

PRICEWATERHOUSE-COOPERS GMBH ★
Erbprinzenstrasse 2a, D-79098 Freiburg

HALDENSLEBEN

LANG UND STOLZ KG ▼
Hagenstrasse 36, 39340 Haldensleben

HALLE

FASSELT & PARTNER WIRTSCHAFTSPRUFUNG-SEGESELSCHAFT ▼
Bernburgerstrasse 4, 06108 Halle

PANNELL KERR FORSTER ▼
Bernburger Strasse 4, 06108 Halle

PRICEWATERHOUSE-COOPERS GMBH ★
Ankerstrasse 3a, D-06108 Halle

HAMBURG

BDO INTERNATIONAL ▽
P.O. Box 10 14 60, 20009 Hamburg

DR SCHLAGE & CO OHG ▼
Jungfernstieg 7, 20354 Hamburg

ERNST & YOUNG GMBH ★
Wirtschaftsprufungsgesillschaft, Steuerberatungsgesellschaft, Rothenbaumshaussee 78, 20148 Hamburg

MS BERATUNGS-UND-TREUHAND-UNION GMBH ▼
Bleichenbrucke 9, 20354 Hamburg

PKF EUROCONSULT GMBH ▼
Jungfernstieg 7, 20354 Hamburg

PRICE WATERHOUSE GMBH ▼
ABC Strabe 45, D-20354 Hamburg

PRICEWATERHOUSE-COOPERS GMBH ★
New-York-Ring 13, D-22297 Hamburg

HANNOVER

BDO INTERNATIONAL ▽
Uhlemeyerstrasse 9 + 11, 30175 Hannover

ERNST & YOUNG ★
Landschaftsstr 8, 30159 Hannover

KPMG DEUTSCHE TREUHAND GROUP ★
Osterstrabe 40, 30159 Hannover

MS BERATUNGS-UND-TREUHAND-UNION GMBH ▼
Hildesheimer Strasse 9, 3000 Hannover

PRICEWATERHOUSE-COOPERS GMBH ★
Fuhrberger Strasse 5, D-30625 Hannover

HAREN (Ems)

PANNELL KERR FORSTER ▼
Ankerstrasse 5, 49733 Haren

HELMSTEDT

PANNELL KERR FORSTER ▼
Botticherstasse 51, 38350 Helmstedt

HOF

KPMG DEUTSCHE TREUHAND GROUP ★
Killmbacher Strasse 47, 95030 Hof

KARLSRUHE

PRICEWATERHOUSE-COOPERS GMBH ★
Postfach 63 29, D-76043 Karlsruhe

PRICEWATERHOUSE-COOPERS GMBH ★
Blucherstr 17, 76185 Karlsruhe

KASSEL

PRICEWATERHOUSE-COOPERS GMBH ★
Bertha-von-Suttner-Strasse 3, D-34131 Kassel

KIEL

BDO INTERNATIONAL ▽
Dahlmannstrasse 1-3, 24103 Kiel

KOBLENZ

BDO INTERNATIONAL ▽
August-Thyssen-Strasse 20, 56070 Koblenz

LEIPZIG

ERNST & YOUNG GMBH ★
Grimmaische Strasse 25, D-04109 Leipzig

PANNELL KERR FORSTER ▼
August Bebel Strasse 61, 04275 Leipzig

PRICEWATERHOUSE-COOPERS GMBH ★
Kathe-Kollwitz-Strasse 21, D-04109 Leipzig

PRICEWATERHOUSE-COOPERS GMBH ★
Inselstrasse 29, D-04103 Leipzig

LORRACH

PRICEWATERHOUSE-COOPERS GMBH ★
Wallbrunnstr 24, D-79539 Lorrach

LUBECK

BDO INTERNATIONAL ▽
Alfstrasse 38, 23552 Lubeck

LUDENSCHEID

MS BERATUNGS-UND-TREUHAND-UNION GMBH ▼
Staberger Strasse 5, 5880 Ludenscheid

MAGDEBURG

PANNELL KERR FORSTER ▼
Klausenerstrasse 29, 39112 Magdeburg

PRICEWATERHOUSE-COOPERS GMBH ★
Hegelstrasse 4, D-39104 Magdeburg

MAINZ

KPMG DEUTSCHE TREUHAND GROUP ★
Issac Fulda Allee 1, 55124 Mainz

PRICEWATERHOUSE-COOPERS GMBH ★
Hindenburgstrasse 32, D-55118 Mainz

MANNHEIM

KPMG DEUTSCHE TREUHAND GROUP ★
Postfach 100743, 68007 Mannheim

MUNICH

BDO INTERNATIONAL ▽
Elisenstrasse 3, 80335 Munich

ERNST & YOUNG GMBH ★
Arnulfstrasse 126, 80636 Munich

INDUSTRIE UND VERKENHRSTREUHAND GMBH ▼
Maximilianstrasse 27, 80539 Munich

KPMG DEUTSCHE TREUHAND GROUP ★
Ganghoferstrasse 29, 80339 Munich

KPMG DEUTSCHE TREUHAND GROUP ★
Elektrastrasse 6, 81925 Munich

KPMG DEUTSCHE TREUHAND GROUP ★
Oskar-von-Miller-Ring 35, 80333, 2 Munich

MACINTYRE STRATER INTERNATIONAL LTD ▼
Bavariaring 18, DW-8000 Munich

MS BERATUNGS-UND-TREUHAND-UNION GMBH ▼
Adalbertstrasse 110, 8000 Munich

PANNELL KERR FORSTER ▼
Maximlianstrasse 27, 80539 Munich

PKF PANNELL KERR FORSTER GMBH ▼
Maximilianstrasse 27, 80539 Munich

PRICEWATERHOUSE-COOPERS GMBH ★
Elsenheimerstrasse 31-33, D-80687 Munich

S.R. CONNELLAN & CO
Johann-Baptist-Lethner, Strasse 9, Langenpreising, 85465 Munich

NURNBERG

DR HELMUT FISHCHER & DR BERTRAM FISCHER ▼
Rankestrasse 56, 90461 Nurnberg

ERNST & YOUNG GMBH ★
Forchheimer Strasse 2, D-90425 Nurnberg

KPMG DEUTSCHE TREUHAND GROUP ★
Maxfeldstrasse 8, 90409 Nurnberg

OLDENBURG

ZINK & PARTNER ▼
Moslestrasse 3, 26122 Oldenburg

OSNABRUCK

MS BERATUNGS-UND-TREUHAND-UNION GMBH ▼
P.O. Box 27 67, Neidersachsenstrasse 14, 4500 Osnabruck

SOCIETAETS TREUHAND GMBH ▼
P O Box 27 67, 49017 Osnabruck

PADERBORN

PKF GREIFFENHAGEN GMBH ▼
Schildern 17-19, 33098 Paderborn

POTSDAM

PRICEWATERHOUSE-COOPERS GMBH ★
Steinstrasse 104-106, (Haus 13), D-14480 Potsdam

RECKLINGHAUSEN

PRICEWATERHOUSE-COOPERS GMBH ★
Postfach 101946, D-45619 Recklinghausen

REGENSBURG

KPMG DEUTSCHE TREUHAND GROUP ★
Albertstrasse 2, 93047 Regensburg

ROSTOCK

PANNELL KERR FORSTER ▼
Am Vogenteich 26, 18055 Rostock

PRICEWATERHOUSE-COOPERS GMBH ★
Rungestrasse 17, D-18055 Rostock

SAARBRUCKEN

PRICEWATERHOUSE-COOPERS GMBH ★
Am Halberg 4, D-66121 Saarbrucken

SCHWERIN

PRICEWATERHOUSE-COOPERS GMBH ★
Werderstrasse 74b, D-19055 Schwerin

SIEGEN

PRICEWATERHOUSE-COOPERS GMBH ★
Koblenzer Strasse 7, D-57072 Siegen

STUTTGART

BDO INTERNATIONAL ▽
P.O. Box 1364, Leonberg, 71203 Stuttgart

ERNST & YOUNG GMBH ★
Mittlerer Pfad 15, D-70499 Stuttgart

KPMG DEUTSCHE TREUHAND GROUP ★
Hessbruhlstrasse 21, D-70565 Stuttgart

MS BERATUNGS-UND-TREUHAND-UNION GMBH ▼
Rotebuehlstrasse 102, 7000 Stuttgart

PRICEWATERHOUSE-COOPERS GMBH ★
Friedrich Str. 14, D-70174 Stuttgart

WIRTSCHAFTSTREUHAN D GMBH ▼
Herdweg 18, 7000 Stuttgart

WIESBADEN

BDO INTERNATIONAL ▽
P.O. Box 2125, 65011 Wiesbaden

WUPPERTAL

DUSSELDORFER TREUHAND-GESELL SCHAFT ALTENBURG & TEWES ▼
Werth 91-93, 5600 Wuppertal

MS BERATUNGS-UND-TREUHAND-UNION GMBH ▼
Wall 39, 5600 Wuppertal

GHANA

ACCRA

ASANTE-WIREDU & ASSOCIATES
East Shiuno Road, Kaneshi Estates Accra, PO Box 20077, Accra

AYEW AGYEMAN TURKSON & CO
Mobil House, P.O. Box 3599, Accra

EMMANUEL KORAM & ASSOCIATES
27 Mankralo Street, East Cantonments, PO Box 3538, Accra

ISSIFU ALI & CO
PO Box 6037, Accra
Tel: 00 233 21230433
Fax: 00 23321224674
Email: hlbia@ghanatel.com.gh
Principal: ICAEW Member
I Ali
Resident Partners (Non-ICAEW Members):
K Duah-Owusu
Registered by another RSB to carry out company audit work

PKF ★
Valley View, Farrar Avenue, Accra

PRICEWATERHOUSE-COOPERS
No. 12 Aviation Road, Una Home, 3rd Floor, Airport City, Accra PMB CT 42

WILLIAMS (AKINTOLA), TETTEY & CO ▼
18 North Ridge, (P.O. Box 6014), Accra

KUMASI

PKF ★
House No. OTB 198, Odum Road, Kumasi

TEMA

PKF ★
Ghana Commercial Bank Building, (P.O.Box 1627), Tema

GIBRALTAR

GIBRALTAR

BAKER TILLY (GIBRALTAR) LTD ◈
Suite 5, International House, Bell Lane, PO Box 178, Gibraltar
Tel: 00 350 20079799
Fax: 00 350 20075141
Email: info@bakertillygibraltar.gi
Website: http://www.bakertillygibraltar.gi
Resident Partners/Directors: ICAEW Members
I P Collinson, A Linares, J Olivera, K A Robinson, C D Serruya
Resident Partners (Non-ICAEW Members):
J J Pisharello, N M Rumford
Other Offices: Regal House, Queensway, Gibraltar (Tel: 00 350 20074015)

BDO ORION LTD
PO Box 1200, Montagu, Pavilion, 8-10 Queensway, Gibraltar
Tel: 00 350 42686
Resident Partners/Directors: ICAEW Members
C P Summerfield

BENADY COHEN & CO
Garrison House, 3 Library Ramp, Gibraltar

BENJAMIN, KAY & BRUMMER
P.O.Box 472 & 104, 50 Town Range, Gibraltar

D.M. CLINTON
116 Rosia Plaza, P O Box 677, Gibraltar
Tel: 00 350 20076679
Principal: ICAEW Member
D M Clinton

DELOITTE & TOUCHE
PO Box 758, Merchant House, 22-24 John Mackintosh Square, Gibraltar

DELOITTE & TOUCHE
Imossi House, 1/5 Irish Town, P.O. Box 758, Gibraltar

DRUMMONDS
PO Box 889, Suite 3F, Eurolife Building, 1 Corral Road, Gibraltar

J. L. FISHER
9/4 Cumberland Road, Gibraltar

KEITH LAWRENCE
Haven Court, 5 Library Ramp, PO Box 900, Gibraltar
Tel: 00 350 20074827
Principal: ICAEW Member
K B Lawrence

KNIGHTS
Europort 932, Gibraltar

MACINTYRE STRATER INTERNATIONAL LTD ▼
P.O. Box 889, Suite 3F, Eurolife Bldg, 1 Corral Road, Gibraltar

MOORE STEPHENS ★
Suite 5, Watergardens 4, Waterport, P O Box 473, Gibraltar

MOORES ROWLAND CORPORATE SERVICES ▼
20-21 Queensway Quay Marina, Queensway, PO Box 925, Gibraltar

P.C. ROBERTS & CO
P.O.Box 561, PMB 6803, International, Commercial Central, Gibraltar

PHILIP OGILVIE
PO Box 29, 1st Floor, 6 Casemates Square, Gibraltar GB1 1ZZ

PRICEWATERHOUSE-COOPERS ★
Intnl Commercial Centre, Casemates Square, Gibraltar

SERFATY & CO
Suite 4, 1st Floor, 123 Main Street, Gibraltar
Tel: 00 350 20049084
Principal: ICAEW Member
M W Serfaty

GRAND DUCHY OF LUXEMBOURG

LUXEMBOURG

DELOITTE & TOUCHE ★
560 rue de Neudorf, L2220 Luxembourg

ERNST & YOUNG ★
5 Boulevard de la Foire, B.P. 351, L-2013 Luxembourg

ERNST & YOUNG ▼
7 Parc d'Activitie, Syrdall Munsbach, L-5365 Luxembourg

HOOGEWERF & CO
PO Box 878, 19 Rue Aldringen, L-2018 Luxembourg

HT GROUP S.A. ◈
15-17 Av Gaston Diderich, L-1420 Luxembourg
Tel: 00 352 4040341
Fax: 00 352 291030
Email: advice@htgroup.lu
Website: http://www.htgroup.lu
Resident Partners/Directors: ICAEW Members
K Horsburgh, F G Thomas
Registered by another RSB to carry out company audit work

SPECIALISATIONS – AUDIT & ASSURANCE
Audit

SPECIALISATIONS – BUSINESS & GENERAL ADVICE
Book-keeping
Company Formation
Company Secretarial Service

SPECIALISATIONS – IT
Computer Consultants

SPECIALISATIONS – SECTOR
New Media

SPECIALISATIONS – TAXATION
Offshore Companies
Payroll Service and Advice
Taxation

Languages Spoken:
English, French, German

KPMG AUDIT ★
9 Allee Scheffer, 2520 Luxembourg

MOORE STEPHENS S.A.R.L ▼
16 Allee Marconi, B P 260, 2012 Luxembourg

PANNELL KERR FORSTER ▼
6 Place de Nancy, L-2212 Luxembourg

PANNELL KERR FORSTER ▼
69 Rue de la Liberation, 4210 Esch-Sur-Alzette, Luxembourg

PRICEWATERHOUSE-COOPERS S.A.R.L. ★
400 route d'Esch, L-1471 Luxembourg

RESOURCE REVISION S.A.R.L
36, Rue Gabriel Lippmann, L-1943 Luxembourg
Tel: 00 352 404206
Principal: ICAEW Member
C F Medlyn

VAINKER & ASSOCIATES SARL
17bd Royal, L-2449 Luxembourg

GREECE

ATHENS

AMIR M. JAZAYERI
15 Fleming Street, Vari, 16672 Athens

DELOITTE HADJIPAVLOU SOFIANOS & CAMBANIS S.A ★
250-254 Kifissias Avenue, P O Box 62091, GR15231, Halandri, Athens

DIMITRIOS CALOUPIS
4 Agias Filotheis, Filothei, 15237 Athens

ERNST & YOUNG ★
11 KLM National Road, Athens Lamia, Metamorphosi, PC 14451 Athens

ERNST & YOUNG ★
Athens Tower A, 4th Floor, 2-4 Messogion Avenue, GR-115 27 Athens

KPMG CERTIFIED AUDITORS AE ★
3 Stratigou Tombra Street, Aghia Paraskevi, GR 153 42 Athens
Tel: 00 30 2106062100
Fax: 00 30 2106062111
Email: postmaster@kpmg.gr
Website: http://www.kpmg.gr
Date Established: 1971
Resident Partners/Directors: ICAEW Members
M Kokkinos, M T Kyriacou
Resident Partners (Non-ICAEW Members):
N Vouniseas, J Achilas, D Caravelis, G Papailiou, H Sirounis, C Douka, S Kyriacou, T Panayides, N Tsiboukas
Other Offices: Thessaloniki
Registered by another RSB to carry out company audit work
Licensed by another DPB to carry on investment business
Individual(s) licensed for insolvency work by another RPB

SPECIALISATIONS – AUDIT & ASSURANCE
Assurance Services

SPECIALISATIONS – BUSINESS & GENERAL ADVICE
Acquisitions and Mergers
Book-keeping

SPECIALISATIONS – FINANCIAL REPORTING
Accounts Preparation

SPECIALISATIONS – SECTOR
Corporate

SPECIALISATIONS – TAXATION
Personal

General Description: Audit, tax, advisory and a variety of other specialised services such as corporate finance.
Languages Spoken:
Greek, English, French, German

MONDAY PAPAKYRIACOU DFK
340 Kifissias Avenue, Psyhico, 15451 Athens

MOORE STEPHENS SA ▼
8 Academias St, GR-106 71 Athens

PANNELL KERR FORSTER ▼
124 Kifissias Avenue, 11526 Athens

PRICEWATERHOUSE-COOPERS ★
268 Kifissias Avenue, Halandri, 15232 Athens

PRICEWATERHOUSE-COOPERS ★
24 Xenias Street, Ilissia, 11 528 Athens

METAMORPHOSIS

ERNST & YOUNG ★
11th KM National Road Athens, Lamia, 14451 Metamorfosis

PIRAEUS

ERNST & YOUNG (HELLAS) SA ▼
87 Akti Miaouli Street, 185 38 Piraeus

MOORE STEPHENS ★
(P.O.Box No. 80 132), 93 Akti Miaouli, GR-185 38, Piraeus

PRICEWATERHOUSE-COOPERS ★
2, II Merarchias Street, 185 35 Piraeus

THESSALONIKI

ERNST & YOUNG ★
4 Polytechneiou Street, 546 26 Thessaloniki

PANNELL KERR FORSTER ▼
33 Alexandrou Papanastasiou, 54639 Thessaloniki

PRICEWATERHOUSE-COOPERS ★
Ethnikis Antistaseos 17, Kalamaria, 55134 Thessaloniki

GRENADA

ST. GEORGES

PANNELL KERR FORSTER ▼
Pannell House, Grand Anse, St Georges

GUADELOUPE

BAIE MAHAULT

PANNELL KERR FORSTER ▼
Immeuble Le Quadrant, Boulevard de Houelbourg, Baie-Mahault, Baie Mahault 97122

PANNELL KERR FORSTER ▼
Immeuble Sopico 14, Boulevard Marquisat de, Houelbourg-Jarry, Baie Mahault 97122

GUAM

AGANA

DELOITTE & TOUCHE LLP
P.O.Box 2996, GCIC Bldg., 414 W Solidad Avenue, 96910 Agana

GUATEMALA

GUATEMALA CITY

BDO INTERNATIONAL ▽
P.O. Box 11-F, Guatemala City, 01910

PANNELL KERR FORSTER ▼
13 Calle 2-60 Zona 10, Officino 1202, Edificio Topacio Azul, Guatemala City 01010

PRAUN, REYES, ALDANA Y ASOCI ADOS ▼
Centro Financiero, Torrel, 7a Avenida 5-10, Zone 4, Guatemala City

PRICEWATERHOUSE-COOPERS ▼
Apartado Postal 868, Guatemala City, 9

GUINEA

CONAKRY

PRICEWATERHOUSE-COOPERS ▼
Immeuble ETI-Bull, 5/F, Blvd du Commerce, BP 478, Face Ambassade de France, Conakry

GUYANA

GEORGETOWN

JACK A. ALLI , SONS & CO ★
145 Crown Street, Georgetown

PKF BARCELLOS NARINE & CO ▼
106/107 Lamaha Street, North Cummingsburg, Georgetown

HAITI

PORT-AU-PRINCE

MEROVE-PIERRE ET ASSOCIES ▼
Route de l'Aeroport, Boite Postale 13270, Delmas, Port-au-Prince

HONDURAS

SAN PEDRO SULA

PEAT, MARWICK, MITCHELL & CO ▼
Edificio banco Atlantica, 7 Piso No.703, 1a.,Calle N.O,.3a. Avenida, San Pedro Sula

TEGUCIGALPA

PEAT, MARWICK, MITCHELL & CO ▼
Colonia Palmira 2A, Calle 2A Av. 212, (Apartado Postal 841), Tegucigalpa

TOVAR LOPEZ & ASOCIADOS ▼
Residencial Florencia Norte, 2DA Calle No 3715, Tegucigalpa

HONG KONG

ABERDEEN

WENDY W F YEE
Unit B, 8/F Tin Fung Industrial Mansion, 63 Wong Chuk Hang Road, Aberdeen

ADMIRALTY

CRA INTERNATIONAL (HONG KONG) LTD
1902A Tower Two, Lippo Centre, 89 Queensway, Admiralty

DAVID C. MINSHAW
3501 Parkside, 88 Queensway, Admiralty

SHINEWING (HK) CPA LTD
16/F, United Centre, 95 Queensway, Admiralty

CAUSEWAY BAY

C M WONG & CO
Flat C, 6/F, Guangdong Tours Centre, 18 Pennington Street, Causeway Bay

CCIF CPA LTD
37/F Hennessy Centre, 500 Hennessy Road, Causeway Bay

CHUNG & PARTNERS LTD ★
Room 1520, 15/F Leighton Centre, 77 Leighton Road, Causeway Bay

F S LAW & CO
Room 1315, Leighton Centre, 77 Leighton Road, Causeway Bay

GARY C.C. LAM & CO
Room 2301-02, 23rd Floor, The Kwangtung Provincial Bank Building, 409 - 415 Hennessy Road, Causeway Bay

GRANT THORNTON ★
6th Floor, Sunning Plaza, 10 Hysan Avenue, Causeway Bay

MABEL CHAN & CO
Suites 2410-11, 24/F, Shell Tower, Times Square, 1 Matheson Street, Causeway Bay

MAZARS CPA LTD
34th Floor, The Lee Gardens, 33 Hysan Avenue, Causeway Bay

MOORES ROWLAND
701 Sunning Plaza, 10 Hysan Avenue, Causeway Bay
Tel: 00 852 22183000
Resident Partners/Directors: ICAEW Members
R W C Ding, M C Fong, D C Y Lin, K F Sim

MORISON HENG
17/F One Hysan Avenue, Causeway Bay

P. C. CHIU & CO
Room 1303, Cameron Commercial Centre, 458-468 Hennessy Road, Causeway Bay

PATRICK LAI & CO ★
6/F, Ko Wah Commercial Building, 67 Percival Street, Causeway Bay

PKF ▼
26/F Citicorp Centre, 18 Whitfield Road, Causeway Bay

PKF ★
26/F Citicorp Centre, 18 Whitfield Road, Causeway Bay

PRICEWATERHOUSE-COOPERS ★
Sunning Plaza,23rd Floor, 10 Hysan Avenue, Causeway Bay

PWPLUS CPA LTD
Room 1301, Eton Tower, 8 Hysan Avenue, Causeway Bay

STEVE AU YEUNG & CO ★
Room 1902 19/F, Ka Nin Wah Commercial Building, 423-425 Hennessy Road, Causeway Bay

CENTRAL

A CHOW & PARTNERS
17/F, Amtel Building, 144-148 Des Voeux Road Central, Central

ADRIAN K C LI & CO
Units A & C, 7/F, 88 Commercial Building, 28-34 Wing Lok Street, Central

ALLIOTT TSOI CPA LTD
22nd Floor, Hing Yip Commercial Centre, 280 Des Voeux Road, Central

ANDREW K.C. LAI & CO
Room 1901 - 1902, Hong Kong Trade Centre, 161-167 Des Voeux Road, Central

ANDREW MA DFK (CPA) LTD
19 Fl, Seaview Commercial Building, 21-24 Connaught Road West, Central
Tel: 00 852 28159988
Resident Partners/Directors: ICAEW Members
A C C Ma

B KWOK & CO ◈
Units 2003 & 2004, 20/F Hua Qin, International Building, 340 Queens Road, Central
Tel: 00 852 91872766
Principal: ICAEW Member
B K B Kwok

BKR LEW & BARR LTD
12th Floor, Dina House, Ruttonjee Centre, 11 Duddell Street, Central

C. K. LIU & CO
13th Floor, Wah Kit Commercial Centre, 302 Des Voeux Road Central, Central

C.M. CHU & CO
Room1302-3, Crocodile House II, 55 Connaught Road, Central

C S YEUNG & CO
Room 204, 2/F Lyndhurst Building, 29 Lyndhurst Terrace, Central

CC CHING & CO
Rooms 801-2, The Centre Mark, 287-299 Queen's Road Central, Central

CHENG YUEN CHING JENNIFER & ASSOCIATES CPA LTD
10/F, Dawning House, 145-6 Connaught Road Central, Central

CIG CPA & CO
Room 401, 4th Floor China Insurance Group Building, 141 Des Voeux Road, Central

D K MAK & CO
Rooms 2101-3, China Insurance Group Building, 141 Des Voeux Road Central, Central

DAVE KWOK & CO
Room 902, General Commercial Building, 156-164 Des Voeux Road, Central

DAVID M.K. YEUNG & CO
14/F, San Toi Building, 137-139 Connaught Road Central, Central

DELOITTE & TOUCHE ▽
35/F One Pacific Place, 88 Queensway, Central

DELOITTE TOUCHE TOHMATSU ★
35/F One Pacific Place, 88 Queensway, Central

DENNIS CHI IN CHOW
35th Floor, One Pacific Place, 88 Queensway, Central

DOMINIC K.F. LI & CO
Room 2107-8,21/F, Kai Tak Commercial Building, 317-319 Des Voeux Road, Central

FL TANG & CO
12/F, Yat Chau Building, 262 Des Voeux Road Central, Central

FRANCIS S L YAN & CO
Rooms 801-803, China Merchants Building, Nos. 303-307 Des Voeux Road, Central

H C WONG & CO
Room 1007, 10th Floor, Won Centre, 111 Connaight Road Central, Central

HARRY C.L. POON
PO Box 9047, General Post Office, 2 Connaught Place, Central

HH LAM & CO
Room 905-909 Yu To Sang Building, 37 Queens Road, Central

JENNINGS T. H. WONG & CO
Unit 401, King Hung Commercial Building, 194-196 Queen's Road, Central

JFU CPA
Unit 1101-02, 11/F, Li Po Chun Chambers, 189 Des Voeux Road, Central

JUNIUS C T LUNG & CO
Units A & B, 21/F World Trust Tower, 50 Stanley Street, Central

K L WONG & CO
14/F, San Toi Building, 137-139 Connaught Road, Central

K W LAU CPA LTD
Room 1203, 12th Floor, United Chinese Bank Building, 31-37 Des Voeux Road, Central
Tel: 00 852 28778002
Principal: ICAEW Member
K Lau

KENNIC L. H. LUI & CO LTD
5/F, Ho Lee Commercial Building, 38 - 44 D' Aguilar Street, Central
Tel: 00 852 21103330
Resident Partners/Directors: ICAEW Members
P Choy, L K Lui, T Yuen

KPMG ★
8/F Prince's Building, 10 Chater Road, Central
Fax: 00 852 28452588
Email: enquiries@kpmg.com.hk
Website: http://www.kpmg.com.hk
Resident Partners/Directors: ICAEW Members
G R Ashford, P J Brough, J P Chattock, D J Collins, N J Debnam, S C Donowho, C Y Fung, Y K P Fung, S J E Gleave, A C Grassick, J B Harrison, K M Ho, P Y L Kan, C W Ko, P W Kung, F K H Lee, S H Y Lee, E S Y Li, T B Liu, Y Liu, C Ma, A A Macpherson, P K McSheaffrey, C Muk, K L Ng, B Nikzad, I C O'Brien, W K Siu, L G Y Y Tang, C Tong, M J Wardle, A W B R Weir, E Y S Wong, M M C Wu, I L K Yan, K S Yiu, K K Yu

KPMG ▽
8/F Prince's Building, 10 Chater Road, Central

KWOK & PARTNERS
Room 2312, 23rd Floor, Nan Fung Tower, 173 Des Voeux Road Central, Central

L & C PARTNERS CPA LTD
17/F, Amtel Building, 144-148 Des Voeux Road Central, Central

LUNA LAM & CO
Room 801, The Centre Mark, 287-299 Queen's Road Central, Central

MAK CHEUNG & CO
Unit 1105, Hua Qin International Building, 340 Queen's Road, Central

NCN CPA LTD
20/F, Hong Kong Trade Centre, 161-167 Des Voeux Road, Central

PHILIP P L CHOI & CO
2702-6 Lucky Commercial Centre, 103-9 Des Voeux Road West, Central

S L LEE & LAU ★
Room 1702, 17/F, Tung Hip Commercial Building, 248 Des Voeux Road, Central

SAMMY K. K. NG
Unit 302, Kam On Building, 176a Queens Road, Central

SUN & CO
Room 801, The Centre Mark, 287 - 299 Queen's Road Central, Central

T P AU & CO
Unit A, 10th Floor, Sun House, 90 Connaught Road, Central

THOMAS CHENG & CO
Units 803-4, 8/F, Nan Fung Tower, 173 Des Voeux Road, Central

VICTOR TSUI & CO
39/F, Shun Tak Centre, West Tower, 200 Connaught Road Central, Central

WAN MAN TSANG ◈
Room 2303-04, Wing on Centre, 111 Connaught Road, Central

WKL & PARTNERS C.P.A LTD
20/F, Ka Wah Bank Centre, 232 Des Voeux Road Central, Central

WONG MIU TING, IVY
Room 21, 2/F, New Henry House, 10 Ice House Street, Central

Y.K. LEUNG & CO
Room 804, 8th Floor, Lap Fai Building, 6-8 Pottinger Street, Central

Y.L. LAW AND CO ★
Room 502, 5/F, Prosperous Building, 48-52 Des Voeux Road, Central

ALBERT WONG & CO ★
Room 701A, Nan Dao Commercial Building, 359-361 Queen's Road Central, Central

ALFRED HK HUEN & CO
14/F Wing On Cheong Building, 5 Wink Lok Street, Central

AU YEUNG HUEN YING & CO
8th Floor, Shum Tower, 268 Des Vouex Road, Central

AZURE LTD
Suite 4708, The Center, 99 Queen's Road, Central

BAKER TILLY HONG KONG LTD
12/F, China Merchants Tower, Shun Tak Centre, 168-200 Connaught Road, Central

BDO MCCABE LO & LTD
8th Floor, Wing On Centre, 111 Connaught Road, Central

BINGLEY WONG & CO
5th Floor, Wah Kit Commercial Centre, 300 Des Voeux Road Central, Central

BUT DO YEUNG C.P.A. LTD
Unit 2203, 22/F, Golden Centre, 118 Des Voeux Road Central, Central

BUT DO YEUNG C.P.A. LTD
Rooms 1801-05, 18th Floor, Hua Qin International Building, 340 Queen's Road Central, Central

CHAN, NG & PARTNERS LTD
Unit 503 5/F Dina House, Ruttonjee Centre, 11 Duddell Street, Central

CHENG, KWOK & CHANG ★
Rm B, 19/F Tung Hip Comm Bldg, 244-252 Des Voeux Road, Central

CHUI & KWOK ★
3/F No. 9 Chiu Lung Street, Central

DELOITTE TOUCHE TOHMATSU ★
26/F Wing On Centre, 111 Connaught Road, Central

DICKSON WONG CPA CO LTD
Room 302, 3/F, The Chinese General Chamber of Commerce Building, 24-25 Connaught Road, Central

EDWIN C. W. YEUNG & CO ★
12/F Lucky Building, 39 Wellington Street, Central

ERNST & YOUNG ★
18/F, Two International Finance Centre, 8 Finance Street, Central

ERNST & YOUNG ★
15/F Hutchison House, 10 Harcourt Road, Central

ERNST & YOUNG TAX SERVICES LTD
18/F, Two IFC, 8 Finance Street, Central

EXCELSIOR CPA & CO
Unit 1, 15th Floor, Workingbond Commercial Centre, 162 Prince Edward Road West, Central

FOK CHAN LEUNG WAN CPA LTD
Rooms904-8 & 403-4, Kai Tak Commercial Building, 317-319 Des Voeux Road, Central

FUNG, YU & CO
Hong Kong Trade Centre 7/F, 161-7 Des Voeux Road Central, Central

GEORGE M.C. MAK & CO ◈
Suites 1801-2, 18th Floor, Alliance Building, 130-136 Connaught Road, Sheung Wan Central
Tel: 00 852 25438060
Principal: ICAEW Member
G M Mak

GRAHAM H Y CHAN & CO ◈
Unit 1, 15/F The Center, 99 Queens Road, Central

GRANT THORNTON ★
13/F Gloucester Tower, The Landmark, 11 Pedder Street, Central
Tel: 00 852 22483166
Resident Partners/Directors: ICAEW Members
R W C Ding, Y Hsiang, D C Y Lin, N Lo, K F Sim, C W Tang

H.H.LAM & CO
Yu To Sang Bldg 9/F, 37 Queens Road, Central

H. H. LIU & CO ★
Rooms 1801-2 18/F, China Insurance Group Building, 141 Des Voeux Road, Central

HENRY WONG & CO
15/F Yue Thai Comm. Bldg, 128 Connaught Road, Central

HERMAN H. Y. NG & CO
20/F, Hong Kong Trade Centre, 161-167 Des Voeux Road, Central
Tel: 00 852 25416622
Principal: ICAEW Member
HY Ng

HLB HODGSON IMPEY CHENG ★ ◈
31/F Gloucester Tower, The Landmark, 11 Pedder Street, Central
Tel: 00 852 28108333
Resident Partners/Directors: ICAEW Members
D K W Cheng, R C C Cheng, J T S Lai, K Young

HO SNEDDON CHOW
Room 1406, China Insurance Group Building, 141 Des Voeux Road, Central

HORACE HO & CO ★
Room 801 8th Floor, Kai Tak Commercial Building, 317-319 Des Voeux Road Central, Central

JOHN K H LI
602 Aon China Bldg, 29 Queen's Road, Central

K.B.TAM & CO
Rooms C-F, 5th Floor, Shing Lee Commercial Building, 6-12 Wing Kut Street, Central

K.C. OH & CO
8th Floor, New Henry House, 10 Ice House Street, Central

K. W. WAN & CO ★
Room 605, 6 Floor Kai Wong Commercial Building, 222-226 Queen's Road Central, Central

KAM CHING YU CPA LTD
Rooms 801-2, The Centre Mark, 287-299 Queen's Road Central, Central

KPMG ★
27/F Alexandra House, 18-20 Chater Road, Central

KWAN WONG TAN & HONG
South China Building, 1 Wyndham Street, Central

LAK & ASSOCIATES C.P.A. LTD ★
Chinachem Tower, 3rd Floor, 34-37 Connaught Road, Central

LAW & PARTNERS CPA LTD
8/F Chinachem Tower, 34-37 Connaught Road, Central

LAW KAM WING & CO
9th Floor, Full View Commercial Bldg, 140-142 Des Voeux Road, Central

LAWRENCE CHEUNG C P A COMPANY LTD
20th Floor, Euro Trade Centre, 21-23 Des Voeux Road, Central

LOUIS LEUNG & PARTNERS CPA LTD
13th Floor, Sun House, 181 Des Voeux Road, Central

M.C. NG & CO
Room 1502, Double Building, 22 Stanley Street, Central

MARK K. LAM & CO ★
Room 2002-03, 20th Floor, Nan Dao Commercial Building, 359-361 Queen's Road, Central

MICHAEL TSOI AND CO
79 - 83 Queen's Road Central, 22nd Floor, Man Hing Commercial Building, Central

NOBLE PONDUS (CPA) LTD
Room B, 7/F, Man Hing Commericial Building, 79-83 Queen's Road Central, Central

NOBLE PONDUS (CPA) LTD
Unit 3003, 30/F, West Tower, Shun Tak Centre, 168-200 Connaught Road Central, Central

P.H.LAM & CO
Room 1602, Tung Hip Commercial Building, 244-252 Des Voeux Road, Central

PATRICK NG & CO
20th Floor, Hong Kong Trade Centre, 161-167 Des Voeux Road, Central

PAUL W.C. HO & CO
20th Floor Golden Centre, No. 188 Des Voeux Road, Central

PHILIP LEE & CO ★
14th Floor, Cnac Group Building, 10 Queen's Road Central, Central

PRICE WATERHOUSE ▼
33/F Cheung Kong Centre, 2 Queens Road, Central

PRICEWATERHOUSE-COOPERS ★
21/F Edinburgh Tower, Edinburgh Tower, 15 Queen's Road Central, Central

PRICEWATERHOUSE-COOPERS ★
Prince's Building, 22nd Floor, Central

PRICEWATERHOUSE-COOPERS ★
33/F Cheung Kong Center, 2 Queen's Road, Central

RAYMOND F.L. WONG
Room 2505, Universal Trade Centre, 3-5A Arbuthnot Road, Central

REGINA L.S. CHOW
5/F Dahsing Life Building, 99-105 Des Voeux Road, Central

RICHARD S K CHAN & CO
Room 1601, Yu Sung Boon Building, 107 Des Vouex Road C, Central

ROCKY SHEK & CO
Room 901, Yip Fung Building, 9/F No 2, D'Aguilar Street, Central
Tel: 00 852 25237012
Resident Partners/Directors: ICAEW Members
R Shek

RONALD H. T. LEE & CO ★
1st Floor Sam Cheong Building, 216-220 Des Voeux Road Central, Central

RONALD W.F. KO & CO ★
4th Floor, Winbase Centre, 208 Queen's Road Central, Central

RYAN IP & CO ★
Room 1801, The Centre Mark, 287-299 Queen's Road Central, Central

S.L. LAM & CO ◈
Rooms 1804-5,The Centre Mark, 287-299 Queen's Road Central, Central

S.L. POON & CO ★
37 Queen's Road, 703 Yu To Sang Building, Central

SUZANNE WONG & CO
Suite 904, 9/F Chinachem Tower, 34-37 Connaught Road, Central

TANG AND FOK ★
Rooms 1801-3 18/Floor, Tung Ning Building, 249-253 Des Voeux Road Central, Central

THOMAS TANG
3404 One Exchange Square, 8 Connaught Place, Central

TING HO KWAN & CHAN
9th Floor, Tung Ning Bldg, 249-253 Des Voeux Road C, Central

TLA CPA LTD
Room 2205, 22/F Nan Fung Tower, 173 Des Voeux Road Central, Central

TSANG TAM & CO
Room 704, 7/F Kai Wong Commercial Building, 222-226 Queens Road, Central

W.K. SUI
8th Floor, Prince's Building, Central

WALLACE KO & CO ★
Room 603-604 6th Floor, Tai Sang Bank Building, 130-132 Des Voeux Road, Central
Tel: 00 852 28540338
Resident Partners/Directors: ICAEW Members
Y W W Ko

WONG LAM LEUNG & KWOK C.P.A LTD
11/F China Insurance Group Building, 141 Des Voeux Road Central, Central

Y.F.PANG & CO
19/F, Dah Sing Life Building, 99 Des Voeux Road Centre, Central

YIP TAI HIM
7/F New York House, 60 Connaught Road, Central

YMT CPA LTD
24/F Golden Centre, 188 Des Voeux Road Central, Central
Tel: 00 852 28518700
Resident Partners/Directors: ICAEW Members
M T Yip

YU HOW YUEN & CO ★
Room 1104-1105 New Victory House, 93-103 Wing Lok Street, Central

CHEUNG SAH WAN

KINSON CPA & CO ★
Room 901, Hang Seng Castle Peak Road Building, 339 Castle Peak Road, Cheung Sha Wan

HUNG HOM

GALA CPA
Unit 1005, 10/F, Tower B, Hunghom Comm Ctr, 37 Ma Tau Wai Road, Hung Hom

K Y LUK & CO
Room 912, 9/F, 655 Nathan Road, Hung Hom

S.Y. YU
Unit 1007, 10/F, Focal Industrial Building, 21 Man Lok Street, Hung Hom

KOWLOON BAY

KTC CPA LTD
Rooms 704 - 705, 7/F, Kowloon Building, 555 Nathan Road, Kowloon Bay

KOWLOON CITY

C K LAM & CO ★
Unit 704, Fourseas Building, 202-212- Nathan Road, Kowloon City

FTW & PARTNERS CPA LTD
1001-3 10th Floor, Manulife Provident Funds Place, 345 Nathan Road, Kowloon City

KWUN TONG

HUI KA HUNG RAYMOND
1902 Westley Square, 48 Hoi Yuen Road, Kwun Tong

TANG YUEN SHUN
Unit K, 18/F, world Tech Centre, 95 How Ming Street, Kwun Tong

MEI FOO SUN CHUEN

ANTHONY WONG
14C, 6/F Nassau Road, Mei Foo Sun Chuen

MONG KOK

ANDREW TSE & CO
Suite 1501, 15th Floor Ginza Plaza, 2A Sai Yeung Choi Street South, Mong Kok

ANOVA
Unit 2205, 22/F Pioneer Centre, 750 Nathan Road, Mong Kok

ANTHONY Y.T.TSE & CO
Room 711, Argyle Centre, 7th Floor, 688 Nathan Road, Mong Kok

BILLY HO AND CO ★
15/F, Hang Seng Mongkok Bldg, 677 Nathan Road, Mong Kok

BLES & PARTNERS CPA LTD
Unit 802, 8/F Bright Way Tower, 33 Mongkok Road, Mong Kok

BT WONG & CO
Unit A, 6/F Rammon House, 101 Sai Yeung Choi Street, Mong Kok

CHENG, YEUNG & CO CPA
Room 1001-2, 10 Floor, Chow Tai Fook Centre, No 580 A-F Nathan Road, Mong Kok
Tel: 00 852 28517998
Principal: ICAEW Member
S Cheng, S H Yeung

CHEUNG LEE NG & CO
Room 1208, Two Grand Tower, 625 Nathan Road, Mong Kok

CK LAW & CO ★
1101 Bank Centre, 630-636 Nathan Road, Mong Kok
Tel: 00 852 23881161
Resident Partners/Directors: ICAEW Members
C K Law

DEREK NG & CO ◈
Room 702, Hollywood Plaza, 610 Nathan Road, Mong Kok
Tel: 00 852 27827186
Principal: ICAEW Member
K K D Ng

EDMUND LAU & CO
Room 1906, 19/F 655 Nathan Road, Mong Kok

FRANCIS HL SHAM & CO
Room 612, 6/F, Hollywood Plaza, 610 Nathan Road, Mong Kok

J & F CO ★
Room 1007, 10/F, 113 Argyle Street, Mong Kok

JENNY KUN & CO ◈
Room 1112, 11/F, Hollywood Plaza, 610 Nathan Road, Mong Kok

KENNETH WONG & CO
Unit B & C, 20/F Full Win Commercial Centre, 573 Nathan Road, Mong Kok

KINSON CPA & CO ★
Room 1003, 10/F Nathan Centre, 580G-K Nathan Road, Mong Kok

LEE SIK WAI & CO ◈
Rooms 2005-7, Bank Centre, 636 Nathan Road, Mong Kok
Tel: 00 852 23599330
Principal: ICAEW Member
S W B Lee

MICHAEL M.C. CHAN & CO
Room 2401, 24/F, 280 Portland Street Commercial Building, 276-280 Portland Street, Mong Kok

MOK & FONG CPA LTD
Flats 2 & 3, 21/F Chung Kiu Commercial Building, 47-51 Shantung Street, Mong Kok

P H TANG & CO
3rd Floor, Rammon House, 101 Sai Yeung Choi Street South, Mong Kok

RICKY LEUNG & CO
Unit 2205, 22/F Pioneer Centre, 750 Nathan Road, Mong Kok

S.W. KAN & CO
Room 704, Kowloon Building, 555 Nathan Road, Mong Kok

SIMON S W LUI & CO
Bank Centre 1013, Nathan Road 636, Mong Kok

THOMAS C.I. LEUNG & CO
Room 1301-1302, Kowloon Building, 555 Nathan Road, Mong Kok

W.O. LO & CO
Room 1901-2, Park-In Commercial Centre, 56 Dundas Street, Mong Kok

WEBSTER NG & CO ★
Rooms 307-9 3/F, Ritz Building, 625 Nathan Road, Mong Kok

WEBSTER NG & CO ★
Room 1117, Hollywood Plaza, 610 Nathan Road, Mong Kok

NORTH POINT

C K YAU & CO ★ ◈
1 Floor, Yuet Ming Building, 129 King's Road, North Point
Tel: 00 852 25781914
Resident Partners/Directors: ICAEW Members
W L Yau

CHAN CHUN KWONG & CO
904 Wellborne Commercial Centre, 8 Java Road, North Point

GEORGE TSO & CO
807 Fortress Tower, 250 King's Road, North Point

KA LUN LAM & CO
Room 1401, 14/F Kwai Hung Holdings Centre, 89 King's Road, North Point

KUNG LOK LAM & CO
Unit 3, 12th Floor Jupiter Tower, 9 Jupiter Street, North Point

LAU CHEUNG FUNG & CHAN
1707, Chinachem Plaza, 338 King's Road, North Point

STEPHEN JASPER
912 Wellbourne Commercial Centre, 8 Java Road, North Point

TAM CHI MING
Room 1805, 18th Floor, Wellborne Commercial Centre, 8 Java Road, North Point
Tel: 00 852 28336366
Principal: ICAEW Member
C M Tam

FELIX W.S. LO & CO
Room 208, Workingberg Commercial Building, 41-47 Marble Road, North Point

PCP CPA LTD
Suite 2205-6, Island Place Tower, 510 King's Road, North Point

TOMMY C.P. SZE & CO ◈
Flat 2003, 20/F, Wellborne Commercial Centre, 8 Java Road, North Point
Tel: 00 852 2806852
Principal: ICAEW Member
C T Sze

POKFULAM

TSANG CHO TAI
8E Fulham Garden, 84 Pokfulam Road, Pok Fu Lam

QUARRY BAY

K H CHUNG & CO ★
Unit 705, 7/F Eastern Centre, No 1065 King's Road, Quarry Bay

LEUNG & CHAN
7th Floor, Hyde Centre, 221-226 Gloucester Road, Quarry Bay

SAI YING PUN

AARON WONG & CO
Room 1603, 16th Floor, Tung Che Commercial Centre, No 246 Des Voeux Road West, Sai Ying Pun

ROGER K C LEE & CO
Room 1109, 11/F, 118 Connaught Road West, Sai Ying Pun

SAN PO KONG

S L WONG & CO
Flat D, 8th Floor, Success Industrial Building, 17 Sheung Hei Street, San Po Kong

SHAU KEI WAN

LAM SIU HUNG & CO
ROOM 1602, Chit Lee Commercial Building, 30-36 Shau Kei Wan Road, Shau Kei Wan

SHEUNG SHUI

H. T. WONG & CO ★
1123A Landmark North, 39 Lung Sum Avenue, Sheung Shui

SHEUNG WAN

CHEUNG PUI CHUNG & CO
Office A, 21/F, Crawford Tower, 99 Jervois Street, Sheung Wan

K. L. LAM & CO
2/F Xiu Ping Commercial Building, 104 Jervois Street, Sheung Wan

LAM & CO
Unit C, 21 Floor, Hong Kong Industrial Building, 444-452 Des Voeux Road West, Sheung Wan

PRICEWATERHOUSE-COOPERS ★
14/F, ING Tower, 308 Des Voeux Road Central, Sheung Wan

ROBIN PANG & CO
2/F, Xiu Ping Comm Bldg, 104 Jervois Street, Sheung Wan

S L WONG & CO
2nd Floor, Teng Fuh Commercial Building, 333 Queen's Road Central, Sheung Wan

WWW.FORENSIC.HK
21 B, Wing Hing Commercial Building, 139 Wing Lok Street, Sheung Wan

ATSA CPA & CO
Room B, 19/F, 88 Commercial Building, 28-34 Wing Lok Street, Sheung Wan
Resident Partners/Directors: ICAEW Members
M F Fung

CHAN, NG & PARTNERS LTD
Rm 1206, Bonham Trade Ctr, 50 Bonham Strand East, Sheung Wan

CHAN YIP KEUNG & CO
Room 1003, 10/F Seaview Commercial Building, 21-24 Connaught Road West, Sheung Wan

CHING SHUN FU & CO
Block B, 14/F Hillier Commercial Building, 89-91 Wing Lok Street, Sheung Wan

FUNG & PANG CPA LTD ◈
1/F & 2/F Xiu Ping Commercial Building, 104 Jervois Street, Sheung Wan

IAN SEE & CO
903 Arion Commercial Centre, 2 Queen's Road West, Sheung Wan

PANG CHAN & CO ◈
Unit A, 13th Floor, E.I.B. Centre, 40-44 Bonham Strand, Sheung Wan
Tel: 00 852 2854 4122
Principal: ICAEW Member
Y W Chan

TOMMY NG & CO
Suite B, 11/F Foo Cheong Building, 82-86 Wing Lok Street, Sheung Wan
Tel: 00 852 2122 9060
Principal: ICAEW Member
F L Ng

VINCENT LEE & CO ★
1/F Xiu Ping Commercial Building, 104 Jervois Street, Sheung Wan
Tel: 00 852 2116 0162
Resident Partners/Directors: ICAEW Members
T C V Lee

W.H. WONG & CO
Room 9, 31/F, China Merchants Tower, Shun Tak Centre, 168 Connaught Road Central, Sheung Wan

TSIM SHA TSUI

BARRY LEE & CO
Unit C, 8th Floor, Charmhill Centre, 50 Hillwood Road, Tsim Sha Tsui

C W LEUNG & CO
Room 403, Wing on House, 71 Des Voeux Road Central, Tsim Sha Tsui

CB WONG & CO
Room 1601, Carnarvon Plaza, 20 Carnarvon Road, Tsim Sha Tsui

CHAN & WAT
Suite A, 19th Floor, Ritz Plaza, 122 Austin Road, Tsim Sha Tsui

CHU AND CHU ★
Suite 1801-5, 18/F, Tower 2, China Hong Kong City, 33 Canton Road, Tsim Sha Tsui
Tel: 00 852 28151133
Resident Partners/Directors: ICAEW Members
K Chan, K T Chan, K A Wong, S Yeung

CLL CPA LTD
Suite C, 9/F Ritz Plaza, 122 Austin Road, Tsim Sha Tsui

DIANA L MA & CO
Room 503, 5/F, Hart Avenue Plaza, 5-9 Hart Avenue, Tsim Sha Tsui

ERNST & YOUNG ★
10/F Tower 2, The Gateway, 25/27 Canton Road, Tsim Sha Tsiu

GEORGE K W HO & CO
Suite 708, 7/F, Chinachem Golden Plaza, 77 Mody Road, Tsim Sha Tsui

H. P. WAN & CO ★
711A Ocean Centre, Canton Road, Tsim Sha Tsiu

H. T. WONG & CO ★
1711 North Tower, Concordia Plaza, 1 Science Museum Road, Tsim Sha Tsiu

HENDRY LAU & CO
Room 704, 7/F Landwide Commercial Building, 118-120 Austin Road, Tsim Sha Tsui

HORACE HO & CO ★ ◈
Unit 511, Tower 1 Silvercord, 30 Canton Road, Tsim Sha Tsui
Tel: 00 852 25210706
Email: info@horaceho.com
Website: http://www.horaceho.com
Resident Partners/Directors: ICAEW Members
Horace M K Ho
Overseas Offices: Shanghai Office: Rm2402, 24/F Shanghai Universal Mansion 172 Yu Yuan Road, Jingan Dis, Shanghai 200040, PRC
Registered by another RSB to carry out company audit work

K. F. WONG & CO
Unit 8, 13/F, Rise Commercial Building, 5-11 Granville Circuit, Granville Road, Tsim Sha Tsiu

K.M. CHAN & CO
Room 1702, One Peking, 1 Peking Road, Tsim Sha Tsui

K.S. LIU & COMPANY, CPA LTD
Unit 1003, 10/F, Rightful Centre, 12 Tak Hing Street, Tsim Sha Tsui

KATON CPA LTD
Room 512, 5/F, Tower 1, Silvercord, 30 Canton Road, Tsim Sha Tsui

KEITH WONG CPA & CO
Room 903, 9/F, Parkes Commercial Centre, 2 - 8 Parkes Street, Tsim Sha Tsui

KEN CHAN & CO
Room 102, 1st Floor, Oriental Centre, 67-71 Chatham Road, Tsim Sha Tsui
Tel: 00 852 23149570
Resident Partners/Directors: ICAEW Members
S K Chan

KMS CPA LTD
Suite 1912, 19th Floor, Tower 1, The Gateway, 25 Canton Road, Tsim Sha Tsui

LAWRENCE CHAN & CO
Suite 1102A, Fourseas Building, 208 - 212 Nathan Road, Tsim Sha Tsui

LEE YUEN KWONG & CO
20th Floor, Quality Education Tower, 476 Nathan Road, Tsim Sha Tsui

LEUNG MING CHI
Unit D 5th Floor, China Insurance Building, 48 Cameron Road, Tsim Sha Tsui

MOORE STEPHENS ★
905 Silvercord, Tower 2, 30 Canton Road, Tsim Sha Tsui

P.K. WONG & CO
Unit 1110, Lippo Sun Plaza, 28 Canton Road, Tsim Sha Tsui

PETER LAM & CO ★ ◈
Suite 1807 The Gateway, Tower II Harbour City, 25 Canton Road, Tsim Sha Tsui
Tel: 00 852 29562803
Resident Partners/Directors: ICAEW Members
K C P Lam

S. F. CHEUNG & CO ★
Room 704 Belgian Bank Building, 721-725 Nathan Road, Tsim Sha Tsui

SHERMAN CHONG & CO
Suite 902, 9th Floor, Parkes Commercial Centre, No. 2-8 Parkes Street, Tsim Sha Tsui
Tel: 00 852 2368 1771
Principal: ICAEW Member
Y S Chong

TO WAI KUM
1711 North Tower, Concordia Plaza, 1 Science Museum Road, Tsim Sha Tsui

ULYSSES YUEN & CO ★
13/F Foo Ho Centre, 3 Austin Avenue, Tsim Sha Tsui

VINCENT MAK & CO
Room 1617-18, Star House, 3 Salisbury Road, Tsim Sha Tsui

WILLIAM M. L. HO & CO LTD
Unit Nos. 301-02 3/F, New East Ocean Centre, No. 9 Science Museum Road, Tsim Sha Tsui

Y L NGAN & CO
Suite 1019, 10/F China Chem Golden Plaza, 77 Mody Road, Tsim Sha Tsui

YIP,NG & CO
Room A-B, 15/F, Ritz Plaza, 122 Austin Road, Tsim Sha Tsui

TSUEN KWAN O NEW

FELIX NG
Dascom Technology Limited, Room 1811-12, Nan Fung Center, 298 Castle Peak Road, Tsuen Kwan O

TSUEN WAN

C M WONG & CO
Room 1245, 12/F Nan Fung Centre, 264-298 Castle Peak Road, Tsuen Wan

FUNG LEUNG & CO
Room 1606, Nan Fung Centre, 264-298, Tsuen Kwan O

W M WONG & CO
Room 1517, 15/F, Nan Fung Centre, 264-298 Castle Peak Road, Tsuen Wan Tsuen Kwan O

WAN CHAI

AIP PARTNERS CPA LTD
Room 1304, C C Wu Building, 302-308 Hennessy Road, Wan Chai
Tel: 00 852 2169 8887
Resident Partners/Directors: ICAEW Members
K K Kwan, T Y Yung Linda

APEX CPA LTD
Unit 1801, 18th Floor, Dominion Centre, 43-59 Queen's Road East, Wan Chai

C.F. CHAN & CO
28th Floor, Times Tower, 393 Jaffe Road, Wan Chai

C Y CHAN & CO
Room B, 5/F, Kiu Yin Com. Building, 361-363 Lockhart Road, Wan Chai

CACHET
13 Floor, Neich Tower, 128 Gloucester Road, Wan Chai

CCIF CPA LTD
Shu Lun Pan Horwath Hong Kong CPA Limited, 20/F Central Plaza, 18 Harbour Road, Wan Chai

CF CHEUNG
Suite 5008, Hopewell Centre, 183 Queen's Road East, Wan Chai

CHAN & MAN ★
701 7/F, Silver Base Centre, 200 Gloucester Road, Wan Chai

CHAN CHEE CHENG & CO ★
19/F, Beverly House, 93-107 Lockhart Road, Wan Chai

CHAN CHOR HUNG & CO
Unit A & B, 15/F Neich Tower, 128 Gloucester Road, Wan Chai

CHAN LI LAW & CO
Unit 1202, 12th Floor, Malaysia Building, No 50, Gloucester Road, Wan Chai

CHARLES WONG & CO
Room A, 6th Floor, Kiu Fu Commercial Building, 300 - 306 Lockhart Road, Wan Chai

DOMINIC CHEUNG AND CO
Room 1502, 15/F, Harcourt House, No.39, Gloucester Road, Wan Chai

EDMUND WONG & CO ★
Unit 2301B, 23/F, BEA Harbour View Centre, 56 Gloucester Road, Wan Chai

EDWIN CHEUNG & SIU
Room 1204, 12/F, Shanghai Ind. Building, 48-62 Hennessy Road, Wan Chai

FC PARTNERS CPA LTD
Room 1201, 12/F Methodist House, 36 Hennessey Road, Wan Chai

HO WAI KI & CO
Unit C 11th Floor, Gaylord Commercial Building, 114-118 Lockhart Road, Wan Chai

HOWARTH
2001 Central Plaza, 18 Harbour Road, Wan Chai

J & D ASSOCIATES
Room 2006, 20/F, Beverly House, 93-107 Lockhart Road, Wan Chai

JESSIE YUNG CPA
17/F Yue On Commercial Building, 385-387 Lockhart Road, Wan Chai

JIMMY C H CHEUNG & CO
1607 Dominion Centre, 43 Queen's Road East, Wan Chai

KP CHENG & CO
Room 2707, 27/E, Shui On Centre, 6-8 Harbour Road, Wan Chai

LEE KA MAN & CO
Room 1001-2, Hang Seng Wan chai Building, 200 Hennessy Road, Wan Chai

LEUNG YAU WING & CO
Unit F, 20/F, CNT Tower, 338 Hennessy Road, Wan Chai

LI, TANG, CHEN & CO ★ ◈
10/F Sun Hung Kai Centre, 30 Harbour Road, Wan Chai
Tel: 00 852 28278663
Resident Partners/Directors: ICAEW Members
W H Chan, P C Law, E K Li, K F D Li, K Yan

LIXIN CPA LTD
Unit 1602, Malaysia Building, 50 Gloucester Road, Wan Chai

LUI & MAK
604 - 607, Dominion Centre, 6th Floor, 43 - 59, Queen's Road East Wan Chai

MORISON HENG
7/F, Allied Kajima Building, 138 Gloucester Road, Wan Chai

NEXIA CHARLES MAR FAN & CO
11th Floor, Fortis Bank Tower, 77-79 Gloucester Road, Wan Chai

NG FUK YAN SAMUEL
1617 Asian House, 1 Hennessy Road, Wan Chai

OLIVER WONG & CO ★
Room B, 25/F, Yam Tze Commercial Building, 23 Thomson Road, Wan Chai

PEGASUS & CO
1301-02, 13/F Kwan Chart Tower, 6 Tonnochy Road, Wan Chai

PROBIZ CPA LTD
20/F, On Hong Commercial Building, 145 Hennessy Road, Wan Chai

RONALD W. F. CHAN & CO
Room 1703, 17/F, Henan Building, 90-92 Jaffe Road, Wan Chai

RSM NELSON WHEELER ★
29th Floor Caroline Centre, Lee Gardens Two, 28 Yun Ping Road, Wan Chai

S F KWOK & CO
Room 1501, East Town Building, 41 Lockhart Road, Wan Chai

S K CHAN & CO
Flat D 8th Floor, Tak LEe Commercial Building, 113-117 Wanchai Road, Wan Chai
Tel: 00 852 28932098
Principal: ICAEW Member
S Chan

SHU LUN PAN HORWATH HONG KONG CPA LTD
2001-2005 Central Plaza, 18 Harbour Road, Wan Chai

W M YU & CO
Flat B1, 11/F, Loyong Court Commercial Building, 212-220 Lockhart Road, Wan Chai

WONG CHAN LAU C.P.A. LTD
Rooms 805 - 6, 8/F, Tai Yau Building, 181 Johnston Road, Wan Chai

WONG CHAN LAU CPA CO LTD
Rooms 805-6, 8/F, Tai Yau Building, 181 Johnston Road, Wan Chai

WS LUI & CO
Unit B, 12/F, Ka Nin Wah Commercial Building, 423 - 425 Hennessy Road, Wan Chai

ALAN H.K.SHING & CO
Unit B, 7/F, Kai Kwong Commercial Building, 332 Lockhart Road, Wan Chai

ANAS NG
Room 708, 7/F Dannies House, 20 Luard Road, Wan Chai

ANTHONY KAM & CO ◈
6307 Central Plaza, 18 Harbour Road, Wan Chai
Tel: 00 852 22466888
Principal: ICAEW Member
A Kam

C.C. KWONG & CO ◈
11/F, No 99 Hennessy Road, Wan Chai
Tel: 00 852 25728226
Website: http://www.cckwongcpa.com
Principal: ICAEW Member
C C Kwong

SPECIALISATIONS – AUDIT & ASSURANCE
Audit

SPECIALISATIONS – BUSINESS & GENERAL ADVICE
Company Formation

General Description: C C Kwong & Co has a strong focus on taxation, migration (Australia) audit and China/HK company formation.

C.K. SHUM & CO
20/F, 88 Lockhart Road, Wan Chai

CHAN LAI PANG & CO
28/F Times Tower, 393 Jaffe Road, Wan Chai

CHAN LI LAW & CO
Unit 1202,12/F, Malaysia Building, 50 Gloucester Road, Wan Chai

CHANG LEUNG HIU & LI CPA LTD
12th Floor, No. 3, Lockhart Road, Wan Chai

CHEUNG KAM SING & CO ★
Rm. 2202 Tung Wai Commercial Building, No. 109-111 Gloucester Road, Wan Chai

CHIU CHOY & CHUNG CPA LTD
Unit A 5/F Yu Fung Commercial Centre, 289-295 Hennesey Road, Wan Chai

CLEMENT C. W. CHAN & CO
3/F & 5/F, Heng Shan Centre, 145 Queen's Road East, Wan Chai

CW IP & CO
9/F Times Media Centre, 133 Wanchai Road, Wan Chai

DOMINIC K.N. TAI & CO
16E Neich Tower, 128 Gloucester Road, Wan Chai
Tel: 00 852 25423293
Principal: ICAEW Member
D K N Tai

FRANCIS WONG CPA CO LTD
19/F, 3 Lockhart Road, Wan Chai

FUNG LAU & CO ★
Room 2604 26/F, C. C. Wu Building, 302-308 Hennessy Road, Wan Chai

GABRIEL TSE
Unit 1601, 16/F Malaysia Building, 50 Gloucester Road, Wan Chai

HENRY LAW & CO ★
Room 301-2, Hang Seng Wanchai Building 3rd Floor, No. 200 Hennessy Road, Wan Chai

HONG KONG GREAT WALL
3/F Malaysia Building, 50 Gloucester Road, Wan Chai

HORACE HO & CO ★
Flat A 13/F, Shun Pont Commercial Building, 5-11 Thomson Road, Wan Chai

HORWATH HONG KONG CPA LTD
2001 Central Plaza, 18 Harbour Road, Wan Chai

JAMES T. W. KONG & CO ★
Room 1901 19/F C C Wu Building, 302-308 Hennessy Road, Wan Chai
Tel: 00 852 28332022
Resident Partners/Directors: ICAEW Members
J Kong

JCK SHUM LEUNG LUK & CO ★
2nd Floor, Jonsim Place, 228 Queen's Road East, Wan Chai

KC NG & CO
Suite B, 13th Floor, Tak Lee Commercial Building, 113-117 Wanchai Road, Wan Chai

KCG & CO ★
Rooms 1401-2, 253-261 Hennessy Road, Wan Chai

KM YEUNG & CO
Room 405, Dominion Centre, 43-59 Queens Road E, Wan Chai

LAI & WONG ★
Unit B, 8th Floor, Success Commercial Building, 245-251 Hennessy Road, Wan Chai

LAU SY & CO ★
Room 1802 Dominion Centre, 43-59 Queen's Road East, Wan Chai

LEHMANBROWN CPA CO LTD
Room 1704, 17-F Jubilee Centre, 18 Fenwick Street, Wan Chai

LEUNG & PUEN CPA LTD
6th Floor, Kwan Chart Tower, 6 Tonnochy Road, Wan Chai
Tel: 00 852 28322831
Resident Partners/Directors: ICAEW Members
J N Leung

LOUIS YEUNG & CO ★
Room 1601 Tung Chiu Commercial Centre, 193 Lockhart Road, Wan Chai

MAURICE FONG & CO ★
Unit 2201-2 22/F Chinachem Johnston Plaza, 178-186 Johnston Road, Wan Chai

MHL CONSULTING LTD
7/F Allied Kajima Building, 138 Gloucester Road, Sar

NEXIA CHARLES MAR FAN & CO ★
11/F Fortis Bank Tower, 77-79 Gloucester Road, Wan Chai

ORIENTAL LINK CPA LTD
Suites 1303 - 1306a, 13/F, Asian House, 1 Hennessey Road, Wan Chai

PK KWONG & CO
Unit 2011, 20/F Hopewell Centre, 183 Queens Road East, Wan Chai

POON & CO ★
Dominion Centre, 6th Floor, 43-59 Queen's Road East, Wan Chai

ROBERT C.L. TSE & CO
Room 1201, 12/F Shanghai Industrial Investment Building, 48-62 Hennessy Road, Wan Chai

S. K. LUK & CO ★
Rooms 502-503 5th Floor, Wanchai Commercial Centre, 194-204 Johnston Road, Wan Chai
Tel: 00 852 28921688
Resident Partners/Directors: ICAEW Members
S K Luk

S. S. LAU & CO
Unit A, 13/F, Empire Land Commercial Centre, 81-85 Lockhart Road, Wan Chai

T. C. NG & CO CPA LTD.
Amber Commercial Building, 13th Floor, 70 Morrison Hill Road, Wan Chai

T.K. CHOI & CO
15th Floor, Empire Land Commercial Centre, 81-85 Lockhart, Wan Chai

TAM AU & CO
Unit B, 22/F Tak Lee Commercial Building, 113 Wan Chai Road, Wan Chai

TONY NEDDERMAN & CO LTD
11th Floor, China Hong Kong Tower, 8 Hennessy Road, Wan Chai

TW CHAN & CO
Unit 2203, 22/F Malaysia Building, 50 Gloucester Road, Wan Chai

UNION ALPHA CPA LTD
19/F No. 3 Lockhart Road, Wan Chai

W S WONG & CO
16th Floor, Jonsim Place, 228 Queen's Road East, Wan Chai

WONG & KWAN
Room A, 9/F Queen Centre, 58-64 Queens Road East, Wan Chai

WONG BROTHERS & CO ★
19th Fl, Mass Mutual Tower, 38 Gloucester Road, Wan Chai

YEUNG, CHAN & ASSOCIATES CPA LTD
Unit A 20/F Success Commercial Building, 245-251 Hennessy Road, Wan Chai

YWC & PARTNERS ★
15th Floor, Empire Land Commercial Centre, 81-85 Lockhart Road, Wan Chai

YAU MA TEI

AU YEUNG & AU YEUNG CPA LTD
Room C 18/F, Nathan Commercial Bldg, 430-436 Nathan Road, Yau Ma Tei

BEN Y S HO & CO
Unit D, 10/F, Nathan Comm Building, 430 - 436 Nathan Road, Yau Ma Tei

KAM & CHEUNG ★
Rooms 1902-4, 19th Floor, Rightful Centre, 11-12 Tak Hing Street, Yau Ma Tei

LAM YIK YIN & CO
Room 802, 8/F, Lee Kiu Building, 51 Jordan Road, Yau Ma Tei

PARKSON & CO
20th Floor, Quality Education Tower, 476 Nathan Road, Yau Ma Tei

PSH & CO
12/F, Nathan Commercial Building, 430-436 Nathan Road, Yau Ma Tei

YUEN LONG

FRANCIS WONG CPA CO LTD
Room 403, Hang Seng Yuen Long Bldg, 91-93 Castle Peak Road, Yuen Long

CHAN LI LAW & CO
Room 2201, Yuen Long Trade Centre, 99 - 109 Castle Peak Road, Yuen Long

CHAN LI LAW & CO
Room 2201, Yuen Long Trade Centre, 99 - 109 Castle Peak Road, Yuen Long

FUNG HOI FUNG & CO
Flat B, 8/F, THY (Yeun Long) Commercial Building, 2 - 8 Tai Cheung Street, Yuen Long

HUNGARY

BUDAPEST

ETYEK CONSULTING
Kapas Utca 26-44 D, 1027 Budapest

KPMG ADVISORY KFT ★
Vaci ut 99, H -1139 Budapest

PKF AUDIT CO ▼
Boloni Gyorgy Ucta 22, Budapest, H1021

PRICEWATERHOUSE-COOPERS ★
Wesselenyi u 16, Budapest, H-1077

ICELAND

AKUREYRI

KPMG ENDURSKODUN HF. ▼
Glerargata 24, Akureyri, 600

PRICEWATERHOUSE-COOPERS ▼
Glerargata 34, Akureyri, 600

HUSAVIK

PRICEWATERHOUSE-COOPERS ▼
Gardarsbraut 15, Husavik, 640

KEFLAVIK

PRICEWATERHOUSE-COOPERS ▼
Tjarnagata 2, Keflavik, 230

REYKJAVIK

KPMG ENDURSKODUN HF. ▼
Borgartun 27, 105 Reykjavik

PRICEWATERHOUSE-COOPERS ▼
Postholf 12370, Reykjavik, 132

STOD-ENDURSKODUN HF ▼
Lynghals 9, P.O. Box 10095, Reykjavik

SELFOSS

PRICEWATERHOUSE-COOPERS ▼
Austurvegi 38, Selfoss, 800

INDIA

BANGALORE

A.F. FERGUSON & CO ▽
Deloitte Centre, Anchorage II, 100/2 Richmond Road, Bangalore 560025

BRAHMAYYA & CO ★
2-2a Kasturba Rd, (Sundaram Motors Bldg), Bangalore

ERNST & YOUNG ▼
RMZ Infinity, Tower C, 3rd Floor, Municipal No-3, Old Madras Road, KR Puram, Bangalore 560 016

FORD, RHODES, PARKS & CO ▼
439, 18th Main, 6th Block, Kormangala, Bangalore 560095

KPMG ★
Maruthi Info Tech Centre, East Wing II Floor, Koramangala Inner Ring Road, Bangalore 560071

MOORE STEPHENS ▼
25/2 Lady Curzon Road, Bangalore 560 001

PRICEWATERHOUSE-COOPERS LTD
Mittal Tower, 10th Floor, C Wing, 47/6 MG Road, Bangalore 560001

PRICEWATERHOUSE-COOPERS LTD
PWC Centre, 3274A 11th Main, HAL II Stage, Indiranagar, Bangalore 560008

RSM & CO ▼
803-804 Prestige Meridian 2, M.G Road, Bangalore 560001

S.B. BILLIMORIA & CO ★
Deloitte House, 70/3 Miller Road, P.O. Box No. 176, Bangalore 560052

BARODA

PANNELL KERR FORSTER ▼
8 2nd Floor, Tower E, Avishkar, Old Padra Road, Baroda 390015

BHUBANESWAR

PRICEWATERHOUSE-COOPERS LTD
26 Forest Park, Ground Floor, Bhubaneswar 751009

CHENNAI

A.F. FERGUSON & CO ▽
No. 5, Nandanam Extn., 1st Street, Nandanam, Chennai 600 035

BRAHMAYYA & CO ★
48 Masilamani Road, Balaji Nagar, Royapettah Town, Chennai 600014

PANNELL KERR FORSTER ▼
7L Century Plaza, 560-562 Anna Salai, Teynampet, Chennai 600018

RSM & CO ▼
7L Century Plaza, 560-562 Anna Salai, Teynampet, Chennai 600018

HARYANA

KPMG ★
4B, DLF Corporate Park, DLF City Phase III, Gurgaon 122 002

HYDERABAD

A.F. FERGUSON & CO ▽
Co Romandel House, 1-2-10 Sardar Patel Road, Secundarabad, Hyderabad 500 003

PANNELL KERR FORSTER ▼
413 Model House, 4th Floor, Panjagutta, Hyderabad 500482

PRICEWATERHOUSE-COOPERS LTD
6-3 550, 11 Floor, LB Bhavan, Somajiguda, Hyderabad 500082

S.B. BILLIMORIA & CO ★
3-6-111/5 Himayatnagar Rd., Hyderabad 500 029

JAIPUR

BDO INTERNATIONAL ▽
Khetan Bhawan, Mirza Ismail Road, Jaipur 1

PANNELL KERR FORSTER ▼
B-12 Bhagirath Colony, Chomu House, Pawan Kunj, Jaipur 302001

JAMNAGAR

G.K.SWARUP & CO
Shyam Kutir, 12/11 Station Road, Teen Batti, Jamnagar 361001

JAMSHEDPUR

S.B. BILLIMORIA & CO ★
72 B Road, Sonary West Layout, Jamshedpur

A.F. FERGUSON & CO ▽
A-1/2, Nirode Apartments, L-Road (West), Bistupur, Jamshedpur 831 001

KOLKATA

A.F. FERGUSON & CO ▽
Apeejay House, 'B' Block, 15 Park Street, Calcutta 700 016

BDO INTERNATIONAL ▽
14 Government Place East, Calcutta 1

BHARAT MALHOTRA & CO
20-6 Bangur Avenue, Block C, Kolkata 700 055

CHOKSEY BHARGAVA & CO ▽
P22, Bondel Road, Calcutta 700 019

D. BASU & CO
10 Old Post Office Street, Calcutta 700001

FORD, RHODES, PARKS & CO ▼
15 Chittaranjan Ave, (PO Box 2064), Calcutta 700072

GEE KAR & CO
22 Kohinoor, 105 Park Street, Calcutta 700 016

LOVELOCK & LEWES
Plot No Y-14, Block EP, Sector V, Salt Lake Electronic Complex, Bidhan Nagar, Calcutta 700091

LOVELOCK & LEWES
4 Lyons Range, Calcutta 700001

MOORE STEPHENS ▼
P O Box 706, Calcutta 700 001

PARTHA MITRA
Plot No. Y-14, Block EP, Sector V,Lake Electronic, Complex, Bidhan Nagar, Kolkata 700 091

PRICEWATERHOUSE-COOPERS LTD
Salt Lake Software Centre, Plot Y14, Block EP, Sector V, Salt Lake Elec. Complex, Calcutta 700091

PRICEWATERHOUSE-COOPERS LTD
Suite 9, 3rd Floor, 20-A Park Street, Calcutta 700016

PRICEWATERHOUSE-COOPERS LTD
Sukh Sagar, 2/5 Sarat Bose Road, 5th Floor, Calcutta 700020

S.B. BILLIMORIA & CO ★
4-A Orient Row, Park Circus, Calcutta

LUCKNOW

KAPUR & CO
17/4 M M Malviya Marg, Lucknow 226001

MADRAS

BDO INTERNATIONAL ▽
Mariam Centre, 2nd Floor, 751 Anna Salai, Madras 600 002

CHOKSEY BHARGAVA & CO ▽
610 Anna Salai, P.O. Box 743, Madras 60006

FORD, RHODES, PARKS & CO ▼
161 Mount Road, Madras 600002

PRICEWATERHOUSE-COOPERS LTD
PO Box 743, 610 Anna Salai, Madras 600006

PRICEWATERHOUSE-COOPERS LTD
Auras Corp Centre, 8th Floor, 98-A Dr Radhakrishnan Salai, Mylapore, Madras 600004

S.B. BILLIMORIA & CO ★
10 Third Main Road, Seethama Colony, Off Mowbrays Road, Alwarpet, Madras 600 018

MADURAI

FORD, RHODES, PARKS & CO ▼
Pandyan Building, West Veli St, Madurai 625001

MUMBAI

A.F. FERGUSON & CO ▽
Maker Towers E, Cuffe Parade, Mumbai, Mumbai 400 005

BDO INTERNATIONAL ▽
Karim Chambers, 40 Hamam Street, Mumbai 23

BHANA & CO
410 Raheja Chambers, Plot No 213,Nariman Point, Mumbai 400 021

BLACKSTONE FRANKS PREMNARAYEN
A401 Business Square, Solitair Corporate Park, Andheri, Mumbai 400093

S.A. BUHARIWALLA & CO
203 Konark Classic, 55 Hill Road, Bandai, Mumbai
Principal: ICAEW Member
M S Buhariwalla

CHOKSEY BHARGAVA & CO ▽
1102/1107 Raheja Chambers, Nariman Point, Mumbai 400021

DADABHOY & CO
7 Darbhanga Mansions, 12 Carmichael Road, Mumbai 400026

ENGINEER & MEHTA ★
45/47 Bombay Samachar Marg, Bank of Maharashtra Building, 5th Floor, Mumbai 400 023

FERGUSON A.F. ASSOCIATES ▽
Maker Towers 'E', Cuffe Parade, Mumbai 400 005

FORD, RHODES, PARKS & CO ▼
312/313 Sai Commercial Complex, BKS Devshi Marg, Govandi, Mumbai 400088
Tel: 00 91 2267979819

H.B. DHONDY & CO
Taj Building, 2nd Floor, 210 Dr. Dadabhai Naoroji Road, Mumbai 400 001

J.D. MISTRI
701 Sharda Chambers, 15 New Marine Lines, Mumbai 400 020

KPMG ★
KPMG House, Kamala Mills Compound, 448 Senapati Bapat Marg, Mumbai 400 013

MAHAJAN & AIBARA
1 Chawla House, 62 Wodehouse Road, Colaba, Mumbai 400 005

MAHAJAN & AIBARA ASSOCIATES ★
1 Chawla House, 62 Wodehouse Road,Colaba, Mumbai 400005

MOORE STEPHENS ▼
A/2 Narayan Plaza, Off Saki Vihar Road, Chandivili, Saki Nala, Mumbai 400 072

PANNELL KERR FORSTER ▼
2-C Vulcan Insurance Building, 2nd Floor, 77 Veer Narman Road, Mumbai

PANNELL KERR FORSTER ▼
Ambit RSM House, 449 Senapati Bapat Marg, Lower Parel, Mumbai 400013

PANNELL KERR FORSTER ▼
109-112 Dalamal Towers, Nariman Point, Mumbai 400021

PANNELL KERR FORSTER ▼
Union Co-op Insurance Building, P.M. Road, Fort, Mumbai 400 001

PANNELL KERR FORSTER CONSULTANTS PVT ▼
Ambit RSM House, 449 Senapati Bapat Marg, Lower Parel, Mumbai 400013

PANNELL KERR FORSTER CONSULTANTS PVT ▼
Pearl Mansion, Groud Floor, 91 Maharshi Karve Road, Mumbai 400020

PHEROZE JAMSHID TARAPORE
802B, Khareghat Road,Dadar, Mumbai 400 014

PRICEWATERHOUSE-COOPERS LTD
252 Veer Savarkar Marg, Shivaji Park, Dadr, Mumbai 400028

PRICEWATERHOUSE-COOPERS LTD
Dubash House, 15 JN Heredia Marg, Ballard Estate, Mumbai 400038

PRICEWATERHOUSE-COOPERS LTD
Trade World, 9th Fl, C Wing, Kamala Mills Compound, Senapti Bapat Marg,Lower Parel, Mumbai 400013

R.B. DUBASH & CO
Firuz-Ara, 160 Maharishi Karve Road, Cooperage, Mumbai 400021

RSM & CO ▼
Ambit RSM House, 449 Senapati Bapat Marg, Lower Parel, Mumbai 400013

RSM & CO ▼
109 -112 Dalamal Towers, Nariman Point, Mumbai 400021

S.A. BUHARIWALLA & ASSOCIATES
203 Konark Classic, 55 Hill Road, Bandai, Mumbai

S.B. BILLIMORIA & CO ★
12 Dr Annie Besant Road, Opp Shiv Sagar Estate, Mumbai 400 018

S.P. CHOPRA & CO ★
15a Horniman Circle, Bharat Insurance Building, Mumbai 400001
Tel: 00 91 226 61298
Resident Partners/Directors: ICAEW Members
Y K Shankardass

S S KOTHARI & CO ▼
109-112 Dalamal Towers, Narlman Point, Mumbai 400021

SHROFF & ASSOCIATES
Hormuzed Building, (Besides Grant Road P.O.), Sleater Road, Mumbai 400 007

TALYARKHAN & CO
Lyndewode House, Bomanji Petit Road, Cumballa Hill, Mumbai 400036

Y.K.SHANKARDASS
15a Horniman Circle, Bharat Insurance Bldg 1, Mumbai 400 023

NEW DELHI

A.F. FERGUSON & CO ▽
Hansalaya, Barakhamba Road, New Delhi 110 001

A.F. FERGUSON & CO ▽
Scindia House, Kasturba Gandhi Marg, New Delhi 110 001

ANIL ANEJA & CO
A1-178 Safdurjung Enclave, New Delhi 110029

BADHWAR & CO
C-28 East of Kailash, New Delhi 110065

BDO INTERNATIONAL ▽
12 Bhagat Singh Marg, New Delhi 1

CHOKSEY BHARGAVA & CO ▽
B-102, Himalaya House, 23 Kasturba Gandhi Marg,P.O Box 466, New Delhi 110 001

ERNST & YOUNG ▼
Ernst & Young Tower, B-26 Qutub Institutional Area, New Delhi 110016

FERGUSON A.F. ASSOCIATES ▽
6H Hansalaya, 15 Barakhamba Rd, New Delhi 110 001

FERGUSON A.F. ASSOCIATES ▽
Scindia House, Kasturba Gandhi Marg, New Delhi 110 001

FORD, RHODES, PARKS & CO ▼
406 Vishal Bhavan, 95 Nehru Place, New Delhi 110019

GRANT THORNTON ★
L41 Connaught Circus, New Delhi 110001
Tel: 00 91 9810093395
Resident Partners/Directors: ICAEW Members
V Chandiok, P Grover

KPMG ★
511 World Trade Centre, Babar Road, New Delhi 110001

MEHRA DHIR BHATIA & CO
248 Hauz Rani, Opp Modi Hospital,Saket, New Delhi 110017

MOORE STEPHENS ▼
Allahabad Bank Building, 17 Parliament Street, New Delhi 110 001

N. BAHL & CO
A 9/34 Vasant Vihar, New Delhi 110057

N. KUMAR & CO
J-14 Hauz Khas, Yusaf Sarai, Mehrauli Road, New Delhi 16

PRICEWATERHOUSE-COOPERS LTD
PO Box 10820, Mehrauli Post Office, New Delhi 110030

PRICEWATERHOUSE-COOPERS LTD
1 Copernicus Marg, 5th Floor, New Delhi 110001

PRICEWATERHOUSE-COOPERS LTD
Sucheta Bhavan, 1st Floor, 11-A Vishnu Digambar Marg, New Delhi 110 002

PURSHOTAM DHIR
A3 Chiragh Enclave, New Delhi 110048
Tel: 00 91 1126410824
Principal: ICAEW Member
P Dhir

R.K. KHANNA & CO ★
RK Khanna Tennis Stadium, West Wing, Tennis Complex, Africa Avenue, New Delhi 110029

RSM & CO ▼
First Floor, Nirlac House, B25 Qutab Insitutional Area, New Delhi 110016

S.B. BILLIMORIA & CO ★
502 Meghdoot, 94 Nehru Place, New Delhi 110 019

PUNE

A.F. FERGUSON & CO ▽
5 The Land Mark, 42 Aundh Road, Range Hills, Khadki, Pune 411020

PANNELL KERR FORSTER ▼
G2 Phoenix Building, Ground Floor, Bund Garden Road, Pune 411 001

PRICEWATERHOUSE-COOPERS LTD
305-307 Century Arcade, 8/3 Narangi Baug Road, Off Boat Club Road, Pune 411001

VADODARA

A.F. FERGUSON & CO ▽
Ground Floor, 20 Sudhanagar, Jetalpur Road, Vadodara 390 007

VIJAYAWADA

BRAHMAYYA & CO ★
18/46 Besant Rd, Gandhinagar, Vijayawada

INDONESIA

BANDUNG

BDO INTERNATIONAL ▽
Taman Sakura Indah, Jalan Kayu Manis No 10, Bandung, 40221

JAKARTA

BDO INTERNATIONAL ▽
P.O. Box 4129, Jakarta, 13041

BDO INTERNATIONAL ▽
Bukit Duri Permai Est Blok B/1, Jalan Jatinegara Barat 54-E, Jakarta, 13320

ERNST & YOUNG ★
Jalan H.R. Rasuna Said Kav, B-6, Kuningan, P.O. Box 2333, Jakarta

HANADI SUBJENDRO & CO ▼
P.O. Box 101/Jkt, Jakarta, 10002

MOORES ROWLAND ▼
Jl Cikini Raya No 9, Jakarta Central, Jakarta, 12950

PANNELL KERR FORSTER ▼
Jl. Barito 2 No. 31, Jakarta, 12130

PRICEWATERHOUSE-COOPERS ★
JI HR Rasuna Said Kav X-7 No. 6, Jakarta, 12940

PRICEWATERHOUSE-COOPERS ★
Gedung PricewaterhouseCoopers, 5/F, Jl HR Rasuna Said Kav C-3, Kuningan, Jakarta, 12920

PRICEWATERHOUSE-COOPERS ★
Gedung PricewaterhouseCoopers, 4/F, Jl HR Rasuna Said Kav C-3, Kuningan, Jakarta, 12920

UTOMO & CO ▼
Chase Plaza Building, P.O.Box 2134, Jakarta, 10001

IRAN

TEHRAN

A.M. MAHALLATI & CO
15 Second Street, Miremad Avenue, Ostad Motahari, Tehran 15875
Tel: 00 98 2188741179
Fax: 00 98 2188742577
Email: majid@mahallati.com
Website: http://www.mahallati.com
Mobile: 00 98 9121218976
Date Established: 1982
Resident Partners/Directors: ICAEW Members
A Mahallati-Kazemeini
Non-resident Partners (ICAEW Members):
M Moaddel
Resident Partners (Non-ICAEW Members):
Z Motallebzadeh
Other Offices: No 9, Beigh Alley, Parsa Ave, Motahri, Tehran

SPECIALISATIONS – AUDIT & ASSURANCE

Assurance Services
Audit
Audit — Private Company
Audit — Public Company

SPECIALISATIONS – BUSINESS & GENERAL ADVICE

Acquisitions and Mergers
Administration
Book-keeping
Book-keeping Systems
Company Formation
Company Secretarial Service
Data Processing Services
Feasibility Studies
Investment Appraisal
Management Accounting Consultancy
Management Consultancy
Overseas Countries
Takeovers

SPECIALISATIONS – BUSINESS RECOVERY & INSOLVENCY

Corporate Recovery
Reorganisations and Company Reconstructions

SPECIALISATIONS – FINANCIAL REPORTING

Accounts Preparation
Financial Reporting
International Reporting Standards (IFRS)
Limited Companies
Limited Company Accounts

SPECIALISATIONS – FORENSIC ACCOUNTING

Expert Witnesses in Litigation

SPECIALISATIONS – INVESTMENT BUSINESS

Financial Planning and Advice
Planning

SPECIALISATIONS – IT

Computerised Accounting Systems

SPECIALISATIONS – SECTOR

Banks/Financial Institutions
Construction
Corporate
Electronics
Food Industry
Oil/Petroleum Industries
Property
Property Development
Property Investment
Transport

SPECIALISATIONS – TAXATION

Employee
Investigations
National Insurance Advice
Personal
Value Added Tax
Languages Spoken:
Persian, English

AGAHAN & CO ★
PO Box 11365-4731, 32/1 Shadab Street, Gharani Avenue, Tehran 15989

ANSARI & ASSOCIATES
107 Sepehr Street, Farahzadi Boulevard, Shahrak Ghods, Tehran 1468673951

AZADRAS & CO
Suite 26, 3rd Floor, Hessari St, Mirdamad Blvd, PO Box 19395-5753, Tehran, 15479

H.M.K. REHMANI
Farmaniyeh, Rouhani St, Koy Ferdos No 32, Tehran, 19547

KPMG BAYAT RAYAN
3rd Floor, 239 Motahari Ave, Tehran, 15876

TADVINCO - ERNST & YOUNG IRAN ★
1303 Vali-e-Asr Avenue, Tehran, 15178

IRAQ

BAGHDAD

AL-JANABI AL-RUBAIE
PO Box 786, Baghdad

AWNI
Nori Buildings, 28 Tunis Street, P.O. Box 3206, Baghdad

ERNST & YOUNG ▽
P.O Box 1140, Al Amerat Street, Al-Mansour, Baghdad
Tel: 00 946 15430357

I.S.BAHRANI
Faris Building, South Gate, Baghdad

NAMIQ RAFIQ
Babil District - 929, Zukak 39, House No 4, Baghdad

IRELAND

ASHBOURNE

ALAN JONES & CO
15 Killegland Street, Ashbourne

BALLA

CATHERINE MONAGHAN
South View, Clairemorris Road, Balla

BALLINA

BOURKE QUINN O'MARA & CO ★
Arran House, James Street, Ballina

BLACKROCK

ALAN WATERHOUSE
106 Mount Albany, Newtownpark Avenue, Blackrock

BOYLE

AHERN & CO
Greatmeadow, Boyle

CAVAN

MCDWYER, LENNON & CO ★
Esker Place, Cathedral Road, Cavan

CLONMEL

SHANNON COLLINS & CO
15 Anne Street, Clonmel

COACHFORD

JOHN J. SHEAHAN & CO
Main Street, Coachford
Tel: 00 353 21 733 4333

COBH

P.J. HIGGINS & CO
2 Cuchulainn Place, Cobh
Tel: 00 353 214812434
Principal: ICAEW Member
P J Higgins

CORK

CATHERINE HUSSEY
3 O'Rahilly Row, Fermoy, Cork
Tel: 00 353 2532413
Fax: 00 353 253 3756
Email: husselaw@iol.ie
Principal: ICAEW Member
A C Hussey

DELOITTE IRELAND
No 6 Lapps Quay, Cork

ERNST & YOUNG BUSINESS ADVISORS ★
City Quarter, Lapps Quay, Cork

GODWIN & CO
16 Railway Place, High Street, Cork

HLB NATHANS ▼ ◈
Nathan House, Lavitts Quay, Cork
Tel: 00 353 214275176

HORGAN, BARRETT & CO ★
Evergreen House, Congress Road, Cork

HYLAND JOHNSON MURRAY ★ ◈
5 Union Quay, Cork

KPMG
Ninety South Mall, Cork

PRICEWATERHOUSE-COOPERS ▼
1 South Mall, Cork

DALKEY

ANTHONY ROSENSHINE & CO
17 Castle Street, Dalkey

DROGHEDA

DOGGETT & CO
26 Laurence Street, Drogheda

DUBLIN

A GRAHAM WILLIAMS
18 Shrewsbury Wood, Cabinteely, Dublin 18

A.J. KING & CO
Hall House, Main Street, Rathcoole, Dublin

DELOITTE IRELAND
Deloitte & Touche House, Earlscourt Terrace, Dublin

ERNST & YOUNG BUSINESS ADVISORS ★
Ernst & Young Building, Harcourt Centre, Harcourt Street, Dublin 2

FITZGERALD POWER ▽
Strawhall Business Park, Athy Road, Dublin

FITZGERALD POWER ▽
Merchants House, Merchants Quay, Dublin 8

HLB NATHANS ▼ ◈
Ulysses House, Foley Street, Dublin 1
Tel: 00 353 1 8881004

J P MILLS & CO
16 Lower Liffey Street, Dublin

KIERAN PIERCE & CO
15 Butterfield Park, Rathfarnham, Dublin 14

KPMG
1 Stokes Place, St Stephen's Green, Dublin 2

KPMG
1 Haslecer Master Place, IFSC, Dublin 1

MCCLOSKEY & CO
12 Magennis Place, Dublin 2
Tel: 00 353 1 6359997
Principal: ICAEW Member
H V McCloskey

MACINTYRE STRATER INTERNATIONAL LTD ▼
28/30 Burlington Road, Dublin 4

MATTHEW EDWARDS & CO
First Floor, Riverview House, 21-23 City Quay, Dublin 2

PRICEWATERHOUSE-COOPERS
One Spencer Dock, North Wall Quay, Dublin 1

PRICEWATERHOUSE-COOPERS ▼
Wilton Place, Dublin 2

PRICEWATERHOUSE-COOPERS ▼
George's Quay, Dublin 2

PRICEWATERHOUSE-COOPERS ▼
One Spencer Dock, North Wall Quay, Dublin 1

R.P.MITCHELL & CO
81 Rochestown Avenue, Dun Laoire, Dublin

SANDRA MCNAMARA & CO ★
9 Vernon Grove, Rathgar, Dublin 6

WALTER SCOTT
3 Clonard Avenue, Sandyford Road, Dublin 16
Tel: 00 353 1294 5511
Principal: ICAEW Member
W Scott

WARREN & PARTNERS
39 Northumberland Road, Ballsbridge, Dublin 4

WARREN & PARTNERS LTD
39 Northumberland Road, Ballsbridge, Dublin 4

DUNDRUM

DELAHUNTY & CO
4 Eagle Terrace, Dundrum 14

GALWAY

ERNST & YOUNG BUSINESS ADVISORS ★
Dockgate, Dock Road, Galway

PATRICK O FLAHERTY BE ACA
Woodpark, Corrandulla, Galway

GREYSTONES

BARRY CALDWELL & CO
135 Hillside, Greystones

KENMARE

HARRINGTON & CO ★
7 Hawthorn Wood, Kenmare
Tel: 00 353 64 40772
Resident Partners/Directors: ICAEW Members
J R Harrington

KILKENNY

PRICEWATERHOUSE-COOPERS ▼
Leggettsrath Business Park, Dublin Road, Kilkenny

KILLEAGH

SCOTT BAIRD & CO
Ardbeg, Drominane, Killeagh
Tel: 00 353 2495003
Principal: ICAEW Member
John H.Scott-Baird

LIMERICK

DELOITTE IRELAND
Deloitte & Touche House, Charlotte Quay, Limerick

ERNST & YOUNG BUSINESS ADVISORS ★
Barrington House, Barrington Street, Limerick

PRICEWATERHOUSE-COOPERS
P.O.Box No 7, Bank Place, Limerick

PRICEWATERHOUSE-COOPERS ▼
Bank Place, Limerick

ROBERT RICHARDSON & CO
The Citadel, Old Clare Street, Limerick

MALLOW

JOHN J. SHEAHAN & CO
Ross House, Cork Road, Mallow
Tel: 00 353 2243200
Principal: ICAEW Member
J J Sheahan

MARK W. LYSAGHT
Hazlewood House, Mallow

PARKMORE

RYAN MCGINTY ▽
Tararock 7, Unit 7, Galway Technology Park, Parkmore

SMITHBORO

TIERNEY TAX CONSULTANCY
Kilcorran House, Kilcorran, Smithboro

THURLES

SPAIN, FEWER, QUINLAN & CO ★
The Mall, Thurles

TRALEE

JD WYNNE & CO ▽ ◈
12 Denny Street, Tralee

WATERFORD

FITZGERALD POWER ▽
Greyfriars, Waterford

MCCARTHY & CO
17 The Village, Knockboy, Waterford
Tel: 00 353 51324518
Resident Partners/Directors: ICAEW Members
P P McCarthy

PRICEWATERHOUSE-COOPERS ▼
Ballycar House, Newtown, Waterford

WESTPORT

MUNRO MOORE
Glynsk, Liscarney, Westport

WEXFORD

PRICEWATERHOUSE-COOPERS ▼
Commarket, Wexford

WICKLOW

LALOR HOLOHAN & CO ★
Church Street, Wicklow

ISRAEL

BINYAMINA

L. HARRIS
38 Rehov Habrosh, Binyamina, 30500

HAIFA

BDO INTERNATIONAL ▽
P.O.B. 33777, Haifa, 31 337

KESSELMAN & KESSELMAN ▼
1 Nathanson Street, (P O Box 33984, 31339), Haifa, 33034

KPMG SOMEKH CHAIKIN ★
18 Haneviim Street, Haifa, 33501

M COOPER & CO
18 Habankim Street, 33265 Haifa
Tel: 00 972 48517604
Resident Partners/Directors: ICAEW Members
M Cooper

M. COOPER
18 Habankim Street, Haifa, 33265

JERUSALEM

BDO INTERNATIONAL ▽
P.O.B. 1011, Jerusalem, 91 010

KESSELMAN & KESSELMAN ▼
9A Diskin Street, Shalom Meir Center, (PO Box 2314, 91022), Jerusalem,96440

KPMG SOMEKH CHAIKIN ★
P O Box 212, 91001 Jerusalem

P.J. KIR-ON
Givat Shaul Business Centre, Lev Hagiva, 11/37 Beit Hadfus St, Jerusalem IL-95483

KFAR SABA

B. RICHMAN
24/5 Sharret Street, Kfar Saba, 44485

NETANYA

HOWARD M. RADLEY ◈
P.O.Box 1644, Independence Square 11, Netanya, 42115
Tel: 00 972 98339785
Principal: ICAEW Member
Howard M Radley

RA'ANANA

L.E. FRIEDMANN
110 Achuza Street, Ra'anana, 43450
Tel: 00 972 97448570
Principal: ICAEW Member
L E Friedmann

RAMAT BET SHEMESH ALEPH

FRANK S LACHMAN
Nachal Sorek 33-16, Remat Beit, Shemesh-aleph

TEL AVIV

BDO INTERNATIONAL ▽
PO Box 9498, Tel Aviv, 61094

GAINSFORD, BELL & CO
111 Arlosoroff St, Tel Aviv, 62098

KESSELMAN & KESSELMAN ▼
35-39 Montefiore Street, (P O Box 452, 61003), Tel Aviv, 65201

KPMG SOMEKH CHAIKIN ★
17 Ha'arba'a Street, Tel Aviv, 64739

MOORE STEPHENS ▼
22 Mazeh Street, Tel Aviv, 65213

PANNELL KERR FORSTER ▼
13th Floor, Toyota Towers, Building A, 65 Igal Alon Street, Tel Aviv 67443

ITALY

ANCONA

DELOITTE & TOUCHE ★
Viale della Vittoria 7, I-60123 Ancona

KPMG S.P.A. ▼
Piazza della Repubblica 15, 60121 Ancona

BARI

KPMG S.P.A. ▼
Via Abate Gimma 30, 70121, Bari

PANNELL KERR FORSTER ▼
Via Cardassi 59, 70121 Bari

PKF ITALIA SPA ▼
Via Caldassi 59, Bari

PRICEWATERHOUSE-COOPERS S.P.A. ★
Viale della Repubblica 110, 70125 Bari

RECONTA ERNST & YOUNG ★
Piazza Umberto, 40, 70100 Bari

BERGAMO

DELOITTE & TOUCHE ★
Via G. Verdi 5, I-24100 Bergamo

KPMG S.P.A. ▼
Piazzale Della Repubblica 2, 24100 Bergamo

RECONTA ERNST & YOUNG ★
Via Locatelli, 24/0, 24121 Bergamo

SERCA SNC ▼
Via Divisione Julia 7, 24100 Bergamo

BOLOGNA

PANNELL KERR FORSTER ▼
Via De Carbonesi 6, 40123 Bologna

PRICEWATERHOUSE-COOPERS S.P.A. ★
Via delle Lame 111, 40122 Bologna

RECONTA ERNST & YOUNG ★
Via M. D'Azeglio, 34, 40123 Bologna

BOLZANO

KPMG S.P.A. ▼
Via Della Resa 20, 39100 Bolzano

BRESCIA

KPMG S.P.A. ▼
via Cefalonia 70, 25125 Brescia

PANNELL KERR FORSTER ▼
Contrada Santa Croce 13, 25188 Brescia

PRICEWATERHOUSE-COOPERS S.P.A. ★
Via Cefalonia 70, 25124 Brescia

RECONTA ERNST & YOUNG ★
Corso Magenta 29, 25121 Brescia

CAGLIARI

DELOITTE & TOUCHE ★
Via Milano 48, I-09125 Cagliari

COMO

KPMG S.P.A. ▼
Via D Fontara 1, 22100 Como

FLORENCE

DELOITTE & TOUCHE ★
Via Cavour 64, I-50129 Florence

KPMG S.P.A. ▼
Corso Italia 2, 50123 Florence

MOORES ROWLAND ITALIA ▼
piazza D'Azeglio N.39, 50121 Florence

PANNELL KERR FORSTER ▼
Via Alfonso La Marmora 39, 50121 Florence

PRICEWATERHOUSE-COOPERS S.P.A. ★
Viale Milton 65, 50121 Florence

GENOA

DELOITTE & TOUCHE ★
Via XX Settembre 10, I-16121 Genoa

KPMG S.P.A. ▼
Piazza della Vittoria 10/7, 16121 Genoa

PRICEWATERHOUSE-COOPERS S.P.A. ★
Piazza Dante 7, 16121 Genoa

RECONTA ERNST & YOUNG ★
Via Roma, 10/2, 16123 Genoa

LE MARCHE

MARCHE ENTERPRISES LTD
Casa Tobia, 340 Contrada Casepulore, Penna San Giovanni, Macerata, 62020 Le Marche

MICHAEL J MURPHY
Casa Tobia, 340 Contrada Casepulore, Penna San Giovanni, Macerata, 62020 Le Marche

LECCE

KPMG S.P.A. ▼
via Imbriani 36, 73100 Lecce

LEGNAGO

BELLUZZO ASSOCIATI ▼
Corso Della Vittoria 55, Legnago

MILAN

BDO INTERNATIONAL ▽
Piazza del Liberty, 20121 Milan

CARLO SALFORD
Via Passo Di Fargorida 6, 20148 Milan

DELOITTE & TOUCHE ★
Via Tortona 25, 20144 Milan

ERNST & YOUNG ★
Via Torino 68, 20123 Milan

ERNST & YOUNG ★
Via Wittgens 6, 20123 Milan

FIDIREVISA ITALIA S.P.A ★
Via Senato 12, 20121 Milan

HUMPHREYS & GATES
Piazza IV Novembre 4, 20124 Milan

KPMG S.P.A. ▼
Via Vittor Pisani 25, 20124 Milan

MOORE STEPHENS & CO S.R.L ▼
Via Cosimo del Fante 16, 20122 Milan

MOORES ROWLAND ITALIA ▼
via Monte Rosa 3, 20149 Milan

PANNELL KERR FORSTER ▼
Via Antonio de Recanonate 1, MI 20124 Milan

PANNELL KERR FORSTER ▼
Via S Paolo 1, 2012 Milan

PKF ITALIA SPA ▼
Viale Vittorio Veneto 10, 20124 Milan

PRICEWATERHOUSE-COOPERS S.P.A. ★
Via Monte Rosa 91, 20149 Milan

RECONTA ERNST & YOUNG ★
Via Della Chiusa 2, 20123 Milan

RECONTA ERNST & YOUNG ★
Via Torino 68, 20123 Milan

ROGER KING S.R.L
Via Amilcare Ponchielli 3, 20129 Milan
Tel: 00 39 3355638187
Principal: ICAEW Member
R G King

SERCA SNC ▼
C.so di Porto Nuova n.34, 20122 Milan

STUDIO TRIBUTARIO E SOCIETARIO ▼
Via Antonio de Recanate I, 20124 Milan
Tel: 00 39 220521401

MODENA

RECONTA ERNST & YOUNG ★
Largo Aldo Moro 28, 41100 Modena

NAPLES

DELOITTE & TOUCHE ★
Centro Direzionale, Via G.Porzio, I-80143 Naples

KPMG S.P.A. ▼
Via Francesco Casacciolo 17, 4th Floor, 80122 Naples

PRICEWATERHOUSE-COOPERS S.P.A. ★
Piazza dei Martiri 30, 80121 Naples

RECONTA ERNST & YOUNG ★
Via F. Crispi 74, 80121 Naples

PADOVA

RECONTA ERNST & YOUNG ★
Via Nicolo Tommaseo 60, 35131 Padova

PADUA

PRICEWATERHOUSE-COOPERS S.P.A. ★
Largo Europa 16, 35137 Padua

PALERMO

KPMG S.P.A. ▼
Piazza Castelnuovo 12, 90141 Palermo

PRICEWATERHOUSE-COOPERS S.P.A. ★
Via Marchese Ugo 60, 90141 Palermo

PARMA

KPMG S.P.A. ▼
via Magnani 10, 43100 Parma

PRICEWATERHOUSE-COOPERS S.P.A. ★
Viale Tanara 20/A, 43100 Parma

PERUGIA

MOORES ROWLAND ITALIA ▼
piazza D'Azeglio N.39, 06128 Perugia

PKF ITALIA SPA ▼
Via Del Campanile n.3, Foligno, 06034 Perugia

PESCARA

RECONTA ERNST & YOUNG ★
Via F.lli Cairoli, 10, 65122 Pescara

REGGIO EMILIA

DELOITTE & TOUCHE ★
Viale Regina Margherita 2, I-42100 Reggio Emilia

ROME

BDO INTERNATIONAL ▽
Viale G Mazzini 113, 00195 Rome

DELOITTE & TOUCHE ★
Via della camilluccia 589/a, 00135 Rome

HAQ AND CO ◈
Via Lombardia 30, 00187 Rome
Tel: 00 39 64814286
Principal: ICAEW Member
S H Haq

KPMG S.P.A. ▼
Via Ettorc Petrolini 2, 00197 Rome

MACINTYRE STRATER INTERNATIONAL LTD ▼
Vaile dell' Esperanto, 71, 00144 Rome

MOORES ROWLAND ITALIA ▼
via Nazionale 172, 00184 Rome

PANNELL KERR FORSTER ▼
Viale Bruno Buozzi N 102, 00197 Rome

PANNELL KERR FORSTER ▼
Via del Tritone n 62/C, 00187 Rome

PKF CONSULTING SRI SINTENNA SRL ▼
Piazza delle Muse 8, 00197 Rome

PKF ITALIA SPA ▼
Corse Vittorio Emanuele, 11287, 00186 Rome

PRICEWATERHOUSE-COOPERS S.P.A. ★
Largo Angelo, Fochetti 29, 00154 Rome

STUDIO ASSOCIATO FRANCESCO GUIDI ▼
Viale Bruno Buozzi N 102, 00197 Rome

ZIA MURSALEEN ★
Deloitte & Touche, Via della Camilluccia 589/A, 00135 Rome

TREVISO

KPMG S.P.A. ▼
via R Zalivani 2, 31100 Treviso

PRICEWATERHOUSE-COOPERS S.P.A. ★
Viale G. Felissent 90, 3110 Treviso

TURIN

DELOITTE & TOUCHE ★
Corso Galileo Ferraris 46, 10129 Turin

KPMG S.P.A. ▼
Corso Vittorio Emanuele II 48, 10123 Turin

PRICEWATERHOUSE-COOPERS S.P.A. ★
Corso Montevecchio 37, 10129 Turin

RECONTA ERNST & YOUNG ★
Corso Vittorio Emanuele, 11,83, 10128 Turin

UDINE

PRICEWATERHOUSE-COOPERS S.P.A. ★
Via Poscolle 43, 33100 Udine

VENICE

A. VON GEBSATTEL
S. Polo 2733, 30125 Venice

VERONA

BELLUZZO & ASSOCIATI ▼
Stradone San Fermo 14, 37121 Verona

KPMG S.P.A. ▼
Corso Cavour 39., Verona, 37121

PANNELL KERR FORSTER ▼
Via XX Settembre, 14, 37129 Verona

PANNELL KERR FORSTER ▼
Strandone San Fermo 14, 37121 Verona

PRICEWATERHOUSE-COOPERS S.P.A. ★
Corso di Porta Nuova 125, 37122 Verona

RECONTA ERNST & YOUNG ★
Via Manin 6, 37122 Verona

VOGHERA

ANTHONY PETER DEEGAN
Via Verdi 64, 27058 Voghera
Tel: 00 39 3476893313
Principal: ICAEW Member
A P Deegan

JAMAICA

KINGSTON

DELOITTE & TOUCHE ★
P.O. Box 13, 7 West Avenue, Kingston 4
Tel: 00 1 876 922682519

DONALD S. REYNOLDS
7 West Avenue, P.O.Box 13, Kingston 4
Principal: ICAEW Member
D S Reynolds

ERNST & YOUNG
8 Olivier Road, Kingston 8

KPMG ★
The Victoria Mutual Bldg, 6 Duke St (P.O. Box 76), Kingston

PANNELL KERR FORSTER ▼
6 Lockett Avenue, Kingston 4

PRICEWATERHOUSE-COOPERS ▼
PO Box 372, Kingston

MONTEGO BAY

DELOITTE & TOUCHE ★
42B & 42C Union Street, Montego Bay
Tel: 00 1 876 9524713

KPMG ★
41 Montego Freeport, Shopping Centre, P.O.Box 220, Montego Bay

PRICEWATERHOUSE-COOPERS ▼
PO Box 180, Montego Bay

OCHO RIOS

PANNELL KERR FORSTER ▼
3rd Floor, 34 Main Street, St Ann, Ocho Rios

JAPAN

KOBE

BDO INTERNATIONAL ▽
Kobe Crystal Tower, 19th Floor, 1-3 Higashi-Kawasaki-cho, Chuo-ku, Kobe 650

NAGOYA

SHOWA OTA & CO ▼
Nagoya Tokyokaijyou Bldg., 2-20-19 Marunouchi, Naka-Ku, Nagoya 460

OSAKA

SHOWA OTA & CO ▼
Osaka Kokusai Buildings, 2-30 Azuchi-Cho, Higashi-ku, Osaka 541

SAPPORO

SHOWA OTA & CO ▼
Hokusei Building, 3-9 Minamishijyo-Nishi, Chuo-Ku, Sapporo 064

SENDAI

SHOWA OTA & CO ▼
Shamboru Ichibancho, 1-6-22 Ichiban-Cho, Sendai 980

TOKYO

ASAHI SHINWA & CO ▼
Nissei Building, 1-18 Agebacho, Shinjoko-ku, Tokyo 162

BDO INTERNATIONAL ▽
Tsutaya Building, 3-1 Shimomiyabi-cho, Shinjuku-ku, Tokyo 162

KPMG AZSA & CO ▼
KPMG Azsa & Co, Marunouchi Trust Tower North 10F, 8-1 Marunouchi 1-Chome, Chiyoda-Ku, Tokyo 100 8250

KPMG AZSA & CO ▼
AZSA Center Building, 1-2 Tsukudo-cho, Shinjuku-ku, Tokyo 162-8551

MOORE STEPHENS ▼
Niu Building 4F, 1 - 17 Nihonbashi 2-Chome, Chuo-ku, Tokyo 103

PRICEWATERHOUSE-COOPERS
Aarata Shion Marunouchi Bldg, Marunouchi 1-5-1, Chiyoda-Ku, Tokyo 100-6506

PRICEWATERHOUSE-COOPERS
Kasumigaseki Building 15F, Kasumigaseki 3-2-5, Chiyoda-Ku, Tokyo 100-6015

PRICEWATERHOUSE-COOPERS AARATA
Sumitomo Mita Building, 12F, 5-37-8 Shiba, Minato-ku, Tokyo 108-0023

SEISHIN & CO ▼
Niu Building 4F, 1 - 17 Nihonbashi 2-Chrome, Cho-ku, Tokyo 103

SHOWA OTA & CO ▼
Hibiya Kokusai Bldg., 2-2-3 Uchisaiwai - Cho, C.P.O. Box 1196, Tokyo 100

TOYAMA

SHOWA OTA & CO ▼
2-4-10 Sogawa, Toyama 930

YOKOHAMA

DAISHOW LTD
Hirado 4-5-23, Totsuka-ku, Yokohama, 244-0802

JORDAN

AMMAN

BAWAB & CO ▼
Shmeisani, Rajab Building 3rd Floor, P O Box 724, Amman, 11118

ERNST & YOUNG ▼
5552, Amman, 11183

ERNST & YOUNG ★
P.O. Box 1140, 4th Floor, Grindlays Center,Shmeissani, Amman

MICHAEL SINDAHA ▼
P.O. Box 925999, ., Amman

MICHAEL SINDAHA & CO ▼
P O Box 925999, Amman, 11110

PANNELL KERR FORSTER ▼
6 Nahawand Street, ground Floor, Al Rabiyah, Amman 11195

PANNELL KERR FORSTER ▼
Al Shmesani, Abu Setta Building, Amman

PRICEWATERHOUSE-COOPERS ▼
Shemeisani, Rajab Building 3rd Floor, P O Box 724, Amman, 11118

KAMPUCHEA

PHNOM PENN

PRICEWATERHOUSE-COOPERS (CAMBODIA) LTD ▼
P O Box 1147, Phnom Penn, 12210

KAZAKHSTAN

ALMATY

ERNST & YOUNG ▼
Almary 480051, Prospect Lenina 212a, Almaty

J.M.M. WALE
Flat 11, Apartment Buildings 66, Kabanbai Batyr Street, Almaty

KPMG AUDIT LLC
180 Dostyk Avenue, Almaty 050051

PRICEWATERHOUSE-COOPERS ▼
Hyatt Regency Office Tower, 29/6 Satpayeva Avenue, 3rd Floor, Almaty 480070

KENYA

ELDORET

ERNST & YOUNG ▼
National Bank Building, Uganda Road, P.O. Box 43, Eldoret

KISUMU

JOHN CUMMING
P.O. Box 327, Kisumu

KLSA PANNELL KERR FORSTER ▼
Mega Plaza, Oglnga Odinga Road, Kisumu, 40100

MALINDI

KLSA PANNELL KERR FORSTER ▼
Plot No 1213, Tourist Road, Malindi, 80200

MOMBASA

EBRAHIM MULLA & CO
P.O. Box 81518, Mombasa

GILL & JOHNSON ▽
Kenya Reinsurance Plaza, 8th Floor, Moi Avenue, (P.O.Box 84712), Mombasa

KLSA - PANNELL KERR FORSTER ★
Jubilee Insurance Building, 3rd Floor, Moi Avenue, PO Box 90553, Mombasa 80100

KLSA PANNELL KERR FORSTER ▼
Jubilee Insurance Building, Mol Avenue, Mombasa, 80100

PRICEWATERHOUSE-COOPERS ★
Ralli House, Nyerere Avenue, PO Box 81411, Mombasa

PSJ & ASSOCIATES ★
P.O. Box 90393, Mombasa

S.M.G. DAYA & CO
P.O.Box 90071, Mombasa

SATISH SHAH
PO Box 82675, Mombasa

NAIROBI

A M PORBUNDERWALLA
PO Box 40248, Nairobi, 00100

A. PRINGLE
P O Box 49561, Nairobi

BDO INTERNATIONAL ▽
P.O. Box 47089, Nairobi

DAVID WHITE & CO
Karen,76 Dagoretti Road, P.O. Box 24911, Nairobi, 00502

DELOITTE & TOUCHE ★
Kirungii, Ring Road, Westlands, P.O. Box 40092 - 00100, Nairobi

ERNST & YOUNG ▼
Hughes Building, Kenyatta Avenue, P.O. Box 42423, Nairobi

ERNST & YOUNG ★
P.O. Box 44286, Alico House, Mamlaka Road, Nairobi

ERNST & YOUNG ▼
Alico House,Mamlaka Road, P.O. Box 44286, Nairobi, 254

GILL & JOHNSON ▽
Kirungii, Ring Road, Westlands, (P.O. Box 40092), Nairobi

KPMG KENYA
P.O. Box 40612, 16 Floor Lonrho HS, Standard Street, Nairobi 00100

MANCHAR LALL & RAI
PO Box 25223, Nairobi, 603

MERALIS
New Rehema House, First Floor, Raphta Road, Westlands, Nairobi

PANNELL KERR FORSTER ▼
Kalamu House, Waiyaki Way, Nairobi, 00100

PRICEWATERHOUSE-COOPERS ★
Rahimtulla Tower, Upper Hill Road, PO Box 43963, Nairobi 00100
Tel: 00 254 202855000
Resident Partners/Directors: ICAEW Members
S J Fisher, W A Hollas, P K B Kinisu, R K Shah, M J Whitehead

PSJ & ASSOCIATES ★
Capitol Hill Towers, 3rd Floor, Cathedral Road, Nairobi

ROPAS LTD
PO Box 63531, Nairobi, 00619

SATISH R. KHIMASIA
P.O. Box 40214, Nairobi

SHAH PATEL & CO ◈
Laxmi Plaza, Biashara Street, PO Box 41652, Nairobi 00100

SUBHASH C. HANDA
PO Box 25223, Nairobi, 00603

Y.P.SENNIK
P.O. Box 45551, Nairobi

NAKURU

ERNST & YOUNG ▼
Kenya Commercial Bank Bldg., Kenyatta Ave, (P.O. Box 45), Nakuru 20100 GPO
Tel: 00 254 512211591
Resident Partners/Directors: ICAEW Members
A Gilani

KLSA PANNELL KERR FORSTER ▼
National Bank Building, Kenyatta Avenue, Nakuru, 20100

NYERI

ERNST & YOUNG ▼
Kang'Aru Annexe, Kimathi Way, P.O. Box 60, Nyeri

KUWAIT

SAFAT

ERNST & YOUNG ★ ◈
P.O. Box 74, Safat, 13001
Tel: 00 965 2655000
Resident Partners/Directors: ICAEW Members
N Shafi, A R Tajdeen

JASSIM AHMAD AL-FAHAD & CO ▼
Al-Shaya Building, Ahmad Jaber Street, P.O. Box 1245, Safat, 13013

KPMG SAFI AL-MUTAWA & PARTNERS ▼
P O Box 24, Safat, 13001

NAWAR & CO
P.O. Box 1545, Safat

SHAAB

PKF BOURESLI & CO ▼
Dana Plaza Building Floor 3, Shaab El Bahree, Arabian Gulf Street, Kuwait City

LATVIA

RIGA

KPMG ★
Balasta Dambis 1a, Riga LV-1048

MOORE STEPHENS (RIGA) LTD ▼
33/1A Kr Valdemara Street, Riga LV 1010

PANNELL KERR FORSTER ▼
3-4 Barona Street, Riga LV1050

PRICEWATERHOUSE-COOPERS ★
KR.Valdemara Iela 19, Riga LV-1010

PRICEWATERHOUSE-COOPERS SIA ★ ◈
Kr. Valdemara iela 19, Riga LV1010
Tel: 00 371 7094400
Resident Partners/Directors:
ICAEW Members
C G Greaves

LEBANON

BEIRUT

BDO INTERNATIONAL ▽
P.O. Box 165, Beirut

ERNST & YOUNG ▽
P.O. Box 11 - 1639, Beirut
Tel: 00 961 1360640

ERNST & YOUNG P.C.C.
Commerce & Finance Building, 1st Floor, Kantari, P.O. Box 11-1639, Riad solh Beirut 1107 2090

KPMG ▼
Beirut Central District, Lazarieh Building - Bloc A3, 6th Floor, BO Box 11-8270, Beirut

PANNELL KERR FORSTER ▼
Fouad Chebab Street, Sin El Fil, Beirut

PRICEWATERHOUSE-COOPERS ★
SNA Building, 5th Floor, PO Box 11-3155, Tabaris Square, Beirut

LESOTHO

MASERU

ERNST & YOUNG ★
Private Bag A169, Maseru

PMB
Maseru Book Centre Building, P.O. Box 1252, Kingsway, Maseru 100

LIBERIA

MONROVIA

PANNELL KERR FORSTER ▼
Lara Bldg (Royal Home), Suite 1C, Randall Street, Monrovia 1000

LIBYA

BENGHAZI

NAWAR & CO
Green Mountain Bldg, Istiklal St P.O.Box 261, Benghazi

TRIPOLI

ERNST & YOUNG
P.O. Box 91873, Tripoli

ERNST & YOUNG ◈
P.O. Box 91873, Tripoli
Tel: 00 218 213344130
Resident Partners/Directors:
ICAEW Members
G R Slater

MOHAMMED SHIRAZ
PO Box 2655, Tripoli

NAWAR & CO
P.O.Box 627, Tripoli

LIECHTENSTEIN

VADUZ

BLEASE LLOYD ASSOCIATES
Banholzsirasse 16, Box 381, FL 9490 Vaduz

KPMG FIDES PEAT ▼
Kirchstrasse 12, Vaduz, FL 9490

MACINTYRE STRATER INTERNATIONAL LTD ▼
Lettstrasse 10, P.O.Box 1518, Vaduz, 9490

LITHUANIA

VILNIUS

PRICEWATERHOUSE-COOPERS UAB ★
Jasinskio 16B, Vilnius LT-01112

REVIZORIOUS UAB ▼
Gerosios Vilties 1, Vilnius LT 01347

MACAU

MACAU

BDO INTERNATIONAL ▽
Av. Dr. Rodrigo Rodrigues, Lote A-3, Edifico Highfield, Court, 12th Floor - Flat A, Macau

DELOITTE TOUCHE TOHMATSU ★
P.O.Box 746 Rua da Praia, Grande 57, Edificio Centro, Commercial da Praia Grande, Macau

PEAT MARWICK E ASSOCIADOS ▼
Edificio Centro Comercial da, Praia Grande, 15 Andar, A15,(P.O. Box 701), Macau

MALAWI

BLANTYRE

DELOITTE & TOUCHE ★
P.O.Box 931, Indebank House, Blantyre

DELOITTE & TOUCHE ★
PO Box 187, First Floor, Indebank House, Kaohsiung Road, Blantyre

ERNST & YOUNG ▼
PO Box 530, Blantyre

KPMG ▼
MASM House, Lower Sclater Road, PO Box 508, Blantyre

PRICEWATERHOUSE-COOPERS ★
First House, Corner Livingstone &, Chilembwe Avenue, PO Box 1147, Blantyre

R.H. SAVJANI
Hannover House, P.O.Box 2126, Blantyre

LILONGWE

KPMG ▼
Murses Central Building, Off Independence Drive, New Capital City Centre, PO Box 30453, Lilongwe

PRICEWATERHOUSE-COOPERS ★
ADL House, 3rd Floor, P O Box 30379,Capital City, Lilongwe,3

MALAYSIA

BATU PAHAT

MONTEIRO & HENG ★
37-IB (2nd Floor), Jalan Mohd. Salleh, Batu Pahat

IPOH

ERNST & YOUNG ★
35 Jalan Hussein, (PO Box 212), 35250 Ipoh

ERNST & YOUNG ★
21 & 23 Jalan Hussein, P.O.Box 212, 30250 Ipoh

EVAN WONG & CO ★
32D Floor,Asia Life Bldg., 45-D Jalan Bandar Raya, (PO Box 212), 30000 Ipoh

KPMG ★
P O Box 104, 30710 Ipoh

PRICEWATERHOUSE-COOPERS ★
Std Chartered Bank Chambers, 21-27 Jalan Dato' Maharajelela, P O Box 136, 30710 Ipoh

JOHOR BAHRU

ERNST & YOUNG ★
Suite 11, 2A Level 11, Menara Pelangi, No 2 Jalan Kuning, Johor Malaysia, Johor Bahru

ERNST & YOUNG ★
Suite 628, 6th Floor, Pan Global,Jalan Wong, Ah Fook, 80000 Johor Bahru

EVAN WONG & CO ★
Room 301. 3rd Floor, 3rd Floor. AIA Building, 2 Jalan Bukit Timbalan, 80000 Johor Bahru

GEP ASSOCIATES ★
Room 1, 15th Floor, Kompleks Tun Abdul Razak, 80000 Johor Bahru

KPMG ★
Level 14 Menara Ansar, 65 Jalan Trus, 80000 Johor Bahru

PRICEWATERHOUSE-COOPERS ★
Menara Ansar,Level 16, Jalan Trus, 80000 Johor Bahru

SEAH & ASSOCIATES
Suite 15.05 Level 15, City Square Office Tower, 106-108 Jalan Wong Ah Fook, 80000 Johor Bahru

SQ ASSOCIATES
Suite 15.05 Level 15, City Square Office Tower, 106-108 Jalan Wong Ah Fook, 80000 Johor Bahru

SQ MORISON
Suite 15.05 Level 15, City Square Office Tower, 106-108 Jalan Wong Ah Fook, 80000 Johor Bahru

KEDAH

KIAT & ASSOCIATES
1st Floor 25 Seberang, Jalan Putera, 05150 Alor Star

LIM HAN HO & CO
502-A Jalan Pintu Sepuluh, 05100 Alor Star

LIM TEOH & CO
503-A Jalan Pintu Sepuluh, 05100 Alor Star

KLANG

K.T. LOW MANAGEMENT SERVICES
85 Leboh Tamarind, Southern Park, 41200 Klang

LEE TECK LEONG & CO
47, Jalan Batai Laut 5, Kawasan 16, Taman Intan, 41300 Klang

THIANG & CO
10 Lebuh Gopeng, 41400 Klang

KLUANG

CHONG ACCOUNTING & MANAGEMENT SERVICES
27 (1st Floor), Jln Syed Abdul Hamid Sagaff, 86000 Kluang

KOTA BAHRU

PANNELL KERR FORSTER ▼
3965, 1st & 2nd Floor, Wisma Geratan, Jalan Temenggung, 15000 Kota Bahru

SQ ASSOCIATES
4213-E 2nd Floor, Jalan Kebun Sultan, 15350 Kota Bahru

KOTA KINABALU

ERNST & YOUNG ★
PO Box 10192, 88802 Kota Kinabalu

EVAN WONG & CO ★
4th Floor Wisma Gek Poh, Jalan Haji,(P.O. Box 10192), 80000 Kota Kinabalu

KEVIN HOW & CO
PO Box 11209, 88813 Kota Kinabalu

KPMG ★
3rd Floor,18 Wisma Gek Poh, Jalan haji Saman, 88000 Kota Kinabalu

LIM CHONG & CO ★
P.O. Box 13661, 88841 Kota Kinabalu

PATRICK KONG & ASSOCIATES ★
2nd Floor, Lot 19, Luyang Phase 8 Kota Kinabalu, Specialist Ctr, POB 11835, 88830 Kota Kinabalu

PRICEWATERHOUSE-COOPERS ★
Lot B1105-B1115, 11th Floor, Wisma Merdeka (Phase II), Jalan Tun Razak, 88000 Kota Kinabalu

ROBERT CHIN LEE & ASSOCIATES ★ ◈
2nd Floor, Lot 15, Bl.B, Lintus Sq, Jalan Lintus, 88300 Kota Kinabalu
Tel: 00 60 88223040
Resident Partners/Directors: ICAEW Members
R K C Chin

S. LIM & CO ★
Lot 46-2, Block E, Damai Plaza, Phase IV,Luyang, 88300 Kota Kinabalu

SQ ASSOCIATES
Block E Lot 38,2nd Floor, Asia City, 88000 Kota Kinabalu

KUALA LUMPUR

ABU BAKAR RAJUDIN & CO
Suite A, Resorts Business Suites, 18-2, Jalan Kampung Attap, 50460 Kuala Lumpur

BDO INTERNATIONAL ▽
12th Floor, Menara Uni. Asia, Jalan sultan Ismail, 1008 Kuala Lumpur

BEH L.H. & CO ★
Suite B-2-1A, North Point Office, Mid Valley City, 1 Medan Syed Putra Utara, 59200 Kuala Lumpur

CHAN CHEE HONG & CO ★
No. 6 & 8 Jalan Gereja, 2nd Floor, Bangunan Keng, 50100 Kuala Lumpur

CHONG & CHONG ▼
4-31 Pertama Office, Tower Complex,Jalan Tuanku Abdul Rahman, Kuala Lumpur

ERNST & YOUNG ★
Level 23A Menara Milenium, Pusat Bandar Damansara, 50490 Kuala Lumpur

ERNST & YOUNG ★
Level 23A, Menara Milenium, Jalan Damanlela, Darrrensara, PO Box 11040, 50734 Kuala Lumpur

ERNST & YOUNG ★
4th Floor, Kompleks Antarabangsa, P O Box 10068, 50704 Kuala Lumpur

ERNST & YOUNG ★
Level 23A, Menara Milenium, Jalan Damanlela, Pusat Bandar Damansara, Damansara Heights, 50490 Kuala Lumpur

EVAN WONG & CO ★
401 4th Floor, Kompleks Antarabangsa,Jalan, Sultan,Ismail, P.O. Box 10068, 50250 Kuala Lumpur

EVAN WONG & PARTNERS ★
4th Floor, Kompleks Antarabangsa,Jalan, Sultan, Ismail PO Box 10068, 01-02 Kuala Lumpur

FOLKS DFK & CO ★
12th Floor, Wisma Tun Sambanthan, No. 2 Jalan Sultan Sulaiman, 50000 Kuala Lumpur

GOMEZ & CO
16-A, 1st Fl, Jalan Tun Sambanthan 3, Brickfields, 50470 Kuala Lumpur

KIAT & ASSOCIATES
24A Persiaran Zaaba, Taman Tun Dr Ismail, 60000 Kuala Lumpur

KPMG ▼
P O Box 10047, 50702 Kuala Lumpur

KPMG ★
Wisma KPMG, Jalan Dungun, Damansara Heights, 50490 Kuala Lumpur

KPMG BUSINESS ADVISORY SDN BHD ▼
Wisma KPMG, Jalan Dungun, Damansara Heights, 50490 Kuala Lumpur

KWONG & CO ★
260 Lorong Maarof, Bukit Bandaraya, 59100 Kuala Lumpur

LIM HON CHEW & CO
25 Jalan Ampang Hilir, Kuala Lumpur

MONTEIRO & HENG ★
20-3 Jalan Tun Sambanthan 3, 50470 Kuala Lumpur

MOORE STEPHENS ★
8A Jalan Sri Semantan Satu, Damansara Heights, 50490 Kuala Lumpur

MOORES ROWLAND ▼
Wisma Selangor Dredging, 7th Floor, South Block, 142-A Jalan Ampang, 50450 Kuala Lumpur
Tel: 00 60 321615222

MUSTAPHARAJ ★
Suite 23.01, 23rd Floor, Plaza Permata (IGB), Jalan Kampar, Jalan Tun Razak, 50400 Kuala Lumpur

NG, LEE & PARTNERS
Suite 20,01 20th Floor, Amoda, 22 Jalan Imbi, Kuala Lumpur

ONG BOON BAH & CO
B10-1 Megan Phileo Promenade, 189 Jalan Tun Razak, 50400 Kuala Lumpur

PANNELL KERR FORSTER ▼
9th Floor MCB Plaza, No 6 Changkat Raja, Chulan, 50200 Kuala Lumpur

PETER CHONG & CO
51 Changkat Bukit Bintang, 50200 Kuala Lumpur
Tel: 00 603 21454991
Fax: 00 603 21454991
Email: info@peterchongco.com
Website: http://www.peterchongco.com
Date Established: 1974
Training Contracts Available.
Principal: ICAEW Member
P T N Chong
Resident Partners (Non-ICAEW Members):
K P Cheng
Other Offices:19th Floor, Gurney Tower, 18 Persiaran, Gurney 10250 Penang, Malaysia (Tel: 00 604 3712150) (Fax: 00 604 3712158)
Registered by another RSB to carry out company audit work
Individual(s) licensed for insolvency work by another RPB

PHILIP WONG & CO
142 Jalan Datuk Sulaiman 6, Taman Tun Dr Ismail, 60000 Kuala Lumpur

PKF KUALA LUMPUR ★
9th Floor, MCB Plaza, No 6 Changkat Raja, Chulan, 50200 Kuala Lumpur

POH & TAN ★ ◈
19-1 Jalan 3/146, Bandar Tasik Selatan, 57000 Kuala Lumpur

PRICEWATERHOUSE-COOPERS ★
P.O.Box 10192, Level 10 1 Sentral, Jalan Travers, 50706 Kuala Lumpur
Tel: 00 603 21731188
Resident Partners/Directors: ICAEW Members
M F Azmi, K F Chin, M A B Haji Yahya, M L Ng, A L Ong, A J Raslan, S Sammanthan, T Sangarapillai, T Somasundaram, U K Vivekananda

PRICEWATERHOUSE-COOPERS ★
11th Floor, Wisma Sime Darby, Jalan Raja Laut, P O Box 10192, 50706 Kuala Lumpur

RABINRAJ & PARTNERS ★
A6-05 Level 6 Carlton Court, Punchak Prima Condominium, Jalan Sri Hartamas 17, 50480 Kuala Lumpur

RSM ROBERT TEO, KUAN & CO ★
Penthouse Wisma RKT Block A No2, Jalan Raja Abdullah, Off Jalan Sultan Ismail, 50300 Kuala Lumpur
Tel: 00 603 26972888
Resident Partners/Directors: ICAEW Members
R K T Teo, K F Yong

S Y KWONG, FOONG & CO
4/F 108 Jalan Tun H.S. Lee, 50000 Kuala Lumpur
Tel: 00 60 320724118
Principal: ICAEW Member
S Y Kwong

SEKHAR & TAN ★
Suite 16-8, Level 16, Wisma UOA II, 21 Jalan Pinang, 50450 Kuala Lumpur

SHAMSIR JASANI GRANT THORNTON ★
No 11-1, Faber Imperial Court, Jalan Sultan Ismail, 50250 Kuala Lumpur
Tel: 00 603 26924022
Resident Partners/Directors: ICAEW Members
N K Jasani

VICTOR & CO ◈
26-5-2 Jalan 2/101c, Cheras Business Centre, 5th Mile, Jalan Cheras, 56100 Kuala Lumpur

VINCENT LOH
Unit 0-1A, Seri Ritchie, 327B Persiarian Ritchie, 55000 Kuala Lumpur

Y.T. YEE & CO
8-12-11a Menara Bangsar, Jalan Liku, P.O. Box 12536, 50782 Kuala Lumpur

YUEN TANG & CO
301 Bangunan Lee Yan Lian, Jalan Tun Perak, 50050 Kuala Lumpur

KUANTAN

PRICEWATERHOUSE-COOPERS ★
HongKong Bank Bldg, 3/F, 1 Jalan Mahkota, 25000 Kuantan

KUCHING

ERNST & YOUNG ★
Room 300-303, 3rd Fl. Wisma Bukit Mata, Jalan Tunku Abdul Rahman, P.O. Box 64, 93700 Kuching

ERNST & YOUNG ★
Rm 300-303 3rd Fl Wisma, Bukit Mata Kuching, Jalan, Tuanku Abdul Rahman, 931000 Kuching

EVAN WONG & CO ★
301 Wisma Bukit Mata, Jalan Tuanku Abdul Rahman, P.O. Box 64, Kuching

HII & LEE ★
1st Floor,250 Jalan Padungan, P.O. Box 1819, 93736 Kuching

HII & LEE ★
2nd Floor, Lot 2765, Block 10, Jalan Tun Ahmad Zaidi Adruce, 93150 Kuching

KPMG ★
Level 6 Westmoore House, Twin Tower Centre,Rock Road, 93200 Kuching

NORDIN, HANIFAH & CO ★
301 Wisma Bukit Mata, Kutching, P.O. Box 64, Kuching

PRICEWATERHOUSE-COOPERS ★
9th Floor, Bangunan Binamas, Jalan Padungan,P O Box 2864, 93756 Kuching

RICHARD KIEW & CO
1st Floor No. 10 A, Lorong 4, Jalan Nanas, PO Box 2536, 93750 Kuching

LABUAN

ERNST & YOUNG ★
Level 9F Main Off Tower, Financial Park Labuan, Jalan Merdka, 87000 Labuan

PRICEWATERHOUSE-COOPERS ★
Level 10(B2) Main Office Tower, Financial Park Labuan, Jalan Merdeka, 87007 Labuan

MALACCA

ERNST & YOUNG ★
1st Floor, Bangunan Madonna, 50-56 Jalan Laksamana, 75000 Malacca

EVAN WONG & CO ★
Bangunan Madonna, 50-56 Jalan Laksamana, (P.O. Box 213), 75000 Malacca

L.K.CHONG & CO
327-A Jalan Melaka Raya 1, Taman Melaka Raya, 75000 Malacca

O.L. YEO & CO
50 Jalan Tokong, 75200 Malacca

PRICEWATERHOUSE-COOPERS ★
12th Floor, Bangunan Yayasan Melaka, Jalan Hang Tuah, PO Box 140, 75300 Malacca

MIRI

ERNST & YOUNG ★
4th Floor, Unit 4.1, Wisma Yong Lung, Lot 698, Pelita Commercial Centre, 98000 Miri

EVAN WONG & CO ★
P.O. Box 1209,15 Jalan Merpati, Ground Fl, 98000 Miri

MUAR

T.H. CHUA & CO
41-24 1st Floor, Jalan Abdul Rahman, 8400 Muar

PENANG

BDO INTERNATIONAL ▽
Suite 12-A, Gurney Tower Office, 18 Persiaran Gurney, 10250 Penang

ERNST & YOUNG ★
37 Jalan Anson, P.O. Box 148, 10400 Penang

EVAN WONG & CO ★
2nd Floor,Hongkong Bank, Chambers, 7 Beach Road, (P.O. Box 148), 10300 Penang

GEP ASSOCIATES ★
11A Lebuhraya Maktab, 10250 Penang

KIAT & ASSOCIATES
No 41-1-1- & 41-2-1, Jalan Cantonment, 10250 Penang

KPMG ★
1st Floor,Wisma Penang Grd., 42 Jalan Sultan Ahmad Shah, (P.O.Box 349), 10050 Penang

PETER CHONG & CO ◈
19th Floor Gurney Tower, 18 Persiaran Gurney, 10250 Penang

SOON & ASSOCIATES
8 Jalan Edgecumbe, 10250 Penang

PERAK

P RETHINASAMY & CO
Kompleks Skomk, Block A, 2nd Floor, Jalan Mankamah, Teluk Intan Perak, 36008 DR Teluk Intan

PETALING JAYA

DELOITTE KASSIMCHAN
Level 19 Uptown 1, Jalan SS 21/ 58, Damansara Uptown, 47400 Petaling Jaya

GEP ASSOCIATES ★ ◈
25 Jalan PJU 1/42A, Dataran Prima, 47301 Petaling Jaya
Tel: 00 603 7033390

H.F. WONG & CO
No.9 Jalan SS 4D/2, Taman People's Park, 47301 Petaling Jaya

H H CHONG & ASSOCIATES
2 Jalan SS 22A/5, 47400 Damansara Jaya

INPANA & ASSOCIATES ★ ◈
2 Jalan 5/41, 46000 Petaling Jaya
Tel: 00 60 3 62501615
Resident Partners/Directors: ICAEW Members
S S Chelliah

KHOO & ASSOCIATES
51 Jalan Alpha SS 20/1, Damansara Utama, 47400 Petaling Jaya

KPMG ★
Level 10, KPMG Tower, 8 First Avenue, Bandar Utama, 47800 Petaling Jaya

M.K.B. HUSSAIN
Unit 1003, Level 10, Block A, Pusat Perdagangan Phileo, Damansara 2, No 15, Jalan 16/ 11, Off Jalan Damansara 46350 Petaling Jaya

NG, HO & PARTNERS
No 4, Jalan 14-52, Petaling Jaya

PETER I M CHIENG & CO
No 2E , 1st Floor, Jalan SS 22/ 25,Damansara, Petaling Jaya

T.L. KWONG & CO
27 Jalan 5/3, 46000 Petaling Jaya

SANDAKAN

PANNELL KERR FORSTER ▼
Bl B, Lot 4&5 3rd FL, Bandar Kim Fung, Mile 4, Nth Rd, PPM459 Elopura, 90000 Sandakan

ERNST & YOUNG ★
11th Floor, Lai Piang Kee Building, Jalan Pryer, (P.O. Box 648), 90000 Sandakan

EVAN WONG & CO ★
Saba Building,Jalan Pelabuhan, (P.O. Box 648), 90007 Sandakan

KPMG ★
P.O. Box 654, 90707, Sandakan

SEREMBAN

BDO INTERNATIONAL ▽
74, 2nd Floor, Jalan Tuanku Antah, 70100 Seremban

SIBU

ERNST & YOUNG ★
5th Flr,Wsma Grand Merlin, P.O. Box 512, 131 kg Nyabor Road, 96000 Sibu

ERNST & YOUNG ★
Units 2.4,2.5,2.6,2.7, 2nd Floor, Kin Orient, Plaza,No10 Jakin Tun Haji Open, 96000 Sibu

EVAN WONG & CO ★
6 Kampong Nyabor Road, (P.O. Box 512), 96000 Sibu

HII & LEE ★
1st Floor, 13 Khoo Peng Loong Road, P.O. Box 505, Sibu

TAWAU

ERNST & YOUNG ★
Sabah Bank Building, Jalan Utara,W.D.T. 46, 91000 Tawau

EVAN WONG & CO ★
Sabah Bank Building,Jalan, Utava,W.D.T. 46, 91000 Tawau

KPMG ★
1144 2nd Fl. Wisma Gek Poh, Mile 1 Dunlop\Kuhara Rd Junc., PO Box 60352, 91013 Tawau

MALDIVES

MALE

PRICEWATERHOUSE-COOPERS ▼
02-05 2nd Floor, STO Trade Centre, Orchid Magu, Male

MALTA

BALZAN

PATRICIA GERA FCA
11 Dr Zammit Street, Balzan BZN 1430

BIRKIRKARA

PANNELL KERR FORSTER ▼
35 Mannarino Road, BKR 08, Birkirkara

FLORIANA

P & C
2nd Floor, Europa Centre, Triq John Lopez, Floriana VLT16

MARSA

R S ATTARD & CO MOORE STEPHENS MALTA ▼
46 Timber Wharf, Marsa, HMR 12

MSIDA

ERNST & YOUNG ▼
Fourth Floor, Regional Business Centre, Achille Ferris Street, Msida MSD1751

PIETA

KPMG ▼
Portico Building, Marina Street, Pieta

KPMG ▼
Portico Buildings, Marina Street, Pieta, MSD 08
Tel: 00 356 25631003
Fax: 00 356 25661000
Email: kpmg@kpmg.com.mt

SLIEMA

DELOITTE & TOUCHE ★
1 Col.Savona Street, Sliema, SLM07

R S ATTARD & CO MOORE STEPHENS MALTA ▼
67 Sir Arturo Merciece Street, Sliema, SLM 10

TA' XBIEX

R.RENDLE
38 Antonio Nani Street, Ta'xbiex XBX 1086

VALLETTA

BDO INTERNATIONAL ▽
136 St Christopher Street, Valletta, VLT 05

BRYANT, MAYL & CO
24 South Street, Valletta VLT 1102

MARK AZZOPARDI-HOLLAND
Valletta Buildings, Flat 20, South Street, Valletta VLT 1103

PRICEWATERHOUSE-COOPERS ★
167 Merchants Street, Valletta, CMR 01

MARTINQUE

FORT-DE-FRANCE

PANNELL KERR FORSTER ▼
Centre Dillon Valmeniere, Route de la Pointe des Sables, 97200 Fort-de-france, Martinque

MAURITIUS

BEAU-BASSIN

CHEONG YOUNE E.K.
7 Remy Ollier Street, Beau Bassin

CUREPIPE

BDO INTERNATIONAL ▽
Cnr. Jerningham and Thomy, d'Arifat Street, Curepipe

RENAUD DESVAUX DE MARIGNY
29 Brown Sequard Street, Curepipe

EBENE

BAKER TILLY MAURITIUS
Level 3, Alexander House, 35 Cybercity, Ebene
Tel: 00 230 4030850
Principal: ICAEW Member
B Lim, D T Lo Seen Chong
Resident Partners (Non-ICAEW Members):
A Ramankhan, J Chan

THREE SIXTY
#02-A8 Cybertower1, Ebene

FLOREAL

SHARON RAMDENEE
Deburg Edwards Street, Floreal

PORT LOUIS

ALLIANCE ASSOCIATES
Suite 401, St James Court, St Denis Street, Port Louis

ASHOKE ROY
3rd Floor, Baroda Bank Building, Sir William Newton St, Port Louis

BACHA & CO
Corner A Feillafe Dr, Rouget Street, Port Louis

BACHA AND BACHA ◈
Les Bacha, Cathedral Square, Port Louis
Tel: 00 230 2088324

BDO DE CHAZAL DU MEE ◈
P.O. Box 799, 10 Frere Felix, De Valois Street, Port Louis
Tel: 00 230 2023000
Resident Partners/Directors: ICAEW Members
A A A Ebrahim, K Hawabhay, J Pougnet, M Y A Ramtoola, G L K F C Seeyave, Y K Teng Hin Voon

BDO INTERNATIONAL ▽
44 St George Street, Port Louis

DE CHAZAL DU MEE & ASSOCIATES LTD Ⓜ
PO Box 799, DCDM Building, 10 Frere Felix De, Valois St, Port Louis
Tel: 00 230 2023000
Resident Partners/Directors: ICAEW Members
J.M. Harel, J Pougnet

ERNST & YOUNG
Anglo Mauritius Building, 1st Floor, Intendance Street, Port Louis

FINACC
3rd Floor, St Louis House, 17 Mgr Gonin Street, Port Louis
Tel: 00 230 2138990
Email: finacc@mazars.mu
Principal: ICAEW Member
O A Rawat

GRANT THORNTON
2nd Floor, Fairfax House, 21 Mgr Gonin Street, Port Louis
Tel: 00 230 2120202
Principal: ICAEW Member
P K Boolaky, A S Hajee Abdoula, Y Thacoor

KEMP CHATTERIS ASSOCIATES LTD Ⓜ
P.O. Box 322, Cerne House, La Chaussee, Port Louis

KEMP CHATTERIS DELOITTE
P.O.Box 322, Cerne House, La Chaussee, Port Louis

KING FOOK BUSINESS LINK LTD
8 Nahaboo Solim Street, Port Louis

KPMG ★
KPMG Centre, 30 St George Street, Port Louis

LAMUSSE SEK SUM & CO ▼
5 Duke of Edinburgh Avenue, Port Louis

M.J.R. LAMUSSE
1st Floor, Ganee Moossa Building, Frere Felix De Valois Street, Port Louis

MOORE STEPHENS ◈
6th Floor, Nirmal House, 22 Sir William Newton Street, Port Louis
Tel: 00 230 2116535
Principal: ICAEW Member
D Busgeeth, A Rogbeer, R Rogbeer

NMC
Suite 306, St James Court, St Denis Street, Port Louis

PRICEWATERHOUSE-COOPERS ★
Training Centre, Champ de Mars, Port Louis

PRICEWATERHOUSE-COOPERS ★
Cerne House, 6th Floor, Chausee Street, Port Louis

PRICEWATERHOUSE-COOPERS ★
TM Building, Pope Hennessy Street, Port Louis

WILTON AUDIT
3 Leoville L' Homme St, Port Louis

Y.A. PEERBAYE
Richard House, 6th Floor, Remy Ollier Street, Port Louis

REDUIT

INTERNATIONAL FINANCIAL SERVICES ★
IFS Court, TwentyEight, Cybercity, Ebene, Reduit
Tel: 00 230 4673000
Resident Partners/Directors: ICAEW Members
C Basanta Lala, K Joory, R A Toorawa

MEXICO

AGUASCALIENTES

MOORE STEPHENS ▼
Av Universidad No 1001, Int 704- 7o piso, Edificio Torreplaza Bosques, Aguascalientes 20120

PRICEWATERHOUSE-COOPERS ▼
Av Aguascalientes Norte 607, Int 402, Fraccionamiento, Bosques del Prado, Aguascalientes CP 20139

CABO SAN LUCAS

BDO INTERNATIONAL ▽
Plaza San Lucas No. 1, Fracc. Pedregal, Cabo San Lucas 23410

CANCUN

PANNELL KERR FORSTER ▼
Alcatraces No 43 Lote 28 SM 22 MZA, 10 Retorno 5, CP775000 Cancun

CD. VICTORIA

MOORE STEPHENS ▼
Lauro Aguirre Nte 214, Centro, CD. Victoria 87000

CELAYA

BDO INTERNATIONAL ▽
Bosques de Chapultepec 110-2, Colonia Arboledas, Primera Seccion, Celaya 38060

CHIHUAHUA

PRICEWATERHOUSE-COOPERS ▼
Apartado Postal 621, Chihuahua 31000

CIUDAD JUAREZ

PRICEWATERHOUSE-COOPERS ▼
Blvd Tomas Fernandez No 8490, Esq con Camino Real SENECU, Fraccionamiento Anglia, Ciudad Juarez CP 32459

COLONIA DEL VALLE

MOORE STEPHENS MEXICO ▼
Providencia 1247, Colonia Del Valle 03100

COL SAN BORJA INSUGENTES

PANNELL KERR FORSTER ▼
Miraflores 236, Col San Borja Insugentes 03310

GUADALAJARA

BDO INTERNATIONAL ▽
Severo Diaz No. 17-601, Sector Hidalgo, Guadalajara 44600

PANNELL KERR FORSTER ▼
AV Moctezuma No 4680, Jardines Del Sol, CP 45650 Guadalajara

PRICEWATERHOUSE-COOPERS ▼
Prol Av de las Americas No, 1592 4 Piso Col Country Club, Sector Hidalgo, Guadalajara 44620

GUAYMAS

BDO INTERNATIONAL ▽
Av. Serdan No. 465-2, Entre Calles 11 y 12, Guaymas 85400

HERMOSILLO

BDO INTERNATIONAL ▽
Rosales y Elias Calles 124 Pte, Edificio Cremi Pitic 2001, Hermosillo 83000

MOORE STEPHENS ▼
Blvd Navarrete 76-1, Col Valle Escondido, Hermosillo 83200

JALISCO

CMR ASESORES SC ▼
Av Moctezuma No 4680, Jardines Del Sol, CP45040, Guadalajara, Jalisco

MEXICO CITY

BDO INTERNATIONAL ▽
Ejercito National, No. 904-7th Floor, Colonia Polanco Los Morales, Mexico City 11510

KPMG MEXICO CARDENAS DOSAL
Boulevard Manuel Avila Camacho 176, Col. Reforma Social, 11650 Mexico City

MANCERA Y FREYSSINIER S.C. ▼
Plaza Polanco Jaime Balmes Num, 11 Torre D 4 & 5th Floors, Colonia Los Morales-Polanco, Mexico City 11510

PANNELL KERR FORSTER ▼
Felix Parra 192, Col San Jose Insurgentes, Mexico City CP 03900

PRICEWATERHOUSE-COOPERS ▼
Mariano Escobedo No 573, Col Polanco Chapultecpec, Mexico City CP 11560

PRIETO, RUIZ DE VELASCO Y CI A SC ▼
Reforma 76-11o Piso, Mexico City 06600

VILLAGARCIA & ASCOIADOS ▼
Av Insurgentes sur 724-8 Piso, Col de Valle, CP 03100 Mexico City

MONCLOVA

MOORE STEPHENS ▼
Ave Monterry 13, Col Guadalupe, Monclova 25750

MONTERREY

BDO INTERNATIONAL ▽
P.O. Box 1238, Monterrey

MOORE STEPHENS ▼
Vicente Ferrara 112, Col Parque Obispado, Monterrey 64060

PANNELL KERR FORSTER ▼
Ocampo No 443 Oriente, Col Centro, Gran Hotel Ancira, Nuevo Leon, 64000 Monterrey

PRICEWATERHOUSE-COOPERS ▼
Apartado Postal 1542, Monterrey NL 64000

PRICEWATERHOUSE-COOPERS ▼
Apartado Postal 2526, Monterrey NL 64000

PRIETO, RUIZ DE VELASCO Y CI A SC ▼
Paras 802-210, Col. Centro, Monterrey 64000

NAUCALPAN

PRICEWATERHOUSE-COOPERS ▼
Apartado Postal 704, Naucalpan 53000

PIEDRAS NEGRAS

MOORE STEPHENS ▼
Juarez 113 Ote, Zona Centro, Piedras Negras 26000

PUEBLA

CMR ASESORES SC ▼
4 Sor No 3746-2CP 72530, Col Ladrillera de Benitez, Puebla

PRICEWATERHOUSE-COOPERS ▼
Circuito Del Sol No 3905-PH, Col Nuevo Amanecer, Puebla 72400

PUERTO VALLARTA

CMR ASESORES SC ▼
Brasillia No 532 Dep 1, Col 5 Diciembre, 48350 Puerto Vallarta

QUERETARO

PRICEWATERHOUSE-COOPERS ▼
Apartado Postal 412, Queretaro QRO 76000

VILLAGARCIA & ASCOIADOS ▼
J Dolores Frias, No 9 Col Cento, 76000 Queretaro

SALTILLO

MOORE STEPHENS ▼
Baja California 1900, Col Republica Ote, Saltillo 64060

SAN LUIS POTOSI

MOORE STEPHENS ▼
Comonfort 805, Zona Centro, San Luis Potosi 78000

PRICEWATERHOUSE-COOPERS ▼
Apartado Postal 977, San Luis Potosi SLP 78000

TAMPICO

PRICEWATERHOUSE-COOPERS ▼
Apartado Postal 494, Tampico 89000

TIJUANA

BDO INTERNATIONAL ▽
Calle Espana 2320 - Piso 3, Colnia Cacho, Tijuana 22150

PRICEWATERHOUSE-COOPERS ▼
Condomino Agua Caliente, Blvd Agua, Caliente 4558-807 Col Aviacion, Tijuana BC 22420

TOLUCA

BDO INTERNATIONAL ▽
Isidro Fabela 724 Sur-Piso 4, P.H., Colonia Americas, Toluca 50130

VERACRUZ

BDO INTERNATIONAL ▽
Primero de Mayo No. 602, Colonia Centro, Veracruz 91700

MONACO

MONTE CARLO

DAVID P STANLEY
Floridian Palace, 21 Boulevard du Larvotto, Monte Carlo, 98000

GEOFFREY NATHAN INTERNATIONAL LTD
1003 Monte Carlo Sun, 74 Boulevard D'Italie, Monte Carlo, 98000

LEIGHTON & LEIGHTON
4 Rue Des Orchidees, MC98000 Monaco

MOORE STEPHENS & CO ◈
L' Estoril, Bloc C, 31 Avenue Princesse Grace, Monte Carlo, MC 98000

MOORES ROWLAND ▼
2 Avenue de Monte Carlo, BP. 343, Monte Carlo, 98006

MOROCCO

CASABLANCA

PANNELL KERR FORSTER ▼
131 Abdelmoumen, Casablanca

PRICE WATERHOUSE ▼
101 Boulevard Massira Al Khedra, Casablanca, 20000

RABAT

KPMG ▼
6 Rue Todgha, Adgal, Rabat

PRICE WATERHOUSE ▼
Residence Es Saada, 1 Boulevard Mohamed V, Rabat, 10000

MOZAMBIQUE

MAPUTO

PRICEWATERHOUSE-COOPERS ★
Rovuma Carlton Hotel, Centro de Escritorios,Piso 3, Sala 1, Rua de Se, Maputo, 114

MYANMAR

YANGON

PRICEWATERHOUSE-COOPERS ▼
P O Box 175, 53/55 Maha Bandoola Garden St, Yangon

NAMIBIA

SANLAM

DELOITTE PIM GOLDBY ▼
P.O. Box 22288, Sanlam, 9000

WALVIS BAY

ERNST & YOUNG ★
P.O. Box 415, Walvis Bay, 9190

WINDHOEK

BDO INTERNATIONAL ▽
P.O. Box 2184, Windhoek, 9000

ERNST & YOUNG ★
P.O. Box 1857, Windhoek

FISHER HOFFMAN PKF ▼
302 Kenya House, Robert Mugabe Avenue, Windhoek

NC TROMP & CO AUDITORS ▼
17 Luderitz Street, Corporate House, Windhoek

PEAT MARWICK NAMIBIA ▼
2nd Floor, Bank Windhoek Building, 262 Independance Avenue, Windhoek

PRICEWATERHOUSE-COOPERS ▼
P O Box 1571, Windhoek

NEW CALEDONIA

NOUMEA

PEAT MARWICK ▼
Rue Des Freres Carcopino, (BP 2353), Noumea

PRICE WATERHOUSE ▼
Port Plaisance, 10 rue Jules Garnier, PO Box 4213, Noumea, 98847

PRICEWATERHOUSE-COOPERS ▼
BP 316, Noumea, 98845

PRICEWATERHOUSE-COOPERS ▼
BP 4192, Noumea, 98846

PRICEWATERHOUSE-COOPERS ▼
BP 4213, Noumea, 98847

PRICEWATERHOUSE-COOPERS ▼
BP 2333, Noumea, 98846

PRICEWATERHOUSE-COOPERS ▼
PO Box 4049, Noumea

NEW ZEALAND

AUCKLAND

BDO INTERNATIONAL ▽
PO Box 2219, Auckland

BILLINGTON & ASSOCIATES ◈
PO Box 28560, Remuera, Auckland 1541

DELOITTE TOUCHE TOHMATSU ★
Deloitte Touche House, 8 Nelson Street, P O Box 33, Auckland

ERNST & YOUNG ▼
41 Shortland Street, PO Box2146, Auckland

GOSLING CHAPMAN ▼
Gosling Chapman Tower, Level 6, 51-53 Shortland Street, P O Box 158, Auckland 1

JAMES CARTER CONSULTING LTD
28 Lingarth Street, Remuera, Auckland

JOHN A. TAYLOR & CO
4 Mizpah Road, Browns Bay, Auckland 0630

KPMG ★
KPMG Centre, 18 Viaduct Harbour Avenue, P.O. Box 1584, Auckland 1

MOORES ROWLAND ▼
6th Floor, 369 Queen Street, Auckland

PKF ▼
Level 5, 50 Anzac Avenue, Auckland

PRICEWATERHOUSE-COOPERS ★
Private Bag 92162, Auckland

PRICEWATERHOUSE-COOPERS ★
Level 21, PWC Tower, 188 Quay Street, Private Bag 92162, Auckland

ROSS MELVILLE PKF ▼
2B William Pickering Drive, North Harbour, Auckland

STAPLES RODWAY ▼
PO Box 3899, Level 9, Tower Centre, 45 Queen Street, Auckland

STAPLES RODWAY ▼
P.O. Box 2146, National Motu, al Centre,37-41 Shortland St, Auckland

CHRISTCHURCH

BDO INTERNATIONAL ▽
P.O. Box 4449, Christchurch

DELOITTE TOUCHE TOHMATSU ★
P.O.Box 248, Deloitte House, 32 Oxford Terrace, Christchurch 8000

ERNST & YOUNG ▼
227 Cambridge Terrace, PO Box 2091, Christchurch 8140

KPMG ★
Clarendon Tower, 78 Worcester St, P.O.Box 274, Christchurch 1

MOORE STEPHENS ▼
12 Main North Road, P O Box 5071, Christchurch 5

MOORES ROWLAND ▼
188-192 Armagh Street, Christchurch

PKF ▼
236 Armagh Street, Christchurch

PRICEWATERHOUSE-COOPERS ★
119 Armagh Street, PO Box 13244, Christchurch

STAPLES RODWAY ▼
Ernst Young House, 227 Cambridge Terrace, P.O. Box 2091, Christchurch

DUNEDIN

DELOITTE TOUCHE TOHMATSU ★
P.O.Box 1245, Wilson Neill House, 481 Moray Place, Dunedin 9000

MOORE STEPHENS ▼
2 Clark Street, P O Box 919, Dunedin

PRICEWATERHOUSE-COOPERS ★
Forsyth Barr House, The Octagon, PO Box 5848, Dunedin 9058

STAPLES RODWAY ▼
Health Board House, P.O. Box 5740, 229 Moray Place, Dunedin

HAMILTON

BDO INTERNATIONAL ▽
P.O. Box 518, Hamilton

DELOITTE TOUCHE TOHMATSU ★
Anchor House, 80 London Street, P.O. Box 17, Hamilton 2000

KPMG ★
KPMG Centre, 85 Alexandra Street, (P.O. Box 929), Hamilton

STAPLES RODWAY ▼
Wel Energy House, Cnr.Victoria & London Sts, P.O. Box 9159, Hamilton

HASTINGS

STAPLES RODWAY ▼
PO Box 46, Hastings 4156

INVERCARGILL

COOK ADAM & CO ★
181 Spey Street, P.O.Box 1109, Invercargill

STAPLES RODWAY ▼
142 Spey Street, P.O. Box 100, Invercargill

LOWER HUTT

MOORE STEPHENS ▼
Auto Point House, 20 Daly Street, P O Box 30-568, Lower Hutt

NAPIER

PRICEWATERHOUSE-COOPERS ★
Corner Raffles & Bower Streets, PO Box 645, Napier

NEW PLYMOUTH

PRICEWATERHOUSE-COOPERS ★ ◈
Corner Devon & Robe Streets, PO Box 144, New Plymouth

STAPLES RODWAY ▼
Ernst & Young House, 109-113 Powderham Street, P.O. Box 146, New Plymouth

NORTH CANTERBURY

PHILIP WOOD & CO LTD
12 Main North Road, Woodend, North Canterbury

NORTHCOTE

BDO INTERNATIONAL ▽
P.O. Box 36264, Takapuna, Northcote

PALMERSTON NORTH

STAPLES RODWAY ▼
State Insurance Bldg., 61 Rangitikei St, P.O. Box 1245, Palmerston North

SOUTH AUCKLAND

BDO INTERNATIONAL ▽
P.O. Box 51-563, Pakuranga, South Auckland

TAURANGA

KPMG ★
35 Grey Street, (P.O.Box 110), Tauranga

WANGANUI

MOORES ROWLAND ▼
249 Wisksteed Street, Wanganui

WELLINGTON

BDO INTERNATIONAL ▽
P.O. Box 10-340, Wellington

DELOITTE TOUCHE TOHMATSU ★
10 Brandon Street, PO Box 1990, Wellington

DELOITTE TOUCHE TOHMATSU ★
P.O.Box 2961, Investment Centre, Featherston/Ballane Sts., Wellington 1

KPMG ★
KPMG Centre, 135 Victoria Street, Wellington 1

MOORE STEPHENS ▼
Real Estate House, Level 2, 354 Lambton Quay, Wellington

PKF ▼
3rd Floor, 85 The Terrace, Wellington

PRICEWATERHOUSE-COOPERS ★
113-119 The Terrace, PO Box 243, Wellington

STAPLES RODWAY ▼
Majestic Centre, 100 Willis Street, P.O. Box 490, Wellington

WHANGAREI

PRICEWATERHOUSE-COOPERS ★
National Mutual Building, 30-34 Rathbone Street, PO Box 445, Whangarei

NIGER

NIAMEY

PKF ▼
Quarter Terminus, BP 12 140, Niamey

NIGERIA

ABUJA

PANNELL KERR FORSTER ★
Plot 2A, herbert Macaulay Way, Abuja

PRICEWATERHOUSE-COOPERS ▽
Katsina House, Ralph Sodeinde Street, Abuja

APAPA

KAY CLIFTON & ASSOCIATES
Bewac Building, 13-15 Wharf Road, Apapa

BAUCHI

PANNELL KERR FORSTER ★
Floor 2, Giwo House, 6 Ahmadu Bellow Way, Bauchi

BENIN CITY

AKINTOLA WILLIAMS ADETONA ISICHEI & CO ★
P.O. Box 376, 83 Sapele Road, Benin City

ANJOUS, UKU, EWEKA & CO
2 Hudson Lane, Ikpoba Road,P.O. Box 420, Benin City

GIWA-OSAGIE DFK & CO ★
6 Ugbague Street, P.O. Box 16, Benin City
Tel: 00 234 803 727 4512
Resident Partners/Directors: ICAEW Members
A R O O Giwa-Osagie

UNUIGBE, AKINTOLA & CO ★
1 Afe Close, Off Ikpokpan Avenue, Benin City

ENUGU

AKINTOLA WILLIAMS ADETONA ISICHEI & CO ★
P.O. Box 334, Valid House, 3A Colliery Avenue, Enugu

EDWIN OYINZE & ASSOCIATES
29 Ogui Road, P.O. Box 2555, Enugu

IBADAN

AIB, FATONA & CO ★
197 Adekunle Fajuyi Street, Adamasingba, Ibadan

OYEDIRAN, FALEYE, OKE & CO ▼
P.M.B. 5614, Wuraola Building, Ring Road,State Hospital Road, Ibadan

IBUSA

C.E. OKOBI & CO
Fed. Govt. Girls College Road, PO Box 555, Ibusa

IKEJA

ADEKUNLE ADESANYA & CO
12 Ogundana Street, Off Allen Avenue, Ikeja

JOS

AKINTOLA WILLIAMS ADETONA ISICHEI & CO ★
P.O. Box 199, Standard House, 5, Jos

OYEDIRAN, FALEYE, OKE & CO ▼
Joseph Gomwalk House, 5, Jos

PANNELL KERR FORSTER ★
Lennap House, Government Secetariat Layout, Jos

KADUNA

AKINTOLA WILLIAMS ADETONA ISICHEI & CO ★
P.O. Box 58, NIDB House, 18 Waff Road, Kaduna

OYEDIRAN, FALEYE, OKE & CO ▼
Box 5260 Investment House, 1st Fl, 27 Aloi Akilu Road, Ahmado Bello Way, Kaduna

PANNELL KERR FORSTER ★
18/19 Ahmadu Bello Way, Kaduna

KANO

AKINTOLA WILLIAMS ADETONA ISICHEI & CO ★
P.O. Box 179, Niger Street/Park Road, Kano

OYEDIRAN, FALEYE, OKE & CO ▼
Development House, 14B Post Office Road, (P.O. Box 2802), Kano

PANNELL KERR FORSTER ★
Gidan Shehu Ahmed, Bank Road, Kano

TEMPLE GOTHARD JOHNSON ABIOY E & CO ★
13A Club Road, Kano

LAGOS

AJIBADE DUROJAIYE & CO ★
27 Ajay Aina Street, Ifako Gbagada, PO Box 70305, Victoria Island, Lagos

AKINTOLA WILLIAMS ADETONA ISICHEI & CO ★
P.O.Box 965, Town Planning Way/ Ade, Akinsanya Street, Ilupeju, Lagos

ANJOUS, UKU, EWEKA & CO
4 Ladipo Labinjo Crescent, Off Bode Thomas Street, Suru Lere, Lagos PMB 12020

ANTHONY ONONYE & CO ★
2 Iya-Agan Lane, Ebute-Metta (West), P O Box 74774, Victoria Island, Lagos

BDO INTERNATIONAL ▽
P.O. Box 3260, Marina, Lagos

EHIEMUA & CO ★
24 Commercial Road, Capl House, 1st Floor Apapa, P O Box 8096, Marina Lagos

EMMANUEL OKECHUKWU & CO
55 Western Avenue, P.O. Box 7923, Lagos

FOLORUNSO OLALEYE & CO
17th Floor(Right Wing), Western House, 8-10 Broad Street, Lagos

GIWA-OSAGIE DFK & CO ★
162 Herbert Macaulay Street, P.M.B. 1111,Yaba, Lagos

HORWATH DAFINONE ▽
Ceddi Towers, 16 Wharf Road, Apapa, PO Box 2151, Marina, Lagos
Tel: 00 234 15451863
Fax: 00 234 15452384
Email: info@dafinone.com
Website: http://www.dafinone.com
Training Contracts Available.
Resident Partners/Directors: ICAEW Members
P K Bhasin, D O Dafinone, E O Dafinone, I O Dafinone, J U Dafinone
Resident Partners (Non-ICAEW Members):
R A Ajibola

INVESTOR IN PEOPLE

SPECIALISATIONS – AUDIT & ASSURANCE
Audit
Audit — Private Company
Audit — Public Company
Internal Audit

SPECIALISATIONS – BUSINESS & GENERAL ADVICE
Acquisitions and Mergers
Book-keeping
Book-keeping Systems
Company Formation
Company Secretarial Service
Data Processing Services
Feasibility Studies
Management Advice to Business
Management Consultancy

SPECIALISATIONS – FINANCIAL REPORTING
Accounts Preparation
Financial Reporting
International Reporting Standards (IFRS)

SPECIALISATIONS – FORENSIC ACCOUNTING
Forensic Accounting

SPECIALISATIONS – IT
Computer Systems and Consultancy
Computerised Accounting Systems

SPECIALISATIONS – SECTOR
Banks/Financial Institutions
Clothing/Textiles
Construction
Food Industry
Human Resources
Manufacturing
Paper/Printing/Publishing
Property Development
Property Investment
Trade Assoc/Unions/Friendly Societies

SPECIALISATIONS – TAXATION
Back Duty
Capital Gains — Limited Companies
PAYE Advice
Payroll Service and Advice
Self Assessment Advice
Taxation
Value Added Tax
Languages Spoken:
English

IGWEOJIKE & CO
55 Western Avenue, GPO Box 7923, Marina, Lagos
Tel: 00 234 17761264
Principal: ICAEW Member
Chief Ojike

JK RANDLE & CO
Lisa Court, 61 Oduduwa Crescent Gra, Ikeja, PO Box 75429, Lagos

KPMG CONSULTING Ⓜ
KPMG House, 233 Ikorodu Road, Ilupeju, Lagos

KUNLE LADEJOBI & CO
G.P.O. Box 6816, Lagos

KUNLE OSHINAIKE & CO ★
P.O. Box 8930, Lagos

MBA & CO
B19 Admirality Towers, 8 Gerrard Road, P O Box 51847, Ikoyi, Lagos

NSOBIARI GEORGE & CO
12 Ijora Causeway, P.O. Box 8342, Lagos

O.A.ADEFESO & CO
Sennia House, 41a Joel Ogunnaike Street, GRA- Ikeja, PO Box 2067, Lagos

OBIORA MONU & CO ★
19 Martins Street, P.O. Box 4130, Lagos

OJIKE, OKECHUKWU & CO ★
5th Floor, 18 Oba Akran Avenue, Ikeja, GPO Box 2495, Marina, Lagos
Tel: 00 234 17761264
Resident Partners/Directors: ICAEW Members
Chief Ojike

OLABODE EMANUEL & PARTNERS
P.O. Box 1443, Lagos

OLUKAYODE AKINDELE & CO
208/212 Broad Street, P.O. Box 70828, Lagos

OLUSEYE JOHNSON & CO ★
16 Modupe Johnson Crecent, Surulere,P.O. Box 6206, Lagos

OLUSOLA AIGBE & CO ★
21 Fagbile Street, Surulere, PO Box 432, Yaba, Lagos

OYEDIRAN, FALEYE, OKE & CO ▼
PO Box 4929, GPO Marina Lagos, Lagos

PANNELL KERR FORSTER ★
Tapa House, 3/5 Imam Dauda Street, off Eric Moore Road, Surulere, Lagos

PRICEWATERHOUSE-COOPERS ▽
Plot 252E Muri Okunola Street, Victoria Island, P O Box 2419, Lagos

UNUIGBE, AKINTOLA & CO ★
Marble House (2nd Floor), 1 Kingsway Road, P.O. Ikoyi, Lagos

V O ODIASE & CO
GPO Box 9209, Marina, Lagos

MAIDUGURI

AKINTOLA WILLIAMS ADETONA ISICHEI & CO ★
P.O. Box 1676, Nicon Building, Sir Kashim Ibrahim Road, Maiduguri

MAKURDI

PANNELL KERR FORSTER ★
45 Barrack Road, Makurdi

MINNA

PANNELL KERR FORSTER ★
Federal Mortgage Bank Building, F Layout, Bosso Road, Minna

ONITSHA

GIWA-OSAGIE DFK & CO ★
9A Modebe Avenue, P.O. Box 3414, Onitsha

OWERRI

AKINTOLA WILLIAMS ADETONA ISICHEI & CO ★
P.O. Box 1778, 23 Wetheral Road, Owerri

PORT HARCOURT

AKINTOLA WILLIAMS ADETONA ISICHEI & CO ★
P.O. Box 939, 67 Ikwerre Road, Port Harcourt

AKINTOLA WILLIAMS ADETONA ISICHEI & CO ★
Orosi House, 28 Forces Avenue, P O Box 3704, Port Harcourt

ALLWELL BROWN & CO
73 Ikwerre Road, P.O. Box 242, Port Harcourt

OYEDIRAN, FALEYE, OKE & CO ▼
18C Forces Avenue, (P.O. Box 8777), Port Harcourt

SAPELE

ANJOUS, UKU, EWEKA & CO
19 Palm Avenue, Sapele

WARRI

ANJOUS, UKU, EWEKA & CO
136 Warri/Sapele Road, Warri

YABA

AIB, FATONA & CO ★
13 Jibowu Street, P.O. Box 461, Yaba

YOLA

GIWA-OSAGIE DFK & CO ★
85 Ahmadu Beloway, P.O. Box 910,Jimeta, Yola

ZARIA

PANNELL KERR FORSTER ★
Gaskiya Building, Gaskiya Road, Zaria

NORTH YEMEN

SANAA

DR AHMED OMAR BAMASHMOOS ▼
PO Box 10018, Al-Shokany Street, Al-Safiah Alganubiyah Zone, Sanaa

NORWAY

ALESUND

ERNST & YOUNG ▼
Grimmergt 4, N-6002 Alesund

KPMG A.S. ▼
Klaus Nelsensgt 4, (Postboks 287), 6001 Alesund

ARENDAL

ERNST & YOUNG ▼
Kittelsbuklveien 1, P.O. Box 299, N-4801 Arendal

KPMG A.S. ▼
Luellskev 4, (Postboks 103), 4800 Arendal

PRICEWATERHOUSE-COOPERS AS ★
Kystveien 40, N-4841 Arendal

BERGEN

ERNST & YOUNG ▼
Lars Hillesgt. 208, P.O. Box 4284, Nygardstangen, N-5028 Bergen

KPMG A.S. ▼
Sandviksboder 5, 5035 Bergen

PRICEWATERHOUSE-COOPERS AS ★
PO Box 1906-Nordnes, N-5817 Bergen

BODO

ERNST & YOUNG ▼
Sjetun-Renviknv 9, P.O. Box 594, N-8001 Bodo

DRAMMEN

ERNST & YOUNG ▼
Nedre Storgt 46, P.O. Box 560, Brakeroeya, N-3002 Drammen

PRICEWATERHOUSE-COOPERS AS ★
PO Box 1621, N-3007 Drammen

ELVERUM

KPMG A.S. ▼
Postboks 58, 2401 Elverum

FORDE

PRICEWATERHOUSE-COOPERS AS ★
PO Box 375, N-6801 Forde

FREDRIKSTAD

KPMG A.S. ▼
Bryggeriveien 6, (Postboks 391), 1600 Fredrikstad

PRICEWATERHOUSE-COOPERS AS ★
Dikeveien 34, N-1661 Fredrikstad

HAMAR

PRICEWATERHOUSE-COOPERS AS ★
P O Box 1100, N-2301 Hamar

HOLMESTRAND

ERNST & YOUNG ▼
Havnegt 7, P.O. Box 43, N-3081 Holmestrand

KONGSBERG

ERNST & YOUNG ▼
Kirketorget 5, N-3600 Kongsberg

KRISTIANSAND

PRICEWATERHOUSE-COOPERS AS ★
Gravane 26, N-4610 Kristiansand

LARVIK

ERNST & YOUNG ▼
Brannvaktsgt 5, P.O. Box 183, N-3251 Larvik

LILLEHAMMER

ERNST & YOUNG ▼
Storgt 132, P.O. Box 324, N-2601 Lillehammer

MO I RANA

PRICEWATERHOUSE-COOPERS AS ★
PO Box 1233, N-8602 Mo I Rana

MOSS

ERNST & YOUNG ▼
Solgaard Skog 104, P.O. Box 720, N-1536 Moss

NARVIK

ERNST & YOUNG ▼
Dronningensgt 33, P.O. Box 444, N-8501 Narvik

NOTODDEN

ERNST & YOUNG ▼
Storgt 54, N-3760 Notodden

OSLO

BDO INTERNATIONAL ▽
Radhusgt 17, 0158, 1 Oslo

KPMG A.S. ▼
Sorkedalsveien 6, 0369 Oslo

MOORES ROWLAND ▼
Munkedamsveien 45, PO Box 1704 Vika, N-0121 Oslo

PANNELL KERR FORSTER ▼
Bogstadveien 27 B, 0355 Oslo

PRICEWATERHOUSE-COOPERS AS ★
Karenslyst alle 12, N-0245 Oslo

PORSGRUNN

ERNST & YOUNG ▼
Olavs gt.26, P.O. Box 64, 3901 Porsgrunn

SANDEFJORD

ERNST & YOUNG ▼
Storgt 27, P.O. Box 2057, N-3201 Sandefjord

SORTLAND

ERNST & YOUNG ▼
Strandgaten 31, P.O. Box .286, N-8401 Sortland

STAVANGER

ERNST & YOUNG ▼
Vassbotnen 11 Forus, P O Box 8015, N-4068 Stavanger

ERNST & YOUNG ▼
Fridtjof Nansens vei 48, PO Box 8015, 4003 Stavanger

KPMG A.S. ▼
Petroleumsveien 6, 4033 Forus, Stavanger

PRICEWATERHOUSE-COOPERS AS ★
PO Box 8017 Forus, N-4068 Stavanger

STORD

KPMG A.S. ▼
Postboks 694, 5404 Stord

TONSBERG

ERNST & YOUNG ▼
Kirkeveien 6, N-3100 Tonsberg

TROMSO

KPMG A.S. ▼
Postboks 898, 9259 Tromso

PRICEWATERHOUSE-COOPERS AS ★
PO Box 2166, N-9267 Tromso

TRONDHEIM

ERNST & YOUNG ▼
Prinsens gt. 34B, N-7011 Trondheim

KPMG A.S. ▼
Postboks 568, 7406 Trondheim

VIKERSUND

ERNST & YOUNG ▼
Hovdeveien 9, P.O. Box 49, N-3371 Vikersund

OMAN

MUSCAT

A.F. FERGUSON & CO ▽
P.O.Box 3848, P.C. 112 Ruwi, Muscat

BDO INTERNATIONAL ▽
P.O. Box 1176, Ruwi, Postal Code 112, Muscat

ERNST & YOUNG ▼ ◈
P.O. Box 1750, Ruwi, 112 Muscat
Tel: 00 968 24559559

KPMG
P O Box 641, 112 Muscat

KPMG
4th Floor HSBC Building, Muttrah Business District, PO Box 641, 112 Muscat

RSM & CO ▼
Suites 107-108, Hatat House, Wadi Adi, Muscat

RUWI

MOORE STEPHENS ▼
Bank Melli Iran Bldg, Office no 201 & 202, 2nd Fl, CBD (South), PO Box 933, 112 Ruwi

PRICEWATERHOUSE-COOPERS
P O Box 3075, 112 Ruwi

PAKISTAN

FAISALABAD

HABIB ALAM & CO
Boly di Chogi, Mandi Quater, Faisalabad 320000

ISLAMABAD

A.F. FERGUSON & CO ★
P.I.A. Building, 49 Blue Area, P.O. Box 3021, Islamabad

AVAIS HYDER LIAQUAT NAUMAN ★
32 Block 8 School Road, Super Market, Islamabad

BDO EBRAHIM & CO
3rd Floor, Saeed Plaza, 22 East Blue Area, Jinnah Avenue, Islamabad 1234

KHALID MAJID REHMAN ★
3rd Floor Al-Malik Centre, 70 West, G-7/F7 Jinnah Avenue, Islamabad 46000

KPMG TASEER HADI & CO ★
6th Floor, State Life Building No 5, Jinnah Avenue, Blue Area, Islamabad

KARACHI

A.F. FERGUSON & CO ★
State Life Building 1C, Off I.I. Chundrigar Road, P.O. Box 4716, Karachi 74000

AVAIS HYDER LIAQUAT NAUMAN ★
5/32 Pir Ali Gohar Road, Off Shaheed-e-Millat Road, N.K.C.H.S., Karachi 748000

BDO EBRAHIM & CO
2nd Floor Block C, Lakson Square Building No 1, Sarwar Shaheed Road, Karachi 74200

BDO INTERNATIONAL ▽
2nd Floor, Block C, Lakson Square Building No. 1, Sarwar Shaheed Road, Karachi 74200

BDO INTERNATIONAL ▽
BDO Ebrahim & Co, 2nd Floor, Block C, Lakson Square Building No1, Sarwar Shahead Road, Karachi 74200

FEROZE SHARIF & CO ★
7-G Block 6, P E C H Society, Karachi 29

FORD RHODES SIDAT HYDER & CO
Progressive Plaza, Beaumont Road, Karachi 75530

IBRAHIM, SHAIKH & CO
259-260 Panorama Centre, Fatima Jinnah Road, Karachi 74400

IBRAHIM, SHAIKH & CO
208 Park Avenue, Sharah-e-Faisal, Karachi

KALEEM MALIK & CO
House No. 9, A-Street, Off Khayaban-e-Shaheen, Defence Hsing Auth, Phase V, Karachi

KHALID MAJID REHMAN ★
1st Floor, Modern Motors House, Beaumont Road, Karachi 46000

KPMG TASEER HADI KHALID & CO ★
1st Floor, Sheikh Sultan Trust Bldg No2, Beaumont Road, Karachi 75530

RAFAQAT MANSHA MOHSIN DOSSANI MASOOM & CO ◈
Suite 113, 3rd Floor, Hafeez Centre, KCHS Block 7&8, Shahra-e-Faisal, Karachi 75350

MUSHTAQ & CO ★
407 Commerce Centre, Hasrat Mohani Road, Karachi 74200

S.H. SIDDIQI & CO
115 1st Flr, Avenue Centre, 264 Statchen Road, R A Lines, G.P.O. Box 1067, Karachi 74200

SAEED METHANI MUSHTAQ & CO ★
602 -Uni Shopping Centre, Abdullah Haroon Road, Sadar, Karachi 74400

SIDDIQI & CO ★
7/G Block 6, P E C H Society, Karachi 29

LAHORE

A.F. FERGUSON & CO ★
Al-Falah Building, PO Box39, Shahrah-e-Quaid-e-Azam, Lahore

A. RAZZAQ & CO
Suite #40 3rd floor, landmark Plaza, Jail Road, Lahore

AFTAB NABI & CO
Alshajar, Nila Gubad, Anarkali, Lahore

AMIN MUDASSAR & CO
4th Floor, 97-B/D-I, Main Building, Gulberg III, Lahore

AVAIS HYDER LIAQUAT NAUMAN ★
1/C-5 Avais Chambers, Sikander Malhi Road, Canal Park, Gulberg 2, Lahore

AVAIS HYDER LIAQUAT NAUMAN ★
Nizam Chambers, Level 4, 7 Fatima Jinah Road, Lahore

BDO EBRAHIM & CO
F-2 First Floor, Grace Centre, Canal Road, I.B Canal Park, Gulberg-II, Lahore 54660

COOPERS & LYBRAND ▼
Abacus House, 11 Main Gulberg, Lahore 54660

FAZAL MAHMOOD & CO
147 Shadman Colony 1, Lahore 54000

FORD RHODES SIDAT HYDER & CO
Mall View Building, 4 Bank Square, Lahore 54000

KPMG TASEER HADI & CO ★
201 Office Block, Siddiq Trade Centre, 72 Main Boulevard, Gulberg II, Lahore

KPMG TASEER HADI KHALID & CO ★
J-8/99 St John's Park, Cantonment, Lahore

M. AKHTAR
171 Shah Jamal, Colony, Lahore

MIAN & CO
178-M Defence Housing Auth., Lahore 54792

MIRZA ARSHED BAIG
190-R, LCCHS, Lahore 54792

MUSHTAQ & CO ★
19-B Block G, Gulherg III, Lahore

NAJEM D TOOR
37-A PCSIR Housing Society, Canal Bank, Lahore

NAZMAN
307 Upper Mall, Lahore 54000

PRICEWATERHOUSE-COOPERS ▼
Abacus House, 4 Noon Avenue, Canal, Muslim Town, Lahore 54600

RAHMAN SARFARAZ RAHIM IQBAL RAFIQ
Apt-4 & 8 Block B, 90 Canal Park, Gulberg II, Lahore

SAEED METHANI MUSHTAQ & CO ★
10/7 Al-Karam, Faiz Road, Old Muslim Town, Lahore

TARIQ AYUB, ANWAR & CO ★
84-B-1 Gulberg III, Lahore

WM PROSERV LLP
313 Eden Towers, Main Boulevard, Gulber III, Lahore

PESHAWAR

SAEED METHANI MUSHTAQ & CO ★
Suite 23c, Block B, Cantonment Board Plaza, Peshawar

RAWALPINDI

FORD RHODES SIDAT HYDER & CO
45 Market Al-Abbas,1st Floor, Adamjee Road,P.O. Box 232, Rawalpindi

PANAMA

PANAMA CITY

ARAUZ, HERMIDA Y PAZMINO ▼
Avenida Cuba y Calle 34, Este 33a-34,Edificio Banco, General,1st Fl.102 La Exposc, Panama City 5

AVILA Y ASOCIADOS SA ▼
Urb Obarrio, Calle Abel Bravo Y Apt 60, Duplex Apt 4, Panama City

AVILA Y ASOCIADOS SA ▼
PO Box 8881, Panama City 5

IRIGOYEN & GARUZ SOAD LTDA ▼
Apartado 6-9009, El Dorado, Panama City

PEAT, MARWICK, MITCHELL & CO ▼
Ave. 4a Sur, (Calle 50), No.54, (Apartado 5307), 5, Panama City

PRICEWATERHOUSE-COOPERS ▼
Avenida Samuel Lewis y Calle, 55e Urbanization Obarrio, Aptdo 6-4493 Zona El Dorado, Panama City

PAPUA NEW GUINEA

LAE

KPMG
IPI Building, 2nd Street, (P.O. Box 1226), Lae

PRICEWATERHOUSE-COOPERS ★
Anz Haus, Central Avenue, Lae

MOUNT HAGEN

GUINN PKF ▼
Section 21, Lot 19, Hagen Drive, PROVICE 281, Mount Hagen

PANNELL KERR FORSTER ▼
Section 21, Lot 19, Hagen Drive, Province 281, Mount Hagen

PORT MORESBY

ERNST & YOUNG ▼
P.O. Box 112, Port Moresby

GUINN PKF ▼
Section 15, Lot 15, Bernal Street, National Capital District, Port Moresby

KPMG
Mogoru Moto Bldg., Champion Parade, (P.O. Box 507), Port Moresby

PRICEWATERHOUSE-COOPERS ★
Credit House, P O Box 484, Cuthbertson Street, Port Moresby

SMITHS
P O Box 487, Port Moresby

PARAGUAY

ASUNCION

PRICEWATERHOUSE-COOPERS ▼
Edificio Asubank, 14 de Mayo 337, Piso 9, (Casilla de Correo 2481), Asuncion

PERU

LIMA

ALEJANDRO TUESTA B. & ASOCIA ▼
Camino Real Aven. No 493-7A, San Isidro, Lima

ALEJANDRO TUESTA B. & ASOCIA ▼
Camino REal Ave. No., 493-, 7A San Isidro,P.O. Box 3210, Lima

BDO INTERNATIONAL ▽
P.O. Box 3661, Lima, 1

CAIPO, DEL BOSQUE Y ASOCIADO ▼
Av. Rep de Chile,388, Apartado 3146, Lima, 11

CAIPO, DEL BOSQUE Y ASOCIDAD OS ▼
Av. Republica de Chile 388, 7th Floor, Lima, 11

MOORE STEPHENS ▼
Av Miraflores 1435, (Antes 28 de Julio), - Miraflores, Lima, 18

PRICEWATERHOUSE-COOPERS ▼
Juan de Arona 830, Apartado 3828, Lima, 27

VILLAGARCIA & ASCOIADOS ▼
Av Paseo de la Republica, No 3557, Lima, 27

PHILIPPINES

MAKATI CITY

PRICEWATERHOUSE-COOPERS ★
Multinational Bancorp., Centre, 14th Floor, 6805 Ayala Avenue, Makati City 1226

R S BERNALDO & ASSOCIATES ▼
18th Floor, Cityland Condominium, 10 Tower 1, 6815 HV De La Costa Ext, Corner Ayala Avenue, Makati City

MANILA

BERRIS & CO ▼
MCPO Box 405, Makati, Manila

FERNADEZ, BERRIS & CO ▼
Metrobank Plaza,21st Floor, Sen. Gil J Puyat Avenue,Makati, Metro, Manila

FERNANDEZ, BERRIS & CO ▼
MCPO Box 405, Makati, Manila

PRICEWATERHOUSE-COOPERS ★
29/F Philamlife Tower, 8767 Paseo De Roxas, Makati, Metro, Manila 1226

SYCIP GORRES VELAY & CO ▼
SGV Building, 6760 Ayala Avenue, Makati, Manila 1200

POLAND

GDANSK

DELOITTE & TOUCHE ★
pok 1110, Waly Piastowskie, Gdansk, 80-995

T & K ABAK GDANSK SP.Z.O.O. ▼
ul Rogaczewskiego 9/19, Gdansk, 80-804

KRAKOW

PANNELL KERR FORSTER ▼
Pl. Na Stawach 1, Krakow, 30-107

PRICEWATERHOUSE-COOPERS SP. Z O.O. ★
Centrum Biurowe Lubicz, ul. Lubicz 23, Krakow, 31-503

RASZYN

KENNEDY & CO
ul Godebskiego 65, Raszyn, 05 090

RZESZOW

PANNELL KERR FORSTER ▼
Al. Pilsudskiego 32, Rzeszow, 35-959

TORUN

PANNELL KERR FORSTER ▼
Zolkiewskiego 37/41, Torun, 87-100

WARSAW

BAKER TILLY SMOCZYNSKI & PARTNERS SP. Z O.O. ★
Ul. Nowogrodzka 12/3, 00511 Warsaw
Tel: 00 48 226221922
Fax: 00 48 226298747
Email: bts@bakertillysmoczynski.eu
Website: http://www.bakertillysmoczynski.eu
Mobile: 00 48 601225588
Resident Partners/Directors:
ICAEW Members
J Smoczynski
Resident Partners (Non-ICAEW Members):
M Byczynska
Other Offices: Krakow, Wroclow
Registered by another RSB to carry out company audit work

SPECIALISATIONS – AUDIT & ASSURANCE
Audit
Audit — Private Company
Audit — Public Company
Internal Audit

SPECIALISATIONS – BUSINESS & GENERAL ADVICE
Acquisitions and Mergers
Book-keeping
Company Formation
Europe
Franchising
Management Accounting Consultancy
Management Advice to Business

SPECIALISATIONS – BUSINESS RECOVERY & INSOLVENCY
Bankruptcies
Corporate Recovery
Liquidations
Reorganisations and Company Reconstructions

SPECIALISATIONS – FINANCIAL REPORTING
Accounts Preparation
Financial Reporting
Foreign Subsidiary Companies
International Reporting Standards (IFRS)

SPECIALISATIONS – FORENSIC ACCOUNTING
Expert Witnesses in Litigation
Forensic Accounting

SPECIALISATIONS – SECTOR
Agriculture
Charities
Corporate
Property
Property Investment
Retailers

SPECIALISATIONS – TAXATION
Capital Gains — Limited Companies
Customs Duty
Investigations
Payroll Service and Advice
Taxation
UK Companies Overseas
UK Nationals Overseas
Value Added Tax
Languages Spoken:
Polish, English

BDO INTERNATIONAL ▽
ul.Jazdow 8a, Warsaw, 00-467

DELOITTE & TOUCHE ★
Piekna 18, 00549 Warsaw

DELOITTE & TOUCHE ★
Ul Piekna 18, 00-549 Warsaw

ERNST & YOUNG AUDIT SP ZOO ★
ul Emilli Plater 53, Warsaw, 00-113

ERNST & YOUNG AUDIT SP ZOO ★
Rondo ONZ 1, 00-124 Warsaw

ERNST & YOUNG AUDIT SP ZOO ★
Ul Sienna 39, Warsaw, 00 121

KPMG POLSKA SP.ZO.O ▼
ul. Chlodna 51, XVI Floor, Warsaw, 00-867

PANNELL KERR FORSTER ▼
Ul Elblaska 15-17, 01 747 Warsaw

PRICEWATERHOUSE-COOPERS SP. Z O.O. ★
Al.Armii Ludowej 14, Warsaw, 00638

WROCLAW

PANNELL KERR FORSTER ▼
Krzyxka 94, Wroclaw, 53-019

PORTUGAL

ALBUFEIRA

PRICEWATERHOUSE-COOPERS ▼
Edificio Altis, 3R, Rua do Indico, Cerro de Alagoa, 8200 Albufeira

FUNCHAL

ERNST & YOUNG ▼
Apartado 315, Funchal Codex, 9000 Funchal

KPMG ★
Edificio Marina Forum, Avenida Arriaga 77, 3D Sala 302, 9000-060 Funchal

MOORE STEPHENS (MADEIRA) ▼
Av Arriaga No. 50-3o Sala 2, 9000 Funchal

LISBON

BDO INTERNATIONAL ▽
Avenida de Republica 50, 10th Floor, 1000 Lisbon

DELOITTE & TOUCHE
Edificio Atrium Saldanha, Praca Ducque de Saldanha 1-6o, 1050904 Lisbon

ERNST & YOUNG ▼
Edificio Republica, Av. da Republica 90-3, 1649-024 Lisbon

HORWATH & ASSOCIADOS SROC LDA ★
Avenida Miquel Bombarda, 21 3 Esq, 1050161 Lisbon

HORWATH & ASSOCIADOS SROC LDA ★
Avenida Miguel Bombarda, No 21 3 Esq, 1050 161 Lisbon

J CAMILO & ASSOCIADO
Rua Odette de Saint Maurice, Piso - 1 Escritorio B, 1700921 Lisbon
Tel: 00 351 217542610
Principal: ICAEW Member
G M Fletcher

KPMG ★
Edificio Monumental, Av. Praia da Vitoria 71-A-11o, 1069-006 Lisbon

MOORE STEPHENS ▼
Av Frei Miguel Contreiras, No 54-10, 1700 Lisbon

PANNELL KERR FORSTER ▼
Av Antonio Augusto de Aguiar, 108 5th and 6th Floor, 1050019 Lisbon

PANNELL KERR FORSTER (PORTUGAL) SA ▼
Av Antonio Augusto de Agviar, 108 5th & 6th Floor, 1050-019 Lisbon

PKF CONSULTORES SA ▼
Av Antonio Augusto de Aguilar 1088, 1050-019 Lisbon

PRICEWATERHOUSE-COOPERS ▼
Edificio Caravelas, Rua Dr Eduardo Neves, 9-6, 1050 Lisbon

PRICEWATERHOUSE-COOPERS ▼
Avenida da Liberdade 245-7, 1269-034 Lisbon

PRICEWATERHOUSE-COOPERS ▼
Rua Marques de Subserra 10, 1070-170 Lisbon

PRICEWATERHOUSECOOPERS LDA
Palacio Sottomayor, Rue Sousa Martins, No 1 - 2 Esq, 1050-217 Lisbon

PRICEWATERHOUSECOOPERS LDA
Rua Marques de Subserra 10, 1070-170 Lisbon

OPORTO

BDO INTERNATIONAL ▽
Rua S.Joao de Brito, 605 E, Escritorio 3.2 - 4100 Porto, Oporto

ERNST & YOUNG ▼
Rua Goncalo Sampaio, No.329-4 DT, 4150 Oporto

MOORE STEPHENS ▼
Rua Joao de Deus No 6-6o, Sala 601, 4100 Oporto

PRICEWATERHOUSE-COOPERS ▼
Edificios do Lago, Rua S Iaoa de Brito, 605-E Esc 1.2, 4100-455 Oporto

PRICEWATERHOUSE-COOPERS ▼
Rua Oliveira Monteiro 168, 4050-438 Oporto

PRICEWATERHOUSECOOPERS LDA
Edificio do Lago, Rua S Joao De Brito, 605-E-Esc 1.2, 4100-455 Oporto

PORTO

KPMG ★
Edifcio Peninsula, Praca Do Bom Sucesso 127/131, 7 Andar-Sala 701, 4150-146 Porto

QATAR

DOHA

ERNST & YOUNG ▼ ◈
P O Box 164, Doha, 164
Tel: 00 974 4414599

KPMG
Arab Bank Building, Second Floor, P O Box 4473, Doha

PRICEWATERHOUSE-COOPERS-QATAR LLC ▼
P O Box 6689, 4th Floor - HSBC Building, Doha

REPUBLIC OF SINGAPORE

SINGAPORE

A.L. HO
101A Sunset Way, Singapore 2159

A. OMAR & CO
6 Commonwealth Lane, 01-01 GMTI Building, Singapore 149547

A.S.H. LOONG & CO
48 Meyer Road, Apt. 08-50, Singapore 437872

B.S. MANGAT & CO
20 Cecil Street, 15-08 Equity Plaza, Singapore 049705

BAKER TILLY TFWLCL
15 Beach Road, Apt. 03-10,Beach Centre, Singapore 189677

BDO INTERNATIONAL ▽
112 Middle Road, 02-00 Midland House, Singapore 0718

BDO RAFFLES ★
19 Keppel Road, 02-01 Jit Poh Building, Singapore 089058
Tel: 00 65 68289118
Resident Partners/Directors: ICAEW Members
S H Chia, S M Lim

BOON SUAN LEE & CO ▼
220 Orchard Road, Apt. 05-02,Midpoint Orhard, Singapore 0923

C.H.ONG & CO
110 Jalan Jurong Kechil, Apt 02-01 Sweebi House, Singapore 2159

C.J. DORAN
239 Arcadia Road, Apt. 03-01, Singapore

DELOITTE & TOUCHE ★
6 Shenton Way, Apt 32-00, DBS Building Tower Two, Singapore 068809

DESAI & CO
1 Tanjong Rhu Road, 05-01, Singapore 436879

E.P. ONG & CO
7 Farrer Drive, Apt 01-05, Sommerville Grandeur, Singapore 259278

EE PENG LIANG & CO ★
10 Collyer Quay, 21-01, Ocean Building, Singapore 0104

ER & CO
336 Smith Street, 04-302, New Bridge Centre, Singapore 050336

ERNST & YOUNG ★
One Raffles Quay, North Tower, Level 18, Singapore 048583

ERNST & YOUNG ★
10 Collyer Quay, 21-01 Ocean Building, Singapore 049315

EVAN WONG & CO ★
P.O. Box 384, 10 Collyer Quay, 21-01 Ocean Building, Singapore 0104

EWE, LOKE & PARTNERS
8 Robinson Road #08-00, ASO Building, Singapore 048544

FOO KON TAN GRANT THORNTON ★
47 Hill Street, 5th Fl. Unit 01, Chinese Chamber of Comm Bldg, Singapore 179365
Tel: 00 65 63312313
Resident Partners/Directors: ICAEW Members
S B Chin

G.S.TAN & CO
110 Middle Rd, Apt 06-03, Chiat Hong Building, Singapore 188968

H.A. CHRISTIE & CO
36 Robinson Road, 14-03, City House, Singapore 068877

H.C.KOH & CO
190 Middle Road, 14-02 Fortune Centre, Singapore 188979

HUANG S.S. & CO
320 Serangoon Road, Apt. 04-46 Serangoon Plaza, Singapore 0821

JAMES SOO & CO
65 Jalan Lanjut, Singapore 577708

K K LEONG & PARTNERS ◈
7500A Beach Road, 12-313 The Plaza, Singapore 199591

K.P. HO & ASSOCIATES ★
80 South Bridge Road 03-01, Golden Castle Building, Singapore 058710

KPMG ★
16 Raffles Quay, # 22-00, Hong Leong Building, Singapore 048581
Tel: 00 65 62133388
Resident Partners/Directors: ICAEW Members
D A Leaver, W Y Tan, D L K Teoh, S Tham, C M Yap

KWAN WONG TAN & HONG
15 Scotts Road, Suite 04-01/03, Thong Teck Building, Singapore 228218

MAZARS
133 Cecil Street, 15-02 Keck Seng Tower, Singapore 069535

MOORE STEPHENS LLP ★
10 Anson Road, Apt 29-15, International Plaza, Singapore 079903
Tel: 00 65 62213771
Resident Partners/Directors: ICAEW Members
C B Johnson

MOORES ROWLAND ★
133 Cecil Street, Apt.15-02 Keck Seng Tower, Singapore 048545

MOORES ROWLAND ▼
14 Robinson Road, 05-01 Far East Finance Bldg, Singapore 048545

OW FOOK SHENG & CO
76 Tanjong Pagar Road, Singapore 088497

PATRICK KAN & CO
80 Marine Parade Road, 16-09, Parkway Parade, Singapore 449269

PAUL WAN & CO ★
10 Anson Road, No. 35-08,International Plaza, Singapore 079903
Tel: 00 65 62203280
Resident Partners/Directors: ICAEW Members
P T C Wan

PHILLIP LEE MANAGEMENT CONSULTANTS PTE LTD
Blk 166 Woodlands St 13, Apartment 02-521, Singapore

PHILLIP LEE MANAGEMENT CONSULTANTS PTE LTD
371 Beach Road, Apt 16-08, Keypoint, Singapore 199597

PKF ▼
Pannell Kerr Forster, 9 Battery Road, 10-01/07 Straits Bldg, Singapore 049910

PRICEWATERHOUSE-COOPERS ★
17-00 PWC Building, 8 Cross Street, Singapore 048424

R. CHOCKALINGHAM & ASSOCIATES
63 Robinson Road, Apt 06-01 Afro Asia Building, Singapore 068894

RGL FORENSIC ACCOUNTANTS (SINGAPORE) PTE LTD
Singapore Land Tower, 37th Floor, 50 Raffles Place, Singapore 048623

ROBERT YAM & CO
Fortune Centre, Apt. 16-03, 190 Middle Road, Singapore 188979

SASHI KALA DEVI ASSOCIATES ★
31 Cantonment Road, Singapore 089747

SHANKER IYER & CO
3 Phillip Street, Unit 18-00, Commerce Point, Singapore 048693
Tel: 00 65 325746
Principal: ICAEW Member
S Iyer

STEPHEN KOH & CO ★
138 Cecil Street, No. 13-03, Cecil Court, Singapore 069538

STEVEN TAN PAC ★
25 International Business Park, #04 - 22/26 German Centre, Singapore 609916
Tel: 00 65 2227088
Resident Partners/Directors: ICAEW Members
S C C Tan

THONG & LIM ★
27 Cantonment Road, Singapore 089745

WONG KOK YEE TAX SERVICES PTE LTD
78 Shenton Way, Apartment 30 - 01, Lippo Centre, Singapore 079120

Y.H. ONG
8 Chee Hoon Avenue, Singapore 1129

REPUBLIC OF SOUTH AFRICA

BELLVILLE

ERNST & YOUNG ★
P.O. Box 504, Bellville, 7532

PRICEWATERHOUSE-COOPERS INC ★
PO Box 168, Bellville, 7535

BENONI

DELOITTE & TOUCHE ★
P.O.Box 58, PFV House, 78 Howard Avenue, Benoni 1500

FISHER HOFFMAN PKF ▼
2nd Floor, Rothburn Building, 61 Woburn Avenue, Benoni 1501

BETHAL

PRICEWATERHOUSE-COOPERS INC ★
PO Box 378, Bethal, 2310

BISHO

PDB PRETORIOUS DONDASME ▼
9 Bisho Business Village, Siwani Avenue, Bisho

BLOEMFONTEIN

DELOITTE & TOUCHE ★
Bloemboard Bldg., 65 Maitland St, PO Box 268, Bloemfontein, 9300

ERNST & YOUNG ★
PO Box 200, Bloemfontein, 9300

FISHER HOFFMAN PKF ▼
40 Victoria Road, Willows, Bloemfontein, 9320

PRICEWATERHOUSE-COOPERS INC ★
PO Box 818, Bloemfontein, 9300

CAPE TOWN

BDO INTERNATIONAL ▽
P.O. Box 2275, Cape Town, 8000

DELOITTE & TOUCHE ★
Sanclare, 21 Dreyer St , Claremont, (P.O.Box 578, 8000), Cape Town 8000

ERNST & YOUNG ★
P.O. Box 656, Cape Town, 8000

MOORE STEPHENS ▼
P O Box 3311, Cape Town, 8000

MOORES ROWLAND ▼
PO Box 2817, Cape Town, 8000

PKF (CPT) INC ▼
4th Floor, Communicare Centre, 2 Roggebaai Square, Cape Town 8001

PRICEWATERHOUSE-COOPERS INC ★
PO Box 2799, Cape Town, 8000

CASCADES

WARMINGTONS INC
PO Box 13774, Cascades, 3202
Tel: 00 27 333940881
Principal: ICAEW Member
P Warmington

CERES

PRICEWATERHOUSE-COOPERS INC ★
PO Box 99, Ceres, 6835

CLAREMONT

PANNELL KERR FORSTER ▼
5th Floor, Protea Place, Protea Road, Claremont

DURBAN

BDO INTERNATIONAL ▽
P.O. Box 1849, Durban, 4000

DELOITTE & TOUCHE ★
P.O. Box 243, Durban, 4000

ERNST & YOUNG ★
P.O. Box 859, Durban, 4000

FISHER HOFFMAN PKF (DBN) INC ▼
2nd Flr, 12 On Palm Boulevard, Gateway, Durban 4319

MOORES ROWLAND ▼
PO Box 2231, Durban, 4000

MORRISON MURRAY ▼
14th Floor, Southern Life House, 88 Field Street, Durban 4000

PRICEWATERHOUSE-COOPERS INC ★
P O Box 1049, Durban, 4000

EAST LONDON

FISHER HOFFMAN PKF ▼
PDB House, 12 Sansom Road, Vincent, East London

JOHN L. FLETCHER
602 The Valley, 70 Jarvis Road, Berea, East London 5241

DELOITTE & TOUCHE ★
Caxton House, Terminus Street, (P.O.Box 271, 5200), East London 5200

PRICEWATERHOUSE-COOPERS INC ★
P O Box 13069, Vincent, East London, CP 5217

EMPANGENI

BDO INTERNATIONAL ▽
P.O. Box 963, Empangeni, 3880

ESHOWE

PRICEWATERHOUSE-COOPERS INC ★
PO Box 4, Eshowe, 3815

GEORGE

ERNST & YOUNG ★
P.O. Box 393, George, 6530

PRICEWATERHOUSE-COOPERS INC ★
PO Box 1195, George, 6530

GRAHAMSTOWN

FISHER HOFFMAN PKF ▼
51A Hill Street, Grahamstown, 6140

GREENACRES

PRICEWATERHOUSE-COOPERS INC ★
PO Box 27013, Greenacres, 6057

GROENKLOOF

PRICEWATERHOUSE-COOPERS INC ★
PO Box 1155, Groenkloof, 0027

HILTON

L.P.H. BENNETT
11 Daisy Road, Hilton, 3245

ILLOVO

ERNST & YOUNG ★
Wanderers Office Park, 52 Corlett Drive, Illovo

JOHANNESBURG

BDO INTERNATIONAL ▽
P.O. Box 8813, Johannesburg, 2000

DELOITTE & TOUCHE ★
Private Bag x 6, Gallo Manor, Johannesburg, 2052

ERNST & YOUNG ★
Wanderers Office Park, 52 Corlett Drive, PO Box 2322, Johannesburg 2000

FISHER HOFFMAN PKF ▼
PKF House, 15 Girton Road, Parktown, Johannesburg 2193

FISHER HOFFMAN SITHOLE ▼
FHS House, 15 Girton Road, Parktown, Johannesburg 2193

HENRI W. ROZEN & CO
PO Box 3039, Johannesburg, 2000

NEXIA LEVITT KIRSON ▼
4th Floor, Aloe Grove, 196 Louis Botha Avenue, Houghton Estate, Johannesburg, Gauteng 2198

PKF (JHB) INC ▼
PKF House, 15 Girton Road, Parktown, Johannesburg 2193

PRICEWATERHOUSE-COOPERS INC ★
2 Eglin Road, Sunninghill

PRICEWATERHOUSE-COOPERS INC ★
90 Rivonia Road, Sandown, Johannesburg, 2196

PRICEWATERHOUSE-COOPERS INC ★
Private Bag X36, Sunninghill, Johannesburg, 2157

KIMBERLEY

DELOITTE & TOUCHE ★
P.O. Box 338, Permanent Bldg., 25 Jones St, Kimberley 8300

PRICEWATERHOUSE-COOPERS INC ★
PO Box 32, Kimberley, 8300

KLERKSDORP

PRICEWATERHOUSE-COOPERS INC ★
PO Box 43, Klerksdorp, 2570

KLOOF

MRMA
Suite 60, Private Bag X4, Kloof, 3640

KRUGERSDORP

ERNST & YOUNG ★
P.O. Box 113, Krugersdorp, 1740

LICHTENBURG

PRICEWATERHOUSE-COOPERS INC ★
PO Box 422, Lichtenburg, 2740

MAFIKENG

ERNST & YOUNG ★
P.O. Box 546, Mafikeng, 2745

PRICEWATERHOUSE-COOPERS INC ★
PO Box 4618, Mafikeng, 2735

MIDDELBURG

DELOITTE & TOUCHE ★
P.O.Box 796, Cnr. Lang & Snyman Sts., Middelburg, 1050

MOORREESBURG

PRICEWATERHOUSE-COOPERS INC ★
PO Box 162, Moorreesburg, 7310

NELSPRUIT

BDO SPENCER STEWARD ▽
P.O. Box 3222, Nelspruit, 1200

DELOITTE & TOUCHE ★
P O Box 27, Nelspruit, 1200

PRICEWATERHOUSE-COOPERS INC ★
PO Box 1875, Nelspruit, 1200

NEWLANDS

FISHER HOFFMAN PKF ▼
5th Floor, Protea Place, Protea Road, Newlands 7700

PANNELL KERR FORSTER ▼
5th Floor, Letterstedt House, Norwich-on-Main, Main Road, Newlands 7700

PAARL

ERNST & YOUNG ★
P.O. Box 257, Paarl, 7620

PRICEWATERHOUSE-COOPERS INC ★
PO Box 215, Paarl, 7620

PIETERMARITZBURG

BDO INTERNATIONAL ▽
P.O. Box 673, Pietermaritzburg, 3200

DELOITTE & TOUCHE ★
PO Box 365, Deloitte House, 181 Berg Street, Pietermaritzburg, 3200

ERNST & YOUNG ★
P.O. Box 574, Pietermaritzburg, 3200

PRICEWATERHOUSE-COOPERS INC ★
PO Box 54, Pietermaritzburg, 3200

PIETERSBURG

PRICEWATERHOUSE-COOPERS INC ★
PO Box 4275, Pietersburg, 0700

PORT ELIZABETH

DELOITTE & TOUCHE ★
P.O.Box 27742, Greenacres, Port Elizabeth, 6057

ERNST & YOUNG ★
1st Floor, PO Box 27214, 145 Cape Road, Port Elizabeth 6057

FISHER HOFFMAN PKF ▼
FHS House, 27 Newton Street, Newton Park, Port Elizabeth 6045

MOORES ROWLAND ▼
Rosebank, 30 Bird Street, PO Box 285, Port Elizabeth 6001

PRICEWATERHOUSE-COOPERS INC ★
PO Box 518, Port Elizabeth, 6000

PRETORIA

BDO INTERNATIONAL ▽
P.O. Box 95436, Waterkloof, Pretoria, 0145

DELOITTE & TOUCHE ★
P.O. Box 11007, Brooklyn, 105 Nicholson Street 0181, Pretoria 0011

ERNST & YOUNG ★
P.O. Box 2128, Pretoria, 0001

FISHER HOFFMAN PKF ▼
Ground Floor, 105 Club Avenue, Waterkloof Heights, Pretoria

MOORE STEPHENS, PRETORIA ▼
P O Box 7750, 407 Lougardia Building, Embankment Road, Centurion, Pretoria 0046

PRICEWATERHOUSE-COOPERS INC ★
PO Box 1093, Pretoria, 0001

PRICEWATERHOUSE-COOPERS INC ★
PO Box 35296, Menlo Park, Pretoria, 0102

RANDBURG

MOORE STEPHENS ▼
P O Box 933, 1st Fl Prk, Randpark Building, Randburg, Gauteng 2125

RICHARDS BAY

DELOITTE PIM GOLDBY ▼
P.O.Box 351, L.A.C. Centre, Angler's Rod, Richards Bay 3900

PRICEWATERHOUSE-COOPERS INC ★
PO Box 1744, Richards Bay, 3900

ROBERTSON

PRICEWATERHOUSE-COOPERS INC ★
PO Box 1, Robertson, 6705

SANDTON

DELOITTE & TOUCHE ★
15 Fredman Drive, Sandown, Private Bag X3, Benmore 2010, Sandton

STELLENBOSCH

PRICEWATERHOUSE-COOPERS INC ★
PO Box 57, Stellenbosch, 7599

TZANEEN

PRICEWATERHOUSE-COOPERS INC ★
PO Box 1985, Tzaneen, 0850

UMTATA

DELOITTE PIM GOLDBY ▼
P.O.Box 928, Metropolitan, Homes Trust Bldg.,23 Alexandra Road, Umtata

PDB PRETORIOUS DONDASME ▼
2nd Floor, Sanlam House, Corner Leeds & Madeira St, Umtata

PRICEWATERHOUSE-COOPERS INC ★
PO Box 931, Umtata

VEREENIGING

ERNST & YOUNG ★
P.O. Box 2305, Vereeniging, 1930

WELKOM

FISHER HOFFMAN PKF ▼
Mylacor Chambers, 3 Argon Street, Welkom, 9459

PRICEWATERHOUSE-COOPERS INC ★
Suite 204 2nd Floor, Nebank Bldng, 10 Ryk Street, (P O Box 9 9460), Welkom 9459

WESTVILLE

MOORE STEPHENS ▼
20 Westville Road, PO Box 1098, Westville, 4000

WITBANK

DELOITTE & TOUCHE ★
201 United Building, 31 President Avenue, (P.O.Box 115, 1035), Witbank 1035

WORCESTER

PRICEWATERHOUSE-COOPERS INC ★
PO Box 62, Worcester, 6849

ROMANIA

BUCHAREST

ERNST & YOUNG ★
Premium Plaza Building, 3rd Floor, 63 - 69 Dr Lacob Felix Street, Sector 1, 011033 Bucharest

ERNST & YOUNG S R L ▼
Premium Plaza Building, 3rd Floor, 63-69 Dr Jacob Felix Street, Sectorl, 011033 Bucharest
Resident Partners/Directors:
ICAEW Members
A Emmanouilidis, M G Evry, A D Papadopoulos

FINCONTA SRL ▼
Intr Vladimir Streinu Nr 2, Sector 2, 021416 Bucharest

PRICEWATERHOUSE-COOPERS ▼
str Costache Negri 1-5, sector 5, Bucharest

PRICEWATERHOUSE-COOPERS ▼
12 Domnita Ruxandra Street, Bucharest, 2

CLUJ-NAPOCA

PRICEWATERHOUSE-COOPERS ▼
67 Dorobantilor Street, Cluj-Napoca, RO-3400

TIMISOARA

PRICEWATERHOUSE-COOPERS ▼
str Paris 2A, Timisoara, 1900

SAINT KITTS AND NEVIS

BASSETERRE

PANNELL KERR FORSTER ▼
Independence House, North Independence Square, Basseterre

CHARLESTOWN

BDO INTERNATIONAL ▽
Suite 1, Barclays Building, Main Street, Charlestown

PANNELL KERR FORSTER ▼
Parkville Complex, Charlestown

SAINT LUCIA

CASTRIES

KPMG ★
4 Manoel St, (P.O. Box 195), Castries

PANNELL KERR FORSTER ▼
PO Box 364, Sabicor Financial Centre, Choc Bay, Castries

PRICEWATERHOUSE-COOPERS ▼
Poine Seraphine, P O Box 195, Castries

SAINT VINCENT AND THE GRENADINES

KINGSTOWN

PANNELL KERR FORSTER ▼
P.O. Box 345, Arnos Vale, Kingstown

SAUDI ARABIA

AL KHOBAR

ERNST & YOUNG ★ ◈
P.O. Box 3795, Al Khobar, 31952
Tel: 00 966 38825414

KPMG AL FOZAN & BANNAGA ★
13th Floor, Al Subeaei Towers, King Abdulaziz Street, PO Box 4803, Al Khobar 31952

DAMMAM

ABDUL AZIZ AL-MOGREN ▼
P O Box 930, Dammam, 31421

AHMED BAJNIED & CO ▼
Al-Sunaid Center, King Khalid Street, P.O. Box 7468, Dammam, 31462

DELOITTE & TOUCHE BAKR ABULKHAIR & CO ★
PO Box 182, Dammam, 31411

NAWAR & CO
Moutlak Bldg, opp Revenue Department, P.O.Box 156, Dammam

JEDDAH

AHMED BAJNIED & CO ▼
King Fahd Street, Al Othman Center, Apt 704,P.O. Box 14306, Jeddah, 21424

DELOITTE & TOUCHE BAKR ABULKHAIR & CO ★
PO Box 442, 12 Floor, Saudi Business Center, Madinah Road, Jeddah 21411

ERNST & YOUNG ★ ◈
P.O. Box 1994, Al Nakheel Centre, Jeddah, 21441
Tel: 00 966 26671040
Resident Partners/Directors:
ICAEW Members
C R D Chatwin, K A Mian

KPMG AL FOZAN AL SADHAN ★
PO Box 55078, Jeddah, 21534

NAWAR & CO
Emir Abdalla El Faysal Bldg, P.O.Box 1308, Jeddah

KHOUBAR

NAWAR & CO
Sorour Bldg, P.O.Box 313, Khoubar

RIYADH

ABDUL AZIZ AL-MOGREN ▼
PO Box 221358, Riyadh, 11311

AHMED BAJNIED & CO ▼
Ibn Salim Center Floor 5, Al Olaya Street, P.O. Box 87293, Riyadh 11642

ERNST & YOUNG ★ ◈
P.O. Box 2732, Riyadh, 11461
Tel: 00 966 12734740

GRIMSDELL & CO
P.O. Box 8080, Sitteen Street, Riyadh, 11482

NAWAR & CO
Emir Moh. Ben Suad Bldg, Sharia El Wazeir, P.O.Box 31, Riyadh

SENEGAL

DAKAR

FIDECA ▼
5 Avenue Carde, Dakar, BP1005

PRICEWATERHOUSE-COOPERS ▼
CPM Fidafrica, 2 Place de l'Independance, Immeuble SDIH, Dakar

SERBIA & MONTENEGRO

BELGRADE

KPMG D.O.O BEOGRAD ★
Studentski trg 4, Belgrade, 11000

SEYCHELLES

VICTORIA, MAHE

POOL & PATEL ★
Maison La Rosiere, P.O. Box 117, Victoria

SIERRA LEONE

FREETOWN

PKF ★
Regent House, 12 Wilberforce Street, Freetown

SLOVAKIA

BRATISLAVA

KPMG SLOVENSKO ★
Mostova 2, 81102 Bratislava

PANNELL KERR FORSTER ▼
Apollo Business Centre, Mlynske Nivv 43, 82109 Bratislava

PANNELL KERR FORSTER ▼
Mileticova 23, Bratislava, 820 06, Slovakia

PRICEWATERHOUSE-COOPERS ★
Hviezdoslavovo namestie 20, Bratislava, 815 32, Slovakia

PRIEVIDZA

HZ PKF SRO ▼
Nabrezie Sv Cyrila 47, 971 01 Prievidza

HZ PKF SRO ▼
Andreja Hlinku 1, Prievidza, 971 01, Slovakia

HZ PRIEVIDZA SRO ▼
Andreja Hlinku 1, Prievidza, 97101, Slovakia

SOLOMON ISLANDS

HONIARA

PEAT MARWICK ▼
L.K.P. Bldg., Mendana Ave., (G.P.O. Box 2), Honiara

PRICEWATERHOUSE-COOPERS ▼
1st Floor, City Centre, Mendana Avenue,(P.O. Box 70), Honiara

SOUTH KOREA

PUSAN

KPMG SAMJONG ACCOUNTING CORP ▼
Pusan Daily News Building, 9th Floor, 1-10 Sujeong-,dong, Dong-ku, Pusan 601-738

SEOUL

BDO INTERNATIONAL ▽
Bo-Sung Building, 4th Floor, 1425-1 So Cho-Dong, Seoul, 137-070

DAEHYUN ACCOUNTING CORPORATION ▼
Room apt 501, 5th Floor, Hanjin Building, Sansung-Dong, Kangnam-Ku, Seoul 135882

KPMG SAMJONG ACCOUNTING CORP ▼
10/F Star Tower, 737 YeokSam Dong, Kangnam GU, Seoul, 135984

PRICEWATERHOUSE-COOPERS
Yongsan, PO Box 266, Seoul, 140-600

SOUTH YEMEN

ADEN

NAWAR & CO
Maala, Crater, P.O.Box 994, Aden

SPAIN

BARCELONA

BDO INTERNATIONAL ▽
San Elias 29-35, 08006 Barcelona

ERNST & YOUNG ★
Edif Sarria Forum, Avda. Sarria 102-106, 08017 Barcelona

KPMG ▼
Edificio la Porta de Barcelona, Avda Diagonal 682, 08034 Barcelona

MACINTYRE STRATER INTERNATIONAL LTD ▼
Bailen 188 30 2A, Barcelona

MOORE STEPHENS SANTACANA GRUP SA ▼
Passatge Foraste 7, 08022 Barcelona

PANNELL KERR FORSTER ▼
Av Diagonal 612, 7-11, 08021 Barcelona

PRICEWATERHOUSE-COOPERS ★
Edifici Caja De Madrid, Avinguda Diagonal, 640 7a Planta, 08017 Barcelona

SPAINACCOUNTANTS
Avenida Diagonal 468,6, 08006 Barcelona

BILBAO

CONSULTORES SAYMA SA ▼
Plaza Circular 3 5B, 48001 Bilbao

ERNST & YOUNG ★
Ibanez de Bilbao,28, 48009 Bilbao

KPMG ▼
Edificio Aurora Polar, Iparraguirre, 29-2a planta, 48011 Bilbao

MOORE STEPHENS ▼
Rodriguez Arias 23 2o, 48011 Bilbao

PRICEWATERHOUSE-COOPERS ★
Avenida de Zugazarte 8, Las Arenas (Vizcaya), Bilbao

CADIZ

BDO INTERNATIONAL ▽
Galerias Paniagua 20, Sotogrande, 11310 Cadiz

SIMSON JONES
Poligno Urbisur, Av de Los Descubrimientos Sin, Parque Empresarial Las Redes, Suite 49L, E11130 Chiclana de la Frontera Cadiz
Tel: 00 34 956537798
Principal: ICAEW Member
B M Jones

WOOD & CO
53b Calle Romo, Jimena de la Frontera, 11330 Cadiz

FUENGIROLA

AFIMAR
c/- Alfonso XIII s/n, Edf Terminal 1 3-8, 29640 Fuengirola

AFIMAR ASESORES ABOGADOS S.L.
c/- Alfonso XIII s/n, Edf Terminal 1,3-8, 29640 Fuengirola

LA CORUNA

ERNST & YOUNG ★
Edificio Ocaso, Canton Pequeno 13-14, 15003 La Coruna

LAS PALMAS

ERNST & YOUNG ★
Edif Atlantico, Avda Alcalde, Ramirez Bethencourt 6, 35003 Las Palmas

PKF AUDIEC SA (JAVIER MARTIN ASOCIADOS) ▼
Triana 4, 1 Planta, 35002 Las Palmas

PRICEWATERHOUSE-COOPERS ★
Pilarillo Seco, Edificio Banco Vitalicio, 35002 Las Palmas

PETER WICKSTEED
El Calvario 12, San Lorenzo, 35018 Las Palmas

LOGRONO

EPG AUDITORES S.R.C ▼
Avda. Portugal, 2 3o Izquierda, 26001 Logrono

MOORE STEPHENS ▼
Avda. Portugal, 2 3o Izquierda, 26001 Logrono

MADRID

ALAN D'SILVA & CO
Paseo De La Castellana, 43, 28046 Madrid

AUDIEC - CHECKAUDIT SA ▼
Espronceda 34, Triplicado 1, 28003 Madrid

BDO INTERNATIONAL ▽
C/Juan Bravo 3 - B, 28006 Madrid

D.M.RADLEY-SEARLE
RSM Audihispana, C/Genova 17, 28004 Madrid

ERNST & YOUNG ★
Torre Picasso, Pza.Pablo Ruiz Picasso 1, 28020 Madrid

EUROCONTROL ASESORES CONTABLES
Oficina 48, Edificio Burgosol, Comunidad de Madrid 35 bis, Las Rozas de Madrid, 28230 Madrid
Tel: 00 34 916406138
Fax: 00 34 916406037
Email: andrew.hall@eurocontrolasesores.com
Website: http://www.eurocontrolasesores.com
Date Established: 1998
Principal: ICAEW Member
A R Hall

SPECIALISATIONS – BUSINESS & GENERAL ADVICE
Book-keeping Systems

SPECIALISATIONS – FINANCIAL REPORTING
Accounts Preparation
Foreign Subsidiary Companies

SPECIALISATIONS – TAXATION
Taxation

Languages Spoken:
English, Spanish

EUROCONTROL AUDITORES SL
Oficina 48, Edificio Burgosol, c/ Comunidad de Madrid 35 bis, Las Rozas de Madrid, 28230 Madrid
Tel: 00 34 916406138
Fax: 00 34 916406037
Email: andrew.hall@eurocontrolasesores.com
Website: http://www.eurocontrolasesores.com
Date Established: 1998
Principal: ICAEW Member
A R Hall
Registered by another RSB to carry out company audit work

SPECIALISATIONS – AUDIT & ASSURANCE
Assurance Services

EUROREVISION ★
Pez Volador 32, 28007 Madrid

KPMG ▼
Edificio Torre Europa, Paseo de la Castellana 95, 28046 Madrid

MACINTYRE STRATER INTERNATIONAL LTD ▼
Paseo De La Harana 5450, Madrid

MOORE STEPHENS SANTACANA GRUP SA ▼
Velazquez 26 3o, 28001 Madrid

PANNELL KERR FORSTER ▼
C/Maldonado 46 5-3, 28006 Madrid

PKF AUDIEC SA ▼
Espronceda, 34 Triplocado 1, 28003 Madrid

PRICEWATERHOUSE-COOPERS ★
Paseo de la Castellana 53, 28046 Madrid

PRICEWATERHOUSE-COOPERS ★
General martinez Campos, 41 - 1st Floor, 28010 Madrid

PRICEWATERHOUSE-COOPERS ★
C/Ulises 18, 28043 Madrid

MALAGA

CHRISTMAS & CO
El Molino de la Nina, Casarabonela, 29566 Malaga

ERNST & YOUNG ★
Edificio Veleria, Paseo de la Farola, 5, 29016 Malaga

GEOFFREY COLLINS SL
Alhaurin Business Centre, Avenida el Grande, 29120 Malaga

GLK FINANCIAL SERVICES S.L.
Cl. Imaculada Conception 7, Edif Europa of 1, Arroyo De La Hiel, 29631 Malaga

M. HOWLAND
Villa Kavensa, Calle Hierbabuena 14, Torreblance, Fuengirola, 29640 Malaga

PKF AUDIEC SA ▼
Duquesa de Parcent 8, 29001 Malaga

MARBELLA

CHURCH & CO
El Rosario 143, 29600 Marbella

CHURCH & PARTNERS SL
El Rosario 143, 29600 Marbella

ROSE & CLAVEL ANGLO - SPANISH CHARTERED ACCOUNTANTS ◈
Centro Plaza, Oficina 10, Nueva Andalucia, 29660 Marbella
Tel: 00 34 952 815 365
Principal: ICAEW Member
S Serrano-Davey

SPENCE CLARKE & CO ★
Edificio Los Pinos L-1, Calle Jacinto Benavente 32, 29600 Marbella
Tel: 00 34 952822943
Fax: 00 34 952827779
Email: admin@spenceclarke.com
Website: http://www.spenceclarke.com
Date Established: 1985
Resident Partners/Directors:
ICAEW Members
A M A Spence Clarke
Resident Partners (Non-ICAEW Members):
S J Spence Clarke
Individual(s) licensed for insolvency work by another RPB

SPECIALISATIONS – BUSINESS & GENERAL ADVICE
Company Formation

SPECIALISATIONS – BUSINESS RECOVERY & INSOLVENCY
Liquidations

SPECIALISATIONS – SECTOR
Entertainers
Property Development
Property Investment

SPECIALISATIONS – TAXATION
Offshore Companies
Taxation
UK Companies Overseas
UK Nationals Overseas

General Description:
Specialists in Spanish tax and accountancy matters for businesses and individuals, property taxation, property investment, resident and non resident personal and inheritance taxation, Spanish company formation and management specialists, investment fund taxation.
Languages Spoken:
English, Spanish, Italian, French
See display advertisement near this entry.

OVIEDO

MOORE STEPHENS ▼
Alonso Quintanilla, 3, 2o H, Apartado No 1240, 33002 Oviedo

VELASCO PEDREGAL, AUDITORES ▼
Alonso Quintanilla, 3, 2o H, Apartado No 1240, 33002 Oviedo

PAMPLONA

ERNST & YOUNG ★
Avda Pio XII 22, 31008 Pamplona

KPMG ▼
Edificio Iruna Park, Arcadio M. Larraona 1, 31008, Pamplona

SALAMANCA

MOORE STEPHENS ▼
Plaza de Espana 13 1oB, 37003 Salamanca

SANTACANA & YGLESIAS, S.L. AUDITORES ▼
Plaza de Espana, 13 1oB, 37003 Salamanca

SAN SEBASTIAN

PANNELL KERR FORSTER ▼
Avda. de la Libertad, 10-Planta 6, 20004 San Sebastian

SANTA CRUZ DE TENERIFE

ERNST & YOUNG ★
Edificio Mapfre, Av. Bravo Murillo 5, 38003 Santa Cruz De Tenerife

PRICEWATERHOUSE-COOPERS ★
Mendez Nunez, 52-2 izq, 38002 Santa Cruz De Tenerife

SEVILLE

ERNST & YOUNG ★
Avd. de la Palmera,19, Edificia Winterthur, 2, 2a planta, 41013 Seville

KPMG ▼
Edificio Menara, Avda. de la Buhaira, E 41018 Seville

MOORE STEPHENS ▼
Federico Sanchez Bedoya, 7.5oH, 41001 Seville

VALENCIA

ERNST & YOUNG ★
Roger de Lauria, 6, 46002 Valencia

KPMG ▼
Edifico Condes de Bunol, Isabel la Catolica 8, 46004 Valencia

MOORE STEPHENS ▼
San Vicente 15 5, 46001 Valencia

PRICEWATERHOUSE-COOPERS ★
Paseo de la Alameda, 35-7a Floor, 46023 Valencia

VALLADOLID

ERNST & YOUNG ★
Santiago 7-2-o, 47001 Valladolid

MOORE STEPHENS ▼
Barbecho, 29 (Huerta del Rey), 47014 Valladolid

VIGO

ERNST & YOUNG ★
Edificio Arenal, C/ Arenal 18, 36201 Vigo

VITORIA

CONSULTORES SAYMA SA ▼
San Prudencio 62, 01005 Vitoria

ZARAGOZA

ERNST & YOUNG ★
Avda. Gomez Laguna,25, Centro Empresarial de Aragon, 50009 Zaragoza

PRICEWATERHOUSE-COOPERS ★
1 de la Constitucion, 4-7a planta, 50008 Zaragoza

SRI LANKA

COLOMBO

ERNST & YOUNG ▼
P.O.Box 101, 201 De Saram Place, 10 Colombo

FORD, RHODES, THORNTON & CO ▼
P.O. Box 186, 3 Colombo

KPMG FORD, RHODES, THORNTON & CO ▼
PO Box 186, 3 Colombo

GALLE

ERNST & YOUNG ▼
35/5 Lower Dickson Road, Galle

KANDY

ERNST & YOUNG ▼
839/2 Peradeniya Road, 20000 Kandy

SUDAN

KHARTOUM

MOHAMED ABDEL HALIM & CO
PO Box 1595, Khartoum, 11111

NAWAR & CO
114 Ghoumhouria St, P.O.Box 1052, Khartoum

SHEIKH & CO ▽
Aboulela New Building, Gamhoria Street, P O Box 1608, Khartoum 1111

PORT SUDAN

NAWAR & CO
P.O.Box 534, Port Sudan

SURINAM

PARAMARIBO

ERNST & YOUNG ★
Kerkplein 11-12, (P.O. Box 1847), Paramaribo

SWAZILAND

MANZINI

PKF ▼
FHS House, Corner Masalesikhundleni &, Mbhabha Streets, Manzini

MATSAPHA

MARTIN ALLISON & CO
First Floor, Liqhaga House, Nkoseluhlaza Street, Manzini, P.O.Box 1131, Matsapha

MBABANE

AKINTOLA WILLIAMS ADETONA ISICHEI & CO ★
P.O. Box 1177, Engungwini Building, Allister Miller St, Mbabane

ERNST & YOUNG ★
P.O. Box 210, Mbabane

PKF ▼
2nd Floor, Development House,Swazi Plaza, P.O.Box 1478, Mbabane

PRICEWATERHOUSE-COOPERS ★
PO Box 569, Mbabane

SWEDEN

ANDERSTORP

OHRLINGS PRICEWATERHOUSECOOPERS ★
Box 162, S-334 23 Anderstorp

ARVIKA

ERNST & YOUNG ▼
Skolgatan 25, (Box 130), 67123 Arvika

AVESTA

OHRLINGS PRICEWATERHOUSECOOPERS ★
Kungsgatan 27, S-774 30 Avesta

BASTAD

PANNELL KERR FORSTER ▼
Kopmansgatan 13, S26939 Bastad

BJASTA

BDO INTERNATIONAL ▽
Box 57, S-890 10 Bjasta

BOLLNAS

OHRLINGS PRICEWATERHOUSECOOPERS ★
Box 171, S-821 21 Bollnas

BORAS

ERNST & YOUNG ▼
Skaraborgsvagen 6, 50234 Boras

OHRLINGS PRICEWATERHOUSECOOPERS ★
Box 274, S-503 10 Boras

BORLANGE

OHRLINGS PRICEWATERHOUSECOOPERS ★
Box 714, S-781 27 Borlange

EKERO

BDO INTERNATIONAL ▽
Knalleborgsvagen 7E, S-178 35 Ekero

ENKOPING

OHRLINGS PRICEWATERHOUSECOOPERS ★
Box 1084, S-745 28 Enkoping

ESKILSTUNA

OHRLINGS PRICEWATERHOUSECOOPERS ★
Fristadstorget 6, S-632 20 Eskilstuna

FALKENBERG

OHRLINGS PRICEWATERHOUSECOOPERS ★
Falkenerarevagen 42, S-311 36 Falkenberg

FALUN

BDO INTERNATIONAL ▽
Stigaregatan 7, S-791 60 Falun

OHRLINGS PRICEWATERHOUSECOOPERS ★
Box 203, S-791 25 Falun

FINSPANG

ERNST & YOUNG ▼
Kalkugnsvagen 1, (Box 121), 61201 Finspang

GAGNEF

OHRLINGS PRICEWATERHOUSECOOPERS ★
Skogsvagen 4, S-780 41 Gagnef

GAVLE

BDO INTERNATIONAL ▽
Box 1251, S-801 37 Gavle

OHRLINGS PRICEWATERHOUSECOOPERS ★
Box 1343, S-801 38 Gavle

SET REVISIONSBYRA AB ▼
Centralplan 5, SE 80311 Gavle

GNOSJO

OHRLINGS PRICEWATERHOUSECOOPERS ★
Box 205, 335 25 Gnosjo

GOTHENBURG

BDO INTERNATIONAL ▽
P.O. Box 53204, S-400 16 Gothenburg

ERNST & YOUNG ▼
Odinsgatan 13, 40182 Gothenburg

OHRLINGS PRICEWATERHOUSECOOPERS ★
Hamntorget 5, Lilla Bommen, S-405 32 Gothenburg

OHRLINGS PRICEWATERHOUSECOOPERS ★
Box 11414, SE-404 29 Gothenburg

PANNELL KERR FORSTER ▼
Bror Nilssons gata 5, S-41755 Gothenburg

HAGFORS

OHRLINGS PRICEWATERHOUSECOOPERS ★
Kopmangatan 6, S-638 30 Hagfors

HALMSTAD

ERNST & YOUNG ▼
Kopmanasgatan 23, 302 42 Halmstad

OHRLINGS PRICEWATERHOUSECOOPERS ★
PO Box 324, S-301 08 Halmstad

HAMMERDAL

OHRLINGS PRICEWATERHOUSECOOPERS ★
Box 77, S-830 70 Hammerdal

HAPARANDA

BDO INTERNATIONAL ▽
Foretagsvagen 3, S-953 33 Haparanda

OHRLINGS PRICEWATERHOUSECOOPERS ★
Box 170, S-953 24 Haparanda

HARNOSAND

OHRLINGS PRICEWATERHOUSECOOPERS ★
Skeppsbron 15, S-871 30 Harnosand

HASSLEHOLM

PANNELL KERR FORSTER ▼
Frykholmsgatan 6, S-26331 Hassleholm

HEDEMORA

OHRLINGS PRICEWATERHOUSECOOPERS ★
Stationsgatan 5, S-776 35 Hedemora

HELSINGBORG

ERNST & YOUNG ▼
Jarnvagsagatan 14, Box 780, 25107 Helsingborg

OHRLINGS PRICEWATERHOUSECOOPERS ★
Kungsgatan 6, S-252 21 Helsingborg

PANNELL KERR FORSTER ▼
Jarnvagsgatan 7, S - 25224 Helsingborg

HOFORS

BDO INTERNATIONAL ▽
Box 19, S-813 21 Hofors

HOGANAS

PANNELL KERR FORSTER ▼
Storgatan 62, S26331 Hoganas

HUDIKSVALL

OHRLINGS PRICEWATERHOUSECOOPERS ★
Box 1124, S-824 13 Hudiksvall

JARFALLA

OHRLINGS PRICEWATERHOUSECOOPERS ★
Box 576, S-175 26 Jarfalla

JONKOPING

ERNST & YOUNG ▼
Ostra Storgatan 17, Box 2224, 55002 Jonkoping

OHRLINGS PRICEWATERHOUSECOOPERS ★
Box 2043, S-550 02 Jonkoping

KALIX

OHRLINGS PRICEWATERHOUSECOOPERS ★
Box 61, S-952 21 Kalix

KALMAR

BDO INTERNATIONAL ▽
Box 211, S-391 22 Kalmar

ERNST & YOUNG ▼
Skeppsbron 5, (Box 753), 39127 Kalmar

OHRLINGS PRICEWATERHOUSECOOPERS ★
Box 740, S-391 27 Kalmar

KARLSHAMN

BDO INTERNATIONAL ▽
Drottninggatan 26, S-374 35 Karlshamn

KARLSKOGA

BDO INTERNATIONAL ▽
Bergsmansgatan 2, S-691 31 Karlskoga

OHRLINGS PRICEWATERHOUSECOOPERS ★
Box 39, S-691 21 Karlskoga

KARLSKRONA

BDO INTERNATIONAL ▽
Krister Hornsgatan 2, S-371 36 Karlskrona

OHRLINGS PRICEWATERHOUSECOOPERS ★
Ronnebygatan 49, S-371 34 Karlskrona

KARLSTAD

BDO INTERNATIONAL ▽
Kopmannagatan 2, S-652 26 Karlstad

ERNST & YOUNG ▼
Kungsgatan 16, (Box 477), 65111 Karlstad

OHRLINGS PRICEWATERHOUSECOOPERS ★
Box 151, S-651 08 Karlstad

KATRINEHOLM

ERNST & YOUNG ▼
Drottninggat, 11 (Box 388), 64123 Katrineholm

OHRLINGS PRICEWATERHOUSECOOPERS ★
Mejerigatan 13, S-641 39 Katrineholm

KIRUNA

BDO INTERNATIONAL ▽
Foreningsgatan 11, S-981 31 Kiruna

OHRLINGS PRICEWATERHOUSECOOPERS ★
Foreningsgatan 7c, S-981 31 Kiruna

KOPING

OHRLINGS PRICEWATERHOUSECOOPERS ★
Ostra Langgatan 6a, S-731 32 Koping

KRISTIANSTAD

MOORES ROWLAND ▼
Langebrogatan 111, 291 59 Kristianstad

OHRLINGS PRICEWATERHOUSECOOPERS ★
Tivoligatan 2, S-291 31 Kristianstad

OHRLINGS PRICEWATERHOUSECOOPERS ★
Dobelnsgatan 6, SE-291 31 Kristianstad

SET REVISIONSBYRA AB ▼
V Boulevarden 41, S-291 31 Kristianstad

KRISTINEHAMN

BDO INTERNATIONAL ▽
Box 288, S-681 26 Kristinehamn

OHRLINGS PRICEWATERHOUSECOOPERS ★
Kungsgatan 38, S-681 30 Kristinehamn

KUNGALV

OHRLINGS PRICEWATERHOUSECOOPERS ★
Box 524, S-442 34 Kungalv

KUNGSBACKA

BDO INTERNATIONAL ▽
Energigatan 10 A, S-434 37 Kungsbacka

OHRLINGS PRICEWATERHOUSECOOPERS ★
Teknikgatan 20, S-434 37 Kungsbacka

SET REVISIONSBYRA AB ▼
Energigatan 10B, S43437 Kungsbacka

LANDSKRONA

PANNELL KERR FORSTER ▼
Parkgatan 2, Landskrona

LEKSAND

OHRLINGS PRICEWATERHOUSECOOPERS ★
Box 146, S-793 23 Leksand

LIDKOPING

OHRLINGS PRICEWATERHOUSECOOPERS ★
Nya Stadens Torg 10, S-531 31 Lidkoping

LINDESBERG

OHRLINGS PRICEWATERHOUSECOOPERS ★
Koppgatan 14, S-711 30 Lindesberg

LINKOPING

BDO INTERNATIONAL ▽
Box 1933, S-581 18 Linkoping

ERNST & YOUNG ▼
Repsiagareatan 21, Box 450, 58105 Linkoping

OHRLINGS PRICEWATERHOUSECOOPERS ★
Linnegatan 7, S-582 25 Linkoping

LJUNGBY

OHRLINGS PRICEWATERHOUSECOOPERS ★
Box 258, S-341 25 Ljungby

LUDVIKA

BDO INTERNATIONAL ▽
Ljungvagen 5, S-771 40 Ludvika

OHRLINGS PRICEWATERHOUSECOOPERS ★
Box 167, S-771 24 Ludvika

LUND

OHRLINGS PRICEWATERHOUSECOOPERS ★
Box 2138, S-220 02 Lund

PANNELL KERR FORSTER ▼
Ostra Martensgatan 15, Lund

LYCKSELE

OHRLINGS PRICEWATERHOUSECOOPERS ★
Skolgatan 11, S-921 31 Lycksele

MALA

BDO INTERNATIONAL ▽
Box 84, S-930 70 Mala

MALMO

ERNST & YOUNG ▼
Torggatan 2, 21140 Malmo

OHRLINGS PRICEWATERHOUSECOOPERS ★
Box 4009, S-203 11 Malmo

OHRLINGS PRICEWATERHOUSECOOPERS ★
Engelbrektsgatan 15, SE-211 33 Malmo

PANNELL KERR FORSTER ▼
Kungsgatan 6, 21149 Malmo

PETERS & CO ▼
Skattekonsulter AB, Stortoget 31, Malmo

MALUNG

OHRLINGS PRICEWATERHOUSECOOPERS ★
Box 42, S-782 21 Malung

MJOLBY

OHRLINGS PRICEWATERHOUSECOOPERS ★
Box 328, S-595 24 Mjolby

MORA

OHRLINGS PRICEWATERHOUSECOOPERS ★
Box 197, S-792 23 Mora

MOTALA

ERNST & YOUNG ▼
Bismotagatan 11a, (Box 384), 59124 Motala

OHRLINGS PRICEWATERHOUSECOOPERS ★
Poppelgatan 3, S-591 35 Motala

NASSJO

OHRLINGS PRICEWATERHOUSECOOPERS ★
Stortoget 1, S-571 31 Nassjo

NORA

OHRLINGS PRICEWATERHOUSECOOPERS ★
Borgmastargatan 8, S-713 23 Nora

NORBERG

OHRLINGS PRICEWATERHOUSECOOPERS ★
Parkgatan 9, S-738 30 Norberg

NORRKOPING

ERNST & YOUNG ▼
Lindovagen 5, (Box 1050), 60040 Norrkoping

OHRLINGS PRICEWATERHOUSECOOPERS ★
S:t Persgatan 95, S-602 33 Norrkoping

NORRTALJE

OHRLINGS PRICEWATERHOUSECOOPERS ★
Box 226, S-761 23 Norrtalje

NORSJO

BDO INTERNATIONAL ▽
Box 27, S-935 21 Norsjo

OREBRO

OHRLINGS PRICEWATERHOUSECOOPERS ★
Box 89, S-701 41 Orebro

ORNSKOLDSVIK

OHRLINGS PRICEWATERHOUSECOOPERS ★
Box 370, S-891 27 Ornskoldsvik

OSKARSHAMN

ERNST & YOUNG ▼
Verkstadsgatan 13, 57235 Oskarshamn

OHRLINGS PRICEWATERHOUSECOOPERS ★
Hantverksgatan 15, S-572 33 Oskarshamn

OSTERSUND

OHRLINGS PRICEWATERHOUSECOOPERS ★
Box 294, S-831 23 Ostersund

PITEA

OHRLINGS PRICEWATERHOUSECOOPERS ★
Box 772, S-941 28 Pitea

RATTVIK

OHRLINGS PRICEWATERHOUSECOOPERS ★
Box 82, 798 22 Rattvik

RONNEBY

BDO INTERNATIONAL ▽
V. Torggatan 5, S-372 30 Ronneby

SALA

OHRLINGS PRICEWATERHOUSECOOPERS ★
Drottninggatan 11a, S-733 30 Sala

SANDVIKEN

OHRLINGS PRICEWATERHOUSECOOPERS ★
Box 100, 811 21 Sandviken

SATER

OHRLINGS PRICEWATERHOUSECOOPERS ★
Box 59, S-783 22 Sater

SAVSJO

OHRLINGS PRICEWATERHOUSECOOPERS ★
Box 177, S-576 24 Savsjo

SKELLEFTEA

BDO INTERNATIONAL ▽
Box 391, S-931 24 Skelleftea

SKOVDE

ERNST & YOUNG ▼
Hogskolevagen, Box 393, 54128 Skovde

OHRLINGS PRICEWATERHOUSECOOPERS ★
Box 41, S-541 21 Skovde

SODERHAMN

OHRLINGS PRICEWATERHOUSECOOPERS ★
Box 87, S-826 22 Soderhamn

SOLLEFTEA

BDO INTERNATIONAL ▽
Box 136, S-881 23 Solleftea

SOLLENTUNA

BDO INTERNATIONAL ▽
Industrivagen 2, S-161 62 Sollentuna

STOCKHOLM

BDO INTERNATIONAL ▽
P.O. Box 70390, S-107 24 Stockholm

MOORES ROWLAND ▼
Karlbergsvagen 77-81, Box 21064, 100 31 Stockholm

OHRLINGS PRICEWATERHOUSECOOPERS ★
Torgatan 21, S-113 97 Stockholm

OHRLINGS PRICEWATERHOUSECOOPERS ★
Box 1000, S-101 38 Stockholm

OHRLINGS PRICEWATERHOUSECOOPERS ★
Box 10018, S-121 26 Stockholm

PANNELL KERR FORSTER ▼
Master Samuelsgatan 56, S-11183 Stockholm

STRANGNAS

OHRLINGS PRICEWATERHOUSECOOPERS ★
Finnigevagen 52, S-645 42 Strangnas

SUNDSVALL

OHRLINGS PRICEWATERHOUSECOOPERS ★
Box 20, S-851 02 Sundsvall

TABY

OHRLINGS PRICEWATERHOUSECOOPERS ★
Kemistvagen 6, S-183 79 Taby

TIDAHOLM

OHRLINGS PRICEWATERHOUSECOOPERS ★
Villagatan 7, S-522 30 Tidaholm

TIMRA

BDO INTERNATIONAL ▽
Box 104, S-861 23 Timra

TROLLHATTAN

OHRLINGS PRICEWATERHOUSECOOPERS ★
Box 307, S-461 27 Trollhattan

UDDEVALLA

OHRLINGS PRICEWATERHOUSECOOPERS ★
Box 350, S-451 18 Uddevalla

UMEA

ERNST & YOUNG ▼
Domareuagen 5, Box 4017, 904 02 Umea

OHRLINGS PRICEWATERHOUSECOOPERS ★
V. Norrlandsgatan 22, S-903 29 Umea

UPPSALA

BDO INTERNATIONAL ▽
P.O. Box 3053, S-750 03 Uppsala

ERNST & YOUNG ▼
Portalgatan 2B, Box 23036, 75141 Uppsala

OHRLINGS PRICEWATERHOUSECOOPERS ★
Box 179, S-751 04 Uppsala

VANERSBORG

OHRLINGS PRICEWATERHOUSECOOPERS ★
Kungsgatan 3, S-462 33 Vanersborg

VANSBRO

OHRLINGS PRICEWATERHOUSECOOPERS ★
Box 27, 780 50 Vansbro

VARA

OHRLINGS PRICEWATERHOUSECOOPERS ★
Box 111, S-534 22 Vara

VARBERG

ERNST & YOUNG ▼
V Vallgatan 13, 43240 Varberg

VARNAMO

OHRLINGS PRICEWATERHOUSECOOPERS ★
Box 303, S-331 23 Varnamo

VASTERAS

OHRLINGS PRICEWATERHOUSECOOPERS ★
Box 885, S-721 23 Vasteras

VASTERVIK

OHRLINGS PRICEWATERHOUSECOOPERS ★
Batmansgatan 28, S-593 30 Vastervik

VAXJO

OHRLINGS PRICEWATERHOUSECOOPERS ★
Box 154, S-351 04 Vaxjo

VETLANDA

OHRLINGS PRICEWATERHOUSECOOPERS ★
Box 11, S-574 21 Vetlanda

VIMMERBY

OHRLINGS PRICEWATERHOUSECOOPERS ★
Storgatan 39, S-598 37 Vimmerby

YSTAD

OHRLINGS PRICEWATERHOUSECOOPERS ★
Hamngatan 128, SE-271 43 Ystad

SET REVISIONSBYRA AB ▼
Nils Ahlins Gatan 2a, SE 27139 Ystad

SWITZERLAND

AARAU

BDO INTERNATIONAL ▽
Entfelderstrasse 5, 5001 Aarau

ERNST & YOUNG ▼
Bahnhofstrasse 78, P.O. Box 2220, CH-5001 Aarau

ALTDORF

BDO INTERNATIONAL ▽
Datwylerstrasse 9, 6460 Altdorf

BADEN-DAETTWIL

BDO INTERNATIONAL ▽
Taefernstrasse 16, 5405 Baden-Daettwil

BASEL

BDO INTERNATIONAL ▽
Rennweg 34, 4020 Basel

DELOITTE & TOUCHE LLP
Steinengraben 22, 4002 Basel

ERNST & YOUNG ▼
Aeschengraben 9, (P.O. Box 2149), CH-4002 Basel

KPMG LTD ▼
P O Box, 4003 Basel

PRICEWATERHOUSE-COOPERS AG ▼
Steinengraben 5, 4003 Basel

PRICEWATERHOUSE-COOPERS AG ★
St Jakobs-Strasse 25, Postfach 4152, 4002 Basel

PRICEWATERHOUSE-COOPERS SA ★
St Jakobs-Strasse 25, CH-4052 Basel

BERNE

ERNST & YOUNG ▼
Schauplatzgasse 21, (P.O. Box 5032), CH-3001 Berne

KPMG LTD ▼
P O Box, 3000 Berne

PANNELL KERR FORSTER ▼
Rue Centrale 47, 2740 Berne

PRICEWATERHOUSE-COOPERS AG ▼
Hallerstrasse 10, 3012 Berne

BIENNE

ERNST & YOUNG ▼
Nidaugasse 8, P.O. Box 1084, CH-2501 Bienne

PANNELL KERR FORSTER ▼
Place General Gusian 16, Bienne Berne, 2502 Bienne

BRIG

ERNST & YOUNG ▼
Furka strasse 25, P.O. Box 27, CH-3900 Brig

BURGDORF

BDO INTERNATIONAL ▽
Kirchbergstrasse 215, 3401 Burgdorf

FRIBOURG

BDO INTERNATIONAL ▽
25 Route des Arsenaux, 1701 Fribourg

ERNST & YOUNG ▼
Route de Chantemerle 39, (P.O. Box 301), CH-1701 Fribourg

KPMG LTD ▼
P.O. Box 324, CH-1701 Fribourg

PANNELL KERR FORSTER ▼
Route du Mont-Carmel 2, 1762 Fribourg

GENEVA

DELOITTE & TOUCHE LLP
20 route de Pre-Bois, ICC Building H, 1215 Geneva

DELOITTE S.A
20 Route de Pre-Bois, CP 1808, CH-1215 Geneva

EDWIN C. BROWN
15 St Joseph, Carouge-GE, CH-1227 Geneva

HUNZIKER ASSOCIATES SA
100 rue du Rhone, CP 1624, 1204 Geneva

KPMG LTD ▼
14 Chemin De-Normandie, 1211-25 Geneva

MACPHAIL & CO ★
12 rue Pierre-Fatio, P.O. Box 3453, 1211 Geneva

PANNELL KERR FORSTER ▼
Route des Acacias 54, 24, 1211 Geneva

PRICEWATERHOUSE-COOPERS AG ▼
Avenue Giuseppe-Motta 50, 1211 Geneva

PRICEWATERHOUSE-COOPERS AG ★
50 Avenue Giuseppe-Motta, CH-1202 Geneva

RAJ NAIR
CRC Cabinet de Revision & Conseil SA, PI des Eaux-Vives 6, PO Box 3444, 1211 Geneva

RAWLINSON & HUNTER SA ▼
18 Rue Le-Corbusier, P.O. Box 225, 1211, 17 Geneva
Tel: 00 41 227891200

GLARUS

BDO INTERNATIONAL ▽
Spielhof 20, 8750 Glarus

GRENCHEN

BDO INTERNATIONAL ▽
Dammstrasse 14, 2540 Grenchen

HERGISWIL

EDWARDS & PARTNER AG
Pilatusstrase 25, CH-6052 Hergiswil

KREUTZLINGEN

BDO INTERNATIONAL ▽
Hauptstrasse 14, 8280 Kreutzlingen

ERNST & YOUNG ▼
Hauptstrasse 110, P.O. Box 70, CH-8280 Kreutzlingen

LAUFEN

BDO INTERNATIONAL ▽
Maiersackerweg 25, 4242 Laufen

LAUSANNE

ERNST & YOUNG ▼
Place Chauderon 18, 9, CH-1000 Lausanne

KPMG LTD ▼
Avenue de Rumine 37, CH-1002 Lausanne

PANNELL KERR FORSTER ▼
Avenue de la Gare 50, 1001 Lausanne

PRICEWATERHOUSE-COOPERS SA ★
Avenue C.-F. Ramuz 45, CH-1001 Lausanne

SOCIETE FIDUCIAIRE ET DE CONSEIL ▼
Chemin des Charmettes 7, Case Postale 3453, 1003 Lausanne

LIESTAL

BDO INTERNATIONAL ▽
Gestadeckplatz 2, 4410 Liestal

LUCERNE

ERNST & YOUNG ▼
Tribschenstrasse 7, P.O. BOX 2066, CH-6002 Lucerne

PRICEWATERHOUSE-COOPERS AG ▼
Murbacherstrasse 3, 6003 Lucerne

LUGANO

COLOMBO FIDUCIARIA SA ▼
Via al Forte 2, 6900 Lugano

ERNST & YOUNG ▼
Via Pretorio 20, P O Box 2915, CH-6901 Lugano

MICHAEL GOLDING
c/o Norconsulting S.A., Via Peri 17, 6900 Lugano

PRICEWATERHOUSE-COOPERS AG ▼
Via Cattori 3, 6902 Lugano

RAJ NAIR
Ilex Trust Lugano SA, 12 Via Pioda, P O Box 3453, 6900 Lugano

LUZERN

BDO INTERNATIONAL ▽
Landenbergstrasse 34, 6002 Luzern

MENZINGEN

B.C. GREEN
Neumattstrasse 13, 6313 Menzingen

NEUCHATEL

ERNST & YOUNG ▼
51 Rue Des Moulins, (P.O. Box 165), CH-2004 Neuchatel

KPMG LTD ▼
P O Box, CH 2000 Neuchatel

OLTEN

BDO INTERNATIONAL ▽
Jurastrasse 20, 4603 Olten

PRANGINS

MICHAEL GUNTON CONSULTING
chemin de la Colline 4, Case Postale 39, 1197 Prangins
Tel: 00 41 223626211
Principal: ICAEW Member
M F Gunton

SARNEN

BDO INTERNATIONAL ▽
Pilatusstrasse 5, 6060 Sarnen

SION

ERNST & YOUNG ▼
29 Place Du Midi, P.O. Box 366, CH-1951 Sion

PANNELL KERR FORSTER ▼
Avenue de la Gare 32, Sion Valais, 1950 Sion

SOLOTHURN

BDO INTERNATIONAL ▽
Fischergarten, 4501 Solothurn

ST GALLEN

BDO INTERNATIONAL ▽
Kornhausstrasse 3, 9001 St Gallen

ERNST & YOUNG ▼
Teufener Strasse 3, P.O. Box 147, CH-9001 St Gallen

KPMG LTD ▼
P O Box 1142, 9001 St Gallen

PRICEWATERHOUSE-COOPERS AG ▼
Neumarkt4/Koruhausstrasse 26, Postfach 1644, CH-9001 St Gallen

SURSEE

BDO INTERNATIONAL ▽
Christoph-Schnyder-Strasse 1C, 6210 Sursee

THUN

PRICEWATERHOUSE-COOPERS AG ▼
Niesenstrasse 1, 3601 Thun

VEVEY

PANNELL KERR FORSTER ▼
Avenue de la Gare 16, 1800 Vevey

VEYRIER

MYLES T. STOTT
12 Chemin du Hameau, 1255 Veyrier

WETZIKON

BDO INTERNATIONAL ▽
Pappelnstrasse 12, 8622 Wetzikon

ZOLLIKON

GRAHAM ASSOCIATES AG ★
Breitackerstr 1, 8702 Zollikon
Tel: 00 41 443913861
Fax: 00 41 443913786/00 41 448053967
Email: aashurst@graham.ch
Website: http://www.graham.ch
Mobile: 00 41 794340800
Date Established: 1980
Resident Partners/Directors:
ICAEW Members
A J Ashurst
Registered by another RSB to carry out company audit work

SPECIALISATIONS – AUDIT & ASSURANCE
Audit

SPECIALISATIONS – BUSINESS & GENERAL ADVICE
Book-keeping
Company Formation
Management Accounting
Consultancy

General Description: Over 20 years in Switzerland. Specialists in reporting services for international companies. Company formation, management and administration services.
Languages Spoken:
English, German

ZUG

ERNST & YOUNG ▼
Bundesstrasse 3, P.O. Box 4523, CH-6304 Zug

KPMG LTD ▼
P O Box 4427, CH 6304 Zug

MOORE STEPHENS A.G. ▼
Postrasse 15, Postfach, 6300 Zug

PANNELL KERR FORSTER ▼
Metallstrasse 9, CH 6304 Zug

ZURICH

BDO INTERNATIONAL ▽
P.O. Box, 8031 Zurich

DELOITTE & TOUCHE LLP
General Guisan-Quai 38, PO Box 2232, 8022 Zurich

ERNST & YOUNG ▼
Bleicherweg 21, P.O. Box 5272, CH-8022 Zurich

MOORE STEPHENS AG ▼
Kanalstrasse 9, Glattbrugg, CH-8152 Zurich

MOORES ROWLAND ▼
Seefeldstrasse 45, CH 8008 Zurich

PANNELL KERR FORSTER ▼
Lavaterstrasse 40, P.O.Box 375, CH-8027 Zurich

PRICEWATERHOUSE-COOPERS AG ▼
Stampfenbachstrasse 109, Postfach, 8035 Zurich

PRICEWATERHOUSE-COOPERS AG ▼
Borsenstrasse 26, 8022 Zurich

PRICEWATERHOUSE-COOPERS SA ★
Birchstrasse 160, 8050 Zurich

SYRIA

DAMASCUS

ERNST & YOUNG ★
PO Box 30595, Damascus
Tel: 00 963 116110104

NAWAR & CO
29 Ayaar St, opp Industrial Bank,P.O.Box 263, Damascus

TAHITI

PAPEETE

COOPERS & LYBRAND ▼
Centre Vaima (B.P. 608), Papeete

TAIWAN

CHIAYI

PRICEWATERHOUSE-COOPERS ▼
419 Chunghsiao Road, 4th Floor, Chiayi, 600

CHUNGLI

PRICEWATERHOUSE-COOPERS ▼
400 Huan Pei Road, 22F-1, Chungli, 320

HSINCHU

PANNELL KERR FORSTER ▼
7th Floor II Park Ave 2nd Road, Science Based Industrial Park, Hsinchu

PRICEWATERHOUSE-COOPERS ▼
11 Innovation Road 1,2nd Floor, Science-Based Ind. Park, Hsinchu,300

KAOHSIUNG

MOORE STEPHENS ▼
21st Floor, 91 Chung Shan 2nd Road, Kaohsiung

PEAT MARWICK MITCHELL & CO ▼
11th Floor, 2 Chung Cheng 3rd Road, Kaohsiung, 80027

PRICEWATERHOUSE-COOPERS ▼
95 Mintzu 2nd Road, 22nd Floor, Kaohsiung, 800

TAICHUNG

MOORE STEPHENS ▼
Golden Enterprize, 9 F/1, 559 Ming Ch'uan Road, Taichung

PANNELL KERR FORSTER ▼
160 Taichang Kan Road, Section 1, Taichung

PRICEWATERHOUSE-COOPERS ▼
345 Chung Kang Road Section 1, 31F, Taichung, 403

TAINAN HAIEN

PANNELL KERR FORSTER ▼
11F-3, 77 Chung Hwa East Road, Section 2, Tainan Haien

PRICEWATERHOUSE-COOPERS ▼
395 Section 1,12th Floor, Lishen Road, Tainan Haien, 701

TAIPEI

BDO INTERNATIONAL ▽
5th and 11th Floor, 65 Sung Chiang Road, Taipei

MOORE STEPHENS ▼
Tuntex Tower, 11th Floor, 99 Tunhwa South Road, Section 2, Taipei

PANNELL KERR FORSTER ▼
7th Floor, 168 Chung Cheng 4th Road, Koahsiung, Taipei

PEAT MARWICK MITCHELL & CO ▼
12th Floor, Concord Bldg., 367 Fu Hsing N. Road, Taipei

PRICEWATERHOUSE-COOPERS ▼
Intl Trade Bldg, 27th Floor, 333 Keelung Road, Sec 1, Taipei, 110

T N SOONG & CO ▼
156 Min Sheng East Road, Section 3, Taipei

TANZANIA

ARUSHA

TIM WILLIAMSON
PO Box 12066, Arusha

DAR ES SALAAM

DELOITTE & TOUCHE ★
P&F Tower 10th Floor, Corner of Ohio Street & Garden Avenue, PO Box 1559, Dar es salaam

DELOITTE & TOUCHE ★
Patel Building 4th Floor, Maktaba Street, (P O Box 1559), Dar es salaam

PRICEWATERHOUSE-COOPERS ★
International House, 5th Floor, Shaaban Robert, Street/Garden Avenue, Dar es salaam

THAILAND

BANGKOK

BDO INTERNATIONAL ▽
22nd Fl, CTI Tower, 191/41 New Ratchadapisek Rd, Klongtoey, Bangkok, 10110

DELOITTE TOUCHE TOHMATSU JAIYOS ★
25th Fl Rajarnakarn Bldg, 183 South Sathorn Road,Yanawa, Bangkok,10120

DELOITTE TOUCHE TOHMATSU JAIYOS CO LTD
Rajanakarn Building, 25 Floor, 183 South Sathorn Rd, Yannawa, Bangkok 10120

PRICEWATERHOUSE-COOPERS ★
15th Floor, Bangkok City Tower, 179/74-80 South Sathorn Road, Bangkok 10120

UNITED AUDITING PKF LTD ▼
100 Rama IV Road,Thaladnoi, Samphanthawong, Bangkok, 10100

UNITED AUDITING PKF (THAILAND) ▼
100 Rama IV Road, Thalandi, Samphan & Hawong, Bangkok 10100

UNITED AUDITING PKF THAILAND ▼
100 Rama IV Road, Thaladnoi, Smaphanthawong, Bangkok 10100

Y.NA THALANG & CO ▼
514/1 Larnluang Road, Beside Manangkasila Mansion, Dusit, Bangkok, 10300

THE NETHERLANDS

ALKMAAR

ERNST & YOUNG ★
Hertog Aalbrechtweg 18, P.O.Box 344, 1800 AH Alkmaar

KPMG ACCOUNTANTS N.V. ★
De Hoefstede Building, Picassolaan 201, 1816 MT, Alkmaar

PRICEWATERHOUSE-COOPERS ★
Kantorenpark Houlvaart, Wognumsebuurt 1, 1817 BH Alkmaar

ALMELO

ERNST & YOUNG ★
Posrbus 328, 7600 AH Almelo

ALMERE

KPMG ACCOUNTANTS N.V. ★
Spoordreef 37, 1315 GK Almere-Stad, Almere

PRICEWATERHOUSE-COOPERS ★
Gebouw 'Saeckenborgh', Spoordreef 22, 1315 GP Almere

ALPHEN A/D RIJN

BDO INTERNATIONAL ▽
P.O. Box 223, 2400 AE Alphen A/D Rijn

AMERSFOORT

ERNST & YOUNG ★
P.O.Box 412, 3800 AK Amersfoort

PRICEWATERHOUSE-COOPERS ★
PO Box 809, 3800 AV Amersfoort

AMSTELVEEN

KPMG ACCOUNTANTS N.V. ★
KPMG Gebouw, Burg.Rijnderslaan 20, 1185 MC Amstelveen

AMSTERDAM

ERNST & YOUNG ▼
Drentestraat 20, 1083 HK Amsterdam

ERNST & YOUNG ★
Antonio Vivaldistraat 150, 1083 HP Amsterdam

GRAHAM, SMITH & PARTNERS
Hemonystraat 11, 1074 BK Amsterdam
Tel: 00 31 206838330
Principal: ICAEW Member
J H Graham

KPMG ACCOUNTANTS N.V. ★
P.O. Box 74500, 1070 DB, Amsterdam

MOORES ROWLAND ▼
Amsteldilk 194, PO Box 7266, 1007 JG Amsterdam

PKF WALLAST ▼
Beechavenue 78-80, Schiphol-Rijk, 1119 PW Amsterdam

PRICEWATERHOUSE-COOPERS ★
De Entree, PO Box 22733, 1100 Amsterdam

PRICEWATERHOUSE-COOPERS ★
Thomas R. Malthusstraat 5, P O Box 90351, 1006 BJ Amsterdam

PRICEWATERHOUSE-COOPERS ★
P O Box 7067, 1007 JB Amsterdam

PRICEWATERHOUSE-COOPERS ★
PO Box 94071, 1090 GB Amsterdam

APELDOORN

BDO INTERNATIONAL ▽
P.O. Box 10147, 7301 GC Apeldoorn

ERNST & YOUNG ★
Prins Willem Alexanderlaan, 1419, P.O. Box 652, 7300 AR Apeldoorn

MOORES ROWLAND ▼
Debenterstraat 184, PO Box 1180, 7301 BK Apeldoorn

ARNHEM

BDO INTERNATIONAL ▽
P.O. Box 1062, 6801 BB Arnhem

ERNST & YOUNG ★
P.O. Box 30116, 6803 AC Arnhem

KPMG ACCOUNTANTS N.V. ★
P.O. Box 30133, 6803 AC Arnhem

PRICEWATERHOUSE-COOPERS ★
Velperweg 35, 6824 BE Arnhem

ASSEN

ERNST & YOUNG ★
Noorderstaete 40, (P.O. Box 900), 9400 AX Assen

BERGEN OP ZOOM

MOORES ROWLAND ▼
Rijtuigwag 14, Bergen Op Zoom

PRICEWATERHOUSE-COOPERS ★
PO Box 524, 4600 AM Bergen Op Zoom

BREDA

ERNST & YOUNG ★
PO Box 2049, 4800 CA Breda

KPMG ACCOUNTANTS N.V. ★
Claudius Prinsenlaan, Topaasstraat 54, 4817 HW, Breda

MOORES ROWLAND ▼
Drulvenstraat 1, Breda

PRICEWATERHOUSE-COOPERS ★
PO Box 1042, 4801 BA Breda

CULEMBORG

MOORES ROWLAND ▼
Landzichtweg 64, PO Box 249, 4100 AE Culemborg

DELFT

ERNST & YOUNG ★
Postbus 5021, 2600 GA Delft

PKF WALLAST ▼
Delf Tech Park 40, 2628 XH Delft

DORDRECHT

BDO INTERNATIONAL ▽
P.O. Box 795, 3300 AT Dordrecht

ERNST & YOUNG ★
P.O. Box 290, 3300 AG Dordrecht

DRACHTEN

KPMG ACCOUNTANTS N.V. ★
Berglaan 56a, 9203 EJ Drachten

EDE

ERNST & YOUNG ★
EDE, Keesomstraat 19, P.O. Box 392, 6710 BJ Ede

EINDHOVEN

BDO INTERNATIONAL ▽
P.O. Box 229, 5600 AE Eindhoven

ERNST & YOUNG ★
P.O. Box 455, 5600 AL Eindhoven

KPMG ACCOUNTANTS N.V. ★
Postbus 2290, 5600 CG Eindhoven

MOORE STEPHENS ▼
Postbus 120, Eindhovenseweg 128, AC Waalre, 5580 Eindhoven

PRICEWATERHOUSE-COOPERS ★
PO Box 6365, 5600 HJ Eindhoven

EMMEN

ERNST & YOUNG ★
P.O.Box 470, 7800 AL Emmen

ETTEN LEUR

MOORES ROWLAND ▼
Schoonhout 40, PO Box 256, 4870 AG Etten Leur

GELEEN

BDO INTERNATIONAL ▽
P.O. Box 1, 6160 AA Geleen

MOORES ROWLAND ▼
Kallen Raeven Groap, Rijksweg Noord 45, 6162 AB Geleen

GOOR

MOORES ROWLAND ▼
Grotestraat 26, PO Box 183, 7470 AD Goor

GOUDA

ERNST & YOUNG ★
Postbus 29, 2800 AA Gouda

KPMG ACCOUNTANTS N.V. ★
Burg Van Reenensingel 101, 2803 PA, Gouda

GRONINGEN

BDO INTERNATIONAL ▽
P.O. Box 253, 9700 AG Groningen

ERNST & YOUNG ★
P.O. Box 997, 9700 AZ Groningen

KPMG ACCOUNTANTS N.V. ★
Post Bus 6153, 9702 HD Groningen

PRICEWATERHOUSE-COOPERS ★
PO Box 8060, 9702 KB Groningen

HAARLEM

ERNST & YOUNG ★
P.O. Box 1119, 2001 BC Haarlem

MOORES ROWLAND ▼
Nieuwegracht 53, 2011 ND Haarlem

HARDERWIJK

ERNST & YOUNG ★
Postbus 126, 3840 AC Harderwijk

HEERENVEEN

ERNST & YOUNG ★
P.O. Box 182, 8440 AD Heerenveen

HEERLEN

ERNST & YOUNG ★
P.O. Box 216, 6400 AE Heerlen

KPMG ACCOUNTANTS N.V. ★
Vlotstraat 10, 6417 CB Heerlen

HELMOND

BDO INTERNATIONAL ▽
P.O. Box 427, 5700 AK Helmond

HENGELO (Ov)

PRICEWATERHOUSE-COOPERS ★
PO Box 65, 7550 AB Hengelo (OV)

HILVERSUM

ERNST & YOUNG ★
P.O. Box 766, 1200 AT Hilversum

HOORN

KPMG ACCOUNTANTS N.V. ★
Postbus 60, 1620 AB Hoorn

LEEUWARDEN

ERNST & YOUNG ★
Westersingel 52, P.O. Box 727, 8901 BM Leeuwarden

KPMG ACCOUNTANTS N.V. ★
Lange Marktstraat 14, 8911 AD, Leeuwarden

PRICEWATERHOUSE-COOPERS ★
PO Box 321, 8901 BC Leeuwarden

LEIDEN

BDO INTERNATIONAL ▽
P.O. Box 16128, 2301 GC Leiden

MAASTRICHT

ERNST & YOUNG ★
P.O. Box 100, 6200 AC Maastricht

PRICEWATERHOUSE-COOPERS ★
PO Box 1314, 6201 BH Maastricht

MEPPEL

MOORES ROWLAND ▼
Blankenstein 102, PO Box 381, 7940 AJ Meppel

MIDDELBURG

ERNST & YOUNG ★
Postbus 201, 4330 AE Middelburg

KPMG ACCOUNTANTS N.V. ★
Molenwater 63, 4331SE Middelburg

NAALDWIJK

BDO INTERNATIONAL ▽
P.O. Box 197, 2670 AD Naaldwijk

ERNST & YOUNG ★
P.O. Box 136, 2670 AC Naaldwijk

NAARDEN

PANNELL KERR FORSTER ▼
Gooimeer 2-20, 1411 DC Naarden

NIJMEGEN

BDO INTERNATIONAL ▽
P.O. Box 40025, 6504 AA Nijmegen

ERNST & YOUNG ★
Nassausingel 2, P.O. Box 473, 6500 AL Nijmegen

KPMG ACCOUNTANTS N.V. ★
Van Schaeck Mathonsingel 4, 6512 AN, Nijmegen

PRICEWATERHOUSE-COOPERS ★
PO Box 1161, 6501 BD Nijmegen

OKRENBROEK

MACINTYRE STRATER INTERNATIONAL LTD ▼
Oerdijk 198, 7435 PK Okrenbroek

RIJSSEN

MOORES ROWLAND ▼
Reggesinge 30, PO Box 246, 7480 AE Rijssen

ROERMOND

ERNST & YOUNG ★
Postbus 1228, 6040 KE Roermond

ROOSENDAAL

BDO INTERNATIONAL ▽
P.O. Box 1415, 4700 BK Roosendaal

ROTTERDAM

BDO INTERNATIONAL ▽
K.P. van der Mandelelaan 60, 3062 MB Rotterdam

ERNST & YOUNG ★
Marten Meesweg 51, P.O. Box 2295, 3000 CG Rotterdam

ERNST & YOUNG ★
Postbus 488, 3000 AL Rotterdam

ERNST & YOUNG ★
Technical Department, Marten Meesweg 95, 3068 Rotterdam

KPMG ACCOUNTANTS N.V. ★
P.O. Box 29174, 3001 GD Rotterdam

MOORES ROWLAND ▼
Central Secretariat, Calandstraat 41, PO Box 23123, 3001 KC Rotterdam

PANNELL KERR FORSTER ▼
P O Box 84030, 3009 Rotterdam

PANNELL KERR FORSTER NEDERLAND BV ▼
P O Box 84030, 3009 Rotterdam

PKF ▼
P O Box 84030, 3009 Rotterdam

PKF WALLAST ▼
Rivium Boulevard 34, Capelle Aan Den Ijssel, 2909 LK Rotterdam

PRICEWATERHOUSE-COOPERS ★
PO Box 8800, 3009 AV Rotterdam

ROZENBURG

MOORE STEPHENS NETHERLANDS BV ▼
Aalsmeerderweg 600-602, 1437 EJ Rozenburg

S'HERTOGENBOSCH

BDO INTERNATIONAL ▽
P.O. Box 3191, 5203 DD S'Hertogenbosch

KPMG ACCOUNTANTS N.V. ★
Pettelaarpark 34, 5216 PD, S'Hertogenbosch

TERNEUZEN

ERNST & YOUNG ★
P.O. Box 113, 4530 AC Terneuzen

MOORES ROWLAND ▼
Herengracht 7, PO Box 1100, 4530 GO Terneuzen

THE HAGUE

BDO INTERNATIONAL ▽
P.O. Box 17408, 2502 CK The Hague

ERNST & YOUNG ▼
Wassenaarseweg 80., The Hague, 2596 CZ

ERNST & YOUNG ★
(P.O. Box 90636), Wassenaarseweg 80, 2509 LP The Hague

KPMG ACCOUNTANTS N.V. ★
Churchillplein 6, 2517 GW, The Hague

MOORES ROWLAND ▼
PO Box 11655, 2502 The Hague

PRICEWATERHOUSE-COOPERS ★
Princes Margrietplantsoen 46, PO Box 30715, 2500 The Hague

PRICEWATERHOUSE-COOPERS ★
Oostduinlaan 2, PO Box 30715, 2500 GS The Hague

TIEL

ERNST & YOUNG ★
P.O. Box 6114, 4000 HC Tiel

TILBURG

BDO INTERNATIONAL ▽
P.O. Box 757, 5000 AT Tilburg

KPMG ACCOUNTANTS N.V. ★
Wilhelminapark 31, EC 5041, Tilburg

PRICEWATERHOUSE-COOPERS ★
PO Box 222, 5000 AE Tilburg

UTRECHT

BDO INTERNATIONAL ▽
P.O. Box 4053, 3502 HB Utrecht

ERNST & YOUNG ★
Postbus 3053, 3502 GB Utrecht

KPMG ACCOUNTANTS N.V. ★
Rijnzathe 10, 3454 PV De Meern, Utrecht

PRICEWATERHOUSE-COOPERS ★
PO Box 85096, 3508 AB Utrecht

VENLO

ERNST & YOUNG ★
Veestraat 5, P.O. Box 391, 5900 AJ Venlo

WAALWIJK

ERNST & YOUNG ★
Postbus 579, 5140 AN Waalwijk

WINSCHOTEN

ERNST & YOUNG ★
Postbus 78, 9670 AB Winschoten

WOERDEN

PKF WALLAST ▼
Pompmolenaan 9, 3447 GJ Woerden

ZWOLLE

ERNST & YOUNG ★
P.O. Box 634, 8000 AP Zwolle

KPMG ACCOUNTANTS N.V. ★
De Zwolse Poort, Burg Roelenweg 11, 8021 EV, Zwolle

PRICEWATERHOUSE-COOPERS ★
PO Box 513, 8000 AM Zwolle

THE RUSSIAN FEDERATION

KAZAN

PANNELL KERR FORSTER ▼
10 Yamashev Avenue, PO Box 134, Tatarstan, 420080 Kazan

MOSCOW

BDO INTERNATIONAL ▽
ul. Tverskaya 15, 3rd Floor, Apt 46, 103009 Moscow

ZAO DELOITTE & TOUCHE CIS
Building 2, 4-7 Vozdvizhenka Street, 125009 Moscow

ERNST & YOUNG ▼
Sadovnicheskaya Nab 77, Building 1, 115035 Moscow

ERNST & YOUNG ▼
Podsosensky Pereulok 20/12, 103062 Moscow

ERNST & YOUNG MOSCOW LLC ▼
Sadovnicheskaya Nab 77, Building 1, 115035 Moscow

KPMG ★
Naberezhnaya Tower Complex, Block C, 18 Krasnopresnenskaya Naberezhnaya, 123317 Moscow

MOORE STEPHENS BALANCE ▼
38 Stremyanny pereulok, 115054 Moscow

PANNELL KERR FORSTER ▼
44/1 Myasnitskaya Street, 101990 Moscow

PRICEWATERHOUSE-COOPERS ★
Kosmodamianskaya Nab 52, Building 5, 115054 Moscow

PRICEWATERHOUSE-COOPERS ★
Nikoloyamskaya, 13, 109240 Moscow

PRICEWATERHOUSE-COOPERS ★
Kosmodamianskaya, Nab. 52, Building 5, 113054 Moscow

THORNTON SPRINGER INTERNATIONAL LTD
No. 6, 3rd Floor, Basmanny Tupik, 103064 Moscow

THORNTON SPRINGER LLP
39 Guilyarouskoqo Street, 129770 Moscow

ZAO PRICEWATERHOUSECOOPERS (AUDIT) ★
Kosmodamianskaya emb, 52, Building 5, 115054 Moscow

ST. PETERSBURG

ERNST & YOUNG ▼
ul. Galernaya 13, 190000 St Petersburg

PANNELL KERR FORSTER ▼
2 Truda Square, 190000 St Petersburg

PRICEWATERHOUSE-COOPERS ★
Proletarskaya Dikatura, Square 6, 3rd Floor, 193124 St Petersburg

PRICEWATERHOUSE-COOPERS ★
Griffon House, 19/21 Dostoyevskogo ul., 191126 St Petersburg

TOGLIATTI

PRICEWATERHOUSE-COOPERS ★
Yuzhnoe Shosse 36, Floor 11, 445633 Togliatti

VLADIVOSTOK

MOORE STEPHENS DALAUDIT ▼
Suite 617, 45-A Aleutskaya Street, 690009 Vladivostok

TOGO

LOME

PKF ★
304 Boulevard du B Janvier, Lome

TRINIDAD AND TOBAGO

MARAVAL

HOMER & CO ★
27A Saddle Road, Maraval

PORT OF SPAIN

D. MONTGOMERY & CO ★
P O Box 119, 118 Abercromby Street, Port Of Spain
Tel: 00 1 868 6234573
Resident Partners/Directors: ICAEW Members
D G Montgomery

DELOITTE & TOUCHE ▼
P.O. Box 231, Bretton Hall, 16 Victoria Avenue, Port Of Spain

ERNST & YOUNG ★
5-7 Sweet Briar Road, St Clair, Port Of Spain

ERNST & YOUNG ★
5-7 Sweet Briar Road, (P.O. Box 158), Port Of Spain

KPMG ★
P O Box 1328, Port Of Spain

PANNELL KERR FORSTER ▼
245 Belmont Circular Road, Port Of Spain

PRICEWATERHOUSE-COOPERS ★
11-13 Victoria Avenue, P O Box 550, Port Of Spain

TERRANCE G. CHANG
5 Hillcrest Avenue, Cascade, Port Of Spain

TRYSTRAM ALLEY & CO
P.O. Box 4377, 29 St Ann's Road, Port Of Spain

WADDELLS
P.O. Box 140, Port Of Spain

SAN FERNANDO

ERNST & YOUNG ★
16-22 Sutton Street, San Fernando

MMS
11 Lower Hillside Street, San Fernando

ST. CLAIR

ERNST & YOUNG ★
5-7 Sweet Briar Road, PO Box 158, St Clair

VALSAYN

HAMLYN MIKE AND CO ★
13 Mayfield Road, Valsayn

I.H. RAMPERSAD & CO
4 Aruac Road, Valsayn

TUNISIA

TUNIS

CABINET RACHED FOURATI (KPMG TUNISIE) ▼
7 rue de Mauritanie, 1002, Tunis

LASSAD MARWANI & CO ▼
Centre Ines, 9 Rue Azzouz Rebai, El Manar 11, Tunis 2092

PRICEWATERHOUSE-COOPERS ▼
Passage du Lac Van, Les Berges du Lac, Tunis, 1053

TURKEY

ANKARA

BDO INTERNATIONAL ▽
Cinnah Caddesi, Hava Sokak 2/5, Cankaya, Ankara

DELOITTE & TOUCHE ★
Attar Sokak No. 9/1-3, Gaziosmanpasa, Ankara, 06700

DRT DENET ★
Cinnah Cad., Hava Sok.2/5, Cankaya, Ankara

PANNELL KERR FORSTER ▼
Nilgun Sokak No 11-10, Cankaya, Ankara

ISTANBUL

ARKAN & ERGIN GRANT THORNTON ★
Yildiz Posta Cad., Dedeman Ishani No 48, Kat 6 80700 Esentepe, Istanbul 80700

ARKAN & ERGIN ULUSLARARASI DENETIM VE YMM AS ★
Abidei Hurriyet Cad, No 285 Bolkan Center, C Blok, Sisli, Istanbul

BDO INTERNATIONAL ▽
Sair Nigar Sk. Yalcinkaya, Is Merkezi, 90/703-704, 80220 Sisli, Istanbul, 80220

BDO INTERNATIONAL ▽
Avni Dilligil Sok, 6 Mecidiyekoy, Istanbul, 34394

DELOITTE & TOUCHE ★
Sun Plaza, Dereboyu Sokak No 24, Maslak, Istanbul 34398

DRT DENET ★
Buyukdere Cad.121,Ercan Han, Kat 4-6,Gayrettepe, Istanbul, 80300

MOORE STEPHENS ▼
Inonu Cad. Akar Palas Apt., No: 22 Kat: 22 Gumussuyu, Istanbul, 80090

PANNELL KERR FORSTER ▼
Mesrutiyet CAD 170 Daire, Apt K4, D9, Beyoglu, 34430 Istanbul

PRICEWATERHOUSE-COOPERS
Blk Plaza, Spor Caddesi No 92, B Blok, Kat 9 Akaretler, Besiktas, Istanbul, 80680

VEGA INDEPENDENT AUDITING & CONSULTING INC - AGN INTERNATIONAL ▼
Aytar Cad. 28/14, Levent, Istanbul

IZMIR

DELOITTE & TOUCHE ★
Sehit Nevres Bulvari,No.5, Sedir Apt., Daire 6,Alsancak, Izmir,35210

PANNELL KERR FORSTER ▼
Ataturk Cad Mayis Ys Merkezi Ekim Apt No 174/1, Passaport, Izmir

KYRENIA MERSIN 10

PARKER RANDALL
Mete Adanir Cad, No 1 Emtan 3 Apt, Kyrenia MERSIN 10

TURKS AND CAICOS ISLANDS

GRAND TURK

MIDGLEY,SNELLING,MORRIS & CO ▼
P.O. Box 156, Hibiscus Square, Pond Street, Grand Turk

MORRIS, COTTINGHAM & CO ★
Hibiscus Square, Pond Street, Grand Turk
Tel: 00 1 649 9462504
Resident Partners/Directors: ICAEW Members
D R Cottingham

PROVIDENCIALES

KPMG ★
Mayfair Hse, Cntr Mews, Providenciales

PRICEWATERHOUSE-COOPERS LTD ★
Abacus House, P O Box 63, Providenciales

UGANDA

KAMPALA

A.H. THAKKAR & SONS
P.O.Box 2903, Kampala

DELOITTE & TOUCHE ★
3rd Floor Rwenzori House, 1 PO Box 10314, 1 Lamumba Avenue, Kampala

GEORGE EGADDU
6 Bandali Close, PO Box 3736, Kampala

PANNELL KERR FORSTER ▼
Plot No 37, Yusuf Lule Road, Kampala

PRICEWATERHOUSE-COOPERS
Crusander House, 3rd Floor, 3 Portal Avenue, Kampala

PRICEWATERHOUSE-COOPERS
Communications House, 1 Colville Street, PO Box 882, Kampala

UKRAINE

KIEV

AUDIT FIRM ANALITIK ▼
3rd Floor, Khreshchatyk Street 44, 01001 Kiev

KYIV

ERNST & YOUNG ▼
19a Khreschatyk Street, 01001 Kyiv

ERNST & YOUNG ▼
3/7 Kyianivsky Provulok, Kyiv 254053

KPMG UKRAINE ▼
Velyka Zhytomyrska 8b, Kyiv 01025

PRICEWATERHOUSE-COOPERS
38 Turgenevska Street, 5th Floor, Kyiv 01054

UNITED ARAB EMIRATES

ABU DHABI

AL-RUBAIE & CO
P.O. Box 46283, Abu Dhabi

BDO INTERNATIONAL ▽
P.O. Box 25836, Abu Dhabi

ERNST & YOUNG ▽ ◈
PO Box 136, Abu Dhabi
Tel: 00 971 2 6277522
Resident Partners/Directors: ICAEW Members
M R Green, A E Kasparian

HLB JIVANJEE & CO
P.O. Box 3401, Abu Dhabi

KPMG
Falcon Tower, 16th Floor, Al Nasr Street, PO Box 7613, Abu Dhabi

PRICEWATERHOUSE-COOPERS ★
9th Floor, East Tower, Abu Dhabi Trade Centre, PO Box 45263, Abu Dhabi

RSM & CO ▼
15th Floor, The Blue Tower, Suite 1501A, Sh Khalifa Street, Abu Dhabi

DUBAI

A.F. FERGUSON & CO ▽
1106, 11th Floor, Office Tower, Holiday Centre, Sheikh Zayad Road, PO Box 7219, Dubai

A.W. ROBINSON
P O Box 3800, Dubai

AGN MAK ★
P.O. Box 6747, Dubai

BDO INTERNATIONAL ▽
P.O. Box 1961, Dubai

BIJAN SHEIBANI
Apt 18D/F, Intercontinental Plaza, P O Box 8811, Dubai

CHOKSY ASSOCIATES
PO Box 11529, Dubai, 75500

ERNST & YOUNG ▽ ◈
Level 28, AL Attar Bus Tower, Sheikh Zayed Road, P.O. Box 9267, Dubai
Tel: 00 971 43324000
Resident Partners/Directors: ICAEW Members
A H Issa, E B Quinlan

G. MARTINS
Villa 12, Khalifa Bin Dhain, Al Safa Park, Al Wasl Rd, Dubai

KPMG
P O Box 3800, Level 32, Emirates Towers, Sheikh Zayed Road, Dubai

MAZARS
Green Corner Building, Al Rigga Street, PO Box 6212, Dubai
Tel: 00 971 42221140
Email: mazars@eim.ae
Website: http://www.mazars.com
Training Contracts Available.
Principal: ICAEW Member
S N Bitar
Resident Partners (Non-ICAEW Members):
Fadi G Khlat
Other Offices: Abu Dhabi, Ajman, Muscat

PANNELL KERR FORSTER ▼
Lease Office Building 15, Office No 43 First Floor, Jelbel Ali Free Zone, Jebel Ali, Dubai

PRICEWATERHOUSE-COOPERS ★
4th Floor, Building 5, The Exchange, Dubai International Finance, Dubai

RSM & CO ▼
Suite 301-303, Al Maidan Tower 2, Al Maktoum Street, Opposite Etisalat Building, Deira, Dubai

RSM & CO ▼
Lease Office Bldg 15, Office No 43, 1st Floor, Jebel Ali Freezone, Jebel Ali, Dubai

SAJJAD HAIDER & CO
P.O. Box 3251, Dubai

WM PROSERV LLP
PO Box 113468, Dubai

SHARJAH

ABDUL KARIM AL-AMIN & CO ★
FAL Oil Co, PO Box 6600, Sharjah

ERNST & YOUNG ▽ ◈
P.O. Box 1350, 3rd Floor, Al Qasimiah Tower,Port Road, Sharjah
Tel: 00 971 6 55830781

KPMG
P O Box 28653, Sharjah

RICHES & CO ★
PO Box 20860, Sharjah

RSM & CO ▼
Golden Towers, 11th Floor Flat No 1101, Al Buhaira Corniche, Sharjah

UNITED STATES

AIKEN

MOORE STEPHENS ELLIOTT DAVIES, LLC ▼
225 Chesterfield Street, NW, P O Box 930, Aiken, SC 29802

AKRON

APPLE GROWTH PARTNERS INC ▼
1540 West Market Street, Suite 201, Akron, OH 44313
Tel: 00 1 3308677350

ERNST & YOUNG ★
222 South Main Street, Third Floor, Akron, OH 44308

ALBUQUERQUE

KPMG LLP
Two Park Square, 6565 America S Parway NE, STE 700,Albuquerque, NM 87110

MOORE STEPHENS ATKINSON, L.L.C. ▼
P O Box 25246, Albuquerque, NM 87125

ALEXANDRIA

PANNELL KERR FORSTER ▼
2034 Eisenhower Avenue, Suite 170, Alexandria, VA 22314

ALLENTOWN

DELOITTE & TOUCHE LLP
7540 Windsor Drive, Suite 200, Allentown, PA 18195

KPMG LLP
4905 Tilghman Street, Allentown, PA 18104

AMARILLO

KPMG LLP
600 First National Place II, (P.O.Box 15650), Amarillo, TX 79105

ANAHEIM

ALOKE BOSU
4175 E La Palma Avenue, Suite 108, Anaheim, CA 92807

ANDERSON

MOORE STEPHENS ELLIOTT DAVIS, L.L.C. ▼
604 N Murray Avenue, PO Box 1486, Anderson, SC 29622-1486

ANN ARBOR

DELOITTE & TOUCHE LLP
101 North Main St, Ann Arbor, MI 48104

ANNISTON

MOORE STEPHENS DUDLEY, LLC ▼
1518 Leighton Avenue, Anniston, AK 36202

ATLANTA

DELOITTE & TOUCHE LLP
285 Peachtree Center Avenue, Atlanta, GA 30303

ERNST & YOUNG ★
600 Peachtree Street N.E., Atlanta, GA 30308-2215

KPMG LLP
303 Peachtree Street, Suite 2000, Atlanta, GA 30308

MOORE STEPHENS TILLER STEWART,L.L.C. ▼
780 Johnson Ferry Road, Suite 325, Atlanta, GA 30342

PANNELL KERR FORSTER ▼
3340 Peachtree Road, Suite 580, Atlanta, GA 30326

PANNELL KERR FORSTER ▼
600 Peachtree Street NE, Suite 1900, Atlanta, GA 30303

AUSTIN

ERNST & YOUNG ★
Suite 1400, 700 Lavacca, Austin, TX 78701

KPMG LLP
Suite 1100, 111 Congress Avenue, Austin, TX 78701

BALTIMORE

ERNST & YOUNG ★
One North Charles Street, Baltimore, MD 21201

KPMG LLP
111 South Calvert Street, Baltimore, MD 21202

BATON ROUGE

KPMG LLP
Bank One Centre - North Tower, Suite 1700,451 Florida St, Baton Rouge,LA 70801

BELLEVUE

KPMG LLP
1900 Rainier Bank Plaza, 777 108th Avenue, Bellevue, WA 98004

BENNINGTON

KPMG LLP
115 Elm Street, P.O. Box 319, Bennington, VT 05201

BIRMINGHAM

DELOITTE & TOUCHE LLP
First Alabama Bank Bldg., 417 North 20th Street, Birmingham, AL 35203

ERNST & YOUNG ★
Amsouth Harbert Plaza, Suite 1900, 1901 Sixth Avenue North, Birmingham, AL 35203

KPMG LLP
Suite 1200 Fin Center, 505 20th St N, Birmingham, AL 35203

MOORE STEPHENS DUDLEY, LLC ▼
2101 Magnolia Avenue, South, Birmingham, AK 35205

DIPIAZZA LA ROCCA MCDOWELL & CO PC ▼
600 Luckie Drive, Suite 300, Birmingham, AL 35223

BOISE

DELOITTE & TOUCHE LLP
101 South Capitol Blvd., Boise, ID 83702

BOSTON

BDO INTERNATIONAL ▽
150 Federal Street, Boston, MA 02110

DELOITTE & TOUCHE LLP
200 Berkeley Street, Boston, MA 02116

ERNST & YOUNG ★
200 Clarendon Street, Boston, MA 02116

KPMG LLP
99 High Street, Boston, MA 02110-2371

PANNELL KERR FORSTER ▼
265 Franklin Street, 17th Floor, Boston, MA 02110

PRICEWATERHOUSE-COOPERS LLP ★
125 High Street, Boston, MA 02109

BUFFALO

DELOITTE & TOUCHE LLP
Key Bank Tower, 50 Fountain Plaza, Buffalo, NY 14202-2212

ERNST & YOUNG ★
1400 Key Tower, 50 Fountain Plaza, Buffalo, NY 14202

CALEXICO

BDO INTERNATIONAL ▽
P.O. Box 2476, Calexico, CA 92231

CENTURY CITY

ERNST & YOUNG ★
2049 Century Park East, Suite 1780, Century City, CA 90067

CHARLESTON

ERNST & YOUNG ★
900 United Center, Charleston, WV 25301

ERNST & YOUNG ★
P.O. Box 2906, Charleston, WV 25330

CHARLOTTE

BDO INTERNATIONAL ▽
1990 Charlotte Plaza, 201 S.College Street, Charlotte, NC 28244-0001

DELOITTE & TOUCHE LLP
1100 Carillon, 227 West Trade Street, Charlotte, NC 28202-1675

ERNST & YOUNG ★
One Independence Centre, Suite 1100, 101 North Tryon Street, Charlotte,NC 28246

KPMG LLP
Suite 2300, 401 South Tryron Street, Charlotte, NC 28202

PANNELL KERR FORSTER ▼
South Tryon Square, Suite 1500, 201 - 800th Tryon Street, Charlotte, NC 28202

CHATTANOOGA

ERNST & YOUNG ★
300 Krystal Building, One Union Square, Chattanooga, TN 37402

CHICAGO

BDO INTERNATIONAL ▽
205 N.Michigan Avenue, Suite 2100, Chicago, IL 60601

ERNST & YOUNG ★
Sears Tower, 233 South Wacker Drive, Chicago, IL 60606

KPMG LLP
303 East Wacker Drive, Chicago, IL 60601-5255

PANNELL KERR FORSTER ▼
2100 Clearwater Drive, Oakbrook, Chicago, IL 60523

PRICEWATERHOUSE-COOPERS LLP ★
One North Wacker, Chicago, IL 60606

CINCINNATI

DELOITTE & TOUCHE LLP
P.O.Box 85340, 250 East Fifth Street, Cincinnati, OH 45201

PANNELL KERR FORSTER ▼
441 Vine Street, Suite 2000, Cincinnati, OH 45202-2905

CLEVELAND

DELOITTE & TOUCHE LLP
127 Public Square, Suite 2500, Cleveland, OH 44114-1303

ERNST & YOUNG ★
1300 Huntington Building, 925 Euclid Avenue, Cleveland, OH 44115

ERNST & YOUNG ★
2000 National City Center, 1900 East Ninth Street, Cleveland, OH 44114

KPMG LLP
Suite 2600, 1375 East North Street, One Cleveland Center, Cleveland, OH 44104

COLUMBIA

DELOITTE & TOUCHE LLP
P.O.Drawer 7128, 1426 Main Street, Columbia, SC 27202

MOORE STEPHENS ELLIOTT DAVIS, L.L.C ▼
1901 Main Street, Suite 1100, PO Box 2227, Columbia, SC 29202-2227

COLUMBUS

DELOITTE & TOUCHE LLP
155 East Broad St, Columbus, OH 43215

ERNST & YOUNG ★
1100 Huntington Centre, 41 South High Street, Columbus, 43215 3400

KPMG LLP
Two Nationwide Plaza, Columbus, OH 43215

CORNWALL

MARTIN NANCE
P.O. Box 223, Cornwall, CT 06796

COSTA MESA

DELOITTE & TOUCHE LLP
P.O.Box 7050, 695 Town Center Drive, Costa Mesa, CA 92626

KPMG LLP
Suite 700,Plaza Tower, 600 Anton Boulevard, Costa Mesa,CA 92626

CRANFORD

MOORE STEPHENS PC ▼
340 North Avenue, 3rd Floor, Cranford, NJ 07016-2496

DALLAS

DELOITTE & TOUCHE LLP
Texas Commerce Tower, 2200 Ross Avenue,Suite 1600, Dallas,TX 75201

ERNST & YOUNG ★
2121 San Jacinto Street, Suite 1500, Dallas, TX 75201

KENNETH LEVENTHAL & CO ▼
2200 Ross Avenue, Suite 1100, Dallas, TX 75201

PANNELL KERR FORSTER ▼
15301 Spectrum Drive, Suite 400, Addison, Dallas, TX 75001

DANVILLE

ERNST & YOUNG ★
120 bridgeside Circle, Danville, CA 94506

DAVENPORT

DELOITTE & TOUCHE LLP
Northwest Bank Building, 101 West 2nd Street, Davenport, IA 52801

DAYTON

DELOITTE & TOUCHE LLP
1700 Courthouse Plaza, Northeast, Dayton, OH 45402

ERNST & YOUNG ★
1 Citizens Federal Centre, Dayton, OH 45402

DENVER

DELOITTE & TOUCHE LLP
555 17th Street, Suite 3600, Denver, CO 80202-3491

ERNST & YOUNG ★
4300 Republic Plaza, Denver, CO 80202

KPMG LLP
Suite 2300, 707 17th Street, Denver, CO 80202-3499

MOORES ROWLAND ▼
717 Seventeenth Street, Suite 1600, Denver, CO 80202

PANNELL KERR FORSTER ▼
7979 E Tufts Avenue, Suite 400, Denver, CO 80237-2843

DES MOINES

DELOITTE & TOUCHE LLP
Two Ruan Center, 601 Locust Street, Des Moines, IA 50309

ERNST & YOUNG ★
801 Grand Avenue, Suite 3400, Des Moines, IA 50309

KPMG LLP
2500 Ruan Center, P.O.Box 772, Des Moines, IA 50309

DETROIT

DELOITTE & TOUCHE LLP
200 Renaissance Center, Detroit, MI 48243

ERNST & YOUNG ★
Comerica Tower at Detroit, Center, 500 Woodward, Suite 1700, Detroit, MI 48226

KPMG LLP
Suite 1200, 150 West Jefferson, Detroit, MI 48226

MOORE STEPHENS DOEREN MAYHEW, P.C. ▼
2300 Top Of Troy, 755 West Big Beaver Road,Troy, Detroit,MI 48084-0231

MOORES ROWLAND ▼
27400 Northwestern Highway, Detroit, MI 48037-0307

PRICEWATERHOUSE-COOPERS LLP ★
400 Renaissance Center, Detroit, MI 48243

EL PASO

BDO INTERNATIONAL ▽
P.O. Box 1889-79950, El Paso, TX 79950

ENCINO

FELIX CHUN NING LEUNG
16027 Ventura Boulevard, Suite 400, Encino, CA 91436

ENGLEWOOD

MICHAEL SHEH & CO
5450 S Lima Street, Englewood, CO 80111

FAIRFAX

PANNELL KERR FORSTER ▼
10304 Eaton Place, Suite 440, Fairfax, VA 22030

FLORHAM PARK

PRICEWATERHOUSE-COOPERS LLP ★
400 Campus Drive, Florham Park, NJ 07932

FORT LAUDERDALE

KPMG LLP
Suite 750 Las Olas Centre, 110 East Broward Blvd, Fort Lauderdale, FL 33301

MACINTYRE STRATER INTERNATIONAL LTD ▼
2929 East Commercial Boulevard, Suite 409, Fort Lauderdale, FL 33308

FORT WAYNE

ERNST & YOUNG ★
2300 Forte Wayne, National Bank Building, 110 West Berry Street, Fort Wayne,IN 46802

FORT WORTH

DELOITTE & TOUCHE LLP
301 Commerce Street, Suite 2950, Fort Worth, TX 76102-4140

KPMG LLP
2500 City Center Tower 11, 301 Commerce Street, Fort Worth, TX 76102

PRICEWATERHOUSE-COOPERS LLP ★
301 Commerce Street, Tower II Suite 2350, Fort Worth, TX 76102-4140

FRESNO

DELOITTE & TOUCHE LLP
5260 N Palm Ave, Siute 300, Fresno, CA 93704

GARDNER

BDO INTERNATIONAL ▽
Shawmut Worcester County, Bank Building, Gardner, MA 01440-0639

GRAND RAPIDS

BDO INTERNATIONAL ▽
99 Monroe, N.W., Suite 800, Grand Rapids, MI 49503-2698

ERNST & YOUNG ★
171 Monroe Avenue N.W., Suite 1000, Grand Rapids, MI 49503

MOORE STEPHENS BEENE GARTER, PLC ▼
50 Monroe Avenue, NW, Suite 600, Grand Rapids, MI 49503-2679

GREENSBORO

BDO INTERNATIONAL ▽
P.O. Box 3072, Greensboro, NC 27402

KPMG LLP
Suite 700, 301 North Elm Street, Greensboro, NC 27401

GREENVILLE

ERNST & YOUNG ★
Insignia Financial Plaza, Suite 800,75 Beattie Place, Greenville, SC 29601

KPMG LLP
Suite 900, 55 Beattie Place, Greenville, SC 29601

MOORE STEPHENS ELLIOTT DAVIS, L.L.C ▼
8705 Pleasanthurg Drive, P.O.Box 6286, Greenville, SC 29606

MOORE STEPHENS ELLIOTT DAVIS, L.L.C. ▼
870 South Pleasantburg Drive, P O Box 6286, Greenville, SC 29606-6286

HARRISBURG

KPMG LLP
Suite 300, 225 Market St, Harrisburg, PA 17108

HARTFORD

DELOITTE & TOUCHE LLP
CityPlace, Hartford, CT 06103

DELOITTE & TOUCHE LLP
City Place,185 Asylum Street, 33rd Floor, Hartford, CT 06103-3402

ERNST & YOUNG ★
Goodwin Square, 225 Asylum Street, Hartford, CT 06103-4304

KPMG LLP
One Financial Plaza, Hartford, CT 06103

HERMITAGE

DELOITTE & TOUCHE LLP
4022 Sells Drive, Hermitage, TN 37076-2930

HIGH POINT

BDO INTERNATIONAL ▽
P.O. Box 2403, High Point, NC 27261-2403

HONOLULU

DELOITTE & TOUCHE LLP
1132 Bishop Street, Suite 1200, Honolulu, HI 96813-2870

KPMG LLP
Suite 2100,Pauahi Tower, 1001 Bishop Street, (P.O. Box 4150), Honolulu, HI 96813

PANNELL KERR FORSTER ▼
1953 S Berentaria Street, 4th Floor, Honolulu, HI 96826

HOUSTON

BDO INTERNATIONAL ▽
1200 Smith Street, Suite 3060, Houston, TX 77002-4501

DELOITTE & TOUCHE LLP
333 Clay Street, Suite 2300, Houston, TX 77002-4196

KPMG LLP
700 Louisana Street, Houston, TX 77002

PANNELL KERR FORSTER ▼
One River Way, Suite 1000, Houston, TX 77056

PANNELL KERR FORSTER ▼
1010 Lamar Street, Suite 400, Houston, TX 77002

PANNELL KERR FORSTER ▼
Suite 2400, 5847 San Felipe, Houston, TX 77057

PRICEWATERHOUSE-COOPERS LLP ★
1201 Louisiana, Suite 2900, Houston, TX 77002

INDIANAPOLIS

ERNST & YOUNG ★
Suite 3400, One Indiana Square, Indianapolis, IN 46204

KPMG LLP
2400 First Indiana Plaza, 135 North Pennsylvania St, Indianapolis, IN 46204

MOORES ROWLAND ▼
201 North Illinois Street, Suite 700, Indianapolis, IN 46204

JACKSON

DELOITTE & TOUCHE LLP
P.O.Box 22561, 1236 Trustmark Bldg., Jackson, MS 39225

KPMG LLP
Suite 1100 One Jackson Pl, 188 East Capitol St, Jackson, MS 39201

JACKSONVILLE

DELOITTE & TOUCHE LLP
One Independent Drive, Jacksonville, FL 32202

ERNST & YOUNG ★
1800 Independent Square, Jacksonville, FL 32202

KPMG LLP
Suite 2700 Independent Sq., One Independent Drive, Jacksonville, FL 32202

JERICHO

DELOITTE & TOUCHE LLP
Two Jericho Plaza, Jericho, NY 11753

KANSAS CITY

DELOITTE & TOUCHE LLP
1010 Grand Avenue, Kansas City, MO 64106

ERNST & YOUNG ★
One Kansas City Place, 1200 Main Street, Kansas City, MO 64105

KPMG LLP
Suite 1600, 1000 Walnut Street, Kansas City, MO 64106

LAFAYETTE

WAI S CHUI
100 Lafayette Circle, Suite 204, Lafayette, CA 94549

LANSING

DELOITTE & TOUCHE LLP
One Michigan Ave., 120 North Washington Square, Lansing, MI 48933

LAS VEGAS

DELOITTE & TOUCHE LLP
3800 Howard Hughes Parkway, Las Vegas, NV 89109

LAWRENCEVILLE

MOORE STEPHENS TILLER STEWART,LLC ▼
1505 Lakes Parkway, Suite 190, Lawrenceville, NJ 30043

LINCOLN

DELOITTE & TOUCHE LLP
1040 NBC Center, 13th & O Streets, Lincoln, NE 68508

KPMG LLP
Suite 1600, 233 South 13th Street, Lincoln, NE 68508

LITTLE ROCK

MOORE STEPHENS FROST, P.A. ▼
425 West Capitol, Suite 3300, Little Rock, AR 72201

LONG BEACH

ERNST & YOUNG ★
One World Trade Center, Suite 2000, Long Beach, CA 90831

LONG ISLAND

ERNST & YOUNG ★
395 North Service Road, Melville, Long Island, NY 11747

LONGWOOD

JEREMY G. STONE
197 Bristol Point, Longwood, FL 32779

LOS ALTOS

POONJA & CO
P O Box 1510, Los Altos, CA 94023-1510

LOS ANGELES

BDO INTERNATIONAL ▽
1900 Avenue of the Stars, 11th Floor, Los Angeles, CA 90067

DELOITTE & TOUCHE LLP
350 South Grand Avenue, Suite 200, Los Angeles, CA 90071

ERNST & YOUNG ★
725 Figueroa Street, Fifth Floor, Los Angeles, CA 90017-5418

KENNETH LEVENTHAL & CO ▼
2049 Century Park East, Suite 1700, Los Angeles, CA 90067

KPMG LLP
KPMG Tower,Suite 2000, 3555 Grand Avenue, Los Angeles, CA 90071

PANNELL KERR FORSTER ▼
400 South Hope Street, Suite 710, Los Angeles, CA 90017

PRICEWATERHOUSE-COOPERS LLP ★
350 South Grand Avenue, Los Angeles, CA 90071

PRICEWATERHOUSE-COOPERS LLP ★
2020 Main Street, Suite 400, Los Angeles, CA 92614

LOUISVILLE

DELOITTE & TOUCHE LLP
510 West Broadway, Louisville, KY 40202

ERNST & YOUNG ★
Suite 2100, 400 West Market Street, Louisville, KY 40202

KPMG LLP
Suite 2600, 400 West Market Street, Louisville, KY 40202

LYNDHURST

ERNST & YOUNG ★
125 Chubb Avenue, Lyndhurst, NJ 07071

MANCHESTER

ERNST & YOUNG ★
Two Wall Street, Manchester, NH 03101

MANHATTAN BEACH

ERNST & YOUNG ★
217 B 5th Street, Manhattan Beach, CA 90266

MANSFIELD

M.J. KEIZER
2113 Castle View Road, Mansfield, TX 76063

MCLEAN

DELOITTE & TOUCHE LLP
1750 Tysons Boulevard, Mclean, VA 22101

MELVILLE

KPMG LLP
Suite 200, 1305 Walt Whitman Road, Melville, NY 11747

MEMPHIS

DELOITTE & TOUCHE LLP
P.O.Box 3030,600 Morgan, Keegan Twr., 50 N.Front St, Memphis,TN 38173

KPMG LLP
STE 900, Morgan Kegan Tower, 50 Nrth Front St, Memphis, TN 38103

MOORE STEPHENS RHEA & IVY, PLC ▼
6000 Poplar Avenue, Suite 250, Memphis, TN 38119-3971

METROPARK

ERNST & YOUNG ★
99 Wood Avenue South, P.O. Box 751, Iselin Metro Pk, Metropark, NJ 08830

MIAMI

BERKOWITZ DICK POLLACK & BRANT LLP ▼
One SE Third Avenue, 15th Floor, Miami, FL 33131

ERNST & YOUNG ★
201 South Biscayne Blvd., Suite 3000, Miami, FL 33131-5313

KPMG LLP
One Biscayne Tower, 2 South Biscayne Boulevard, Miami, FL 33131

MILWAUKEE

BDO INTERNATIONAL ▽
Two Plaza East, 330 East Kilbourne Avenue, Suite 950, Milwaukee, WI 53202-3143

KPMG LLP
777 East Wisconsin Avenue, Milwaukee, WI 53202

MINNEAPOLIS

PANNELL KERR FORSTER ▼
100 Washington Avenue South, Suite 1600, Minneapolis, MN 55401-2192

DELOITTE & TOUCHE LLP
900 Pillsbury Center, Minneapolis, MN 55402

ERNST & YOUNG ★
220 South Sixth Street, 1400 Pillsbury Center, Minneapolis, MN 55402

KPMG LLP
4200 Norwest Center, 90 South Seventh Street, Minneapolis, MN 55402

MONTVALE

KPMG LLP
Three Chestnut Ridge Road, Montvale, NJ 07645-0435

MOUNTAIN VIEW

KPMG LLP
500 East Middlefield Road, Mountain View, CA 94043

MUSKEGON

BDO INTERNATIONAL ▽
801 West Norton Avenue, Muskegon, MI 49441-4155

NAPLES

MACINTYRE STRATER INTERNATIONAL LTD ▼
3001 Tamiami Trail, North, P O Box 413032, Naples, FL 33941-3032

NASHVILLE

DELOITTE & TOUCHE LLP
424 Church Street, Nashville, TN 37219-2398

KPMG LLP
1900 Nashville City Center, 511 Union Street, Nashville, TN 37219

NEW JERSEY

KPMG LLP
300 Tice Boulevard, Woodcliff Lake, New Jersey, NJ 07677

NEW ORLEANS

DELOITTE & TOUCHE LLP
701 Poydras Street, New Orleans, LA 70139

ERNST & YOUNG ★
4200 One Shell Square, 701 Poydras Street, New Orleans, LA 70139

NEW YORK

A.E.C SCRUTON
271 State Street, Brooklyn, NY 11201

BDO INTERNATIONAL ▽
Executive Office, 330 Madison Avenue, New York, NY 10017

DELOITTE & TOUCHE LLP
1633 Broaway, New York, NY 10019-6754

DELOITTE & TOUCHE LLP
Two World Financial Center, New York, NY 10281-1414

ERNST & YOUNG ★
5 Times Square, New York, NY 10036

HUSSAIN MIRZA
78 Crawford Terrace, New Rochelle, New York, NY 10804

KPMG LLP
345 Park Avenue, New York, NY 10154

KPMG LLP
757 Third Avenue, New York, NY 10017

MCDOWELL CPA PC ◈
410 Park Avenue, 15th Floor, New York, NY 10022
Tel: 00 1 2129491966
Website: http://www.mcdowell.com
Principal: ICAEW Member
A McDowell

PANNELL KERR FORSTER ▼
420 Lexington Avenue, Suite 2400, New York, NY 10170-0002

PANNELL KERR FORSTER ▼
29 Broadway, New York, NY 10006

PRICEWATERHOUSE-COOPERS LLP ★
300 Madison Avenue, New York, NY 10017

PRICEWATERHOUSE-COOPERS LLP ★
1177 Avenue of the Americas, New York, NY 10036

NORFOLK

KPMG LLP
2100 Dominion Tower, 999 Waterside Drive, Norfolk, VA 23510

NORWELL

PANNELL KERR FORSTER PC ▼
600 Longwater Drive, Norwell, MA 02061

OKLAHOMA CITY

KPMG LLP
700 First Oklahoma Tower, 210 West Park Avenue, Oklahoma City, OK 73102

OMAHA

DELOITTE & TOUCHE LLP
2000 First National Center, Omaha, NE 68102

KPMG LLP
Suite 1501, Two Central Park Plaza, 222 South 15th Street, Omaha, NE 68102

ORLANDO

BDO INTERNATIONAL ▽
201 S.Orange Avenue, Suite 950, Orlando, FL 32801-3421

DELOITTE & TOUCHE LLP
200 South Orange Ave., Orlando, FL 32801

ERNST & YOUNG ★
Suite 1700, 390 N. Orange Avenue, Orlando, FL 32801-1671

KPMG LLP
111 North Orange Avenue, Orlando, FL 32801

MOORE STEPHENS - LOVELACE, P.A. ▼
1201 South Orlando Avenue, Ste 400, Winter Park, Orlando, FL 32789

PRICEWATERHOUSE-COOPERS LLP ★
420 South Orange Avenue, Suite 200, Orlando, FL 32801

OSTERVILLE

PANNELL KERR FORSTER PC ▼
901 Main Street, Osterville, MA 02655

PALO ALTO

ERNST & YOUNG ★
Suite 200, Building 1, 1001 Page Mill Road, Palo Alto, CA 94304

PARSIPPANY

DELOITTE & TOUCHE LLP
P.O.Box 319, Two Hilton Court, Parsippany, NJ 07054-0319

PHILADELPHIA

DELOITTE & TOUCHE LLP
1700 Market Street, Philadelphia, PA 19103

ERNST & YOUNG ★
Two Commerce Square,Suite 4000, 2001 Market Street, Philadelphia,PA 19103-7096

KPMG LLP
1601 Market Street, Philadelphia, PA 19103

MOORE STEPHENS ASHER & COMPANY, P.C. ▼
1845 Walnut Street, Suite 1300, Philadelphia, PA 19103-4755

PANNELL KERR FORSTER ▼
8 Penn Center - 19th Floor, Philadelphia, PA 19103

PRICEWATERHOUSE-COOPERS LLP ★
2 Commerce Square, Suite 1700, 2001 Market Street, Philadelphia, PA 19103-7042

PHOENIX

DELOITTE & TOUCHE LLP
2901 North Central Avenue, Phoenix, AZ 85012-2799

ERNST & YOUNG ★
Two Renaissance Square, 40 North Central Avenue, Suite 900, Phoenix, AZ 85004

PANNELL KERR FORSTER ▼
1313 East Osborn Road, Suite 220, Phoenix, AZ 85014

PITTSBURGH

DELOITTE & TOUCHE LLP
2400 One PPG Place, Pittsburgh, PA 15222

KPMG LLP
One Mellon Bank Centre, Pittsburgh, PA 15219

PORTLAND

DELOITTE & TOUCHE LLP
3900 U.S. Bancorp Tower, Portland, OR 97204

DELOITTE & TOUCHE LLP
111 S W Fifth Avenue, 3900 U S Bancorp Tower, Portland, OR 97204-3698

PRINCETON

PANNELL KERR FORSTER ▼
PO Box 7648, Princeton, NJ 08543-7648

PROVIDENCE

KPMG LLP
600 Fleet Center, 50 Kennedy Plaza, Providence, RI 02903

RALEIGH

DELOITTE & TOUCHE LLP
P.O.Box 2778, 2000 Center Plaza Building, Raleigh, NC 27602

ERNST & YOUNG ★
P.O. Box 40789, 3200 Beech Leaf Court, Raleigh, NC 27629-0789

PRICEWATERHOUSE-COOPERS LLP ★
150 Fayetteville Street Mall, Suite 2300, Raleigh, NC 27601

REEDS SPRING

M L EASTWOOD
P.O. Box 2033, Reeds Spring, MO 65737

RENO

ERNST & YOUNG ★
200 S. Virginia Street, Reno, NV 89501

RICHMOND

BDO INTERNATIONAL ▽
300 Arboretum Place, Suite 520, Richmond, VA 23236

ERNST & YOUNG ★
Suite 1500,One James Center, 901 E Cary Street, Richmond, VA 23219

KPMG LLP
1021 East Cary Street, Suite 1900, Richmond, VA 23219

PANNELL KERR FORSTER PC ▼
1001 Boulders Parkway, Suite 500, Richmond, VA 23225

RIVERSIDE

ERNST & YOUNG ★
P.O. Box 1270, Riverside, CA 92502

ROANOKE

KPMG LLP
Suite 1710,First Union Street, 10 South Jefferson Street, Roanoke,VA 24011

MOORE STEPHENS BROWN EDWARDS, LLP ▼
P O Box 12388, Roanoke, VA 24014

ROCHESTER

DELOITTE & TOUCHE LLP
One Lincoln First Square, Rochester, NY 14604-1998

MOORE STEPHENS BONADIO, LLP
One Cambridge Place, 1850 Winton Road South, Rochester, NY 14618-3993

SACRAMENTO

KPMG LLP
Suite 800, 400 Capitol Mall, Sacramento, CA 95814

SAIPAN

DELOITTE & TOUCHE LLP
P.O.Box 308, Saipan, 96950

SALT LAKE CITY

DELOITTE & TOUCHE LLP
50 South Main Street, Salt Lake City, UT 84144

KPMG LLP
Suite 900-65, 60 East South Temple, Salt Lake City, UT 84111

SAN ANTONIO

DELOITTE & TOUCHE LLP
700 North St Mary's, San Antonio, TX 78205

ERNST & YOUNG ★
1900 Frost Bank Tower, 100 W. Houston Street, San Antonio, TX 78205

KPMG LLP
Suite 2400, 112 E Pecan, San Antonio, TX 78205

SAN DIEGO

DELOITTE & TOUCHE LLP
701 B Street, San Diego, CA 92101

ERNST & YOUNG ★
501 West Broadway, Suite 1100, San Diego, CA 92101

KPMG LLP
750 B Street, San Diego, CA 92101

PKF ▼
2020 Camino Del Rio North, Suite 500, San Diego, CA 92108

SAN FRANCISCO

DATTANI, & CO ★
2218 Lombard Street, San Francisco, CA 94123

DELOITTE & TOUCHE LLP
50 Fremont Street, San Francisco, CA 94105

ERNST & YOUNG ★
560 Mission Street, Suite 1600, San Francisco, CA 94105-2907

KPMG LLP
55 Second Street, Suite 1400, San Francisco, CA 94105

PANNELL KERR FORSTER ▼
425 California Street, Suite 1600, San Francisco, CA 94104

PRICEWATERHOUSE-COOPERS LLP ★
Three Embarcadero Center, San Francisco, CA 94111

SAN JOSE

DELOITTE & TOUCHE LLP
60 South Market Street, San Jose, CA 95113

ERNST & YOUNG ★
303 Almaden Boulevard, San Jose, CA 95110

PRICEWATERHOUSE-COOPERS LLP ★
10 Almaden Boulevard, Suite 1600, San Jose, CA 95113

SAN JUAN

KPMG LLP
American International Plaza, 250 Munoz Rivera Avenue, 11th Floor, Hato Rey, San Juan, PR 00918

PANNELL KERR FORSTER ▼
1056 Munoz Rivera Avenue, Suite 304, San Juan, PR 00927

SAN MARINO

AU YOUNG, TSE & WU ★
2390 Ridgeway Road, San Marino, CA 91108

SANTA ROSA

ANDERSON & COMPANY LLP
110 Stony Point Road, Suite 210, Santa Rosa, CA 95401

DELOITTE & TOUCHE LLP
149 Stony Circle, Santa Rosa, CA 95401-4105

SAVANNAH

MOORE STEPHENS TILLER STEWART,L.L.C. ▼
7 East Congress Street, Suite 803, Savannah, GA 31401

SCOTTSDALE

MOORE STEPHENS - HENRY & HORNE, P.L.C. ▼
7098 E.Cochise, Suite 101, Scottsdale, AZ 85253

N.A. LANE
17394 N 77th Street, Scottsdale, AZ 85255

SEAFORD

PANNELL KERR FORSTER ▼
2234 Jackson Avenue, Seaford, NY 11783

SEATTLE

BDO INTERNATIONAL ▽
One Union Square, Suite 2528, 600 University, Seattle, WA 98101

ERNST & YOUNG ★
999 Third Avenue, Suite 3500, Seattle, WA 98104

KPMG LLP
801-2nd Avenue, Suite 900, Seattle, WA 98104

MOORE STEPHENS BENSON & MCLAUGHLIN, P.S. ▼
1400 Blanchard Plaza, 2201 Sixth Avenue, Seattle, DC 98121-1810

SHERMAN OAKS

KRYCLER ERVIN TAUBMAN & WALHEIM ★
15303 Ventura Boulevard, Suite 1040, Sherman Oaks, CA 91403

SHORT HILLS

KPMG LLP
150 John F. Kennedy Parkway, Short Hills, NJ 07078

SHREVEPORT

KPMG LLP
1900 Commercial National, Tower, 333 Texas Street, Shreveport, LA 71101

SOUTH JERSEY

PRICEWATERHOUSE-COOPERS LLP ★
500 Campus Drive, Florham Park, South Jersey, NJ 07932

SOUTH PASADENA

MACINTYRE STRATER INTERNATIONAL LTD ▼
1015 Fremont Avenue, P O Box 1566, South Pasadena, CA 91031

SOUTHFIELD

PANNELL KERR FORSTER ▼
27777 Franklin Road, Suite 1200, Southfield, MI 48034-8262

SPARTANBURG

PANNELL KERR FORSTER ▼
350 East St John Street, PO Box 6404, 29302, Spartanburg, SC 29304-6404

ST. PETERSBURG

DELOITTE & TOUCHE CIS LTD
St Petersburg Branch, Gustaf Business Centre, Lit K 36/40 Sredniy Prospekt, St Petersburg

ST.LOUIS

MOORE STEPHENS SMITH WALLACE, L.L.C. ▼
1050 N Lindbergh Blvd, St Louis, MO 63132-2912

STAMFORD

KPMG LLP
Stamford Square, 3001 Summer Street, Stamford, CT 06905

MACINTYRE STRATER INTERNATIONAL LTD ▼
Four Stamford Plaza, P.O.Box 120, Stamford, CT 06904

PRICEWATERHOUSE-COOPERS LLP ★
Four Stamford Plaza, 107 Elm Street, Stamford, CT 06901

SYRACUSE

ERNST & YOUNG ★
1800 One Mony Plaza, Syracuse, NY 13202

TALLAHASSEE

MOORE STEPHENS LOVELACE ▼
307 West Park Avenue, P O Box 470, Tallahassee, FL 32302-0470

TAMPA

DELOITTE & TOUCHE LLP
201 East Kennedy Blvd., Tampa, FL 33602

KPMG LLP
Suite 2400, 100 North Tampa Street, Tampa, FL 33602

TOLEDO

ERNST & YOUNG ★
One Seagate, Toledo, OH 43604

KPMG LLP
Edison Plaza, Toledo, OH 43604

PRICEWATERHOUSE-COOPERS LLP ★
1 Seagate, Suite 1800, Toledo, OH 43604-1574

TRENTON

DELOITTE & TOUCHE LLP
144 West State Street, Trenton, NJ 08608

TROY

BDO INTERNATIONAL ▽
755 West Big Beaver, Suite 1900, Troy, MI 48084-0178

TULSA

ERNST & YOUNG ★
3900 One Williams Center, (P.O.Box 1529), Tulsa, OK 74101

TUSTIN

SALAH ALHAFIDH & CO
14571 Emerywood Road, Tustin, CA 92780-6273

VERO BEACH

KPMG LLP
700 20th Street, (P.O. Box 249), Vero Beach, FL 32961

WALNUT CREEK

ERNST & YOUNG ★
Suite 200, 1331 North California, Boulevard, Walnut Creek, CA 94596

WASHINGTON

BDO INTERNATIONAL ▽
1129 20th Street NW, Suite 500, Washington, DC 20036

DELOITTE & TOUCHE LLP
555 12th Street, NW, Suite 500, Washington, DC 20004

KENNETH LEVENTHAL & CO ▼
2000 K Street, N.W.,Suite 750, Washington, DC 20006

KPMG LLP
2001 M Street, N.W., Washington, DC 20036

PRICEWATERHOUSE-COOPERS LLP ★
1301 K Street NW, Suite 800W, Washington, DC 20005-3333

WEST PALM BEACH

BDO INTERNATIONAL ▽
1601 Forum Place, Centurion Plaza, Suite 904, West Palm Beach, FL 33401

DELOITTE & TOUCHE LLP
1645 Palm Beach Lakes Blvd., West Palm Beach, FL 33401

WILTON

DELOITTE & TOUCHE LLP
P.O.Box 820, Ten Westport Road, Wilton, CT 06897-0820

WOODBRIDGE

BDO INTERNATIONAL ▽
90 Woodbridge Center Drive, 7th Floor, Woodbridge, NJ 07095

WOODLAND HILLS

DELOITTE & TOUCHE LLP
21550 Oxnard Street, Woodland Hills, CA 91367

ERNST & YOUNG ★
21800 Oxnard Street, Suite 500, Woodland Hills, 91367

PRICEWATERHOUSE-COOPERS LLP ★
21650 Oxnard Street, Suite 1900, Woodland Hills, CA 91367

URUGUAY

MONTEVIDEO

AUDITORES Y CONTADORES PUBLICOS ASOCIADOS ▼
Av. 18 de Julio 1474, Piso 12, Montevideo

BDO INTERNATIONAL ▽
Rincon 487 - Piso 11, 11.000, Montevideo, 19000

KPMG URUGUAY LTDA. ▼
Plaza de Cagancha 1335, Piso 7o, ific. 702, Montevideo, 11 100

MACINTYRE STRATER INTERNATIONAL LTD ▼
Av 18 de Julio, 1357, Suite 501, Montevideo

PKF CHIARINO & ASOCIADOS ▼
Misiones 1481, Piso 1, Montevideo

PRICEWATERHOUSE-COOPERS
Treinta y Tres 1374, Piso 5, Montevideo, 5

PRICEWATERHOUSE-COOPERS
Cerrito-461, 1st Floor, Montevideo, 11000

PRICEWATERHOUSE-COOPERS
Ruta 8, Km 17,5,Edificio M1, Zona Franca de Montevideo, Montevideo,12200

VANUATU

PORT VILA

HAWKES LAW
Hawkes Law House, PO Box 212, Port Vila

MOORE STEPHENS ▼
Moore Stephens House, P O Box 95, Kumul Highway, Port Vila

MOORES ROWLAND ▼
2nd Floor, Windsor House, Kumul Highway, P.O.Box 257, Port Vila

VENEZUELA

BARQUISIMETO

DOMINGUEZ DEBERA ALCARAZ VAZQUEZ ▼
Edifico Torre Ejecutiva, Planta Baja Calle 26, entre Carreras 16 y 17, Barquisimeto

CARACAS

DOMINGUEZ DEBERA ALCARAZ VAZQUEZ ▼
Centro Plaza, Torre A, 7y8 Av Francisco de Miranda, LOs Palos Grandes, Apt 5972, Caracas,1010-A

KPMG ▼
Interseccion de las Avs, FCO de Miranda y Libestador, Chacao, Caracas, 1060A

PRICEWATERHOUSE-COOPERS
Edificio Del Rio, Avenida Principal de Chuao, Caracas, 1061-A

VILLAGARCIA & ASCOIADOS ▼
AV FCO De Miranda Y Tamanaco, EDF Centro Seguro, Sud America, Piso 2, OFC 2-H, El Rosal, Caracas 1060

MARACAIBO

DOMINGUEZ DEBERA ALCARAZ VAZQUEZ ▼
Centro Comercial Montielco, Calle 72 con Av 20, Piso 7,Oficina 2, Apt. 15191, Maracaibo,2002-A

VALENCIA

DOMINGUEZ DEBERA ALCARAZ VAZQUEZ ▼
Centro Prof. Majay,Piso 5, Av Bolivar, Apt. 681, Valencia, 2002-A

VIETNAM

HANOI

KPMG LTD
16th Floor, Pacific Place, 83B Ly Thuong Kiet Street, Hoan Kiem District, Hanoi

HO CHI MINH CITY

PRICEWATERHOUSE-COOPERS (VIETNAM) LTD
4th Floor, Saigon Tower, 29 Le Duan Boulevard, District 1, Ho Chi Minh City

YEMEN

SANAA

DR AHMED OMAR BAMASHMOOS ▼
P O Box 10016, Al-Shokany Street, Al-Safiah Alganubiyah Zone, Sanaa

ZAMBIA

KITWE

DELOITTE & TOUCHE ★
P.O.Box 20416, 30 Pamo Ave., Kitwe

PRICEWATERHOUSE-COOPERS ▼
P O Box 21604, Kitwe

LUSAKA

DELOITTE & TOUCHE ★
Kafue House, 1 Nairobi Place, PO Box 30030, Lusaka

GADSDEN GRILLO & CO
P.O.Box 35931, Lusaka
Tel: 00 260 1290331
Principal: ICAEW Member
B L Gadsden

KPMG ▼
Kambendekela House, Dedan Kimathi Road, P.O. Box 31014, Lusaka

PRICEWATERHOUSE-COOPERS ▼
P O Box 30942, Lusaka, 10101

NDOLA

DELOITTE & TOUCHE ★
P.O.Box 70138, Mpelembe House, Broadway, Ndola

PRICEWATERHOUSE-COOPERS ▼
P O Box 70042, Ndola

ZIMBABWE

BULAWAYO

ERNST & YOUNG ★
P.O. Box 1426, Bulawayo

HARARE

ERNST & YOUNG ★
Angwa City, cnr Julius Nyerere & Union Ave, Box 62, Harare

PRICEWATERHOUSE-COOPERS ★
Building No 4, Arundel Office Park, Norfolk Road, Mount Pleasant, Harare

KWE KWE

ERNST & YOUNG ★
PO Box 642, Kwe Kwe

MUTARE

ERNST & YOUNG ★
P.O.Box 261, Mutare

THE OFFICIAL ICAEW DIRECTORY OF FIRMS 2009

INDEX

NUMERICAL

A

Bold type indicates entries with display advertising

Bold type indicates entries with display advertising

Bold type indicates entries with display advertising

Bold type indicates entries with display advertising

B

Bold type indicates entries with display advertising

Bold type indicates entries with display advertising

Bold type indicates entries with display advertising

Bold type indicates entries with display advertising

C

Bold type indicates entries with display advertising

Bold type indicates entries with display advertising

D

Bold type indicates entries with display advertising

Bold type indicates entries with display advertising

Bold type indicates entries with display advertising

E

Bold type indicates entries with display advertising

F

Bold type indicates entries with display advertising

G

Bold type indicates entries with display advertising

H

Bold type indicates entries with display advertising

Bold type indicates entries with display advertising

Bold type indicates entries with display advertising

I

J

Bold type indicates entries with display advertising

Bold type indicates entries with display advertising

K

Bold type indicates entries with display advertising

Bold type indicates entries with display advertising

L

Bold type indicates entries with display advertising

M

Bold type indicates entries with display advertising

Bold type indicates entries with display advertising

Bold type indicates entries with display advertising

Bold type indicates entries with display advertising

N

O

Bold type indicates entries with display advertising

P

Bold type indicates entries with display advertising

Bold type indicates entries with display advertising

Bold type indicates entries with display advertising

Q

R

Bold type indicates entries with display advertising

Bold type indicates entries with display advertising

S

Bold type indicates entries with display advertising

Bold type indicates entries with display advertising

Bold type indicates entries with display advertising

T

Bold type indicates entries with display advertising

Bold type indicates entries with display advertising

U

V

W

Bold type indicates entries with display advertising

Bold type indicates entries with display advertising

Bold type indicates entries with display advertising

X

Y

Z